WORLDMARK
YEARBOOK
2000

ISSN 1527-6503

WORLDMARK
YEARBOOK
2000

Volume 2
I–R

Mary Rose Bonk, Editor

GALE GROUP

Detroit
New York
San Francisco
London
Boston
Woodbridge, CT

Editor: Mary Rose Bonk
Associate Editors: Nancy Matuszak, Matthew May, John F. McCoy, Michael Reade
Assistant Editors: R. David Riddle, Chris Romig, Christy Wood
Permissions Manager: Maria Franklin
Permissions Specialist: Margaret Chamberlain
Permissions Associate: Shalice Shah-Caldwell
Image Cataloger: Mary Grimes

Composition Manager: Mary Beth Trimper
Assistant Production Manager: Evi Seoud
Manufacturing Manager: Dorothy Maki
Senior Buyer: Wendy Blurton
Product Design Manager: Cynthia Baldwin
Senior Art Director: Michelle DiMercurio
Graphic Specialist: Christine O'Bryan
Indexing Specialists: Susan Kelsch, Amy Suchowski, Cindy Tsiang

Copyright © 2000 by The Gale Group
27500 Drake Rd.
Farmington Hills, MI 48331-3535

British Library Cataloguing in Publication Data. A Catalogue record of this book is available from the British Library.
ISBN 0–7876–4931–7 (2-Volume set)
ISBN 0–7876–4932–5 (Volume 1)
ISBN 0–7876–4933–3 (Volume 2)
ISBN 0–7876–5088–9 (Volume 3)
ISSN 1527–6503

Printed in the United States of America

10 9 8 7 6 5 4 3 2 1

CONTENTS

Contents

FOREWORD

A NEW, YEARLY REFERENCE FOR A NEW ERA

As a new addition to the Worldmark family, *Worldmark Yearbook* presents to users a comprehensive profile of 229 of the world's nations and terrritories and their current events. Information often scattered throughout books, articles, and various agencies is compiled here in an easy to use reference. It complements other Worldmark publications by presenting the most current information on countries around the world. The Worldmark line already provides you with an in-depth historical account for these countries in *Worldmark Encyclopedia of the Nations*. With the introduction of the *Worldmark Yearbook*, you can be kept up-to-date with the latest developments.

The Year in Review

Worldmark Yearbook begins with a look at the year in review. From Tokyo to Berlin, and from Moscow to Auckland and Pretoria, major events from the past year are highlighted and placed in an international perspective. The main focus of the *Yearbook* is on national events, so the Year in Review provides a broader look at how national issues can affect regional neighbors and the world.

Where in the World?

Each country is accompanied by a map that places it within its area of the world and which details major cities and landmarks. Geography often plays an important role in a nation's politics and economy. The expansive maps can help *Yearbook* users better understand how geography may affect what goes on within a nation. In addition, in a world increasingly referred to as a "global village," national events often spill over into neighboring states. To easily identify neighbors, six color regional maps are on hand for reference.

National Symbols

An added feature of the *Worldmark Yearbook* is the color illustration of national symbols, including flags and official insignia. Each country's official flag is represented and a brief description is included in each entry. A country's official insignia, such as an emblem or seal, is also represented.

Profiles

A national profile highlights basic information for each country. The national capital, monetary unit, anthem, and climate are a few examples of the data available at the beginning of each entry.

Background Check

A yearbook of current events would be of little use without a context in which to put those events. *Worldmark Yearbook*'s introductory survey provides users with this context. Recent history from the mid-twentieth century onward is outlined to provide background in and support for the events of the past year. But history itself does not present a comprehensive picture of how a nation operates. Do you want to know how a country's government is set up? Who can participate in it? How the economy operates? What are the major industrial and economic developments of the past few years? The answers to these questions, and more, can be found in the introductory survey.

Analyzing the Year's Events

A timeline is included in each entry and lists chronologically the events of the past year. Selecting the most significant of these events, an analysis explains them in greater depth and pulls together the threads of politics, economy, and culture to create a cohesive picture of a distinct nation. Economic struggles, cultural revivals, political triumphs: the analysis paints a more personal picture of each country, which can not be as easily portrayed through the simple listing of facts or statistics.

Who's Who?

Who's been running the country while these events have taken place? To find out, users can reference the *Yearbook*'s directory, which, when possible, includes information on how to contact an individual or group. Main government functionaries, including the heads and ministers of state, are listed, as are political organizations active within the country and its major judicial courts. In this "global village," knowing one's neighbors is important, and maintaining official contact with them is a vital part of government operations. In this light, users will find a comprehensive listing of diplomatic representation for each country.

Just the Facts

If hard data is what you're looking for, you can find it in the statistical survey. Population size and growth, economic output and development, major industrial production, and more can be located in the statistical survey. Statistics complement the analysis by explaining numerically much of what's going on in a country's society and economy. It creates a numerative picture that can be easily compared with that of other nations.

Want More?

Check out the Further Reading section for sources of additional information on statistics, current events, and historical background. You can also refer to the International Organizations listing. It provides contact information and a brief description of over 1,800 international organizations that are involved in a variety of global concerns.

At Your Fingertips

Are you looking for something specific? A glance at the *Yearbook*'s comprehensive index will help you find your way. The user-friendly index covers personal names, subjects, and geographies and can refer you quickly to the information you need.

A COMPREHENSIVE TOOL TO TODAY'S WORLD

The *Worldmark Yearbook* pulls together the many components that make up a government and a society to give users a well-balanced, comprehensive, and illustrative source of information on the world's nations. Its many headers make quick reference points to easily locate information. *Worldmark Yearbook* is a proud new edition to the Worldmark line and will enhance the libraries of all reference users. This is just the beginning.

We encourage you to contact us with comments or suggestions. Tell us what you want to see in the *Yearbook* and how we can better meet your needs. Comments and suggestions can be sent to: The Editors, *Worldmark Yearbook*, The Gale Group, 27500 Drake Road, Farmington Hills, MI 48331. Or, call toll free at 1-800-877-4253.

ACKNOWLEDGEMENTS

For editorial and technical assistance that helped keep this project on track and on time, the editors are extremely grateful to the following Gale Group contributors:

Richard Antonowicz, programmer/analyst, **Pamela A. Dear**, associate editor, **Shelly Dickey**, senior editor, **Kathy Droste**, editor, **Anthony Gerring**, technical support, **Bernard Grunow**, editor, **Amanda Moran**, senior market analyst, **Rita Runchock**, managing editor, and **Phyllis Spinelli**, associate editor.

For editorial and textual contributions to the *Worldmark Yearbook*, the editors are indebted to the following:

Advanced Information Consultants, Canton, Michigan, **Kimberly Burton**, Ann Arbor, Michigan, **Michael Dawson**, Carlsbad, California, **Eastword Publications Development**, Cleveland, Ohio, **Editorial Code and Data, Inc. (ECDI)**, Southfield, Michigan, **GGS Information Services**, York, Pennsylvania, **Richard Clay Hanes**, Eugene, Oregon, **Margery Heffron**, Exeter, New Hampshire, **Paul Kobel**, Charlotte, North Carolina, **John Macaulay**, Miami, Florida, and **Vocabula Communications Company**, Lexington, Massachusetts.

For permission to take material from personal or published sources, use of images, and for other courtesies extended during the preparation of this edition, the editors are grateful to the following sources:

Eastword Publications Development, **The Flag Institute**, **International Monetary Fund**, **Publications Services Unit**, **Maryland Cartographics**, **UNESCO (United Nations Education, Scientific and Cultural Organization)**, **UNIDO (United Nations Industrial Development Organization)**, **United Nations Publications**, author of original material, **Oxford University Press, Inc.**, **Pascal Vagnat**, and the **World Bank**.

KEY TO ABBREVIATIONS

ABEDA: Arab Bank for Economic Development in Africa

ACC: Arab Cooperation Council

ACCT: Agence de Cooperation Culturelle et Technique; see Agency for Cultural and Technical Cooperation

ACP: African, Caribbean, and Pacific Countries

AfDB: African Development Bank

AFESD: Arab Fund for Economic and Social Development

AG: Andean Group

AL: Arab League

ALADI: Asociacion Latinamericana de Intergracion; see Latin American Integration Association (LAIA)

AMF: Arab Monetary Fund

AMU: Arab Maghreb Fund

ANZUS: Australia-New Zealand-United States Security Trust

APEC: Asia Pacific Economic Cooperation

AsDB: Asian Development Bank

ASEAN: Association of Southeast Asian Nations

BAD: Banque Africaine de Developpement; see African Development Bank (AfDB)

BADEA: Banque Arabe de Developpement Economique en Afrique; see Arab Bank for Economic Development in Africa (ABEDA)

BCIE: Banco Centroamericano de Integracion Economico; see Central American Bank for Economic Integration (BCIE)

BDEAC: Banque de Development des Etats de l'Afrique Centrale; see Central African States Development Bank

Benelux: Benelux Economic Union

BID: Banco Interamericano de Desarrollo; see Inter-American Development Bank (IADB)

BIS: Bank for International Settlements

BOAD: Banque Ouest-Africaine de Developpement; see West African Development Bank (WADB)

BSEC: Black Sea Economic Coorperation Zone

C: Commonwealth

CACM: Central American Common Market

CAEU: Council of Arab Economic Unity

CARICOM: Caribbean Community and Common Market

CBSS: Council of Baltic Sea States

CCC: Customs Cooperation Council

CDB: Caribbean Development Bank

CE: Council of Europe

CEAO: Communaute Economique de l'Afrique de l'Ouest; see West African Economic Community (CEAO)

CEEAC: Communaute Economique des Etats de l' Afrique Centrale; see Economic Community of Central African States (CEEAC)

CEI: Central European Initiative

CEMA: Council for Mutual Economic Assistance; also known as CMEA or Comecon

CEPGL: Communaute Economique de Pays des Grands Lacs; see Economic Community of the Great Lakes Countries (CEPGL)

CERN: Conseil European pour la Recherche Nucleaire; see European Organization for Nuclear Research (CERN)

CG: Contadora Group

CIS: Commonwealth of Independent States

CMEA: Council for Mutual Economic Assistance (CEMA); also known as Comeecon

COCOM: Coordinating Committee on Export Controls

Comecon: Council for Mutual Economic Assistance (CEMA); also known as CMEA

CP: Colombo Plan

CSCE: Conference on Security and Cooperation in Europe

DC: Developed country

EADB: East African Development Bank

EBRD: European Bank for Reconstruction and Development

EC: European Community; see European Union (EU)

ECA: Economic Commission for Africa

ECAFE: Economic Commission for Asia and the Far East; see Economic and Social Commission for Asia and the Pacific (ESCAP)

ECE: Economic Commission for Europe

ECLA: Economic Commission for Latin America; see Economic Commission for Latin America and the Caribbean (ECLAC)

ECLAC: Economic Commission for Latin America and the Caribbean

ECO: Economic Cooperation Organization

ECOSOC: Economic and Social Council

ECOWAS: Economic Community of West African States

ECSC: European Coal and Steel Community

ECWA: Economic Commission for Western Asia; see Economic and Social Council for Western Asia (ESCWA)

EEC: European Economic Community

EFTA: European Free Trade Association

EIB: European Investment Bank

Entente: Council of the Entente

ESA: European Space Agency

ESCAP: Economic and Social Commission for Asia and the Pacific

ESCWA: Economic and Social Commission for Western Asia

EU: European Union

Euratom: European Atomic Energy Community

FAO: Food and Agriculture Organization

FLS: Front Line States

FZ: Franc Zone

G-2: Group of 2

G-3: Group of 3

G-5: Group of 5

G-6: Group of 6

G-7: Group of 7

G-8: Group of 8

G-9: Group of 9

G-10: Group of 10

G-11: Group of 11

G-15: Group of 15

G-19: Group of 19

G-24: Group of 24

G-30: Group or 30

G-33: Group of 33

G-77: Group of 77

GATT: General Agreement on Tariff and Trade

Habitat: Commission on Human Settlements

IADB: Inter-American Development Bank

IAEA: International Atomic Energy Agency

IBEC: International Bank for Economic Cooperation

IBRD: International Bank for Reconstruction and Development

ICAO: International Civil Aviation Organization

ICC: International Chamber of Commerce

ICEM: Intergovernmental Committee for European Migration; see International Organization for Migration (IOM)

ICFTU: International Confederation of Free Trade Unions

ICJ: International Court of Justice

ICM: Intergovernmental Committee for Migration; see International Organization for Migration (IOM)

ICRC: International Committee of the Red Cross

ICRM: International Red Cross and Red Crescent Movement

IDA: International Development Association

IDB: Islamic Development Bank

IEA: International Energy Agency

IFAD: International Fund for Agriculture Development

IFC: International Finance Corporation

IFCTU: International Federation of Christian Trade Unions

IFRCS: International Federation of Red Cross and Red Crescent Societies

IGADD: Inter-Governmental Authority on Drought and Development

IIB: International Investment Bank

ILO: International Labor Organization

IMCO: Intergovernmental Maritime Consultative Organization; see International Maritime Organization (IMO)

IMF: International Monetary Fund

IMO: International Maritime Fund

INMARSAT: International Maritime Satelite Organization

INTELSAT: International Telecommunications Satellite Organization

INTERPOL: International Criminal Police Organization

IOC: International Olympic Committee

IOM: International Organization for Migration

ISO: International Organization for Standardization

ITU: International Telecommunications Union

LAES: Latin American Economic System

LAIA: Latin American Integration Association

LAS: League of Arab States; see Arab League (AL)

LDC: Less developed country

LLDC: Least developed country

LORCS: League of Red Cross and Red Crescent Societies

MERCOSUR: Mercado Commun del Cono Sur; see Southern Cone Common Market

MINURSO: United Nations Mission for the Referendum in Western Sahara

MTCR: Missile Technology Control Regime

NACC: North Atlantic Cooperation Council

NAM: Nonaligned Movement

NATO: North Atlantic Treaty Organization

NC: Nordic Council

NEA: Nuclear Energy Agency

NIB: Nordic Investment Bank

NIC: Newly industrializing country; see newly industrializing economy (NIE)

NIE: Newly industrializing economy

NSG: Nuclear Suppliers Group

OAPEC: Organization of Arab Petroleum Exporting Countries

OAS: Organization of American States

OAU: Organization of African Unity

OECD: Organization for Economic Cooperation and Development

OECS: Organization of Eastern Caribbean States

OIC: Organization of the Islamic Conference

ONUSAL: United Nations Observer Mission in El Salvador

OPANAL: Organismo para la Proscripcion de las Armas Nuclearea en la America Latina y el Caribe; see Agency for the Prohibition of Nuclear Weapons in Latin America and the Caribbean

OPEC: Organization of Petroleum Exporting Countries

OSCE: Organization on Security and Cooperation in Europe

PCA: Permanent Court of Arbitration

PPP: Partnership for Peace

RG: Rio Group

SAARC: South Asian Association for Regional Cooperation

SACU: South African Customs Union

SADC: South African Development Community

SADCC: South African Development Coordination Conference

SELA: Sistema Economico Latinamericana; see Latin American Economic System (LAES)

SPARTECA: South Pacific Regional Trade and Economic Cooperation Agreement

SPC: South Pacific Commission

SPF: South Pacific Forum

UDEAC: Union Douaniere et Economique de l'Afrique Centrale; see Central African Customs and Economic Union (UDEAC)

UN: United Nations

UNAVEM II: United Nations Angola Verification Mission

UNAMIR: United Nations Assistance Mission for Rwands

UNCTAD: United Nations Conference on Trade and Development

UNDOF: United Nations Disengagement Observer Force

UNDP: United Nations Development Program

UNEP: United Nations Environment Program

UNESCO: United Nations Educational, Scientific, and Cultural Organization

UNFICYP: United Nations Forces in Cyprus

UNFPA: United Nations Fund for Population Activities; see UN Population Fund (UNFPA)

UNHCR: United Nations Office of the High Commissioner for Refugees

UNICEF: United Nations Children's Fund

UNIDO: United Nations Industrial Development Organization

UNIFIL: United Nations Interim Force in Lebanon

UNIKOM: United Nations Iraq-Kuwait Observation Mission

UNITAR: United Nations Institute for Training and Research

UNMIH: United Nations Mission in Haiti

UNMOGIP: United Nations Military Observer Group in India and Pakistan

UNOMIG: United Nations Observer Mission in Georgia

UNOMIL: United Nations Observer Mission in Liberia

UNOMOZ: United Nations Operation in Mozambique

UNOMUR: United Nations Observer Mission Uganda-Rwanda

UNOSOM: United Nations Operation in Somalia

UNPROFOR: United Nations Protection Force

UNRISD: United Nations Research Institute for Social Development

UNRWA: United Nations Relief and Works Agency for Palestine Refugees in the Near East

UNTAC: United Nations Transitional Authority in Cambodia

UNTSO: United Nations Truce Supervision Organization

UNU: United Nations University

UPU: Universal Postal Union

USSR/EE: USSR/Eastern Europe

WADB: West African Development Bank

WCL: World Confederation of Labor

WEU: Western European Union

WFC: World Food Council

WFP: World Food Program

WFTU: World Federation of Trade Unions

WHO: World Health Organization

WIPO: World Intellectual Property Organization

WMO: World Meteorological Organization

WP: Warsaw Pact

WTO: World Trade Organization

WtoO: World Tourism Organization

ZC: Zangger Committee

IMPERIAL/METRIC CONVERSION KEY

WHEN YOU KNOW	MULTIPLY BY	TO FIND	WHEN YOU KNOW	MULTIPLY BY	TO FIND
Length			**Length**		
Millimeters (mm)	0.04	inches (in)	inches (in)	25.4	millimeters
Centimeters (cm)	0.4	inches (in)	inches (in)	2.54	centimeters (cm)
Meters (m)	3.3	feet (ft)	feet (ft)	30.5	centimeters (cm)
Meters (m)	1.1	yards (yd)	yards (yd)	0.9	meters (m)
Kilometers (km)	0.6	miles (mi)	miles (m)	1.1	kilometers (km)
Area			**Area**		
sq. centimeters (cm²)	0.155	sq. inches (in²)	sq. inches (in²)	6.45	sq. centimeters (cm²)
sq. meters (m²)	10.76	sq. feet (ft²)	sq. feet (ft²)	0.09	sq. meters (m²)
sq. meters (m²)	1.2	sq. yards (yd²)	sq. yards (yd²)	0.84	sq. meters (m²)
sq. kilometers (km²)	0.4	sq. miles (mi²)	sq. miles (mi²)	0.4	sq. kilometers (km²)
hectares (ha)	2.5	acres	acres	0.4	hectares (ha)
Weight			**Weight**		
grams (g)	0.035	ounces (oz)	ounces (oz)	28.0	grams (g)
kilograms (km)	2.2	pounds (lbs)	pounds (lbs)	0.45	kilograms (kg)
metric tons (t)	1.1	short tons (2,000 lbs)	short tons (2,000 lbs)	0.9	metric tons (t)
Volume			**Volume**		
milliliters (ml)	0.03	fluid ounces (fl oz)	fluid ounces (fl oz)	30.0	milliliters (ml)
liters (L)	2.1	pints (pt)	pints (pt)	0.47	liters (L)
liters (L)	1.06	quarts (qt)	quarts (qt)	.95	liters (L)
liters (L)	0.26	gallons (gal)	gallons (gal)	3.8	liters (L)
cubic meters (m³)	35.0	cubic feet (ft³)	cubic feet (ft³)	0.03	cubic meters (m³)
cubic meters (m³)	1.3	cubic yards (yd³)	cubic yards (yd³)	0.76	cubic meters (m³)
Temperature			**Temperature**		
Celsius (°C)	9/5 + 32	Fahrenheit (°F)	Fahrenheit (°F)	5/9 − 32	Celsius (°C)

STATUS OF NATIONS

COUNTRY NAME: SYSTEM OF GOVERNMENT

Afghanistan: transitional government

Albania: emerging democracy

Algeria: republic

American Samoa: unincorporated territory of the United States

Andorra: parliamentary democracy

Angola: transitional government, nominally a multiparty democracy with a strong presidential system

Anguilla: British crown colony

Antigua and Barbuda: parliamentary democracy

Argentina: republic

Armenia: republic

Aruba: parliamentary

Australia: democratic, federal-state system recognizing the British monarch as sovereign

Austria: federal republic

Azerbaijan: republic

Bahamas, The: commonwealth

Bahrain: traditional monarchy

Bangladesh: republic

Barbados: parliamentary democracy

Belarus: republic

Belgium: federal parliamentary democracy under a constitutional monarch

Belize: parliamentary democracy

Benin: republic under multiparty democratic rule

Bermuda: British crown colony

Bhutan: monarchy

Bolivia: republic

Bosnia and Herzegovina: emerging democracy

Botswana: parliamentary republic

Brazil: federal republic

British Virgin Islands: British crown colony

Brunei: constitutional sultanate

Bulgaria: republic

Burkina Faso: parliamentary

Burundi: republic

Cambodia: multiparty liberal democracy under a constitutional monarchy

Cameroon: unitary republic; multiparty presidential regime (opposition parties legalized in 1990)

Canada: federation with parliamentary democracy

Cape Verde: republic

Cayman Islands: British crown colony

Central African Republic: republic

Chad: republic

Chile: republic

China: Communist state

Christmas Island: territory of Australia

Colombia: republic; executive branch dominates government structure

Comoros: independent republic

Congo, Democratic Republic of: dictatorship; presumably undergoing a transition to representative government

Congo, Republic of: republic

Cook Islands: self-governing parliamentary democracy

Costa Rica: democratic republic

Cote d'Ivoire: republic

Croatia: presidential/parliamentary democracy

Cuba: Communist state

Cyprus: republic

Czech Republic: parliamentary democracy

Denmark: constitutional monarchy

Djibouti: republic

Dominica: parliamentary democracy

Dominican Republic: republic

Ecuador: republic

Egypt: republic

El Salvador: republic

Equatorial Guinea: republic in transition to multiparty democracy

Eritrea: transitional government

Estonia: parliamentary democracy

Ethiopia: federal republic

Falkland Islands: British crown colony

Faroe Islands: part of the Kingdom of Denmark; self-governing overseas administrative division of Denmark since 1948

Fiji: republic

Finland: republic

France: republic

French Guiana: French overseas department

French Polynesia: territory of France

Gabon: republic; multiparty presidential regime

Gambia, The: republic under multiparty democratic rule

Georgia: republic

Germany: federal republic

Ghana: constitutional democracy

Gibraltar: British crown colony

Greece: parliamentary republic

Greenland: part of the Kingdom of Denmark; self-governing overseas administrative division of Denmark since 1979

Grenada: parliamentary democracy

Guadeloupe: overseas department and administrative region of France

Guam: unincorporated territory of the United States

Guatemala: republic

Guernsey: dependency of the British crown

Guinea: republic

Guinea-Bissau: republic

Guyana: republic

Haiti: republic

Honduras: republic

Hungary: republic

Iceland: constitutional republic

India: federal republic

Indonesia: republic

Iran: theocratic republic

Iraq: republic

Ireland: republic

Israel: republic

Italy: republic

Jamaica: parliamentary democracy

Japan: constitutional monarchy

Jersey: dependency of the British crown

Jordan: constitutional monarchy

Kazakstan: republic

Kenya: republic

Kiribati: republic

Korea, North: Communist state; one-man dictatorship

Korea, South: republic

Kuwait: nominal constitutional monarchy

Kyrgyzstan: republic

Laos: Communist state

Latvia: parliamentary democracy

Lebanon: republic

Lesotho: parliamentary constitutional monarchy

Liberia: republic

Libya: Jamahiriya (a state of the masses) in theory, governed by the populace through local councils; in fact, a military dictatorship

Liechtenstein: hereditary constitutional monarchy

Lithuania: parliamentary democracy

Luxembourg: constitutional monarchy

Macau: Chinese province

Macedonia: emerging democracy

Madagascar: republic

Malawi: multiparty democracy

Malaysia: constitutional monarchy

Maldives: republic

Mali: republic

Malta: parliamentary democracy

Man, Isle of: British crown dependency

Marshall Islands: constitutional government in free association with the US

Martinique: overseas department and administrative region of France

Mauritania: republic

Mauritius: parliamentary democracy

Mayotte: territory of France

Mexico: federal republic operating under a centralized government

Micronesia, Federated States of: constitutional government in free association with the US

Midway Islands: territory of the United States

Moldova: republic

Monaco: constitutional monarchy

Mongolia: republic

Montenegro: republic

Montserrat: British crown colony

Morocco: constitutional monarchy

Mozambique: republic

Myanmar: military regime

Namibia: republic

Nauru: republic

Nepal: parliamentary democracy

Netherlands: constitutional monarchy

Netherlands Antilles: parliamentary

New Caledonia: territory of France

New Zealand: parliamentary democracy

Nicaragua: republic

Niger: republic

Nigeria: republic transitioning from military to civilian rule

Niue: self-governing parliamentary democracy

Norfolk Island: territory of Australia

Northern Mariana Islands: commonwealth

Norway: constitutional monarchy

Oman: monarchy

Pakistan: federal republic

Palau: constitutional government in free association with the US

Panama: constitutional republic

Papua New Guinea: parliamentary democracy

Paraguay: republic

Peru: republic

Philippines: republic

Poland: democratic state

Portugal: parliamentary democracy

Puerto Rico: commonwealth

Qatar: traditional monarchy

Reunion: overseas department of France

Romania: republic

Russia: republic

Rwanda: republic

Saint Helena: British dependency

Saint Kitts and Nevis: constitutional monarchy

Saint Lucia: constitutional monarchy

Saint Pierre and Miquelon: French territorial collectivity

Saint Vincent and the Grenadines: constitutional monarchy

Samoa: constitutional monarchy under native chief

San Marino: republic

Sao Tome and Principe: republic

Saudi Arabia: monarchy

Senegal: republic under multiparty democratic rule

Serbia: republic

Seychelles: republic

Sierra Leone: constitutional democracy

Singapore: republic within Commonwealth

Slovakia: parliamentary democracy

Slovenia: parliamentary democratic republic

Solomon Islands: parliamentary democracy

Somalia: none

South Africa: republic

Spain: parliamentary monarchy

Sri Lanka: republic

Sudan: transitional

Suriname: republic

Swaziland: monarchy

Sweden: constitutional monarchy

Switzerland: federal republic

Syria: republic under military regime since March 1963

Taiwan: multiparty democratic regime headed by popularly elected president

Tajikistan: republic

Tanzania: republic

Thailand: constitutional monarchy

Togo: republic under transition to multiparty democratic rule

Tonga: hereditary constitutional monarchy

Trinidad and Tobago: parliamentary democracy

Tunisia: republic

Turkey: republican parliamentary democracy

Turkmenistan: republic

Turks and Caicos: British dependency

Tuvalu: constitutional monarchy with a parliamentary democracy

Uganda: republic

Ukraine: republic

United Arab Emirates: federation with specified powers delegated to the UAE federal government and other powers reserved to member emirates

United Kingdom: constitutional monarchy

United States: federal republic; strong democratic tradition

Uruguay: republic

Uzbekistan: republic; effectively authoritarian presidential rule, with little power outside the executive branch; executive power concentrated in the presidency

Vanuatu: republic

Vatican City: monarchical-sacerdotal state

Venezuela: republic

Vietnam: Communist state

Virgin Islands: territory of the United States

Wallis and Futuna: French overseas territory

Yemen: republic

Zambia: republic

Zimbabwe: parliamentary democracy

SOURCES OF STATISTICS

GEOGRAPHY—1

SOURCE. U.S. Central Intelligence Agency (CIA) 1998, *The World Factbook 1998* [Online]. Available: http://www.cia.gov/cia/publications/factbook/index.html [October 1999].

NOTES.

Comparative area—Based on total area equivalents. Most entities are compared with the entire United States or one of the 50 states. The smaller entities are compared with Washington, D.C. (178 square km, 69 square miles), or the Mall in Washington, D.C. (0.59 square km, 0.23 square miles, 146 acres).

km—Kilometers.

Land area—Aggregate of all surfaces delimited by international boundaries and/or coastlines, excluding inland water bodies (lakes, reservoirs, rivers).

Land use—Human use of the land surface is categorized as *arable land*—land cultivated for crops that are replanted after each harvest (wheat, maize, rice); *permanent crops*—land cultivated for crops that are not replanted after each harvest (citrus, coffee, rubber); *meadows and pastures*—land permanently used for herbaceous forage crops; *forest and woodland*—land under dense or open stands of trees; and *other*—any land type not specifically mentioned above (urban areas, roads, deserts).

mi—Miles.

NA—Data are not available.

Total area—Sum of all land and water area delimited by international boundaries and/or coastlines.

DEMOGRAPHICS—2A

SOURCE. U.S. Bureau of the Census (1998). *International Database 1998* [Online]. Available: http://www.census.gov:80/ipc/www/wp98.html [October 1999].

NOTES.

NA—Data are not available.

DEMOGRAPHICS—2B

SOURCE. U.S. Central Intelligence Agency (CIA) 1998, *The World Factbook 1998* [Online]. Available: http://www.cia.gov/cia/publications/factbook/index.html [October 1999].

NOTES.

NA—Data are not available.

HEALTH PERSONNEL—3

SOURCE. The World Bank, *World Development Indicators 1999* (March 1999), pages 90–92. Reprinted with permission.

United Nations Development Program (UNDP) and Oxford University Press, *Human Development Report 1999*, pages 172–175. Reprinted with permission.

NOTES.

Public Health Expenditure—This category consists of recurrent and capital spending from government (central and local) budgets, external borrowings and grants (including donations from international agencies and nongovernmental organizations), and social (or compulsory) health insurance funds.

Private Health Expenditure—This category includes direct household (out-of-pocket) spending, private insurance, charitable donations, and direct service payments by private corporations.

FOOTNOTES.

a—Data are for the most recent year available.

b—Data may not sum to totals because of rounding.

c—Data refer to 1993 or a year around 1993.

HEALTH CARE INDICATORS—4

SOURCE. The World Bank, *World Development Indicators 1999* (March 1999), pages 94–112. Reprinted with permission.

United Nations Development Program (UNDP) and Oxford University Press, *Human Development Report 1999*, pages 211–214. Reprinted with permission.

NOTES.

Percentage of Population with Access to Safe Water.—This is the share of the population with reasonable access to an adequate amount of safe water (including treated surface water and untreated but uncontaminated water, such as from springs, sanitary wells, and protected boreholes). In urban areas the source may be a public fountain or standpipe located not more than 200 meters away. In rural areas the definition implies that members of a household do not have to spend a disproportionate part of the day fetching water. An adequate amount of safe water is that needed to satisfy metabolic, hygienic, and domestic requirements—usually about 20 liters a person a day. The definition of safe water has changed over time.

Percentage of Population with Access to Sanitation.—This is the share of the population with at least adequate excreta disposal facilities that can effectively prevent human, animal, and insect contact with excreta. Suitable facilities range from simple but protected pit latrines to flush toilets with sewerage. To be effective, all facilities must be correctly constructed and properly maintained.

Adult HIV Prevalence—This is the percentage of people aged 15-49 who are infected with human immunodeficiency virus (HIV).

FOOTNOTES.

...—Data are not available.

a—Data are for most recent year available.

b—Official estimate.

c—UNICEF-WHO estimate based on statistical modeling.

d—Indirect estimate based on a sample survey.

e—Based on a survey covering 30 provinces.

f—Based on a sample survey.

INFANTS & MALNUTRITION—5

SOURCE. United Nations Children's Fund (UNICEF), *The State of the World's Children 1999*, pages 94–105.

The World Bank and Oxford University Press, *Entering the 21st Century: World Development Report 1999/2000* (August 1999), pages 232 and 233. Reprinted with permission.

The World Bank, *World Development Indicators 1999* (March 1999), pages 98–101. Reprinted with permission.

NOTES.

Under-five mortality rate—Probability of dying between birth and exactly five years of age expressed per 1,000 live births.

Low birthweight—Weights at birth that are less than 2,500 grams.

TB—Tuberculosis

DPT—Diphtheria, pertussis (whooping cough) and tetanus.

Prevalence of child malnutrition—Expressed in percentage of children under age 5.

FOOTNOTES.

NA—Data are not available.

x—Indicates data that refer to years other than those specified, differ from the standard definitions, or refer to only part of a country.

a—Data are for the most recent year available within the range listed.

b—Data are for the most recent year available within the range.

ETHNIC DIVISION—6

SOURCE. U.S. Central Intelligence Agency (CIA) 1998, *The World Factbook 1998* [Online]. Available: http://www.cia.gov/cia/publications/factbook/index.html [October 1999].

NOTES.

Tables show the major ethnic divisions of peoples in the given country for the most recent year available. When available, the distribution is shown in percent.

NA—Data are not available.

RELIGION—7

SOURCE. U.S. Central Intelligence Agency (CIA) 1998, *The World Factbook 1998* [Online]. Available: http://www.cia.gov/cia/publications/factbook/index.html [October 1999].

NOTES.

Tables show major religious denominations of the peoples of the given country for the most recent year available. When available, the distribution is shown in percent.

NA—Data are not available.

MAJOR LANGUAGES—8

SOURCE. U.S. Central Intelligence Agency (CIA) 1998, *The World Factbook 1998* [Online]. Available: http://www.cia.gov/cia/publications/factbook/index.html [October 1999].

NOTES.

Tables show major language(s) spoken by inhabitants of the given country for the most recent year available. When available, the distribution is shown in percent.

NA—Data are not available.

PUBLIC EDUCATION EXPENDITURES—9

SOURCE. The World Bank, *World Development Indicators 1999* (March 1999), pages 74–77. Reprinted with permission.

NOTES.

The data on education spending refer solely to public spending—that is, government spending on public education plus subsidies for private education. The data generally exclude foreign aid for education.

They also may exclude religious schools, which play a significant role in many developing countries.

The percentage of GNP devoted to education can be interpreted as reflecting a country's effort in education. Often it bears a weak relationship to measures of output of the education system, as reflected in educational attainment. The pattern suggests wide variations across countries in the efficiency with which the government's resources are translated into education outcomes.

Public Expenditures of Education.—This is the percentage of GNP accounted for by public spending on public education plus subsidies to private education at the primary, secondary, and tertiary levels.

Expenditure of Teaching Materials.—The public spending on teaching materials (textbooks, books, and other scholastic supplies) as a percentage of total public spending on primary or secondary education.

FOOTNOTES.

1—Data are for years or periods other than those specified.

EDUCATION ATTAINMENT—10

SOURCE. United Nations Education, Scientific, and Cultural Organization and Bernan Press, *UNESCO 1999 Statistical Yearbook*, pages 51–64. Reprinted with permission.

NOTES.

The percentage distribution of the population aged 25 years and over according to the highest level of education attained reflects both the outcomes of participation in education in the past and the educational composition of the population. These data have been collected mainly during national population censuses and sample surveys. The six levels of educational attainment presented here are based on the International Standard Classification of Education (ISCED) and are defined as follows:

No schooling—Refers to persons who have completed less than one year of primary education.

Primary education incomplete—Includes all persons who have completed at least one grade of primary education but who did not complete the final grade of this level of education.

Primary education completed—Refers to all persons who have completed the final grade of primary education but did not enter secondary education.

Attended lower secondary education—Comprises all persons who have attended lower secondary education but not (upper) secondary education.

Attended (upper) secondary education—Includes all persons who have attended (upper) secondary education but not post-secondary education.

Post-secondary education—Refers to all persons who have completed secondary education and attended post-secondary education.

FOOTNOTES.

1—Not including persons with no schooling or less than one year of primary education.

2—The category "No Schooling" comprises illiterates.

3—"Completed primary education" refers to the last two years of primary education.

4—Persons who can read and write have been counted with "incomplete primary."

5—Not including population attending and never attended school.

6—Data refer only to persons who have attended school but left school.

7—Based on a sample survey of 35,502 persons.

8—Not including persons still in school.

9—Based on a sample survey of 51,372 persons.

10—Post-secondary education refers to universities only.

11—Not including transients and residents of former canal zone.

12—The category "No schooling" refers to those who have attended less than one grade of primary education.

13—Not including armed forces stationed in the area.

14—Lower secondary education refers to "intermedio" level of education. (Upper) secondary education refers to "Media," "Tecnica" and "Normal" education.

15—Not including rural population of Northern Brazil.

16—Not including persons whose level of education is unknown.

17—Not including Jammu and Kashmir.

18—Not including persons still attending school for whom the level is unknown.

19—Household survey results based on a sample of 6,393 households. The category of "No schooling" includes illiterates.

20—(Upper) secondary education includes 'polytechnic'; post-secondary education refers to universities only.

21—Data are based on a sample of 8,619 households (5,563 urban and 3,056 rural) from the 1993 Demographic and Health Survey.

22—"Incomplete primary education" refers to grades 1 to 4 and "Complete primary education" refers to grades 5 to 8.

23—Not including expatriate workers and their families.

24—The category "No schooling" includes persons who are still in school.

25—The category "No schooling" comprises persons who did not state their level of education.

26—Based on a 20% sample of census returns.

LITERACY RATES—11A

SOURCE. United Nations Education and Culture Organization (UNESCO), *Compendium of Statistics on Illiteracy* (1995 Edition), pages 40–49. Reprinted with permission.

NOTES.

Literacy statistics are concerned with the stock of persons who have successfully acquired the basic reading, writing and numerical skills essential for personal growth and cohesion within contemporary societies. Levels of literacy within a population constitute on the one hand a reflection of the level of development and accomplishments of the education systems, and on the other hand a pointer on the potential for human input into further economic, social and cultural development. Literacy rate has therefore been widely used as a key common indicator for monitoring and assessing progress in the current world thrusts of Education for All and Human Resources Development, and has been regularly incorporated into various reports and publications.

As the national statistics on literacy made available to UNESCO are collected during population censuses that usually take place once every ten years, estimations and projections are carried out to fill the data gaps for the years between two censuses, as well as to provide projections showing likely progress in literacy for the future.

Literacy continues to progress in the world. Adult literacy rate, or the percentage of literates within the adult population aged 15 years and over, has been steadily growing in all countries. Entering the 1990s, over three-quarters (75.3 percent) of the world's adult population have become literate—increasing from 69.5 percent in 1980. Based on the past trends, it is estimated that the overall literacy rate in the world has further improved to 77.4 percent in 1995, and is projected to reach 80 percent at the beginning of the 21st century.

The literate adult population in the world has undergone phenomenal expansion during the past fifteen years from 1980 to 1995, and is projected to further increase in the future. In absolute numbers, the adult literate population in the world rose from 2 billion in 1980 to an estimated 3 billion in 1995, i.e. by 1 billion persons. If the current rate of progress can be maintained, the number of adult literates in the world may reach 3.4 billions in the year 2000, and 4.2 billion in 2010.

Despite these signs of positive progress in both literacy rates and number of literates, one may notice that there remains a large illiterate population in the world of today—numbering some 885 million adults aged 15 years and over—and that this illiterate population increased from an estimated 877 million in 1980. The expansion of the world's illiterate population seems to have reached its turning point during the first half of the 1990s. The projections show that if the past trend were to continue, this world total would gradually decrease to some 881 million by the year 2000. But the huge mass of more than 880 million illiterates shall continue to constitute major challenges to education in the future.

Literate—A person is literate who can with understanding both read and write a short simple statement on his everyday life.

Illiterate—A person is illiterate who cannot with understanding both read and write a short simple statement on his everyday life.

Adult—Refers to persons aged 15 years or older.

LITERACY RATES—11B

SOURCE. United Nations Children's Fund (UNICEF), *The State of the World's Children 1999*, pages 106–109.

NOTES.

Adult Literacy Rate—Percentage of persons aged 15 years and over who can read and write.

-—Data not available.

X—Indicates data that refer to years or periods other than those specified, differ from the standard definitions, or refer to only part of a country.

POLITICAL PARTIES—12

SOURCE. U.S. Central Intelligence Agency (CIA) 1998, *The World Factbook 1998* [Online]. Available: http://www.cia.gov/cia/publications/factbook/index.html [October 1999].

NOTES.

When available, political party representation is shown for the lower house of the legislative branch of government. The lower house was chosen in order to present, in most cases, a picture of the electoral results of voting by the general public. The name of this legislative body is shown in the legend of the given table.

When available, election results are shown as a percent distribution of votes in the most recent election. Otherwise, percent distribution of seats, or number of seats, by political party is shown. If there are no political parties or there is one-party rule, this information is provided in place of tabular data.

Wherever possible, political party names have been presented in English translation.

NA—Data are not available.

GOVERNMENT BUDGETS—13A

SOURCE. International Monetary Fund (IMF), *Government Finance Statistics Yearbook 1998*, pages 18–421.

FOOTNOTES.

f—Forecast.

p—Preliminary / provisional.

....—Data not available.

——Zero or less than half a significant digit.

GOVERNMENT BUDGET—13B

SOURCE. U.S. Central Intelligence Agency (CIA) 1998, *The World Factbook 1998* [Online]. Available: http://www.cia.gov/cia/publications/factbook/index.html [October 1999].

NOTES.

IMF data were obtained primarily by means of a detailed questionnaire distribution to government finance statistics correspondents, who are usually located in each country's respective ministry of finance or central bank. Three of the six categories of central government expenditure shown in the IMF tables are comprised of subcategories, whose subtotals have been summed. Below is a list of these subcategories.

Education/Health—Also includes *Welfare* and *Social security.*

Industry—Includes *Fuel and energy; Agriculture, forestry, fishing, and hunting; Mining, manufacturing, and construction; Transportation and communication;* and *Other economic affairs and services.*

Other—Includes *Recreational, cultural, and religious affairs and other expenditures.*

Some of the subcategory data are incomplete for Guatemala, India, and Nepal, and consequently have been calculated as zero (0).

Minor differences between published totals and the sum of components are attributable to rounding.

Following are definitions of acronyms and terms pertinent to these tables.

Central government—All units representing the territorial jurisdiction of the central authority throughout a country.

CY—Calendar year: 12-month year beginning January 1 and ending the following December 31.

A dash (-)—Data are nil or negligible.

est.—Estimate.

Expenditure—All nonrepayable payments by government, including both capital and current expenditures and regardless of whether goods or services were received for such expenditures.

FY—Fiscal Year: presented within the calendar year containing the greatest number of months for that fiscal year. Fiscal years ending June 30 are presented within the same calendar year. For example, the fiscal year July 1, 1995–June 30, 1996 is shown within the calendar year 1996.

Government—All units that implement public policy by providing nonmarket services and transferring income; these units are financed mainly by compulsory levies on other sectors.

NA—Data are not available.

Revenue—All nonrepayable government receipts other than grants.

MILITARY AFFAIRS—14A

SOURCE. U.S. Central Intelligence Agency (CIA) 1998, *The World Factbook 1998* [Online]. Available: http://www.cia.gov/cia/publications/factbook/index.html [October 1999].

FOOTNOTES.

e—Estimate based on partial or uncertain data.

NA—Data not available.

0—Nil or negligible.

MILITARY AFFAIRS—14B

SOURCE. U.S. Arms Control and Disarmament Agency, *World Military Expenditures and Arms Transfers 1996* (WMEAT), (July 1997), pages 57–99 and 108–150.

NOTES.

Military Expenditures

For NATO countries, military expenditures are from NATO publications and are based on the NATO definition. In this definition, (a) civilian-type expenditures of the defense ministry are excluded and military-type expenditures of other ministries are included; (b) grant military assistance is included in the expenditures of the donor country; and (c) purchases of military equipment for credit are included at the time the debt is incurred, not at the time of payment.

For other non-communist countries, data are generally the expenditures of the ministry of defense. When these are known to include the costs of internal security, an attempt is made to remove these expenditures. A wide variety of data sources is used for these countries, including the publications and data resources of other U.S. government agencies, standardized reporting to the United Nations by country, and other international sources.

It should be recognized by users of the statistical tables that the military expenditure data are of uneven accuracy and completeness. For example, there are indications or reasons to believe that the military expenditures reported by some countries consist mainly or entirely of recurring or operating expenditures and omit all or most capital expenditures, including arms purchases.

In some cases it is believed that a better estimate of total military expenditures is obtained by adding to nominal military expenditures the value of arms imports. It must be cautioned, however, that this method may over- or underestimate the actual expenditures in a given year due to the fact that payment for arms may not coincide in time with deliveries. Also, arms acquisitions in some cases may be financed by, or consist of grants from, other countries.

For countries that have major clandestine nuclear or other military weapons development programs, such as Iraq, estimation of military expenditures is extremely difficult and especially subject to errors of underestimation.

Further information in the quality of the military expenditure data presented for countries throughout the world will be difficult to achieve without better reporting by the countries themselves. As has been noted elsewhere, "There is growing evidence that important amounts of security expenditures may not enter the accounts or the national budgets of many developing countries." Among the mechanisms commonly used to obscure such expenditures are: double-bookkeeping budget categories, military assistance, and manipulation or foreign exchange.

Particular problems arise in estimating the military expenditures of communist countries due to the exceptional scarcity and ambiguity of released information. As in past editions of this publication, data on the military expenditures of the Soviet Union are based on Central Intelligence Agency (CIA) estimates. For most of the series, these are estimates of what it would cost in the United States in dollars to develop, procure, staff, and operate a military force similar to that of the Soviet Union. Estimates of this type—that is, those based entirely on one country's price pattern—generally overstate the relative size of the second country's expenditures in intercountry comparisons. Also, such estimates are not consistent with the methods used here for converting other countries' expenditures into dollars.

Nevertheless, the basic CIA estimates are the best available for present purposes; in fact, there are no alternative estimates that can inspire confidence and have the capability to detect relatively small changes over time, such as the slowdown and decline in Soviet military spending that the CIA estimates have indicated.

For Russia, estimated military spending trends in rubles are used in conjunction with dollar estimates for earlier years to make rough estimates of spending in dollars.

For former Warsaw Pact countries other than the Soviet Union, the estimates of military expenditures through 1989 are from Thad P. Alton et al. These estimates cover the officially announced state budget expenditures on national defense and thus understate total military expenditures to the extent of possible defense outlays by non-defense agencies of the central government, local governments, and economic enterprises. Possible subsidization of military procurement may also cause understatement. The dollar estimates were derived by calculating pay and allowances at the current full U.S. average rates for officers and for lower ranks. After subtraction of pay and allowances, the remainder of the official defense budgets in national currencies was converted into dollars at overall rates based on comparisons of the various countries' GNPs expressed in dollars and in national currencies. The

rates are based in part on the purchasing power parites (PPPs) estimated by the International Comparison Project of the United Nations, including there latest (Phase V) versions.

Estimates for these countries in 1990 and 1991 are based on total military spending in national currency as reported by the respective governments to the UN (in most cases) or the IMF. These expenditures in toto are converted to dollars at the Alton GNP conversion rates for 1989 as adjusted to 1991 by the respective U.S. and national GNP deflators (per the World Bank), without estimating personnel compensation separately at U.S. dollar rates, as was done for earlier years. The resulting military conversion rates (in national currency per dollar) are substantially lower than the 1991 market rate, and approximately the same as the implied rate for GNP.

Estimates for the newly independent states of the former Soviet Union, Yugoslavia, and Czechoslovakia and other former Warsaw Pact countries present difficulties due to scarcity of reliable data in national currencies and to problems in converting to dollars. The basic method employed for most of these countries was to establish the ratio of military expenditures to GNP in national currency and then to multiply this ratio by the World Bank's estimate of GNP in dollars as converted to international dollars by estimate PPPs and reported in the *World Bank Atlas 1997.* This method implicitly converts military spending at the GNP-wide PPP, which, as with conversion by exchange rates, preserves the same ME/GNP ratio in dollars as obtains in national currency.

Data for China are based on U.S. Government estimates of the yuan costs of Chinese forces, weapons, programs, and activities. Costs in yuan are here converted to dollars using the same estimated conversion rate as used for GNP. Due to the exceptional difficulties in both estimating yuan costs and converting them to dollars, comparisons of Chinese military spending with other data should be treated as having a wide margin of error.

Other published sources used include the *Government Finance Statistics Yearbook,* issued by the International Monetary Fund; *The World Factbook,* produced annually the Central Intelligence Agency; *The Military Balance,* issued by the International Institute for Strategic Studies (London); and the *SIPRI Yearbook: World Armaments and Disarmament,* issued by the Stockholm International Peach Research Institute.

Gross National Product (GNP)

GNP represents the total output of goods and services produced by residents of a country, valued at market prices. The source of GNP data for most noncommunist countries is the International Bank for Reconstruction and Development (World Bank).

For a number of countries whose GNP is dominated by oil exports (Bahrain, Kuwait, Libya, Oman, Qatar, Saudi Arabia, and the United Arab Emirates), the World Bank's estimate of deflated (or constant price) GNP in domestic currency tends to understate increases in the monetary value of oil exports, and thus of GNP, resulting from oil price increases. These World Bank estimates are designed to measure real (or physical) product. An alternative estimate of constant-price GNP was therefore obtained using the implicit price deflator for U.S. GNP (for lack of a better national deflator). This considered appropriate because a large share of the GNP of these countries is realized in U.S. dollars.

GNP estimates of the Soviet Union are by the CIA, as published in its *Handbook of Economic Statistics 1990* and updated. GNP estimates for other Warsaw Pact countries through 1989 are from ''East European Military Expenditures, 1965–1978,'' by Thad P. Alton and others, *op. cit.,* as updated and substantially revised by the authors. These estimates through 1989 have been extended to 1990 and 1991 on the basis of estimates for those years in the CIA's *Handbook of Economic Statistics, 1992.*

Estimates of GNP in 1992–1994 for successor states to the Soviet Union, Yugoslavia, and Czechoslovakia are based on World Bank estimates of GNP per capita employing PPPs and population, as published in the *World Bank Atlas 1997.*

GNP data for China are based on World Bank estimates in yuan. These are in line with estimates of GDP in Western accounting terms made by Chinese authorities. Converting estimates in yuan to dollars is highly problematic, however, due to the inappropriateness of the official exchange rate and lack of sufficient yuan price information by which to reliably estimate PPPs. (The ratio of the highest to the lowest estimates by various sources of China's GNP is on the order of 6 or 7 to 1, which would make the world rank of China's GNP vary between about third or fourth and twelfth). The conversion rate used here is based on a PPP estimated for 1981 and moved by respective U.S. and China implicit GNP deflators to 1994.

GNP estimates for a few non-communist countries are from the CIA's *Handbook of Economic Statistics* cited above. Estimates for the other communist countries are rough approximations.

Military Expenditures-to-GNP Ratio

It should be noted that the meaning of the ratio of military expenditures to GNP differs somewhat between most communist (or previously communist) and other countries. For non-communist countries, both military expenditures and GNP are converted from the national currency unit to dollars at the same exchange rate; consequently, the ratio of military expenditures to GNP is the same in dollars as in the national currency and reflects national relative prices. For communist countries, however, military expenditures and GNP are converted differently. Soviet military expenditures, as already noted, are estimated in a way designed to show the cost of the Soviet armed forces in U.S. prices, as if purchased in this country. On the other hand, the Soviet GNP estimates used here are designed to

show average relative size when both U.S. and Soviet GNP are valued and compared at both dollar and ruble prices. The Soviet ratio of military expenditures to GNP in ruble terms, the preferred method of comparison, is estimated to have been 15-18% in that country's latest years.

The estimated ratio for Russia derived here in dollars is probably somewhat overstated since military spending in dollars is relative to earlier estimates for the Soviet Union, while GNP estimates (at PPPs) are by the World Bank. Russia's burden ratio in ruble term is preferably estimated to be under 10%.

For Eastern European countries before 1992, the ratios of military expenditures to GNP in dollars were about twice the ratios that would obtain in domestic currencies. However, since official military budgets in these countries probably substantially understated their actual military expenditures, the larger ratios on dollar estimates are believed to be the better approximations of the actual ratios.

Central Government Expenditures (CGE)

These expenditures include current and capital (developmental) expenditures plus net lending to the government enterprises by central (or federal) governments. A major source is the International Monetary Fund's *Government Finance Statistics Yearbook.* The category used here is ''Total Expenditures and Lending minus Repayment, Consolidated Central Government.''

Other sources for these data are the International Monetary Fund, *International Financial Statistics* (monthly); OECD, *Economics Surveys;* and CIA, *The World Factbook* (annual). Data for Warsaw Pact countries are from national publications and are supplied by Thad P. Alton and others. For all Warsaw Pact countries and China, conversion to dollars is at the implicit rates used for calculating dollar estimates of GNP.

For all countries, with the same exceptions as noted above for the military expenditures-to-GNP ratio, military expenditures and central government expenditures are converted to dollars at the same rate; the ratio of the two variables is thus the same in dollars as in national currency.

It should be noted that for the Soviet Union, China, Iran, Jordan, and possibly others, the ratio of military expenditures to central government expenditures may be overstated, inasmuch as the estimate for military expenditures is obtained at least in part independently of nominal budget or government expenditure data, and it is possible that not all estimated military expenditures pass through the nominal central government budget.

Population

Population estimates are for midyear and are made available to ACDA by the U.S. Bureau of the Census.

Armed Forces

Armed forces refer to active-duty military personnel, including paramilitary forces if those forces resemble regular units in their organization, equipment, training, or mission. Reserve forces are not included unless specifically noted.

Figures for the United States and all other North American Treaty Organization (NATO) countries are as reported by NATO. Estimates of the number of personnel under arms for other countries are provided by U.S. Government sources. The armed forces series for the Soviet Union includes all special forces judged to have national security missions (e.g., KGB border guards) and excludes uniformed forces primarily performing noncombatant services (construction, railroad, civil defense, and internal security troops).

Arms Transfers

Arms transfers (arms imports and exports) represent the international transfer (under terms of grant, credit, barter, or cash) of military equipment, usually referred to as "conventional," including weapons of war, parts thereof, ammunition, support equipment, and other commodities designed for military use. Among the items included are tactical guided missiles use. Among the items included are tactical guided missiles and rockets, military aircraft, naval vessels, armored and nonarmored military vehicles, communications and electronic equipment, artillery, infantry weapons, small arms, ammunition, other ordinance, parachutes, and uniforms. Dual use equipment, which can have application in both military and civilian sectors, is included when its primary mission is identified as military. The building of defense production facilities and licensing fees paid as royalties for the production of military equipment are included when they are contained in military transfer agreements. There have been no international transfers of purely strategic weaponry. Military services such as training, supply operations, equipment repair, technical assistance, and construction are included where data are available. Excluded are foodstuffs, medical equipment, petroleum products and other supplies.

Redefinition of U.S. Arms Exports. The scope of U.S. arms exports data was modified in the *WMEAT 1995* edition. These exports include both government-to-government transfers under the Foreign Military Sales (FMS), Military Assistance Program (MAP), and other programs administered by the Department of Defense, and commercial (enterprise-to-government) transfers licensed by the Department of State under International Traffic in Arms Regulations. Under the previous practice, the material component (arms, equipment, and "hardware" items) of FMS and MAP sales was included, while the military services component was excluded (although the magnitude and general destination of the omitted services was reported in these Statistical Notes).

Beginning with the previous edition, both the material and the military services components of FMS and other government-to-government sales (such as the International Military Education and Training Program—IMET) are included in total U.S. arms exports as reported here. The commercial sales category, covering both material and military services, was included in its entirety.

The omission of FMS and other military services prior to the previous edition had been intended to improve comparability with available estimates of the arms exports of other countries, which tended to contain a much smaller services component and/or were subject to significant underestimation (services being less easily observed). The increasing importance of these services and the desire to present a full picture of U.S. arms exports consistent with other sources prompted the change to inclusion. Users should be aware, however, of both the lower true share of services in other countries' arms exports and the tendency to underestimate them. It should also be noted that a portion of the IMET program is devoted to programs that promote improved civil-military relations.

The change in scope of U.S. arms exports increased their overall volume by amounts ranging over the last decade from $2.3 billion (current dollars) to $3.7 billion for deliveries and $2.3 billion to $7.3 billion for agreements.

The statistics contained herein are estimates of the value of goods actually delivered during the reference year, in contrast both to payments and the value of programs, agreements, contracts, or orders concluded during the period, which are expected to result in future deliveries.

U.S. Arms Imports. U.S. arms import data in this and the previous four editions of WMEAT are revised upward substantially from earlier editions. The present series consist of data obtained from the Department of Commerce, Bureau of Economic Analysis (BEA), including (a) imports of military-type (formerly "special category") goods, as compiled by the Bureau of the Census, and (b) Department of Defense direct expenditures abroad for major equipment, as compiled from DOD data by BEA. The goods in (a) include: complete military aircraft, all types; engines and turbines for military (naval) ships and boats; tanks, artillery, missiles, guns, and ammunition; military apparel and footwear; and other military goods, equipment, and parts.

Data on countries other than the United States are estimates by U.S. Government sources. Arms transfer data for the Soviet Union and other former communist countries are approximations based on limited information.

It should be noted that the arms transfer estimates for the most recent year, and to a lesser extent for several preceding years, tend to a lesser extent for several preceding years, tend to be understated. This applies to both foreign and U.S. arms exports. In former case, information on transfers comes from a variety of sources and is sometimes acquired and processed with a considerable time lag. In the U.S. case, commercial arms transfer licenses are now valued for three years, causing a delay in the reporting of deliveries made on them to statistical agencies.

Close comparisons between the estimated values shown for arms transfers and for GNP and military expenditures are not warranted. Frequently, weapons prices do not reflect true production costs. Furthermore, much of the international arms trade involves offset or barter arrangements, multiyear loans, discounted prices, third party payments, and partial debt forgiveness. Acquisitions of armaments thus may not [necessarily] impose the burden on an economy, whether in the same or in other years, that is implied by the estimated equivalent U.S. dollar value of the shipment. Therefore, the value of arms imports should be compared to other categories of data with care.

Total Imports and Exports

The values for imports and exports cover merchandise transactions and come mainly from International Financial Statistics published by the IMF. The trade figures for presently and formerly communist countries and from the CIA's *Handbook of Economic Statistics, 1996* edition.

FOOTNOTES.

e—Estimate based on partial or uncertain data.

NA—Data not available.

p—Estimate based on purchasing power parities.

r—Rough estimate.

0—Nil or negligible.

1—Estimated by adding arms imports to data on military expenditures, which are believed to exclude arms purchases. However, it should be noted that the value of arms deliveries in a given year may differ significantly from actual expenditures on arms imports in that year.

2—This ratio is calculated from the dollar values shown in previous columns. In most cases it also is equal to the ratio that could be calculated from national currency values, since both numerator and denominator are usually converted into dollars by the same exchange rate or other conversion factor. In the case of this country, however, the two variables are converted at different rates, yielding a different ratio than would obtain in national currency. The ratio for Russia in rubles terms, for example, is believed to be less than 10 percent in 1995.

3—This series or entry is believed to omit a major share of total military expenditures, probably including most expenditures on arms procurement.

4—Germany, (The Federal Republic of), was known as West Germany through 1990. Thereafter, Germany refers to the unified Germany.

5—In order to reduce distortions in the trend for worked, region, and organization totals caused by

data gaps for individual countries and years, rough approximations for all gaps are included in the totals.

6—To avoid the appearance of excessive accuracy, arms transfer data by country are rounded, with greater severity for larger amounts. All country group totals for arms exports and arms imports shown here are the sums of rounded country data. Consequently, world totals for arms imports and arms exports will not be equal.

7—Total imports and exports usually are as reported by individual countries and the extent to which arms transfers are included is often uncertain. Imports are reported ''cif'' (including cost of shipping, insurance, and freight) and exports are reported ''fob'' (excluding these costs). For these reasons and because of divergent sources, world totals for imports and exports are not equal.

8—Because some countries exclude arms imports or exports from their trade statistics and their ''total'' imports and exports are therefore understated, and because arms transfers may be estimated independently for trade data, the resulting ratios of arms to total imports or exports may be overstated and may even exceed 100 percent.

9—Some part of estimated total military expenditures may not be included in announced central budget expenditures. The ratio of ME to CGE therefore may be overstated.

10—Included major equipment purchased by the U.S. Army Corps of Engineers for use in military construction projects in Saudi Arabia, recorded in U.S. accounts as U.S. imports.

11—U.S. arms imports data shown here is revised upward substantially form reports before 1993.

12—Little data are available because of an ongoing civil war.

CRIME—15

SOURCE. Crime Prevention and Criminal Justice Division, United Nations Criminal Justice Information Network (UNCJIN), *The Fifth United Nations Survey of Crime Trends and Operations of Criminal Justice Systems* [Online], Available: http://www.uncjin.org/stats/wcs.html [October 1999]. Reprinted with permission.

NOTES.

The major goal of the Fifth United Nations Survey is to collect data on the incidence of reported crime and the operations of criminal justice systems with a view to improving the dissemination of that information globally. To that end, the Survey should facilitate an overview of trends and interrelationships between various parts of the criminal justice system so as to promote informed decision making in its administration, nationally and cross-nationally.

As with data collected for the Fourth United Nations Survey, these data demonstrate the difficulty of comparing crime internationally. One difficulty is that the vast majority of incidents that become known to the police come from reports by victims. Thus, credibility becomes a statistical determinant. Another difficulty is that comparison is severely undermined by differences in legal definitions and by administrative procedures regarding counting, classification, and disclosure. The researcher should be aware of these shortcomings when using these data.

NA—Data are not available.

TOTAL LABOR FORCE—16

SOURCE. U.S. Central Intelligence Agency (CIA) 1998, *The World Factbook 1998* [Online]. Available: http://www.cia.gov/cia/publications/factbook/index.html [October 1999].

NOTES.

Data show the number of persons in the labor force for the most recent year available.

NA—Data are not available.

UNEMPLOYMENT RATE—17

SOURCE. U.S. Central Intelligence Agency (CIA) 1998, *The World Factbook 1998* [Online]. Available: http://www.cia.gov/cia/publications/factbook/index.html [October 1999].

NOTES.

Data show the rate of unemployment in percent for the most recent year available.

NA—Data are not available.

ENERGY PRODUCTION—18

SOURCE. U.S. Central Intelligence Agency (CIA) 1998, *The World Factbook 1998* [Online]. Available: http://www.cia.gov/cia/publications/factbook/index.html [October 1999].

NOTES.

Btu—British thermal units.

TRANSPORTATION—19

SOURCE. U.S. Central Intelligence Agency (CIA) 1998, *The World Factbook 1998* [Online]. Available: http://www.cia.gov/cia/publications/factbook/index.html [October 1999].

NOTES.

Following are CIA definitions of terms used in these tables.

Airports—Only airports with usable runways are included in this listing. Not all airports have facilities for refueling, maintenance, or air traffic control. Paved runways have concrete or asphalt surfaces; unpaved runways have grass, dirt, sand, or gravel surfaces.

DWT—Deadweight tons.

GRT—Gross register tons.

km—Kilometers.

m—Meters.

Merchant marine—All ships engaged in the carriage of goods. All commercial vessels (as opposed to all nonmilitary ships), which excludes tugs, fishing vessels, offshore oil rigs, etc. Also, a grouping of merchant ships by nationality or register.

NA—Data are not available.

TOP AGRICULTURAL PRODUCTS—20

SOURCE. U.S. Central Intelligence Agency (CIA) 1998, *The World Factbook 1998* [Online]. Available: http://www.cia.gov/cia/publications/factbook/index.html [October 1999].

NOTES.

GDP—Gross Domestic Product: the value of all goods and services produced within a nation in a given year.

GDP & MANUFACTURING SUMMARY—21

SOURCE. United Nations Industrial Development Organization (UNIDO), *Industrial Development Global Report 1996*, pages 129—254. Reprinted with permission.

NOTES.

Gross domestic product (GDP)—All economic activity in a given country, including activity engaged in by foreign nationals. For example, assets of a General Motors plant in Mexico would contribute to Mexico's GDP. *Real GDP* measures economic activity in constant prices, that is, after adjustments for inflation.

Manufacturing value added (MVA)—The value of output minus the cost of raw materials and other inputs.

FOOTNOTES.

1—Value originating from the National Accounts Statistics.

2—In 1990 constant prices.

3—The data presented here are for activities in the former Federal Republic of Germany and do not include those of the former Democratic Republic of Germany, even after unification in 1990.

Numbers in *italics*—Estimated by UNIDO, Research and Publication Division, Research and Studies Branch.

NA—No value available.

——Value is less than half a unit.

ECONOMIC INDICATORS—22

SOURCE. U.S. Central Intelligence Agency (CIA) 1998, *The World Factbook 1998* [Online]. Available: http://www.cia.gov/cia/publications/factbook/index.html [October 1999].

NOTES.

Following are CIA definitions of acronyms and terms used in these tables.

est.—Estimate.

External debt—The amount of debt owed to foreign entities by the given country.

GDP—Gross domestic product: the value of all goods and services produced within a nation in a given year. Methodology: GDP dollar estimates for all countries are derived from purchasing power parity (PPP) calculations rather than from conversions at official currency exchange rates. The PPP method involves the use of international dollar price weights, which are applied to the quantities of goods and services produced in a given economy. The data derived from the PPP method provide a better comparison of economic well-being between countries. The division of a GDP estimate in domestic currency by the corresponding PPP estimate in dollars gives the PPP conversion rate. When priced in PPPs, $1,000 will buy the same market basket of goods in any country. Whereas PPP estimates for OECD countries are quite reliable, PPP estimates for developing countries are often rough approximations. Most of the GDP estimates are based on extrapolation of numbers published by the UN International Comparison Program and by Professors Robert Summers and Alan Heston of the University of Pennsylvania and their colleagues. Note: the numbers for GDP and other economic data can not be chained together from successive volumes of the *Factbook* because of changes in the U.S. dollar measuring rod, revisions of data by statistical agencies, use of new or different sources of information, and changes in national statistical methods and practices.

Inflation rate—An increase in prices unrelated to value.

NA—Data are not available.

National product—The total output of goods and services in a given country. (See gross domestic product).

BALANCE OF PAYMENTS SUMMARY—23

SOURCE. United Nations Conference on Trade and Development, *Handbook of International Trade and Development Statistics*, pages 214–241.

NOTES.

The following explanatory notes are intended to provide a brief description of the balance of payments categories presented. In actual practice, there are many exceptions to the definitions of categories, and for these the reader should refer to the country notes in the *Balance of Payments Yearbook*.

Exports of goods (fob)—The export figure here differs from that reported in the trade returns because of adjustments for coverage, valuation, timing, inland freight, etc. Such adjustments to the reported export and import figures are necessary in order to make the trade statistics compatible with the concepts employed in the balance of payments. In particular, valuation adjustments are required in those cases in which the market price at which goods have been sold differs from the price used for customs' purposes. This problem in valuation is probably more important for imports than for exports and is likely to be a factor whenever there is a long delay between the date of sale and the date at which an import duty becomes payable.

The coverage of goods in Balance of Payments Manual, 5th edition, has been expanded to include (a) the value of goods (on a gross basis) received/sent for processing and their subsequent export/import in the form of processed goods; (b) the value of repairs on goods; and (c) the value of goods procured in ports by carriers. In Balance of Payments Manual, 4th edition, the net value between goods imported for processing and subsequently re-exported was included in processing services; repairs of goods and goods procured in ports by carriers were also included under services.

Imports of goods (fob)—Adjustments for coverage, valuation, timing, etc., are made to imports reported in trade returns, as described in the notes above. In addition, an adjustment is made to convert imports from a cif to an fob basis for those countries reporting imports cif. The import figures reported here include imports of non-monetary gold.

Balance of goods—Measured on a fob/fob basis and including transactions in monetary gold.

Services and income-debit (total)—Total payments for services and income.

The Balance of Payments Manual, 5th edition, classifies income and services separately; in Balance of Payments Manual, 4th edition, income was a subcomponent of services. Balance of Payments Manual, 5th edition, also reclassifies certain income and services transactions. In Balance of Payments Manual, 4th edition, labor income included non-resident workers' expenditures as well as workers' earnings; in Balance of Payments Manual, 5th edition, workers' earnings are classified under compensation of employees in the income category, and their expenditures appear under travel services. In Balance of Payments Manual, 4th edition, compensation of resident staff of foreign embassies and military bases and of international organizations was included under government services; this compensation is classified as a credit item of compensation of employees in Balance of Payments Manual, 5th edition. Balance of Payments Manual, 4th edition, treated payments for the use of patents, copyrights, and similar non-financial intangible assets as property income; these are regarded as subcomponents of other services in Balance of Payments Manual, 5th edition. In general, the Balance of Payments Manual, 5th edition, concept of income covers investment income plus all forms of compensation of employees; whereas, in Balance of Payments Manual, 4th edition, the concept included investment income, most forms of labor income (including workers' expenditures abroad), and property income.

Services and income-credit (total)—Counterpart to service and income-debit (total).

Current transfers: government-net—Current transfers are classified, according to the sector of the compiling economy, into two main categories: general government and other sectors. General government transfers comprise current international cooperation, which covers current transfers—in cash or in kind—between governments of different economies or between governments and international organizations.

Current transfers: other sectors-net—Current transfers between other sectors of an economy and non-residents comprise those occurring between individuals, between non-governmental institutions or organizations (or between the two groups), or between non-resident governmental institutions and individuals or non-governmental institutions. The same basic items (described in paragraphs 298 to 300 of the IMF Manual) for the government sector are generally applicable to other sectors, although there are some differences within components. In addition, there is the category of workers' remittances.

Balance of current account—Covered in the current account are all transactions (other than those in financial items) that involve economic values and occur between resident and non-resident entities. Also covered are offsets to current economic values provided or acquired without a quid pro quo. Specifically, the major classifications are goods and services, income, and current transfers.

FOOTNOTES.

f.o.b—Free On Board, i.e., the value of goods does not include insurance and freight charges.

..—Data are not available.

———Data are nil or negligible.

EXCHANGE RATES—24

SOURCE. U.S. Central Intelligence Agency (CIA) 1998, *The World Factbook 1998* [Online]. Available: http://www.cia.gov/cia/publications/factbook/index.html [October 1999].

NOTES.

Following are CIA definitions of acronyms and terms used in these tables.

Exchange rate—The official value of a nation's monetary unit, at a given date or over a given period of time, as expressed in units of local currency per U.S. dollar and as determined by international market forces or official fiat. These often have little relation to domestic output. In developing countries with weak currencies, the exchange rate estimate in GDP (gross domestic product) in dollars is typically one-fourth to one-half the PPP (purchasing power parity) estimate. Although exchange rates may suddenly go up or down by 10% or more, real output

may have remained unchanged. On January 12, 1994, for example, the 14 countries of the African Financial Community (whose currencies are tied to the French franc) devalued their currencies by 50%. This move, of course, did not cut the real output of their countries by half.

BMR—Black Market rate.

NA—Data are not available.

SOURCE. U.S. Central Intelligence Agency (CIA) 1998, *The World Factbook 1998* [Online]. Available: http://www.cia.gov/cia/publications/factbook/index.html [October 1999].

NOTES.

Top import origins are distributed in percent when data are available.

Following are CIA definitions of the acronyms and terms used here.

BLEU—Belgium-Luxembourg Economic Union.

Caricom—Caribbean Community and Common Market.

CEMA—Council for Mutual Economic Assistance; also known as CMEA or Comecon.

c.i.f.—Cost, insurance, freight.

CIS—Commonwealth of Independent States.

CMEA—Council for Mutual Economic Assistance; also known as CEMA or Comecon.

ECOWAS—Economic Community of West African States.

EFTA—European Free Trade Association.

est.—Estimate.

EU—European Union.

f.o.b.—Free on board.

FSU—Former Soviet Union.

NA—Data are not available.

OECD—Organization for Economic Cooperation and Development.

OECS—Organization of Eastern Caribbean States.

OPEC—Organization of Petroleum Exporting Countries.

SACU—South African Customs Union.

UAE—United Arab Emirates.

UK—United Kingdom.

U.S.—United States.

U.S.S.R.—Union of Soviet Socialist Republics (Soviet Union).

TOP EXPORT—26

SOURCE. U.S. Central Intelligence Agency (CIA) 1998, *The World Factbook 1998* [Online]. Available: http://www.cia.gov/cia/publications/factbook/index.html [October 1999].

NOTES.

Top export destinations are distributed in percent when data are available.

Following are CIA definitions of the acronyms and terms used in these tables.

BLEU—Belgium-Luxembourg Economic Union.

Caricom—Caribbean Community and Common Market.

CEMA—Council for Mutual Economic Assistance; also known as *CEMA* or *Comecon.*

c.i.f.—Cost, insurance, freight.

CIS—Commonwealth of Independent States.

CMEA—Council for Mutual Economic Assistance; also known as *CEMA* or *Comecon.*

ECOWAS—Economic Community of West African States.

EFTA—European Free Trade Association.

est.—Estimate.

EU—European Union.

f.o.b.—Free on board.

FSU—Former Soviet Union.

NA—Data are not available.

OECD—Organization for Economic Cooperation and Development.

OECS—Organization of Eastern Caribbean States.

OPEC—Organization of Petroleum Exporting Countries.

SACU—South African Customs Union.

UAE—United Arab Emirates.

UK—United Kingdom.

U.S.—United States.

U.S.S.R.—Union of Soviet Socialist Republics (Soviet Union).

FOOTNOTES.

f.o.b—Free on board, i.e., the value of goods does not include insurance and freight charges.

..—Data are not available.

———Data are nil or negligible.

FOREIGN AID—27

SOURCE. U.S. Central Intelligence Agency (CIA) 1998, *The World Factbook 1998* [Online]. Available: http://www.cia.gov/cia/publications/factbook/index.html [October 1999].

NOTES.

Following are CIA definitions of terms used in these tables.

Donor—Country that pledges official economic aid to another country.

NA—Data are not available.

ODA—Official development assistance. ODA refers to financial assistance which is concessional in characters, has the main objective of promoting economic development and welfare in less developed countries (LDCs), and contains a grant element of at least 25 percent.

OOF—Other official flows. OOF also refers to official government assistance, but with a main objective other than development and with a grant element less than 25 percent. Transactions include official export credits (such as Export-Import Bank credits), official equity and portfolio investment, and debt reorganization by the official sector that does not meet concessional terms. Aid is considered to have been committed when the parties involved initial agreements constituting a formal declaration of intent.

Recipient—Country that receives official economic aid from another country.

IMPORT AND EXPORT COMMODITIES—28

SOURCE. U.S. Central Intelligence Agency (CIA) 1998, *The World Factbook 1998* [Online]. Available: http://www.cia.gov/cia/publications/factbook/index.html [October 1999].

NOTES.

Category 39: *Top Import Origins* and Category 40: *Top Export Destinations* provide corresponding year of commodity imports/exports respectively.

When available, commodities are distributed in percent.

ICELAND

Republic of Iceland
Lveldi Ísland

INTRODUCTORY SURVEY

RECENT HISTORY

Cut off from Denmark during World War II (1939–45) by the German occupation of that country, Iceland established diplomatic relations with the United Kingdom and the United States. British forces, who took over the protection of the island in 1940, were replaced the following year by U.S. troops, who remained until early 1947. In May 1944, more than 97% of those participating voted to end the union with the king of Denmark and, on 17 June 1944, Iceland became an independent republic.

In 1946, Iceland was admitted to United Nations membership, and three years later, it became a party to the North Atlantic Treaty Organization (NATO). In March 1970, Iceland joined the European Free Trade Association (EFTA), and a trade agreement was reached with the European Community in February 1973. To protect its fishing industry, Iceland extended its fishing zone in 1958, 1972, and 1975, provoking conflict with the United Kingdom and other countries.

GOVERNMENT

Iceland is an independent republic. Executive power is vested in the president and the government, legislative power in the president and the legislative assembly *(Althing)*. The president is elected by universal voting for a four-year term. Executive power is exercised by a prime minister selected by the president.

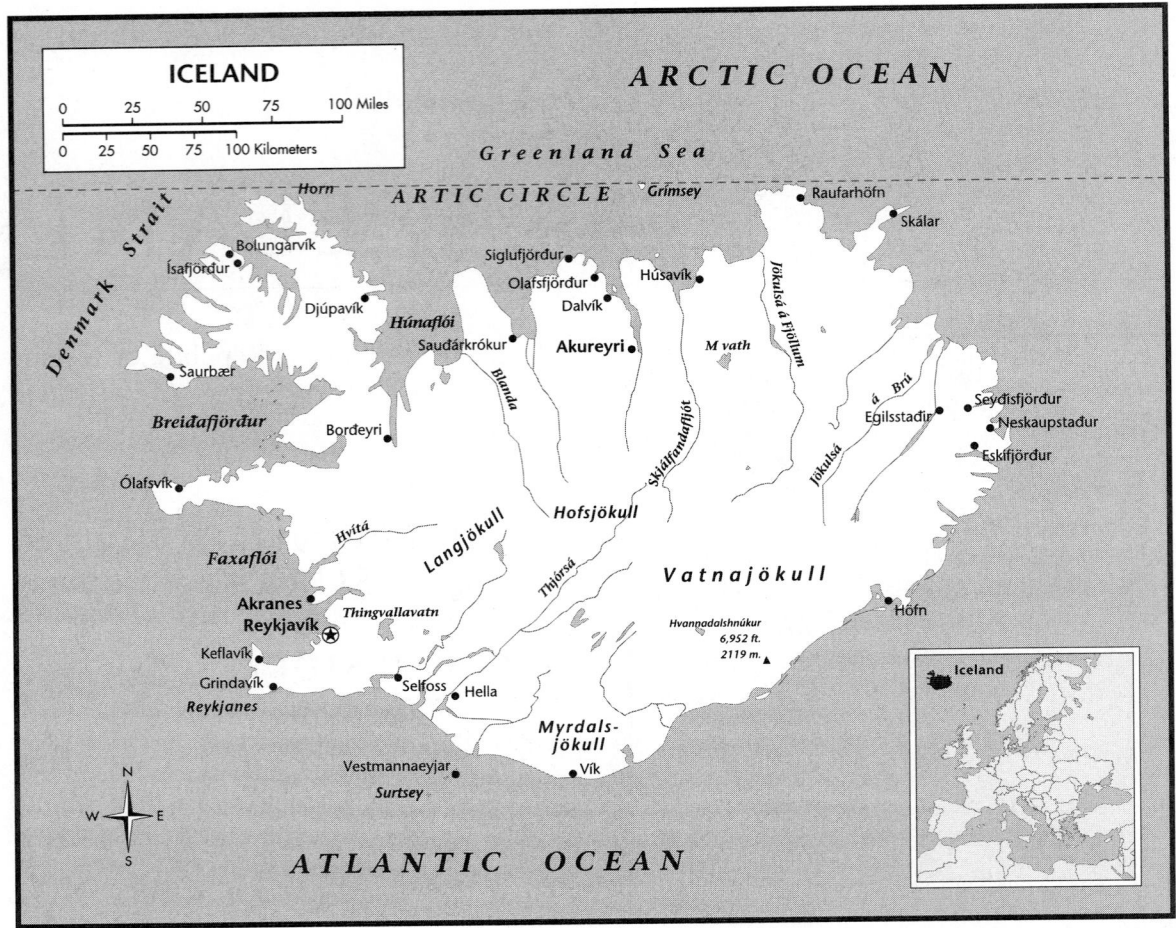

Judiciary

The district magistrates *(sslumenn)* and the town magistrates *(bæjarfógetar)* administer justice on a local level in twenty-six lower courts. Appeals are heard by the Supreme Court, consisting of eight justices (all appointed for life by the president), who elect one of their number as chief justice for a two-year term. There are special courts for maritime cases, labor disputes, and other types of cases.

Political Parties

No one major party in recent years has been able to command a majority of the votes, and coalition governments have been the rule. The general election of April 1991 resulted in a new center-right coalition led by Daví Oddsson of the Independence Party and members of the Social Democratic People's Party. Oddson formed a new coalition government following the 1995 elections between the Independence Party and the Progressive Party.

DEFENSE

Iceland is the only NATO member with no military force of its own, although the government does maintain armed fishery protection vessels and planes manned by 130 personnel.

ECONOMIC AFFAIRS

Iceland's economy, once primarily agricultural, is now based on services and the fish processing industry. Sheep raising and dairying are the chief agricultural activities, with horse breeding also substantial. Since Iceland has almost no known mineral resources and has had no concentrations of population until recent decades, industry is small-scale and local. The growth rate of the domestic economy was estimated at 5.6% in 1996 and 3.3% in 1997.

Public Finance

Since 1984, Iceland's budget has shown a deficit averaging nearly 2% of GDP raising its net indebtedness relative to GDP to almost 30% in

1994. Government attempts to balance the budget were frustrated by the economic downturn during 1987–93 and by fiscal concessions to expedite wage settlements. The U.S. CIA estimates that, in 1994, government revenues totaled approximately $1.9 billion and expenditures $2.1 billion, including capital expenditures of $297 million. External debt totaled $2.5 billion, approximately 58% of which was financed abroad.

Income

In 1998, Iceland's gross national product (GNP) was $7.67 billion, or about $28,010 per person. Between 1985 and 1995, the average annual real growth rate of GNP per person was 0.3% and the average annual inflation rate was 11.8%.

Industry

Fish processing is the most important industry. Facilities for freezing, salting, sun-curing, and reducing fish to oil or fish meal are flexible enough to allow shifting from one process to another based on demand.

Banking and Finance

In March 1961, the Central Bank of Iceland was founded to issue notes and assume other central bank functions previously exercised by the National Bank of Iceland, a wholly state-owned bank established in 1885.

In 1997, there were four commercial banks, two of which are still state owned. The country's two other banks, Islandsbanki and Sparisjodabanki, are privately owned.

The whole basis on which the financial system is supervised and regulated, however, has been transformed by Iceland's accession to the European Economic Area (EEA) agreement in 1994. Under the agreement, Iceland has been required to implement into national law the common minimum standards for the supervision of financial institutions—banks, insurance companies, and securities firms—developed at EU level.

The money supply, as measured by M2, totaled K135,353 million in 1995.

The Securities Exchange of Iceland (SEI) was established in 1985 on the basis of rules set by the Central Bank.

Economic Development

The national government and some local governments are involved in trawler fishing, herring processing, merchant shipping, electric power facilities, and certain other industries. The central government largely supervises the export-import trade and the fishing and fish-processing industries. Further, the government supports farmers in the rebuilding or enlarging of their homes, livestock sheds, and barns, and assists them in the purchase of machinery.

The government fixes prices of essential foods and other basic consumption items and subsidizes them, both to limit prices for the consumer and to maintain farm incomes. It also fixes markups that manufacturers, wholesalers, retailers, and importers may place on a wide variety of products.

SOCIAL WELFARE

The national health insurance scheme includes insurance against sickness, accident, and unemployment; pensions for the aged and disabled; and a health service that provides treatment and care of the sick.

Studies show that women earn about 40% less than men in comparable jobs.

Healthcare

The incidence of tuberculosis, once widespread, has been greatly reduced. There were two reported cases of AIDS in 1995. Life expectancy is 79 years, among the highest in the world.

Housing

The total number of dwellings at the end of 1993 was 95,757. Traditional turf houses were replaced long ago by wooden ones. In the 1980s and 1990s, most new housing was concrete. Virtually all dwellings have electricity, piped water, and central heating.

EDUCATION

There is practically no adult illiteracy. Education is compulsory for children aged 7 to 15. In 1993, there were 24,711 students at primary schools, 30,914 in secondary schools, and 6,050 students at post-secondary institutions.

1999 KEY EVENTS TIMELINE

May

- The center-right coalition retains a majority in the general elections.

June

- Russian bombers are intercepted by a U.S. fighter jets 60 miles from Icelandic coast.

July

- Iceland is ranked among the world's ten most prosperous nations.

October

- An Iceland supermarket chain taps into the burgeoning U.K. Internet sales market.

- Hillary Clinton speaks at a women's rights conference of 400 in Reykjavik.

November

- A red kite, a rare bird which had flown in 1997 from Scotland (where it had been reared and banded) to Iceland, is captured and returned to Scotland on board an Iceland Air flight. There are just 34 breeding pairs of red kite known to exist in Scotland.

December

- The Organization for Economic Cooperation and Development (OECD) recommends Iceland raise its interest rates to slow its economy. Iceland's central bank reports consumer prices increased 5.6 percent in 1999.

ANALYSIS OF EVENTS: 1999

BUSINESS AND THE ECONOMY

After forecasting an average annual inflation rate of 3.0 percent for 1999 in July, Iceland's central bank adjusted its projection to 3.3 percent in the face of a strong economy that pushed Iceland's consumer price index to a six-year high. The primary factors cited for the increase in inflation were rising prices for energy and housing. The central bank predicted a 3.7 percent inflation rate for the year 2000, based on the appreciation of the Icelandic crown, the 2000 budget, and stabilizing wages, which are expected to average out at a 6.5 percent increase in 1999. The economy of Iceland was expected to continue or surpass its growth rate of 5 percent a year, which it has maintained for the past three years. Unemployment remains low at 2 percent, necessitating the importation of foreign laborers. Iceland's strong and diversified economy, based on fishing, energy, technology, and tourism, allows it to maintain an economic and political independence that justifies its lack of interest in joining the European Union.

In October, the Iceland supermarket chain, which has stores in Britain, took advantage of rapidly growing Internet sales in the U.K. and began to offer groceries over its Internet website. Customers can order around the clock, though the service requires a minimum order of 40 pounds and a delivery area within a 10-mile radius of one of their stores; the company says that this covers virtually all of Britain. Iceland supermarket representatives have touted the Internet venture as Britain's first free nationwide grocery shopping service.

GOVERNMENT AND POLITICS

General elections in May resulted in the retention of a majority by a center-right coalition between Iceland's conservative Independence Party, led by the prime minister, and the centrist Progressive Party, which is headed by Iceland's foreign minister. The coalition has kept control of the Althing, the world's oldest parliament, on a platform promising continued economic stability and prosperity.

In April, in the face of NATO military actions in Yugoslavia, the European Union asked Iceland and other non-EU nations to comply with its ban on oil exports to Yugoslavia except for humanitarian purposes.

Memories of Cold War tensions were briefly revived in June when two Russian TU-95 Bear bombers flew to within 60 miles of Iceland. The bombers were intercepted by two U.S. F-15s from NATO's Keflavik base in Iceland, and escorted out of NATO airspace. Russian Bears are large propeller-driven planes dating back to the 1950s but capable of carrying nuclear weapons. U.S. Defense Department officials dismissed the incident as a non-threatening display of Russian military capability meant primarily to impress critics in Russia. The incident off Iceland occurred almost simultaneously with a Norwegian interception of two Russian TU-140 Blackjack bombers off Norway. U.S. officials said all four planes were part of military exercises the Russians had been planning for almost a year, though they had failed to notify Washington of their actual execution in June.

CULTURE AND SOCIETY

In July, Iceland was ranked among the world's 10 most prosperous nations. In October, Transparency International, a group that monitors government corruption around the globe, rated Iceland as the sixth-least corrupted nation in the world.

In October, Reykjavik was the site of a conference of 400 women activists from the U.S., Russia, the Baltics, and Scandinavia. Featured speaker at the conference was U.S. First Lady Hillary Rodham Clinton, who used the occasion to call for international efforts to end prostitution. Citing an inseparable link between democracy and the guarantee of women's rights, Mrs. Clinton cited Iceland and the Scandinavian countries as models for women's equality.

DIRECTORY

CENTRAL GOVERNMENT

Head of State

President

Olafur Ragnar Grimsson, Office of the President, Soleyjargotu 1, IS-150 Reykjavik, Iceland
PHONE: +354 5404400
FAX: +354 5624802

Prime Minister

David Oddsson, Office of the Prime Minister, Stjornarraoshusinu, IS-150 Reykjavik, Iceland
PHONE: +354 5609400
FAX: +354 5628626
E-MAIL: postur@for.stjr.is

Ministers

Minister of Foreign Affairs and External Trade

Halldor Asgrimsson, Ministry of Foreign Affairs and External Trade, Rauoararstig 25, IS-150 Reykjavik, Iceland
PHONE: +354 5609900
FAX: +354 5622373
E-MAIL: external@utn.stjr.is

Minister of Finance

Geir H. Haarde, Ministry of Finance, Arnarhvali, IS-150 Reykjavik, Iceland
PHONE: +354 5609200
FAX: +354 5628280
E-MAIL: postur@fjr.stjr.is

Minister of Culture and Education

Bjorn Bjarnason, Ministry of Culture and Education, Solvholsgotu 4, IS-150 Reykjavik, Iceland
PHONE: +354 5609504
FAX: +354 5623068
E-MAIL: postur@mrn.stjr.is

Minister of Justice

Solveig Petursdottir, Ministry of Justice, Arnarhvali, IS-150 Reykjavik, Iceland
PHONE: +354 5609010
FAX: +354 5527340
E-MAIL: postur@dkm.stjr.is

Minister of Fisheries

Arni M. Mathiesen, Ministry of Fisheries, Skulagotu 4, IS-150 Reykjavik, Iceland
PHONE: +354 5609670
FAX: +354 5621853
E-MAIL: postur@sjr.stjr.is

Minister of Communications

Sturla Boovarsson, Ministry of Communications, Hafnarhusinu v/Tryggvagotu, IS-150 Reykjavik, Iceland
PHONE: +354 5609630
FAX: +354 5621702
E-MAIL: postur@sam.stjr.is

Minister of Agriculture

Guoni Agustsson, Ministry of Agriculture, Rauoararstig 25, IS-150 Reykjavik, Iceland
PHONE: +354 5609750
FAX: +354 5521160
E-MAIL: postur@lan.stjr.is

Minister of the Environment

Siv Frioleifsdottir, Ministry of the Environment, Vonarstraeti 4, IS-150 Reykjavik, Iceland
PHONE: +354 5609600
FAX: +354 5624566
E-MAIL: postur@umh.stjr.is

Minister of Trade and Industry

Finnur Ingolfsson, Ministry of Trade and Industry, Arnarhvali, IS-150 Reykjavik, Iceland
PHONE: +354 5609070
FAX: +354 5621289
E-MAIL: postur@ivr.stjr.is

Minister of Health and Social Security

Ingibjorg Palmadottir, Ministry of Health and Social Security, Laugavegi 116, IS-150 Reykjavik, Iceland
PHONE: +354 5609700
FAX: +354 5519165
E-MAIL: postur@htr.stjr.is

Minister of Social Affairs

Pall Petursson, Ministry of Social Affairs, Hafnarhusinu v/Tryggvagotu, IS-150 Reykjavik, Iceland
PHONE: +354 5609100
FAX: +354 5524804
E-MAIL: postur@fel.stjr.is

POLITICAL ORGANIZATIONS

Sjalfstaedisflokkurinn-IP (Independence Party)

Haaleitisbraut 1, 105 Reykjavik, Iceland
PHONE: +354 5682900
FAX: +354 5692927
TITLE: Chairman
NAME: David Oddsson

Althdubandalagid-PA (People's Alliance)

Laugavegi 3, 101 Reykjavik, Iceland
PHONE: +354 5517500
FAX: +354 5517599
TITLE: Chairwoman
NAME: Margret Frimannsdottir

Thjodvaki (People's Movement)

c/o Althing, Reykjavik, Iceland

Framsoknarflokkurinn-PP (Progressive Party)

Hafnarstraeti 20, 101 Reykjavik, Iceland
PHONE: +354 5624480
FAX: +354 5623325
TITLE: Chair
NAME: Halldor Asgrimsson

Althyduflokkurinn-SDP (Social Democratic Party)

Hverfisgatu 8-10, 101 Reykjavik, Iceland
PHONE: +354 5529244
FAX: +354 5629155
TITLE: Chair
NAME: Sighvatur Bjorgvinsson

Samtok um Kvennalista-WA (Women's Alliance)

Laugavegi 17, 101 Reykjavik, Iceland
PHONE: +354 5513725
FAX: +354 5527560
TITLE: Chair
NAME: Kristin Astgeirsdottir

DIPLOMATIC REPRESENTATION

Embassies in Iceland

Denmark
Hverfsgata 29, IS-101 Reykjavik, Iceland
PHONE: +354 5621230
FAX: +354 5623316
TITLE: Ambassador
NAME: Klaus Otto Kappel

Germany
Laufasvegur 3 POB 400, IS-121 Reykjavik, Iceland
PHONE: +354 5301100
FAX: +354 5301101
TITLE: Ambassador
NAME: Reinhart W. Ehni

United Kingdom
Laufasvegur 31, IS-101 Reykjavik, Iceland
PHONE: +354 5505100
FAX: +354 5505104
TITLE: Ambassador
NAME: James McCulloch

United States
Laufasvegur 21, IS-101 Reykjavik, Iceland
PHONE: +354 5629100
FAX: +354 5629118
TITLE: Ambassador
NAME: Day Olin Mount

JUDICIAL SYSTEM

Supreme Court

Domshusinu vio Arnarhol, IS-150 Reykjavik, Iceland
PHONE: +354 5103030
FAX: +354 5623995

FURTHER READING

Articles

"Fuel Cells Meet Big Business." *The Economist* 352 (July 24, 1999): 59.

Gardner, Marilyn. "A Former President Who Listened to the Young." *Christian Science Monitor* 91 (April 21, 1999): 16.

Gdula, Steven. "Novel Sounds." *The Advocate* (May 25, 1999): 99.

Gibson, Helen. "Protester in Pinstripes." *Time* 154 (October 1, 1999): 95.

McDevitt, Bette. "Discovering Iceland." *National Catholic Reporter* 35 (October 15, 1999): 36.

Wallis, David. "What Little Elves Tell Icelanders." *New York Times,* 19 September 1999.

Internet

Daily News From Iceland. Available Online @ http://www.icenews.is//daily1.html (November 12, 1999).

ICELAND: STATISTICAL DATA

For sources and notes see "Sources of Statistics" in the front of each volume.

GEOGRAPHY

Geography (1)

Area:

Total: 103,000 sq km.

Land: 100,250 sq km.

Water: 2,750 sq km.

Area—comparative: slightly smaller than Kentucky.

Land boundaries: 0 km.

Coastline: 4,988 km.

Climate: temperate; moderated by North Atlantic Current; mild, windy winters; damp, cool summers.

Terrain: mostly plateau interspersed with mountain peaks, icefields; coast deeply indented by bays and fiords.

Natural resources: fish, hydropower, geothermal power, diatomite.

Land use:

Arable land: 0%

Permanent crops: 0%

Permanent pastures: 23%

Forests and woodland: 1%

Other: 76% (1993 est.).

HUMAN FACTORS

Demographics (2A)

	1990	1995	1998	2000	2010	2020	2030	2040	2050
Population	254.7	267.5	271.0	274.1	287.3	295.5	298.5	292.2	278.8
Net migration rate (per 1,000 population)	NA	NA	NA	NA	NA	NA	NA	NA	NA
Births	NA	NA	NA	NA	NA	NA	NA	NA	NA
Deaths	NA	NA	NA	NA	NA	NA	NA	NA	NA
Life expectancy - males	76.1	75.9	76.8	76.9	77.7	78.4	78.9	79.4	79.8
Life expectancy - females	80.5	80.1	81.1	81.3	82.6	83.7	84.5	85.2	85.8
Birth rate (per 1,000)	18.7	16.0	15.1	14.7	12.4	11.0	9.5	8.3	7.6
Death rate (per 1,000)	6.8	7.2	7.0	7.0	7.6	8.4	10.0	11.9	13.3
Women of reproductive age (15-49 yrs.)	65.1	68.5	69.2	69.4	69.6	67.5	65.1	61.4	55.1
of which are currently married	NA	NA	NA	NA	NA	NA	NA	NA	NA
Fertility rate	2.3	2.1	2.0	2.0	1.8	1.6	1.5	1.5	1.4

Except as noted, values for vital statistics are in thousands; life expectancy is in years.

Infants and Malnutrition (5)

Under-5 mortality rate (1997) 5

% of infants with low birthweight (1990-97) . . . . . .NA

Births attended by skilled health staff % of total[a] . . .NA

% fully immunized (1995-97)

TB 98

DPT 98%

Polio 99

Measles 98

Prevalence of child malnutrition under age 5
(1992-97)[b] . . . . .NA

Ethnic Division (6)

Homogeneous mixture of descendants of Norwegians and Celts.

Religions (7)

Evangelical Lutheran 96%

Other Protestant and Roman Catholic 3%

None 1% (1988)

Languages (8)

Icelandic.

GOVERNMENT & LAW

Political Parties (12)

Parliament	% of seats
Independence Party	.37.1
Progressive Party	.23.3
Social Democratic Party	.11.4
Socialists	.14.3
People's Movement	.7.2
Women's Party	.4.9

Government Budget (13A)

Year: 1996

Total Expenditures: 156,454 Millions of Kronur

Expenditures as a percentage of the total by function:

General public services and public order 9.35

Defense . . . .-

Education 12.83

Health 23.17

Social Security and Welfare 22.76

Housing and community amenities 83

Recreational, cultural, and religious affairs 2.62

Fuel and energy 62

Agriculture, forestry, fishing, and hunting 5.66

Mining, manufacturing, and construction 42

Transportation and communication 8.96

Other economic affairs and services 1.73

LABOR FORCE

Labor Force (16)

Total 131,000

Manufacturing 12.9%

Fishing and fish processing 11.8%

Construction 10.7%

Other services 59.5%

Agriculture 5.1%

Data for 1996 est. Percent distribution for 1996 est.

Unemployment Rate (17)

3.8% (1997 est.)

PRODUCTION SECTOR

Electric Energy (18)

Capacity . . . . .1.083 million kW (1995)

Production . . . . .4.916 billion kWh (1995)

Consumption per capita . . . . .18,481 kWh (1995)

Transportation (19)

Highways:

total: 12,341 km

paved: 3,196 km

unpaved: 9,145 km (1996 est.)

Merchant marine:

total: 5 ships (1,000 GRT or over) totaling 22,594 GRT/29,322 DWT ships by type: cargo 1, chemical tanker 1, container 1, oil tanker 1, refrigerated cargo 1 (1997 est.)

Airports: 90 (1997 est.)

Airports—with paved runways:

total: 11

over 3,047 m: 1

1,524 to 2,437 m: 4

914 to 1,523 m: 6 (1997 est.)

Airports—with unpaved runways:

total: 79

1,524 to 2,437 m: 3

914 to 1,523 m: 22

under 914 m: 54 (1997 est.)

Top Agricultural Products (20)

Potatoes, turnips; cattle, sheep; fish catch of about 1.1 million metric tons in 1992.

GOVERNMENT & LAW

Military Affairs (14B)

	1990	1991	1992	1993	1994	1995
Military expenditures						
Current dollars (mil.)	0	0	0	0	0	0
1995 constant dollars (mil.)	0	0	0	0	0	0
Armed forces (000)	0	0	0	0	0	0
Gross national product (GNP)						
Current dollars (mil.)	5,681	5,991	6,014	6,184	6,539	6,851[e]
1995 constant dollars (mil.)	6,529	6,621	6,468	6,484	6,703	6,851[e]
Central government expenditures (CGE)						
1995 constant dollars (mil.)	2,170	2,324	2,265	2,271	2,422	2,398[e]
People (mil.)	.3	.3	.3	.3	.3	.3
Military expenditure as % of GNP	0	0	0	0	0	0
Military expenditure as % of CGE	0	0	0	0	0	0
Military expenditure per capita (1995 $)	0	0	0	0	0	0
Armed forces per 1,000 people (soldiers)	0	0	0	0	0	0
GNP per capita (1995 $)	25,630	25,780	24,970	24,820	25,200	25,560
Arms imports[6]						
Current dollars (mil.)	0	0	0	0	0	0
1995 constant dollars (mil.)	0	0	0	0	0	0
Arms exports[6]						
Current dollars (mil.)	0	0	0	0	0	0
1995 constant dollars (mil.)	0	0	0	0	0	0
Total imports[7]						
Current dollars (mil.)	1,680	1,760	1,684	1,349	1,472	1,756
1995 constant dollars (mil.)	1,931	1,945	1,811	1,414	1,509	1,756
Total exports[7]						
Current dollars (mil.)	1,592	1,550	1,528	1,399	1,623	1,804
1995 constant dollars (mil.)	1,830	1,713	1,644	1,467	1,664	1,804
Arms as percent of total imports[8]	0	0	0	0	0	0
Arms as percent of total exports[8]	0	0	0	0	0	0

MANUFACTURING SECTOR

GDP & Manufacturing Summary (21)

Detailed value added figures are listed by both International Standard Industry Code (ISIC) and product title.

	1980	1985	1990	1994
GDP ($-1990 mil.)[1]	4,657	5,225	6,080	6,193
Per capita ($-1990)[1]	20,425	21,681	23,844	23,282
Manufacturing share (%) (current prices)[1]	20.3	18.6	16.7	NA

Manufacturing

Value added ($-1990 mil.)[1]	813	823	819	727
Industrial production index	100	101	101	89
Value added ($ mil.)	518	429	755	818
Gross output ($ mil.)	1,676	1,471	2,602	2,475
Employment (000)	28	30	22	21
Profitability (% of gross output)				
Intermediate input (%)	69	71	71	67

GDP & Manufacturing Summary (21)

	1980	1985	1990	1994
Wages and salaries inc. supplements (%)	25	22	22	22
Gross operating surplus	6	7	7	11
Productivity ($)				
Gross output per worker	61,052	51,071	111,991	116,366
Value added per worker	18,864	14,907	32,498	38,630
Average wage (inc. supplements)	15,021	11,345	25,775	26,773
Value added ($ mil.)				
311/2 Food products	188	175	285	397
313 Beverages	11	10	21	21
314 Tobacco products	NA	NA	NA	NA
321 Textiles	23	17	21	15
322 Wearing apparel	15	10	10	12
323 Leather and fur products	6	6	5	8
324 Footwear	1	1	1	—
331 Wood and wood products	—	—	1	1
332 Furniture and fixtures	45	29	40	40
341 Paper and paper products	4	4	9	9
342 Printing and publishing	35	36	84	84
351 Industrial chemicals	8	7	17	15
352 Other chemical products	7	8	15	19
353 Petroleum refineries	—	—	—	—
354 Miscellaneous petroleum and coal products	—	—	—	—
355 Rubber products	—	—	—	—
356 Plastic products	11	11	27	27
361 Pottery, china and earthenware	1	—	1	—
362 Glass and glass products	3	3	4	4
369 Other non-metal mineral products	23	21	37	34
371 Iron and steel	6	11	9	5
372 Non-ferrous metals	39	13	36	21
381 Metal products	62	44	85	56
382 Non-electrical machinery	—	—	—	—
383 Electrical machinery	—	—	—	—
384 Transport equipment	21	13	20	21
385 Professional and scientific equipment	—	—	—	—
390 Other manufacturing industries	10	11	27	28

FINANCE, ECONOMICS, & TRADE

Economic Indicators (22)

National product: GDP—purchasing power parity—$5.71 billion (1997 est.)

National product real growth rate: 4.9% (1997 est.)

National product per capita: $21,000 (1997 est.)

Inflation rate—consumer price index: 2.3% (1996)

Exchange Rates (24)

Exchange rates:

Icelandic kronur (IKr) per US$1

January 1998	72.707
1997	70.904
1996	66.500
1995	64.692
1994	69.944
1993	67.603

Top Import Origins (25)

$2 billion (f.o.b., 1996) Data are for 1995.

Origins	%
Germany	11
Norway	10
United Kingdom	10
Denmark	9
United States	8
Sweden	7

Balance of Payments (23)

	1991	1992	1993	1994	1995
Exports of goods (f.o.b.)	1,552	1,529	1,398	1,561	1,804
Imports of goods (f.o.b.)	−1,599	−1,527	−1,217	−1,288	−1,598
Trade balance	−47	2	181	273	206
Services - debits	−902	−882	−856	−836	−911
Services - credits	640	669	673	682	761
Private transfers (net)	−8	−7	−8	−7	−10
Government transfers (net)	−1	4	5	−1	5
Overall balance	−318	−214	−5	111	51

Top Export Destinations (26)

$1.8 billion (f.o.b., 1996) Data are for 1995.

Destinations	%
United Kingdom	19
Germany	14
United States	12
Japan	11
Denmark	8
France	7

Economic Aid (27)

$NA. NA stands for not available.

Import Export Commodities (28)

Import Commodities	Export Commodities
Machinery and transportation equipment	Fish and fish products 75%
Petroleum products	Animal products
Foodstuffs	Aluminum
Textiles	Ferrosilicon
	Diatomite

INDIA

Republic of India
Bharat Ganarajya

INTRODUCTORY SURVEY

RECENT HISTORY

The end of World War II in 1945 led to renewed negotiations on independence between Britain and the Hindu and Muslim leaders. In mid-August 1947, with Hindu-Muslim tensions rising, British India was divided into the two self-governing dominions of India and Pakistan. Known as Partition, this division caused a mass movement of Hindus, Muslims, and Sikhs who found themselves on the "wrong" side of new international boundaries. As many as twenty million people moved, and up to three million of these were killed in bloodletting on both sides of the new international frontier. Gandhi, who opposed Partition and worked untiringly for Hindu-Muslim cooperation, became a casualty of the inflamed feelings of the period. He was assassinated by a Hindu extremist five months after Partition.

Among the unresolved legacies of Partition was the fate of the independent state of Jammu and Kashmir, bordering both new nations. A Muslim-majority state with a Hindu maharaja, Kashmir has been the site of periodic Indian-Pakistani clashes since 1948. While Pakistan governs its portion of the former princely state as Azad ("free") Kashmir and as the Northern Areas, the Indian portion is governed as Jammu and Kashmir, a state in the Indian Union.

In the late 1980s, India's cancellation of election results and dismissal of the state government led to the start of an armed rebellion by Muslim militants. Indian repression and Pakistan's un-

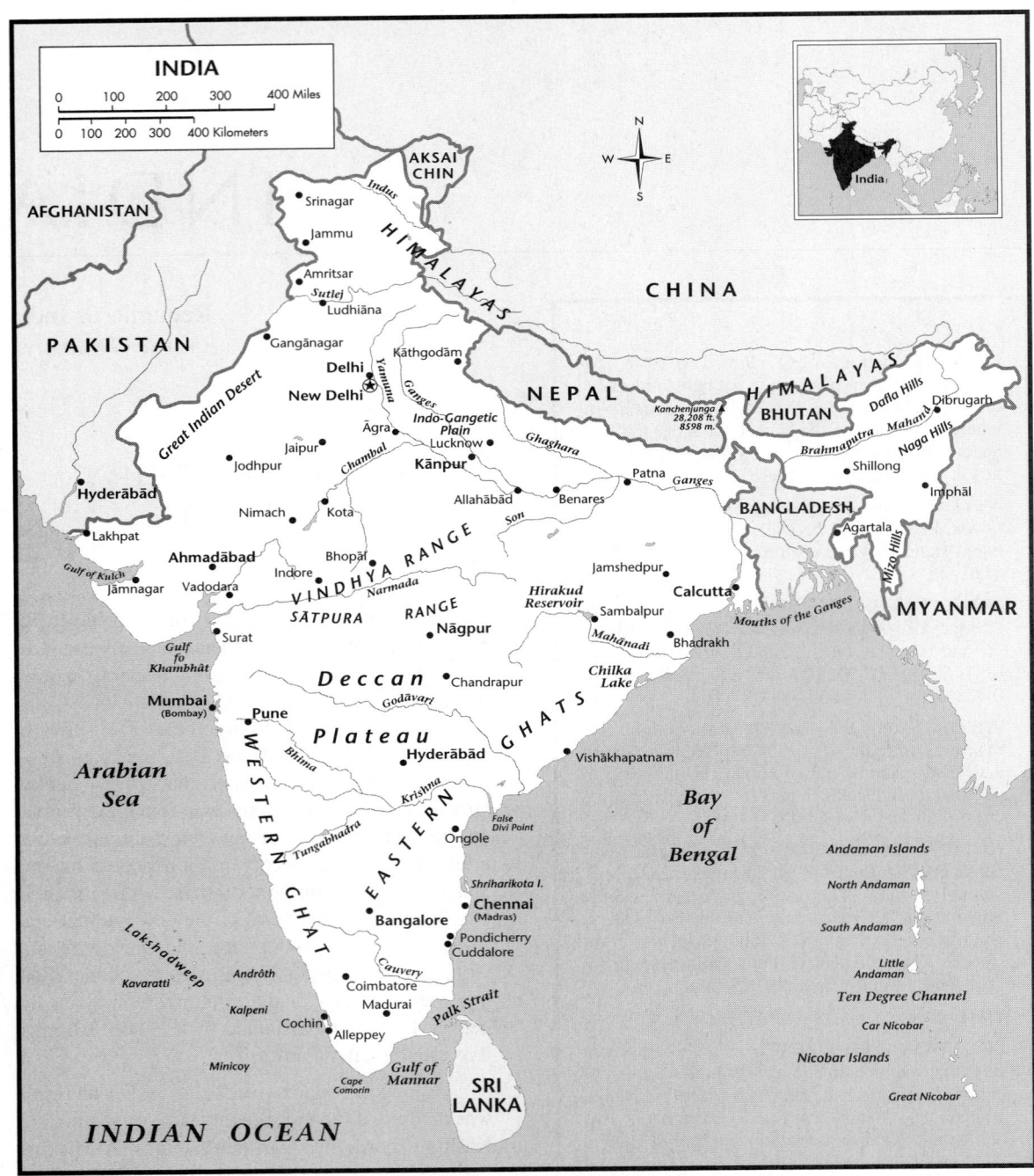

declared support of the militants have threatened to spark renewed warfare and keep the issue unresolved.

India and China have been at odds over their Himalayan border since the Chinese occupation of Tibet in 1959, leading to clashes between Indian and Chinese troops at a number of locations along the disputed border. The border dispute with China remains unresolved, although tensions have been eased by a stand-still accord signed by the two countries in September 1993.

After the death of India's first prime minister, Jawaharlal Nehru, on 27 May 1964, his successor, Lal Bahadur Shastri, led India in dealing with Hindu-Muslim violence in Kashmir. Shastri died of a heart attack while at Tashkent, Uzbekistan, to sign a peace agreement. His successor, Indira Gandhi (Nehru's daughter), pledged to honor the accords. India again went to war with Pakistan in December 1971, this time to support East Pakistan in its civil war with West Pakistan. Indian forces tipped the balance in favor of the separatists, which ultimately led to the creation of Bangladesh from the former East Pakistan.

In June 1975, Gandhi's conviction on minor election law violations in the 1972 polls required her to resign. She continued in power by proclaiming a state of emergency. She imposed press censorship, arrested opposition political leaders, and sponsored legislation that cleared her of the election law violations. These actions, although later upheld by the Supreme Court, resulted in widespread public disapproval.

Two years later, Ghandi was defeated in parliamentary elections, forcing her Congress Party into the parliamentary opposition for the first time. Morarji Desai, of the winning five-party Janata coalition, became prime minister. But Janata, formed solely to oppose Mrs. Gandhi, had no unity or agreed program, and it soon collapsed. Mrs. Gandhi's newly reorganized Congress Party/I (''I'' for Indira) gained Hindu votes to win a huge election victory in January 1980, and she regained office.

In October 1983, Sikh discontent led to widespread violence by Sikh separatist militants in Punjab and to the imposition of direct rule in that state. A year later, with the Sikh separatist violence unchecked, Gandhi herself became one of its victims—assassinated by Sikh members of her own guard.

Rajiv Gandhi immediately followed his mother as prime minister. However, during the next two years, his popularity declined quickly as the public reacted to government-imposed price increases for basic commodities, his inability to stem rising ethnic violence, and charges of military kickbacks and other scandals.

After a rise in Indo-Pakistan tensions in 1986–87, Rajiv Gandhi and Prime Minister Benazir Bhutto of Pakistan signed an agreement by which both nations agreed not to attack the nuclear facilities of the other in 1988. And in September 1989, Gandhi agreed with Sri Lanka's request to pull his 100,000 troops out of their bloody stand-off with Tamil separatists by the end of the year.

During the election campaign in the spring of 1991, Rajiv Gandhi was assassinated by a disgruntled Sri Lankan Tamil. P.V. Narasimha Rao, a former minister under both Rajiv and Indira Gandhi, formed a minority government. As prime minister, Rao introduced new economic reforms, opening India to foreign investors and market economics. Rao lost his power in 1996 after three cabinet members resigned from corruption charges and two elections weakened the Congress Party's rule. Between May 1996 and April 1997, political instability caused India to change its government four times. In March 1998, Hindu nationalist Atal Bihari Vajpayee became prime minister.

In May 1998, India conducted several underground nuclear test explosions, prompting international clamor. The tests were India's first since 1974. Pakistan responded with its own nuclear testing later that month, raising concerns that India and Pakistan would begin a nuclear arms race. India and Pakistan conducted tests of medium-range missiles in April 1999.

Despite their arms race, the two sides did make efforts to improve relations. In February 1999, India and Pakistan started a bus service between the two countries. On the first day of service, Vajpayee rode to Lahore to meet Pakistan's prime minister, Nawaz Sharif.

On April 17, 1999, Vajpayee's coalition government fell. Congress Party leader Sonia Gandhi (widow of Rajiv Gandhi) failed to form a new government and elections were scheduled for that September.

GOVERNMENT

India is an independent socialist democratic republic, with no religious ties to the government. Its constitution, which became effective 26 January 1950, provides for a parliamentary form of government. The constitution also contains an extensive set of guidelines similar to the United States Bill of Rights. The right to vote is granted to all at age 21.

Judiciary

The laws and judicial system of British India were continued after independence with only slight modifications. The Supreme Court consists of a chief justice and up to seventeen judges. The Court's duties include interpreting the constitution, handling disputes between the states, and judging appeals from lower courts.

In addition, each state's judicial system is headed by a high court. Judgments from these courts may be appealed to the Supreme Court.

Islamic law (Shari'a) governs many noncriminal matters involving Muslims, including family law, inheritance, and divorce.

Political Parties

In various forms, the Indian National Congress has controlled the government for most of the years since independence in 1947. Founded in 1885, the Indian National Congress, known after 1947 as the Congress Party (CP), was the most powerful mass movement fighting for independence in British India. It became the ruling party of free India due to its national popularity and because most leaders of the independence movement were among its members, including India's first prime minister, Jawaharlal Nehru.

With the decline of the Congress Party as a national party, there has been a rise in the number of single state, linguistic, ethnic, and regional parties capable of governing only at the state level but available for coalition building at the national level.

DEFENSE

In 1995, armed forces members totaled 1.1 million. The army had 980,000 members; the navy (including the naval air force) had 55,000 members; the air force had 110,000 members; and the coast guard had 3,000 members.

Budgeted defense expenditures in 1996 were around $8.4 billion.

ECONOMIC AFFAIRS

Agriculture provides the livelihood for 67% of the population. These agricultural workers produce 30% of the gross national product (GNP). The country is rich in mineral, forest, and power resources, and its ample reserves of iron ore and coal provide a substantial base for heavy industry.

Under a planned development program since independence, the government was the driving force behind the nation's industries. India has placed greater emphasis on private enterprise to stimulate growth and modernization.

The domestic economy grew at an annual rate of about 6% during 1993–96. By 1997, however, the steep rise in imports signaled that reforms were needed in order to keep up the economic recovery.

Public Finance

The executive branch has considerable control over public finance. Thus, while parliament can oversee and investigate public expenditures and may reduce the budget, it cannot expand the budget, and checks exist that prevent it from delaying passage.

Budgets in recent decades have reflected the needs of rapid economic development under rising expenditures of the five-year plans. Insufficient government receipts for financing this development have led to yearly deficits and a resulting increase of new tax measures and deficit financing.

The U.S. CIA estimates that, in 1995, government revenues totaled approximately $36.5 billion and expenditures $54.9 billion. External debt totaled $97.9 billion, approximately 10% of which was financed abroad.

High interest rates, 8% inflation, slow industrial growth, and weak foreign investment prompted the government to recommend dramatic new initiatives in the 1997–98 budget, including cuts in taxes and duties.

Income

In 1998, India's gross national product (GNP) was $421 billion, or $430 per person. During 1985–95, the average annual real growth rate of the GNP per person was 3.1%, while inflation averaged 9.8%.

Industry

Textile production dominates the industrial field. Millions of cottage workers throughout the country handloom cotton, wool, silk, and rayon. Total cotton cloth production in 1995–96 was 17.25 billion square meters (22.56 billion square yards).

In 1995–96, India produced 17.8 million tons of finished steel and 518 million tons of aluminum ingots. Vehicle production in 1995–96 included 9.9 million bicycles, 2.6 million motorcycles and scooters, 675,000 passenger vehicles, 202,800 tractors, and 18,900 railroad cars.

The production of computers and a wide range of consumer electronics has been boosted by the recent liberalization of imports of component parts. Production of computer software for export accounted for about 9% of the value of electronics production in 1995–96.

The oil-refining industry yielded 345 million tons of refined petroleum products in 1995. Nitrogen fertilizer production grew to 11.3 million tons in 1995–96, and cement production to 69.3 million tons. Refined sugar production totaled 16.5 million tons in 1995–96.

Banking and Finance

A well-established banking system exists in India. At the end of 1995, there were 62,300 branches of public sector and commercial banks. The largest public-sector bank is the State Bank of India, which, at the end of 1996, accounted for one-third of income.

The Reserve Bank of India, founded in 1935 and nationalized in 1949, is the central banking and note-issuing authority. As of May 1996, total foreign reserves, excluding gold, totaled $17,418 million. A new institution, the Export-Import Bank of India, was established in 1982 to finance medium- and long-term credit for the exporting of goods and services.

In an attempt to regulate lending practices and interest rates, the government has encouraged the formation of cooperative credit societies.

Of India's twenty-three stock exchanges, the Bombay Stock Exchange (BSE) and National Stock Exchange (NSE) are the most important. Major efforts have been made to strengthen the stock market institutionally and make it less like a casino. A statutory regulatory body, the Security and Exchange Board of India (SEBI), is charged with providing international standards of investor protection.

Economic Development

Under a series of five-year plans through 1990, the government became a participant in many industrial fields and increased its regulation of existing private commerce and industry. Long the owner-operator of most railway facilities, all radio broadcasting, post, and telegraph facilities, arms and ammunition factories, and river development programs, the government reserved for itself the right to nationalize any industries it deemed necessary. Yet the government's socialist approach was pragmatic, not doctrinaire; agriculture and large segments of trade, finance, and industry remained in private hands. Planning is supervised by an eight-member Planning Commission, established in 1950 and chaired by the prime minister.

The eighth development plan (for 1992–97) most analysts proclaimed a success; economic growth averaged 6% a year, employment rose, poverty was reduced, exports increased, and infla-

tion declined. Although impressed with India's economic performance since 1991, observers see a need for substantial further reform if growth is to be increased to 9% or 10% a year in the future. Areas for improvement include a reduction in the government's deficit, privatization of state-owned enterprises, increased investment in infrastructure, a further reduction in tariffs, and increased fiscal responsibility.

SOCIAL WELFARE

India's governments have established an extensive social welfare system. Programs for children include supplementary nutrition for expectant mothers and for children under 7 years of age, immunization and health programs, vacation camps for low-income families, and prevocational training for adolescents. Programs for women include welfare grants, women's adult education, and working women's hostels. There are also services for the blind, deaf, mentally retarded, and orthopedically handicapped.

Special measures are aimed at rehabilitating juvenile delinquents, prostitutes, and convicts. Begging in public places is forbidden by law in most states and localities. Other social welfare programs cover displaced persons; family planning and maternity care; rural community development; emergency relief programs for drought, flood, earthquake, and other disasters; untouchability (the *Harijans*); and underdeveloped tribal peoples.

Below the highest political levels, and especially in rural India, the position of women remains inferior to that of men. Laws aimed at preventing employment discrimination, female bondage and prostitution, and the *sati* (the burning of widows) are often not enforced. A National Commission for Women was established in 1992 to investigate abuses against women. Despite laws against it, child marriages are still arranged in many parts of India.

In 1995, there were an estimated 500,000 children living and working on the streets. Child prostitution is widespread.

Healthcare

The government is paying increased attention to integrated health, maternity, and child care in rural areas. In 1991, there were a total of 39,026 hospitals and dispensaries. There were 637,604 hospital beds (0.76 per 1,000 people). In the same year, India had 331,630 physicians (0.4 per 1,000 people). There are also some 278,000 registered health care providers following the Ayurvedic (ancient Hindu) and Unani systems.

Average life expectancy has increased from 48 years in 1971 to 63 in the late 1990s. However, many diseases remain, especially deficiency diseases such as goiter, malnutrition (due to lack of protein), rickets, and beriberi.

Housing

Progress has been made toward improving the generally primitive housing in which most Indians live. By 1992, total housing stock numbered 121 million units. The government's goal is to provide 8 million new housing units between 1990 and the year 2000, 2 million to meet the existing need and 6 million to meet the needs that will be created by population growth.

EDUCATION

According to estimates, the population of India is 52% literate. In 1988, a national literacy mission was begun, following which some states achieved 100% literacy. In 1992, the second program of action on education was introduced to reaffirm the 1986 policy with plans to achieve total literacy and free education for all children up to grade eight by the year 2000.

Free and compulsory elementary education is a guiding principle of the constitution. In 1993, there were 572,923 primary level schools with 1.7 million teachers and 108.2 million pupils. In general secondary schools, there were 64.1 million pupils the same year.

India's system of higher education is still basically British in structure and approach. The university system is second only to that of the United States in size with 150 universities and over 5,000 colleges and higher-level institutions.

1999 KEY EVENTS TIMELINE

January

- Clashes between Indian and Pakistani soldiers are reported in the disputed territory of Kashmir.
- Sectarian violence intensifies. An Australian-born Christian missionary and his two sons are killed, allegedly by members of a Hindu militant group, the Bajrang Dal, in Orissa. In Bihar, a private militia sponsored by upper-caste landlords attacks and massacres several Dalits (formerly called untouchables).
- Alarmed by a widening trade deficit, the government hikes import duties on gold.

February

- Prime Minister Vajpayee takes the bus to Lahore in Pakistan for talks with Pakistani premier, Nawaz Sharif.
- Strobe Talbott, the American deputy secretary of state, holds talks with Indian officials in Delhi on nuclear proliferation issues.
- The government submits budget for the new fiscal year. Proposed tax increases coupled with interest rate cuts buoy the stock market.

April

- The AIADMK, a Tamil Nadu-based party that had been the BJP's largest coalition partner, withdraws from the government. Three days later, on April 17, Vajpayee's government loses a confidence motion in Parliament by a solitary vote. Congress and other opposition parties cannot muster enough support to form a new government and Vajpayee remains in office, leading a caretaker administration until new elections are held.
- India test-fires the Agni 2, an intermediate range ballistic missile that can deliver a nuclear payload 1,500 miles.

May

- Large scale fighting erupts in the Kargil region on May 9 along the line of control separating Indian and Pakistani-held sectors of Kashmir.
- Infiltrators from Pakistan seize mountaintops in Indian-controlled territory, sparking the most serious military confrontation between the two rival nations in a decade. India loses two air force jets as it escalates attacks on the infiltrators.

June

- Indian foreign minister, Jaswant Singh meets with his Pakistani counterpart Sartaj Aziz and reiterates India's demand that Pakistan unconditionally withdraw its infiltrators from Kargil. Singh also travels to China for talks.

July

- After secret negotiations, India and Pakistan agree to a phased withdrawal of forces from Kargil peaks.

August

- Nearly 300 people are killed in one of the nation's worst rail disasters.

- The National Security Advisory Board issues a draft of India's nuclear doctrine, favoring development of a minimum credible deterrence capability.

- India downs a Pakistani naval patrol aircraft over the Rann of Kutch, claiming the plane violated Indian air space.

September

- General elections begin on September 5 and are scheduled to end October 3.

October

- The National Democratic Alliance, a BJP-led coalition of more than twenty parties, captures a narrow majority of seats in the Lok Sabha, returning to power acting Prime Minister Atal Behari Vajpayee.

- Bangalore-based software maker Infosys Technologies reports a 134 percent increase in half-year profits.

November

- Pope John Paul says the Catholic Church will continue to recruit in India, ignoring Hindu objections.

- The death toll from last month's cyclone in eastern India rises above 3,400.

December

- An Indian jetliner is hijacked on December 24 during a flight from Katmandu, Nepal to New Delhi. The hijackers demands for the release of a Pakistani Islamic religious leader, Maulana Masood Azhar, and several others who were being held in jails in India, were met and the crisis ended in Afghanistan on December 31.

- The Taj Majal was to be opened for moonlight viewing on December 22 for the first time in since the mid-1980s. The Supreme Court overrode the plan, citing security concerns.

ANALYSIS OF EVENTS: 1999

BUSINESS AND THE ECONOMY

India's economy runs the gamut from traditional farming to heavy industries and modern services. Nearly two-thirds of the population is employed in agriculture, which contributes 25 percent of GDP. In recent years, the information technology sector has boomed. Software companies' revenues have grown at an annual rate of over 50 percent, and software and remote service exports to overseas clients are expected to more than quadruple in the next couple of years. Experts see India's large and growing pool of cheap but skilled knowledge workers giving the country a significant competitive advantage in the new global information economy. In the first half of 1999, the economy rebounded from its disappointing performance in 1998 to post 5.5 percent growth. The growth was led by a strong recovery in the industrial sector that offset a decline in agriculture.

On October 8, India's financial markets celebrated the NDA's election victory, which is expected to result in a more stable government and aggressive pursuit of economic reforms. The BSE Sensex rose more than 5 percent to top the 5000 mark for the first time. However, there are worries that a burgeoning fiscal deficit could derail the newly re-elected government's ambitious economic agenda.

GOVERNMENT AND POLITICS

Domestic political uncertainties, tensions with Pakistan and the diplomatic fallout from India's nuclear tests continued to dominate the attention of the BJP-led coalition government of Prime Minister Atal Behari Vajpayee in early 1999. The Hindu-nationalist BJP came to power at the head of an 18-party coalition in March 1998. In May that year, the new government conducted a series of nuclear tests, demonstrating India's nuclear weapons capability. International condemnation and sanctions followed, but the government's decision earned approval at home.

However, as the year wore on, the government's popularity waned among India's citizens. Bickering among coalition members and a failure to effectively tackle the nation's economic and social woes contributed to this decline. With the economy stagnant and prices rising, the BJP was humiliated at the hands of the opposition Congress party in state elections held in November 1998. The electoral losses prompted a struggle between the BJP's hard-liners and pragmatists for control of the government's policy agenda. Hard-liners accused the Vajpayee government of abandoning the defining Hindu-nationalist principles of the party. Pragmatists argued that the government's survival took precedence over dogma. Since many coalition partners did not share the BJP's Hindu-nationalist credo, compromises were necessary for the BJP to remain in power. The internecine conflict stalled passage of legislation introduced by the government to open up the insurance sector to foreign investors and protect patent rights. Opposition by the BJP's swadeshi (buy Indian) faction contributed to these bills' demise, raising concerns about the government's ability to make progress on needed economic reforms.

As the year drew to a close, the government was embarrassed by an upsurge in violence against minority Christians, allegedly perpetrated by Hindu militants linked to the RSS, an umbrella organization of the Hindu nationalist movement closely tied to the BJP. This issue and the controversial dismissal of the Navy chief created fresh tensions within an increasingly unstable coalition. In January 1999, at the National Executive meeting of the BJP, Vajpayee stressed unity but emphasized his government's policies would reflect consensus national priorities rather than the more contentious aspects of party ideology. He followed up with some concessions to coalition partners and appeared to regain their trust.

In February, the government scored two diplomatic coups. Progress was reported in U.S.-Indian negotiations towards a deal linking India agreeing to sign the Comprehensive Test Ban Treaty to a lifting of remaining multilateral economic sanctions. Vajpayee also met with Pakistan's prime minister, Nawaz Sharif for talks that yielded a declaration of principles on efforts to settle the dispute over Kashmir and avoid accidental nuclear confrontation. Domestic developments were less salutary. The government narrowly escaped defeat on a parliamentary vote by withdrawing legislation ratifying the dismissal of Bihar's state government on grounds of misrule. The reprieve was brief. In April, the south Indian party, AIADMK, whose 18 members provided the government a thin majority, bolted the coalition causing the government's col-

lapse. Congress, the second largest party, proved unable to muster support to head a new government. Parliament was dissolved, new elections were scheduled for the autumn and Vajpayee stayed on as interim prime minister.

Warming relations between India and Pakistan suffered a serious blow in May when the two countries teetered on the brink of war. India accused Pakistani-backed infiltrators of seizing territory on its side of the line of control separating Indian and Pakistani held parts of disputed Kashmir. India's strong military response and refusal to strike any deal short of the intruders' unconditional withdrawal won Vajpayee support at home and abroad. Although Pakistan denied involvement, most Western governments blamed Pakistan for the incident. Kashmir has been a sore point for both nations since their independence in 1947. Pakistan claims all of Kashmir and insists that peaceful relations with India hinge on the latter's acceptance of Kashmiris' right to self-determination. Although the intruders retreated in July, tensions in the region continued with new clashes reported.

The election campaign, meanwhile, featured the BJP-led National Democratic Alliance promising stability under the seasoned and popular leadership of Vajpayee. Congress leader Sonia Gandhi's Italian birth became an issue for some senior members of her own party and among voters. Some observers described the campaign as highly negative. Balloting began in September and ended in October. The results confirmed several exit polls. The NDA won a comfortable majority while Congress suffered its worst ever defeat. On October 13, Vajpayee was sworn in as prime minister. Indian and U.S. officials are scheduled for talks in November on nuclear disarmament and president Clinton's impending visit to India.

CULTURE AND SOCIETY

India is ethnically and culturally diverse. Out of nearly 600 languages and dialects, 17 are recognized as official languages. More than 80% of Indians are Hindus; Muslims are the largest religious minority. India's constitution established a secular state. However, in recent years, extremist Hindu nationalist organizations that promote Hindutva, a majoritarian doctrine proclaiming Hindu cultural and social hegemony in India, have emerged from the fringe to gain significant political influence. The BJP's detractors accuse the party, which has close ties to the Hindu nationalist movement and, in principle, embraces Hindutva, of abandoning secularism and fanning religious tensions. The BJP's governing agenda, however, sidesteps Hindutva's cherished but contentious policy objectives. Indeed, the party's 1999 election manifesto dropped communally charged issues. Hindu militants are blamed for a campaign of violence against minority Christians, many of whom are converts from poverty stricken Hindu castes. Vajpayee touched a raw nerve in January when he called for a national debate on conversions. The topic's sensitivity was highlighted by the controversy surrounding the Pope's visit in November. Hindu fervor has also made the country's largest cultural establishment, the movie industry, reluctant to make films that could be considered offensive to Hindu values.

Unofficial estimates suggest that India's population has crossed the one billion threshold, straining the country's resources and social infrastructure. Although India boasts a 300 million-strong middle class, a third of the people live in poverty and nearly half of all adults are illiterate. Millions are caught in a poverty trap by circumstances of birth. Nobel Prize winning economist Amartya Sen toured his native India in early 1999 with a message that emphasized improving social opportunities for the chronically poor through increased spending on mass literacy and better health care.

DIRECTORY

CENTRAL GOVERNMENT
Head of State

President
Kocheril Raman Narayanan, Office of the President, Rashtrapati Bhavan, New Delhi 110 004, India

Vice President
Krishan Kant, Office of the Vice President

Prime Minister
Atal Bihari Vajpayee, Office of the Prime Minister, 3 Race Course Road, New Delhi 110 001, India
PHONE: +91 (11) 3018939

Ministers

Minister of Agriculture
Satyanarayana Rao, Ministry of Agriculture

Minister of Chemical and Fertilization
Ramesh Bais, Ministry of Chemical and Fertilization

Minister of Civil Aviation
Chaman Lal Gupta, Ministry of Civil Aviation

Minister of Commerce and Industry
Dr. Raman, Ministry of Commerce and Industry

Minister of Communications
Tapan Sikdar, Ministry of Communications

Minister of Consumer Affairs and Public Distribution
V. Sreenivasa Prasad, Ministry of Consumer Affairs and Public Distribution

Minister of Culture, Youth Affairs and Sports
Chaoba Singh, Ministry of Culture, Youth Affairs and Sports

Minister of Defense
Harin Pathak, Ministry of Defense

Minister of Environment and Forests
Babu Lal Marandi, Ministry of Environment and Forests

Minister of External Affairs
Ajit Kumar Panja, Ministry of External Affairs

Minister of Finance
Venur Dhananjaya Kumar, Ministry of Finance

Minister of Food Processing
Syed Hussain, Ministry of Food Processing

Minister of Health and Family Welfare with Independent Charge
N. T. Shanmugam, Ministry of Health and Family Welfare with Independent Charge

Minister of Heavy Industry and Public Enterprises
Vallabhbhai Kathiria, Ministry of Heavy Industry and Public Enterprises

Minister of Home Affairs
Vidyasagar Rao, Ministry of Home Affairs

Minister of Human Resources Development
Jaisingrao Gaikwad Patil, Ministry of Human Resources Development

Minister of Information and Broadcasting
M. Kannappan, Ministry of Information and Broadcasting

Minister of Mines and Minerals
Rita Verma, Ministry of Mines and Minerals

Minister of Non-Conventional Energy Sources
Arun Jaitley, Ministry of Non-Conventional
Energy Sources

Minister of Labour and Employment
Lall Muni, Ministry of Labour and Employment

Minister of Law, Justice and Company Affairs
O. Rajagopal, Ministry of Law, Justice and
Company Affairs

Minister of State Parliamentary Affairs
Shriram Chauhan, Minister for Parliamentary
Affairs

Minister of State
Faggan Singh Kuleste, Ministry of Parliamentary
Affairs

Minister of Petroleum
E. Ponnuswamy, Ministry of Petroleum, Shastri
Bhawan, New Delhi 110 001, India

**Minister of Planning and Program
Implementation**
Bangaru Laxman, Ministry of Planning and
Program Implementation

Minister of Power
Jayawanti Mehta, Ministry of Power

Minister of Railways
Digvijay Singh, Ministry of Railways

Minister of Rural Development
A. Raja, Ministry of Rural Development

**Minister of Science and Technology and
Parliamentary Affairs**
Santosh Kumar Gangwar, Ministry of Science
and Technology and Parliamentary Affairs

Minister of Surface Transportation
Debendra Pradhan, Ministry of Surface
Transportation

Minister of Steel and Parliamentary Affairs
Dilip Ray, Ministry of Steel and Parliamentary
Affairs

**Minister of Small Scale Industries, Agro and
Rural Industries**
Vasundhara Raje, Ministry of Small Scale
Industries, Agro and Rural Industries

Minister of Textiles
Gingee N. Ramachandran, Ministry of Textiles

Minister of Tourism
Sadhvi Uma Shree Bharati, Ministry of Tourism

Minister of Urban Development
Bandaru Dattatreya, Ministry of Urban
Development

Minister of Social Justice and Empowerment
Maneka Gandhi, Ministry of Social Justice and
Empowerment, A-4, Maharani Bagh, New Delhi
110 065, India
PHONE: +91 (11) 6840402
FAX: +91 (11) 6823144

Minister of Water Resources
Bijoya Chakravarty, Ministry of Water
Resources

Secretary of Agriculture and Cooperation
Bhaskar Barua, Department of Agriculture and
Cooperation
PHONE: +91 (11) 3382651
FAX: +91 (11) 3386004

**Minister of Atomic Energy and Animal
Husbandry**
Atal Behari Vajpayee, Ministry of Atomic
Energy and Animal Husbandry

**Minister of Chemicals and Fertilizers and
Food and Consumer Affairs**
Surjit Singh Barnala, Ministry of Chemicals and
Fertilizers and Food and Consumer Affairs

Minister of Civil Aviation
Ananth Kumar, Ministry of Civil Aviation

Minister of Chemicals and Fertilizers
Suresh Prabhakar Prabhu, Ministry of Chemicals
and Fertilizers, Tughlak Road, New Delhi 110
001, India
PHONE: +91 (11) 3017105; 3017106
FAX: +91 (11) 3017102
E-MAIL: commerce@hub.nic.in

Minister of Civil Aviation
Sharad Yadav, Ministry of Civil Aviation, 16
Sati, 3rd Main Vyalikaval, Bangalore 560003,
India
PHONE: +91 (80) 3310139
FAX: +91 (80) 3310070
E-MAIL: commerce@hub.nic.in

Minister of Commerce and Industry
Murasoli Maran, Ministry of Commerce and
Industry, Udyog Bhavan, New Delhi 110 011,
India
PHONE: +91 (11) 3015299; 3016917
FAX: +91 (11) 3014418
E-MAIL: commerce@hub.nic.in

Minister of Communications
Ram Vilas Paswan, Ministry of Communications

Minister of Consumer Affairs and Public Distribution
Kumar Shanta, Ministry of Consumer Affairs and Public Distribution

Minister of Culture, Youth Affairs and Sports
Kumar Ananth, Ministry of Culture, Youth Affairs and Sports, Shastri Bhawan, Dr. Rajendra Prasad Road, New Delhi 110 001, India
PHONE: +91 (11) 3382897
FAX: +91 (11) 3387418

Minister of Defense
George Fernandes, Ministry of Defense, Krishna Menon Marg, New Delhi 110 011, India
PHONE: +91 (11) 3017172; 3016035
FAX: +91 (11) 3793397
E-MAIL: Ramesh@dhs.unv.ernet.in

Minister of Environment and Forests
T. R. Baalu, Ministry of Environment and Forests, Paryavaran Bhavan, CGO Complex, Lodhi Road, New Delhi 110 003, India
PHONE: +91 (11) 4361896
FAX: +91 (11) 3014418
E-MAIL: secy@envfor.delhi.nic.in

Minister of External Affairs with additional charge of Department of Electronics
Jaswant Singh, Ministry of External Affairs with additional charge of Department of Electronics

Minister of Finance
Yashwant Sinha, Ministry of Finance

Minister of Family Welfare
Ministry of Family Welfare, Nirman Bhawan, New Delhi 110 011, India
E-MAIL: cdireifw@mohfw.delhi.nic.in

Minister of Food Processing Industries
Ministry of Food Processing Industries, Panchseel Bhawan, August Kranti Marg, New Delhi 110 049, India
PHONE: +91 (11) 6493012; 6492476; 6492475
FAX: +91 (11) 6493228
E-MAIL: mofpi@hub.nic.in

Minister of Heavy Industries and Public Enterprises
Manohar Joshi, Ministry of Heavy Industries and Public Enterprises

Minister of Home Affairs
Lal Krishna Advani, Ministry of Home Affairs, North Block, Central Secretariat, New Delhi 110 001, India
PHONE: +91 (11) 3011011; 3010161

FAX: +91 (11) 3015750; 3017763

Minister of Human Resource Development
Murli Manohar Joshi, Ministry of Human Resource Development, Technology Bhawan, New Mehrauli Road, New Delhi 110 016, India

Minister of Information and Broadcasting with additional charge of Food Processing Industries
Pramod Mahajan, Ministry of Information and Broadcasting with additional charge of Food Processing Industries, Panchsheel Bhawan, August Kranti Marg, New Delhi 110 049, India
PHONE: +91 (11) 6493012; 6492476; 6492475
FAX: +91 (11) 6493228
E-MAIL: mofpi@hub.nic.in

Minister of Law, Justice and Company Affairs
Ram Jethmalani, Ministry of Law, Justice and Company Affairs, 4th Floor, A-Wing, Shastri Bhavan, New Delhi 110 001, India
PHONE: +91 (11) 3387557; 3384777; 3384617
FAX: +91 (11) 3384241; 3387259; 3382733
E-MAIL: lawmin@caselaw.delhi.nic.in

Minister of Labour
Satyanarayan Jatia, Ministry of Labour, Shram Shakti Bhawan, Rafi Marg, New Delhi 110 001, India
PHONE: +91 (11) 3001425
E-MAIL: labour@lisd.delhi.nic.in

Minister of Mines and Minerals
Naveen Patnaik, Ministry of Mines and Minerals

Minister of Petroleum and Natural Gas
Ram Naik, Ministry of Petroleum and Natural Gas, Government of India, New Delhi, 110 001, India
PHONE: +91 (11) 3381462

Minister of Power and Non-Conventional Energy Sources
P. R. Kumaramangalam, Ministry of Power and Non-Conventional Energy Sources, Block-14, C.G.O. Complex, Lodhi Road, New Delhi 110 003, India
PHONE: +91 (11) 4361604
FAX: +91 (11) 4361604
E-MAIL: dirmnes@ren02.nic.in

Minister of Railways
Mamta Bannerjeeb, Ministry of Railways

Minister of Rural Development
Sunder Lal Patwa, Ministry of Rural Development

Minister of Surface Transportation
Kumar Nitish, Ministry of Surface
Transportation

Minister of Steel and Mines
Naveen Patnaik, Ministry of Steel and Mines

Minister of Textiles
Kashiram Rana, Ministry of Textiles, Udyog
Bhavan, New Delhi 110 011, India
PHONE: +91 (11) 3014069
FAX: +91 (11) 3013711/3013681
E-MAIL: dirmnes@ren02.nic.in

Minister of Tourism
Ministry of Tourism, 88 Janpath, New Delhi 110
011, India
PHONE: +91 (11) 3320342; 3320005; 3320109
FAX: +91 (11) 3320342
E-MAIL: newdelhi@tourisminindia.com

Minister of Tribal Affairs
Jual Oram, Ministry of Tribal Affairs

Minister of Urban Development
Jagmohan, Ministry of Urban Development,
Nirman Bhawan, Maulana Azad Road, New
Delhi 110 011, India
PHONE: +91 (11) 3018495; 3019162; 3018998
FAX: +91 (11) 3019089
E-MAIL: secyurban@alpha.nic.in

**Minister of Urban Unemployment and Poverty
Alleviation**
Satya Narayan Jatiya, Ministry of Urban
Unemployment and Poverty Alleviation

**Minister of Water Resources and
Parliamentary Affairs**
Pramod Mahajan, Ministry of Water Resources
and Parliamentary Affairs, Shram Shakti Bhavan,
New Delhi 110 011, India
PHONE: +91 (11) 3717129
FAX: +91 (11) 3710253
E-MAIL: mowr@hub.nic.in

POLITICAL ORGANIZATIONS

Bharatiya Janata Party-BJP (Indian People's Party)

11 Ashoka Road, New Delhi 110 001, India
PHONE: +91 (11) 3382234; 3382235
FAX: +91 (11) 3782163
E-MAIL: bjpco@bjp.org
TITLE: Party President
NAME: Kushabhau Thakre

Ajeya Bharat Party

D-56 South Extension, New Delhi 110 001,
India
PHONE: +91 (11) 4697410
E-MAIL: members@ajeyabharat.com
TITLE: Party President
NAME: Santosh Singh

Shiromani Akali Dal-SAD (Akali Religious Party)

All-India Anna Dravida Munnetra Kazagham-ADMK (All-India Anna Diravida Progressive Foundation)

275 Aavai Shanmugam Road, Chennai 600 014,
India
TITLE: General Secretary
NAME: Jayaram Jayalalitha

Congress Party

TITLE: President
NAME: P. V. Narasimha Rao

Dravida Munnetra Kazhagam (DMK)

Biju Janta Dal (BJD)

Samata Party-SAP (Equality Party)

NAME: George Fernandes

Haryana Vikas Party (HVP)

Lok Shakti (LS)

Marumalarchi Dravida Munnetra Kazhhagam (MDMK)

Pattali Makkal Katchi (PMK)

Shiva Sena (SS)

Mumbai 400 051, India
TITLE: General Secretary
NAME: Shivsenapramukh Balasaheb Thackeray

Trinamool Congress (TC)

Indian Union Muslim League (IUML)

Kerala Congress-Mani (KC-M)

NAME: K. M. Mani

Republican Party of India (RPI)

National Front/Left Front/United Front (NF)

All India Forward Block (AIFB)

TITLE: Chairman
NAME: Prem Dutta Paliwal

Asom Gana Parishad-AGP (Assam People's Council)

Bhartiya Kissan Kamagar Party

Communist Party of India (CPI)

NAME: Vinod Mishra

Communist Party of India (Marxist)

A. K. Gopalan Bhawan, 27-29 Bhai Vir Singh Marg, New Delhi 110 001, India
PHONE: +91 (11) 3344918
FAX: +91 (11) 3747483
E-MAIL: cpim@vsnl.com
TITLE: General Secretary
NAME: Harkishan Singh Surjeet

Communist Party of India Liberation

AU-90 Shakarpur, New Delhi 110 092, India
PHONE: +91 (11) 2221067
FAX: +91 (11) 2218248
E-MAIL: cpim@vsnl.com
TITLE: General Secretary
NAME: Dipankar Bhattacharya

Dravida Munnetra Kazhagam-DMK (Dravida Progressive Federation)

NAME: M. Karunanidhi

Humanist Party of India

Jammu and Kashmir National Conference (JKNC)

Janata Dal-JD (People's Party)

NAME: Laloo Prasad Yadav

People's Party, Ajit Singh faction

NAME: Ajit Singh

Revolutionary Socialist Party (RSP)

NAME: Tridip Chowdhury

Samajwadi Party-SP (Socialist Party)

18 Coppernicus Lane, New Delhi 110 001, India
PHONE: +91 (11) 3386842
FAX: +91 (11) 3382430
TITLE: President
NAME: Mulayam Singh Yadav

Tamil Maanila Congress (TMC)

8 Kalakshetra Avenue, Thiruvanmiyur, India
PHONE: +91 (44) 8583945; 8583940
E-MAIL: icmcomp@md2.vsnl.net.in

TITLE: President
NAME: G. K. Moopanar

Telugu Desam-TD (Telugu Land)

NAME: Chandrababu Naidu

Rashtriya Janata Dal-RJD (National People's Party)

Victory of India Party (VIP)

DIPLOMATIC REPRESENTATION

Embassies in India

Algeria
E-12/4, Vasant Vihar, New Delhi 110 001, India
PHONE: +91 (11) 6882014; 6883910; 6112249
FAX: +91 (11) 6882289

Australia
1/50-G Shantipath, Chanakyapuri, New Delhi 110 021, India
PHONE: +91 (11) 6888223; 6885556; 6885637
FAX: +91 (11) 6885199; 6887366; 6872228

Austria
EP-13 Chandergupta Marg, Chanakyapuri, New Delhi 110 021, India
PHONE: +91 (11) 6882014; 6883910; 6112249
FAX: +91 (11) 6886929

Bangladesh
56 Ring Road, Lajpat Nagar, New Delhi 110 024, India
PHONE: +91 (11) 6834668; 6839209; 6834065
FAX: +91 (11) 6839237; 6840596

Belgium
50 N Shanti Path, Chanakyapuri, New Delhi 110 021, India
PHONE: +91 (11) 608295; 608067; 607957
FAX: +91 (11) 6885821; 6889115

Brazil
8 Aurangazeb Road, New Delhi 110 011, India
PHONE: +91 (11) 3017301
FAX: +91 (11) 3793684

Brunei Darussalam
A-42 Vasant Vihar, Vasant Marg, New Delhi 110 059, India
PHONE: +91 (11) 6888341; 6881545
FAX: +91 (11) 6881808

Bulgaria
EP 16-17 Chandragupta Marg, Chanakyapuri, New Delhi 110 021, India
PHONE: +91 (11) 607413; 607716; 608048

FAX: +91 (11) 6876190

Canada
7/8 Shantipath, Chanakyapuri, New Delhi 110
021, India
PHONE: +91 (11) 6876500
FAX: +91 (11) 6870031; 6875387; 6876579

China
50-D Shantipath, Chanakyapuri, New Delhi 110
021, India
PHONE: +91 (11) 6871585; 6871586; 6871587
FAX: +91 (11) 6885486

Colombia
82-D Malacha Marg, Chanakyapuri, New Delhi
110 021, India
PHONE: +91 (11) 3012771; 3012773
FAX: +91 (11) 3792485

Democratic Republic of Congo
C-56 Panchsheel Enclave, New Delhi 110 017,
India
PHONE: +91 (11) 6222796
FAX: +91 (11) 6227226

Croatia
70 Ring Road, Lajpat Nagar-III, New Delhi 110
024, India
PHONE: +91 (11) 6924761; 6924762
FAX: +91 (11) 4924763

Cyprus
106 Jor Bagh, New Delhi 110 003, India
PHONE: +91 (11) 4697503; 4697508
FAX: +91 (11) 4628828

Czech Republic
50-M Niti Marg, Chanakyapuri, New Delhi 110
021, India
PHONE: +91 (11) 6110205; 6110318; 6110382
FAX: +91 (11) 6886221

Denmark
11 Aurangzeb Road, New Delhi 110 011, India
PHONE: +91 (11) 3010900
FAX: +91 (11) 3010961; 3011502

Egypt
1/50-M Niti Marg, Chanakyapuri, New Delhi
110 021, India
PHONE: +91 (11) 6114096; 6114097
FAX: +91 (11) 6885355

Ethiopia
7/50-G Satya Marg, Chanakyapuri, New Delhi
110 021, India
PHONE: +91 (11) 6119513; 6119514; 6884931

European Community
65 Golf Links, New Delhi 110 003, India
PHONE: +91 (11) 4629237; 4629238
FAX: +91 (11) 4629206; 6875731

Finland
E-3 Nyaya Marg, Chanakyapuri, New Delhi 110
021, India
PHONE: +91 (11) 6115258; 6118096
FAX: +91 (11) 6886713; 6885380

France
2/50-E Shantipath, Chanakyapuri, New Delhi
110 021, India
PHONE: +91 (11) 6118790
FAX: +91 (11) 6872305; 6872306

Germany
No. 6 Block 50-G, Shantipath, Chanakyapuri,
New Delhi 110 021, India
PHONE: +91 (11) 6873117

Ghana
50-N Satya Marg, Chanakyapuri, New Delhi 110
021, India
PHONE: +91 (11) 6883315; 6883298
FAX: +91 (11) 6883202

Greece
6 Sundar Nagar, Chanakyapuri, New Delhi 110
021, India
PHONE: +91 (11) 4617800
FAX: +91 (11) 4601363

Hungary
2/50-M Niti Marg, Chanakyapuri 110 021, India
PHONE: +91 (11) 4617800
FAX: +91 (11) 6886742

Indonesia
50-A, Chanakyapuri, New Delhi 110 021, India
PHONE: +91 (11) 6118642; 6118643; 6118644
FAX: +91 (11) 6874402; 6886763

Iran
5 Barakhamba Road, New Delhi 110 001, India
PHONE: +91 (11) 4617800
FAX: +91 (11) 3325493

Iraq
169-171 Jor Bagh, New Delhi 110 003, India
PHONE: +91 (11) 4618011; 4618012
FAX: +91 (11) 4631547

Ireland
230 Jor Bagh, New Delhi 110 003, India
PHONE: +91 (11) 4626733; 4626741; 4626743
FAX: +91 (11) 4697053

Israel
3 Aurangzeb Road, New Delhi 110 011, India
PHONE: +91 (11) 3013238
FAX: +91 (11) 3014298

Italy
50-E Chandragupta Marg, Chanakyapuri, New Delhi 110 021, India
PHONE: +91 (11) 6114355; 6114359; 6114353
FAX: +91 (11) 6873889

Japan
50-G Shantipath, Chanakyapuri, New Delhi 110 021, India
PHONE: +91 (11) 6876581; 6876582; 6876564
FAX: +91 (11) 6885587

Jordan
1/21 ShantiNiketan, New Delhi 110 021, India
PHONE: +91 (11) 6889857; 6889733
FAX: +91 (11) 6883763

Kazakhstan
EP 16-17 Chandragupta Marg, Chanakyapuri, New Delhi 110 021, India
PHONE: +91 (11) 6888252; 6881461
FAX: +91 (11) 6888464

Kenya
66 Vasant Marg, Vasant Vihar, New Delhi 110 057, India
PHONE: +91 (11) 6876538; 6876539; 6876540
FAX: +91 (11) 6876550

North Korea
H-1 Maharani Bagh, New Delhi 110 065, India
PHONE: +91 (11) 6829644; 6829645; 6466357
FAX: +91 (11) 6466357

Kuwait
5-A Shantipath, Chanakyapuri, New Delhi 110 021, India
PHONE: +91 (11) 600791; 600972
FAX: +91 (11) 6873516

Lebanon
10 Sardar patel Marg, New Delhi 110 021, India
PHONE: +91 (11) 3013174; 3013637
FAX: +91 (11) 3015555

Libya
22 Golf Links, New Delhi 110 003, India
PHONE: +91 (11) 4697717; 4697771; 4698027
FAX: +91 (11) 4633005

Malaysia
50-M Satya Marg, Chanakyapuri, New Delhi 110 021, India
PHONE: +91 (11) 601291; 601292; 601296
FAX: +91 (11) 6881538

Mauritius
5 Kautilya Marg, Chanakyapuri, New Delhi 110 021, India
FAX: +91 (11) 3019925

Mexico
10 Jor Bagh, New Delhi 110 003, India
PHONE: +91 (11) 4697991; 4697992; 4615128
FAX: +91 (11) 4692360

Myanmar
3/50F Nyaya Marg, Chanakyapuri, New Delhi 110 021, India
PHONE: +91 (11) 6889007; 6889008
FAX: +91 (11) 6877942

Namibia
D-6/ 24, Vasant Vihar, New Delhi 110 003, India
PHONE: +91 (11) 6110389; 6110309; 6114772
FAX: +91 (11) 6116120

Nepal
Barakhamba Road, New Delhi 110 001, India
PHONE: +91 (11) 3329969; 3327361; 3329218
FAX: +91 (11) 3326857

Netherlands
6/50 F Shantipath, Chanakyapuri, New Delhi 110 021, India
PHONE: +91 (11) 6884951; 6884952; 6884953
FAX: +91 (11) 6884956

New Zealand
50-N Nyaya Marg, Chanakyapuri, New Delhi 110 021, India
PHONE: +91 (11) 6883170
FAX: +91 (11) 6872317

Norway
5 Shantipath, Chanakyapuri, New Delhi 110 021, India
PHONE: +91 (11) 6110389; 6110309; 6114772
FAX: +91 (11) 6873814

Oman
16 Olof Palam Marg, Vasant Vihar, New Delhi 110 057, India
PHONE: +91 (11) 670215; 674798; 671704
FAX: +91 (11) 6876478

Pakistan
2/50-G Shantipath, Chanakyapuri, New Delhi 110 021, India
PHONE: +91 (11) 600601; 600603; 600604
FAX: +91 (11) 687239

Philippines
50-N Nyaya Marg, Chanakyapuri, New Delhi 110 021, India

PHONE: +91 (11) 601120
FAX: +91 (11) 6866401

Poland
550-M Shantipath, Chanakyapuri, New Delhi
110 021, India
PHONE: +91 (11) 6889211; 608321
FAX: +91 (11) 6871914; 686604

Portugal
13 Sundar Nagar, New Delhi 110 003, India
PHONE: +91 (11) 4601262
FAX: +91 (11) 4601252

Qatar
G-5 Anand Niketan, New Delhi 110 021, India
PHONE: +91 (11) 6117241; 6117240
FAX: +91 (11) 6886080; 6882184

Romania
A-52 Vasant Marg, Vasant Vihar, New Delhi
110 057, India
PHONE: +91 (11) 6870447; 6870611; 6870700
FAX: +91 (11) 6870611

Russia
Shantipath, Chanakyapuri, New Delhi 110 021,
India
PHONE: +91 (11) 6873799; 6873800; 6873802
FAX: +91 (11) 6886080; 6882184

Saudi Arabia
D-12 New Delhi South Extn., Chanakyapuri,
New Delhi 110 049, India
PHONE: +91 (11) 6442471; 6445419
FAX: +91 (11) 6222790

Serbia
3/50 G Niti Marg, Chanakyapuri, New Delhi 110
021, India
PHONE: +91 (11) 6872073; 6873661
FAX: +91 (11) 6885535

Singapore
E-6 Chandergupta Marg, Chanakyapuri, New
Delhi 110 021, India
PHONE: +91 (11) 6885659; 6886506; 6877939
FAX: +91 (11) 6886798

Slovakia
50-M Niti Marg, Chanakyapuri, New Delhi 110
021, India
PHONE: +91 (11) 6889071; 6885340; 6111075
FAX: +91 (11) 6877941

South Africa
B-18 Vasant Marg, Vasant Vihar, New Delhi
110 057, India
PHONE: +91 (11) 6119411; 6113505

Spain
512 Prithiviraj Road, New Delhi 110 011, India
PHONE: +91 (11) 63792085; 3792082; 3792074
FAX: +91 (11) 3753375

Sri Lanka
527 Kautilya Marg, Chanakyapuri, New Delhi
110 021, India
PHONE: +91 (11) 3010201; 3010202; 3010203
FAX: +91 (11) 3015295

Sweden
Nyaya Marg, Chanakyapuri, New Delhi 110 021,
India
PHONE: +91 (11) 6875760; 608135
FAX: +91 (11) 6885401

Switzerland
28 Vasant Marg, Vasant Vihar, New Delhi 110
057, India
PHONE: +91 (11) 6878372; 6878373; 6878374
FAX: +91 (11) 6873093; 6112220

Syria
28 Vasant Vihar, New Delhi 110 057, India
PHONE: +91 (11) 670233; 670285
FAX: +91 (11) 6873107

Thailand
56-N Nyaya Marg, Chanakyapuri, New Delhi
110 021, India
PHONE: +91 (11) 605679; 6118103; 6118104
FAX: +91 (11) 6872029

Trinidad and Tobago
131 Jor Bagh, New Delhi 110 003, India
PHONE: +91 (11) 4618187
FAX: +91 (11) 4624581

Turkey
N-50 Nyaya Marg, Chanakyapuri, New Delhi
110 021, India
PHONE: +91 (11) 601921; 6889053; 6889054
FAX: +91 (11) 6881409

Uganda
B-3/26 Vasant Vihar, New Delhi 110 057, India
PHONE: +91 (11) 6874412; 6885817
FAX: +91 (11) 6874405

Ukraine
176 Jor Bagh, New Delhi 110 003, India
PHONE: +91 (11) 4616019; 4616086
FAX: +91 (11) 4616085; 4616087

United Arab Amirates
EP-12 Chandragupta Marg, Chanakyapuri, New
Delhi 110 021, India
PHONE: +91 (11) 670830; 670945; 6872822
FAX: +91 (11) 6873272

United Kingdom

Shantipath, Chanakyapuri, New Delhi 110 021, India

PHONE: +91 (11) 6872161

FAX: +91 (11) 6872882

United States

Shantipath, Chanakyapuri, New Delhi 110 021, India

PHONE: +91 (11) 6889033

FAX: +91 (11) 6113933

Uzbekistan

D-4/6 Vasant Vihar, New Delhi 110 057, India

PHONE: +91 (11) 6119035; 6119036

FAX: +91 (11) 6873246

Zambia

F-8/22 Vasant Vihar, New Delhi 110 057, India

PHONE: +91 (11) 6877681; 6877848; 6877862

FAX: +91 (11) 6877928

JUDICIAL SYSTEM

Supreme Court

FURTHER READING

Articles

Clifton, Tony. "A Gandhi in the Wings: Whipped, Congress Looks to a Political Heiress." *Newsweek International* (October 18, 1999): 44.

———. "'Hindustan for the Hindus!': Muslims and Christians Still Fear the Power of the RSS." *Newsweek International* (October 18, 1999): 42.

"From Mild-Mannered to Man of Action." *Business Week* (February 8, 1999): 38.

Kuchment, Anna. "Nuclear Dread in South Asia." *Newsweek International* (October 18, 1999): 5.

Rao, Kala. "The Power and the Glory." *The Banker* 149 (October 1999): 83.

"Reform Grabs More Seats in Delhi." *Business Week* (October 25, 1999): 32.

Books

Economist Intelligence Unit. *India Business Intelligence.* Hong Kong: EIU, 1997.

McCullin, Don. *India.* London: Jonathan Cape, 1999.

Thomas, Raju G. C. *Democracy, Security, and Development in India.* New York: St. Martin's Press, 1996.

Wolpert, Stanley A. *India.* Berkeley: University of California Press, 1999.

Internet

Discover India. Available Online @ http://www.meadev.gov.in/1page.htm (November 17, 1999).

INDIA: STATISTICAL DATA

For sources and notes see "Sources of Statistics" in the front of each volume.

GEOGRAPHY

Geography (1)

Area:

Total: 3,287,590 sq km.

Land: 2,973,190 sq km.

Water: 314,400 sq km.

Area—comparative: slightly more than one-third the size of the US.

Land boundaries:

Total: 14,103 km.

Border countries: Bangladesh 4,053 km, Bhutan 605 km, Burma 1,463 km, China 3,380 km, Nepal 1,690 km, Pakistan 2,912 km.

HUMAN FACTORS

Demographics (2A)

	1990	1995	1998	2000	2010	2020	2030	2040	2050
Population	NA	933,285.6	984,003.7	1,017,645.2	1,182,170.8	1,340,864.8	1,484,847.0	1,607,751.8	1,706,950.6
Net migration rate (per 1,000 population)	NA	NA	NA	NA	NA	NA	NA	NA	NA
Births	NA	NA	NA	NA	NA	NA	NA	NA	NA
Deaths	NA	NA	NA	NA	NA	NA	NA	NA	NA
Life expectancy - males	NA	60.8	62.1	63.0	66.9	70.2	72.9	75.0	76.6
Life expectancy - females	NA	62.1	63.7	64.9	69.9	74.2	77.6	80.2	82.2
Birth rate (per 1,000)	NA	27.5	25.9	24.9	20.9	18.1	15.9	14.5	13.4
Death rate (per 1,000)	NA	9.3	8.7	8.3	7.1	6.7	6.9	7.5	8.4
Women of reproductive age (15-49 yrs.)	NA	229,471.8	245,315.5	256,330.9	307,890.1	346,756.1	376,514.9	389,495.1	393,298.7
of which are currently married	NA	NA	NA	NA	NA	NA	NA	NA	NA
Fertility rate	NA	3.4	3.2	3.1	2.5	2.3	2.1	2.1	2.0

Except as noted, values for vital statistics are in thousands; life expectancy is in years.

Geography (1) (cont.)

Coastline: 7,000 km.

Climate: varies from tropical monsoon in south to temperate in north.

Terrain: upland plain (Deccan Plateau) in south, flat to rolling plain along the Ganges, deserts in west, Himalayas in north.

Natural resources: coal (fourth-largest reserves in the world), iron ore, manganese, mica, bauxite, titanium ore, chromite, natural gas, diamonds, petroleum, limestone.

Land use:

Arable land: 56%

Permanent crops: 1%

Permanent pastures: 4%

Forests and woodland: 23%

Other: 16% (1993 est.).

HUMAN FACTORS

Health Personnel (3)

Total health expenditure as a percentage of GDP, 1990-1997[a]

Public sector	.0.7
Private sector	.4.4
Total[b]	.5.6

Health expenditure per capita in U.S. dollars, 1990-1997[a]

Purchasing power parity	.64
Total	.18

Availability of health care facilities per 100,000 people

Hospital beds 1990-1997[a]	.80
Doctors 1993[c]	.48
Nurses 1993[c]	.NA

Health Indicators (4)

Life expectancy at birth

1980	.54
1997	.63

Daily per capita supply of calories (1996) 2,415

Total fertility rate births per woman (1997) 3.3

Maternal mortality ratio per 100,000 live births (1990-97) ....440[d]

Safe water % of population with access (1995) 85

Sanitation % of population with access (1995) 16

Consumption of iodized salt % of households (1992-98)[a] 70

Smoking prevalence

Male % of adults (1985-95)[a]	.40
Female % of adults (1985-95)[a]	.3

Tuberculosis incidence per 100,000 people (1997) 187

Adult HIV prevalence % of population ages 15-49 (1997) 0.82

Infants and Malnutrition (5)

Under-5 mortality rate (1997) 108

% of infants with low birthweight (1990-97) 33

Births attended by skilled health staff % of total[a] ...35

% fully immunized (1995-97)

TB	.96
DPT	.90
Polio	.91
Measles	.81

Prevalence of child malnutrition under age 5 (1992-97)[b] 53

Ethnic Division (6)

Indo-Aryan	.72%
Dravidian	.25%
Mongoloid and other	.3%

Religions (7)

Hindu	.80%
Muslim	.14%
Christian	.2.4%
Sikh	.2%
Buddhist	.0.7%
Jains	.0.5%
Other	.0.4%

Languages (8)

English enjoys associate status but is the most important language for national, political, and commercial communication, Hindi the national language and primary tongue of 30% of the people, Bengali (official), Telugu (official), Marathi (official), Tamil (official), Urdu (official), Gujarati (official), Malayalam (official), Kannada (official), Oriya (official), Punjabi (official), Assamese (official), Kashmiri (official), Sindhi (official), Sanskrit (official), Hindustani a popular variant of Hindu/Urdu, is spoken widely throughout northern India. 24 languages each spoken by a million or more persons; numerous other languages and dialects, for the most part mutually unintelligible.

EDUCATION

Public Education Expenditures (9)

Public expenditure on education (% of GNP)

1980 . . . . .3.0

1996 . . . . .3.4[1]

Expenditure per student

Primary % of GNP per capita

1980 . . . . .10.5

1996 . . . . .11.6[1]

Secondary % of GNP per capita

1980 . . . .

1996 . . . .

Tertiary % of GNP per capita

1980 . . . . .88.5

1996 . . . . .74.8

Expenditure on teaching materials

Primary % of total for level (1996) . . . .

Secondary % of total for level (1996) . . . .

Primary pupil-teacher ratio per teacher (1996) . . . . .64[1]

Duration of primary education years (1995) 5

Educational Attainment (10)

Age group (1991)[17] . . . . .25+

Total population 368,004,483

Highest level attained (%)

No schooling 57.5

First level

Not completed 28.0

Completed . . . . .NA

Entered second level

S-1 . . . . .7.2

S-2 . . . . .NA

Postsecondary 7.3

Literacy Rates (11A)

In thousands and percent[1]	1990	1995	2000	2010
Illiterate population (15+ yrs.)	279,610	290,705	300,833	313,647
Literacy rate - total adult pop. (%)	48.4	52.0	55.8	62.6
Literacy rate - males (%)	62.4	65.5	68.6	73.8
Literacy rate - females (%)	33.5	37.7	42.1	50.7

GOVERNMENT & LAW

Political Parties (12)

Legislative branch is a bicameral Parliament (it consists of the Council of States, a body consisting of not more than 250 members, up to 12 of which are appointed by the president, the remainder are chosen by the elected members of the state and territorial assemblies members serve six-year terms; and the People's Assembly (545 seats; 543 elected by popular vote, 2 appointed members serve five-year terms). No election results are available.

Government Budget (13A)

Year: 1997

Total Expenditures: 2,331.5 Billions of Rupees

Expenditures as a percentage of the total by function:

General public services and public order . . . . . . .8.28[f]

Defense . . . . .15.21[f]

Education . . . . .2.49[f]

Health . . . . .1.54[f]

Social Security and Welfare . . . .

Housing and community amenities . . . . .6.28[f]

Recreational, cultural, and religious affairs . . . .

Fuel and energy . . . .

Agriculture, forestry, fishing, and hunting . . . . . .5.31[f]

Mining, manufacturing, and construction . . . . . .1.70[f]

Transportation and communication . . . . .1.50[f]

Other economic affairs and services . . . . .6.26[f]

Crime (15)

Crime rate (for 1997)

Crimes reported 6,411,300

Total persons convicted 5,353,400

Crimes per 100,000 population 675

Persons responsible for offenses

Total number of suspects 7,377,500

Total number of female suspects 317,200

Total number of juvenile suspects 14,800

LABOR FORCE

Labor Force (16)

Total (million) 390

Agriculture 67%

Services 18%

Industry 15%

Data for 1997 est. Percent distribution for 1995 est.

Unemployment Rate (17)

Rate not available.

PRODUCTION SECTOR

Electric Energy (18)

Capacity . . . . .83.288 million kW (1996)

Production . . . . .398.28 billion kWh (1995)

Consumption per capita . . . . .427 kWh (1995)

Transportation (19)

Highways:

total: 2.06 million km

paved: 1,034,120 km

unpaved: 1,025,880 km (1996 est.)

Waterways: 16,180 km; 3,631 km navigable by large vessels

Pipelines: crude oil 3,005 km; petroleum products 2,687 km; natural gas 1,700 km (1995)

Merchant marine:

total: 299 ships (1,000 GRT or over) totaling 6,605,619 GRT/10,988,439 DWT

Airports: 343 (1997 est.)

Airports—with paved runways:

total: 237

GOVERNMENT & LAW

Military Affairs (14B)

	1990	1991	1992	1993	1994	1995
Military expenditures						
Current dollars (mil.)	6,635	6,390	6,500	7,509	8,294	7,831
1995 constant dollars (mil.)	7,626	7,061	6,991	7,872	8,502	7,831
Armed forces (000)	1,262	1,265	1,265	1,256	1,305	1,265
Gross national product (GNP)						
Current dollars (mil.)	228,700	238,600	257,900	274,400	299,000	326,200
1995 constant dollars (mil.)	262,800	263,600	277,400	287,600	306,500	326,200
Central government expenditures (CGE)						
1995 constant dollars (mil.)	57,940	54,740	56,510	59,500	62,080	61,800
People (mil.)	855.6	872.3	888.6	904.7	920.7	936.5
Military expenditure as % of GNP	2.9	2.7	2.5	2.7	2.8	2.4
Military expenditure as % of CGE	13.2	12.9	12.4	13.2	13.7	12.7
Military expenditure per capita (1995 $)	9	8	8	9	9	8
Armed forces per 1,000 people (soldiers)	1.5	1.5	1.4	1.4	1.4	1.4
GNP per capita (1995 $)	307	302	312	318	333	348
Arms imports[6]						
Current dollars (mil.)	1,800	925	650	270	230	410
1995 constant dollars (mil.)	2,069	1,022	699	283	236	410
Arms exports[6]						
Current dollars (mil.)	10	5	0	10	10	5
1995 constant dollars (mil.)	11	6	0	10	10	5
Total imports[7]						
Current dollars (mil.)	23,640	20,420	23,580	22,760	26,850	34,520
1995 constant dollars (mil.)	27,170	22,560	25,360	23,860	27,520	34,520
Total exports[7]						
Current dollars (mil.)	17,970	17,660	19,560	21,550	25,070	30,760
1995 constant dollars (mil.)	20,660	19,520	21,040	22,600	25,700	30,760
Arms as percent of total imports[8]	7.6	4.5	2.8	1.2	.9	1.2
Arms as percent of total exports[8]	.1	0	0	0	0	0

over 3,047 m: 12

2,438 to 3,047 m: 47

1,524 to 2,437 m: 87

914 to 1,523 m: 72

under 914 m: 19 (1997 est.)

Airports—with unpaved runways:

total: 106

2,438 to 3,047 m: 2

1,524 to 2,437 m: 6

914 to 1,523 m: 47

under 914 m: 51 (1997 est.)

Top Agricultural Products (20)

Rice, wheat, oilseed, cotton, jute, tea, sugarcane, potatoes; cattle, water buffalo, sheep, goats, poultry; fish catch of about 3 million metric tons ranks India among the world's top 10 fishing nations.

MANUFACTURING SECTOR

GDP & Manufacturing Summary (21)

Detailed value added figures are listed by both International Standard Industry Code (ISIC) and product title.

	1980	1985	1990	1994
GDP ($-1990 mil.)[1]	173,216	224,966	303,282	352,516
Per capita ($-1990)[1]	251	293	357	384
Manufacturing share (%) (current prices)[1]	17.7	17.9	18.6	17.9
Manufacturing				
Value added ($-1990 mil.)[1]	24,608	34,472	50,174	56,223
Industrial production index	100	129	181	203
Value added ($ mil.)	13,086	15,526	25,097	24,396
Gross output ($ mil.)	71,387	88,304	140,511	137,990
Employment (000)	6,992	6,578	7,299	8,382
Profitability (% of gross output)				
Intermediate input (%)	82	82	82	82
Wages and salaries inc. supplements (%)	11	10	8	8
Gross operating surplus	8	8	10	10
Productivity ($)				
Gross output per worker	10,210	13,423	19,250	16,456
Value added per worker	1,872	2,360	3,438	2,911
Average wage (inc. supplements)	1,083	1,298	1,592	1,269
Value added ($ mil.)				
311/2 Food products	899	1,436	2,212	2,019
313 Beverages	99	135	246	241
314 Tobacco products	196	230	489	508
321 Textiles	2,642	2,135	3,264	2,503
322 Wearing apparel	62	87	316	427
323 Leather and fur products	48	52	123	102
324 Footwear	37	52	104	106
331 Wood and wood products	74	73	102	79
332 Furniture and fixtures	8	7	8	6
341 Paper and paper products	296	233	574	451
342 Printing and publishing	256	280	340	396
351 Industrial chemicals	778	1,200	1,833	2,601
352 Other chemical products	1,062	1,146	1,647	1,922
353 Petroleum refineries	203	344	1,072	1,154
354 Miscellaneous petroleum and coal products	151	152	146	204
355 Rubber products	234	363	566	522
356 Plastic products	93	166	297	317
361 Pottery, china and earthenware	47	27	52	40

GDP & Manufacturing Summary (21)

	1980	1985	1990	1994
362 Glass and glass products	67	101	111	109
369 Other non-metal mineral products	399	775	1,122	954
371 Iron and steel	1,489	1,790	2,551	1,983
372 Non-ferrous metals	81	115	654	726
381 Metal products	421	425	614	554
382 Non-electrical machinery	1,130	1,506	2,011	2,021
383 Electrical machinery	1,061	1,201	2,009	2,052
384 Transport equipment	1,088	1,231	2,374	2,065
385 Professional and scientific equipment	92	118	165	168
390 Other manufacturing industries	72	146	92	165

FINANCE, ECONOMICS, & TRADE

Economic Indicators (22)

National product: GDP—purchasing power parity—$1.534 trillion (1997 est.)

National product real growth rate: 5% (1997 est.)

National product per capita: $1,600 (1997 est.)

Inflation rate—consumer price index: 7% (1997 est.)

Exchange Rates (24)

Exchange rates:

Indian rupees (Rs) per US$1

January 1998	39.358
1997	36.313
1996	35.433
1995	32.427
1994	31.374
1993	30.493

Top Import Origins (25)

$39.7 billion (c.i.f., 1997)

Origins	%
United Kingdom	NA

NA stands for not available.

Top Export Destinations (26)

$33.9 billion (f.o.b., 1997).

Destinations	%
United States	NA
Hong Kong	NA
United Kingdom	NA
Germany	NA

NA stands for not available.

Balance of Payments (23)

	1991	1992	1993	1994	1995
Exports of goods (f.o.b.)	18,095	20,019	22,016	25,523	31,239
Imports of goods (f.o.b.)	−21,087	−22,931	−24,108	−29,673	−37,957
Trade balance	−2,992	−2,911	−2,093	−4,150	−6,719
Services - debits	−10,180	−11,024	−10,618	−12,570	−15,487
Services - credits	5,157	5,311	5,482	6,859	8,261
Private transfers (net)	460	460	307	422	334
Government transfers (net)	3,263	3,679	5,046	7,763	8,048
Overall balance	−4,292	−4,485	−1,876	−1,676	−5,564

Economic Aid (27)

Recipient: ODA, $1.237 billion (1993); US ODA bilateral commitments $171 million; US Ex-Im bilateral commitments $680 million; Western (non-US) countries, ODA bilateral commitments $2.48 billion; OPEC bilateral aid $200 million; World Bank (IBRD) multilateral commitments $2.8 billion; Asian Development Bank (AsDB) multilateral commitments $760 million; International (IFC) multilateral commitments $200 million; other mult.

Import Export Commodities (28)

Import Commodities	Export Commodities
Crude oil and petroleum products	Gems and jewelry
Machinery	Clothing
Gems	Engineering goods
Fertilizer	Chemicals
Chemicals	Leather manufactures
	Cotton yarn
	Fabric

INDONESIA

Republic of Indonesia
Republik Indonesia

INTRODUCTORY SURVEY

RECENT HISTORY

Following the formation of the Volkstraad (a representative body), an Indonesian nationalist movement began to develop that steadily gained strength. Nationalists under the leadership of Untung Sukarno and Mohammad Hatta proclaimed an independent republic on 17 August 1945. After four years of fighting and negotiations, the Dutch recognized the independence of all the former Dutch East Indies (except West New Guinea) as the Republic of the United States of Indonesia on 27 December 1949.

Sukarno became the first president of the new nation, and Hatta the vice-president. Eventually, longstanding tensions between Java and the other islands erupted in violence. In response, the Sukarno regime turned to an increasingly authoritarian, anti-Western policy of "guided democracy." In March 1967, following a 1965 communist-led takeover attempt and widespread military action against hundreds of thousands of Indonesian Chinese, the People's Consultative Assembly (Majetis Permusyawaratan Rakyat—MPR) voted unanimously to withdraw all Sukarno's governmental power and appoint the commander of the army, General Suharto, acting president. One year later, it conferred full presidential powers on Suharto, and he was sworn in as president for a five-year term.

Under Suharto's "New Order," Indonesia turned to the West and began following a conservative economic course stressing private investment.

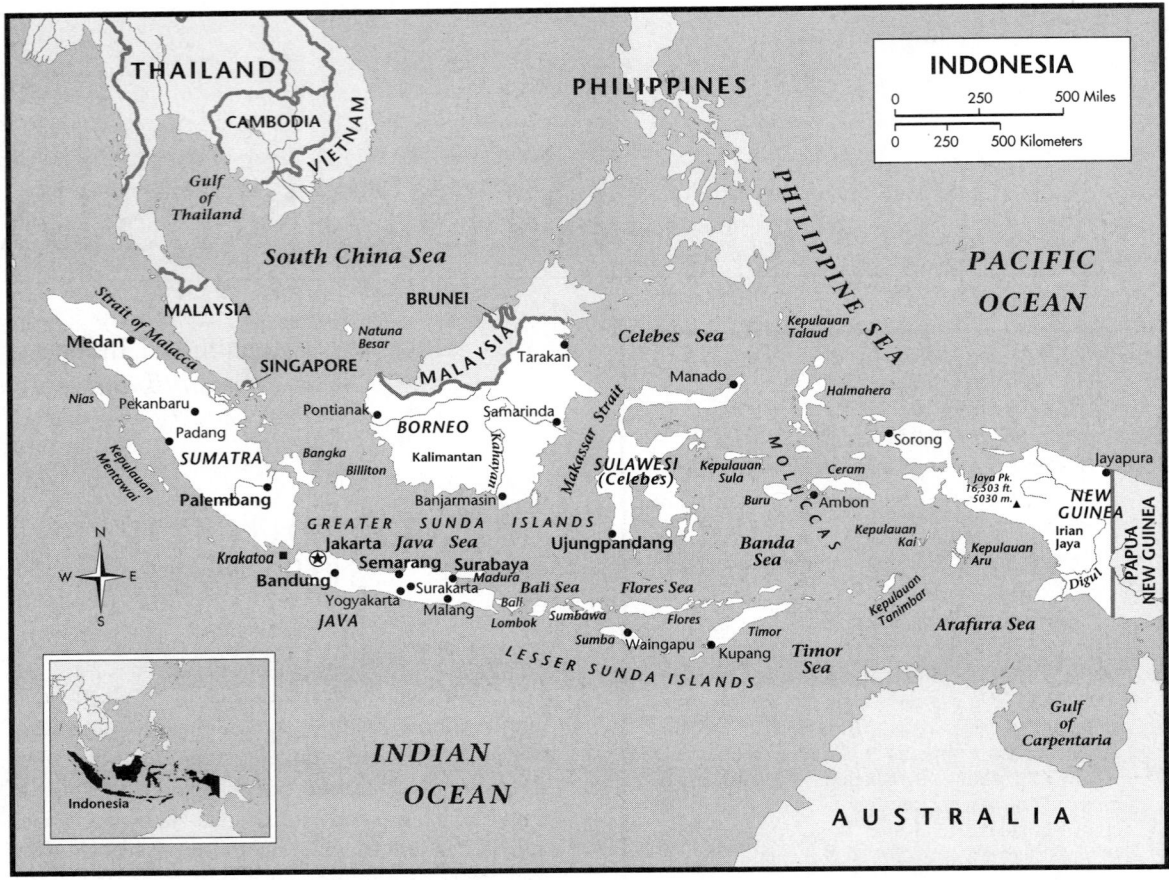

In foreign affairs, Suharto's government achieved closer ties with the United States, Japan, and Western Europe while maintaining links with the Soviet Union.

Following Portugal's withdrawal from East Timor in December 1975, Indonesia sent troops into the former Portuguese colony and gained full control of the territory, which it incorporated as an Indonesian Province. This action was opposed by both the United Nations (UN) and the military group that was then in control of the island. The war against Fretilin continued into the 1980s, with reports of massacres by government troops and severe economic hardship among the Timorese. The military and diplomatic struggle over East Timor continued into the 1990s unresolved.

Between 1969 and 1992, the Transmigration Program, a policy aimed at overcoming uneven population distribution in Indonesia by moving families from the inner islands to the outer islands, moved 1.5 million families. The program suffered from land disputes with local residents and environmental concerns over loss of forest land. In 1989 tension from land disputes in Java and the outer islands produced social unrest that resulted in clashes between villagers and the armed forces.

On 12 November 1991, during a funeral for a young Timorese killed in demonstrations against Indonesia's rule of East Timor, soldiers opened fire on the defenseless mourners in a massacre that received worldwide attention. Western governments threatened to halt aid, and by 1993 United States policy toward Indonesia shifted toward criticism of Indonesia's rule in East Timor, and a threat to revoke trade privileges. A UN resolution on Indonesia's human rights violations placed the country on a rights "watch" list in 1993.

Violent labor unrest broke out in Medan in April 1994, and ethnic Chinese became the target of such violence. Many incidents of rural unrest continued in 1995–96 in East Timor and in Kalimantan.

In late 1997, the value of Indonesia's currency crashed and foreign debt soared as the country was drawn into the financial crisis spreading in Asia.

The government agreed to impose reforms outlined by the International Monetary Fund (IMF), but then it went back on some of those pledges. The IMF delayed the second half of the assistance package. In March 1998, Suharto was elected to a seventh term as president.

As the economic crisis continued into 1998, political instability increased and troops were sent into the streets to deal with a growing number of demonstrations. By May, public defiance to Suharto and the death toll from riots were on the rise. The troubled economy stagnated, and many foreigners left the country. Suharto resigned on 20 May 1998. His deputy, Bacharuddin Jusuf Habibie, succeeded him. Habibie at first inititated only modest reforms. Under public pressure, Habibie promised to hold a general election, revise or get rid of many restrictive laws, and to review the cases of political prisoners.

In August 1998, Indonesia and Portugal agreed on a plan to give East Timor local autonomy and control over its own educational and cultural affairs. In January 1999, Habibie took this policy a step further and declared that he would propose to the People's Consultative Assembly that if the East Timorese rejected autonomy within Indonesia, they would receive independence. Not all Indonesians and East Timorese favored the independence of the former Portugese colony. The 1999 presidential candidate Megawati Sukarnoputri opposed East Timor's independence, and East Timorese who favored integration with Indonesia took up arms against those who supported independence.

GOVERNMENT

In 1967, Suharto officially became leader of Indonesia (he had become Indonesia's unoffical ruler in March 1966). Suharto reorganized the cabinet, making all of its twelve ministers responsible to him. In 1987, memberships in the house of representatives, or DPR, and the People's Consultative Assembly (MPR) were increased to 500 and 1,000, respectively. Under the new system, legislative responsibility rested with the DPR, which consists of 400 elected members and 100 members appointed by the president. Under the Suharto government, the MPR acted as a consultative body, setting guidelines for national policy. In 1998, the MPR elected President Suharto to a seventh term, but he resigned soon after being elected. Bacharuddin Jusuf Habibie succeeded him. According to the constitution, Habibie would serve out the remain-

der of Suharto's term (until 2003), but in response to public pressure, Habibie agreed to hold elections on June 7, 1999.

Judiciary

Government courts, each with a single judge, have jurisdiction in original civil and criminal cases. The High Court hears appeals in civil cases and reviews criminal cases. The Supreme Court is the highest court in the country. Its primary function is judicial review. Judgment in civil cases involving Muslims is based on the principles of Muslim law. Judges are appointed by the central government. Customary law (adat) continues in the villages unchanged.

Islamic law (Shari'a) governs many noncriminal matters involving Muslims, including family law, inheritance and divorce. A civil code based on Roman law is applied to Europeans. A combination of codes is applied to other groups such as ethnic Chinese and Indians.

Political Parties

Before the 1971 elections, the government formed Golkar (Golongan Karya), a political party. An act of 1975 provided for the fusion of the major political organizations into two parties—the United Development Party (Partai Persuatan Pembangunan—PPP) and the Indonesian Democratic Party (Partai DemoKrasi Indonesia—PDI). The PPP, Golkar's chief opposition, is a fusion of Muslim groups, while the PDI represents the merger of the Indonesian Nationalist Party (PNI), the Christian Party, the Roman Catholic Party, and smaller groups. In the 1997 elections, Golkar won 74% of the popular vote. The PPP took 22%, and the PDI took 3%. The 1997 campaign was the most violent in recent years, with over 200 people killed during the campaign. Suharto resigned shortly after being elected.

Going into the 1999 elections, the four leading presidential candidates were Habibie of the Golkar party and three candidates from newly formed political groupings: Megawati Sukarnoputri of the Indonesian Democratic Party of Struggle, Amien Rais of the National Mandate Party, and Abdurrahman Wahid of the National Awakening Party. Sukarnoputri is the daughter of Untung Sukarno.

DEFENSE

The Indonesian armed forces consist of an army, a navy, and an air force, numbering 299,200 in 1995. The army has 235,200 personnel; the air force, 21,000; the navy, 43,000. Paramilitary forces include a 174,000-man police force and three other armed security forces, including a trained People's Security force of 300,000.

Indonesia spent $2.8 billion for defense in 1995, or about 3% of its gross domestic product (GDP).

ECONOMIC AFFAIRS

In the twentieth century, production of oil, tin, timber, and rubber has become central to the economy. However, agriculture, with rice as the chief crop, remains the main occupation of the vast majority of Indonesians, and standards of living are low, but improving. Indonesia is exceptionally rich in coal, oil, and other industrial raw materials.

Government policies have held the inflation rate at under 10%. Export performance has remained strong, and the government has continued deregulation to stimulate growth. An increasingly important element of national income and foreign exchange earnings is tourism with over three million visitors to Indonesia annually.

Public Finance

Government expenditures have outrun public income by a considerable margin each year since 1952, and this cash deficit has been met by foreign aid receipts. Since 1985, however, Indonesia has discouraged public sector and monetary growth, resulting in an overall budgetary surplus in 1991–2, despite a significant drop in oil revenues from falling prices.

The U.S. CIA estimates that, in 1995, government revenues totaled approximately $38.1 billion and expenditures $38.1 billion. External debt totaled $97.6 billion, approximately 99% of which was financed abroad.

Income

In 1998, Indonesia's gross national product (GNP) was $138 billion, or $680 per person. For the period 1985–95, the average inflation rate was 8.8%, resulting in a real growth rate in gross national product of 6% per person.

Industry

Despite new industries, overall industrial growth has been small since World War II with agriculture foremost in the Indonesian economy. However, in 1991, manufacturing took over as the dominant area. In that year textiles were the key industrial export, accounting for 47% of the total. In 1995, Indonesia's oil refineries, dominated by Pertamina, produced 300,200 barrels of refined petroleum products per day.

Banking and Finance

The government's Bank Negara Indonesia (BNI) was established in 1953 as the successor to the Java Bank. Bank Indonesia, as the central bank, is responsible for the administration and regulation of the six state banks and other banking operations. Among the state banks, Bank Export Import Indonesia specializes in credits for the production, processing, and marketing of export products. Bank Rakjat Indonesia specializes in credits to agricultural cooperative societies but also provides fishing and rural credit in general. BNI specializes in credits to the industrial sector; Bank Bumi Daya, in credits to estates and forestry operations; Bank Dagang Negara, in credits to the mining sector; and Bank Tabungan Negara, in the promotion of savings among the general public. The Development Bank of Indonesia (Bank Pembangunan Indonesia– or BAPINDO) provides financial assistance to government enterprises and approved new industries.

The Indonesian banking system has been transformed since the early 1980s through a process of gradual but steady reform, which culminated in the enactment of a new banking law in 1992. The liberalization of the banking industry had a dramatic impact on its growth.

Indonesia's first stock exchange was established in December 1912 in Jakarta, although both this and two subsequent exchanges established in Surabaya and Semarang in 1925 were shut down during the Japanese occupation. It was not until August 1977 that the Jakarta Stock Exchange (JSE) was successfully relaunched.

Economic Development

From the late 1960s through the mid-1980s, the Suharto government focused its efforts on financial stabilization, relying heavily on advice and assistance from multilateral aid donors. The results were mixed.

Efforts to restructure the economy in the 1980s resulted in an expansion of real GDP 6% annually on average, and in 1993 Indonesia's per capita GNP passed $700.

The 1988 Guidelines of State Policy introduced Transmigration Development, a policy aimed at overcoming uneven population distribution in Indonesia. The policy had multiple objectives: to ease the burden of densely populated regions, to upgrade regional development, to expand job opportunities, to support national unity, and to strengthen national defense.

Bilateral and multinational assistance has played a major role in Indonesia's development.

SOCIAL WELFARE

There is nothing similar to a welfare program in the Western sense, but the society is one in which family and clan relationships run strong. In addition, many orphanages, homes for the aged, youth activities, and private volunteer organizations meet special needs, in some cases receiving government subsidies.

Women in Indonesia enjoy a more favorable position than is customary in Muslim societies. In spite of women's official equality, in practice they often find it hard to exercise their legal rights.

Ethnic Chinese face discrimination. There are restrictions on the rights of noncitizen Chinese to own and operate businesses. It is illegal to import Chinese-language publications and the celebration Chinese New Year is prohibited by law.

Outright violations of human rights exist in the former Portuguese colony of East Timor. An estimated 200,000 people have died in the violence in East Timor since Indonesia gained control over the region.

Healthcare

National health programs, of which family planning is an important part, stress the building of small and healthy families. Elimination of contagious diseases focuses on malaria, rabies, elephantiasis, tuberculosis, cholera, and leprosy. Overcrowded cities, poor sanitation, impure water supplies, substandard urban housing, and dietary deficiencies are contributing factors to health problems. In 1994–95, only 63% of the population had access to safe water and 55% had adequate sanitation. Average life expectancy is 65 years for men and women. During 1989–95, 39% of children under 5 years old were considered malnourished.

In 1991, Indonesia had 1,552 hospitals, with about 120,711 beds. In addition, there were 5,656 public health centers.

Housing

Housing is a serious problem in both urban and rural areas. In 1989, 55% of all households received their drinking water from wells, 13% from springs, and only 13% from pipes. Lighting was provided to 45% of all households by kerosene lamps, and only 43% of dwellings had private toilet facilities.

In 1990 alone, 210,000 new housing units were completed, and the total number of dwellings stood at 44.9 million in 1992.

EDUCATION

Under the constitution, six years of primary education are free and compulsory. In practice, however, the supply of schools and teachers is inadequate to meet the needs of the fast-growing under-15 age group. In 1993, there were 29.9 million primary school students and 11.4 million secondary school students.

There are fifty-one universities, the largest of which are the University of Indonesia (in Jakarta) and the University of Gajah Mada (in Yogyakarta).

1999 KEY EVENTS TIMELINE

January

- Separatist supporters riot in Aceh province.
- The Indonesian government reports that 130 million Indonesians are living in poverty.
- Rioting breaks out between Christians and Muslims.

February

- New election laws are passed.
- Imprisoned East Timor independence leader Xanana Gusmao is transferred to house arrest.
- Troops fire on Muslim and Christian mobs battling on Ambon Island.
- Students rally in Jakarta for President Habibies's resignation.

March

- Violence between Christians and Muslims continues on Ambon Island.
- The foreign ministers of Indonesia and Portugal agree to allow the people of East Timor to choose between independence and Indonesia's offer of greater autonomy.
- Ethnic violence in the West Kalimantan province on the island of Borneo reportedly claims 200 lives.

April

- The government restructures its armed forces, and places the police under a separate command from the military.

- Armed militia members attack parishioners seeking refuge in a church in Liquica, East Timor.

- Government supporters kill 30 alleged separatists in Dili, the capitol of East Timor.

- Militias rampage through Dili, burning and ransacking buildings and property. Among the dead is the son of Manuel Carrascalao, the leader of the Council of National Timorese Resistance.

- Separatists and pro-government militias sign a peace accord in Dili.

- President Habibie announces that an East Timor referendum on independence will be held August 8.

May

- Security forces open fire on rioting Christians and Muslims, killing eight and injuring seven.

- Three leading reformist parties unite in opposition to President Habibie.

June

- Elections are held on June 7th for 462 national assembly seats, the first open elections in Indonesia in 40 years.

- The IMF approves release of $450m in loans to Indonesia.

July

- Vote counting continues as rioters in Jakarta allege election rigging by the ruling Golkar party.

- Separatist unrest in the largely Muslim Aceh province claims ten lives.

- Aid workers and United Nations staff are attacked in East Timor.

- Final election results show the opposition leader Megawati Sukarnoputri's coalition party, the Indonesian Democratic Party, winning more votes than President Habibie's Golkar Party.

- Ex-president Suharto suffers a mild stroke.

August

- Thick smog from the perennial burning of forests in Indonesia blankets the region.

- The East Timorese referendum takes place; the East Timorese people vote overwhelmingly in favor of independence.

September

- Indonesia ends its security pact with Australia.

- The chief of the Indonesian Armed Forces, General Wiranto, concedes he has lost control of elements in the military in East Timor.

- 3000 people take refuge in a UN compound in Dili.

- International peacekeepers, led by Australians, arrive in East Timor.

- The Indonesian government offers to help importing businesses find new sources of goods, rather than buying Australian goods, in protest of Australia's stand on East Timor.

- Martial law is declared in East Timor.

- Parliament approves a measure granting the military the authority to take over all systems of communication and restrict freedom of expression. Violent protests by thousands of university students erupt across Indonesia; at least three are killed in clashes with riot police.

October

- Habibie bows out of the election after a vote of no confidence from the legislative body.

- Abdurrahman Wahid is elected president.

- A car bomb explodes in Jakarta hours after voting ends.

- Megawati Sukarnoputri is elected vice president.

- Thousands of students rally in Makassar, South Sulawesi, demanding an independent state of Sulawesi.

November

- President Abdurrahman Wahid gives his agreement in principle to a referendum on independence for the province of Aceh, where hundreds of people died this year in a war between separatist guerillas and the Indonesian army.

- Tens of thousands of people demonstrate in Aceh, calling for a referendum on independence.

- Leaked Australian intelligence documents emerge as the strongest proof yet that the Indonesian government had closer ties than it has acknowledged to the violence carried out by its troops and their affiliates in East Timor.

- A senior delegation from the United States arrives in East Timor for talks with the new United Nations' transitional authority and leaders of the pro-independence movement.

- Richard Holbrooke, America's ambassador to the UN and leader of the U.S. delegation visiting East Timor, warns the Indonesian government not to let the camps, where 200,000 East Timorese refugees languish in West Timor, become its Gaza strip, as efforts by aid agencies are being blocked by pro-Indonesia militia groups who have been allowed to take control of many of the camps.

- At an informal meeting in Manila, Philippines, six members of the Association of Southeast Asian Nations (ASEAN)—Brunei, Indonesia, Malaysia, Philippines, Singapore, and Thailand—agree to establish a free-trade zone by eliminating duties on most goods traded in the region by 2010. The remaining four newer and less-developed nation members—Cambodia, Laos, Myanmar (Burma), and Vietnam—will eliminate duties by 2015. Rice will be excluded from trade agreements, however.

December

- President Abdurrahman Wahid presses for arrest warrants to be issued for some of Indonesia's worst debtors after a $1.3 billion banking scandal.

- Approximately 20,000 demonstrators demand independence for Irian Jaya as Indonesian President Abdurrahman Wahid warns that ''repressive efforts'' might be used to settle unrest.

- Indonesia's new agreement with the International Monetary Fund calls for the country to run a budget deficit of about four percent of the gross domestic product next year.

- Indonesian Defense Minister Juwono Sudarsono says no senior officers will be held accountable for past human rights abuses and warns of the risk of a military coup.

- The attorney general announces that a case against former President Suharto, alleging that he illegally accumulated billions of dollars while in office, will be reopened based on new information.

- Hundreds protest at the offices of the Jakarta city manager on December 14, demanding that bars and nightclubs be closed during Muslim holy month of Ramadan.

ANALYSIS OF EVENTS: 1999

BUSINESS AND THE ECONOMY

In 1999 the Indonesian economy continued to suffer from the regional economic crisis which began in 1997 and was marked by the collapse of the Indonesian rupiah, bank insolvency, and the flight of both foreign and Indo-Chinese investors. This year has seen Indonesian banks closed and nationalized as the government struggled to control the situation. The banks remaining are burdened with $80 billion in corporate debt, more that two thirds of which is non-performing. The Indonesian economy has additional complications in the form of violence on several fronts. The separatist movement in Aceh, the anti-Madurese bloodshed in West Kalimantan, and the situation in East Timor have spotlighted a nation wracked by internal unrest, an unattractive climate for investment.

The free elections held in June of this year, with their promise of greater democracy and stability, opened the world's pocketbooks to Indonesia. Investors poured money into local stocks, sending prices in June up 12 percent to their highest level since 1997. The International Monetary Fund (IMF) approved the release of $450 million in loans. It appeared that the situation was improving for the beleaguered nation; however, scandal surrounding payments made by Bank Bali to several highly placed politicians placed a roadblock in the economic turn-about.

The scandal, dubbed ''Baligate,'' involves approximately $80 million paid in unnecessary commissions to a firm connected with the ruling Golkar party. President Habibie denied that the money was used to fund his re-election campaign; however, the fact that his Golkar party, as well as officials close to him, including Finance Minister Bambang Subianto, were implicated made Baligate look suspiciously like an attempt to influence the presidential election.

In response to the Baligate scandal, the IMF suspended talks on its bailout installments to Jakarta, and the Asian Development Bank stated that it would hold up further loans until the case was cleared up. In late October, the Indonesian Supreme Court gave approval for the release of the audit into the Bank Bali scandal; IMF loan payments were expected to resume soon after.

While some economists fear that the newly elected President Wahid has little experience in economic matters, he brings diplomatic skills to the job of uniting factions in the legislative body. It is hoped that the new democratically elected leadership will bring greater stability to the nation and to the Indonesian economy.

GOVERNMENT AND POLITICS

The year 1999 was a landmark year for democracy in Indonesia as on June 7 the first free general elections in 40 years were held with 48 parties participating. The 462 legislators elected in June, along with 238 appointed representatives, comprise the People's Consultative Assembly (MPR), Indonesia's highest legislative body. This body faced the task of selecting their country's new president and vice president during the national assembly in October.

There were three candidates for the country's highest office: incumbent president B.J. Habibie; opposition leader Megawati Sukarnoputri; moderate Muslim Abdurrahman ''Gus Dur'' Wahid. After receiving a vote of no confidence from the legislature only hours before the election, Habibie withdrew, and Wahid was elected Indonesia's fourth president. Shortly following the presidential election, Megawati was elected vice president, a move that could enhance the stability of the new government if it succeeds in uniting political opponents and building coalitions in the legislature.

President Wahid will not enjoy the unlimited reign of his predecessors, for the legislature has amended the nation's constitution to restrict a president to no more than two consecutive terms. The presidential powers have been further amended, requiring the president to approve all bills passed by the legislature and to consult with the legislature on appointments of military commanders, consuls, and ambassadors. In addition, the presidential right to grant medals and titles will be governed by law. Presidential pardons and amnesty grants will have to be made in consultation with the Supreme Court.

While President Wahid will not have the autocratic rule traditional to Indonesia, he faces challenges as great as any faced by previous presidents. In 1999, Indonesia was marked by violence in East Timor, unrest in Aceh and other provinces seeking independence, and ethnic bloodshed in West Kalimantan and other provinces.

In March the foreign ministers of Portugal and Indonesia agreed to allow the people of East Timor a referendum in which they could choose between independence and greater autonomy from Indonesia. On August 30, the East Timorese voted overwhelmingly in favor of independence. Following the vote, armed militias took to the streets in the East Timor capitol Dili, burning the city and targeting especially those most vocal in the quest for independence. It is estimated that at least one quarter of the nation's population of 800,000 are now refugees. The violence in East Timor has isolated Indonesia diplomatically from its closest neighbor, Australia. In response to Australia's criticism of Indonesia's failure to protect the civilian population, Indonesia ended its security pact with Australia in mid-September.

United Nations peacekeeping forces, led by Australia, entered East Timor on September 20. They were welcomed by the East Timorese, but not by those Indonesians who saw the East Timorese vote for independence as a dangerous precedent in a nation beset by other separatist movements, most notably in Aceh, Irian Jaya and South Sulawesi.

The violence in West Kalimantan stems from a different cause. The Indonesian government promotes the movement of settlers from the more populous areas of Indonesia, such as Java and Madura, to less populous areas such as West Kalimantan. Designed in part to create a greater sense of national unity, the policy has in fact led to sectarian violence and unexpected alliances in West Kalimantan as the local population unites to drive out the Madurese settlers.

Ethnic violence has disrupted life in other areas of Indonesia. Fighting between Christians and Muslims on Ambon Island broke out in January and has produced 53,000 mostly Muslim refugees. As in East Timor and West Kalimantan, the Indonesian armed forces do not seem able to contain the violence or to protect the civilian population. President Wahid and Vice President Megawati face a difficult task as they undertake the leadership of this diverse and currently troubled nation.

CULTURE AND SOCIETY

In 1999 Indonesia struggled to live up to its motto, ''Bhinneka Tunggal Ika,'' which means ''Unity in Diversity.'' The country experienced both political and ethnic violence, as East Timor voted to separate from Indonesia, groups in the provinces of Aceh and Irian Jaya also sought independence, and the native population of West

Kalimantan turned against the settlers from Madura. Unrest in Indonesia cost several hundred lives in 1999 and resulted in tens of thousands fleeing their homelands.

As difficult as 1999 was, the year's events were not all negative and destabilizing for the Indonesians. Free elections took place for the first time in 40 years. The newly elected government united two leaders with strong followings, Muslim moderate Abdurrahman Wahid and Megawati Sukarnoputri. The coalition embodied in this pairing could help bring peace and stability to Indonesia.

DIRECTORY

CENTRAL GOVERNMENT

Head of State

President
Abdurrahman Wahid, Office of the President

Vice President
Megawati Sukarnoputri, Office of the Vice President

Ministers

Minister of Home Affairs
Ministry of Home Affairs, Jl. Merdeka Utara No. 7, Jakara Pusat, Indonesia
PHONE: +62 373908; 3842222
FAX: +62 360091; 372812

Minister of Foreign Affairs
Alwi Shihab, Ministry of Foreign Affairs, Jl. Pejambon No. 6, Jakarta Pusat, Indonesia
PHONE: +62 3441508
FAX: +62 360517; 380511; 363750

Minister of Defense and Security
General Wiranto, Ministry of Defense and Security, Jl. Merderka Barat No. 13-14, Jakarta Pusat, Indonesia
PHONE: +62 374408
FAX: +62 7501490; 3844500; 3804149

Minister of Justice
Haji Muladi, Ministry of Justice, Jl. H.R. Rasuna Said Kav. 4-5, Kuningan, Jakarta Selatan, Indonesia
PHONE: +62 513006; 513004
FAX: +62 5253095; 3104149; 5225036

Minister of Information
Yosfiah Yunus, Ministry of Information, Jl. Merdeka Barat 9, Jakarta Pusat, Indonesia
PHONE: +62 377408; 351363
FAX: +62 375953; 360113

Minister of Finance
Bambang Subianto, Ministry of Finance, Jl. Lapangan Banten Timur 2-4, Jakarta Pusat, Indonesia
PHONE: +62 373309; 365364
FAX: +62 375295; 375492; 353710

Minister of Industry and Trade
Rahadi Ramelan, Ministry of Industry and Trade, Jl. Jend. Gatot Subroto kav. 52-53, Jakarta Selatan, Indonesia
PHONE: +62 515509
FAX: +62 512720; 516458; 5201604

Minister of Agriculture
Soleh Solahuddin, Ministry of Agriculture, Jl. Harsono R.M. No. 3, Ragunan, Pasar Minggu, Jakarta Selatan, Indonesia
PHONE: +62 7806131
FAX: +62 7804237; 7800220; 7804377

Minister of Mining and Energy
Mangkusubroto Kuntoro, Ministry of Mining and Energy, Jl. Merdeka Selatan No. 18, Jakarta Pusat, Indonesia
PHONE: +62 360232
FAX: +62 3847461; 5255863

Minister of Public Works
Rachmadi Bambang Sumadio, Ministry of Public Works, Jl. Pattimura No. 20, Kebayoran Baru, Jakarta Selatan, Indonesia
PHONE: +62 7395588
FAX: +62 7390769

Minister of Forestry and Plantations
Muslimin Nasution, Ministry of Forestry and Plantations, Gedung Manggala Wanabakti (Blok I), Jl. Gatot Subroto, Jakarta Selatan, Indonesia
PHONE: +62 5704503; 5733037
FAX: +62 5700226; 588732

Minister of Communications
Giri Hadiharjono Suseno, Ministry of Communications, Jl. Merdeka Barat No. 8, Jakarta Pusat, Indonesia
PHONE: +62 361308
FAX: +62 3107788; 451657; 5229850

Minister of Tourism, Arts, and Culture
Usman Marzuki, Ministry of Tourism, Arts, and Culture, Jl. Merdeka Barat 16-19, Jakarta 10110, Indonesia
PHONE: +62 3860822
FAX: +62 3867589; 3860828

Minister of Co-Operative and Small Enterprises
Adi Sasono, Ministry of Co-Operative and Small Enterprises, Jl. H.R. Rasuna Said Kav. 3-4-5, Jakarta Selatan, Indonesia
PHONE: +62 5240366
FAX: +62 520438

Minister of Manpower
Fahmi Idris, Ministry of Manpower, Jl. Jend. Gatot Subroto Kav. 51, Jakarta Selatan, Indonesia
PHONE: +62 5255685; 5255688
FAX: +62 5255659; 5253913

Minister of Transmigration
Priyono Hendro, Ministry of Transmigration, Jl. Taman Makam Pahlawan, Kalibata No. 17, Jakarta Selatan, Indonesia
PHONE: +62 7999912

Minister of Education
Juwono Sudarsono, Ministry of Education, Jl. Jend. Sudirman, Senayan, Jakarta Selatan, Indonesia
PHONE: +62 5731665
FAX: +62 5736870; 5738181; 5733127

Minister of Health
Farid Antara Muluk, Ministry of Health, Jl. H.R. Rasuna Said B1 X/5 Kav. 4-9, Jakarta Selatan, Indonesia
PHONE: +62 5201590
FAX: +62 5201591; 5201588

Minister of Religious Affairs
Fajar Malik, Ministry of Religious Affairs, Jl. Lapangan Banteng Barat No. 3-4, Jakarta Pusat, Indonesia
PHONE: +62 360244
FAX: +62 361720

Minister of Social Affairs
Yustika Sjarifudin Baharsjah, Ministry of Social Affairs, Jl. Salemba Raya No. 28, Jakarta, Indonesia
PHONE: +62 3103591
FAX: +62 3103783

Minister of State and State Secretary
H. Muladi, Ministry of State and State Secretary, Jl. Veteran No. 17, Jakarta Pusat, Indonesia
PHONE: +62 3847198; 3847199
FAX: +62 352685

Minister of National Development Planning
Budiono, Ministry of National Development Planning, Jl. Taman Suropati No. 2, Jakarta Pusat, Indonesia
PHONE: +62 336207; 3905650
FAX: +62 3145374; 334779

Minister of Research and Technology
Zuhalmans Gedung BPPT Lt. III, Ministry of Research and Technology, Jl. M.H. Thamrin No. 8, Jakarta Pusat, Indonesia
PHONE: +62 324714
FAX: +62 328169; 362439; 330728

Minister of Food and Horticulture
A. M. Syaifuddin, Ministry of Food and Horticulture, Jl. Gatot Subroto No. 49, Jakarta Selatan, Indonesia
PHONE: +62 510075
FAX: +62 5255306; 5255425

Minister of Population
Ida Bagus Oka, Ministry of Population, Jl. Permata No. 1, Halim Perdana Kusuma, Jakarta Timur 13650, Indonesia
PHONE: +62 8098018; 8009029
FAX: +62 8194532

Minister of Land and Agrarian Affairs
Hasan Basri, Ministry of Land and Agrarian Affairs, Jl. Sisingamangaraja No. 2, Kebayoran Baru, Jakarta Selatan, Indonesia
PHONE: +62 7222420

Minister of Housing
Theo Leo Sambuaga, Ministry of Housing, Jl. Kebon sirih No. 31, Jakarta Pusat, Indonesia
PHONE: +62 323235
FAX: +62 327430

Minister of Environment
Panagian Siregar, Ministry of Environment, Jl. Merdeka Barat No. 15, Lantai III, Jakarta Pusat, Indonesia
PHONE: +62 374627
FAX: +62 3857579; 3847075; 374371

Minister of Women's Affairs
Tutty Alawiyah, Ministry of Women's Affairs, Jl. Merdeka Barat No. 15, Jakarta Pusat, Indonesia
PHONE: +62 3805540

FAX: +62 3805562

Minister of Youth and Sports

Agung Laksono, Ministry of Youth and Sports, Jl. Gerbang Pemuda No. 3, Senayan, Jakarta Selatan, Indonesia
PHONE: +62 5738310; 5738152; 5738153
FAX: +62 588313

Minister of Reform of State Enterprises

Tanri Abeng, Ministry of Reform of State Enterprises, Jl. Veteran III No. 2, Jakarta Pusat, Indonesia
PHONE: +62 3847028
FAX: +62 3847028

POLITICAL ORGANIZATIONS

Partai Persatuan Pembangunan-PPP (Development Unity Party)

TITLE: Chairman
NAME: Hamzah Haz

Golongan Karya-GOLKAR (Functional Groups)

Jl. Anggrek Nellymurni, Slipi Jakarta Barat 11480, Indonesia
PHONE: +62 5302222
TITLE: General Chairman
NAME: Akbar Tansung

Partai Demokrasi Indonesia-PDI (Indonesia Democracy Party)

TITLE: Chairman
NAME: Budi Hardjono

DIPLOMATIC REPRESENTATION

Embassies in Indonesia

Afghanistan

Jl. Kusumaatmaja S.H. #15, Menteng, Jakarta 10310, Indonesia
PHONE: +62 (21) 3143169
FAX: +62 (21) 335390

Algeria

Jl. H.R. Rasuna Said Kav.10, Kuningan, Jakarta 12950, Indonesia
PHONE: +62 (21) 5254719; 5254809
FAX: +62 (21) 5254654

Argentina

Menara Mulia Building, Suite 1901, 19th Floor, Jl. Jenderal Gatot Subroto, Kav. 9-11, Jakarta 12930, Indonesia

PHONE: +62 (21) 5265661
FAX: +62 (21) 5265664

Australia

Jl. H.R. Rasuna Said, Kav. C15-16, Jakarta 12940, Indonesia
PHONE: +62 (21) 5227111
FAX: +62 (21) 5227101

Austria

Jl. Diponegoro #44, Menteng, Jakarta 10310, Indonesia
PHONE: +62 (21) 338090; 338101; 3107451
FAX: +62 (21) 3904927

Bangladesh

Jl. Denpasar Raya #3, Block A-13, Kav. 10, Kuningan, Jakarta 12950, Indonesia
PHONE: +62 (21) 5251986; 5221574; 5221729
FAX: +62 (21) 5261807

Belgium

Wisma BCA Building, 16th Floor, Jl. Jenderal Sudirman Kav. 22-23, Jakarta 10310, Indonesia
PHONE: +62 (21) 3162030
FAX: +62 (21) 3162035

Brazil

Menara Mulia Building, 16th Floor, Suite 1602, Jl. Jenderal Gatot Subroto Kav. 9-11, Jakarta 12390, Indonesia
PHONE: +62 (21) 5265656; 5265660
FAX: +62 (21) 5265659

Brunei

Wisma GKBI, Suite 1901, Jl. Jenderal Sudirman # 28, Jakarta 10210, Indonesia
PHONE: +62 (21) 5741437; 5741438; 5741439
FAX: +62 (21) 5741463

Bulgaria

Jl. Imam Bonjol # 34-36, Jakarta 10310, Indonesia
PHONE: +62 (21) 3904049; 3904048

Cambodia

Panin Bank Plaza, 4th Floor, Jl. Palmerah Utara #52, Jakarta 11480, Indonesia
PHONE: +62 (21) 5484840; 5483716
FAX: +62 (21) 5483684

Canada

Wisma Metropolitan I, 5th Floor, Jl. Jenderal Sudirman Kav.29, Jakarta 12920, Indonesia
PHONE: +62 (21) 5250709
FAX: +62 (21) 5712251

Chile

Bina Mulia I Building, 7th Floor, Jl. H.R. Rasuna Said, Kav.10, Jakarta 12950, Indonesia

PHONE: +62 (21) 5201131
FAX: +62 (21) 5201955

China
Mega Kuningan No.2, Jakarta, Indonesia
PHONE: +62 (21) 5761037; 5761039
FAX: +62 (21) 5761034

Colombia
Central Plaza Building, 16th Floor, Jl. Jenderal
Sudirman Kav. 47, Jakarta 12920, Indonesia
PHONE: +62 (21) 5701422
FAX: +62 (21) 5207717

Croatia
Menara Mulia Building, Suite 2101, Jl. Gatot
Subroto, Kav.9-11, Jakarta 12930, Indonesia
PHONE: +62 (21) 5257822; 5257611
FAX: +62 (21) 5204073

Cuba
Villa Pejaten Mas, Block G/#4, Pejaten, Pasar
Minggu, Jakarta 12520, Indonesia
PHONE: +62 (21) 7806673
FAX: +62 (21) 7807345; 7806673

Czech Republic
Jl. Gereja Theresia #20, P.O. Box 1319, Jakarta,
Indonesia
PHONE: +62 (21) 3904075; 3904077
FAX: +62 (21) 336282

Denmark
Bina Mulia Building, 4th Floor, Jl. H.R. Rasuna
Said, Kav.10, Jakarta 12950, Indonesia
PHONE: +62 (21) 5204350
FAX: +62 (21) 5201962

Egypt
Jl. Teuku Umar #68, Menteng, Jakarta 10350,
Indonesia
PHONE: +62 (21) 3143440; 331141; 335350
FAX: +62 (21) 3145073

Finland
Bina Mulia Building I, 10th Floor, Jl. H.R.
Rasuna Said, Kav.10, Kuningan, Jakarta 12950,
Indonesia
PHONE: +62 (21) 5207408
FAX: +62 (21) 5252033

France
Jl. M.H. Thamrin #20, Jakarta Pusat, Indonesia
PHONE: +62 (21) 3142807
FAX: +62 (21) 3143338

Germany
Jl. M.H. Thamrin # 1, Jakarta Pusat, Indonesia
PHONE: +62 (21) 3901750
FAX: +62 (21) 3901757

Greece
Plaza 89, 12th Floor, Jl. HR. Rasuna Said Kav
X-7/No.6, Kuningan, Jakarta 12950, Indonesia
PHONE: +62 (21) 5207776
FAX: +62 (21) 5207753

Hungary
Jl. H.R. Rasuna Said, Kav.X/#3, Kuningan,
Jakarta 12950, Indonesia
PHONE: +62 (21) 5203459; 5203460
FAX: +62 (21) 5203461

India
Jl. H.R. Rasuna Said S-1, Kuningan, Jakarta
12950, Indonesia
PHONE: +62 (21) 5204150; 5204152; 5204157
FAX: +62 (21) 5204160

Iran
Jl. H.O.S. Cokroaminoto 110, Menteng, Jakarta
Pusat, Indonesia
PHONE: +62 (21) 331391; 334637; 331378
FAX: +62 (21) 3107860

Iraq
Jl. Teuku Umar # 38, Menteng, Jakarta 10350,
Indonesia
PHONE: +62 (21) 3904067
FAX: +62 (21) 3904066

Italy
Jl. Diponegoro #45, Menteng, Jakarta 10310,
Indonesia
PHONE: +62 (21) 337445; 323490; 337440
FAX: +62 (21) 337422

Japan
Jl. M.H. Thamrin #24, Jakarta Pusat, Indonesia
PHONE: +62 (21) 324308
FAX: +62 (21) 325460

Jordan
Jl.Denpasar Raya Block A-13, Kav.01-02,
Kuningan, Jakarta 12950, Indonesia
PHONE: +62 (21) 5204400; 5204401
FAX: +62 (21) 5202447

North Korea
Jl. H.R. Rasuna Said Kav. X-5, Kuningan,
Jakarta 12950, Indonesia
PHONE: +62 (21) 5210181; 5222442; 5260066
FAX: +62 (21) 5210183

South Korea
Jl. Jenderal Gatot Subroto # 57, P.O. Box 4187
JKTM, Jakarta Selatan, Indonesia
PHONE: +62 (21) 5201915
FAX: +62 (21) 5254159

Kuwait
Jl. Denpasar Raya Block A-XII/#1, Kuningan Timur, Jakarta 12950, Indonesia
PHONE: +62 (21) 5202477; 5202478; 5202479
FAX: +62 (21) 5204359; 5224931; 5265886

Laos
Jl. Kintamani Raya C-15/#33, Jakarta 12950, Indonesia
PHONE: +62 (21) 5202673; 5229602
FAX: +62 (21) 5229601

Lebanon
Jl. YBR V/#82, Kuningan, Jakarta 12950, Indonesia
PHONE: +62 (21) 5264306; 5253074; 5207121
FAX: +62 (21) 5207121

Libya
Jl. Pekalongan #24, Menteng, Jakarta 10310, Indonesia
PHONE: +62 (21) 335308; 335754
FAX: +62 (21) 335726

Malaysia
Jl. H.R. Rasuna Said, Kav.X/6, # 1-3 Kuningan, Jakarta 12950, Indonesia
PHONE: +62 (21) 5224947
FAX: +62 (21) 5224974

Mali
Jl. Mendawai III/#18, Kebayoran Baru, Jakarta 12130, Indonesia
PHONE: +62 (21) 7208472; 7268504
FAX: +62 (21) 7229589

Mexico
Menara Mulia Building, Suite 2306, Jl. Gatot Subroto Kav. 9-11, Jakarta 12930, Indonesia
PHONE: +62 (21) 5203980
FAX: +62 (21) 5203978

Morocco
Kuningan Plaza, South Tower Suite 512, Jl. H.R. Rasuna Said, Kav.C 11-14, Kuningan, Jakarta 12950, Indonesia
PHONE: +62 (21) 5200773; 5200956
FAX: +62 (21) 5200586

Myanmar
Jl. Haji Agus Salim #109, Menteng, Jakarta Pusat, Indonesia
PHONE: +62 (21) 3140440; 327684
FAX: +62 (21) 327204

Netherlands
Jl. H.R. Rasuna Said Kav. S-3, Kuningan, Jakarta 12950, Indonesia
PHONE: +62 (21) 5251515
FAX: +62 (21) 5700734

New Zealand
BRI II Building, 23rd Floor, Jl. Jenderal Sudirman, Kav.44-46, Jakarta 10210, Indonesia
PHONE: +62 (21) 5709460; 5709470
FAX: +62 (21) 5709457; 5709471

Nigeria
Jl. Taman Patra XIV/ #11-11A, Kuningan Timur, 12950 Jakarta, Indonesia
PHONE: +62 (21) 5260922; 5260923
FAX: +62 (21) 5260924

Norway
Bina Mulia Building I, 4th Floor, Jl. H.R. Rasuna Said Kav.10, Kuningan, Jakarta 12950, Indonesia
PHONE: +62 (21) 5251990
FAX: +62 (21) 5207365

Pakistan
Jl. Teuku Umar #50, Menteng, Jakarta 10350, Indonesia
PHONE: +62 (21) 3144008; 3144009; 3144011
FAX: +62 (21) 3103947; 3103946; 3103945

Palestine
Jl. Diponogoro #59, Menteng, Jakarta 10310, Indonesia
PHONE: +62 (21) 323521; 3145444; 3108005
FAX: +62 (21) 3108011

Papua New Guinea
Panin Bank Centre, 6th Floor, Jl. Jenderal Sudirman # 1, Jakarta 10270, Indonesia
PHONE: +62 (21) 7251218
FAX: +62 (21) 7201012

Peru
Bina Mulia Building 2, 3rd Floor, Jl. H.R. Rasuna Said Kav. 11, Kuningan, Jakarta 12950, Indonesia
PHONE: +62 (21) 5201176; 5201866
FAX: +62 (21) 5201932

Philippines
Jl. Imam Bonjol # 6-8, Menteng, Jakarta 10310, Indonesia
PHONE: +62 (21) 3100302; 3149329; 3100334
FAX: +62 (21) 3159773; 3151167

Poland
Jl. Diponegoro #65, Menteng, Jakarta 10310, Indonesia
PHONE: +62 (21) 3140509
FAX: +62 (21) 327343

Qatar
Jl. Taman Ubud I/ No.5, Kuningan Timur,
Jakarta 12920, Indonesia
PHONE: +62 (21) 5277751; 5277752
FAX: +62 (21) 5277754

Romania
Jl. Teuku Cik Ditiro #42A, Menteng, Jakarta
Pusat, Indonesia
PHONE: +62 (21) 3106240; 3106241
FAX: +62 (21) 3907759

Russia
Jl. H.R. Rasuna Said, Kav.X-7/1-2, Kuningan,
Jakarta 12950, Indonesia
PHONE: +62 (21) 5222912; 5222914; 5225195
FAX: +62 (21) 5222916; 5222915

Saudi Arabia
Jl. M.T. Haryono, Kav.27, Cawang Atas, Jakarta
13630, Indonesia
PHONE: +62 (21) 8011553; 8011537
FAX: +62 (21) 8011527

Serbia
Jl. HOS Cokroaminoto #109, Menteng, Jakarta
10310, Indonesia
PHONE: +62 (21) 3143560; 334157
FAX: +62 (21) 3143613

Singapore
Jl. H.R. Rasuna Said, Block X/4, Kav. 2,
Kuningan, Jakarta 12950, Indonesia
PHONE: +62 (21) 5201489

Slovakia
Jl. Prof. Moh.Yamin, SH # 29, Menteng, Jakarta
10310, Indonesia
PHONE: +62 (21) 3101068; 3151429
FAX: +62 (21) 3101180

South Africa
Wisma GKBI, 7th Floor, Suite 705, Jl. Jenderal
Sudirman #28, Jakarta 10210, Indonesia
PHONE: +62 (21) 5740660
FAX: +62 (21) 5740661

Spain
Jl. Haji Agus Salim #61, Menteng, Jakarta
10350, Indonesia
PHONE: +62 (21) 335937; 335940; 335771
FAX: +62 (21) 325996

Sri Lanka
Jl. Diponegoro # 70, Menteng, Jakarta 10310,
Indonesia
PHONE: +62 (21) 3141018; 3161886; 3919364
FAX: +62 (21) 3107962

Sudan
Wisma Bank Dharmala, 7th Floor, Suite 01, Jl.
Jenderal Sudirman Kav. 28, Jakarta 12910,
Indonesia
PHONE: +62 (21) 5212075
FAX: +62 (21) 5212077

Sweden
Bina Mulia Building I, 7th Floor, Jl. H.R.
Rasuna Said, Kav. 10, Kuningan, Jakarta 12950,
Indonesia
PHONE: +62 (21) 5201551
FAX: +62 (21) 5252652

Switzerland
Jl. H.R. Rasuna Said, Block X3/2, Kuningan,
Jakarta 12950, Indonesia
PHONE: +62 (21) 5256061
FAX: +62 (21) 5202289

Syria
Jl. Karang Asem I /#8, Kuningan Raya, Jakarta
12950, Indonesia
PHONE: +62 (21) 5204117; 5201641; 5255991
FAX: +62 (21) 5202511

Thailand
Jl. Imam Bonjol #74, Jakarta 10310, Indonesia
PHONE: +62 (21) 3904052; 3147925; 3915651
FAX: +62 (21) 3107469

Tunisia
Wisma Dharmala Sakti, 11th Floor, Jl. Jenderal
Sudirman #32, Jakarta 10220, Indonesia
PHONE: +62 (21) 5703432; 5704220
FAX: +62 (21) 5700016

Turkey
Jl. H.R. Rasuna Said, Kav. 1, Jakarta 12950,
Indonesia
PHONE: +62 (21) 5256250; 5264143; 5227440
FAX: +62 (21) 5226056; 5275673

Ukraine
Jl. Simprug Permata I / No. 39, Jakarta 12220,
Indonesia
PHONE: +62 (21) 7267575; 7205356
FAX: +62 (21) 7266969

United Arab Emirates
Jl. Sisingamangaraja C-4, Kav. 16-17, Kuningan
12950, Indonesia
PHONE: +62 (21) 5206518; 5206552
FAX: +62 (21) 5206526

United Kingdom
Jl. M.H. Thamrin # 75, Jakarta Pusat, Indonesia
PHONE: +62 (21) 3156264
FAX: +62 (21) 3141824; 3902726; 3907493

United States
Jl. Medan Merdeka Selatan #5, Jakarta 10110, Indonesia
PHONE: +62 (21) 3442211
FAX: +62 (21) 3862259
TITLE: Ambassador
NAME: J. Stapleton Roy

Uzbekistan
Jl. Brawijaya Raya #7, Block P-5, Jakarta Selatan, Indonesia
PHONE: +62 (21) 7399009; 7221640; 9134212
FAX: +62 (21) 7221640

Vatican City
Jl. Medan Merdeka Timur #18, P.O. Box 4227, Jakarta Pusat, Indonesia
PHONE: +62 (21) 3841142; 3810736
FAX: +62 (21) 3841143

Venezuela
Menara Mulia, Suite 2005, 20th Floor, Jl. Jenderal Gatot Subroto Kav.9-11, Jakarta Selatan, Indonesia
PHONE: +62 (21) 5227547; 5257548
FAX: +62 (21) 5227549
E-MAIL: evenjakt@indo.net.id

Vietnam
Jl. Teuku Umar #25, Menteng, Jakarta 10350, Indonesia
PHONE: +62 (21) 9100163; 3158537; 3100358
FAX: +62 (21) 3149615

Yemen
Jl. Yusuf Adiwinata #29, Menteng, Jakarta 10350, Indonesia
PHONE: +62 (21) 3904074; 3108029; 3108035
FAX: +62 (21) 3904946

JUDICIAL SYSTEM
Supreme Court

FURTHER READING
Articles
"Asia Holds Its Breath." *The Economist* (June 12, 1999): 35.

"B Negative." *The Economist* (March 20, 1999): 75.

"Dangerous Horizon." *The Economist* (May 29, 1999): 37.

"The Dangers in East Timor." *The Economist* (September 18, 1999): 39.

"Descent into Darkest Borneo." *The Economist* (March 27, 1999): 42.

"Enemies of the Ballot." *The Economist* (July 10, 1999): 37.

"Four Months in Review." *Current History* (September 1999): 301.

"Fraying at the Edges." *The Economist* (August 21, 1999): 32.

"Friends No More." *The Economist* (September 25, 1999): 44.

"Friend or Foe in East Timor." *The Economist* (September 25, 1999): 43.

"Indonesia's Peace Starts at the Top." *The Christian Science Monitor* (October 22, 1999): 6.

"Indonesia's Opposition Revs Up." *The Economist* (May 22, 1999): 39.

"Indonesia's Second Chance." *The Economist* (June 5, 1999): 37.

"The Mystery and Muddle Surrounding East Timor." *The Economist* (February 13, 1999): 39.

"On Democracy's Front Line." *The Economist* (January 30, 1999): 37.

"The Price of Freedom in East Timor." *The New Leader* (September 20–October 4, 1999): 3.

"The Robin Hood of Java." *The Economist* (March 20, 1999): 43.

"The Scramble at the Ballot Box." *The Economist* (May 1, 1999): 40.

"A Survival Guide." *The Economist* (January 30, 1999): 58.

"Terror in the Spice Islands." *The Economist* (March 6, 1999): 38.

"Through the Glass, Darkly." *The Economist* (August 14, 1999): 32.

"The Wild Bunch." *The Economist* (April 24, 1999): 38.

"Will the Army Defend or Defeat Indonesia's New Democracy?" *The Economist* (April 10, 1999): 39.

Books
Jardine, Matthew and Noam Chomsky (Introduction). *East Timor: Genocide in Paradise*. Real Story Series, 2nd Ed. Ondonian Press, 1999.

Kohen, Arnold S. *From the Place of the Dead: The Epic Struggles of Bishop Belo of East Timor*. New York: St. Martin's Press, 1999.

Prawiro, Radius. *Indonesia's Struggle for Economic Development: Pragmatism in Action.* New York: Oxford University Press, 1999.

Schwartz, Adam and Jonathan Paris. *The Politics of Post-Suharto Indonesia.* Brookings Institute Press/American Development Bank, 1999.

Soesastro, M. Hadi and Richard W. Baker, J. Kristiadi, Douglas E. Ramage, ed. *Indonesia: The Challenge of Change.* New York: St. Martin's Press, 1999.

Internet

BPS Statistics Indonesia. Available Online @ http://www.bps.do.id/ (December 15, 1999).

The Business Times. Available Online @ http://business-times.asia1.com.sg/ (December 15, 1999).

Department of Foreign Affairs, Republic of Indonesia. Available Online @ http://www.dfa-deplu.go.id/ (December 15, 1999).

General Consulate of the Republic of Indonesia. Available Online @ http://www.kjri-la.com/ (December 15, 1999).

Inside Indonesia Magazine. Available Online @ http://www.insideindonesia.org/ (December 15, 1999).

INDONESIA: STATISTICAL DATA

For sources and notes see "Sources of Statistics" in the front of each volume.

GEOGRAPHY

Geography (1)

Area:

Total: 1,919,440 sq km.

Land: 1,826,440 sq km.

Water: 93,000 sq km.

Area—comparative: slightly less than three times the size of Texas.

Land boundaries:

Total: 2,602 km.

Border countries: Malaysia 1,782 km, Papua New Guinea 820 km.

Coastline: 54,716 km.

Climate: tropical; hot, humid; more moderate in highlands.

Terrain: mostly coastal lowlands; larger islands have interior mountains.

Natural resources: petroleum, tin, natural gas, nickel, timber, bauxite, copper, fertile soils, coal, gold, silver.

Land use:

Arable land: 10%

Permanent crops: 7%

Permanent pastures: 7%

Forests and woodland: 62%

Other: 14% (1993 est.).

HUMAN FACTORS

Demographics (2A)

	1990	1995	1998	2000	2010	2020	2030	2040	2050
Population	187,727.6	203,459.3	212,941.8	219,266.6	249,678.9	276,017.0	299,126.4	317,561.4	330,566.2
Net migration rate (per 1,000 population)	NA	NA	NA	NA	NA	NA	NA	NA	NA
Births	NA	NA	NA	NA	NA	NA	NA	NA	NA
Deaths	NA	NA	NA	NA	NA	NA	NA	NA	NA
Life expectancy - males	57.0	59.1	60.3	61.1	64.7	67.9	70.6	72.9	74.7
Life expectancy - females	60.8	63.4	64.8	65.8	70.1	73.8	76.9	79.4	81.4
Birth rate (per 1,000)	25.9	23.9	23.1	22.4	18.9	16.4	15.1	13.8	13.1
Death rate (per 1,000)	9.1	8.5	8.2	8.1	7.5	7.5	8.0	8.9	9.8
Women of reproductive age (15-49 yrs.)	48,926.0	55,364.2	59,255.0	61,535.0	68,602.4	73,567.7	74,993.5	75,452.5	75,482.7
of which are currently married	61,960.4	NA	NA	NA	NA	NA	NA	NA	NA
Fertility rate	3.0	2.7	2.6	2.5	2.3	2.1	2.0	2.0	2.0

Except as noted, values for vital statistics are in thousands; life expectancy is in years.

Health Indicators (4)

Life expectancy at birth

1980 55

1997 65

Daily per capita supply of calories (1996) 2,930

Total fertility rate births per woman (1997) 2.8

Maternal mortality ratio per 100,000 live births
(1990-97) . . . . .390[d]

Safe water % of population with access (1995) 65

Sanitation % of population with access (1995) 55

Consumption of iodized salt % of households
(1992-98)[a] 62

Smoking prevalence

Male % of adults (1985-95)[a] 53

Female % of adults (1985-95)[a] 4

Tuberculosis incidence per 100,000 people
(1997) 285

Adult HIV prevalence % of population ages
15-49 (1997) 0.05

Infants and Malnutrition (5)

Under-5 mortality rate (1997) 68

% of infants with low birthweight (1990-97) 8

Births attended by skilled health staff % of total[a] . . .36

% fully immunized (1995-97)

TB 100

DPT 91

Polio 90

Measles 92

Prevalence of child malnutrition under age 5
(1992-97)[b] 34

Ethnic Division (6)

Javanese 45%

Sundanese 14%

Madurese 7.5%

Coastal Malays 7.5%

Other 26%

Religions (7)

Muslim 87%

Protestant 6%

Roman Catholic 3%

Hindu 2%

Buddhist 1%

Other 1% (1985)

Languages (8)

Bahasa Indonesia (official, modified form of Malay),
English, Dutch, local dialects, the most widely spoken
of which is Javanese.

EDUCATION

Public Education Expenditures (9)

Public expenditure on education (% of GNP)

1980 . . . . .1.7

1996 . . . . .1.4

Expenditure per student

Primary % of GNP per capita

1980 . . . .

1996 . . . .

Secondary % of GNP per capita

1980 . . . .

1996 . . . . .6.6[1]

Tertiary % of GNP per capita

1980 . . . .

1996 . . . . .12.9

Expenditure on teaching materials

Primary % of total for level (1996) . . . .

Secondary % of total for level (1996) . . . .

Primary pupil-teacher ratio per teacher (1996) . . . . .23[1]

Duration of primary education years (1995) 6

Educational Attainment (10)

Age group (1990) . . . . .25+

Total population .78,497,680

Highest level attained (%)

No schooling 54.5

First level

Not completed 26.4

Completed . . . . .NA

Entered second level

S-1 . . . . .16.8

S-2 . . . . .NA

Postsecondary 2.3

Literacy Rates (11A)

In thousands and percent[1]	1990	1995	2000	2010
Illiterate population (15+ yrs.)	20,899	21,507	18,740	12,726
Literacy rate - total adult pop. (%)	81.6	83.8	87.3	92.7
Literacy rate - males (%)	88.3	89.6	92.1	95.7
Literacy rate - females (%)	75.3	78.0	82.6	89.9

GOVERNMENT & LAW

Political Parties (12)

House of Representatives	% of seats
Golkar	.74.5
Development Unity Party (PPP)	.22.43
Indonesia Democracy Party (PDI)	.3.07

Government Budget (13A)

Year: 1996

Total Expenditures: 77,964 Billions of Rupiah

Expenditures as a percentage of the total by function:

General public services and public order . . . . .18.70[P]

Defense . . . . .7.30[P]

Education . . . . .9.03[P]

Health . . . . .2.52[P]

Social Security and Welfare . . . . .7.24[P]

Housing and community amenities . . . . .20.29[P]

Recreational, cultural, and religious affairs . . . . .2.39[P]

Fuel and energy . . . .69[P]

Agriculture, forestry, fishing, and hunting . . . . .12.48[P]

Mining, manufacturing, and construction . . . . . .1.35[P]

Transportation and communication . . . . .7.34[P]

Other economic affairs and services . . . . .1.78[P]

Military Affairs (14B)

	1990	1991	1992	1993	1994	1995
Military expenditures						
Current dollars (mil.)	1,699	1,862	1,962	2,091	2,364	3,398
1995 constant dollars (mil.)	1,952	2,058	2,110	2,192	2,423	3,398
Armed forces (000)	283	278	283	271	280	280
Gross national product (GNP)						
Current dollars (mil.)	113,400	128,400	141,500	156,500	172,200	189,400
1995 constant dollars (mil.)	130,400	141,900	152,200	164,100	176,500	189,400
Central government expenditures (CGE)						
1995 constant dollars (mil.)	25,110	24,590	29,180	28,080	31,870	38,090[e]
People (mil.)	187.7	190.9	194.0	197.2	200.3	203.5
Military expenditure as % of GNP	1.5	1.5	1.4	1.3	1.4	1.8
Military expenditure as % of CGE	7.8	8.4	7.2	7.8	7.6	8.9
Military expenditure per capita (1995 $)	10	11	11	11	12	17
Armed forces per 1,000 people (soldiers)	1.5	1.5	1.5	1.4	1.4	1.4
GNP per capita (1995 $)	694	743	784	832	881	931
Arms imports[6]						
Current dollars (mil.)	300	30	50	90	50	170
1995 constant dollars (mil.)	345	33	54	94	51	170
Arms exports[6]						
Current dollars (mil.)	5	6	20	20	40	10
1995 constant dollars (mil.)	6	6	22	21	41	10
Total imports[7]						
Current dollars (mil.)	21,840	25,870	27,280	28,330	31,980	40,920
1995 constant dollars (mil.)	25,100	28,590	29,340	29,700	32,790	40,920
Total exports[7]						
Current dollars (mil.)	25,670	29,140	33,970	36,820	40,050	45,420
1995 constant dollars (mil.)	29,510	32,200	36,540	38,600	41,060	45,420
Arms as percent of total imports[8]	1.4	.1	.2	.3	.2	.4
Arms as percent of total exports[8]	0	0	.1	.1	.1	0

Crime (15)

Crime rate (for 1997)

Crimes reported 123,700

Total persons convicted 59,400

Crimes per 100,000 population 61

Persons responsible for offenses

Total number of suspects . . . . .NA

Total number of female suspects . . . . .NA

Total number of juvenile suspects . . . . .NA

LABOR FORCE

Labor Force (16)

Total (million) 67

Agriculture 44%

Manufacturing 13%

Construction 5%

Transport and communications 4%

Other 34%

Data for 1995 est.

Unemployment Rate (17)

15%; underemployment 50% (1998 est.)

PRODUCTION SECTOR

Electric Energy (18)

Capacity . . . . .16.265 million kW (1995)

Production . . . . .60.4 billion kWh (1995)

Consumption per capita . . . . .297 kWh (1995)

Transportation (19)

Highways:

total: 393,000 km

paved: 178,815 km

unpaved: 214,185 km (1996 est.)

Waterways: 21,579 km total; Sumatra 5,471 km, Java and Madura 820 km, Kalimantan 10,460 km, Sulawesi (Celebes) 241 km, Irian Jaya 4,587 km

Pipelines: crude oil 2,505 km; petroleum products 456 km; natural gas 1,703 km (1989)

Merchant marine:

total: 503 ships (1,000 GRT or over) totaling 2,433,857 GRT/3,510,818 DWT ships by type: bulk 35, cargo 291, chemical tanker 8, container 11, liquefied gas tanker 5, livestock carrier 1, oil tanker 105, passenger 8, passenger-cargo 12, roll-on/roll-off cargo 10, short-sea passenger 6, specialized tanker 6, vehicle carrier 5 (1997 est.)

Airports: 442 (1997 est.)

Airports—with paved runways:

total: 124

over 3,047 m: 4

2,438 to 3,047 m: 11

1,524 to 2,437 m: 40

914 to 1,523 m: 41

under 914 m: 28 (1997 est.)

Airports—with unpaved runways:

total: 318

1,524 to 2,437 m: 5

914 to 1,523 m: 32

under 914 m: 281 (1997 est.)

Top Agricultural Products (20)

Rice, cassava (tapioca), peanuts, rubber, cocoa, coffee, palm oil, copra, other tropical products; poultry, beef, pork, eggs.

MANUFACTURING SECTOR

GDP & Manufacturing Summary (21)

Detailed value added figures are listed by both International Standard Industry Code (ISIC) and product title.

	1980	1985	1990	1994
GDP ($-1990 mil.)[1]	61,524	78,453	106,141	137,690
Per capita ($-1990)[1]	408	469	581	707
Manufacturing share (%) (current prices)[1]	13.0	16.0	19.9	21.2
Manufacturing				
Value added ($-1990 mil.)[1]	6,923	12,730	21,115	30,162
Industrial production index	100	117	190	245
Value added ($ mil.)	4,371	8,103	15,295	28,605
Gross output ($ mil.)	13,226	23,120	40,944	79,062
Employment (000)	964	1,673	2,649	3,801
Profitability (% of gross output)				
Intermediate input (%)	67	65	63	64
Wages and salaries inc. supplements (%)	6	7	5	5

	1980	1985	1990	1994
Gross operating surplus	27	28	33	31
Productivity ($)				
Gross output per worker	11,237	12,320	14,363	19,818
Value added per worker	3,499	3,852	5,127	6,954
Average wage (inc. supplements)	744	921	674	1,001
Value added ($ mil.)				
311/2 Food products	376	870	1,910	3,546
313 Beverages	51	77	112	192
314 Tobacco products	649	741	1,732	2,330
321 Textiles	420	687	1,306	2,379
322 Wearing apparel	15	105	458	1,938
323 Leather and fur products	5	14	43	100
324 Footwear	26	31	189	985
331 Wood and wood products	239	612	1,382	2,250
332 Furniture and fixtures	6	18	117	284
341 Paper and paper products	43	110	477	774
342 Printing and publishing	51	92	150	358
351 Industrial chemicals	145	385	687	1,284
352 Other chemical products	241	430	535	1,028
353 Petroleum refineries	978	1,611	1,636	2,239
354 Miscellaneous petroleum and coal products	4	5	8	12
355 Rubber products	164	328	494	498
356 Plastic products	25	175	228	611
361 Pottery, china and earthenware	8	24	77	231
362 Glass and glass products	36	98	64	236
369 Other non-metal mineral products	200	262	374	667
371 Iron and steel	107	301	1,045	1,542
372 Non-ferrous metals	—	168	188	189
381 Metal products	118	278	402	955
382 Non-electrical machinery	53	76	171	282
383 Electrical machinery	180	246	403	882
384 Transport equipment	217	331	1,036	2,544
385 Professional and scientific equipment	2	4	10	22
390 Other manufacturing industries	13	24	61	245

FINANCE, ECONOMICS, & TRADE

Economic Indicators (22)

National product: GDP—purchasing power parity—$960 billion (1997 est.)

National product real growth rate: 4% (1997 est.)

National product per capita: $4,600 (1997 est.)

Inflation rate—consumer price index: 50% (1998 est.)

Exchange Rates (24)

Exchange rates:

Indonesian rupiahs (Rp) per US$1

April 1998 8,000
1997 . . . . .2,909.4
1996 . . . . .2,342.3
1995 . . . . .2,248.6
1994 . . . . .2,160.8
1993 . . . . .2,087.1

Top Import Origins (25)

$41.6 billion (f.o.b., 1997) Data are for 1995.

Origins	%
Germany	11
Norway	10
United Kingdom	10
Denmark	9
United States	8
Sweden	7

Top Export Destinations (26)

$53.4 billion (f.o.b., 1997) Data are for 1995.

Destinations	%
Japan	27.1
United States	13.9
Singapore	8.3
South Korea	6.4
Taiwan	3.9
China	3.8
Hong Kong	3.6

Economic Aid (27)

Recipient: IMF program, $42 billion (1998 est.).

Import Export Commodities (28)

Import Commodities	Export Commodities
Manufactures 75.3%	Textiles/garments 20.6%
Raw materials 9.0%	Wood products 15.7%
Foodstuffs 7.8%	Electronics 9.9%
Fuels 7.7%	Footwear 6.1%

Balance of Payments (23)

	1991	1992	1993	1994	1995
Exports of goods (f.o.b.)	29,635	33,796	36,607	40,223	45,479
Imports of goods (f.o.b.)	−24,834	−26,774	−28,376	−32,322	−39,769
Trade balance	4,801	7,022	8,231	7,901	5,710
Services - debits	−13,062	−14,582	−15,861	−17,157	−20,598
Services - credits	3,739	4,209	4,987	5,845	7,026
Private transfers (net)	132	342	191	170	210
Government transfers (net)	130	229	346	449	629
Overall balance	−4,260	−2,780	−2,106	−2,792	−7,023

IRAN

Islamic Republic of Iran
Jomhuri-ye Eslami-ye Iran

CAPITAL: Tehran.

FLAG: The national flag is a tricolor of green, white, and red horizontal stripes, the top and bottom stripes having the Arabic inscription *Allah Akbar* (''God Is Great'') written along the edge nearest the white stripe. In the center, in red, is the coat of arms, consisting of a stylized representation of the word *Allah.*

MONETARY UNIT: The rial (R) is a paper currency of 100 dinars. There are coins of 1, 5, 10, 20, and 50 rials, and notes of 100, 200, 500, 1,000, 2,000, 5,000, and 10,000 rials. R1 = $0.00057 (or $1 = R1,749.9).

WEIGHTS AND MEASURES: The metric system is the legal standard, but local units are widely used.

HOLIDAYS: National Day, 11 February; Oil Nationalization Day, 20 March; No Ruz (New Year), 21–24 March; Islamic Republic Day, 1 April; 13th Day of No Ruz (Revolution Day), 2 April. Religious holidays (according to the lunar calendar) include Birthday of Imam Husayn; Birthday of the Twelfth Imam; Martyrdom of Imam 'Ali; Death of Imam Ja'afar Sadiq; 'Id al-Fitr; Birthday of Imam Reza; 'Id-i-Qurban; 'Id-i-Qadir; Shab-i-Miraj; Martyrdom of Imam Husayn; 40th Day after the Death of Imam Husayn; Birthday of the Prophet; Birthday of Imam 'Ali.

TIME: 3:30 PM = noon GMT.

LOCATION AND SIZE: Located in southwestern Asia, Iran covers an area of 1,648,000 square kilometers (636,296 square miles). It has a total boundary length of 8,620 kilometers (5,356 miles), and its territory includes several islands in the Persian Gulf.

Iran's capital city, Tehran, is located in the northwestern part of the country.

CLIMATE: Cold winters and hot summers are prevalent across the plateau. On the plateau, the annual rainfall does not exceed 30 centimeters (12 inches), with the deserts and the Persian Gulf area receiving less than 13 centimeters (5 inches). The Caspian Sea coastal region is warm and humid throughout the year, with annual rainfall about 100 to 150 centimeters (40–60 inches).

INTROCTORY SURVEY

RECENT HISTORY

Oil, the source of nearly all Iran's national wealth, quickly came to dominate post-World War II politics. Between 1947 and 1953, there were conflicts over nationalizing Iran's oil industry, still dominated by British interests in the form of the Anglo-Iranian Oil Co. (AIOC). After 1953, Shah Muhammad Reza Pahlavi began to increase his power. New arrangements between the National Iranian Oil Co. and a group of United States, United Kingdom, and Dutch oil companies were negotiated during April–September 1954. Iran joined the Western alliance through the Baghdad Pact in 1955, later the Central Treaty Organization.

U.S. assistance and goodwill were plainly essential for the Shah. In 1961, President John F. Kennedy urged him to undertake a more liberal program. Under the ''white revolution'' of 1962–63, the Shah initiated land reform, political changes (including, for the first time, the right of women to hold and vote for public office), and broad economic development.

The Shah's dictatorial methods, his use of the secret police (known as SAVAK), his program of rapid Westernization (at the expense of Islamic tradition), his emphasis on lavish display and costly arms imports, and his perceived tolerance of corruption and of U.S. domination fed opposition in the late 1970s. The economic boom of the previous fifteen years also came to an end. Practically the entire population turned against the Shah. Following nine months of demonstrations and violent army reactions, martial law was declared in Iran's

major cities in September 1978, but antigovernment strikes and massive marches could not be stopped. The leader of the Islamic opposition, Ayatollah Ruhollah Khomeini (the term *ayatollah* is the highest rank of the Shi'ite Muslim clergy), had spent fifteen years in exile, first in Iraq and briefly in France. On 1 February 1979, the Ayatollah returned to an enthusiastic welcome in Tehran. He quickly asserted control and appointed a provisional government, which took power after the final collapse of the Shah's regime on 11 February.

On 1 April, Khomeini declared Iran an Islamic Republic. Revolutionary groups made random arrests and illegal executions of political opponents. On 4 November 1979, fifty-three U.S. hostages were seized by militant Iranian students who demanded the return of the Shah from the United States (where he was receiving medical treatment)

to stand trial in Iran. Despite vigorous protests by the U.S. government, the hostages were held for 444 days. A U.S. attempt to free them by military force failed, and the Shah died in Egypt on 27 July 1980. The crisis was finally resolved on 20 January 1981, in an agreement providing for release of the prisoners.

However, conflict between rival political groups within Iran continued, accompanied by repeated bombings and assassinations. By 1982, at least 4,500 people had been killed in political violence, and some estimates placed the total much higher. In September 1982, Sadegh Ghotbzadeh, who had been foreign minister during the hostage crisis, was executed on charges of plotting to kill Khomeini and establish a secular government.

Iraq, meanwhile, had taken advantage of Iran's political chaos and economic disorder to revive an old border dispute, and full-scale war erupted in

---

September 1980, when Iraqi forces invaded Khuzistan in the southwest, and captured the town of Khorramshahr and the oil refinery center of Abadan. Iran then launched its own offensive, invading Iraq but failing to make significant gains. The land war became deadlocked, and in 1983 Iraq broadened the war zone to include oil-tanker traffic in the northern Persian Gulf.

Hostilities continued until 1988, when Iran finally yielded to terms for a cease-fire. On 3 June 1989, a few months after calling for the death of novelist Salman Rushdie for blasphemy, Khomeini died of a heart attack. Over 3 million people attended his funeral. He was succeeded as spiritual guide by President Ali Khamenei.

Iran remained neutral during the Gulf War, receiving (and retaining) Iraqi planes that were flown across the border for safekeeping. Iran also accepted thousands of Kurdish refugees from Iraq to add to its heavy burden of Afghan refugees from the civil war in that country. Inflation, shortages, and unemployment—the products of revolution, war, and mismanagement— generated widespread popular discontent.

In June 1997, moderate candidate Mohammad Khatami was elected president. His election marked a move toward greater political and cultural tolerance by the Islamic government. In April 1998, Gholamhossein Karabaschi, the mayor of Teheran, was arrested on corruption charges. Karabaschi was also a political moderate and many Iranians demonstrated in protest of the arrest, which they considered politically motivated by conservatives. The mayor was later released.

GOVERNMENT

The constitution of December 1979 established an Islamic republic in conformity with the principles of the Shi'ite faith. Guidance of the republic is entrusted to the country's spiritual leader (faqih) or to a council of religious leaders. An appointed Council of Guardians consists of six religious leaders, who consider all legislation for conformity to Islamic principles, and six Muslim lawyers appointed by the Supreme Judicial Council, who rule on limited questions of constitutionality.

The executive branch consists of a president and Council of Ministers. The president is elected by popular vote to a four-year term and supervises government administration. The presidency has limited power since all laws must be approved by

an elite group of clerics. The Majlis consists of 270 members elected directly to four-year terms. Voting is universal for those over age 15.

Judiciary

In August 1982, the Supreme Court invalidated all previous laws that did not conform with the dictates of Islam, and all courts set up before the 1979 revolution were abolished in October 1982. An Islamic system of punishment, introduced in 1983, included flogging, stoning, and amputation for various crimes. There are two different court systems: civil courts and revolutionary courts.

The judicial system is under the authority of the religious leader (faqih). A Supreme Judicial Council responsible to the faqih oversees the Supreme Court, which has sixteen branches. The Ministry of Justice oversees law courts in the provinces. The revolutionary courts try cases involving political offenses, narcotics trafficking, and "crimes against God." The trials in revolutionary courts are rarely held in public, and there is no guarantee of access to an attorney.

Political Parties

After the overthrow of the Shah's regime in February 1979, new political parties were formed. In elections to the Majlis (parliament) in March and May 1980, the Islamic Republican Party (IRP), which was closely identified with Ayatollah Khomeini, emerged as the dominant group.

All parties found not to be acceptable by Islamic standards have been banned.

DEFENSE

Two years' military service is required for all males at age 18. In 1995, the army had 345,000 soldiers (250,000 draftees); the navy, 18,000 men.

The Revolutionary Guards unit (Pasdaran) has an estimated 100,000-man army and 20,000 sailors and marines. Complementing the Pasdaran are the baseej, radical young volunteers devoted to an Islamic Iran. Membership is estimated at 200,000. The police force numbers 150,000. The official military budget in 1996 was $3.4 billion.

ECONOMIC AFFAIRS

Iran witnessed rapid economic growth during the reign of Shah Muhammad Reza Pahlavi. With the astonishing growth of its oil revenues, Iran became a major world economic power. Development of its extensive agricultural, mineral, and power resources was financed through oil revenues.

The economy has changed drastically since 1979. The war with Iraq, which reduced oil exports, coupled with the decrease in the price of oil, sent oil revenues downward from $20.5 billion in 1979 to an estimated $5.3 billion in 1986.

Government economic reforms begun after Iran accepted a UN cease-fire resolution in 1988 led to economic growth and lowered budget deficits and inflation, which dropped from 29% in 1988 to around 10% in 1990. In 1997, 86% of the domestic economy came from state-owned businesses. During 1994–96, Iran's economy grew at a steady rate of about 2% per year.

Public Finance

The budget is prepared by the Finance Ministry and submitted to Parliament. Trade reforms implemented since 1991 have boosted economic growth and reduced budget deficits. The general government deficit fell from 9% of GDP in 1988 to 2% in 1992.

Income

In 1998, the gross national product (GNP) of Iran was $109.6 billion, or $1,770 per person.

Industry

Main industries are oil refining, petrochemicals, steel, and copper. Major refinery products are motor fuel, distillate fuel oil, and residual fuel oil. In 1995, output of refined petroleum products amounted to 398,500 barrels per day.

The textile industry has prospered in recent years with increased production of cotton, woolen, and synthetic fabrics. The making of handwoven carpets is a traditional industry in Iran that flourishes despite competition from machine-made products.

Banking and Finance

Before the modern era in Iranian banking, which dates to the opening of a branch of a British bank in 1888, credit was available only at high rates from noninstitutional lenders such as relatives, friends, wealthy landowners, and bazaar money lenders. As recently as 1988 these noninstitutional sources of credit were still available, particularly in the more isolated rural communities. The Central Bank of Iran–Bank Markazil–established by the Monetary and Banking Law of 1960, issues notes, controls foreign exchange, and supervises the banking sector.

The revolutionary government nationalized all commercial banks shortly after taking office in 1979 and announced that banking practices would be brought in line with Islamic principles, which include a ban on interest payments.

In 1991, measures to promote competition between banks, and to loosen Bank Markazi's control in order to encourage savings within the official banking sector were introduced.

Bank Melli, which has acted for the central bank, handles most Iranian banking operations outside the country. The requirements to abide by Islamic principles were never imposed on Bank Melli.

The Tehran Stock Exchange, locally known as the Bourse, was created in 1971.

Economic Development

Iran's five-year economic plan (1989/90–1993/94) authorized up to $27 billion in foreign borrowing. It aimed to increase productivity in key industrial and economic sectors and to promote the non-oil export sector. The 1994/95–1998/99 plan aimed at investing money in transport, particularly in the railroad system and in the construction of a public underground for Tehran. Other projects were aimed at revitalizing the petroleum sector. In 1995, the French company Total was contracted to develop a new oil gas site.

SOCIAL WELFARE

Traditionally, the family and the tribe were supplemented by Islamic *waqf* (obligatory charity) institutions for the care of the infirm and the indigent. In 1974, the Ministry of Social Welfare was created. At that time, it was anticipated that by the end of the fifth plan (1973–78), some 50% of the urban population would enjoy insurance coverage, but coverage for the whole country was not expected until the end of the 1980s. The 1979 constitution provided for health, unemployment, and old-age insurance.

Healthcare

Average life expectancy is estimated at 70 years for both women and men. In 1995, 80% of the population had access to health care services.

The Islamic republic has continued to provide health care programs to the rural areas. In 1993, there was one physician for every 3,142 people. As of 1990, Iran had 1.5 hospital beds per 1,000 people and total health care expenditures of over $3 billion.

Housing

In 1986, 43% of all housing units were constructed of brick with iron beams, 19% were adobe and wood, and 16% were brick with wooden beams. Electricity was available in 84% of all housing units, 95% had a water toilet, 75% had piped water, 54% had a kitchen, and 47% had a bath.

EDUCATION

Literacy training has been a prime concern in Iran. In 1994, the illiteracy rate was estimated at 27.7%, 21.6% for males and 34.2% for females. In 1994, there were 9.7 million elementary-school pupils, and 7.3 million total secondary-school students.

Education is financed by the state at all levels, from elementary school through university. At university level, however, every student is required to later serve the government for a number of years equivalent to those spent at the university.

The country's 16 universities were closed after the 1979 revolution and then reopened gradually between 1982 and 1983 with Islamic curriculums. In 1994, all higher level institutions had 478,455 students.

1999 KEY EVENTS TIMELINE

January

- The ministry of information announces that intelligence officers were responsible for the killings of five dissidents in November and December 1998.

- The United States imposes sanctions against three Russian institutes for allegedly helping Iran develop nuclear and missile capability.

February

- The first nationwide election for local council since the 1979 revolution takes place on February 26.

March

- President Khatami, in his first visit to a Western state, holds talks with Pope John Paul II at the Vatican.

- The falling oil prices force the Organization of Petroleum Exporting Countries (OPEC) and other major exporters to agree on production cuts.

June

- The state-run radio reports the arrest of thirteen Jewish Iranians on charges of spying for the United States and Israel.

July

- Students protesting the closure of a pro-reform newspaper set off widespread unrest.

September

- President Khatami presents his five-year development plan to the parliament.

November

- Twenty years after the US-Iranian hostage crisis, the annual commemorative burning of the U.S. flag in Iran is boycotted by students who hold a protest instead.

- Journalists at Iran's pro-reform daily *Khordad* report for work despite a clerical court ruling banning their newspaper and jailing their managing editor.

- Former president Akbar Hashemi Rafsanjani announces his plan to run for parliament in February 2000.

December

- Iran agrees to send its soccer team to play an exhibition game in the United States at the Rose Bowl on January 16, after receiving assurances that Iranian soccer players would not be fingerprinted.

ANALYSIS OF EVENTS: 1999

BUSINESS AND THE ECONOMY

The fall of crude oil prices from late 1997 to March 1999 forced Iran to cut government spending, restrain imports, renegotiate its external debt repayments schedule, and to seek further finance. The rising oil prices driven by OPEC members' compliance with the March production cuts boosted growth prospects for 1999–2000. The increasing oil revenue would help with current expenses and external debt repayments.

In his five years, Khatami has proposed extensive structural reforms based on reducing dependence on oil, curtailing state monopolies, encouraging private investment, ensuring social justice, and improving economic security. The pace of economic recovery and structural reform will be affected by the outcome of next year's parliamentary elections, future oil prices, and the extent of government success in improving the fiscal balance, privatizing money-losing state enterprises, reducing government regulations, and attracting domestic and foreign investors. Iran's economic development could be somewhat restrained by the U.S. economic sanctions.

GOVERNMENT AND POLITICS

President Mohammad Khatami, elected in May 1997, continued the process of transforming revolutionary Iran into a civil society through the rule of law, transparency, accountability, tolerance, and social justice. The Khatami administration succeeded in setting up local councils, promoting tolerance, and establishing more political and social liberties. Khatami's reform programs attracted increasing popular support and were challenged by his conservative opponents. They closed a number of liberal newspapers and proposed new restrictive press laws. The February 2000 parliamentary elections will be a critical factor in the contest between reformists and their opponents and will determine the pace and scope of political, social, and economic development. President Khatami continued to advocate for a dialogue of civilizations. His official visits to Italy, Syria, Saudi Arabia, and France facilitated Iran's closer rapprochement with the Arab world and the European Union. Unresolved dispute with the United Arab Emirate over islands marred Iranian-Arab ties. Iran's foreign policy will be conditioned by its domestic power struggle. Foreign policy issues including Iran's relations with the United States were debated in media. There is no prospect for the resumption of diplomatic ties or the lifting of U.S. economic sanctions on Iran in the near future.

CULTURE AND SOCIETY

Among the most important achievements of the Khatami government were greater press freedom, relaxation of certain cultural and social restrictions, more attention to the needs of women and the younger generation, and greater public participation in policy making process. There was more tolerance of artistic expression, and new newspapers flourished. In the absence of serious political parties, the press played an effective role in creating civil society by promoting public debates on the role of religion in politics, human rights, the press laws, and the nature of government intervention in economy. The "people-to-people" exchanges brought greater contacts between Iranian and American societies. Iranian scholars, newspaper editors, journalists, film directors, musicians, and writers visited the United States and an increasing number of Americans traveled to Iran. A number of Iranian films were shown across the United States. The enhanced mutual understanding between the two countries created opportunities for further cultural and scientific exchanges.

DIRECTORY

CENTRAL GOVERNMENT

Head of State

Leader of the Islamic Revolution
Ayatollah Ali Hoseini-Khamenei, Office of the Islamic Revolution

President
Mohammad Khatami-Ardakani, Office of the President, al-Shariati Ave., Tehran, Iran
E-MAIL: iranemb@salamiran.org

Ministers

Minister of Foreign Affairs
Kamal Kharazi, Ministry of Foreign Affairs, Kushak Mersi Street, Ferdusi Ave., 11200 Tehran, Iran
FAX: +98 (21) 3116276

Minister of Agriculture and Rural Development
Isa Kalantari, Ministry of Agriculture and Rural Development

Minister of Commerce
Mohammad Shariat-Madari, Ministry of Commerce

Minister of Reconstruction Jihad
Mohammad Saidi-Kia, Ministry of Reconstruction Jihad

Minister of Cooperatives
Morteza Haji-Qaem, Ministry of Cooperatives

Minister of Culture and Higher Education
Mostafa Moin-Najafabadi, Ministry of Culture and Higher Education

Minister of Defense and Armed Forces Logistics
Ali Shamkhani, Ministry of Defense and Armed Forces Logistics

Minister of Economic Affairs and Finance
Hosein Namazi, Ministry of Economic Affairs and Finance

Minister of Education and Training
Hosein Mozafar, Ministry of Education and Training

Minister of Energy
Habibollah Bitaraf, Ministry of Energy

Minister of Health, Treatment, and Medical Education
Mohammad Farhadi, Ministry of Health, Treatment, and Medical Education

Minister of Housing and Urban Development
Abdol-Alizadeh, Ministry of Housing and Urban Development

Minister of Industries
Qolam Reza Shafei, Ministry of Industries

Minister of Intelligence and Security
Hojjat al-Eslam Mohammad Ali Yunesi, Ministry of Intelligence and Security

Minister of Interior
Hojjat al-Eslam Abdol Vahed Musavi-Lari, Ministry of Interior

Minister of Islamic Culture and Guidance
Ataollah Mohajerani, Ministry of Islamic Culture and Guidance

Minister of Justice
Hojjat al-Eslam Mohammad Esmail Shoshtari, Ministry of Justice

Minister of Labor and Social Affairs
Hosein Kamali, Ministry of Labor and Social Affairs

Minister of Mines and Metals
Eshaq Jahangiri, Ministry of Mines and Metals

Minister of Petroleum/Oil
Bijan Namdar-Zanganeh, Ministry of Petroleum/Oil

Minister of Post, Telegraph, and Telephone
Mohammad Reza Aref-Yazdi, Ministry of Post, Telegraph, and Telephone

Minister of Roads and Transport
Mahmud Hojati-Najafabadi, Ministry of Roads and Transport

POLITICAL ORGANIZATIONS

Jameh-ye Ruhaniyat Mobarez-JRM (Militant Clerics Association)
NAME: Mehdi Mahdavi-Karubi

Servants of Reconstruction

Executives of Construction

Islamic Iran Solidarity Party

Islamic Partnership Front

DIPLOMATIC REPRESENTATION

Embassies in Iran

Australia
No. 11, 23rd St., Khalid Islambuli Ave., P.O. Box 15875-4334, Abbasabad, 15138 Tehran, Iran
PHONE: +98 (21) 8866153
FAX: +98 (21) 8720484

Belgium
Ave. Shahid Fayyaz Babak Street 3, Tehran, Iran
PHONE: +98 (21) 2044574
FAX: +98 (21) 2040733

Denmark
18 Dashti Street, Tehran, Iran
PHONE: +98 (21) 2030009
FAX: + 98 (21) 2030007
E-MAIL: ambadane.teheran@inet.uni2.dk
TITLE: Ambassador
NAME: Hugo Østergaard-Andersen

Ireland
Ave. Mirdamad Khiaban Razane Shomali 8, Tehran, Iran
PHONE: +98 (21) 2227672
FAX: +98 (21) 2222731

Italy
81 Ave. Neuphle le Chateau, Tehran, Iran
PHONE: +98 (21) 6496955; 6496956; 6496957
FAX: +98 (21) 6496961

New Zealand
Ave. Mirza-ye-ShiraziShahid, Ali-ye-MirzaHassani Street No. 29, Tehran, Iran
PHONE: +98 (21) 8715083; 8860336
FAX: +98 (21) 8861715; 8860336

Russia
39 Neauphle-le-Chateau, Tehran, Iran

United Kingdom
Ferdossi Ave., Tehran, Iran
TITLE: Chargé d'Affaires
NAME: J. R. James

JUDICIAL SYSTEM
Supreme Court

FURTHER READING
Articles

Amuzegar, Jahangir. "Khatami and the Iranian Economy at Mid-Term." *Middle East Journal* (Autumn 1999).

Balali, Mehrdad. "Clinton's Remarks Spark Iran Debate on U.S. Ties." Reuters, 18 April 1999.

Clawson, Patrick. "How the U.S. Can Bolster Reform in Iran." *The Wall Street Journal,* 16 July 1999.

"Conflicting Voices From Iran" *New York Times,* 7 November 1999.

Hooglund, Eric. "Khatami's Iran." *Current History* (February 1999).

"Iran's Economy Ailing, Still." *The Economist* (August 14, 1999).

Sherman, Besty. "Iran's Film Revolution Continues." *Boston Globe,* 7 November 1999.

Books

Aldrich, George H. *The Jurisprudence of the Iran-United States Claims Tribunal.* New York: Oxford University Press, 1996.

Economic Trends in the MENA Region. Cairo: Economic Research Forum for the Arab Countries, Iran and Turkey, 1998.

Rahnema, Saeed and Sohrab Behdad, eds. *Iran After the Revolution: Crisis of an Islamic State.* New York: I.B. Taurus, 1995.

Internet

"Iran." *United States Energy Information Association.* Available Online @ http://www.eia.doe.gov/emeu/cabs/iran.html (November 12, 1999).

National Council of Resistance. Available Online @ http://www.iran-e-azad.org/english/boi.html (November 12, 1999).

Presidency of the Islamic Republic of Iran. Available Online @ http://www.gov.ir/ (November 12, 1999).

IRAN: STATISTICAL DATA

For sources and notes see "Sources of Statistics" in the front of each volume.

GEOGRAPHY

Geography (1)

Area:

Total: 1.648 million sq km.

Land: 1.636 million sq km.

Water: 12,000 sq km.

Area—comparative: slightly larger than Alaska.

Land boundaries:

Total: 5,440 km.

Border countries: Afghanistan 936 km, Armenia 35 km, Azerbaijan-proper 432 km, Azerbaijan-Naxcivan exclave 179 km, Iraq 1,458 km, Pakistan 909 km, Turkey 499 km, Turkmenistan 992 km.

Coastline: 2,440 km.

Note: Iran also borders the Caspian Sea (740 km).

Climate: mostly arid or semiarid, subtropical along Caspian coast.

Terrain: rugged, mountainous rim; high, central basin with deserts, mountains; small, discontinuous plains along both coasts.

Natural resources: petroleum, natural gas, coal, chromium, copper, iron ore, lead, manganese, zinc, sulfur.

Land use:

Arable land: 10%

Permanent crops: 1%

Permanent pastures: 27%

Forests and woodland: 7%

Other: 55% (1993 est.).

HUMAN FACTORS

Demographics (2A)

	1990	1995	1998	2000	2010	2020	2030	2040	2050
Population	NA	NA	64,411.5	65,865.3	75,742.9	87,131.5	96,235.4	104,357.6	110,326.2
Net migration rate (per 1,000 population)	NA	NA	NA	NA	NA	NA	NA	NA	NA
Births	NA	NA	NA	NA	NA	NA	NA	NA	NA
Deaths	NA	NA	NA	NA	NA	NA	NA	NA	NA
Life expectancy - males	NA	NA	68.0	68.8	72.1	74.7	76.5	77.9	78.8
Life expectancy - females	NA	NA	70.7	71.7	75.8	79.1	81.5	83.2	84.4
Birth rate (per 1,000)	NA	NA	21.3	20.1	20.6	16.3	14.1	13.7	12.2
Death rate (per 1,000)	NA	NA	5.5	5.3	4.8	4.6	5.3	6.6	8.2
Women of reproductive age (15-49 yrs.)	NA	NA	16,462.2	17,558.4	22,007.7	24,161.1	25,376.5	23,929.1	23,887.7
of which are currently married	NA	NA	NA	NA	NA	NA	NA	NA	NA
Fertility rate	NA	NA	2.6	2.3	2.0	2.0	2.0	2.0	2.0

Except as noted, values for vital statistics are in thousands; life expectancy is in years.

Health Personnel (3)

Total health expenditure as a percentage of GDP, 1990-1997[a]

Public sector 1.7

Private sector 2.5

Total[b] 4.2

Health expenditure per capita in U.S. dollars, 1990-1997[a]

Purchasing power parity 210

Total 89

Availability of health care facilities per 100,000 people

Hospital beds 1990-1997[a] 140

Doctors 1993[c] . . . . .NA

Nurses 1993[c] . . . . .NA

Health Indicators (4)

Life expectancy at birth

1980 60

1997 69

Daily per capita supply of calories (1996) 2,824

Total fertility rate births per woman (1997) 2.8

Maternal mortality ratio per 100,000 live births (1990-97) . . . . .120[c]

Safe water % of population with access (1995) 90

Sanitation % of population with access (1995) 81

Consumption of iodized salt % of households (1992-98)[a] 94

Smoking prevalence

Male % of adults (1985-95)[a] . . . .

Female % of adults (1985-95)[a] . . . .

Tuberculosis incidence per 100,000 people (1997) 55

Adult HIV prevalence % of population ages 15-49 (1997) . . . .<0.005

Infants and Malnutrition (5)

Under-5 mortality rate (1997) 35

% of infants with low birthweight (1990-97) 10

Births attended by skilled health staff % of total[a] . . .74

% fully immunized (1995-97)

TB 99

DPT 97

Polio 97

Measles 96

Prevalence of child malnutrition under age 5 (1992-97)[b] 16

Ethnic Division (6)

Persian 51%

Azerbaijani 24%

Gilaki and Mazandarani 8%

Kurd 7%

Arab 3%

Lur 2%

Baloch 2%

Turkmen 2%

Other 1%

Religions (7)

Shi'a Muslim 89%

Sunni Muslim 10%

Zoroastrian, Jewish, Christian, and Baha'i 1%

Languages (8)

Persian and Persian dialects 58%, Turkic and Turkic dialects 26%, Kurdish 9%, Luri 2%, Balochi 1%, Arabic 1%, Turkish 1%, other 2%.

EDUCATION

Public Education Expenditures (9)

Public expenditure on education (% of GNP)

1980 . . . . .7.5

1996 . . . . .4.0[1]

Expenditure per student

Primary % of GNP per capita

1980 . . . . .16.2[1]

1996 . . . . .7.6

Secondary % of GNP per capita

1980 . . . .

1996 . . . . .10.1

Tertiary % of GNP per capita

1980 . . . . .67.5[1]

1996 . . . . .43.2

Expenditure on teaching materials

Primary % of total for level (1996) . . . .

Secondary % of total for level (1996) 1.2

Primary pupil-teacher ratio per teacher (1996) 31

Duration of primary education years (1995) 5

Educational Attainment (10)

Age group (1987) . . . . .10+

Total population .10,628,447

Highest level attained (%)

  No schooling 52.8

  First level

    Not completed 21.6

    Completed . . . . .NA

  Entered second level

    S-1 . . . . .11.6

    S-2 . . . . .NA

  Postsecondary 4.1

GOVERNMENT & LAW

Political Parties (12)

The legislative branch is a unicameral Islamic Consultative Assembly (270 seats; members elected by popular vote to serve four-year terms). Iran has no political parties.

Government Budget (13B)

Revenues . . . .$34.6 billion

Expenditures . . . .$34.9 billion

  Capital expenditures . . . .$11.8 billion

Data for FY96/97.

Military Affairs (14B)

	1990	1991	1992	1993	1994	1995
Military expenditures						
Current dollars (mil.)[1]	8,098	7,831	5,029	6,041	5,449	4,191
1995 constant dollars (mil.)[1]	9,307	8,654	5,410	6,333	5,586	4,191
Armed forces (000)	440	465	528	528	528	440
Gross national product (GNP)						
Current dollars (mil.)	133,900	153,700	167,600	175,800	157,500	158,200[e]
1995 constant dollars (mil.)	153,900	169,900	180,300	184,300	161,500	158,200[e]
Central government expenditures (CGE)						
1995 constant dollars (mil.)	30,860	32,660	36,420	45,060	41,210	NA
People (mil.)	56.9	59.1	60.9	62.0	63.1	64.6
Military expenditure as % of GNP	6.0	5.1	3.0	3.4	3.5	2.6
Military expenditure as % of CGE	30.2	26.5	14.9	14.1	13.6	NA
Military expenditure per capita (1995 $)	163	146	89	102	88	65
Armed forces per 1,000 people (soldiers)	7.7	7.9	8.7	8.5	8.4	6.8
GNP per capita (1995 $)	2,702	2,875	2,961	2,972	2,558	2,449
Arms imports[6]						
Current dollars (mil.)	1,900	1,600	850	1,100	390	270
1995 constant dollars (mil.)	2,184	1,768	914	1,153	400	270
Arms exports[6]						
Current dollars (mil.)	0	20	20	80	80	290
1995 constant dollars (mil.)	0	22	22	84	82	290
Total imports[7]						
Current dollars (mil.)	15,720	21,790	23,110	16,650	11,640	12,410
1995 constant dollars (mil.)	18,060	24,080	24,850	17,450	11,930	12,410
Total exports[7]						
Current dollars (mil.)	15,320	15,920	19,870[e]	18,570[e]	17,300[e]	18,600[e]
1995 constant dollars (mil.)	17,600	17,590	21,370[e]	19,470[e]	17,730[e]	18,600[e]
Arms as percent of total imports[8]	12.1	7.3	3.7	6.6	3.4	2.2
Arms as percent of total exports[8]	0	.1	.1	.4	.5	1.6

LABOR FORCE

Labor Force (16)

Total (million) 15.4

Agriculture 33%

Manufacturing 21%

Shortage of skilled labor. Data for 1988 est.

Unemployment Rate (17)

More than 30% (January 1998 est.)

PRODUCTION SECTOR

Electric Energy (18)

Capacity . . . . .25.117 million kW (1995)

Production . . . . .79 billion kWh (1995)

Consumption per capita . . . . .1,222 kWh (1995)

Transportation (19)

Highways:

total: 162,000 km

paved: 81,000 km (including 470 km of expressways)

unpaved: 81,000 km (1996 est.)

Waterways: 904 km; the Shatt al Arab is usually navigable by maritime traffic for about 130 km; channel has been dredged to 3 m and is in use

Pipelines: crude oil 5,900 km; petroleum products 3,900 km; natural gas 4,550 km

Merchant marine:

total: 135 ships (1,000 GRT or over) totaling 3,465,226 GRT/6,128,443 DWT ships by type: bulk 47, cargo 34, chemical tanker 4, combination bulk 2, container 4, liquefied gas tanker 1, multifunction large-load carrier 6, oil tanker 23, refrigerated cargo 3, roll-on/roll-off cargo 10, short-sea passenger 1

Airports: 280 (1997 est.)

Airports—with paved runways:

total: 103

over 3,047 m: 36

2,438 to 3,047 m: 14

1,524 to 2,437 m: 27

914 to 1,523 m: 21

under 914 m: 5 (1997 est.)

Airports—with unpaved runways:

total: 177

over 3,047 m: 1

2,438 to 3,047 m: 4

1,524 to 2,437 m: 14

914 to 1,523 m: 124

under 914 m: 34 (1997 est.)

Top Agricultural Products (20)

Wheat, rice, other grains, sugar beets, fruits, nuts, cotton; dairy products, wool; caviar.

MANUFACTURING SECTOR

GDP & Manufacturing Summary (21)

Detailed value added figures are listed by both International Standard Industry Code (ISIC) and product title.

	1980	1985	1990	1994
GDP ($-1990 mil.)[1]	67,761	87,299	88,173	107,581
Per capita ($-1990)[1]	1,726	1,785	1,496	1,636
Manufacturing share (%) (current prices)[1]	9.1	8.5	12.3	13.5
Manufacturing				
Value added ($-1990 mil.)[1]	6,234	7,920	10,621	13,947
Industrial production index	100	139	151	199
Value added ($ mil.)	8,186	5,374	7,994	5,839
Gross output ($ mil.)	15,870	10,994	17,373	13,302
Employment (000)	470	611	653	626
Profitability (% of gross output)				
Intermediate input (%)	48	52	54	56
Wages and salaries inc. supplements (%)	29	28	15	16
Gross operating surplus	23	19	31	28
Productivity ($)				
Gross output per worker	33,756	17,161	26,007	20,553
Value added per worker	17,411	8,790	11,966	9,120
Average wage (inc. supplements)	9,668	4,893	3,925	3,465
Value added ($ mil.)				
311/2 Food products	930	553	737	755
313 Beverages	145	133	152	127
314 Tobacco products	190	46	82	52
321 Textiles	1,329	931	1,355	635
322 Wearing apparel	78	33	85	16
323 Leather and fur products	36	30	69	21

	1980	1985	1990	1994
324 Footwear	100	71	85	35
331 Wood and wood products	68	52	108	40
332 Furniture and fixtures	33	21	32	19
341 Paper and paper products	135	115	130	96
342 Printing and publishing	80	42	114	54
351 Industrial chemicals	93	102	227	281
352 Other chemical products	278	266	412	317
353 Petroleum refineries	1,652	386	31	19
354 Miscellaneous petroleum and coal products	2	14	38	18
555 Rubber products	93	79	116	122
356 Plastic products	198	103	164	92
361 Pottery, china and earthenware	45	33	41	33
362 Glass and glass products	115	73	73	68
369 Other non-metal mineral products	819	601	688	451
371 Iron and steel	367	313	893	890
372 Non-ferrous metals	48	84	413	209
381 Metal products	319	244	338	261
382 Non-electrical machinery	208	277	724	230
383 Electrical machinery	391	329	332	461
384 Transport equipment	399	407	504	473
385 Professional and scientific equipment	24	24	23	39
390 Other manufacturing industries	11	12	28	24

FINANCE, ECONOMICS, & TRADE

Economic Indicators (22)

National product: GDP—purchasing power parity—$371.2 billion (1997 est.)

National product real growth rate: 3.2% (1997 est.)

National product per capita: $5,500 (1997 est.)

Inflation rate—consumer price index: 23% (1996)

Exchange Rates (24)

Exchange rates:

Iranian rials (IR) per US$1

January 1998	1,752.14
1996	1,750.76
1997	1,752.92
1995	1,747.93
1994	1,748.75
1993	1,267.77

Black market rate: 4,600 rials per US$1 (March 1997); As of May 1995, the "official rate" of 1,750 rials per US$1 is used for imports of essential goods and services and for oil exports, whereas the "official export rate" of 3,000 rials per US$1 is used for non-oil exports and imports not covered by the official rate.

Balance of Payments (23)

	1992	1993	1994	1995	1996
Exports of goods (f.o.b.)	19,868	18,080	19,434	18,360	22,391
Imports of goods (f.o.b.)	−23,274	−19,287	−12,617	−12,774	−14,989
Trade balance	−3,406	−1,207	6,817	5,586	7,402
Services - debits	−5,940	−5,743	−3,639	−3,133	−3,981
Services - credits	846	1,235	580	909	1,348
Private transfers (net)	—	—	−2	−4	−8
Government transfers (net)	1,996	1,500	1,200	—	471
Overall balance	−6,504	−4,215	4,956	3,358	5,232

Top Import Origins (25)

$15.6 billion (f.o.b., 1997 est.)

Origins	%
Germany	NA
Italy	NA
Japan	NA
UAE	NA
United Kingdom	NA
Belgium	NA

NA stands for not available.

Top Export Destinations (26)

$19 billion (f.o.b., 1997 est.).

Destinations	%
Japan	NA
United States	NA
United Kingdom	NA
Germany	NA
South Korea	NA
UAE	NA

NA stands for not available.

Economic Aid (27)

Recipient: ODA, $40 million (1993).

Import Export Commodities (28)

Import Commodities	Export Commodities
Machinery	Petroleum 80%
Military supplies	Carpets
Metal works	Fruits
Foodstuffs	Nuts
Pharmaceuticals	Hides
Technical services	Iron
Refined oil products	Steel

IRAQ

CAPITAL: Baghdad.

FLAG: The national flag is a tricolor of red, white, and black horizontal stripes, with three five-pointed stars in green in the center of the white stripe. In 1991 the phrase *Allahu Akbar* (''God is Great'') in green Arabic script was added between the stars.

ANTHEM: *Al-Salaam al-Jumhuri (Salute of the Republic)*.

MONETARY UNIT: The Iraqi dinar (ID) is a paper currency of 1,000 fils. There are coins of 1, 5, 10, 25, 50, 100, and 250 fils, and notes of 250 and 500 fils and 1, 5, 10, 50, and 100 dinars. The dinar is extremely unstable, falling to $1 = ID3,000 in 1995.

WEIGHTS AND MEASURES: The metric system is the legal standard, but weights and measures in general use vary, especially in domestic transactions. The unit of land is the dunam, which is equivalent to approximately 0.25 hectare (0.62 acre).

HOLIDAYS: New Year's Day, 1 January; Army Day, 6 January; 14th Ramadan Revolution Day, 8 February; Declaration of the Republic, 14 July; and Peaceful Revolution Day, 17 July. Muslim religious holidays include `Id al-Fitr, `Id al-`Adha', Milad an-Nabi, and Islamic New Year.

TIME: 3 PM = noon GMT.

LOCATION AND SIZE: Iraq comprises an area of 437,072 square kilometers (168,754 square miles), slightly more than twice the size of the state of Idaho. It has a total boundary length of 3,681 kilometers (2,288 miles). Iraq's capital city, Baghdad, is located in the east central part of the country.

CLIMATE: Summers are intensely hot and dry, and during the hottest time of the day—often reaching 49°C (120°F) in the shade—people take refuge in underground shelters. Winters are damp and comparatively cold, with temperatures averaging about 10°C (50°F). With annual rainfall of less than 15.1 centimeters (5.9 inches), agriculture is dependent on irrigation.

INTRODUCTORY SURVEY

RECENT HISTORY

Iraq gained independence in 1932 and was admitted to membership in the League of Nations.

On 14 July 1958, a military takeover led by General `Abd al-Karim al-Qasim (Kassim) abolished the monarchy and established a republic in its place. Iraq left the anti-communist Baghdad Pact, which the monarchy had joined in 1955. A farm reform law broke up the great land holdings of feudal leaders, and a new economic development program emphasized industrialization. Qasim continued to rule Iraq for four and a half years. On 9 February 1963, however, another military takeover, led by Colonel `Abd as-Salam Muhammad `Arif, overthrew his government and executed him.

In July 1968, General (later Marshal) Ahmad Hasan al-Bakr, heading a section of the Ba`th Party, staged a takeover and established a new government with himself as president. In July 1970, the Bakr government granted limited political, economic, and cultural independence to Iraq's Kurdish minority. But in March 1974, Kurdish rebels revolted, with Iranian military support, and the Iraqi army replied with a major offensive. On 6 March 1975, Iraq and Iran concluded an agreement by which Iran gave up support for the Kurds.

Bakr ruled until July 1979, when he was followed as president by his chosen successor, Saddam Hussein (Husayn) al-Takriti. Tensions between Iraq and Iran rose after the Iranian revolu-

IRAQ

0   50   100 Miles
0   50   100 Kilometers

tion of 1979 and the coming to power of Saddam Hussein. In September 1980, Iraq mounted a full-scale invasion of Iran. Iranian forces launched a slow but successful counterattack and major offensives aimed at the Iraqi oil port of Al Basxrah. Iraqi soldiers repelled the attacks, and the war came to a stalemate, with tens of thousands of casualties on each side.

Attempts by the UN and by other Arab states to resolve the conflict were unsuccessful. In the latter stages of the war, Iraq accepted but Iran regularly rejected proposals for a compromise peace. The war eventually spread to Persian Gulf shipping, as both sides attacked oil tankers and ships transporting oil, goods, and arms. It ended on 20 August 1988 after Iran accepted a UN cease-fire proposal. Having suffered enormous casualties and physical damage, Baghdad began the postwar process of reconstruction.

When Iraq's wartime allies seemed unwilling to help or critical of Iraqi policies, Saddam Hussein turned bitterly against them. Kuwait was the principal target. After threats and troop movements, Iraq invaded and occupied it on 2 August 1990.

A devastating air war began on 17 January 1991 followed by ground attack on 24 February. Iraq was defeated, but not occupied. Despite vast destruction and several hundred thousand casualties, Saddam's government remained firmly in control. Since 1990 economic sanctions have banned oil sales and require Iraq to submit its nonconventional weapons centers to inspection and monitoring. In 1996, the UN agreed to let Iraq export $2 billion in oil to buy food and medical supplies. Iraq has provided inconsistent and false information to the UN Security Council regarding its possession of chemical and other weapons of mass annihilation.

Numerous incidents of failing to cooperate with UN arms inspectors have also increased the Security Council's distrust of Iraq. In late 1997, ten American members of the UN weapons inspection team were denied access to strategic sites. In January 1998 the United States sent 20 ships and 30,000 troops to the area as tension grew. UN secretary-general Kofi Annan went to Iraq in February and persuaded Hussein to comply to the inspections. By April 1998, however, the UN reported that Iraq still showed no progress in meeting its requirement for disarmament. The Iraqi failure to cooperate resulted in American-led air strikes in late December 1998. These bombardments resumed in 1999 when Iraq violated the northern no-fly zone (an area of northern Iraq forbidden to Iraqi military aircraft) almost daily.

GOVERNMENT

Since the 1968 takeover, the Ba'th Party has ruled Iraq by means of the Revolutionary Command Council, which selects the president and a cabinet composed of military and civilian leaders. The president (Saddam Hussein since 1979) serves as chairman of the Revolutionary Command Council, which exercises both executive and legislative powers. He is also prime minister, commander-in-chief of the armed forces, and secretary-general of the Ba'th Party. A National Assembly of 250 members has little real power. Most senior officials are relatives or close associates of Saddam Hussein.

Judiciary

The court system is made up of two distinct branches: security courts and a more conventional court system to handle other charges. The security courts have jurisdiction in all cases involving spy-ing, treason, political dissent, smuggling and currency exchange violations, and drug trafficking. The ordinary civil courts have jurisdiction over civil, commercial, and criminal cases except for those that fall under the jurisdiction of the religious courts.

Although there are no Shari'a (Islamic) courts, family courts may administer Shari'a law according to Iraqi custom.

Political Parties

Since the 1968 takeover, the Ba'thists, organized as the Arab Ba'th Socialist Party, have been the ruling political group in Iraq. Other parties are allowed in order to give the appearance of political tolerance. Outside Iraq, ethnic, religious, and political opposition groups have come together to organize a common front against Saddam Hussein, but they have achieved little. The Shia al Dawa Party was brutally suppressed by Saddam before the Iran-Iraq war.

DEFENSE

Damaged by its defeat in the Gulf War of 1991, the Iraqi armed forces are estimated at 382,500 men, half their prewar strength. The army has a strength of 350,000 men (100,000 recalled reservists); the navy has 1,000 men; and the air force has 30,000 men.

During 1981–90, Iraq purchased some $45 billion in arms from the Soviet Union, France, and China. It was the world's principal arms importer for this period. During the war with Iran, Iraq's defense budget averaged more than $13 billion a year.

ECONOMIC AFFAIRS

Oil is the most important sector of the economy. Petroleum production was badly hurt by the war with Iran, however, and the economy was in serious trouble in 1987. In response to the Iraqi invasion of Kuwait on 2 August 1990, the UN imposed comprehensive economic, financial, and military sanctions, totally isolating the Iraqi economy. However, UN Security Council resolutions authorized the export of Iraqi crude oil worth up to $1.6 billion over a limited time to finance humanitarian imports for the Iraqi people.

Public Finance

An undeclared budget for the military is believed to have absorbed over half of state funds during the war with Iran. Since 1980, the decline in oil exports and huge war expenditures forced Iraq to borrow and to raise funds from abroad. Iraq's invasion of Kuwait in 1990, with the consequent infrastructural damage, UN sanctions, and oil embargo, have severely diminished revenues.

Income

There are no reliable statistics on Iraq's economy. In 1995, different government and international organizations estimated Iraq's gross national product (GNP) at between $766 and $3,035 per person. In 1993, the inflation rate may have been as high as 1000%.

Industry

Main industries are oil refining, food processing, textiles, leather goods, cement and other building materials, tobacco, paper, and sulfur extraction. In 1995, Iraq produced an estimated 200 million tons of refined petroleum products.

Banking and Finance

Data on the financial situation in Iraq are not generally available since the main source of official statistics, the Central Bank of Iraq, has not released figures since 1977. However, data from external authorities are available. After 1991, six new banks were established as a result of liberalizing legislation and the opportunity for large-scale profits from currency speculation.

The Central Bank is striving to maintain the value of the dinar against the dollar through strict monetary policies. Because of the devastated state of the economy, however, it has largely failed in this attempt. In 1994, the black market value of the dinar stood at 750 to the dollar; by 1995, it had fallen to 3,000.

The establishment of a stock exchange in Baghdad was delayed by practical considerations such as a lack of computers, but it was eventually inaugurated in March 1992.

Economic Development

The government both controls and participates in petroleum, agriculture, commerce, banking, and industry.

Iraq has an estimated foreign debt of more than $87 billion. The imposition of sanctions against Iraq has destroyed all attempts to stabilize Iraq's payments. Iraq also faces reparation claims. Iran is separately pursuing its claim for massive separation payments arising from the 1980–88 war. Iraq is also obligated by UN resolutions to pay for various UN agency activities.

SOCIAL WELFARE

A social security law passed in 1971 provides benefits or payments for disability, maternity, old age, unemployment, sickness, and funerals. Although Iraq's constitution guarantees individual rights, the government sharply limits political freedoms and tolerates little public expression of dissent. The government supports equality for women, who make up about 20% of the work force. However, women are not allowed to travel abroad unaccompanied. A 1990 decree grants immunity to men who kill female family members who have committed an ''immoral act'' (such as adultery).

Although the constitution guarantees individual rights, Iraqis are not free to express their opposition to the government. Political offenders are subject to arbitrary arrest, imprisonment, and torture. Amputation and branding are used as a form of punishment for serious crimes.

Healthcare

During 1985–95, 93% of the population had access to health care services. Considerable effort has been made to expand medical facilities to small towns and more remote areas of the country. In 1992, Iraq had 58 doctors per 100,000 people. In 1990, there were 1.6 hospital beds per 1,000 inhabitants. Life expectancy averages 62 years.

Housing

Since 1980, living conditions for the vast majority of the population have improved greatly. Electricity and running water are normal features of all Iraqi villages in rural areas. Mud huts in remote places are rapidly being replaced by brick dwellings. According to the latest available information, total housing units numbered 2.5 million with 6.5 people per dwelling.

EDUCATION

An estimated 42% of adults were illiterate in 1995, 29.3% of men and 55% of women. In 1992, 2.9 million students attended 8,003 primary schools, and 1.1 million attended secondary schools. Primary schools provide a six-year course, and secondary schools have a three-year intermediate course, followed by a two-year course in preparation for entrance to college. There are seven universities in Iraq, the most important being the University of Baghdad.

1999 KEY EVENTS TIMELINE

January

- About 6,000 Iraqis march in the streets of Baghdad on January 16 to mark the eighth anniversary of the start of the Gulf War. They proclaim support for Iraqi leader Saddam Hussein, and call for an end to United Nations economic sanctions.

- The Pentagon admits that a United States missile flew off course and struck a residential neighborhood in southern Iraq. Iraqi authorities claim three missiles hit the area, killing 11 people.

February

- Iraqi officials warn Saudi Arabia and Kuwait that they will retaliate if the two nations continue to allow the United States and Britain to use military bases in their territories to launch attacks against Iraq. They later warn Turkey of the same consequences.

March

- U.S. jets attack air defense sites in the northern no-flight zone for three consecutive days.

April

- Iraqi authorities say foreign air attacks in the last three months have killed and wounded hundreds of civilians.

- The Iraqi government says it has executed four men for the killing of prominent Shiite Muslim leader Mohammed Sadeq al-Sadr and his two sons.

May

- Iraqi officials say at least 21 people are killed and more than two dozen wounded during separate attacks by the U.S. and Britain.

- Saddam Hussein celebrates his 62nd birthday with week-long festivities.

June

- Six leaders of an Iranian exile group based in Iraq, and an Iraqi are killed by a car bomb. A second car bomb explodes in Baghdad, injuring several people.

August

- The United Nations said Iraqi babies are dying at twice the rate they were before the Gulf War, and

after nine years of U.N. sanctions. The United States blames Iraq for the rise in mortality rates among infants.

- Iraq condemns embargo on ninth anniversary of sanctions. Iraqi government officials call the United Nations sanctions criminal.

September

- The five permanent members of the United Nations Security Council fail to reach an agreement on a new policy of sanctions against Iraq. The group could not reach a conclusion on how to resume stalled weapons inspections.

- The Iraqi foreign minister says his country was committed to repair damaged relations with the rest of the Arab world, during a semi-annual meeting of the 21 members of the Arab League. Kuwait and Saudi Arabia remain cool to Iraq's friendship overtures.

- Iraq donates $10 million in oil to Turkey for earthquake relief. The dramatic gesture is seen as an attempt by Iraqi leader Saddam Hussein to embarrass the United States, which had sent $9 million in aid when the gift was announced.

October

- Pope John Paul II decides to put his trip to Iraq on hold. The Vatican was under pressure by the United States and Britain to cancel the visit for fear that it would be seen as support for Saddam Hussein. The Iraqi leader sends a letter congratulating the Pope on the 21st anniversary of his pontificate.

November

- Iraq accuses U.S. and British aircraft of bombing a primary school in the northern city of Mosul, injuring eight people; the U.S. European Command says fighters bombed anti-aircraft batteries that fired at them.

December

- Iraq cancels plans for a visit by Pope John Paul II to Ur, believed to be the birthplace of Abraham.

- The government announces that it will resume oil exports under the terms of the United Nations "oil for food" program which the Security Council renewed for six more months.

ANALYSIS OF EVENTS: 1999

BUSINESS AND THE ECONOMY

Economic sanctions continued to hurt the nation during 1999. In May, the United Nations Security Council voted unanimously to extend for six months the oil-for-food program that allows Iraq to buy humanitarian supplies. Under the plan, Iraq was allowed to sell $5.25 billion in oil to buy food, medicine and other supplies. During the first six months of the year, Iraq sold about $3.9 billion worth of oil. Also in May, the Iraqi government declined a proposal by Britain and the Netherlands to permit international investment in Iraq's oil fields if Baghdad cooperated with UN inspectors. India, in the meantime, also expressed interest in Iraqi oil fields, proposing that some of its major firms be allowed to develop unexplored oil fields. However, India said it would not break UN sanctions. In October, the Iraqi government accused the United States and Britain of blocking needed spare parts to rehabilitate its oil industry.

GOVERNMENT AND POLITICS

On January 16, several thousand Iraqis gathered in Baghdad to mark the eighth anniversary of the start of the Gulf War. Organized by Saddam Hussein's ruling Baath Party, the demonstrators called for an end to the debilitating United Nations economic embargo imposed after Iraq invaded Kuwait in 1990. The war began on January 16, 1991, when a U.S.-led coalition attacked Iraqi forces occupying Kuwait. The conflict lasted only 43 days, but the impasse with Hussein has lasted almost a decade. With 1999 coming to an end, there were no signs that Hussein would come to terms with the United Nations any time soon.

Exactly what to do about Iraq has confounded the UN. In September, the five permanent members of the Security Council could not agree on a new policy on sanctions against Iraq after months of negotiations. Foreign ministers from the United States, Britain, China, Russia and France pledged to work on how best to resume stalled weapons inspections in Iraq. UN weapons inspectors pulled out of Iraq in December 1998, shortly before the United States and Britain launched air strikes after Iraq refused to cooperate with inspectors.

The Security Council has considered a resolution that would suspend all sanctions if Iraq cooperates with a new commission that would monitor its banned weapons program. But Hussein's government has repeatedly said it will not consider any plan that does not include a complete lifting of the sanctions. The United Nations has allowed Iraq to sell a limited amount of oil for food and medicine, about $5.25 billion worth of oil between May and December 1999.

American and British jets patrolling the skis above Iraq attacked Iraqi targets nearly every day during the first three months of the year. Critics said the bombings disrupted the distribution of food and medical supplies, and sometimes killed Iraqi civilians. But the Americans and the British defended the attacks, saying they were simply defending themselves when threatened by Iraqi forces. The constant barrage kept Iraq's government under constant pressure.

Despite the dropping bombs, Hussein has remained defiant at a high, although not personal, cost. Living conditions for his country's 22 million people have deteriorated, with an alarming mortality rate among infants, and widespread poverty and hunger. In August, three U.S. activists joined the Iraqi government to condemn the embargo during the ninth anniversary of sanctions. The United Nations estimates that 1 million Iraqis, mostly children, have died under the sanctions. Most people barely survive on 2,100 calories a day, the organization said.

Iraqi officials in 1999 began to project a "kinder and gentler image," according to *The Economist*, to capitalize on widespread sympathy for the Iraqi people. They looked for allies in the United Nations, the Arab League, and the Vatican. After a devastating earthquake hit Turkey, Hussein sent $10 million worth of oil as a show of solidarity, and critics said, to score political points. Hussein has been more successful with some Arab League nations, including Egypt, which has sent trade delegations to Iraq. In late 1999, Iraq assumed the rotating chairmanship of the 22-member Arab League. Iraq said it was committed to repairing relationships with other Arab countries, but Kuwait, and Saudi Arabia were not ready for reconciliation. Other Arab nations were not likely to circumvent the UN sanctions for the sake of Hussein.

Pope John Paul II criticized the embargo for making the Iraqi people suffer needlessly, and said he was planning to visit Iraq sometime in December. But the United States embarked on its own publicity campaign to focus attention back on Hussein's brutal regime. The pope, under heavy pressure from the U.S., Britain and Iraqi political dissidents, postponed his visit. In the meantime, American and British planes continued to fly over Iraq.

CULTURE AND SOCIETY

While Saddam Hussein continued to challenge the west, UNICEF, the UN children's agency, said mortality among children under five more than doubled from 56 per 1,000 live births in 1984–89 to 131 deaths 10 years later. According to calculations made by the organization, if the reduction in child mortality throughout Iraq in the 1980s had continued into the 1990s, there would have been a half million fewer deaths of children under five during the eight years covered by economic sanctions. There was no shortage of blame. Iraq said the sanctions were hurting the nation, and should be lifted. But the United States vowed to keep the sanctions in place and blamed Hussein for the dramatic increase in infant mortality.

The sanctions were supposed to force Hussein to give up weapons of mass destruction. Yet, on the ninth anniversary of sanctions, the Iraqis, and not Hussein, were on the losing end. In October, CNN reported the country's educational system was deteriorating, with a steady decline in the number of students and teachers. Supplies are so scarce that students bring chalk for their teachers. According to UNICEF, the money allocated to education has dropped by 90 percent since the Gulf War. Some teachers earn $5 per month, less than 1 percent of a typical teacher's salary before the war. According to the Iraqi government, more than 1 million students have failed to enroll in school. And yet while school materials appear to be short, Hussein reportedly sent 3 million textbooks to the northern Kurdish region, which has been outside Baghdad's control since 1991. The books were seen as the latest overture by Hussein to negotiate with the Kurds.

While Iraq's people suffered, Hussein celebrated his 62nd birthday in May with week-long celebrations which included the unveiling of a large mural that depicts Hussein as the 6th century B.C. ruler of Babylon, Nebuchadnezzar. The celebrations included the opening of a new resort, which houses the mural, and a dam project on the River Tigris. During large parades, supporters carried signs that read "with your birth Iraq was reborn."

DIRECTORY

CENTRAL GOVERNMENT
Head of State

President
Saddam Hussein, Office of the President, Presidential Palace, Karadat Mariam, Baghdad, Iraq
E-MAIL: irqun@undp.org

Vice President
Taha Muhyi al-Din Maruf, Office of the Vice President

Vice President
Taha Yasin Ramadan, Office of the Vice President

Ministers

Prime Minister
Saddam Hussein, Office of the Prime Minister

Deputy Prime Minister
Tariq Aziz, Office of the Deputy Prime Minister

Deputy Prime Minister
Hikmat Mizban Ibrahim al-Azzawi, Office of the Deputy Prime Minister

Deputy Prime Minister
Muhammad Hamza al-Zubaydi, Office of the Deputy Prime Minister

Minister of Agriculture
Abdallah Hamid Mahmud al-Salih, Ministry of Agriculture

Minister of Awqaf and Religious Affairs
Abd al-Munim Ahmad, Ministry of Awqaf and Religious Affairs

Minister of Culture and Information
Humam Abd al-Khaliq Abd al-Ghafur, Ministry of Culture and Information

Minister of Defense
Hashim Ahmad al-Jabburi Tai, Ministry of Defense

Minister of Education
Fahd Salim Shaqrah, Ministry of Education

Minister of Finance
Hikmat Mizban Ibrahim al-Azzawi, Ministry of Finance

Minister of Foreign Affairs

Muhammad Said Kazim al-Sahhaf, Ministry of Foreign Affairs

PHONE: +964 (1) 8879638; 5370091

FAX: +964 (1) 5433746

Minister of Health

Umid Midhat Mubarak, Ministry of Health

Minister of Higher Education and Scientific Research

Abd al-Jabbar Tawfiq, Ministry of Higher Education and Scientific Research

Minister of Housing and Reconstruction

Maan Abdallah al-Sarsam, Ministry of Housing and Reconstruction

Minister of Industry and Minerals

Adnan Abd al-Majid Jasim al-Ani, Ministry of Industry and Minerals

Minister of Interior

Muhammad Zimam Abd al-Razzaq, Ministry of Interior

Minister of Irrigation

Mahmud Dhiyab al-Ahmad, Ministry of Irrigation

Minister of Justice

Shabib Lazim al-Maliki, Ministry of Justice

Minister of Labor and Social Affairs

Sadi Tumah Abbas, Ministry of Labor and Social Affairs

Minister of Oil

Amir Rashid Muhammad al-Ubaydi, Ministry of Oil

Minister of State

Abd al-Wahhab Umar Mirza al-Atrush, Ministry of State

Minister of State

Arshad Muhammad Ahmad Muhammad al-Zibari, Ministry of State

Minister of State for Military Affairs

Abd al-Jabbar Khalil Shanshal, Ministry of State for Military Affairs

Minister of Trade

Muhammad Mahdi al-Salih, Ministry of Trade

Minister of Transport and Communications

Ahmad Murtada Ahmad Khalil, Ministry of Transport and Communications

POLITICAL ORGANIZATIONS

Hizb al Baath al'Arabiyah al Ishtiraki (Socialist Arab Rebirth Party)

Assyrian Democratic Movement

Christian Union

Partiya Demokrata Kurdistane (Democratic Party of Kurdistan)

Patriotic Union of Kurdistan

Assyrian Democratic Movement Zowaa

Assyrian Progressive Nationalist Party

Constitutional Monarchy Movement

Islamic Party of Iraq

Kurdistan Communist Party

Worker Communist Party of Iraq

Ba'th Arab Socialist Party

DIPLOMATIC REPRESENTATION

Embassies in Iraq

Afghanistan

NAME: Shareh Al-Machreb

Greece

Jadriyah University Square, P.O. Box 10003, Baghdad, Iraq

PHONE: +964 (1) 7182433; 7762273; 7764360

FAX: +964 (1) 7188729

Italy

1, Zukak, 73 Mahalla 913 Hay Al-Jamiaa, Baghdad, Iraq

PHONE: +964 (1) 7765058; 7769105

Portugal

P.O. Box 2123, Alwika, Baghdad, Iraq

PHONE: +964 (1) 7187542

FAX: +964 (1) 7183508

Russia

Al Mouthanabbi 605/5/4, Baghdad, Iraq

PHONE: +964 (1) 5414749; 5414754; 5418913

JUDICIAL SYSTEM

Court of Cassation

FURTHER READING

Articles

"Baby Powder and Death." *The Economist* (August 21, 1999): 36.

"Battle with Iraq Continues." *The Economist* (June 12, 1999).

"Charming: Iraqi Officials Are Trying to Project a Kinder, Gentler Image." *The Economist* (September 8, 1999): 51.

"Iraq as It Ever Was." *The Economist* (February 6, 1999): 47.

"Iraq Said to Execute 123, Including 19 Dissidents." Reuters, 25 October 1999.

"Iraqi Sideshow Continues." *The Nation* (June 7, 1999): 5.

"Iraq's Opposition: Not Up to It." *The Economist* (September 11, 1999): 52.

"Monumental: Monuments in Iraq." *The Economist* (March 6, 1999): 77.

"The Number-One Son. Saddam Hussein's Son, Uday, Is Heir Apparent for Iraq." Reuters, 25 October 1999.

"School Daze: Grades Are Dropping, Hunger Is Increasing as Iraqi Teens Feel the UN Sanctions." *Scholastic Update* (February 22, 1999): 14.

"U.S. Warplanes Bomb Iraq." *Washington Post,* 28 May 1999.

"Why the Bombs Are Falling in Iraq." *The Economist* (March 6, 1999): 42.

Books

Laizer, S. J. *Martyrs, Traitors, and Patriots: Kurdistan after the Gulf War.* Atlantic Highlands, N.J.: Zed Books, 1996.

Mofid, Kamran. *The Economic Consequences of the Gulf War.* New York: Routledge, 1990.

Internet

Iraqi News Agency. Available Online @ http://www.nisciraq.net/ (October 28, 1999).

Permanent Mission of Iraq to the United Nations. Available Online @ http://www.iraqi-mission.org/ (October 28, 1999).

IRAQ: STATISTICAL DATA

For sources and notes see "Sources of Statistics" in the front of each volume.

GEOGRAPHY

Geography (1)

Area:

Total: 437,072 sq km.

Land: 432,162 sq km.

Water: 4,910 sq km.

Area—comparative: slightly more than twice the size of Idaho.

Land boundaries:

Total: 3,631 km.

Border countries: Iran 1,458 km, Jordan 181 km, Kuwait 242 km, Saudi Arabia 814 km, Syria 605 km, Turkey 331 km.

Coastline: 58 km.

Climate: mostly desert; mild to cool winters with dry, hot, cloudless summers; northern mountainous regions along Iranian and Turkish borders experience cold winters with occasionally heavy snows that melt in early spring, sometimes causing extensive flooding in central and southern Iraq.

Terrain: mostly broad plains; reedy marshes along Iranian border in south with large flooded areas; mountains along borders with Iran and Turkey.

Natural resources: petroleum, natural gas, phosphates, sulfur.

Land use:

Arable land: 12%

Permanent crops: 0%

Permanent pastures: 9%

Forests and woodland: 0%

Other: 79% (1993 est.).

HUMAN FACTORS

Demographics (2A)

	1990	1995	1998	2000	2010	2020	2030	2040	2050
Population	18,134.7	19,713.3	21,722.3	23,150.9	31,151.5	39,713.3	48,656.3	57,484.7	65,529.2
Net migration rate (per 1,000 population)	NA	NA	NA	NA	NA	NA	NA	NA	NA
Births	NA	NA	NA	NA	NA	NA	NA	NA	NA
Deaths	NA	NA	NA	NA	NA	NA	NA	NA	NA
Life expectancy - males	65.5	65.5	65.5	65.5	68.7	71.0	72.8	74.4	75.7
Life expectancy - females	67.6	67.6	67.6	67.6	71.7	75.0	77.7	79.8	81.6
Birth rate (per 1,000)	38.9	38.8	38.6	38.2	31.8	26.2	22.7	19.3	17.0
Death rate (per 1,000)	7.1	6.6	6.6	6.6	4.9	4.2	4.2	4.6	5.5
Women of reproductive age (15-49 yrs.)	3,915.3	4,492.3	5,085.0	5,491.5	7,638.6	10,242.8	12,782.5	14,952.7	16,791.1
of which are currently married	NA	NA	NA	NA	NA	NA	NA	NA	NA
Fertility rate	6.1	5.6	5.2	5.0	4.0	3.2	2.7	2.4	2.2

Except as noted, values for vital statistics are in thousands; life expectancy is in years.

Health Personnel (3)

Total health expenditure as a percentage of GDP, 1990-1997[a]

Public sector . . . . .NA

Private sector . . . . .NA

Total[b] . . . . .NA

Health expenditure per capita in U.S. dollars, 1990-1997[a]

Purchasing power parity . . . . .NA

Total . . . . .NA

Availability of health care facilities per 100,000 people

Hospital beds 1990-1997[a] 170

Doctors 1993[c] 51

Nurses 1993[c] 64

Health Indicators (4)

Life expectancy at birth

1980 62

1997 58

Daily per capita supply of calories (1996) 2,252

Total fertility rate births per woman (1997) 4.7

Maternal mortality ratio per 100,000 live births (1990-97) . . . . .310[c]

Safe water % of population with access (1995) 77

Sanitation % of population with access (1995) 70

Consumption of iodized salt % of households (1992-98)[a] 10

Smoking prevalence

Male % of adults (1985-95)[a] 40

Female % of adults (1985-95)[a] 5

Tuberculosis incidence per 100,000 people (1997) 160

Adult HIV prevalence % of population ages 15-49 (1997) . . . .<0.005

Infants and Malnutrition (5)

Under-5 mortality rate (1997) 122

% of infants with low birthweight (1990-97) 15

Births attended by skilled health staff % of total[a] . . .54

% fully immunized (1995-97)

TB 97

DPT 92

Polio 92

Measles 98

Prevalence of child malnutrition under age 5 (1992-97)[b] . . . . .NA

Ethnic Division (6)

Arab 75%-80%

Kurdish 15%-20%

Turkoman, Assyrian or other 5%

Religions (7)

Muslim 97%

Shi'a 60%-65%

Sunni 32%-37%

Christian or other 3%

Languages (8)

Arabic, Kurdish (official in Kurdish regions), Assyrian, Armenian.

EDUCATION

Public Education Expenditures (9)

Public expenditure on education (% of GNP)

1980 . . . . .3.0

1996 . . . .

Expenditure per student

Primary % of GNP per capita

1980 . . . . .7.1

1996 . . . .

Secondary % of GNP per capita

1980 . . . . .6.5

1996 . . . .

Tertiary % of GNP per capita

1980 . . . . .87.8

1996 . . . .

Expenditure on teaching materials

Primary % of total for level (1996) . . . .

Secondary % of total for level (1996) . . . .

Primary pupil-teacher ratio per teacher (1996) . . . . .20[1]

Duration of primary education years (1995) 6

Educational Attainment (10)

Age group (1987) . . . . .10+

Total population 10,628,447

Highest level attained (%)

No schooling 52.8

First level

Not completed 21.6

Completed . . . . .NA

Entered second level

S-1 . . . . .11.6

S-2 . . . . .NA

Postsecondary 4.1

Literacy Rates (11A)

In thousands and percent[1]	1990	1995	2000	2010
Illiterate population (15+ yrs.)	4,808	4,848	4,982	5,007
Literacy rate - total adult pop. (%)	52.3	58.0	63.5	73.6
Literacy rate - males (%)	66.0	70.7	74.9	82.4
Literacy rate - females (%)	38.2	45.0	51.8	64.7

GOVERNMENT & LAW

Political Parties (12)

The legislative branch is a unicameral National Assembly (250 seats; 30 appointed by Saddam Hussein to represent the three northern provinces of Dahuk, Arbil, and As Sulaymaniyah; 220 elected by popular vote; members serve four-year terms). The Ba'th Party is the only party in Iraq.

Government Budget (13B)

Revenues . . . . .NA

Expenditures . . . . .NA

  Capital expenditures . . . . .NA

NA stands for not available.

Military Affairs (14B)

	1990	1991	1992	1993	1994	1995
Military expenditures						
Current dollars (mil.)[1]	14,110	8,776	NA	NA	NA	NA
1995 constant dollars (mil.)[1]	16,210	9,698	NA	NA	NA	NA
Armed forces (000)	1,390	475	407	407	425	390
Gross national product (GNP)						
Current dollars (mil.)	23,010	11,720	15,560	NA	NA	NA
1995 constant dollars (mil.)	26,440	12,960	16,740	NA	NA	NA
Central government expenditures (CGE)						
1995 constant dollars (mil.)	NA	NA	NA	NA	NA	NA
People (mil.)	18.4	17.9	18.5	19.2	19.9	20.6
Military expenditure as % of GNP	61.3	74.9	NA	NA	NA	NA
Military expenditure as % of CGE	NA	NA	NA	NA	NA	NA
Military expenditure per capita (1995 $)	880	541	NA	NA	NA	NA
Armed forces per 1,000 people (soldiers)	75.4	26.5	22.0	21.2	21.4	18.9
GNP per capita (1995 $)	1,435	723	907	NA	NA	NA
Arms imports[6]						
Current dollars (mil.)	2,900	0	0	0	0	0
1995 constant dollars (mil.)	3,333	0	0	0	0	0
Arms exports[6]						
Current dollars (mil.)	40	0	0	0	0	0
1995 constant dollars (mil.)	46	0	0	0	0	0
Total imports[7]						
Current dollars (mil.)	6,526	423	603	520	297	611[e]
1995 constant dollars (mil.)	7,499	467	648	545	305	611[e]
Total exports[7]						
Current dollars (mil.)	10,380[e]	468[e]	595[e]	NA	612[e]	1,000[e]
1995 constant dollars (mil.)	11,930[e]	517[e]	640[e]	NA	627[e]	1,000[e]
Arms as percent of total imports[8]	44.4	0	0	0	0	0
Arms as percent of total exports[8]	.4	0	0	NA	0	0

LABOR FORCE

Labor Force (16)

Total (million) 4.4

Services 48%

Agriculture 30%

Industry 22%

Severe labor shortage; expatriate labor force was about 1,600,000 (July 1990); since then, it has declined substantially. Data for 1989.

Unemployment Rate (17)

Rate not available.

PRODUCTION SECTOR

Electric Energy (18)

Capacity . . . . .6.83 million kW (1996)

Production . . . . .31.8 billion kWh (1996)

Consumption per capita . . . . . . .1,362 kWh (1996 est.)

Transportation (19)

Highways:

total: 47,400 km

paved: 40,764 km

unpaved: 6,636 km (1996 est.)

Waterways: 1,015 km; Shatt al Arab is usually navigable by maritime traffic for about 130 km; channel has been dredged to 3 meters and is in use; Tigris and Euphrates Rivers have navigable sections for shallow-draft watercraft; Shatt al Basrah canal was navigable by shallow-draft craft before closing in 1991 because of the Persian Gulf war

Pipelines: crude oil 4,350 km; petroleum products 725 km; natural gas 1,360 km

Merchant marine:

total: 35 ships (1,000 GRT or over) totaling 791,485 GRT/1,428,307 DWT ships by type: cargo 14, oil tanker 16, passenger 1, passenger-cargo 1, refrigerated cargo 1, roll-on/roll-off cargo 2 (1997 est.)

Airports: 111 (1997 est.)

Airports—with paved runways:

total: 76

over 3,047 m: 22

2,438 to 3,047 m: 33

1,524 to 2,437 m: 7

914 to 1,523 m: 7

under 914 m: 7 (1997 est.)

Airports—with unpaved runways:

total: 35

over 3,047 m: 3

2,438 to 3,047 m: 6

1,524 to 2,437 m: 4

914 to 1,523 m: 12

under 914 m: 10 (1997 est.)

Top Agricultural Products (20)

Wheat, barley, rice, vegetables, dates, other fruit, cotton; cattle, sheep.

MANUFACTURING SECTOR

GDP & Manufacturing Summary (21)

Detailed value added figures are listed by both International Standard Industry Code (ISIC) and product title.

	1980	1985	1990	1994
GDP ($-1990 mil.)[1]	98,479	73,401	64,898	19,529
Per capita ($-1990)[1]	7,571	4,792	3,590	980
Manufacturing share (%) (current prices)[1]	4.5	9.5	8.4	4.1
Manufacturing				
Value added ($-1990 mil.)[1]	6,983	7,445	5,735	1,753
Industrial production index	100	106	131	61
Value added ($ mil.)	2,070	3,676	3,623	606
Gross output ($ mil.)	5,155	7,162	7,560	1,387
Employment (000)	177	174	134	117
Profitability (% of gross output)				
Intermediate input (%)	60	49	36	56
Wages and salaries inc. supplements (%)	13	13	64	16
Gross operating surplus	27	39	−1	27
Productivity ($)				
Gross output per worker	29,100	41,091	6,611	11,707
Value added per worker	11,686	21,089	27,250	5,153
Average wage (inc. supplements)	3,700	5,242	3,552	1,933
Value added ($ mil.)				
311/2 Food products	183	396	306	59
313 Beverages	91	125	139	19
314 Tobacco products	108	140	125	7
321 Textiles	246	248	362	20
322 Wearing apparel	42	53	47	7
323 Leather and fur products	24	1	1	—
324 Footwear	18	81	70	22

	1980	1985	1990	1994
331 Wood and wood products	1	1	1	—
332 Furniture and fixtures	10	13	14	1
341 Paper and paper products	48	52	78	20
342 Printing and publishing	29	33	50	8
351 Industrial chemicals	67	151	167	79
352 Other chemical products	187	389	362	6
353 Petroleum refineries	405	868	836	127
354 Miscellaneous petroleum and coal products	27	40	56	19
355 Rubber products	5	10	11	4
356 Plastic products	11	33	28	10
361 Pottery, china and earthenware	1	1	1	—
362 Glass and glass products	21	35	31	4
369 Other non-metal mineral products	190	565	557	100
371 Iron and steel	7	20	17	24
372 Non-ferrous metals	—	—	—	—
381 Metal products	53	47	56	28
382 Non-electrical machinery	160	149	111	13
383 Electrical machinery	122	185	139	26
384 Transport equipment	15	40	56	3
385 Professional and scientific equipment	1	—	—	—
390 Other manufacturing industries	1	—	—	—

FINANCE, ECONOMICS, & TRADE

Economic Indicators (22)

National product: GDP—purchasing power parity—$42.8 billion (1997 est.)

National product real growth rate: 0% (1997 est.)

National product per capita: $2,000 (1997 est.)

Inflation rate—consumer price index: NA%

Exchange Rates (24)

Exchange rates:

Iraqi dinars (ID) per US$1

Fixed official rate since 1982 . . . . .0.3109

Black market rate

Iraqi dinars (ID) per US$1

December 1997 1,530

December 1995 3,000

Subject to wide fluctuations

Economic Aid (27)

Recipient: ODA, $NA. NA stands for not available.

Import Export Commodities (28)

Import Commodities	Export Commodities
Manufactures	Crude oil
Food	

Balance of Payments (23)

	1969	1970	1973	1975	1977
Exports of goods (f.o.b.)	NA	1,098	2,204	8,301	10,838
Imports of goods (f.o.b.)	NA	−459	−849	−4,162	−5,867
Trade balance	NA	639	1,355	4,139	4,971
Services - debits	NA	−679	−800	−1,712	−2,707
Services - credits	NA	143	256	543	761
Private transfers (net)	NA	1	1	1	NA
Government transfers (net)	NA	1	−11	−266	−35
Direct investments	NA	18	297	−436	−5
Short-term capital (net)	NA	−2	18	−2,041	−2
Errors and omissions	NA	−127	−254	−726	−510
Overall balance	NA	−6	663	−498	2,473

IRELAND

Éire

INTRODUCTORY SURVEY

RECENT HISTORY

The desire for independence from England grew until the Anglo-Irish Treaty was signed in 1921. The treaty did not give Ireland complete independence but did establish an Irish Free State with dominion status in the British Commonwealth. Dominion status gave Ireland more control over its affairs, but forced Ireland to accept the British monarch as its chief-of-state. The treaty also split Ireland along religious lines. Unlike the rest of Ireland, Protestant-dominated Northern Ireland remained a part of the United Kingdom. Violent opposition to dominion status and to a separate government in Northern Ireland precipitated a civil war that lasted almost a year (1922–23). Pro-treaty forces won the war, and the Irish Free State was officially proclaimed. In 1937 a new Irish constitution was enacted and the name of the country was officially changed to Ireland (Éire in Irish).

Dominion status proved to be short-lived, and in 1948 Ireland voted itself out of the Commonwealth of Nations. On 18 April 1949, it declared itself a republic. Ireland was admitted to the UN in 1955 and became a member of the European Community (EC) in 1973.

Even after independence, sentiment in favor of a reunified Irish Republic remained strong, represented at its extreme by the terrorist activities of the Irish Republican Army (IRA). During the civil violence that disrupted Northern Ireland from the late 1960s on, the Irish government attempted to curb the ''pro-visional wing'' of the IRA. This part of

IRELAND

0   25   50   75   100 Miles

0 25 50 75 100 Kilometers

NORTH
ATLANTIC
OCEAN

SCOTLAND

Letterkenny
Donegal
Donegal Bay
Sligo
Lough Conn
Castlebar
Lough Mask
Roscommon
Lough Corrib *Lough Ree*
Athlone
Galway
Galway Bay
Aran Is.
Cliffs of Moher
Ennis
Limerick
Tipperary
Tralee
Killarney
Dingle Bay
Carrauntuohill
3,414 ft.
1041 m.
Bantry
Bantry Bay

NORTHERN
IRELAND
(U.K.)

Finn
Monaghan
Carrick on Shannon
Longford
Drogheda
Dundalk
Boyne
Mullingar
Shannon
Tullamore
Naas
WICKLOW MTS.
Carlow
Kilkenny
Barrow
Clonmel
Suir
Waterford
Wexford
Blackwater
Blarney Castle
Lee
Cork

Irish Sea
Swords
Dublin
Dun Laoghaire
Wicklow
Arklow

Saint George's Channel

Celtic Sea

Ireland

the IRA tried to intimidate the government through ongoing bombings, assassinations, and other types of terrorist means, often using Ireland as a base for attacks in the north. Despite all government efforts, terrorist acts continued.

In 1997, Ireland's new prime minister, Bernie Ahern, revived the peace effort and resumed talks with the British government and with Sinn Fein leader Gerry Adams. In April 1998, the Irish Parliament approved a peace agreement that had been authorized by the leaders of Northern Ireland a month earlier. The accord was voted on simultaneously by the people of the Irish Republic and Northern Ireland in May 1998 and approved. The accord stated that the Irish Republic would give up its territorial claim to Northern Ireland.

On 15 August 1998, a car bomb exploded in Omagh, Northern Ireland, killing 28 and wounding

over 200. The bombing appeared to be conducted by a Roman Catholic splinter group opposed to the accord, and it raised doubts about the new peace agreement.

GOVERNMENT

Under the Irish constitution, legislative power is vested in the national parliament (Oireachtas), which consists of the president and two houses—House of Representatives (Dáil Éireann) and Senate (Seanad Éireann). The parliament sits in Dublin, the capital city. The president is elected by popular vote for seven years. The Dáil consists of 166 seats and the Seanad 60. Suffrage is universal at age 18.

Judiciary

Justice is administered by a Supreme Court, a high court with full original jurisdiction, and circuit and district courts with local and limited jurisdiction. Individual liberties are protected by the 1937 Constitution and by Supreme Court decisions.

Political parties

The major political parties are Fianna Fáil, Fine Gael, the Progressive Democrats, the Democratic Left, and the Labour Party.

Fianna Fáil, the Republican party, was in power for all but six years during the period from 1932 to 1973, when it lost its majority to a Fine Gael–Labour coalition. In recent years, both Fine Gael and Fianna Fáil have lost seats to the Labour Party, which is now the third largest political party in Ireland. Sinn Fein, the political arm of the Provisional IRA, ended its sixty-five-year boycott of the Dáil in 1986 and won a single seat in the 1997 elections. Fianna Fáil won 77 of the 166 seats in the 1997 elections.

DEFENSE

The army and its reserves, the air corps, and the naval service are small but well trained. The army (10,500 regulars, 15,000 reserves) is supplied with British and European weapons and equipment. A navy has 1,100 members, and the air force, another 1,100.

ECONOMIC AFFAIRS

Until the 1950s, Ireland had a predominantly agricultural economy. However, liberal trade policies and the drive for industrialization have stimulated economic expansion. Ireland's economic growth has been faster than any other European

Union (EU) nation. Unemployment, however, has remained high; the rate was 12–14% in 1996. Inflation was 2.8% in 1995. Today, Ireland is among the least developed countries in the EU. Ireland depends on the EU for substantial financial assistance.

Public Finance

Expenditures of local authorities are principally for health, roads, housing, and social welfare.

The U.S. CIA estimates that, in 1994, government revenues totaled approximately $19.3 billion and expenditures $20.3 billion.

The annual budget deficit has remained below 3% since 1989, which meets the Maastricht criteria for adopting a single European currency (the Euro) in 1999. Ireland still needs, however, to reduce its $43.8 billion debt burden from its current level of over 90% of GDP to the Maastricht mandated level of 60%. The debt has generally been financed by the sale of government securities and cost the government $3.3 billion a year in debt service, which is about 9% of exports and 7% of GNP.

Income

In 1998, Ireland's gross national product (GNP) was $67.5 billion, or about $18,340 per person. During 1985–95, the average annual real growth rate in the GNP per person was 5.2%, and the average annual inflation rate was 2.5%.

Industry

Today, the most important products of manufacturing are food, metal and engineering goods, electronics and data processing, engineering, chemicals and chemical products, nonmetallic minerals, and paper and printing.

Banking and Finance

In 1979, Ireland joined the European Monetary System, thus severing the 150-year-old tie with the British pound. The Central Bank of Ireland, established in 1942, is both the monetary authority and the bank of issue. Its role has expanded considerably, particularly in monetary policy.

The commercial banking sector is dominated by two main Irish-owned groups, the Bank of Ireland Group and the Allied Irish Banks Group. Foreign reserves minus gold totaled $8,630 million at end-year 1995. Wide-money supply (M3) was £26,520 million at the end of the first quarter of 1997.

The Irish Stock Exchange has its trading floor in Dublin. The Stock Exchange Act came into effect on 4 December 1995, and separated the Dublin Stock Exchange from the London Stock Exchange. Since that date, the Dublin Stock Exchange has been regulated by the Central Bank of Ireland.

Economic Development

Government policies are premised on private enterprise as a predominant factor in the economy. Specific economic programs adopted in recent decades have attempted to increase efficiency in agriculture and industry, stimulate new export industries, create employment opportunities for labor leaving the agricultural sector, and reduce unemployment and net emigration.

The 1987–90 Program for National Recovery is generally credited with creating the conditions to bring government spending and the national debt under control. The 1991–93 Program for Economic and Social Progress was to further reduce the national debt and budget deficit and to establish a schedule of wage increases.

A 1994–99 national development plan calls for investment of £20 billion and aims to achieve an average annual GDP growth rate of 3.5%. The government hopes to create 200,000 jobs through this plan, with funding by the state, the EC, and the private sector. Half of the money is earmarked for industry, transport, training, and energy.

SOCIAL WELFARE

Since April 1974, all wage and salary earners between the ages of 16 and 68 have been covered by a compulsory social insurance program, including unemployment insurance, disability benefits, retirement and old-age pensions, widows' pensions, maternity benefits, and a death grant.

The prominence of the Roman Catholic Church has had a significant impact on social legislation. Both divorce and abortion are illegal in Ireland. Contraceptives, the sale of which had been entirely prohibited, became available to married couples by prescription in the early 1980s; the need for a prescription was abolished in 1985. Also in 1985, the minimum age for marriage was raised from 14 to 18 for girls and from 16 to 18 for boys. Since then, Ireland's birth rate has plummeted and now is in line with those of most other European countries.

In 1990, the government established the Second Commission on the Status of Women, to help bring about the participation of women in all aspects of Irish society. Although the number of married women who hold paying jobs has increased in recent years, only a third of Irish women work outside the home.

Healthcare

Health services are provided by the Department of Health. A comprehensive health service, with free hospitalization, treatment, and medication, is provided for low-income groups. A somewhat reduced list of services is offered free to the rest of the population. There are about 2 physicians for every 1,000 people.

Infant mortality has been reduced from 50.3 per 1,000 live births in 1948 to 18 in 1972 and 5 in 1992. Tuberculosis, long a major cause of adult deaths, declined from 3,700 cases in 1947 to only 18 per 100,000 in 1990. Average life expectancy at birth in 1995 was 76 years.

Housing

Government subsidies are given to encourage home ownership, and local authorities provide housing for those unable to house themselves adequately. In 1992, over 20,600 new private dwellings were completed.

EDUCATION

Education is compulsory for nine years. In 1993, there were 391,998 pupils in 3,276 primary schools; 362,230 students were in secondary schools; 117,641 students were enrolled in higher level institutions. Ireland has two universities, the University of Dublin (Trinity College) and the National University of Ireland.

1999 KEY EVENTS TIMELINE

January

- New allegations of financial wrongdoing by EU commissioner Padraig Flynn add to scandals threatening the future of ruling Fianna Fail party.

- Ireland is one of eleven EU nations to adopt the euro as its currency.

February

- Legislative approval of North-South Ministerial Council to oversee cooperation in tourism and other areas is the latest step in the Northern Ireland peace process.

- Ulster Unionists and Sinn Fein hold the first bilateral talks to address IRA disarmament dispute.

- Televised statements by politician Padraig Flynn, in response to corruption allegations, embarrass the ruling Fianna Fail party and raise specter of a possible government collapse.

- Four Irish Republican Army members are sentenced to prison terms for role in a 1996 bank robbery.

March

- The deadline for the creation of a Northern Ireland assembly cabinet is moved back to April 1 pending agreement on decommissioning of the IRA.

- Anti-abortion protesters, including members of American abortion-rights group, occupy a family planning clinic in Dublin.

April

- The peace process stalls as talks fail to end the deadlock over IRA disarmament issue.

- A corporate tax rate cut is expected to strengthen Irish stocks.

May

- British prime minister Tony Blair sets a new June deadline for the next step in the implementation of the Northern Ireland peace agreement.

- The Ulster Unionist Party rejects the latest compromise measure by British and Irish governments.

June

- The impasse over Northern Ireland persists as the latest peace agreement deadline passes.

July

- Irish police detain three people in connection with the smuggling of arms from the U.S. to Northern Ireland by Catholic guerrillas.

- The number of unemployed falls below 100,000 for the first time in twenty years.

- The Irish government sells a 50.1 percent stake in Telecom Eireann.

- A U.N. study finds Ireland has one of highest illiteracy rates in the developed world.

- British and Irish prime ministers propose a new compromise plan for the Northern Ireland cabinet, but it is rejected by the Ulster Unionists.

August

- A British official rules that the IRA cease-fire is intact.

September

- The Irish government releases a Green Paper to encourage reasonable debate on the abortion issue.

- Former U.S. Senator George Mitchell returns to Belfast to lead a new attempt at salvaging the stalled Northern Ireland peace process.

November

- The IRA agrees to negotiate with the Northern Ireland disarmament commission in a show of support for the Good Friday Accords if a joint Catholic-Protestant administration for Northern Ireland was appointed.

ANALYSIS OF EVENTS: 1999

BUSINESS AND THE ECONOMY

In January 1999, Ireland became one of eleven European Union members—and the only English-speaking country—to adopt the euro, the new currency introduced to pave the way toward eventual economic union among EU nations. Like the other ten participating nations, Ireland would actually continue to issue its own currency until 2002, but its exchange rate would be pegged to the euro.

The year's most eagerly awaited Irish stock issue was probably the government's July sale of its 50.1 percent stake in Telecom Eireann, the state-operated telephone monopoly, which was expected to have the third-largest market capitalization of any stock traded in Dublin. The sale raised about 4.2 billion euros ($4.3 billion). A government reduction in the corporate tax rate in April was expected to strengthen Irish stocks even further.

The phenomenal economic success that Ireland—which is now being called "the Celtic Tiger"—had enjoyed for much of the 1990s continued through the final year of the decade. Economic growth, which has averaged over eight percent a year since 1993, remained strong. The nation's unemployment rate of 5.8 percent was about half the European Union average, and Irish unemployment fell below 100,000 for the first time

in twenty years. Ireland's high-tech industry, which has led the country's current economic boom, continued to prosper: 33 percent of all personal computers in Europe were manufactured in Ireland, and the nation was second only to the U.S. in software exports.

GOVERNMENT AND POLITICS

In spite of Ireland's flourishing economy and the optimism occasioned by the historic 1998 Northern Ireland peace agreement, the coalition government headed by Prime Minister Bertie Ahern and his conservative-nationalist Fianna Fail party was endangered by a series of scandals that unfolded throughout 1999. Although none of the scandals centered on Ahern personally, they reflected poorly on his party and lessened his government's chances of political survival until the constitutionally mandated general elections in 2002. Perhaps the most damaging were allegations of financial impropriety by Ahern's political mentor, former prime minister Charles Haughey. By the fall of 1999, four different tribunals were investigating corruption charges against Haughey and other politicians, including Ray Burke, a former foreign minister, and Padraig Flynn, a European Union commissioner posted in Brussels. Most of the charges involved alleged payoffs by businessmen in exchange for political favors.

In February legislators from Ireland and Northern Ireland voted to create a North-South Ministerial council to oversee cooperation between Ireland and Northern Ireland in tourism and other matters. After this point, however, the Northern Ireland peace process began to unravel. Progress toward implementation of the 1998 Good Friday peace agreement between leaders of Northern Ireland, Britain, and the Irish Republic was stalled for much of the year over the issue of decommissioning the Irish Republican Army (IRA). Under the terms of the agreement, a ten-member Protestant-Catholic cabinet, the Northern Ireland Executive, was to have been formed by March 10, heading a new provincial government and returning home rule to Northern Ireland for the first time since 1974. However, the Protestant Ulster Unionist Party headed by David Trimble insisted that Sinn Fein, the political wing of the IRA, not be allowed to assume its two seats in the cabinet until the IRA turned over its weapons. The IRA claimed that the 1998 peace agreement had not mandated disarmament as a precondition for forming the new government, and insisted that it was not required to disarm until 2000.

As the year progressed, the deadline for forming the Executive was pushed back repeatedly. As successive compromises were proposed and rejected, the impasse between the Unionists and Sinn Fein persisted through the summer. In September, former U.S. senator George Mitchell, who had been instrumental in brokering the original agreement, spearheaded a new effort to revive the faltering peace process. At the end of August, Marjorie Mowlam, the British secretary for Northern Ireland, found that the IRA had not violated the cease-fire the group had declared in July 1997. Such a finding was a precondition for Sinn Fein to continue its participation in peace talks and in the new Northern Ireland government. Protestant spokespersons condemned the finding, citing alleged IRA involvement in a plot, uncovered in July, to smuggle arms from the United States into Northern Ireland, as well as in the murder of a Catholic taxicab driver suspected of being a police informant.

CULTURE AND SOCIETY

At the end of the 1990s, after years of an economic boom spearheaded by high-tech industries, many Irish were enjoying a level of optimism and well-being not normally associated with this traditionally poor country. Instead of emigrating, young people were able to find jobs at home: in 1999, 60 percent of Ireland's population was under 44 years old; 41 percent was younger than 24. The capital city of Dublin had become a chic, cosmopolitan population center that drew young people from all over Europe to its pubs and coffee bars.

Even in the midst of unprecedented change, however, traditional cultural legacies and battles persisted, including the debate over abortion in this heavily Catholic society. Two separate events in 1999 refocused attention on the issue, recalling the heated national debate of 1992, when voters had rejected proposed changes to the nation's abortion law and a judge had upheld the right of a pregnant schoolgirl to seek an abortion outside the country. In March, members of Ireland's most hard-line anti-abortion group, Youth Defense, joined by protesters from the American Christian Defense Coalition, broke into and occupied the office of a family planning clinic in Dublin, forcing the clinic to close temporarily. (The clinic did not actually perform abortions, which are illegal in Ireland unless the

mother's life is in danger.) The following week, an Irish court issued an injunction barring both groups from further picketing or protesting at the site. In September the government issued a Green Paper outlining seven possible positions on abortion and inviting public discussion of the issue.

Another social struggle that was highlighted in 1999 was the battle against illiteracy. A report issued by the United Nations found that 23 percent of Irish adults are functionally illiterate—one of the highest illiteracy rates in the developed world. The long-standing problem was closely linked to the nation's traditional poverty, which kept class sizes large and made it necessary for many youths to leave school and begin working before their education was complete. Although the government operated literacy programs in Dublin and elsewhere in the country, a spokesperson said that many more would need to be launched to truly address the magnitude of the problem.

DIRECTORY

CENTRAL GOVERNMENT
Head of State

President
Mary McAleese, Office of the President

Head of State

Taoiseach (Prime Minister)
Bertie Ahern, Office of the Taoiseach

Ministers

Minister for Marine and Natural Resources
Michael Woods, Ministry of Marine and Natural Resources, Leeson Lane, Dublin 2, Ireland
PHONE: +353 (1) 6199200
E-MAIL: minister@marine.irlgov.ie

Minister of Foreign Affairs
David Andrews, Ministry of Foreign Affairs, 80 St. Stephen Green, Dublin 2, Ireland
E-MAIL: library1@iveagh.irlgov.ie

Minister of Public Enterprise
Mary O'Rourke, Department of Public Enterprise, Kildare Street, Dublin 2, Ireland
PHONE: +353 (1) 6312121
FAX: +353 (1) 6312827
E-MAIL: Webmaster@entemp.irlgov.ie

Minister of Defense
Michael Smith, Ministry of Defense
E-MAIL: defence@iol.ie

Minister of Agriculture and Food
Joe Walsh, Ministry of Agriculture and Food, Kildare Street, Dublin 2, Ireland
PHONE: +353 (1) 6072000
E-MAIL: information@daff.irlgov.ie

Minister of Finance
Charlie McCreevey, Ministry of Finance, Upper Merrion Street, Dublin 2, Ireland
PHONE: +353 (1) 676571
FAX: +353 (1) 6789936
E-MAIL: wemaster@finance.irlgov.ie

Minister of Health and Children
Brian Cowen, Ministry of Health and Children, Hawkins Street, Dublin 2, Ireland
PHONE: +353 (1) 6714711
FAX: +353 (1) 6711947

Minister of the Environment and Local Government
Noel Dempsey, Ministry of the Environment and Local Government, Custom House, Dublin 1, Ireland
PHONE: +353 (1) 8882000
FAX: +353 (1) 8788640
E-MAIL: minister@environ.irlgov.ie

Minister of Social, Community and Family Affairs
Dermot Ahern, Ministry of Social, Community and Family Affairs, Store Street, Dublin 1, Ireland
PHONE: +353 (1) 6797777
E-MAIL: webweaver@welfare.eirmail400.ie

Minister of Arts, Heritage, Gaeltacht and the Islands
Sile de Valera, Ministry of Arts, Heritage, Gaeltacht and the Islands, Dun Aimhirgin, 43-49 Mespil Road, Dublin 4, Ireland
PHONE: +353 (1) 6473000
FAX: +353 (1) 6670826
E-MAIL: eolas@ealga.irlgov.ie

Minister of Justice, Equality and Law Reform
John O'Donoghue, Ministry of Justice, Equality and Law Reform, 72-76 St. Stephens Green, Dublin 2, Ireland
PHONE: +353 (1) 6028202
FAX: +353 (1) 6615461
E-MAIL: pagemaster@justice.irlgov.ie

Minister of Tourism, Sport and Recreation
Jim McDaid, Ministry of Tourism, Sport and Recreation

Minister of Education and Science
Micheál Martin, Ministry of Education and Science, Marlborough Street, Dublin 1, Ireland
PHONE: +353 (1) 8734700

FAX: +353 (1) 8786712

POLITICAL ORGANIZATIONS
Fianna Fáil
13 Upper Mount Street, Dublin 2, Ireland
PHONE: +353 (1) 6761551; 6613415
FAX: +353 (1) 6785690
NAME: Bertie Ahern

The Labour Party
17 Ely Place, Dublin 2, Ireland
PHONE: +353 (1) 6612615
FAX: +353 (1) 6612640
E-MAIL: ruairi_quinn@oireachtas.irlgov.ie
NAME: Ruairi Quinn

Fine Gael
51 Upper Mount Street, Dublin 2, Ireland
PHONE: +353 (1) 6198444
FAX: +353 (1) 6625046; 6627648
E-MAIL: finegael@finegael.com
NAME: John Bruton

Communist Party of Ireland
NAME: Michael O'Riordan

Sinn Féin
51/55 Falls Road, Belfast, Northern Ireland
PHONE: +44 (1232) 624421
FAX: +44 (1232) 622112
E-MAIL: sinnfein@iol.ie
NAME: Gerry Adams

Progressive Democrats
25 South Frederick Street, Dublin 2, Ireland
PHONE: +353 (1) 6794399
FAX: +353 (1) 6794757
E-MAIL: jackm@iol.ie
NAME: Mary Harney

The Workers' Party
NAME: Marion Donnelly

The Socialist Party
PHONE: +353 (1) 6772686
E-MAIL: dublinsp@clubi.ie
NAME: Joe Higgins

Green Alliance
5a Upper Fownes Street, Temple Bar, Dublin 2, Ireland
PHONE: +353 (1) 6790012
FAX: +353 (1) 6797168
E-MAIL: greenpar@iol.ie

NAME: Patricia Howard

DIPLOMATIC REPRESENTATION
Embassies in Ireland

Australia
Second Floor, Fitzwilton House, Wilton Terrace, Dublin 2, Ireland
PHONE: +353 (1) 6761517
FAX: +353 (1) 6785185
E-MAIL: austremb.dublin@dfat.gov.au

Belgium
Shrewsbury House, Shrewsbury Road, Ballsbridge, Dublin 4, Ireland
PHONE: +353 (1) 2692082
FAX: +353 (1) 2838488

France
36 Ailesbury Road, Ballsbridge, Dublin 4, Ireland
PHONE: +353 (1) 2601666
FAX: +353 (1) 2830178
E-MAIL: consul@ambafrance.ie

Israel
Carrisbrook House, 122 Pembroke Road, Dublin 4, Ireland
PHONE: +353 (1) 6680303
FAX: +353 (1) 6680418
E-MAIL: embisrael@iol.ie

Italy
63 Northumberland Road, Dublin, Ireland
PHONE: +353 (1) 6601744
FAX: +353 (1) 6682759
E-MAIL: italianembassy@tinet.ie

Netherlands
160 Merrion Road, Dublin 4, Ireland
PHONE: +353 (1) 2693444
FAX: +353 (1) 2839690
E-MAIL: nethemb@indigo.ie

New Zealand
46 Upper Mount Street, Dublin 2, Ireland
PHONE: +353 (1) 6762464
FAX: +353 (1) 6762489

Russia
186 Orwell Road, Rathgar, Dublin, Ireland
PHONE: +353 (1) 4923525; 4922048
FAX: +353 (1) 4923525

United Kingdom
29 Merrion Road Ballsbridge, Dublin 4, Ireland
PHONE: +353 (1) 2053700; 2053757

FAX: +353 (1) 2053885

JUDICIAL SYSTEM
Supreme Court
Four Courts, Inns Quay, Dublin 7, Ireland
PHONE: +353 (1) 8886000
E-MAIL: courtsinfo@justice.ie

FURTHER READING
Articles

"Angela's Offspring." *The Economist* (February 27, 1999): 83

Clarity, James F. "In the Land of Joyce and Yeats, a Struggle to Read A B C's." *The New York Times International*, 24 July 1999, p. A5.

———. "Unabashed Politician's Statements Jeopardize Irish Government." *The New York Times*, 14 February 1999, p. 9.

"Honey Pot." *The Economist* (August 28, 1999): 39.

"The Luck of the Irish." *Fortune* (October 25, 1999): 194.

Martin, Neil A. "Celtic Tiger Burning Bright, Ireland Won't Follow Asia's Script." *Barron's* (1 March 1999): MW8.

"Northern Ireland: Mitchell 'Hopeful'." *The New York Times*, 24 September 1999, p. A8.

Pesek, William. "Will Labor Woes Snare Ireland's Economic Leprechaun?" *Barron's* (11 October 1999): MW10.

"Teflon Taoiseach." *The Economist* (16 October 1999): 53.

"The Whiff of Something Fishy." *The Economist* (30 January 1999): 46.

Books

Douglas, Roy, Liam Harte, and Jim O'Hara. *Ireland Since 1690: A Concise History.* Belfast: Blackstaff, 1999.

MacCarthy-Morrogh, Michael. *The Irish Century: A Photographic History of the Last Hundred Years.* Boulder, Colo.: Roberts Rinehart Publishers, 1998.

Townshend, Charles. *Ireland: The 20th Century.* New York: Oxford University Press, 1999.

IRELAND: STATISTICAL DATA

For sources and notes see "Sources of Statistics" in the front of each volume.

GEOGRAPHY

Geography (1)

Area:

Total: 70,280 sq km.

Land: 68,890 sq km.

Water: 1,390 sq km.

Area—comparative: slightly larger than West Virginia.

Land boundaries:

Total: 360 km.

Border countries: UK 360 km.

Coastline: 1,448 km.

Climate: temperate maritime; modified by North Atlantic Current; mild winters, cool summers; consistently humid; overcast about half the time.

Terrain: mostly level to rolling interior plain surrounded by rugged hills and low mountains; sea cliffs on west coast.

Natural resources: zinc, lead, natural gas, barite, copper, gypsum, limestone, dolomite, peat, silver.

Land use:

Arable land: 13%

Permanent crops: 0%

Permanent pastures: 68%

Forests and woodland: 5%

Other: 14% (1993 est.).

HUMAN FACTORS

Demographics (2A)

	1990	1995	1998	2000	2010	2020	2030	2040	2050
Population	3,508.2	3,583.9	3,619.5	3,647.3	3,809.9	3,909.7	3,892.7	3,791.7	3,599.7
Net migration rate (per 1,000 population)	NA	NA	NA	NA	NA	NA	NA	NA	NA
Births	NA	NA	NA	NA	NA	NA	NA	NA	NA
Deaths	31.9	NA	NA	NA	NA	NA	NA	NA	NA
Life expectancy - males	71.7	72.8	73.4	73.8	75.6	77.0	78.1	79.0	79.7
Life expectancy - females	77.5	78.4	79.1	79.5	81.4	82.9	84.1	85.0	85.7
Birth rate (per 1,000)	15.1	13.5	13.5	13.7	12.7	9.6	8.3	7.9	6.7
Death rate (per 1,000)	9.1	8.8	8.5	8.4	8.0	8.5	9.9	11.6	13.5
Women of reproductive age (15-49 yrs.)	850.8	924.8	951.6	961.6	961.0	945.2	860.5	759.6	684.6
of which are currently married	NA	NA	NA	NA	NA	NA	NA	NA	NA
Fertility rate	2.1	1.9	1.8	1.8	1.6	1.5	1.4	1.3	1.3

Except as noted, values for vital statistics are in thousands; life expectancy is in years.

Health Personnel (3)

Total health expenditure as a percentage of GDP, 1990-1997[a]

Public sector 5.1

Private sector 1.7

Total[b] 6.7

Health expenditure per capita in U.S. dollars, 1990-1997[a]

Purchasing power parity 1,331

Total 1,337

Availability of health care facilities per 100,000 people

Hospital beds 1990-1997[a] 500

Doctors 1993[c] 167

Nurses 1993[c] . . . . .NA

Health Indicators (4)

Life expectancy at birth

1980 73

1997 76

Daily per capita supply of calories (1996) 3,636

Total fertility rate births per woman (1997) 1.9

Maternal mortality ratio per 100,000 live births (1990-97) . . . . .10[c]

Safe water % of population with access (1995) . . . .

Sanitation % of population with access (1995) . . . .

Consumption of iodized salt % of households (1992-98)[a] . . . .

Smoking prevalence

Male % of adults (1985-95)[a] 29

Female % of adults (1985-95)[a] 28

Tuberculosis incidence per 100,000 people (1997) 21

Adult HIV prevalence % of population ages 15-49 (1997) 0.09

Infants and Malnutrition (5)

Under-5 mortality rate (1997) 7

% of infants with low birthweight (1990-97) 4

Births attended by skilled health staff % of total[a] . . .NA

% fully immunized (1995-97)

TB . . . . .NA

DPT . . . . .NA

Polio 63

Measles . . . . .NA

Prevalence of child malnutrition under age 5 (1992-97)[b] . . . . .NA

Ethnic Division (6)

Celtic, English.

Religions (7)

Roman Catholic 93%

Anglican 3%

None 1%

Unknown 2%

Other 1% (1981)

Languages (8)

Irish (Gaelic), spoken mainly in areas located along the western seaboard, English is the language generally used.

EDUCATION

Public Education Expenditures (9)

Public expenditure on education (% of GNP)

1980 . . . . .6.3

1996 . . . . .5.8

Expenditure per student

Primary % of GNP per capita

1980 . . . . .11.6

1996 . . . . .14.4[1]

Secondary % of GNP per capita

1980 . . . . .24.3

1996 . . . . .22.3[1]

Tertiary % of GNP per capita

1980 . . . . .60.0

1996 . . . . .36.5

Expenditure on teaching materials

Primary % of total for level (1996) 0.3

Secondary % of total for level (1996) . . . .

Primary pupil-teacher ratio per teacher (1996) . . . . .23[1]

Duration of primary education years (1995) 6

Educational Attainment (10)

Age group (1991) . . . . .25+

Total population .1,983,547

Highest level attained (%)

No schooling 0.0

First level

Not completed 0.0

Completed 38.5

Entered second level

S-1 . . . . .43.7

S-2 . . . . .NA

Postsecondary 14.6

GOVERNMENT & LAW

Political Parties (12)

House of Representatives	No. of seats
Fianna Fail	77
Fine Gael	54
Labor Party	17
Progressive Democrats	4
Democratic Left	4
Greens	2
Sinn Fein	1
Independents	7

Government Budget (13A)

Year: 1995

Total Expenditures: 15,319 Millions of Pounds

Expenditures as a percentage of the total by function:

General public services and public order 8.36
Defense 2.84
Education 13.17
Health 15.25
Social Security and Welfare 28.09
Housing and community amenities 2.74
Recreational, cultural, and religious affairs ..... .54
Fuel and energy .... .71

Continued on next page.

Military Affairs (14B)

	1990	1991	1992	1993	1994	1995
Military expenditures						
Current dollars (mil.)	538	599	622	570	639	689
1995 constant dollars (mil.)	618	662	669	597	655	689
Armed forces (000)	13	13	13	13	17	13
Gross national product (GNP)						
Current dollars (mil.)	35,900	39,080	41,910	44,420	48,150	54,450[e]
1995 constant dollars (mil.)	41,250	43,190	45,080	46,570	49,360	54,450[e]
Central government expenditures (CGE)						
1995 constant dollars (mil.)	18,670	19,340	21,130	18,150	19,340	20,330
People (mil.)	3.5	3.5	3.5	3.6	3.6	3.6
Military expenditure as % of GNP	1.5	1.5	1.5	1.3	1.3	1.3
Military expenditure as % of CGE	3.3	3.4	3.2	3.3	3.4	3.4
Military expenditure per capita (1995 $)	176	187	188	168	183	193
Armed forces per 1,000 people (soldiers)	3.7	3.7	3.7	3.6	4.8	3.6
GNP per capita (1995 $)	11,760	12,240	12,700	13,070	13,830	15,250
Arms imports[6]						
Current dollars (mil.)	5	10	5	0	60	0
1995 constant dollars (mil.)	6	11	5	0	62	0
Arms exports[6]						
Current dollars (mil.)	0	10	0	0	0	0
1995 constant dollars (mil.)	0	11	0	0	0	0
Total imports[7]						
Current dollars (mil.)	20,670	20,770	22,480	21,390	25,510	32,570
1995 constant dollars (mil.)	23,750	22,950	24,180	22,420	26,150	32,570
Total exports[7]						
Current dollars (mil.)	23,740	24,220	28,330	28,610	34,370	44,190
1995 constant dollars (mil.)	27,290	26,770	30,470	29,990	35,230	44,190
Arms as percent of total imports[8]	0	0	0	0	.2	0
Arms as percent of total exports[8]	0	0	0	0	0	0

Government Budget (13A) cont.

Agriculture, forestry, fishing, and hunting 3.99

Mining, manufacturing, and construction 3.31

Transportation and communication 3.50

Other economic affairs and services 2.75

Crime (15)

Crime rate (for 1997)

Crimes reported 90,900

Total persons convicted 39,100

Crimes per 100,000 population 2,600

Persons responsible for offenses

Total number of suspects 5,200

Total number of female suspects 425

Total number of juvenile suspects 475

LABOR FORCE

Labor Force (16)

Total (million) 1.52

Services 62.1%

Manufacturing and construction 27.0%

Agriculture, forestry, fishing 10.0%

Utilities 0.9%

Data for 1997 est. Percent distribution for 1996 est.

Unemployment Rate (17)

11.8% (1997)

PRODUCTION SECTOR

Electric Energy (18)

Capacity . . . . .3.62 million kW (1995)

Production . . . . .16.586 billion kWh (1995)

Consumption per capita . . . . .4,672 kWh (1995)

Transportation (19)

Highways:

total: 92,500 km

paved: 87,042 km (including 80 km of expressways)

unpaved: 5,458 km (1996 est.)

Waterways: limited for commercial traffic

Pipelines: natural gas 225 km

Merchant marine:

total: 39 ships (1,000 GRT or over) totaling 116,059 GRT/149,149 DWT ships by type: bulk 1, cargo 30, chemical tanker 1, container 3, oil tanker 2, short-sea passenger 2 (1997 est.)

Airports: 44 (1997 est.)

Airports—with paved runways:

total: 15

over 3,047 m: 1

2,438 to 3,047 m: 1

1,524 to 2,437 m: 3

914 to 1,523 m: 3

under 914 m: 7 (1997 est.)

Airports—with unpaved runways:

total: 29

914 to 1,523 m: 4

under 914 m: 25 (1997 est.)

Top Agricultural Products (20)

Turnips, barley, potatoes, sugar beets, wheat; meat and dairy products.

MANUFACTURING SECTOR

GDP & Manufacturing Summary (21)

Detailed value added figures are listed by both International Standard Industry Code (ISIC) and product title.

	1980	1985	1990	1994
GDP ($-1990 mil.)[1]	31,322	35,523	44,930	52,691
Per capita ($-1990)[1]	9,210	10,001	12,826	14,889
Manufacturing share (%) (current prices)[1]	25.5	27.3	30.8	29.1
Manufacturing				
Value added ($-1990 mil.)[1]	7,339	9,323	11,445	14,510
Industrial production index	100	116	168	226
Value added ($ mil.)	5,700	5,995	15,013	20,101
Gross output ($ mil.)	15,905	15,394	33,527	42,642
Employment (000)	225	186	194	209
Profitability (% of gross output)				
Intermediate input (%)	64	61	55	52
Wages and salaries inc. supplements (%)	17	14	14	13
Gross operating surplus	19	25	31	34
Productivity ($)				
Gross output per worker	70,084	82,216	172,604	201,607

	1980	1985	1990	1994
Value added per worker	25,118	32,017	77,289	100,050
Average wage (inc. supplements)	11,907	11,606	23,773	26,817
Value added ($ mil.)				
311/2 Food products	1,264	1,194	3,068	4,331
313 Beverages	325	331	792	1,004
314 Tobacco products	83	83	166	189
321 Textiles	266	181	349	375
322 Wearing apparel	147	118	207	171
323 Leather and fur products	28	12	21	16
324 Footwear	42	22	19	12
331 Wood and wood products	93	66	170	210
332 Furniture and fixtures	59	40	86	105
341 Paper and paper products	105	75	190	215
342 Printing and publishing	265	219	561	695
351 Industrial chemicals	236	315	757	1,154
352 Other chemical products	536	715	1,718	2,701
353 Petroleum refineries	22	15	30	32
354 Miscellaneous petroleum and coal products	—	—	—	—
355 Rubber products	52	58	118	150
356 Plastic products	113	125	332	478
361 Pottery, china and earthenware	28	13	28	30
362 Glass and glass products	109	113	144	195
369 Other non-metal mineral products	322	206	560	653
371 Iron and steel	31	37	92	102
372 Non-ferrous metals	15	8	10	5
381 Metal products	335	216	469	504
382 Non-electrical machinery	449	854	2,235	2,644
383 Electrical machinery	337	512	1,840	2,876
384 Transport equipment	190	116	309	287
385 Professional and scientific equipment	168	261	611	833
390 Other manufacturing industries	79	39	132	132

FINANCE, ECONOMICS, & TRADE

Economic Indicators (22)

National product: GDP—purchasing power parity—$59.9 billion (1997 est.)

National product real growth rate: 6% (1997 est.)

National product per capita: $18,600 (1997 est.)

Inflation rate—consumer price index: 1.6% (1997)

Balance of Payments (23)

	1992	1993	1994	1995	1996
Exports of goods (f.o.b.)	28,107	28,728	33,642	44,423	48,500
Imports of goods (f.o.b.)	−21,062	−20,553	−24,275	−30,866	−33,306
Trade balance	7,045	8,175	9,366	13,557	15,194
Services - debits	−15,911	−14,876	−17,371	−23,738	−27,115
Services - credits	7,336	6,549	7,832	10,127	11,142
Private transfers (net)	528	472	276	250	41
Government transfers (net)	1,609	1,445	1,474	1,526	2,144
Overall balance	607	1,766	1,577	1,721	1,406

Exchange Rates (24)

Exchange rates:

Irish pounds £ per US$1

January 1997	.0.7233
1997	.0.6588
1996	.0.6248
1995	.0.6235
1994	.0.6676
1993	.0.6816

Top Import Origins (25)

$44.9 billion (c.i.f., 1997)

Origins	%
European Union	.52
UK	.29
Germany	.10.2
France	.4
United States	.12

Top Export Destinations (26)

$54.8 billion (f.o.b., 1997).

Destinations	%
European Union	.66
UK	.22
Germany	.13
France	.8
United States	.6

Economic Aid (27)

Donor: ODA, $81 million (1993).

Import Export Commodities (28)

Import Commodities	Export Commodities
Food	Chemicals
Animal feed	Data processing equipment
Data processing equipment	Industrial machinery
Petroleum and petroleum products	Live animals
Machinery	Animal products
Textiles	
Clothing	

ISRAEL

State of Israel
Arabic—*Dawlat Israel*
Hebrew—*Medinat Yisrael*

INTRODUCTORY SURVEY

RECENT HISTORY

After World War II (1939–45), several nations began to support the establishment of a Jewish state as a haven for the survivors of the Nazi Holocaust. The British government finally decided to give up their rule over Palestine. On 29 November 1947, the UN General Assembly adopted a plan for the division of Palestine into two economically united but politically independent states, one Jewish and the other Arab.

The Arabs of Palestine at once rose up against this division. The Jews accepted the plan. On 14 May 1948, they proclaimed the formation of the State of Israel. The next day, the Arab League states—Egypt, Iraq, Jordan, Lebanon, Sa'udi Arabia, and Syria—launched a joint armed attack. Hundreds of thousands of Palestinian Arabs fled abroad.

The war left Israel in possession of a much larger territory than that awarded the Jews under the UN plan. The Arab state failed to take shape, as Jordan annexed the West Bank. Meanwhile, Palestinian refugees were resettled in camps on both banks of the Jordan River, in the Gaza Strip, in southern Lebanon, and in Syria.

Arabs periodically raided the borders, and the Israelis fought back. Tensions rose as Arab countries declared economic boycotts and Egypt nationalized the Suez Canal on 26 July 1956. On 29 October 1956, Israel (with British and French support) invaded Egypt and gained control of the Gaza

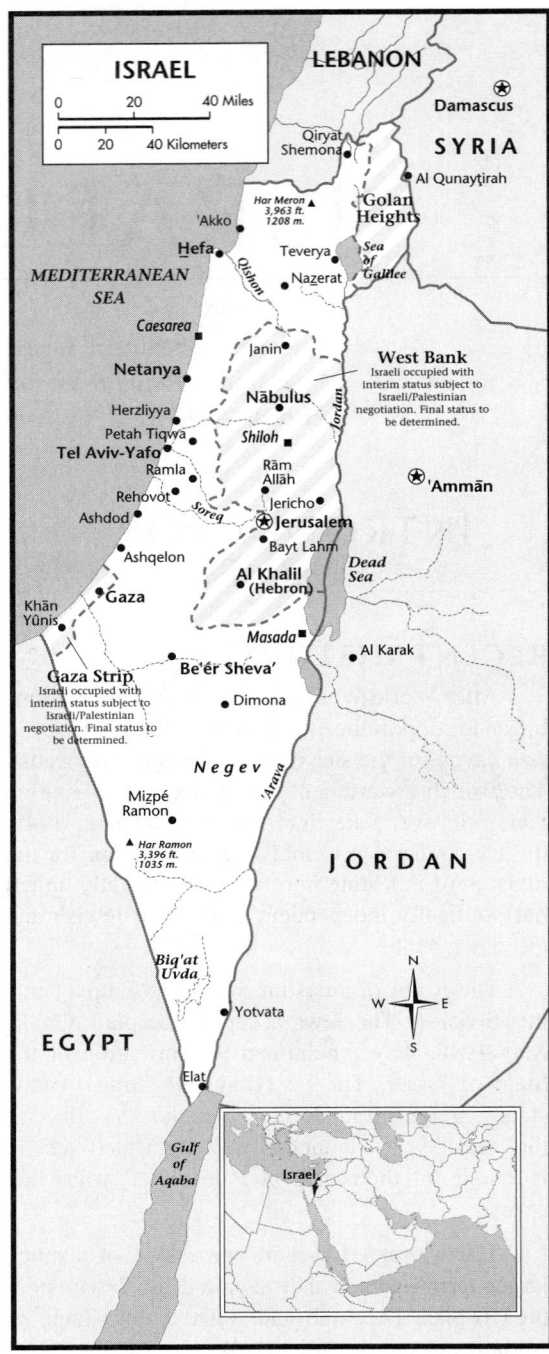

ISRAEL

0   20   40 Miles

0   20   40 Kilometers

LEBANON

Damascus

SYRIA

Qiryat
Shemona

Al Qunayṭirah

Har Meron
3,963 ft.
1,208 m.

Golan
Heights

'Akko

Hefa

Teverya

Sea
of
Galilee

MEDITERRANEAN
SEA

Nazerat

Caesarea

Janin

Netanya

Nābulus

West Bank
Israeli occupied with
interim status subject to
Israeli/Palestinian
negotiation. Final status to
be determined.

Herzliyya

Shiloh

Petah Tiqwa

Tel Aviv-Yafo

Ramla

Rām
Allāh

Rehovot

Jericho

'Ammān

Ashdod

Jerusalem

Bayt Lahm

Ashqelon

Dead
Sea

Al Khalil
(Hebron)

Khān
Yūnis

Gaza

Masada

Al Karak

Be'ér Sheva'

Gaza Strip
Israeli occupied with
interim status subject to
Israeli/Palestinian
negotiation. Final status to
be determined.

Dimona

Negev

Mizpé
Ramon

Har Ramon
3,396 ft.
1,035 m.

JORDAN

Biq'at
Uvda

N
W   E
S

Yotvata

EGYPT

Elat

Gulf
of
Aqaba

Israel

scored a decisive victory in the conflict, since termed the Six-Day War. Israel took control of the Sinai Peninsula, the Gaza Strip, the Golan Heights, and the West Bank (including Jordanian-ruled East Jerusalem).

The UN Security Council unanimously adopted Resolution 242, calling for withdrawal of Israeli armed forces from territories occupied during the war. Israel said that return of the captured territories would have to be part of a general agreement guaranteeing peace. In 1967, the Israeli government began Jewish settlement in these areas. By 1994, there were some 120,000 settlers in the occupied territories.

In 1969, the government of neighboring Lebanon signed an agreement with the organization made up of Palestinian guerrillas known as the Palestine Liberation Organization (PLO). Lebanon agreed to allow the PLO to operate within its borders. A cease-fire between Israel and the PLO took effect in August 1970, but the PLO continued an international campaign of terrorism, highlighted in September 1972 by the kidnap and murder of Israeli athletes at the Olympic Games in Munich, Germany.

On 6 October 1973, during the Jewish high holiday of Yom Kippur, Egypt and Syria attacked Israeli-held territory in the Sinai Peninsula and the Golan Heights at the same time. The Arabs won initial victories, but by 24 October, when a UN cease-fire took effect, the Israelis had beaten back their attackers. Although victorious, Israel gave up some territory in the Sinai in return for concessions from Egypt.

The thirty-year cycle of Egyptian-Israeli hostilities was broken in September 1978. Israeli Prime Minister Menachem Begin and Egyptian President Anwar al-Sadat agreed on the general framework for a peace treaty, which they signed in Washington, D.C., on 26 March 1979. However, the two countries failed to reach agreement on Palestinian self-rule in the West Bank and the Gaza Strip, and Israel continued to establish Jewish settlements in the West Bank despite Egyptian protests.

Other Arab countries condemned Egypt for signing the peace accord, and their relations with Israel remained tense. Hostilities between Israel and the PLO and Syria reached a climax in early June 1982. Israel launched a full-scale invasion of southern Lebanon, aimed at destroying bases from

Strip and the Sinai Peninsula. Fighting ended on 4 November, and Israel (under pressure from the United States) withdrew from the occupied areas in March 1957.

Violations of the truce by both sides continued, and on 5 June 1967, Israel attacked Egypt and its allies, Syria and Jordan. By 11 June, Israel had

which the PLO had shelled northern Israel and initiated terrorist attacks. A negotiated ceasefire was arranged by U.S. envoy Philip Habib on 25 June, and a multinational peacekeeping force was stationed in the Beirut area.

Israeli feelings about the Lebanese war were divided. Ariel Sharon resigned as defense minister. In 1985, Israel withdrew from southern Lebanon. In December 1987, unarmed Palestinians in Gaza began what became a long series of stone-throwing riots against Israeli troops in the occupied territories. In this uprising (or *intifada* in Arabic), over 1,000 Palestinians were killed as well as several hundred Israelis and Palestinian collaborators.

During the Gulf War of 1991, Israel was hit by Iraqi missile attacks, convincing some Israelis of the need to move toward peace with the Arabs. Israeli and Palestinian representatives met secretly in Oslo, Norway to work out a peace agreement involving the transfer of authority in the Gaza Strip and the West Bank city of Jericho to interim Palestinian rule. The final form of Palestinian independence was to be resolved in five years. The agreement was signed at the White House in Washington, D.C., on 13 September 1993.

The agreement was opposed by extremists on both sides and was set back by a massacre of thirty Muslims at prayer in the Al Khalil (Hebron) mosque on 25 February 1994 by a militant Israeli settler. Finally, delayed by several months, the withdrawal of Israeli forces and establishment of Palestinian self-rule in Gaza and Jericho took place on 18 May 1994. By 1997, six West Bank cities had been turned over to Palestinian control.

On 24 September 1995, Israel and the PLO reached a further agreement that would transfer control of much of the rest of the occupied West Bank to its Arab residents. In November 1995, a militant Israeli assassinated Prime Minister Yitzhak Rabin in retaliation for slowing Jewish settlement in the occupied territories. Rabin's assassination created political uncertainty in Israel and was a setback to the peace process.

In May 1996, Benjamin Netanyahu won Israel's first direct election for the office of prime minister. He immediately took a tougher stance on the occupied territories, increasing the construction of Jewish settlements. This action angered Palestinians. In 1997, Netanyahu was involved in an influence-peddling scandal, but no charges were filed.

In March 1998, Israel officially recognized the 1978 UN resolution calling for it to withdraw its military forces from Lebanon. The government, however, indicated that it would leave only when Lebanon was able to maintain its own security.

In May 1999, Labor Party leader Ehud Barak defeated Likud Party Prime Minister Benjamin Netanyahu. The election was widely seen as a public rejection of the policies of Netanyahu who was widely blamed for having stalled the peace process.

GOVERNMENT

Israel is a democratic republic, with no written constitution. Legislative power resides in the single-chamber Knesset (parliament), whose 120 members are elected for 4-year terms by secret vote of all citizens 18 years of age and over. The head of state is the president, who performs ceremonial duties. In 1996, a new law went into effect that allowed voters to directly elect the prime minister. The cabinet, headed by the prime minister, is collectively responsible to the Knesset.

Judiciary

Magistrates' courts in all towns are the first to hear most cases and settle petty property claims and lesser criminal charges. Three district courts, serving mainly as courts of appeal, have jurisdiction over all other actions except marriage and divorce cases. These are heard, along with other personal and religious matters, in the religious courts of the Jewish (rabbinical), Muslim (Shari'ah), Druze, and Christian communities. The eleven-member Supreme Court is the court of last appeal. There is no jury system.

Political Parties

Israel's multiparty system reflects the diverse origins of the people and their long practice of party politics in Zionist organizations. The Mapai (Israel Workers Party) led the first coalition governments to rule Israel after independence. It also formed the nucleus of the present socialist Israel Labor Party, which controlled Israel's governments during 1969–74 under prime minister Golda Meir and during 1974–77 under prime minister Yitzhak Rabin.

In September 1973, four right-wing nationalist parties combined to form the Likud, which thus became the major opposition bloc in the Knesset (parliament). The Likud became the largest party in the Knesset by winning forty-three seats in the May 1977 elections, and its leader Menachem Begin became prime minister. The Likud and Labor parties have been Israel's two main political groupings since that time. In recent years, however, both Likud and Labor have lost seats in the Knesset as minor religious parties, such as Shas, have gained followers.

DEFENSE

Jewish and Druze men between the ages of 18 and 26 are drafted. Drafted Jewish women are trained for noncombat duties. Christians and Muslims may serve on a voluntary basis, but Muslims are rarely allowed to bear arms.

In 1995, the Israeli army had 175,000 active duty soldiers (138,500 draftees) and could mobilize as many as 598,000 more soldiers. The navy had 9,000 regulars, 3,000 draftees, and 10,000 reservists.

The air force had 32,000 regulars, 21,800 draftees, and 37,000 reserves. There are 6,000 paramilitary border police.

The Ministry of Defense's expenditure was $7.2 billion in 1995, or 12% of the gross domestic product (GDP).

ECONOMIC AFFAIRS

The government is obliged to spend a large part of its income on defense. In addition, traditional Middle Eastern sources of supply (oil and wheat) and nearby markets for goods and services have been closed off. Israel must export on a large scale to maintain its relatively high standard of living.

The average annual growth during 1990–96 was 6%. Much of the economic expansion in the 1990s has come from the construction, infrastructure expansion, and capital investment brought on by the influx of thousands of Russian immigrants.

Income

In 1998, Israel's gross national product (GNP) was US $95.1 billion, or about US $15,940 per person.

Industry

Major expansion has taken place in textiles, machinery and transport equipment, metallurgy, mineral processing, electrical products, precision instruments, and chemicals. However, industry remains handicapped by reliance on imported raw materials, relatively high wage costs, and inflation.

Banking and Finance

The Bank of Israel, with headquarters in Jerusalem, began operations as the central state bank in December 1954. Foreign currency reserves stood at $11.8 billion in November 1996, due to an adoption of a restrictive monetary policy.

The structure of the banking industry is based on the central European model of "universal banking," whereby the banks operate as retail, wholesale, and investment banks, as well as being active in all main areas of capital market activity, brokerage, underwriting, and mutual and provident fund management.

In 1994, the Palestinian Authority (PA) began to take over the management of an economy with a limited capacity to support its expanding population. The PA has acted within the constraints of the economic protocol to revive the financial sector.

In expectation of a boom in the financial sector, a number of Jordanian and Palestinian banks opened, or re-opened, branches in the West Bank and Gaza. By 1996, 42 branches of ten banks were operating. A key factor in the success of the banks will be the supervisory activities of the Palestinian Monetary Authority (PMA), set up as a result of the Paris protocol.

The Arab Palestine Investment Bank (APIB), was scheduled to open in early 1997. Total deposits of the Palestinian banking system expanded by over 125% during the year ended June 1996, reaching $2.06 trillion. Money supply, as measured by M1, totaled nis 17,202 at the end of May 1996.

Economic Development

Economic policy is dictated by goals of national security, full utilization of resources, integration of immigrants, and institution of a broad welfare program. Major government projects include an expansion of the Ben-Gurion Airport, a subway for Tel-Aviv, a tunnel through Mt. Carmel, and a major new North-South highway.

The tourism sector was expected to bloom in 1994 with approximately 2 million arrivals.

SOCIAL WELFARE

A national insurance law, which came into force in April 1954, provides insurance for the disabled and for survivors. It also grants maternity benefits and monthly allowances for large families. Workers' compensation provisions cover employees, members of rural cooperatives, and since 1957, all the self-employed.

Women's rights are protected by the Equal Rights for Women Law (1951) and the Employment of Women Law (1954), which requires equal pay for equal work. In 1993, a new law barred discrimination in unemployment compensation for elderly female citizens.

International organizations cite police harassment of Arabs on the West Bank and Gaza Strip as an ongoing problem, while Israeli officials point to the threat of Arab terrorist attacks as a source of social instability.

Healthcare

Estimated life expectancy is 77 years for both men and women. In 1992, there were 3 doctors per 1,000 people. The Ministry of Health also operates infant welfare clinics, nursing schools, and laboratories.

Housing

From 1960 to 1985, a total of 943,350 housing units were constructed. In 1986, 94% of all housing units had piped water, 58.2% had flush toilets, and 99% had electric lighting. Between 1989 and 1991, a sudden rise in immigration from the former Soviet Union and Ethiopia resulted in a dramatic increase in housing demand. As of 1992, the total number of dwellings in Israel was 1.5 million.

EDUCATION

Education is compulsory for 11 years and free for all children between 5 and 16 years of age. Primary education is for eight years followed by four years of secondary education. The language of instruction in Jewish schools is Hebrew; in Arab schools it is Arabic. In the period of 1988–93 the estimated literacy rate among Israelis aged 15 and over was 95% total, 97% for men, and 93% for women. In 1993, primary schools had 780,575 students with 48,010 teachers, and secondary level schools had 338,288 students with 53,581 teachers.

Israel has eight institutions of higher learning. In 1993, the total number of students in all higher-level institutions of Israel was 91,480.

1999 KEY EVENTS TIMELINE

January

- Israel's parliament deposes Prime Minister Benjamin Netanyahu and begins the search for a new government head. They set the election for May 17.

- The upcoming election delays peace talks. The Palestinian Authority, led by Yassir Arafat, is in conflict with Hamas, an opposition terrorist group.

March

- The murder case involving an American Jew, Samuel Sheinbein, who fled to Israel to avoid prosecution in the United States, will be tried in Israel. Sheinbein will not be extradited. The United States is opposed to this decision.

- Israel is still wrestling with the idea that the army occupation of Lebanon is a failure and Israel may withdraw its troops. This could become an election issue for Netanyahu.

- Aryeh Deri, leader of the Orthodox Shas party, is found guilty of taking bribes. A panel of three judges issues a unanimous decision of guilt. Deri still plans to stand for election in May.

April

- Israel occupies Arnoun, a village in southern Lebanon, after the death of an Israeli soldier.

- Yassir Arafat announces his intention to declare a Palestinian state on May 4.

May

- Yassir Arafat, head of the Palestinian Authority, fails to declare Palestinian statehood. This comes after many statements by Arafat of his intention to do so on May 4, 1999.

- All political parties are courting the Arab vote in an attempt to win the May national elections.

- The Shas party appeals to all Sephardic Jews for political support, claiming the Sephardim are oppressed.

- Ehud Barak emerges the winner of the May 17 elections, defeating Prime Minister Benjamin Netanyahu.

- Barak must form a coalition government.

June

- Israel continues to build settlements on the West Bank and is criticized by Arabs for negotiating in bad faith. Barak has promised to halt the development of the settlements but so far has not done so,

- Barak must choose a coalition government, but so far he is still negotiating with the Shas, the liberal Meretz, and the Likud, his former enemy and party of the defeated Netanyahu.

- Barak meets with Yassir Arafat to discuss the implementation of the Wye Agreement from October 1998. The release of Palestinian prisoners has been delayed since the May elections.

July

- Barak forms a coalition government with Likud having the most influence. Barak also delegates seats to the Shas, Meretz and Arab parties.

- Barak begins peace initiatives with Israel's Middle East neighbors.

- An extreme Orthodox sect issues a ''Fatwa'' (ritual killing) of two rabbis it considers in violation of Jewish law. The group denies this accusation, claiming they only endorse censure of the rabbis.

- Employees of Mekorot, a water company, go out on strike because of a wage dispute. This threatens not only public safety, but business as well.

August

- Barak is accused by the Palestinians of reneging on the Wye plan for withdrawal of settlements from the West Bank. Netanyahu had pledged to have a thirteen percent withdrawal, but Barak is considering only a two percent withdrawal.

September

- Israel frees some jailed Palestinians in an effort to renew peace talks.

- Ariel Sharon, a leader of Barak's rival Likud Party, indicates his willingness to co-operate with the new government. He wants his defeated party to be a leader in the future. Sharon is a hardliner and will probably be at odds with Barak's land-for-peace deals.

October

- Benjamin Netanyahu and his wife are accused of taking government gifts. They deny any wrongdoing.

- Samuel Sheinbein is found guilty and sentenced to twenty-four years in an Israeli prison.

- Palestinian residents of Judea, Samaria and Gaza will be allowed safe passage in these areas.

- The Popular Front Liberation of Palestine wants Arafat to break off peace talks with Israel.

- Israel again promises a swift withdrawal of settlements from the West Bank.

November

- Three pipe bombs simultaneously explode in the center of the coastal town of Netanya, wounding 21 Israelis; authorities claim the bomb is a terror attack by Palestinian militants set on derailing upcoming peace talks.

- Jacob Frenkel, governor of the Bank of Israel, announces his resignation.

- Israel's premier offers the post of Bank of Israel governor to economics professor Elhanan Helpman.

December

- Palestinians give Israel a draft document spelling out their conditions for a final peace deal, which Israeli Prime Minister Ehud Barak wants to reach by September 2000.

- Palestinians say they are suspending all peace talks until Israel stops expanding Jewish settlements in the West Bank; Israeli Prime Minister Barak responds by saying he will freeze plans to expand Jewish settlements around Jerusalem.

- Peace talks with Syria begin in Washington.

ANALYSIS OF EVENTS: 1999

BUSINESS AND THE ECONOMY

Israel seems to be making progress in the development of the medical and technological industries. Tourism is still the most prominent revenue producing industry, but more western countries such as the United States and member countries of the European Union have made trade agreements with Israel to produce medical and scientific materials. General Electric Medical has opened a Global Center of Excellence in Israel. Also, as of October 1999, Israel has combined with Le Bonheur Hospital in Memphis, Tennessee, to produce medical technological supplies. Israel has a large percentage of highly trained and educated people. This, combined with being a country that is compatible with western democratic ideals, has fostered confidence in Israel's economic growth.

Not only has an upscale economy benefited Israel, but it has also been favorable for other countries to see Israel's emergence in the field of investment banking. Of all the nations in the Middle East, Israel has the leading edge for emerging markets. It has capitalized on its political stability to increase confidence in foreign investors. Israel has also recently discovered oil and gas reserves that were previously unknown to exist in Israel, thus creating a possible source of revenue as well as a source of self-sufficiency with regard to its oil-producing neighbors. Israel has always been in the forefront of military aircraft production. Recently Turkey has ordered an upgrade of its fighter aircraft and Israel is filling that order. The diamond industry has also begun to show profitability. At the close of 1999, Israel has shown itself to be more profitable with a substantial drop in its foreign debt. Investors are waiting to see if Israel can emerge as a high tech giant in its own right, combining smaller companies to become a conglomerate heavyweight.

GOVERNMENT AND POLITICS

Israel's political history has been shaped by its quest to regain biblical lands, the struggle for peace with its Arab neighbors, and the fight to maintain a secular democracy while appeasing the religious right-wing faction. Unfortunately, Israel has many political parties, necessitating the formation of a coalition government. These governments are always courting clamoring political minorities, which then exact concessions to their causes. The population of Israel has always been largely secular in their lifestyles while supporting an Orthodox control over ceremonies and some public affairs. Some of the Orthodox policies, such as the refusal to grant land for peace and opposition to the use of public facilities during the Sabbath, have come under harsh scrutiny by the secular populace. Also, the refusal of the Orthodox to serve in the military has caused an uproar in the rest of the population. The May election unseated Prime Minister Benjamin Netanyahu, a Likud party leader and opponent of land-for-peace deals, in favor of Ehud Barak of the One Israel (formerly Labor) party which favors negotiation of lands for peace. However, even though Barak won the election, he was still forced to form a coalition government. Barak succeeded against high odds in creating a new government in which his party is the largest among many—which means he is relatively secure from overthrow by a vote of no confidence. The other parties would have to agree to unseat him and they are all so disparate they would probably never combine an effective offense. Barak has included the Shas (a Sephardic-Orthodox party), a Russian immigrant party, an Arab party and the rival Likud party in his coalition. By giving some political plums and cabinet positions to his rivals, Barak has managed to achieve a tentative peace in his own government and can perhaps finish the job of obtaining peace in the Middle East.

Barak must also deal with Israel's withdrawal of troops from Lebanon and the negotiation with Syria over the Golan Heights, which Israel conquered in the Six-Day War. Since that war Israel has also heavily settled much of the disputed West Bank area. In order to achieve a land-for-peace agreement, Israel must dismantle some of the existing communities and put a freeze on the development of new communities. In an effort to preempt the government, some Israelis have been quickly putting up makeshift houses to increase the occupied territory. This has angered the Israeli government and stalled peace talks. Now Barak is talking of dismantling these cities and the citizens of these areas have rebelled and vowed never to leave. Barak's pledge to offer land for peace is now on the line and he must deliver his promise to the people in order to maintain his credibility.

CULTURE AND SOCIETY

Israel has been a melting pot for many cultures. Even though about 80 percent of its present population is of the Jewish faith, that group is far from being united on issues of religion and politics. The most recent divisions have occurred between those of Ashkenazic (western European) descent and those of Sephardic (eastern European, Spanish and Portuguese, and northern African) descent. These two groups differ on religious customs and intensity of commitment to Orthodoxy. There exists severe antipathy between the two groups, each claiming to be the Israeli ''elite.'' Up to the present, the Ashkinazim have dominated politics, although the Sephardim have controlled the religious arm of the government. With the election of the Barak government, the Shas party (Sephardic-Orthodox) took over more parliamentary seats than ever and became a thorn in the side of the Israeli people. For one, the Sephardim adamantly refuse to concede any land for peace. This is diametrically opposed to the principle of the Barak government. Also, the Sephardim control all life-cycle ceremonies and have defined who is a Jew. This may seem trivial, but someone who has converted to Judaism through the Reform or Conservative movement may not be considered a Jew in Israel. Thus, his children are not Jewish and may be denied marriage to an Orthodox Jewish person. Although most Israeli Jews are not strict followers of Orthodoxy, they have no say in religious law, which is hard to distinguish from some civil laws in many cases.

Jews in the United States, who are overwhelmingly Reform and Conservative, are at odds with Israel's dependence on the Sephardim. American Jews are important to Israel because of their huge economic support in the past. Now the American Jewish community has become severely critical of the theocracy in Israel and may try to control government leanings by tightening its pursestrings. The Orthodox have also protected many of their community by having able-bodied men and women exempt from military service. There are branches in the military (everyone must serve) reserved for the Orthodox, but those who are pursuing religious studies have so far been exempt. They retain this exemption while they are studying. The ruse is that they continue to ''study'' until they are too old for service. This puts a financial hardship on their families who become welfare recipients at the expense of the rest of the Israeli citizens. Barak has promised to investigate some of these bogus exemptions, much to the consternation of the Orthodox. Israeli art and culture has also suffered from the fragmentation of society. Art that is too secular or avant-garde is criticized by the Orthodox, and political art is criticized by the pro-Arab population.

DIRECTORY

CENTRAL GOVERNMENT

Head of State

President
Ezer Weizman, Office of the President

Prime Minister and Minister of Defense
Ehud Barak, Office of the Prime Minister, 3 Kaplan St., PO Box 187, Kiryat Ben-Gurion, IL-91919 Jerusalem, Israel
PHONE: +972 (2) 6705555
FAX: +972 (2) 6512631

Ministers

Minister of Justice
Yossi Beilin, Ministry of Justice, 29 Salah A-din St., IL-91010 Jerusalem, Israel
PHONE: +972 (2) 6708511
FAX: +972 (2) 6288618

Minister of Public Security
Shlomo Ben-Ami, Ministry of Public of Security, Kiryat Hamemshala, PO Box 18182, IL-91181 Jerusalem, Israel
PHONE: +972 (2) 5308003
FAX: +972 (2) 5847872

Minister of Communications and Deputy Prime Minister
Benjamin Ben-Eliezer, Ministry of Communications, 23 Yaffo St., IL-91999 Jerusalem, Israel
PHONE: +972 (2) 6706320
FAX: +972 (2) 6706372

Minister of Health
Shlomo Benizri, Ministry of Health, 2 Ben-Tabai St., PO Box 1176, IL-91010 Jerusalem, Israel
PHONE: +972 (2) 6705705
FAX: +972 (2) 6796491

Minister of Industry and Trade
Ran Cohen, Ministry of Industry and Trade, 30 Agron St., PO Box 299, IL-91002 Jerusalem, Israel
PHONE: +972 (2) 6220339
FAX: +972 (2) 6259274

Minister of Religious Affairs
Yitzhak Cohen, Ministry of Religious Affairs, 36 Yaffo St., PO Box 13059, IL-91130 Jerusalem, Israel
PHONE: +972 (2) 5311171
FAX: +972 (2) 5311183

Minister of the Environment
Dalia Itzik, Ministry of the Environment, 5 Kanfei Nesharim St., Givat Shaul, PO Box 34033, IL-95464 Jerusalem, Israel
PHONE: +972 (2) 6553777
FAX: +972 (2) 6553777

Minister of Foreign Affairs
David Levy, Ministry of Foreign Affairs
PHONE: +972 (2) 5303111
FAX: +972 (2) 5303367

Minister of Construction and Housing
Yitzhak Levy, Ministry of Construction and Housing, PO Box 18110, IL-91180 Jerusalem, Israel
PHONE: +972 (2) 5825501
FAX: +972 (2) 5825501

Minister of Tourism
Amnon Lipkin-Shahak, Ministry of Tourism, 24 King George St., PO Box 1018, IL-91009 Jerusalem, Israel

PHONE: +972 (2) 6754811
FAX: +972 (2) 6250890

Minister of Diaspora and Social Affairs
Michael Melchior, Ministry of Diaspora and
Social Affairs

Minister of Transport
Yitzhak Mordechai, Ministry of Transport, 97
Yaffo St., IL-91000 Jerusalem, Israel
PHONE: +972 (2) 6228211
FAX: +972 (2) 6228693

Minister of Agriculture and Rural Development
Haim Oron, Ministry of Agriculture and Rural
Development, 8 Arania St., Hakirya, IL-61070
Tel Aviv, Israel
PHONE: +972 (3) 6971444
FAX: +972 (3) 6968899

Minister of Regional Cooperation
Shimon Peres, Ministry of Regional Cooperation

Minister of Jerusalem Affairs
Haim Ramon, Ministry of Jerusalem Affairs

Minister of Education, Culture and Sports
Yossi Sarid, Ministry of Education, Culture and
Sports, 34 Shivtei Israel St., PO Box 292,
IL-91911 Jerusalem, Israel
PHONE: +972 (2) 5602222
FAX: +972 (2) 5602752

POLITICAL ORGANIZATIONS
Likud Party
TITLE: Prime Minister
NAME: Binyamin Netanyahu

Tzomet
NAME: Rafael Eitan

National Religious Party
NAME: Yitzhak Levi

Yisra'el Ba'Aliya
NAME: Natan Sharansky

United Jewish Torah
NAME: Meir Porush

Third Way
NAME: Avigdor Kahalani

DIPLOMATIC REPRESENTATION
Embassies in Israel
Argentina
3A, Rehov Jabotinsky, IL-52520 Ramat-Gan, Israel
PHONE: +972 (3) 5759170
FAX: +972 (3) 5759178

Australia
37 Shaul Hamelech Blvd., IL-64928 Tel Aviv, Israel
PHONE: +972 (3) 6950451
FAX: +972 (3) 6968404

Belarus
2 Rehov Kaufman, IL-68012 Tel Aviv, Israel
PHONE: +972 (3) 5102236
FAX: +972 (3) 5102235

Belgium
266 Rehov Hayarkon, IL-63504 Tel Aviv, Israel
PHONE: +972 (3) 6054164
FAX: +972 (3) 5465345

Bolivia
7A Rehov Hashalom, IL-90805 Mevasseret Zion, Israel
PHONE: +972 (2) 5335195
FAX: +972 (2) 5335196

Brazil
2 Rehov Kaplan, IL-64734 Tel Aviv, Israel
PHONE: +972 (3) 6919292
FAX: +972 (3) 6916060

Bulgaria
124 Ibn Gvirol, IL-62308 Tel Aviv, Israel
PHONE: +972 (3) 5241759
FAX: +972 (3) 5241798

Cameroon
79 Rehov Yehuda Hamaccabi, IL-62300 Tel Aviv, Israel
PHONE: +972 (3) 6043640
FAX: +972 (3) 6043639

Canada
3 Nirim Beit Hasapanut, Yad Eliyahu, IL-67060 Tel Aviv, Israel
PHONE: +972 (3) 6363300

China
222 Rehov Ben Yehuda, IL-63473 Tel Aviv, Israel
PHONE: +972 (3) 5467277
FAX: +972 (3) 5467251

Columbia
52 Rehov Pinkas, 6th floor Apt. 26, IL-62261
Tel Aviv, Israel
PHONE: +972 (3) 5461434
FAX: +972 (3) 5461404

Congo
25 Rehov Leisen, PO Box 21352, IL-61212 Tel
Aviv, Israel
PHONE: +972 (3) 6912414
FAX: +972 (3) 6952825

Costa Rica
13 Rehov Diskin, Apt. 1, PO Box 1318,
IL-91012 Jerusalem, Israel
PHONE: +972 (2) 5666197
FAX: +972 (2) 5632591

Côte d'Ivoire
14 Rehov He Be'Iyar, Kikar HaMedina,
IL-62093 Tel Aviv, Israel
PHONE: +972 (3) 6963727
FAX: +972 (3) 6968888

Cyprus
Top Tower, 50 Rehov Dizengoff, IL-64332 Tel
Aviv, Israel
PHONE: +972 (3) 5250212
FAX: +972 (3) 6290535

Czech Republic
23 Zeitlin, IL-64955 Tel Aviv, Israel
PHONE: +972 (3) 6918282
FAX: +972 (3) 6918286

Denmark
23 Rehov Bnei Moshe, IL-62308 Tel Aviv,
Israel
PHONE: +972 (3) 5442144
FAX: +972 (3) 5465502

Dominican Republic
4 Sderot Shaul Hamelech, IL-64733 Tel Aviv,
Israel
PHONE: +972 (3) 6957580
FAX: +972 (3) 6962032

Egypt
PHONE: +972 (3) 5464151
FAX: +972 (3) 5441615

El Salvador
34 Rehov Rahel Imeinu, IL-93228 Jerusalem,
Israel
PHONE: +972 (2) 5633575
FAX: +972 (2) 5638528

Equador
Asia House, 4 Rehov Weizman, IL-64239 Tel
Aviv, Israel

PHONE: +972 (3) 6958764
FAX: +972 (3) 6969437

Ethiopia
48 Derech Petach Tikva, IL-66184 Tel Aviv,
Israel
PHONE: +972 (3) 6397831
FAX: +972 (3) 6397837

European Community
3 Rehov Daniel Frisch, IL-64731 Tel Aviv,
Israel
PHONE: +972 (3) 6964160
FAX: +972 (3) 6951983

Finland
Beit Eliyahu 8th Floor, 2 Rehov Ibn Gvirol,
IL-64077 Tel Aviv, Israel
PHONE: +972 (3) 6950527
FAX: +972 (3) 6966311

France
112 Herbert Samuel, IL-63572 Tel Aviv, Israel
PHONE: +972 (3) 5245371
FAX: +972 (3) 5465937

Gabon
32 Rehov Jabotinsky, IL-52495 Ramat-Gan,
Israel

Germany
3 Rehov Daniel Frisch, IL-64731 Tel Aviv,
Israel
PHONE: +972 (3) 6931313
FAX: +972 (3) 6969217

Ghana
15 Abba Hillel Silver, IL-52522 Ramat-Gan,
Israel

Greece
47 Rehov Bodenheimer, IL-62008 Tel Aviv,
Israel
PHONE: +972 (3) 6055461
FAX: +972 (3) 6054374

Guatemala
74 Rehov He Be'Iyar, IL-62198 Tel Aviv, Israel
PHONE: +972 (3) 5467372
FAX: +972 (3) 5467317

Honduras
46 Rehov He Be'Iyar, Kikar HaMedina,
IL-62093 Tel Aviv, Israel
PHONE: +972 (3) 5469506
FAX: +972 (3) 5469505

Hungary
18 Rehov Pinkas, IL-62661 Tel Aviv, Israel
PHONE: +972 (3) 5466860

FAX: +972 (3) 5468968

India
PHONE: +972 (3) 5101431
FAX: +972 (3) 5101434

Ireland
Carlton Hotel, 10 Rehov Eliezer Peri, IL-63573
Tel Aviv, Israel

Italy
PHONE: +972 (3) 6964223
FAX: +972 (3) 6918428

Japan
Asia House, 4 Rehov Weizman, IL-64239 Tel
Aviv, Israel
PHONE: +972 (3) 6957292
FAX: +972 (3) 6910516

Jordan
12 Abba Hillel Silver, IL-52506 Ramat-Gan,
Israel
PHONE: +972 (3) 7517722
FAX: +972 (3) 7517712

Kazakhstan
33 Rehov Jabotinsky, IL-52511 Ramat-Gan,
Israel

Kenya
50 Rehov Jabotinsky, PO Box 22115, IL-61220
Tel Aviv, Israel
PHONE: +972 (3) 5249935
FAX: +972 (3) 5241611

Korea
38 Chen Blvd, IL-64166 Tel Aviv, Israel
PHONE: +972 (3) 6963244
FAX: +972 (3) 6963243

Kyrgyzstan
7 Abba Hillel Silver, IL-52522 Ramat-Gan,
Israel
PHONE: +972 (3) 6136546
FAX: +972 (3) 6136548

Latvia
Rehov Pinkas, Apt. 51, IL-62261 Tel Aviv,
Israel
PHONE: +972 (3) 5462438

Liberia
6 Rehov Frug, IL-52482 Ramat-Gan, Israel
PHONE: +972 (3) 6728532
FAX: +972 (3) 6727167

Lithuania
50 Rehov Dizengoff, Suite 1404, IL-64332 Tel
Aviv, Israel
PHONE: +972 (3) 5288514

FAX: +972 (3) 5257265

Mauritania
18/12 Rehov He Be'Iyar, IL-62093 Tel Aviv,
Israel

Mexico
3 Rehov Bograshov, IL-63808 Tel Aviv, Israel
PHONE: +972 (3) 5230367
FAX: +972 (3) 5237399

Moldova
7 Rehov Havakook, Apt. 303, IL-63505 Tel
Aviv, Israel
PHONE: +972 (3) 6040014

Morocco
67 Rehov Weizman, Apt. 5, IL-62155 Tel Aviv,
Israel
PHONE: +972 (3) 5464007

Myanmar
26 Hayarkon, Tel Aviv, Israel
PHONE: +972 (3) 5170760
FAX: +972 (3) 5171440

Netherlands
4 Rehov Weizman, IL-64239 Tel Aviv, Israel
PHONE: +972 (3) 6957377
FAX: +972 (3) 6957370

Nigeria
34 Rehov Gordon, IL-63414 Tel Aviv, Israel
PHONE: +972 (3) 5222144
FAX: +972 (3) 5248991

Norway
40 Hanamal, IL-63506 Tel Aviv, Israel
PHONE: +972 (3) 5442030
FAX: +972 (3) 5442034

Oman
79 Rehov Yehuda Hamaccabi, IL-62300 Tel
Aviv, Israel

Panama
10 Rehov He Be'Iyar, Kikar HaMedina,
IL-62998 Tel Aviv, Israel
PHONE: +972 (3) 6956711
FAX: +972 (3) 6910045

Paraguay
1/4 Rehov Carmel, IL-90805 Mevasseret Zion,
Israel
PHONE: +972 (2) 5334830
FAX: +972 (2) 5333878

Peru
37 Rehov Hamarganit, IL-52584 Ramat-Gan,
Israel
PHONE: +972 (3) 6135591

FAX: +972 (3) 7512286

Philippines
2 Rehov Kaufman, IL-68012 Tel Aviv, Israel
PHONE: +972 (3) 5104651
FAX: +972 (3) 5102229

Poland
16 Rehov Soutine, IL-64684 Tel Aviv, Israel
PHONE: +972 (3) 5240188
FAX: +972 (3) 5237806

Portugal
4 Rehov Weizman, IL-64585 Tel Aviv, Israel
PHONE: +972 (3) 6956372
FAX: +972 (3) 6956366

Romania
24 Rehov Adam Hacohen, IL-64662 Tel Aviv, Israel
PHONE: +972 (3) 5230066
FAX: +972 (3) 5247379

Russia
120 Rehov Hayarkon, Tel Aviv, Israel
PHONE: +972 (3) 5226733
FAX: +972 (3) 5226713

Rwanda
30 Rehov He Be'Iyar, Kikar Hamedina, IL-62093 Tel Aviv, Israel
PHONE: +972 (3) 6912319
FAX: +972 (3) 6963408

Serbia
8 Rehov Shaul Hamelech, IL-64776 Tel Aviv, Israel
PHONE: +972 (3) 6938412
FAX: +972 (3) 6938411

Slovakia
37 Rehov Jabotinsky, PO Box 6459, IL-61064 Tel Aviv, Israel
PHONE: +972 (3) 5440066
FAX: +972 (3) 5440069

Slovenia
2 Rehov Kaufman, IL-68012 Tel Aviv, Israel
PHONE: +972 (3) 5163425
FAX: +972 (3) 5163530

South Africa
Top Tower, Floor 16, 50 Rehov Dizengoff, IL-64332 Tel Aviv, Israel
PHONE: +972 (3) 5252566
FAX: +972 (3) 5253230

Spain
Dubnov Tower, Floor 16, 3 Rehov Daniel Frisch, IL-64731 Tel Aviv, Israel

PHONE: +972 (3) 6965218
FAX: +972 (3) 6965217

Sweden
4 Rehov Weizman, IL-64239 Tel Aviv, Israel
PHONE: +972 (3) 6958111
FAX: +972 (3) 6958116

Switzerland
228 Rehov Hayarkon, IL-63405 Tel Aviv, Israel
PHONE: +972 (3) 5464455
FAX: +972 (3) 5464408

Turkey
202 Rehov Hayarkon, IL-63405 Tel Aviv, Israel
PHONE: +972 (3) 5241101
FAX: +972 (3) 5240499

Ukraine
12 Rehov Striker, IL-62006 Tel Aviv, Israel
PHONE: +972 (3) 6040311
FAX: +972 (3) 6042512

United States
71 Rehov Hayarkon, IL-63903 Tel Aviv, Israel
PHONE: +972 (3) 5197575
FAX: +972 (3) 5102444

Uruguay
52 Rehov Pinkas, Apt. 10, Floor 2, IL-62261 Tel Aviv, Israel
PHONE: +972 (3) 6040411
FAX: +972 (3) 5441452

Uzbekistan
1 Rehov Ben Yehuda, IL-63801 Tel Aviv, Israel
PHONE: +972 (3) 5104684
FAX: +972 (3) 5104679

Vatican City
PO Box 150, IL-61001 Jaffa, Israel
PHONE: +972 (3) 6835658
FAX: +972 (3) 6835659

Venezuela
2 Rehov Kaufman, Floor 16, IL-61500 Tel Aviv, Israel
PHONE: +972 (3) 5176287
FAX: +972 (3) 5176210

Zaire
1 Rehov Rachel, IL-64584 Tel Aviv, Israel
PHONE: +972 (3) 5248306
FAX: +972 (3) 5229951

JUDICIAL SYSTEM
Supreme Court

FURTHER READING
Articles

"Bolters Take Off" *The Economist* (January 2, 1999): 40.

"Has the Romance Ended?" *Society* 36 (May-June 1999): 15.

"Israel's High Tech Promised Land." *Business Week* (April 26, 1999): 8.

"Jailed in Jordan." *The Economist* (September 25, 1999): 6.

Lambert, Miriam Udel. "Challenging Orthodoxy." *The New Republic* (June 21, 1999): 20.

Makovsky, David and Larry Derfner. "The Politics of Resentment." *U.S. News and World Report* (May 31, 1999): 36.

Rees, Matt. "Courting the Arab Vote." *Newsweek International* (May 3, 1999): 36.

———. "Giving Up the Golan Heights in the Name of Peace." *Newsweek International* (June 14, 1999): 41.

"Sharon's Way." *The Economist* (September 25, 1999): 52.

Books

Bregman, Ahron and el-Tahri Jihan. *The Fifty Years' War: Israel and the Arabs.* TV Books, Harper Collins, 1999.

Griver, Simon. *Essential Israel.* Lincolnwood, Ill.: Passport Books, 1999.

Sachar, Howard M. *Israel and Europe: an Appraisal in History.* New York: Alfred A. Knopf, 1999.

Internet

Israel News Online. Available Online @ http://members.aol.com/Israel/Hr/index.html (December 15, 1999).

Israel Radio. Available Online @ www.kolisrael.net (December 15, 1999).

Israel's Government Page. Available Online @ www.israel.org (December 15, 1999).

ISRAEL:
STATISTICAL DATA

For sources and notes see "Sources of Statistics" in the front of each volume.

GEOGRAPHY

Geography (1)

Area:

Total: 20,770 sq km.

Land: 20,330 sq km.

Water: 440 sq km.

Area—comparative: slightly smaller than New Jersey.

Land boundaries:

Total: 1,006 km.

Border countries: Egypt 255 km, Gaza Strip 51 km, Jordan 238 km, Lebanon 79 km, Syria 76 km, West Bank 307 km.

Coastline: 273 km.

Climate: temperate; hot and dry in southern and eastern desert areas.

Terrain: Negev desert in the south; low coastal plain; central mountains; Jordan Rift Valley.

Natural resources: copper, phosphates, bromide, potash, clay, sand, sulfur, asphalt, manganese, small amounts of natural gas and crude oil.

Land use:

Arable land: 17%

Permanent crops: 4%

Permanent pastures: 7%

Forests and woodland: 6%

Other: 66% (1993 est.).

HUMAN FACTORS

Demographics (2A)

	1990	1995	1998	2000	2010	2020	2030	2040	2050
Population	4,512.1	5,306.0	5,644.0	5,851.9	6,696.0	7,438.5	8,086.7	8,593.8	8,960.9
Net migration rate (per 1,000 population)	NA	NA	NA	NA	NA	NA	NA	NA	NA
Births	NA	NA	NA	NA	NA	NA	NA	NA	NA
Deaths	28.7	NA	NA	NA	NA	NA	NA	NA	NA
Life expectancy - males	75.4	76.0	76.5	76.9	78.3	79.2	79.8	80.2	80.5
Life expectancy - females	79.1	79.7	80.4	80.8	82.6	83.8	84.7	85.4	85.8
Birth rate (per 1,000)	21.7	20.5	20.0	19.6	17.6	15.7	14.4	13.2	12.3
Death rate (per 1,000)	6.2	6.3	6.2	6.1	6.0	6.2	7.2	8.1	9.0
Women of reproductive age (15-49 yrs.)	1,098.0	1,333.8	1,414.9	1,462.1	1,626.4	1,794.8	1,888.3	1,949.5	1,973.3
of which are currently married	NA	NA	NA	NA	NA	NA	NA	NA	NA
Fertility rate	3.0	2.8	2.7	2.6	2.4	2.2	2.1	2.0	2.0

Except as noted, values for vital statistics are in thousands; life expectancy is in years.

Health Personnel (3)

Total health expenditure as a percentage of GDP, 1990-1997[a]

Public sector 0.3

Private sector 0.3

Total[b] 4.1

Health expenditure per capita in U.S. dollars, 1990-1997[a]

Purchasing power parity 651

Total 551

Availability of health care facilities per 100,000 people

Hospital beds 1990-1997[a] 600

Doctors 1993[c] 459

Nurses 1993[c] 671

Health Indicators (4)

Life expectancy at birth

1980 73

1997 77

Daily per capita supply of calories (1996) 3,272

Total fertility rate births per woman (1997) 2.7

Maternal mortality ratio per 100,000 live births (1990-97) . . . . .7[c]

Safe water % of population with access (1995) 99

Sanitation % of population with access (1995) 100

Consumption of iodized salt % of households (1992-98)[a] . . . .

Smoking prevalence

Male % of adults (1985-95)[a] 45

Female % of adults (1985-95)[a] 30

Tuberculosis incidence per 100,000 people (1997) 7

Adult HIV prevalence % of population ages 15-49 (1997) 0.07

Infants and Malnutrition (5)

Under-5 mortality rate (1997) 6

% of infants with low birthweight (1990-97) 7

Births attended by skilled health staff % of total[a] . . .99

% fully immunized (1995-97)

TB . . . . .NA

DPT 92

Polio 93

Measles 94

Prevalence of child malnutrition under age 5 (1992-97)[b] . . . . .NA

Ethnic Division (6)

Jewish 82% (Israel-born 50%, Europe/Americas/ Oceania-born 20%, Africa-born 7%, Asia-born 5%) Non-Jewish 18% (mostly Arab) (1993 est.).

Religions (7)

Judaism 82%

Islam . . . . .14% (mostly Sunni Muslim)

Christian 2%

Druze and other 2%

Languages (8)

Hebrew (official), Arabic used officially for Arab minority, English most commonly used foreign language.

EDUCATION

Public Education Expenditures (9)

Public expenditure on education (% of GNP)

1980 . . . . .7.9

1996 . . . . .7.2[1]

Expenditure per student

Primary % of GNP per capita

1980 . . . . .15.4

1996 . . . . .19.6[1]

Secondary % of GNP per capita

1980 . . . .

1996 . . . . .32.7[1]

Tertiary % of GNP per capita

1980 . . . . .72.5

1996 . . . . .35.2

Expenditure on teaching materials

Primary % of total for level (1996) 9.9

Secondary % of total for level (1996) . . . .

Primary pupil-teacher ratio per teacher (1996) . . . . .16[1]

Duration of primary education years (1995) 6

Educational Attainment (10)

Age group (1983) . . . . .25+

Total population .2,043,720

Highest level attained (%)

No schooling 10.5

First level

Not completed 42.4

Completed . . . . .NA

Entered second level

S-1 . . . . .35.9

S-2 . . . . .NA

Postsecondary 11.2

Literacy Rates (11B)

Adult literacy rate

1980

Male 93x

Female 83x

1995

Male 98

Female 94

GOVERNMENT & LAW

Political Parties (12)

Knesset	No. of seats
Labor Party	.34
Likud Party	.32
SHAS	.10
MERETZ	.9
National Religious Party	.9
Yisra'el Ba'Aliya	.7
Hadash-Balad	.5
Third Way	.4
United Arab List	.4

Military Affairs (14B)

	1990	1991	1992	1993	1994	1995
Military expenditures						
Current dollars (mil.)	7,168	5,641	7,735	7,452	8,171	8,734
1995 constant dollars (mil.)	8,237	6,233	8,320	7,812	8,376	8,734
Armed forces (000)	190	190	181	181	185	185
Gross national product (GNP)						
Current dollars (mil.)	56,820	64,000	70,440	75,470	82,520	90,560e
1995 constant dollars (mil.)	65,300	70,720	75,770	79,120	84,590	90,560e
Central government expenditures (CGE)						
1995 constant dollars (mil.)	33,250	27,710	35,670	35,330	37,810	41,470
People (mil.)	4.5	4.8	4.9	5.1	5.2	5.3
Military expenditure as % of GNP	12.6	8.8	11.0	9.9	9.9	9.6
Military expenditure as % of CGE	24.8	22.5	23.3	22.1	22.2	21.1
Military expenditure per capita (1995 $)	1,826	1,311	1,685	1,543	1,615	1,646
Armed forces per 1,000 people (soldiers)	42.1	39.9	36.7	35.8	35.7	34.9
GNP per capita (1995 $)	14,470	14,870	15,350	15,630	16,310	17,070
Arms imports[6]						
Current dollars (mil.)	600	600	800	1,100	600	340
1995 constant dollars (mil.)	690	663	861	1,153	615	340
Arms exports[6]						
Current dollars (mil.)	625	725	550	600	725	775
1995 constant dollars (mil.)	718	801	592	629	743	775
Total imports[7]						
Current dollars (mil.)	16,790	18,660	20,250	22,620	25,240	29,580
1995 constant dollars (mil.)	19,300	20,620	21,780	23,720	25,870	29,580
Total exports[7]						
Current dollars (mil.)	11,580	11,920	13,120	14,830	16,880	19,050
1995 constant dollars (mil.)	13,300	13,170	14,110	15,540	17,310	19,050
Arms as percent of total imports[8]	3.6	3.2	4.0	4.9	2.4	1.1
Arms as percent of total exports[8]	5.4	6.1	4.2	4.0	4.3	4.1

Political Parties (12)

Knesset	No. of seats
United Jewish Torah	.4
Moledet	.2

Government Budget (13A)

Year: 1997

Total Expenditures: 163,530 Millions of New Sheqalim

Expenditures as a percentage of the total by function:

General public services and public order	.5.10[P]
Defense	.17.89[P]
Education	.14.02[P]
Health	.13.65[P]
Social Security and Welfare	.24.91[P]
Housing and community amenities	.3.75[P]
Recreational, cultural, and religious affairs	.96[P]
Fuel and energy	.26[P]
Agriculture, forestry, fishing, and hunting	.1.21[P]
Mining, manufacturing, and construction	.2.60[P]
Transportation and communication	.1.90[P]
Other economic affairs and services	.84[P]

Crime (15)

Crime rate (for 1997)

Crimes reported	.366,300
Total persons convicted	.101,800
Crimes per 100,000 population	.6,550

Persons responsible for offenses

Total number of suspects	.89,300
Total number of female suspects	.10,700
Total number of juvenile suspects	.7,100

LABOR FORCE

Labor Force (16)

Total (million)	.2.3
Public services	.31.3%
Manufacturing	.20.2%
Finance and business	.13.1%
Commerce	.12.8%
Construction	.7.5%
Personal and other services	.6.4%
Transport, storage, and communications	.6.2%
Agriculture, forestry, and fishing	.2.6%

Data for 1997. Percent distribution for 1996.

Unemployment Rate (17)

7.7% (1997)

PRODUCTION SECTOR

Electric Energy (18)

Capacity	.7.736 million kW (1996)
Production	.32.5 billion kWh (1996)
Consumption per capita	.5,387 kWh (1995)

Transportation (19)

Highways:

total: 15,065 km

paved: 15,065 km (including 56 km of expressways)

unpaved: 0 km (1996)

Pipelines: crude oil 708 km; petroleum products 290 km; natural gas 89 km

Merchant marine:

total: 27 ships (1,000 GRT or over) totaling 803,383 GRT/947,678 DWT ships by type: cargo 2, container 24, roll-on/roll-off cargo 1 (1997 est.)

Airports: 54 (1997 est.)

Airports—with paved runways:

total: 31

over 3,047 m: 2

2,438 to 3,047 m: 5

1,524 to 2,437 m: 8

914 to 1,523 m: 9

under 914 m: 7 (1997 est.)

Airports—with unpaved runways:

total: 23

2,438 to 3,047 m: 1

1,524 to 2,437 m: 1

914 to 1,523 m: 3

under 914 m: 18 (1997 est.)

Top Agricultural Products (20)

Citrus and other fruits, vegetables, cotton; beef, poultry, dairy products.

MANUFACTURING SECTOR

GDP & Manufacturing Summary (21)

Detailed value added figures are listed by both International Standard Industry Code (ISIC) and product title.

	1980	1985	1990	1994
GDP ($-1990 mil.)[1]	38,687	44,907	54,910	69,365
Per capita ($-1990)[1]	9,973	10,609	11,783	12,709
Manufacturing share (%) (current prices)[1]	16.0	21.1	20.9	21.7

	1980	1985	1990	1994
Manufacturing				
Value added ($-1990 mil.)[1]	6,303	7,513	8,394	11,185
Industrial production index	100	119	133	168
Value added ($ mil.)	6,490	6,655	10,193	12,030
Gross output ($ mil.)	14,332	16,351	24,574	33,407
Employment (000)	259	292	292	343
Profitability (% of gross output)				
Intermediate input (%)	55	59	59	64
Wages and salaries inc. supplements (%)	30	30	32	31
Gross operating surplus	15	11	10	5
Productivity ($)				
Gross output per worker	54,619	55,297	83,073	96,122
Value added per worker	24,733	22,506	34,461	34,618
Average wage (inc. supplements)	16,734	16,765	26,622	29,689
Value added ($ mil.)				
311/2 Food products	706	748	1,221	1,249
313 Beverages	66	56	146	153
314 Tobacco products	24	10	33	23
321 Textiles	422	243	404	393
322 Wearing apparel	293	229	427	561
323 Leather and fur products	18	13	19	22
324 Footwear	38	42	55	65
331 Wood and wood products	112	78	116	149
332 Furniture and fixtures	90	81	131	180
341 Paper and paper products	150	135	241	269
342 Printing and publishing	184	227	470	648
351 Industrial chemicals	256	317	498	614
352 Other chemical products	250	241	420	462
353 Petroleum refineries	93	106	115	152
354 Miscellaneous petroleum and coal products	93	106	115	152
355 Rubber products	104	64	76	74
356 Plastic products	212	290	468	666
361 Pottery, china and earthenware	26	25	30	36
362 Glass and glass products	30	23	37	31
369 Other non-metal mineral products	239	143	306	433
371 Iron and steel	148	118	113	137
372 Non-ferrous metals	61	36	61	66
381 Metal products	1,060	967	1,228	1,426
382 Non-electrical machinery	245	224	279	359
383 Electrical machinery	831	1,415	2,200	2,784
384 Transport equipment	610	522	742	614
385 Professional and scientific equipment	66	129	125	171
390 Other manufacturing industries	63	67	120	141

FINANCE, ECONOMICS, & TRADE

Economic Indicators (22)

National product: GDP—purchasing power parity— $96.7 billion (1997 est.)

National product real growth rate: 1.9% (1997 est.)

National product per capita: $17,500 (1997 est.)

Inflation rate—consumer price index: 9% (1997)

Exchange Rates (24)

Exchange rates:

New Israeli shekels (NIS) per US$1

December 1997	3.5340
1997	3.4494
1996	3.1917
1995	3.0113
1994	3.0111
1993	2.8301

Balance of Payments (23)

	1992	1993	1994	1995	1996
Exports of goods (f.o.b.)	13,382	14,888	16,782	19,146	20,436
Imports of goods (f.o.b.)	−18,389	−20,532	−22,752	−26,834	−28,405
Trade balance	−5,007	−5,644	−5,970	−7,688	−7,969
Services - debits	−9,432	−9,929	−11,634	−13,916	−15,078
Services - credits	7,374	7,277	7,738	9,477	9,765
Private transfers (net)	3,897	3,637	3,326	3,035	3,481
Government transfers (net)	1,930	2,101	2,378	2,754	2,745
Overall balance	−1,239	−2,557	−4,162	−6,339	−7,057

Top Import Origins (25)

$28.6 billion (c.i.f., 1997) Data are for 1996.

Origins	%
European Union	.52
United States	.20
Japan	.NA

NA stands for not available.

Top Export Destinations (26)

$20.7 billion (f.o.b., 1997) Data are for 1996.

Destinations	%
European Union	.32
United States	.31
Japan	.7

Economic Aid (27)

Recipient: $1.2 billion (1997) from the US.

Import Export Commodities (28)

Import Commodities	Export Commodities
Military equipment	Machinery and equipment
Investment goods	
Rough diamonds	Cut diamonds
Oil	Chemicals
Consumer goods	Textiles and apparel
	Agricultural products
	Metals

ITALY

CAPITAL: Rome (Roma).

FLAG: The national flag is a tricolor of green, white, and red vertical stripes.

ANTHEM: *Fratelli d'Italia (Brothers of Italy).*

MONETARY UNIT: The lira (L) is a paper currency of 100 centesimi. There are coins of 5, 10, 20, 50, 100, 200, 500, and 1,000 lire, and notes of 1,000, 2,000, 5,000, 10,000, 50,000, and 100,000 lire. The lira has floated freely since February 1973. L1 = $0.00066 (or $1 = L1,515.1).

WEIGHTS AND MEASURES: The metric system is the legal standard.

HOLIDAYS: New Year's Day, 1 January; Epiphany, 6 January; Liberation Day, 25 April; Labor Day, 1 May; Assumption, 15 August; All Saints' Day, 1 November; National Unity Day, 5 November; Immaculate Conception, 8 December; Christmas, 25 December; St. Stephen's Day, 26 December. Easter Monday is a movable holiday. In addition, each town has a holiday on its Saint's Day.

TIME: 1 PM = noon GMT.

LOCATION AND SIZE: Situated in southern Europe, the Italian Republic, including the major islands of Sicily and Sardinia, covers a land area of 301,230 square kilometers (116,306 square miles), slightly larger than the state of Arizona. Within the frontiers of Italy are the sovereign Republic of San Marino and the sovereign state of Vatican City.

Italy's capital city, Rome, is located in the west central part of the country.

CLIMATE: Climate varies with elevation and region. The coldest period occurs in December and January; the hottest in July and August. In the Po Plain, the average annual temperature is about 13°C (55°F); in Sicily, about 18°C (64°F); and in the coastal lowlands, about 14°C (57°F).

INTRODUCTORY SURVEY

RECENT HISTORY

Italy joined Germany against the United States and its allies in World War II (1939–45). Defeats in Greece and North Africa and the Allied invasion of Sicily toppled Mussolini's regime on 25 July 1943. Soon Italy was divided into two warring zones, one controlled by the Allies in the south and the other held by the Germans. When German power collapsed, Mussolini was captured and executed by Italian partisans.

In 1946, Italy became a republic by popular referendum; the following year, a new constitution was drafted. The conclusion of the war left Italy poverty stricken and in political chaos. By the early 1950s, however, with foreign assistance (including $1.5 billion from the United States under the Marshall Plan), Italy managed to restore its economy to prewar levels.

Politically, postwar Italy has been marked by a pattern of instability, with a different coalition government coming to power on average about once a year since 1946. Left-wing terrorism plagued Italy during the 1970s and early 1980s. By the mid-1980s, internal security had improved and a major effort against organized crime was under way. Corruption and scandals involving senior politicians and government officials in the early 1990s led to hundreds of investigations and arrests. The scandals discredited the major parties that had governed since 1948 and boosted the popularity of new reformist groups.

GOVERNMENT

The head of the Italian Republic is the president, who is elected for a seven-year term by Parliament. Presidential powers and duties include nomination of the prime minister, who, in turn, chooses a Council of Ministers (cabinet) with the approval of Parliament. Legislative power is vested in the two-chamber Parliament, consisting of the 630-member Chamber of Deputies and the 315-member Senate. Parliament is elected by universal direct vote.

Judiciary

Civil cases and lesser criminal cases are tried before judges called *pretori*. There are 159 tribunals, each with jurisdiction over its own district; 90 assize courts, where cases are heard by juries; and 26 assize courts of appeal. The Court of Cassation in Rome acts as the highest level of appeal in all cases except those involving constitutional matters, which are brought before the special Constitutional Court. For many years, the number of civil and criminal cases has been increasing more rapidly than the judicial resources to deal with them.

Political Parties

The Christian Democratic Party (Partito Democrazia Cristiana—DC) dominated the government from 1948–81. The DC is referred to as the Popular Party and was part of the Pact for Italy coalition in the 1994 election.

To the right and the left of the DC stand a wide range of parties. The most important of these has traditionally been the Italian Communist Party (Partito Comunista Italiano—PCI), which is now split into two parties: Communist Refounding and the Democratic Party.

DEFENSE

Since 1949 Italy, as a member of the North Atlantic Treaty Organization (NATO), has maintained large and balanced modern forces. The total strength in 1995 was 325,100 (163,800 draftees), not including 113,200 *carabinieri,* or paramilitary national police. The total reserve strength was 584,000. Mandatory military service is for 12 months for all services.

Army personnel numbered 167,200, including 126,700 draftees. Navy personnel totaled 44,000, including 17,600 draftees and 1,000 marines, and 600 naval commandos. The air force had a total strength of 68,000 personnel, including 19,500 draftees. Italy's military budget for 1996 was $20 billion, or 2% of the gross domestic product (GDP).

ECONOMIC AFFAIRS

As the Italian economy has expanded since the 1950s, its structure has changed markedly. The role of agriculture has declined, while the importance of industry has increased dramatically. Precision machinery and motor vehicles have led the surge in manufacturing, and Italy has generally been a leader in European industrial design and fashion in recent decades. By 1989, Italy had the fifth largest Organization for Economic Cooperation and Development (OECD) economy. Unemployment has hovered around 10% to 12% for most of the 1990s. Italy's large public debt, public sector deficit, and complicated tax system are restrictions to economic growth.

Public Finance

Reflecting both increasing economic activity and the pressures of inflation, the Italian budget has expanded continually since 1950. The U.S. CIA estimates that, in 1994, government revenues totaled approximately $339 billion and expenditures $431 billion. External debt totaled $67 billion.

Income

In 1998, Italy's gross national product (GNP) was $1.16 trillion, or about $20,250 per person. During 1985–95, the annual average real growth rate in GNP per person was 1.7%, while the average annual inflation rate was 6%.

Industry

Italian industry expanded rapidly in the postwar period. Industrial production almost tripled between 1955 and 1968, and has generally showed continued growth. The automotive industry, which registered major gains during the 1960s and early 1970s, peaked in 1989, when 2.2 million vehicles were produced. In 1994, crude steel production was 26.1 million tons, ferroalloys, 99.2 million tons; and pig iron, 11.2 million tons. Italy is the second-largest producer of crude steel in the European Union (EU) after Germany.

Banking and Finance

The Bank of Italy (Banca d'Italia), the central bank, is the sole bank of issue and exercises credit control functions. Foreign reserves, excluding gold, totaled $35,297 million in March 1996.

Three banks are of nationwide standing: the Bank of Rome, Credito Italiano, and the Italian Commercial Bank. At the end of 1992 there were numerous foreign banks operating in Italy.

A new banking law was passed in 1993, to bring Italy into conformity with the EU's Second Banking directive, and to introduce two major innovations that aim to move Italy toward a model of universal banking. It allows banks to hold shares in industrial concerns; and it eliminates the distinction between banks (aziende di credito) and special credit institutions (aziende di credito speciale), thus allowing all banks to perform operations previously limited to specific types of intermediary.

On 30 January 1997, the government drafted legislation to promote restructuring and consolidation in Italy's largely inefficient and highly fragmented banking sector. The bill is the latest in a series of attempts since 1990 to rationalize the sector.

There are 10 stock exchanges in operation. The most important is that in Milan (established in 1808). Since 1974, the markets have been regulated by the National Commission for Companies and the Stock Exchange.

Economic Development

The combined effects of inflation, increased energy prices, and political instability posed serious economic problems during the 1970s. With Italy mired in recession in the early 1980s, economic policy was directed at reducing the public sector deficit, tightening controls on credit, and maintaining a stable exchange rate, chiefly through a variety of short-term constraints. A period of recovery began in 1983, leading to expanded output and lower inflation but also to expanded unemployment. The economic policy aims in 1987 included the reduction of the public-sector deficit and unemployment. Furthermore, improvement in the external sector (due mainly to the fall of oil prices and depreciation of the dollar) led to liberalization of the foreign exchange market in May 1987.

Priorities of the early 1990s were cutting government spending, fighting tax evasion to reduce public debt, and selling off state-owned enterprises.

Italy provided $3,352 million in aid to developing countries in 1991, or 0.3% of GNP.

SOCIAL WELFARE

Under current social insurance, all workers and their families are covered and receive old-age, disability, and survivor pensions, unemployment and injury benefits, health and maternity coverage, and family allowances.

Women fill only about 10% of managerial positions and are not well represented in professional positions.

Healthcare

A national health plan, begun in 1980, seeks to provide free health care for all citizens, but certain minimum charges remain. The shortage of medical personnel and hospital facilities in Italy's rural areas remains serious. In 1994, the government announced plans to dismantle public universal insurance. In 1992, there were 296,385 doctors (one for every 210 people) and 389,432 hospital beds (1 for every 147 people). Average life expectancy was estimated to be 78 years for women and men in 1995.

Housing

Italy's housing and public building program was a major item in the general program of postwar reconstruction. Between 1940–45, almost 20% of the habitable rooms in the country were destroyed. In 1985, a total of 39,385 new residential buildings were started. In 1992, the total number of housing units was 24.8 million.

EDUCATION

About 3% of adults are illiterate. Education is free and compulsory for eight years. In the academic year 1993, there were 21,378 public and private elementary schools providing education for 2.9 million pupils. Also, 4.7 million students were enrolled in secondary schools.

Higher education had a total enrollment of 1.7 million in 1993 with 59,770 teaching staff. There are forty-one state universities and fifteen other universities, colleges, and higher learning institutes.

1999 KEY EVENTS TIMELINE

January

- Abdullah Ocalan, the leader of Turkey's separatist guerrilla army, is released by Italian officials after being arrested in December 1998.

- Oskar Piskulic, a 78-year-old Croatian citizen, is tried on charges for his role in a mass murder in northern Italy just after the end of World War II.

- Organized crime and illegal immigrants are blamed for a new rash of street violence in Milan—nine murders in the first nine days of the year.

- The launch of the euro (European Currency Unit) brings a fixed currency rate for eleven European nations including Italy.

February

- Italy's highest appeals court sparks international outrage when it overturns a rape conviction, claiming as one reason that the victim wore blue jeans on the day of the attack.

- Olivetti S.p.A. makes a surprising $65 billion offer in a hostile takeover bid February 20 for telecommunications giant Telecom Italia.

March

- Italy supports the NATO air war on Serbia. NATO aircrafts are allowed to use Italian airbases.

- Italians are angered by the acquittal of a United States Air Force pilot on 20 counts of manslaughter stemming from a ski resort gondola accident in the Italian Alps in 1998. The acquittal was announced March 4.

- United States President Bill Clinton meets with Prime Minister Massimo D'Alema on March 7 and apologizes for the ski resort accident.

- During ceremonies in Los Angeles, California, on March 21, director and actor Roberto Benigni wins the Academy Award for Best Actor and for Best Foreign Film for his film, *Life is Beautiful.*

April

- Two thousand Italian troops are sent to Albania to deliver humanitarian aid for the victims of the Kosovo crisis.

- A surprisingly low voter turnout for the election on April 18 fails to give effect to a referendum on changing the parliamentary electoral system.

May

- The Burger King Corporation signs an agreement with Italian restaurant company Autogrill to open 500 Burger King units in Italy.

- Carlo Azeglio Ciampi is elected the new president by the Italian Parliament on May 14.

- The senior adviser to the Minister of Labor, Massimo D'Antona, is assassinated in Rome on May 20. The Red Brigade terrorist group claims responsibility.

- The bid by telecommunications company Olivetti to take over the much larger Telecom Italia is accepted on May 21.

June

- European elections are held, with Italian voters turning out in higher numbers than any other European country.

- Media tycoon Silvio Berlusconi's Forza Italia party wins the most votes to the European Parliament.

- The world's oldest bank, Monte dei Paschi di Siena, founded in 1472, offers public stock shares for sale for the first time.

- Cyclist Marco Pantani, the 1998 Tour de France winner, is ejected from the Tour of Italy race for failing a drug test.

July

- The Italian government says it will not allow any more refugees from Yugoslavia to enter its borders and will treat them as illegal immigrants.

- Suspected insurance swindler Martin Frankel, sought by American authorities, is suspected of hiding out in Italy after nearly $500,000 in wire transfers is traced to Rome.

- Minister of Culture Giovanna Melandri vows to improve the circulation of Italian films in the United States and internationally.

August

- A joint venture between the University of Pittsburgh and the Italian government will bring liver transplant technology and other specialized medical care to Sicily and southern Italy.

- Shareholders of Banca Intesa S.p.A. approved management's move to acquire Banca Commerciale Italiana and create the largest bank in Italy and the eleventh largest in Europe.

September

- Former seven-time prime minister Giulio Andreotti is acquitted of conspiring with organized crime after a four year trial.

- Prominent anti-fascist writer and post-war senator Leo Valiani dies at his home in Milan. He was 90 years old.

- A two-year investigation discovers evidence of Russian organized crime members laundering millions of dollars through Italian banks.

- The oldest film festival in the world, the 56th Venice International Film Festival, opens on September 1.

- A re-creation of the Leonardo da Vinci-inspired 24-foot-tall bronze horse sculpture is unveiled in Milan on September 10.

October

- Former prime minister and fugitive Bettino Craxi is hospitalized in Tunisia.

- Italian financier Giancarlo Paretti is arrested on long-standing warrants for perjury and fraud.

- Boxes of personal effects belonging to World War II fascist dictator Benito Mussolini are found in a Treasury Ministry vault.

- Leo Lionni, 89, creator of children's books, dies at his home in Radda.

- A unit of Germany's Deutsche Bank takes control of Piaggio, maker of Italy's Vespa Scooters.

- The Italian national soccer team qualifies for the European 2000 championship tournament.

November

- A judge in Milan rules that Silvio Berlusconi, media mogul who leads Italy's center-right opposition, must face a trial for a crime alleged to have happened in 1985; Berlusconi is accused of bribing judges to fix the sale of a state-owned food group.

- The basilica in Assisi reopens after two years of restoration following damage to the thirteenth-century and fourteenth-century frescoes and the vaulted ceiling in a 1997 earthquake.

December

- Massimo D'Alema, Italy's prime minister, seeks to boost trade links with Libya by becoming the first Western leader to meet Colonel Moamar Qadaffi in Tripoli in seven years.

- Italy and the U.S. formally sign a bilateral "open skies" aviation agreement.

ANALYSIS OF EVENTS: 1999

BUSINESS AND THE ECONOMY

The year 1999 saw the introduction of the euro (European Currency Unit) representing a unified fixed-rate currency for eleven countries in the European Union, including Italy. The hope of all the nations involved is for the euro to stimulate each of their economies and challenge the U.S. dollar's lead in international value. The Italian monetary unit, the liré, will be permanently replaced by euro coins and paper money in July 2002. Until then, both currencies will co-exist, but the liré will be tied to the fluctuations in the euro. Through the first six months of the year, however, the euro steadily decreased in value against the dollar.

With much hope riding on the new currency alliance, the economy, however, failed to see much improvement for the first half of the year. Analysts observed a small growth rate in the gross domestic product (GDP) with the unemployment rate at 12 percent, and were fearing that a recession was on the way. There were much more positive reports for the second half of the year with several signs of an economic turnaround. An increased demand for goods and services from abroad along with plans from the treasury minister to cut budget deficits and public spending had business analysts predicting a revival in the economy as only a matter of time.

This was also the year for large American-style corporate mergers in several industries, including telecommunications, real estate, banking, and insurance. The biggest surprise was the $60 billion hostile takeover bid by Olivetti S.p.A. in February of the former state-run Telecom Italia. Olivetti's takeover attempt was compared to a "minnow swallowing a whale." Although Telecom's CEO Franco Bernabe vigorously fought the takeover bid, it was finally accepted in May. In March, four of the country's five largest banks announced merger plans. Banca Commerciale Italiana and Banca Intesa completed their merger in August to form Italy's largest bank and the eleventh largest in Europe. In October, a German bank gained control over the company that produces Italy's trademark Vespa motor scooters.

In the retail and service sectors, Burger King Corporation forged an agreement with Autogrill S.p.A. to open five hundred Burger King units throughout Italy. Luxury good producer and design house Fendi was taken over by Louis Vuitton of France, ending a months-long battle for control. Finally, Italy's strong travel and tourism market was negatively affected by the ongoing conflict in Kosovo as travelers became wary of European trips in general.

GOVERNMENT AND POLITICS

The Italian government has a reputation for being unstable and fractious; fifty-six different governments have been in place since the end of World War II. But in May, the Italian parliament, seeking political stability and consensus, elected 78-year-old Carlo Azeglio Ciampi as the new president by secret ballot on the first round of balloting. President Ciampi had served as the treasury minister prior to assuming the responsibilities of his new position. It is believed that President Ciampi will build stability in Italian government and bring together the forty or so political parties in Italy. In his acceptance speech, he also urged for a stronger European Union.

In April, voters had an opportunity to vote on a referendum to change electoral laws. The system-in-place was criticized for allowing small political parties too much influence in government over the larger parties, resulting in instability. Although the referendum was supported, the percentage of registered voters who turned out to vote fell short of what was necessary to give effect to the referendum. This was seen as a lost opportunity for Italian citizens to have more control over their government. In June, Silvio Berlusconi's right-wing Forza Italia party gained the most votes from Italian voters for seats in the European Parliament.

On May 20, a dark chapter in Italian political life was re-opened when a senior adviser to the Minister of Labor, Massimo D'Antona, was assassinated near his home in Rome. The communist terrorist organization known as the Red Brigade claimed responsibility for the murder. The Red Brigade terrorized Italy in the 1970s, culminating in the kidnapping and murder of Prime Minister Aldo Moro in 1978. Experts were divided over whether this was the beginning of a new wave of Brigade violence.

Prime Minister Massimo D'Alema gained the Italian Parliament and people's confidence in supporting the NATO intervention in Kosovo and war on Serbia. Although he did not permit Italian planes to take part in any bombing, he allowed NATO aircraft to use Italian airbases. Also, 2000 army troops were sent to Albania to assist in the refugee relief effort.

A final chapter was written on Italy's government corruption scandal from the early 1990s when former Prime Minister Giulio Andreotti was acquitted by a three-judge panel on charges of conspiring with organized crime after a four-year trial deemed the "trial of the century" by Italians.

CULTURE AND SOCIETY

The highlight of the year in arts came when Tuscan Roberto Benigni joyously accepted the Oscar for Best Actor and for Best Foreign Film at the 71st annual Academy Awards for his film "La Vita è Bella" ("Life is Beautiful"). He became the first actor to win the Oscar for Best Actor in a non-English language film. The 56th annual Venice Film Festival was held in September under the direction of new director Alberto Barbera who promises to bring new life into the world's oldest film festival. Although Roberto Benigni's success made great strides for Italian cinema, the Minister of Culture, Giovanna Melandri, plans to develop projects and legislation to improve the circulation of Italian films in the United States and throughout the world.

Rome continued to ready itself for the Holy Jubilee, a celebration of 2000 years of Christianity. Twenty-nine million visitors are expected to travel to Rome in 2000 which is twice the number of visitors during a normal year. A total of $4 billion is being spent on infrastructure improvements and new cultural attractions. In September, workers building a new garage ramp at the Vatican discovered the walls of an ancient Roman villa causing construction to halt.

The Supreme Court of Appeals rendered a decision in February that outraged virtually everyone in Italy and internationally from feminists to right-wing politicians. The court overturned a man's rape conviction citing as one reason for the reversal that the female victim was wearing blue jeans at the time of the alleged attack. The court reasoned that it is impossible to remove jeans from a person without their cooperation casting doubt on the credibility of the victim. Female members of parliament showed up to work in blue jeans to protest of the court's lack of insight into sexual violence issues. Italians were also angered over the acquittal of United States Air Force Pilot Richard Ashby who flew his jet too low and cut a ski gondola cable in northern Italy causing the deaths of twenty Europeans. President Bill Clinton met with Prime Minister Massimo D'Alema after the acquittal and expressed his regrets to the Italian people. The Prime Minister was unmoved by President Clinton's apology.

In sports, the Italian national soccer team qualified for the European 2000 Championship tournament. AC Milan, owned by media tycoon and right-wing politician Silvio Berlusconi, won this year's Italian league championship. In June, Ivan Gotti won his second Tour of Italy cycling race in three years. In a race marked with controversy, cyclist Marco Pantani was disqualified after failing a drug test. In July, Ferrari Formula One driver Michael Schumacher was injured in a crash at the British Grand Prix.

DIRECTORY

CENTRAL GOVERNMENT
Head of State

President
Carlo Azeglio-Ciampi, Office of the President, Palazzo del Quirinale, I-00187 Rome, Italy
FAX: +39 (6) 46992384

Ministers

Prime Minister
T. H. Massimo D'Alema, Office of the Prime Minister, Piazza Colonna 370, I-00187 Rome, Italy
FAX: +39 (6) 6783998; 6796894

Minister of Culture
Giovanna Melandri

Minister of Justice
Oliviero Diliberto, Ministry of Justice, Via Arenula 70, I-00186 Rome, Italy
FAX: +39 (6) 5227855

Minister of Finance
Vincenzo Visco, Ministry of Finance, Viale Europa 242, I-00144 Rome, Italy
PHONE: +39 (6) 59971
FAX: +39 (6) 5917240; 5910993

Minister of Treasury
Giuliano Amato, Ministry of Treasury, Via XX Settembre 97, I-00187 Rome, Italy
FAX: +39 (6) 4882146

Minister of Defense
Carlo Scognamiglio, Ministry of Defense, Via XX Settembre 8, I-00187 Rome, Italy
PHONE: +39 (6) 4882126
FAX: +39 (6) 4747775; 4885756

Minister of University and Scientific and Technological Research
Ortensio Zecchino, Ministry of University and Scientific and Technological Research, Piazzale Kennedy 20, I-00144 Rome, Italy
FAX: +39 (6) 5926146

Minister of Education
Luigi Berlinguer, Ministry of Education, Viale Trastevere 76/A, I-00153 Rome, Italy
FAX: +39 (6) 58492057

Minister of Public Works
Enrico Micheli, Ministry of Public Works, Piazza di Porta Pia 1, I-00198 Rome, Italy
FAX: +39 (6) 44124308; 44267275

Minister of Environment
Edo Ronchi, Ministry of Environment, Piazza Venezia 11, I-00187 Rome, Italy
PHONE: +39 (6) 6783331
FAX: +39 (6) 6783844

Minister of Agricultural, Food and Forestry Resources
Paolo De Castro, Ministry of Agricultural, Food and Forestry Resources, Via XX Settembre 20, I-00187 Rome, Italy
FAX: +39 (6) 4746168

Minister of Transport and Merchant Marine
Tiziano Treu, Ministry of Transport and Merchant Marine, Piazza della Croce Rossa 1, I-00161 Rome, Italy
FAX: +39 (6) 44241539; 8540664

Minister of Communications
Salvatore Cardinale, Ministry of Communications, Viale America 201, I-00144 Rome, Italy
FAX: +39 (6) 5942274; 6780408

Minister of Industry, Commerce and Crafts
Pierluigi Bersani, Ministry of Industry, Commerce and Crafts, Via Molise 2, I-00187 Rome, Italy
FAX: +39 (6) 47052215

Minister of Labor and Social Welfare
Cesare Salvi, Ministry of Labor and Social Welfare, Via Flavia 6, I-00187 Rome, Italy
FAX: +39 (6) 47887174; 4881087

Minister of Foreign Trade
Piero Fassino, Ministry of Foreign Trade, Viale America 341, I-00144 Rome, Italy
FAX: +39 (6) 59647507; 59647494

Minister of Health
Rosi Bindi, Ministry of Health, Piazzale dell'Industria 20, I-00144 Rome, Italy
FAX: +39 (6) 59945328

Minister of National Patrimony
Giovanna Melandri, Ministry of National Patrimony, Via del Collegio Romeno 27, I-00186 Rome, Italy
FAX: +39 (6) 6791905; 6793156

POLITICAL ORGANIZATIONS

Forza Italia-FI (Italy Ahead)
Via dell'Umilta 48, I-00187 Rome, Italy
PHONE: +39 (6) 6731268; 6731276
FAX: +39 (6) 69941392; 69941315
NAME: Silvio Berlusconi

Partito Democratico della Sinistra (PDS)
Via delle Botteghe Oscure 4, I-00186 Rome, Italy
PHONE: +39 (6) 6711318; 6711558
FAX: +39 (6) 6792085

Partito della Rifondazione Comunista (PRC)
Via Barberini 11, I-00187 Rome, Italy
PHONE: +39 (6) 4870871
FAX: +39 (6) 4883252

Partito Popolare Italiano (PPI)

Piazza del Gesu' 46, I-00186 Rome, Italy
FAX: +39 (6) 67753951

Cristiani Democratici Uniti (CDU)

Piazza del Gesu' 46, I-00186 Rome, Italy
PHONE: +39 (6) 67751; 67753844
FAX: +39 (6) 67753951

Comitato per l'Italia che Vogliamo (Ulivo)

Largo Pietro di Brazza 26, I-00187 Rome, Italy
PHONE: +39 (6) 69920282; 69920464
FAX: +39 (6) 69920457

Centro Cristiano Democratico

Via di Ripetta 142, I-00186 Rome, Italy
PHONE: +39 (6) 68806108
FAX: +39 (6) 68806414

Alleanza Nazionale (AN)

Via della Scrofa 39, I-00186 Rome, Italy
PHONE: +39 (6) 6833769; 6872918; 6864364
FAX: +39 (6) 6879581; 4879252

Lega Nord (Northern League)

Via Carlo Bellerio 41, 20161 Milano, Italy
FAX: +39 (2) 66211298; 66202375

Federazione dei Verdi

Via Catalana 1/A, I-00186 Rome, Italy
PHONE: +39 (6) 68802879
FAX: +39 (6) 68803023

Partito Radicale

Via Uffici del Vicario 21, I-00186 Rome, Italy
PHONE: +39 (6) 6760592; 67603311; 6780804
FAX: +39 (6) 6781904; 6780804

Partito Radicale Transnazionale

PHONE: +39 (6) 689791
FAX: +39 (6) 68805396

La Rete-Movimento per la Democrazia

Lungotevere Marzio 3, I-00186 Rome, Italy
PHONE: +39 (6) 68300448; 68300447
FAX: +39 (6) 68300446

Patto Segni

Via Belsiana 100, I-00187 Rome, Italy
PHONE: +39 (6) 6786240; 6786240; 6780840
FAX: +39 (6) 6789890

Unione di Centro

Via della Stelletta 23, I-00186 Rome, Italy
PHONE: +39 (6) 6872344

Partito Repubblicano Italiano

Piazza dei Caprettari 70, I-00186 Rome, Italy
PHONE: +39 (6) 6834037; 6834038; 6834039
FAX: +39 (6) 68300903

Federazione dei Liberali Italiani

Via Frattina 89, I-00187 Rome, Italy
PHONE: +39 (6) 6783252
FAX: +39 (6) 6797102

Partito Socialista Italiano (PSI)

Via Tomacelli 146, I-00186 Rome, Italy
PHONE: +39 (6) 68604274
FAX: +39 (6) 68604282

Rinascita Socialista

Via G. De Calvi 6, I-00151 Rome, Italy
PHONE: +39 (6) 5371371
FAX: +39 (6) 538041

Alleanza Democratica

Via del Plebiscito 102, I-00186 Rome, Italy
PHONE: +39 (6) 69942200
FAX: +39 (6) 69942435

Movimento Cristiano-Sociali

Piazza Adriana 5, I-00193 Rome, Italy
PHONE: +39 (6) 68300537
FAX: +39 (6) 68300539

DIPLOMATIC REPRESENTATION
Embassies in Italy

Albania
Via Asmara 9, Rome, Italy
PHONE: +39 (6) 8380725

Argentina
Piazza Esquilino 2, Rome, Italy
PHONE: +39 (6) 4742551

Austria
Via Pergolesi 3, Rome, Italy
PHONE: +39 (6) 8558241

Belgium
Via Monti Parioli 49, Rome, Italy

Brazil
Piazza Navona 14, Rome, Italy
PHONE: +39 (6) 6838841

Bulgaria
Via Rubens 21, Rome, Italy
PHONE: +39 (6) 3224643

Canada
Via G.B. de Rossi 27, I-00161 Rome, Italy
FAX: +39 (6) 44598754

Croatia
Via SS. Cosma e Damiano 26, Rome, Italy
PHONE: +39 (6) 33250242

Czech Republic
Via Colli Farnesina 144, Rome, Italy
PHONE: +39 (6) 3296711

Denmark
Via Monti Parioli 50, Rome, Italy
PHONE: +39 (6) 3200441

Finland
Via Lisbona 3, Rome, Italy
PHONE: +39 (6) 8548329; 8848182

Germany
Via Po 25/c, Rome, Italy
PHONE: +39 (6) 884741

Greece
Via Mercadante 36, Rome, Italy
PHONE: +39 (6) 8442584

Hungary
Via Villini 12/16, Rome, Italy
PHONE: +39 (6) 4402032

Iceland
Via Donatello 21, Milan, Italy
PHONE: +39 (02) 70638515

Ireland
Largo Nazareno 3, Rome, Italy
PHONE: +39 (6) 6782541

Japan
Via Sella 60, Rome, Italy
PHONE: +39 (6) 4817151

Lithuania
Piazza Farnese 44, Rome, Italy
PHONE: +39 (6) 6865786

Luxembourg
Via Ardeatina 134, Rome, Italy
PHONE: +39 (6) 5180885

Malta
Lungotevere Marzio 12, Rome, Italy
PHONE: +39 (6) 6892687; 6879990

Monaco
Via Bertoloni 36, Rome, Italy
PHONE: +39 (6) 8077692

Netherlands
Via Mercati 8, Rome, Italy
PHONE: +39 (6) 3221141

Norway
Via Terme Deciane 79, Rome, Italy
PHONE: +39 (6) 5755853

Poland
Via Rubens 20, Rome, Italy
PHONE: +39 (02) 3224455; 3224597

Portugal
Via Pezzana 9, Rome, Italy
PHONE: +39 (6) 8073801

Romania
Via Tartaglia 36, Rome, Italy
PHONE: +39 (6) 8078807; 8084423

Russia
Via Gaeta 5, Rome, Italy
PHONE: +39 (6) 4941649

Serbia
Via Monti Parioli 20, Rome, Italy
PHONE: +39 (6) 3200805; 3200897

Slovakia
Via Colli Farnesina 144, Rome, Italy
PHONE: +39 (6) 36308617

Slovenia
Via Pisano 10, Rome, Italy
PHONE: +39 (6) 8081075

South Africa
Via Tanaro 14/16, Rome, Italy
PHONE: +39 (6) 8419794

Spain
Via Garibaldi 35, Rome, Italy
PHONE: +39 (6) 5800144

Sweden
Piazza Rio de Janeiro 3, Rome, Italy
PHONE: +39 (6) 44231459

Switzerland
Via Oriani 61, Rome, Italy
PHONE: +39 (6) 8083641

Turkey
Via Palestro 28, Rome, Italy
PHONE: +39 (6) 4469932; 4941526

Ukraine
Via Castelfidardo 50, Rome, Italy
PHONE: +39 (6) 44700172

United Kingdom
Via XX Settembre 80/a, Rome, Italy
PHONE: +39 (6) 4825441

United States

Via Veneto 119/a, I-00187 Rome, Italy

FAX: +39 (6) 4882672

JUDICIAL SYSTEM

Corte Suprema di Cassazione (Supreme Court of Cassation)

Palazzo di Giustizea, Piazza Cavour, I-00193 Rome, Italy

FAX: +39 (6) 6874170

Corte Costituzionale (Constitutional Court)

Palazzo della Consulta, Piazza del Quirinale 41, I-00187 Rome, Italy

Consiglio Superiore della Magistratura (Superior Council of the Judiciary)

Piazza dell'Indipendenza 6, I-00185 Rome, Italy

FURTHER READING
Articles

Andrews, Edmund L. "Slide in Currency Is Chilling Europe." *The New York Times,* 10 July 1999.

"Berlusconi's Back." *The Economist* (June 26, 1999): 60.

Burke, Greg and Thomas Sancton. "Return of the Red Brigades: A Brutal Political Killing in Rome Points to the Resurgence of a Feared Leftist Terrorist Organization." *Time International* (May 31, 1999): 32.

"A Canny Breed, Those Jolly Italians." *The Economist* (March 27, 1999): 55.

"Carlo Azeglio Ciampi, Italy's New President." *The Economist* (May 22, 1999): 60.

"The Euro's First Success." *The Seattle Times,* 31 December 1998.

"French-Italian Alliance Takes Controlling Stake in Fendi." *The New York Times,* 13 October 1999.

Hughes, Candice. "Venice Film Festival Gets Fresh Eye." *The Seattle Times,* 2 September 1999.

"Italian Outrage." *Maclean's* (March 15, 1999): 29.

"Italy Breaks the Old Mold." *Business Week* (April 5, 1999): 22.

"Italy's Ex-Premier Acquitted." *San Jose Mercury News,* 24 October 1999.

"Italy's Prime Minister Is Unswayed by Clinton Apology." *The New York Times,* 8 March 1999.

"Italy's Reformers Thwarted." *The Economist* (April 24, 1999): 52.

"Italy Tries Croat Charged with Participation in Massacre Just After WWII." *The Chicago Tribune,* 11 January 1999.

"Judged By Her Jeans: Italian Women Are Up in Arms After a Court Declares That a Woman Who Is Wearing Jeans Can't Be Raped." *Time International* (March 1, 1999): 51.

Lane, David. "Against All Odds." *Accountancy* (July 1999): 24.

"Loyal Italians." *The Economist* (April 17, 1999): 53.

Mondellini, Luciano. "Afternoon Mega-Merger." *Euromoney* (April 1999): 10.

"Rome's Face-Lift Is Behind Schedule . . . But the Souvenir Vendors Are Ready." *Business Week* (March 15, 1999): 4.

Simon, Roger. "Italy's Prime Minister Is Unswayed by Clinton Apology." *The Chicago Tribune* (March 8, 1999): K2204.

Tagliabue, John. "International Business; In Europe's Big Economies, New Signs of Brisk Growth." *The New York Times,* 10 August 1999.

"Take It to the People." *The Economist* (February 6, 1999): 53.

Trevelyan, Robert. "Italy Special Report." *Middle East Economic Report* (July 2, 1999): 7.

Young, Deborah. "Minister Vows to Protect Italo Pix." *Variety* (August 30, 1999): 18.

Zulli, Heather. "Cosmopolitan Criminal." *The Economist* (January 16, 1999): 47.

ITALY: STATISTICAL DATA

For sources and notes see "Sources of Statistics" in the front of each volume.

GEOGRAPHY

Geography (1)

Area:

Total: 301,230 sq km.

Land: 294,020 sq km.

Water: 7,210 sq km.

Note: includes Sardinia and Sicily.

Area—comparative: slightly larger than Arizona.

Land boundaries:

Total: 1,932.2 km.

Border countries: Austria 430 km, France 488 km, Holy See (Vatican City) 3.2 km, San Marino 39 km, Slovenia 232 km, Switzerland 740 km.

Coastline: 7,600 km.

Climate: predominantly Mediterranean; Alpine in far north; hot, dry in south.

Terrain: mostly rugged and mountainous; some plains, coastal lowlands.

Natural resources: mercury, potash, marble, sulfur, dwindling natural gas and crude oil reserves, fish, coal.

Land use:

Arable land: 31%

Permanent crops: 10%

Permanent pastures: 15%

Forests and woodland: 23%

Other: 21% (1993 est.).

HUMAN FACTORS

Demographics (2A)

	1990	1995	1998	2000	2010	2020	2030	2040	2050
Population	NA	56,908.7	56,782.7	56,686.6	55,297.2	52,209.2	48,342.0	43,711.8	38,290.1
Net migration rate (per 1,000 population)	NA	NA	NA	NA	NA	NA	NA	NA	NA
Births	NA	NA	NA	NA	NA	NA	NA	NA	NA
Deaths	NA	NA	NA	NA	NA	NA	NA	NA	NA
Life expectancy - males	NA	74.8	75.3	75.5	76.7	77.7	78.6	79.2	79.8
Life expectancy - females	NA	81.3	81.7	81.9	83.0	83.9	84.7	85.3	85.8
Birth rate (per 1,000)	NA	9.1	9.1	9.4	7.3	6.4	6.2	5.6	5.3
Death rate (per 1,000)	NA	9.8	10.2	10.4	11.8	13.2	14.8	17.2	20.0
Women of reproductive age (15-49 yrs.)	NA	14,310.9	14,013.1	13,778.8	12,530.8	10,464.3	8,493.4	7,314.2	6,192.1
of which are currently married	NA	NA	NA	NA	NA	NA	NA	NA	NA
Fertility rate	NA	1.2	1.2	1.3	1.3	1.3	1.3	1.3	1.3

Except as noted, values for vital statistics are in thousands; life expectancy is in years.

Health Personnel (3)

Total health expenditure as a percentage of GDP, 1990-1997[a]

Public sector 5.3

Private sector 2.3

Total[b] 7.6

Health expenditure per capita in U.S. dollars, 1990-1997[a]

Purchasing power parity 1,589

Total 1,515

Availability of health care facilities per 100,000 people

Hospital beds 1990-1997[a] 640

Doctors 1993[c] . . . . .NA

Nurses 1993[c] . . . . .NA

Health Indicators (4)

Life expectancy at birth

1980 74

1997 78

Daily per capita supply of calories (1996) 3,504

Total fertility rate births per woman (1997) 1.2

Maternal mortality ratio per 100,000 live births (1990-97) . . . . .12[c]

Safe water % of population with access (1995) . . . .

Sanitation % of population with access (1995) . . . .

Consumption of iodized salt % of households (1992-98)[a] . . . .

Smoking prevalence

Male % of adults (1985-95)[a] 38

Female % of adults (1985-95)[a] 26

Tuberculosis incidence per 100,000 people (1997) 10

Adult HIV prevalence % of population ages 15-49 (1997) 0.31

Infants and Malnutrition (5)

Under-5 mortality rate (1997) 6

% of infants with low birthweight (1990-97) 5

Births attended by skilled health staff % of total[a] . . .NA

% fully immunized (1995-97)

TB . . . . .NA

DPT 92

Polio 93

Measles 94

Prevalence of child malnutrition under age 5 (1992-97)[b] . . . . .NA

Ethnic Division (6)

Italian (includes small clusters of German-, French-, and Slovene-Italians in the north and Albanian-Italians and Greek-Italians in the south).

Religions (7)

Roman Catholic 98%

Other 2%

Languages (8)

Italian, German (parts of Trentino-Alto Adige region are predominantly German speaking), French (small French- speaking minority in Valle d'Aosta region), Slovene (Slovene-speaking minority in the Trieste-Gorizia area).

EDUCATION

Public Education Expenditures (9)

Public expenditure on education (% of GNP)

1980 . . . .

1996 . . . . .4.7[1]

Expenditure per student

Primary % of GNP per capita

1980 . . . .

1996 . . . . .21.5[1]

Secondary % of GNP per capita

1980 . . . .

1996 . . . .

Tertiary % of GNP per capita

1980 . . . .

1996 . . . . .21.9

Expenditure on teaching materials

Primary % of total for level (1996) . . . .

Secondary % of total for level (1996) . . . .

Primary pupil-teacher ratio per teacher (1996) . . . . .11[1]

Duration of primary education years (1995) 5

Educational Attainment (10)

Age group (1981) . . . . .6+

Total population 53,481,852

Highest level attained (%)

No schooling[2] 2.1

First level

Not completed 12.2

Completed 32.5

Entered second level

S-1 . . . . .30.7

S-2 . . . . .18.6

Postsecondary 3.8

Literacy Rates (11B)

Adult literacy rate

1980

Male 95%

Female 92%

1995

Male 99

Female 98

GOVERNMENT & LAW

Political Parties (12)

Chamber of Deputies	No. of seats
Olive Tree	.284
Freedom Alliance	.246
Northern League	.59
Refounded Communists	.35
Southern Tyrol List	.3
Autonomous List	.2
Other	.1

Military Affairs (14B)

	1990	1991	1992	1993	1994	1995
Military expenditures						
Current dollars (mil.)	19,150	19,940	20,010	20,670	20,700	19,380
1995 constant dollars (mil.)	22,010	22,030	21,530	21,670	21,220	19,380
Armed forces (000)	493	473	471	450	436	435
Gross national product (GNP)						
Current dollars (bil.)	886,400	930,800	960,400	980,200	1,025,000	1,082,000[e]
1995 constant dollars (bil.)	1,019,000	1,029,000	1,033,000	1,028,000	1,050,000	1,082,000[e]
Central government expenditures (CGE)						
1995 constant dollars (mil.)	505,900	517,500	552,500	559,400	543,400	NA
People (mil.)	57.7	57.8	57.2	57.2	57.3	57.4
Military expenditure as % of GNP	2.2	2.1	2.1	2.1	2.0	1.8
Military expenditure as % of CGE	4.4	4.3	3.9	3.9	3.9	NA
Military expenditure per capita (1995 $)	382	381	377	379	370	338
Armed forces per 1,000 people (soldiers)	8.5	8.2	8.2	7.9	7.6	7.6
GNP per capita (1995 $)	17,670	17,800	18,070	17,950	18,330	18,850
Arms imports[6]						
Current dollars (mil.)	240	280	120	110	110	110
1995 constant dollars (mil.)	276	309	129	115	115	110
Arms exports[6]						
Current dollars (mil.)	200	300	370	350	140	150
1995 constant dollars (mil.)	230	332	398	367	144	150
Total imports[7]						
Current dollars (mil.)	182,000	182,700	188,500	148,300	169,200	204,100
1995 constant dollars (mil.)	209,100	201,900	202,700	155,400	173,400	204,100
Total exports[7]						
Current dollars (mil.)	170,500	169,500	178,200	169,200	191,400	231,300
1995 constant dollars (mil.)	195,900	187,300	191,600	177,300	196,200	231,300
Arms as percent of total imports[8]	.1	.2	.1	.1	.1	.1
Arms as percent of total exports[8]	.1	.2	.2	.2	.1	.1

Government Budget (13B)

Revenues . . . .$416 billion

Expenditures . . . .$506 billion

  Capital expenditures . . . .$47 billion

Data for 1996 est.

Crime (15)

Crime rate (for 1997)

  Crimes reported .2,440,800

  Total persons convicted 604,800

  Crimes per 100,000 population 4,250

Persons responsible for offenses

  Total number of suspects 784,700

  Total number of female suspects . . . . .NA

  Total number of juvenile suspects 22,700

LABOR FORCE

Labor Force (16)

Total (million) 22.851

Services 61%

Industry 32%

Agriculture 7%

Data for 1996.

Unemployment Rate (17)

12.2% (December 1997 est.)

PRODUCTION SECTOR

Electric Energy (18)

Capacity . . . . .57.186 million kW (1995)

Production . . . . .225.179 billion kWh (1995)

Consumption per capita . . . . .4,509 kWh (1995)

Transportation (19)

Highways:

total: 317,000 km

paved: 317,000 km (including 9,500 km of expressways)

unpaved: 0 km (1996 est.)

Waterways: 2,400 km for various types of commercial traffic, although of limited overall value

Pipelines: crude oil 1,703 km; petroleum products 2,148 km; natural gas 19,400 km

Merchant marine:

total: 365 ships (1,000 GRT or over) totaling 5,032,728 GRT/7,076,307 DWT ships by type: bulk 29, cargo 47, chemical tanker 39, combination ore/oil 2, container 15, liquefied gas tanker 30, multifunction large-load carrier 1, oil tanker 98, passenger 5, roll-on/roll-off cargo 51, short-sea passenger 30, specialized tanker 11, vehicle carrier 7 (1997 est.)

Airports: 136 (1997 est.)

Airports—with paved runways:

total: 96

over 3,047 m: 5

2,438 to 3,047 m: 33

1,524 to 2,437 m: 16

914 to 1,523 m: 30

under 914 m: 12 (1997 est.)

Airports—with unpaved runways:

total: 40

1,524 to 2,437 m: 2

914 to 1,523 m: 20

under 914 m: 18 (1997 est.)

Top Agricultural Products (20)

Fruits, vegetables, grapes, potatoes, sugar beets, soybeans, grain, olives; meat and dairy products; fish catch of 525,000 metric tons in 1990.

MANUFACTURING SECTOR

GDP & Manufacturing Summary (21)

Detailed value added figures are listed by both International Standard Industry Code (ISIC) and product title.

	1980	1985	1990	1994
GDP ($-1990 mil.)[1]	878,864	942,069	1,095,122	1,138,253
Per capita ($-1990)[1]	15,573	16,594	19,205	19,914
Manufacturing share (%) (current prices)[1]	28.1	24.5	22.7	20.8
Manufacturing				
Value added ($-1990 mil.)[1]	191,990	202,705	245,232	255,658
Industrial production index	100	96	112	110
Value added ($ mil.)	97,032	64,726	144,733	128,486

	1980	1985	1990	1994
Gross output ($ mil.)	250,912	212,913	478,032	428,813
Employment (000)	3,333	2,875	2,757	2,692
Profitability (% of gross output)				
Intermediate input (%)	61	70	70	70
Wages and salaries inc. supplements (%)	21	18	27	28
Gross operating surplus	18	12	4	2
Productivity ($)				
Gross output per worker	74,433	73,115	170,315	156,427
Value added per worker	28,784	22,227	51,566	46,871
Average wage (inc. supplements)	15,647	13,630	46,298	44,166
Value added ($ mil.)				
311/2 Food products	6,362	3,618	9,599	10,333
313 Beverages	1,672	1,354	2,015	1,739
314 Tobacco products	307	224	556	552
321 Textiles	6,716	5,062	10,327	8,584
322 Wearing apparel	3,197	2,322	4,876	4,986
323 Leather and fur products	718	560	1,234	1,243
324 Footwear	1,495	1,260	2,231	2,171
331 Wood and wood products	1,318	786	1,616	1,421
332 Furniture and fixtures	1,936	1,257	2,900	2,553
341 Paper and paper products	2,260	1,661	3,878	3,124
342 Printing and publishing	3,017	2,271	6,171	5,661
351 Industrial chemicals	6,354	4,219	5,906	4,807
352 Other chemical products	4,068	2,471	3,974	3,001
353 Petroleum refineries	1,128	936	1,718	1,707
354 Miscellaneous petroleum and coal products	206	170	406	438
355 Rubber products	1,832	1,107	2,254	1,876
356 Plastic products	1,465	1,729	4,799	4,547
361 Pottery, china and earthenware	1,984	1,178	2,860	2,463
362 Glass and glass products	1,336	806	1,673	1,467
369 Other non-metal mineral products	3,361	1,864	4,299	3,458
371 Iron and steel	8,354	3,846	8,117	4,899
372 Non-ferrous metals	1,315	875	1,788	1,418
381 Metal products	5,687	3,405	8,014	7,390
382 Non-electrical machinery	9,326	8,914	20,330	19,846
383 Electrical machinery	8,435	5,813	14,990	14,198
384 Transport equipment	10,280	6,172	14,550	12,325
385 Professional and scientific equipment	2,032	550	1,761	1,291
390 Other manufacturing industries	871	297	1,890	989

FINANCE, ECONOMICS, & TRADE

Economic Indicators (22)

National product: GDP—purchasing power parity—$1.24 trillion (1997 est.)

National product real growth rate: 1.5% (1997 est.)

National product per capita: $21,500 (1997 est.)

Inflation rate—consumer price index: 1.9% (1997 est.)

Balance of Payments (23)

	1992	1993	1994	1995	1996
Exports of goods (f.o.b.)	178,155	169,153	191,421	233,998	250,843
Imports of goods (f.o.b.)	−174,969	−136,328	−155,827	−189,240	−190,021
Trade balance	3,186	32,825	35,595	44,758	60,821
Services - debits	−114,102	−103,880	−100,733	−114,923	−122,553
Services - credits	88,363	86,565	85,440	99,904	110,052
Private transfers (net)	−7,274	−7,869	−7,158	−5,382	−7,631
Government transfers (net)	−264	−637	67	777	352
Overall balance	−30,091	8,279	13,211	25,134	41,040

Exchange Rates (24)

Exchange rates:

Italian lire (Lit) per US$1

January 1998	1,787.7
1997	1,703.1
1996	1,542.9
1995	1,628.9
1994	1,612.4
1993	1,573.7

Top Import Origins (25)

$190 billion (c.i.f., 1996).

Origins	%
European Union	45.5
OPEC	4.8
United States	4.3

Top Export Destinations (26)

$250.8 billion (f.o.b., 1996).

Destinations	%
European Union	53.4
United States	7.8
OPEC	3.8

Economic Aid (27)

Donor: ODA, $3.043 billion (1993).

Import Export Commodities (28)

Import Commodities	Export Commodities
Industrial machinery	Metals
Chemicals	Textiles and clothing
Transport equipment	Production machinery
Petroleum	Motor vehicles
Metals	Transportation equipment
Food	Chemicals
Agricultural products	

JAMAICA

CAPITAL: Kingston.

FLAG: Two diagonal yellow gold bars forming a saltire divide the flag into four triangular panels. The two side panels are black, and the top and bottom panels are green.

ANTHEM: First line, ''Eternal father, bless our land . . .''

MONETARY UNIT: The Jamaican dollar (J $) of 100 cents was introduced on 8 September 1969. There are coins of 1, 5, 10, and 25 cents, and 1 dollar, and notes of 2, 5, 10, 20, 50, and 100 dollars. J $1 = US $0.02865 (or US $1 = J $34.909).

WEIGHTS AND MEASURES: Both metric and imperial weights and measures are used.

HOLIDAYS: New Year's Day, 1 January; Labor Day, 23 May; Independence Day, 1st Monday in August; National Heroes' Day, 3rd Monday in October; Christmas, 25 December; Boxing Day, 26 December. Movable religious holidays include Ash Wednesday, Good Friday, and Easter Monday.

TIME: 7 AM = noon GMT.

LOCATION AND SIZE: Jamaica is an island in the Caribbean Sea situated about 160 kilometers (90 miles) south of Cuba. It has a total area of 10,990 square kilometers (4,243 square miles), slightly smaller than the state of Connecticut. The total coastline is 1,022 kilometers (634 miles).

Jamaica's capital city, Kingston, is located on the country's southeastern coast.

CLIMATE: The climate ranges from tropical at sea level to temperate in the uplands; there is relatively little seasonal variation in temperature. The average annual temperature in the coastal lowlands is 27°C (81°F); for the Blue Mountains, 13°C (55°F). The island has an average annual rainfall of 198 centimeters (78 inches), with wide variations during the year between the north and south coasts. The rainy seasons are May to June and September to November.

INTRODUCTORY SURVEY

RECENT HISTORY

In 1944, Jamaica was granted self-government by England, and had its first election. Jamaica became an independent state on 6 August 1962, with dominion status in the Commonwealth of Nations. The Jamaica Labour Party (JLP) became the ruling party, and its leader, Sir Alexander Bustamante, became the nation's first prime minister.

The JLP held power through the 1960s. In February 1972, the rival People's National Party (PNP) gained a majority in Parliament, and Michael Manley headed a new democratic socialist government. Manley established friendly relations with Cuba, which the United States criticized.

Deteriorating economic conditions led to violence in Kingston and elsewhere during the mid-1970s, discouraging tourism. By 1976, Jamaica was faced with declining exports and an unemployment rate estimated at 30–40%. Tourism suffered another blow in January 1979 with three days of rioting in Kingston at the height of the tourist season.

Manley called for elections in the fall of 1980. The opposition JLP won a landslide victory, and Edward Seaga became prime minister and minister of finance. He announced a conservative economic program that brought an immediate harvest of aid from the United States and the International Monetary Fund (IMF). In October 1981, Jamaica broke off diplomatic relations with Cuba, and two years

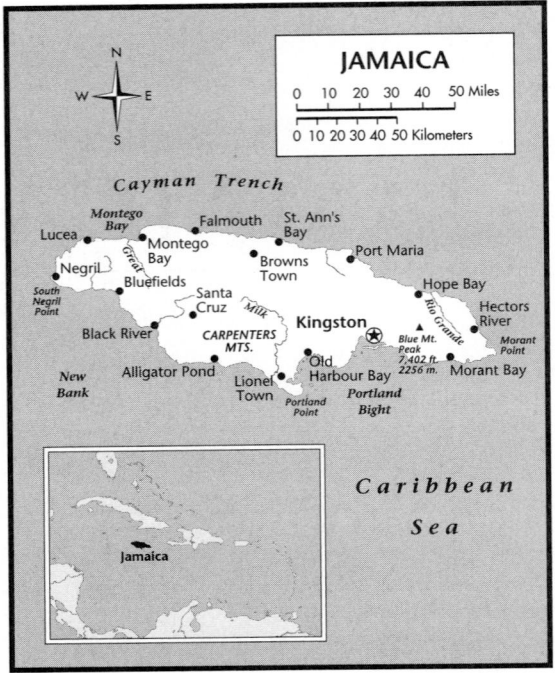

The Senate—the upper house—consists of twenty-one appointed members. The popularly elected House of Representatives consists of sixty members. The House is by far the more important of the two chambers.

The governor-general appoints both the prime minister and the leader of the opposition. The normal term of office in Parliament is five years, but elections can be called at any time. Voting is universal at age 18.

The cabinet consists of the prime minister and at least eleven additional ministers, appointed by the governor-general on the advice of the prime minister.

Judiciary

Cases may be heard first before a lay magistrate (justice of the peace), a magistrate, or a judge in the Supreme Court, according to the seriousness of the offense or the amount of property involved. The Supreme Court also hears appeals. Final appeal rests with the seven-member Court of Appeals.

Political Parties

Two political parties dominate Jamaican politics. The Jamaica Labour Party (JLP), the more conservative of the two parties, held a parliamentary majority during the first ten years of independence, and again from 1980–89 under Edward Seaga. Seaga remains opposition leader.

The People's National Party (PNP), which was returned to power in 1989 under Norman W. Manley, its founder, holds to a moderate socialist program. Both the JLP and PNP stand for a broad program of social reform and welfare, and economic development with the participation of foreign investment.

A third political party, the National Democratic Movement (NDM), was formed in October 1995 by Bruce Golding, the former leader of the JLP. Tensions between the NDM and the JLP have resulted in ten political murders.

DEFENSE

The Jamaica Defense Force in 1995 numbered 3,320 personnel, including 870 reserves. In 1992, Jamaica spent U.S. $28 million on defense.

ECONOMIC AFFAIRS

The structure of the Jamaican economy has undergone major changes since 1945, when it was

later it participated in the U.S.-led invasion of Grenada.

The conservative JLP under Seaga remained in power through the 1980s, but its support eroded as it carried out unpopular economic policies mandated by the IMF.

Criticizing the decline in social services under Seaga and promising to attract foreign investment, Manley and the PNP were returned to office in the 1989 elections. Manley reversed many of Seaga's policies, but by 1992, inflation was on the rise and the economy slowed. Unemployment hovered around 20%.

Manley retired in 1992, leaving the government to Percival J. Patterson, who moved politically further to the right, encouraging more reforms.

Patterson encouraged more market-oriented reforms. Violence erupted during the campaigning of the 1995 elections, and political violence resurged again in 1996. Patterson was reelected in 1997.

GOVERNMENT

The 1962 constitution provides for a governor-general appointed by the British crown, a cabinet presided over by a prime minister, and a two-chamber legislature.

primarily dependent on tropical agricultural products—sugar, bananas, coffee, and cocoa. The island has since become one of the world's largest producers of bauxite. It also has developed as a major tourist center for North Americans.

Public Finance

The 1993–94 budget called for a total expenditure of J$40,370 million, an increase of 54.2% over the previous fiscal year's budget. Recurrent account expenditures rose to a larger share (70.3%) of the total budget, a reversal of the trend over the previous several years. The budget deficit of J$11 billion was financed from external debt (60%) and internal debt (40%). As a result of debt forgiveness, Jamaica's external debt fell by 11.4% to $3.68 billion during 1991–93. The U.S. CIA estimates that, in 1995, government revenues totaled approximately $1.45 billion and expenditures $2 billion, including capital expenditures of $732 million. External debt totaled $3.6 billion.

Income

In 1998, Jamaica's gross national product (GNP) was U.S. $4.3 billion, or about U.S. $1,680 per person. For the period 1985–95, the average inflation rate was 28.3%, resulting in a real growth rate in GNP of 3.7% per person.

Industry

Since 1945, when Jamaican manufacturing was confined largely to processing local agricultural products and making beer, clothing, and furniture, the industries have grown and diversified considerably. The island now produces a wide range of goods.

Banking and Finance

The Bank of Jamaica, the central bank, acts as the government's banker and is authorized to act as agent for the government in the management of the public debt. It also issues and redeems currency, administers Jamaica's external reserves, oversees private banks, and influences the volume and conditions of the supply of credit.

The extent of the drain upon public finances caused by the precarious state of the financial sector became clear in mid-February 1997, when it was reported that net advances by the Bank of Jamaica to financial institutions had risen by J$607 million (U.S.$17.4 million) in January alone, bringing the total outstanding to J$8.7 billion. Century National Bank, which was taken over by the government in July 1996, has so far received a total of J$5.5 billion, and it is clear that several other financial institutions are still dependent upon the government to solve their liquidity problems.

In September 1968 the Jamaican Stock Exchange was incorporated. Jamaica's security market merged with the stock markets in Barbados and Trinidad and Tobago in 1989.

Economic Development

Key sectors in this island economy are bauxite (aluminum and bauxite account for more than half of exports) and tourism. Since assuming office in 1992, Prime Minister Patterson has consolidated the market-oriented reforms initiated by his predecessor, Michael Manley, to make Jamaica a regional leader in economic reform. Patterson has eliminated most price controls, streamlined tax schedules, and privatized government enterprises. Tight monetary and fiscal policies under an IMF program have helped slow inflation and stabilize the exchange rate, but, as a result, economic growth has slowed down and unemployment remains high.

SOCIAL WELFARE

Jamaica has pioneered in social welfare in the West Indies since 1938. Government assistance is provided to those in need, and rehabilitation grants and family allowances are made. A National Insurance Scheme (NIS) came into effect in April 1966, providing benefits in the form of old-age and disability health and maternity coverage, pensions, workers' compensation, widows' and widowers' pensions, and grants.

Cultural traditions, economic discrimination, and workplace sexual harassment have prevented women from achieving full equality.

Crime is a serious social problem, with 900 reported homicides in 1996.

Healthcare

The central government provides most medical services in Jamaica through the Ministry of Health. In 1992, 90% of the population had access to health care services.

The government conducts a broad public health program, involving epidemic control, health education, industrial health protection, and campaigns against tuberculosis, venereal diseases, yaws, and malaria. Tuberculosis, hookworm, and venereal diseases remain the most prevalent diseases. Life expectancy in 1995 averaged 74 years for both men and women.

Housing

Although middle- and upper-income housing is comparable to that in neighboring areas of North America, facilities for low-income groups are poor by any standard. The problem has been aggravated by constant migration from the rural areas to the cities, causing the growth of urban slums. Most new urban housing is built of cinder block and steel on the edges of cities. Rural housing is primarily built of wood and roofed with zinc sheeting. Squatter settlements surround the major cities of Jamaica.

EDUCATION

Jamaica's estimated illiteracy rate is 15%. In 1992, there were 333,104 primary school students and 235,071 secondary students. Education is compulsory for six years of primary education.

At the university and higher level institutions, there were 15,891 students enrolled in 1991.

1999 KEY EVENTS TIMELINE

March

- Jamaica deploys soldiers in tourist areas to prevent thefts and harassment of visitors.

April

- Fears rise as killers shoot police officers. In a two-week period, four current and former police officers are killed, and six more are wounded.

- Jamaicans protest a 30 percent increase in gas prices. Many loot stores, stone motorists and set flaming tire barricades in Kingston. At least nine die and many are injured in the riots.

July

- Jamaica's Prime Minister, P.J. Patterson gives the military broad powers to intervene in gang wars that have driven hundreds of people from their homes in Kingston's poorest neighborhoods.

- Mikel Wallace, a member of the internationally renowned reggae group Third World, is fatally shot during an attempted carjacking in Kingston. He was 43.

- Britain's conservatives blame the upsurge in gun violence on Jamaican immigrants. Jamaica opposes calls for visa restrictions.

- Dennis Brown, the singer who took over from Bob Marley as Jamaica's "Crown Prince of Reggae," dies from pneumonia after long illness. The singer was one of the most influential exponents of reggae music. He was 42.

August

- Madam Rose Agatha Leon, beloved former government minister and leader of the Jamaica Labor Party, is murdered inside her home. She was 80.

- Amnesty International seeks an inquiry into the forced removal of homeless people from the resort town of Montego Bay.

- Jamaican track star Merlene Ottey, the most successful athlete in the history of the world championships, tests positive for the banned steroid nandrolone.

September

- The government announces that 1,000 police officers have been disciplined and 29 fired in 1999.

- Australian swimmer Susie Maroney, 24, becomes the first person to swim from Jamaica to Cuba. She arrives in Cuba after a 36-hour, 119-mile swim in seas whipped up by Hurricane Floyd.

October

- The National Minority Business Council in cooperation with the Jamaica Economic Development Agency (JAMPRO) holds its 2nd Annual Trade and investment Mission in Kingston October 29 to November 2 to help businesses owned by women and minorities identify opportunities.

December

- The government reports that the economy continues to decline for the fourth year in a row, with interest on the nation's debt consuming about 40 percent of the government's revenue.

ANALYSIS OF EVENTS: 1999

BUSINESS AND THE ECONOMY

In April, riots broke out after Prime Minister P.J. Patterson announced gasoline prices would go up by 30 percent. At least nine people were killed in the resulting three-day riots and many more were injured.

Patterson said the price hike was inevitable. His government was under pressure to keep up payments on $3.2 billion worth of loans. The price for the island's main commodity, bauxite, was falling in world markets. Bauxite is used to make aluminum, and accounts for about 53 percent of the country's foreign earnings. Tourism accounts for about 45 percent. The government was trying to find $100 million in new tax revenues to make up for the fall in bauxite prices and sagging tourism.

The riots forced Patterson to cut the gasoline tax increase by half. He said he would tax interest on stocks and shares to make up the difference. Tourism was only growing by 1 to 2 percent, and Patterson in March sent troops to resort centers to protect visitors after highly publicized muggings.

GOVERNMENT AND POLITICS

Rose Leon, a beloved former member of the government, and successful businesswoman, was bound, gagged and choked to death in her home in August. The murder of the 80-year-old woman shocked the nation.

During the 1970s and 1980s, the Jamaica Labor Party and the People's National Party, caught in a bitter struggle for power, relied on armed gangs to sway voters. Over time, the competing gangs turned to crime, and began to sell illegal drugs and kill each other over turf wars. Much of the violence in Jamaica today is blamed on these gangs.

Rose Leon had been a member of both parties, and some of her former political colleagues called for an examination into the country's increasing violence, a legacy of the political wars. One by one, they apologized after her death, in radio, television, and newspapers. Many Jamaicans talked about the need for a truth and reconciliation commission similar to the one used in South Africa. Not all politicians wanted such a commission. Even some of those who apologized were not ready to take any blame for the nation's crime problems. Prime Minister P.J. Patterson rejected calls for a panel, saying the nation had other major problems to worry about. One thing was clear: Jamaicans were not happy with the country's two major parties or its leadership.

CULTURE AND SOCIETY

In August, the Jamaica Observer newspaper conducted a poll, and asked 1,200 people whether people known to be criminals should be killed by police when detained or formally charged and tried in court. The findings were shocking, even for Jamaicans numbed by unprecedented violence during 1999. Twenty-six percent of those who were surveyed said police should kill criminals on the spot.

A "mood of despair grips Jamaica," *The Miami Herald* reported on September 26, 1999. More than 500 Jamaicans in a nation of 2.6 million had been murdered by the time the article was published. Thirty-nine people were murdered during a seven-day period in late June. No segment of society had been spared by the violence, unlike past years when officials said crime was mainly centered in the poverty-stricken town of Kingston. During the turbulent months of 1999, a famous musician was shot in an attempted carjacking, a respected politician was bound, gagged and choked to death in her home, and police officers were killed and injured. Even the beloved national soccer team did not go untouched, with people close to the team being shot or killed. By July, the crime wave affecting the small island nation had reached beyond its borders, and English conservative politicians sought to require visas for Jamaican visitors. There was no shortage of excuses. Jamaica's minister of national security said 1,000 convicted criminals deported to Jamaica after serving sentences in the United States each year had worsened crime rates. Jamaica, deeply concerned about its international reputation and its tourism industry, deployed military forces in the country's resort centers to protect tourists.

As the nation decried the violence, army troops were called to pacify Kingston, where soldiers set up military outposts in the neighborhoods, and began helicopter patrols during the night in July. A dusk-to-dawn curfew was imposed in some areas, and military patrols were allowed to conduct searches for weapons and drugs. In the meantime, the government was having problems with its police force, which began an unofficial strike over a pay dispute in July, with officers calling in sick. In their increasing role, soldiers guarded the country's jails when guards went on strike. The union representing 7,100 police officers finally accepted a 24 percent raise, easing some of the tensions. In September, to answer criticism against police violence, the government announced it had disciplined more than 1,000 officers and fired 29.

DIRECTORY

CENTRAL GOVERNMENT

Head of State

Monarch
Elizabeth II, Queen of England

Governor-General
Howard Felix Cooke

Prime Minister
P.J. Patterson, Office of the Prime Minister, Jamaica House, Kingston 6, Jamaica
PHONE: 9279941
FAX: 9290005

Ministers

Minister without Portfolio
Maxine Henry-Wilson, Office of Minister without Portfolio, Jamaica House, Kingston 6, Jamaica
PHONE: 9279941
FAX: 9290005

Minister of State
Derrick Kellier, Ministry of State, Jamaica House, Kingston 6, Jamaica
PHONE: 9279941
FAX: 9290005

Minister of Tourism
Francis Tulloch, Ministry of Tourism, 64 Knutsford Boulevard, Kingston 5, Jamaica
PHONE: 9204956
FAX: 9204944
E-MAIL: Opmt@cwjamaica.com

Minister of Foreign Affairs and Foreign Trade
Seymour Mullings, Ministry of Foreign Affairs and Foreign Trade, 21 Dominica Drive, Kingston 5, Jamaica
PHONE: 9264220
FAX: 9295112
E-MAIL: Mfaftjam@cwjamaica.com

Minister of Finance and Planning
Omar Davies, Ministry of Finance and Planning, 30 National Heroes Circle, Kingston 4, Jamaica
PHONE: 9228600
FAX: 9228804
E-MAIL: Mfaftjam@cwjamaica.com

Minister of Labor, Social Security and Sports
Portia Simpson-Miller, Ministry of Labor, Social Security and Sports, 14 National Heroes Circle, Kingston 4, Jamaica
PHONE: 9228000; 9229500; 9671900
FAX: 9226902
E-MAIL: Mfaftjam@cwjamaica.com

Minister of Mining and Energy
Robert Pickersgill, Ministry of Mining and Energy, 36 Trafaglar Road, Kingston 10, Jamaica
PHONE: 9269170
FAX: 9682082
E-MAIL: Hmme@cwjamaica.com

Minister of Industry and Investment
Paul Robertson, Ministry of Industry and Investment, 36 Trafaglar Road, Kingston 10, Jamaica
PHONE: 9298990
FAX: 9298196
E-MAIL: Gojmii@infochan.com

Minister of Transportation and Works
Peter Phillips, Ministry of Transportation and Works, 140 Maxfield Avenue, Kingston 10, Jamaica
PHONE: 9263110
FAX: 9292996

Minister of National Security and Justice
K.D. Knight, Ministry of National Security and Justice, 12 Ocean Bouvelard, Kingston, Jamaica
PHONE: 9220080
FAX: 9226950
E-MAIL: inform@infochan,com

Minister of Environment and Housing
Easton Douglas, Ministry of Environment and Housing, 2 Hagley Park Road, Kingston 10, Jamaica
PHONE: 9261590; 9267008
FAX: 9262591
E-MAIL: Mehsys@hotmail.com

Minister of Education and Housing
Burchell Whiteman, Ministry of Education and Housing, 2 National Heroes Circle, Kingston 4, Jamaica
PHONE: 9221400
FAX: 9671837

Minister of Agriculture
Roger Clarke, Ministry of Agriculture, Hope Gardens, Kingston 6, Jamaica
PHONE: 9271731
FAX: 9271904

Minister of Health

John Junor, Ministry of Health, Oceana Hotel Complex, 2 King St., Kingston, Jamaica
PHONE: 9671092
FAX: 9271904

Minister of Local Government, Youth and Community Development

Arnold Bertram, Ministry of Local Government, Youth and Community Development, 85 Hagley Park, Kingston 10, Jamaica
PHONE: 7540994
FAX: 9600725

Minister of Water

Karl Blythe, Ministry of Water, 7th floor, Island Life Building, 6 St. Lucia Avenue, Kingston 5, Jamaica
PHONE: 7540973
FAX: 7540975
E-MAIL: prumow@cwjamaica.com

Minister of Commerce and Technology

Phillip Paulwell, Ministry of Commerce and Technology
PHONE: 9298990
FAX: 9601623
E-MAIL: prumow@cwjamaica.com

POLITICAL ORGANIZATIONS

People's National Party (PNP)

89 Old Hope Road, Kingston 6, Jamaica
PHONE: 9277805
FAX: 9274389
TITLE: Leader
NAME: P.J. Patterson

Jamaica Labour Party (JLP)

20 Belmont Road, Kingston 5, Jamaica
PHONE: 9290987
FAX: 9291276
TITLE: Leader
NAME: Edward Seaga

National Democratic Movement (NDM)

15A Old Hope Road, Kingston 5, Jamaica
PHONE: 9207848
FAX: 9207846
TITLE: Leader
NAME: Bruce Golding

Natural Law Party

c/o 21st Century Integrated Medical Centre Shop Of. 3, Overton Plaza, 49 Union Street, Montego Bay, Jamaica
PHONE: (876) 9719107
FAX: (876) 9719109
TITLE: Leader
NAME: Leo Campbell
E-MAIL: nlp@cwjamaica.com

DIPLOMATIC REPRESENTATION

Embassies in Jamaica

Canada

30-36 Knutsford Boulevard, Kingston 5, Jamaica
PHONE: 9261500
FAX: 9261702
E-MAIL: carol.hart@kngno1.x400.gc.ca
TITLE: High Commissioner
NAME: Gavin Stewart

China

8 Sea View Avenue, Kingston 10, Jamaica
PHONE: 9273871
FAX: 9276920
TITLE: Ambassador
NAME: Li Shangsheng

Germany

10 Waterloo Road, PO Box 444, Kingston 10, Jamaica
PHONE: 9266728
FAX: 9298282
TITLE: Ambassador
NAME: Wilfried Bolewski

India

4 Retreat Avenue, Kingston 6, Jamaica
PHONE: 9273114
FAX: 9782801
E-MAIL: hicomind@toj.com
TITLE: High Commissioner
NAME: Vidya Bhushan Soni

Japan

3rd Floor, 32 Trafalgar Road, Kingston 10, Jamaica
PHONE: 9273114
FAX: 9782801
TITLE: Ambassador
NAME: Motoi Okubo

Nigeria

5 Waterloo Road, Kingston 10, Jamaica
PHONE: 9266400
FAX: 9687371

TITLE: Acting High Commissioner
NAME: Baba Gana Zanna

Russia
22 Norbrook Drive, Kingston 8, Jamaica
PHONE: 9241048
FAX: 9258290
TITLE: Ambassador
NAME: Igor Iakovlev

United Kingdom
28 Trafalgar Road, Kingston 10, Jamaica
PHONE: 9269050
FAX: 9297869
E-MAIL: emjam@sysnet.net
TITLE: High Commissioner
NAME: A. Richard Thomas

United States
Mutual Life Building, 3rd Floor, 2 Oxford Road, Kingston 5, Jamaica
PHONE: 9294850
FAX: 9356000

JUDICIAL SYSTEM
Supreme Court of Jamaica

Public Building E, 134 Tower Street, Kingston, Jamaica
PHONE: 9228300; 9225606; 9674859

E-MAIL: webmaster@sc.gov.jm

Court of Appeal

FURTHER READING
Articles

"Crime Problems in Jamaica Worsened by Deportees from U.S., Officials Say." *The Miami Herald,* 27 September 1999.

"Jamaica Rediscovers Reggae's Message." *The Seattle Times*, 24 September 1999.

"Jamaica Uses Army Troops to Fight Street Gangs." *The Seattle Times*, 14 July 1999.

"Jamaican School Leads Nation Into Computer Sector." *The Miami Herald,* 17 October 1999.

"Jamaicans Tired of Parties In and Out of Power." *The Miami Herald*, 1 October 1999.

"A Killing Shocks Jamaicans Into Soul-Searching." *The New York Times,* 18 October 1999.

"A Mood of Despair Grips Jamaica." *The Miami Herald,* 26 September 1999.

"Political Confession Urges Seize Jamaica." *The Miami Herald*, 20 September 1999.

JAMAICA: STATISTICAL DATA

For sources and notes see "Sources of Statistics" in the front of each volume.

GEOGRAPHY

Geography (1)

Area:

Total: 10,990 sq. km.

Land: 10,830 sq. km.

Water: 160 sq. km.

Area—comparative: slightly smaller than Connecticut.

Land boundaries: 0 km.

Coastline: 1,022 km.

Climate: tropical; hot, humid; temperate interior.

Terrain: mostly mountains with narrow, discontinuous coastal plain.

Natural resources: bauxite, gypsum, limestone.

Land use:

Arable land: 14%

Permanent crops: 6%

Permanent pastures: 24%

Forests and woodland: 17%

Other: 39% (1993 est.).

Note: irrigated land—3% (350 sq km) (1993 est.).

HUMAN FACTORS

Health Personnel (3)

Total health expenditure as a percentage of GDP, 1990-1997[a]

   Public sector 2.5

   Private sector 2.4

   Total[b] 4.9

Health expenditure per capita in U.S. dollars, 1990-1997[a]

   Purchasing power parity 176

   Total 76

Availability of health care facilities per 100,000 people

   Hospital beds 1990-1997[a] 210

   Doctors 1993[c] 57

   Nurses 1993[c] 69

Demographics (2A)

	1990	1995	1998	2000	2010	2020	2030	2040	2050
Population	2,466.1	2,573.8	2,634.7	2,668.7	2,900.3	3,213.2	3,475.4	3,643.8	3,712.0
Net migration rate (per 1,000 population)	NA	NA	NA	NA	NA	NA	NA	NA	NA
Births	NA	NA	NA	NA	NA	NA	NA	NA	NA
Deaths	NA	NA	NA	NA	NA	NA	NA	NA	NA
Life expectancy - males	71.2	72.4	73.0	73.4	75.2	76.6	77.7	78.5	79.1
Life expectancy - females	75.4	77.0	77.8	78.4	80.7	82.5	83.8	84.7	85.4
Birth rate (per 1,000)	24.4	22.8	20.9	19.5	16.2	14.6	12.5	11.3	10.8
Death rate (per 1,000)	6.1	5.6	5.4	5.3	5.1	5.3	6.2	8.1	10.3
Women of reproductive age (15-49 yrs.)	633.7	679.9	706.9	725.4	804.7	842.7	843.8	825.2	780.0
of which are currently married	NA	NA	NA	NA	NA	NA	NA	NA	NA
Fertility rate	2.7	2.5	2.3	2.2	2.0	1.9	1.8	1.8	1.8

Except as noted, values for vital statistics are in thousands; life expectancy is in years.

Health Indicators (4)

Life expectancy at birth

1980 71

1997 75

Daily per capita supply of calories (1996) 2,575

Total fertility rate births per woman (1997) 2.7

Maternal mortality ratio per 100,000 live births
(1990-97) . . . . .120[c]

Safe water % of population with access (1995) 93

Sanitation % of population with access (1995) 74

Consumption of iodized salt % of households
(1992-98)[a] 100

Smoking prevalence

Male % of adults (1985-95)[a] 43

Female % of adults (1985-95)[a] 13

Tuberculosis incidence per 100,000 people
(1997) 8

Adult HIV prevalence % of population ages
15-49 (1997) 0.99

Infants and Malnutrition (5)

Under-5 mortality rate (1997) 11

% of infants with low birthweight (1990-97) 10

Births attended by skilled health staff % of total[a] . . .92

% fully immunized (1995-97)

TB 97

DPT 90

Polio 90

Measles 88

Prevalence of child malnutrition under age 5
(1992-97)[b] 10

Ethnic Division (6)

Black 90.4%

East Indian 1.3%

White 0.2%

Chinese 0.2%

Mixed 7.3%

Other 0.6%

Religions (7)

Protestant 61.3%

Church of God 21.2%

Baptist 8.8%

Anglican 5.5%

Seventh-Day Adventist .9%

Pentecostal 7.6%

Methodist 2.7%

United Church 2.7%

Brethren 1.1%

Jehovah's Witness 1.6%

Moravian 1.1%

Roman Catholic 4%

Other 34.7%

Other includes some spiritual cults.

Languages (8)

English, Creole.

EDUCATION

Public Education Expenditures (9)

Public expenditure on education (% of GNP)

1980 . . . . .7.0

1996 . . . . .7.4

Expenditure per student

Primary % of GNP per capita

1980 . . . . .13.8

1996 . . . .

Secondary % of GNP per capita

1980 . . . . .22.0

1996 . . . .

Tertiary % of GNP per capita

1980 . . . . .202.6

1996 . . . .

Expenditure on teaching materials

Primary % of total for level (1996) 1.7

Secondary % of total for level (1996) . . . . .1.1[1]

Primary pupil-teacher ratio per teacher (1996) . . . .

Duration of primary education years (1995) 6

Educational Attainment (10)

Age group (1991) . . . . .25+

Total population 970,086

Highest level attained (%)

No schooling 0

First level

Not completed 67.5

Completed . . . . .NA

Entered second level

S-1 . . . . .29.9

S-2 . . . . .NA

Postsecondary[10] 2.7

Literacy Rates (11A)

In thousands and percent[1]	1990	1995	2000	2010
Illiterate population (15+ yrs.)	271	254	248	221
Literacy rate - total adult pop. (%)	82.9	85.0	86.4	89.7
Literacy rate - males (%)	78.5	80.8	82.4	85.7
Literacy rate - females (%)	87.1	89.1	90.3	93.7

GOVERNMENT & LAW

Political Parties (12)

House of Representatives	No. of seats
People's National Party (PNP)	50
Jamaica Labor Party (JLP)	10

Government Budget (13B)

Revenues . . . .$3 billion
Expenditures . . . .$3 billion
  Capital expenditures . . . .$1.163 billion
Data for FY97/98 est.

Military Affairs (14B)

	1990	1991	1992	1993	1994	1995
Military expenditures						
Current dollars (mil.)	25	21	18	24	24	28
1995 constant dollars (mil.)	28	12	19	26	25	28
Armed forces (000)	3	3	3	3	3	3
Gross national product (GNP)						
Current dollars (mil.)	2,560	2,670	2,970	3,344	3,425	3,528
1995 constant dollars (mil.)	2,943	2,951	3,194	3,506	3,511	3,528
Central government expenditures (CGE)						
1995 constant dollars (mil.)	867[e]	676[e]	NA	NA	NA	2,000[e]
People (mil.)	2.5	2.5	2.5	2.5	2.6	2.6
Military expenditure as % of GNP	1.0	.8	.6	.7	.7	.8
Military expenditure as % of CGE	3.3	3.4	NA	NA	NA	1.4
Military expenditure per capita (1995 $)	12	9	8	10	10	11
Armed forces per 1,000 people (soldiers)	1.2	1.2	1.2	1.2	1.2	1.2
GNP per capita (1995 $)	1,193	1,186	1,273	1,386	1,376	1,371
Arms imports[6]						
Current dollars (mil.)	0	10	10	5	5	0
1995 constant dollars (mil.)	0	11	11	5	5	0
Arms exports[6]						
Current dollars (mil.)	0	0	0	0	0	0
1995 constant dollars (mil.)	0	0	0	0	0	0
Total imports[7]						
Current dollars (mil.)	1,859	1,491	1,668	2,097	2,164	2,757
1995 constant dollars (mil.)	2,136	1,648	1,794	2,198	2,218	2,757
Total exports[7]						
Current dollars (mil.)	1,135	1,053	1,102	1,069	1,192	1,414
1995 constant dollars (mil.)	1,304	1,164	1,185	1,121	1,222	1,414
Arms as percent of total imports[8]	0	.7	.6	.2	.2	0
Arms as percent of total exports[8]	0	0	0	0	0	0

Crime (15)

Crime rate (for 1997)

Crimes reported 51,200

Total persons convicted 41,000

Crimes per 100,000 population 2,000

Persons responsible for offenses

Total number of suspects 41,100

Total number of female suspects . . . . .NA

Total number of juvenile suspects . . . . .NA

LABOR FORCE

Labor Force (16)

Total (million) 1.14

Services 41%

Agriculture 22.5%

Industry 19%

Unemployed 17.5%

Data for 1996 Percent distribution for 1989.

Unemployment Rate (17)

16% (1996 est.)

PRODUCTION SECTOR

Electric Energy (18)

Capacity . . . . .1.182 million kW (1995)

Production . . . . .3.87 billion kWh (1995)

Consumption per capita . . . . .1,503 kWh (1995)

Transportation (19)

Highways:

total: 18,700 km

paved: 13,100 km

unpaved: 5,600 km (gravel 3,200 km; improved earth 2,400 km) (1997 est.)

Pipelines: petroleum products 10 km

Merchant marine:

total: 3 ships (1,000 GRT or over) totaling 5,931 GRT/10,545 DWT ships by type: bulk 1, oil tanker 1, roll-on/roll-off cargo 1 (1997 est.)

Airports: 36 (1997 est.)

Airports—with paved runways:

total: 11

2,438 to 3,047 m: 2

1,524 to 2,437 m: 1

914 to 1,523 m: 3

under 914 m: 5 (1997 est.)

Airports—with unpaved runways:

total: 25

914 to 1,523 m: 2

under 914 m: 23 (1997 est.)

Top Agricultural Products (20)

Sugarcane, bananas, coffee, citrus, potatoes, vegetables; poultry, goats, milk.

MANUFACTURING SECTOR

GDP & Manufacturing Summary (21)

Detailed value added figures are listed by both International Standard Industry Code (ISIC) and product title.

	1980	1985	1990	1994
GDP ($-1990 mil.)[1]	3,369	3,382	4,242	4,397
Per capita ($-1990)[1]	1,579	1,463	1,793	1,810
Manufacturing share (%) (current prices)[1]	16.1	19.3	18.2	17.4
Manufacturing				
Value added ($-1990 mil.)[1]	619	658	824	771
Industrial production index	100	106	133	124
Value added ($ mil.)	436	363	831	728
Gross output ($ mil.)	1,661	1,498	2,549	3,063
Employment (000)	44	54	65	73
Profitability (% of gross output)				
Intermediate input (%)	79	76	73	77
Wages and salaries inc. supplements (%)	11	10	10	10
Gross operating surplus	9	14	17	13
Productivity ($)				
Gross output per worker	48,137	27,805	48,821	40,629
Value added per worker	9,883	6,737	11,620	9,641
Average wage (inc. supplements)	5,427	2,797	4,449	4,096
Value added ($ mil.)				
311/2 Food products	78	74	182	194
313 Beverages	63	44	103	83

	1980	1985	1990	1994
314 Tobacco products	61	40	56	44
321 Textiles	3	4	8	9
322 Wearing apparel	15	12	25	26
323 Leather and fur products	2	2	2	1
324 Footwear	8	4	7	5
331 Wood and wood products	3	2	5	2
332 Furniture and fixtures	12	11	19	10
341 Paper and paper products	8	3	6	6
342 Printing and publishing	13	13	35	29
351 Industrial chemicals	5	7	23	20
352 Other chemical products	22	23	38	37
353 Petroleum refineries	55	51	151	87
354 Miscellaneous petroleum and coal products	—	—	16	20
355 Rubber products	12	3	6	6
356 Plastic products	13	2	4	4
361 Pottery, china and earthenware	1	2	5	6
362 Glass and glass products	2	3	8	9
369 Other non-metal mineral products	8	11	29	33
371 Iron and steel	1	10	21	22
372 Non-ferrous metals	—	—	—	—
381 Metal products	12	13	29	27
382 Non-electrical machinery	8	4	6	6
383 Electrical machinery	6	4	8	7
384 Transport equipment	24	19	32	30
385 Professional and scientific equipment	—	—	—	—
390 Other manufacturing industries	4	3	6	3

FINANCE, ECONOMICS, & TRADE

Economic Indicators (22)

National product: GDP—purchasing power parity—$9.5 billion (1996 est.)

National product real growth rate: -1.4% (1996 est.)

National product per capita: $3,660 (1996 est.)

Inflation rate—consumer price index: 17% (1996 est.)

Exchange Rates (24)

Exchange rates:

Jamaican dollars (J$) per US$1

November 1997	36.051
1996	37.120
1995	35.142
1994	33.086
1993	24.949

Balance of Payments (23)

	1991	1992	1993	1994	1995
Exports of goods (f.o.b.)	1,197	1,116	1,105	1,551	1,793
Imports of goods (f.o.b.)	−1,588	−1,541	−1,920	−2,065	−2,606
Trade balance	−392	−425	−815	−514	−813
Services - debits	−1,169	−1,083	−1,136	−1,304	−1,501
Services - credits	1,052	1,179	1,378	1,377	1,534
Private transfers (net)	100	92	71	10	17
Government transfers (net)	169	266	319	448	518
Overall balance	−240	29	−184	17	−245

Top Import Origins (25)

$2.9 billion (f.o.b., 1996 est.).

Origins	%
United States	.52
Trinidad and Tobago	.8
Japan	.6
United Kingdom	.4
Canada	.3

Top Export Destinations (26)

$1.4 billion (f.o.b., 1996).

Destinations	%
United States	.37
United Kingdom	.13
Canada	.12
Netherlands	.9
Norway	.7

Economic Aid (27)

Recipient: ODA, $306 million (1996).

Import Export Commodities (28)

Import Commodities	Export Commodities
Machinery and transport equipment	Alumina
	Bauxite
Construction materials	Sugar
Fuel	Bananas
Food	Rum
Chemicals	

JAPAN

Nippon

INTRODUCTORY SURVEY

RECENT HISTORY

Following World War II, with economic aid from the United States and the determination of the Japanese people to rebuild their country, the Japanese economy rapidly recovered. The standard of living quickly surpassed the prewar level by a wide margin. In 1956, Japan was elected to United Nations membership.

During the 1960s, Japan's remarkable economic expansion raised it to the level of a great trading power. In 1968, it surpassed the Federal Republic of Germany (FRG) to stand second after the United States among non-communist nations in total value of its gross national product (GNP). The lack of domestic petroleum resources, however, caused two separate oil crises. Another oil crisis during the 1970s led to long-range programs for energy conservation and diversification.

The yen declined in value in the early 1980s, causing Japanese exports to become cheaper in overseas markets. The United States and other leading trading partners began to demand that Japan limit certain exports and remove import barriers to Japan's domestic market.

Emperor Hirohito died of cancer on 7 January 1989, at the age of 87. He was succeeded by the Crown Prince Akihito, who was enthroned in a formal ceremony in November 1990. The sense of entering a new era brought increased controversy over Japan's actions in the earlier part of the century, particularly during World War II.

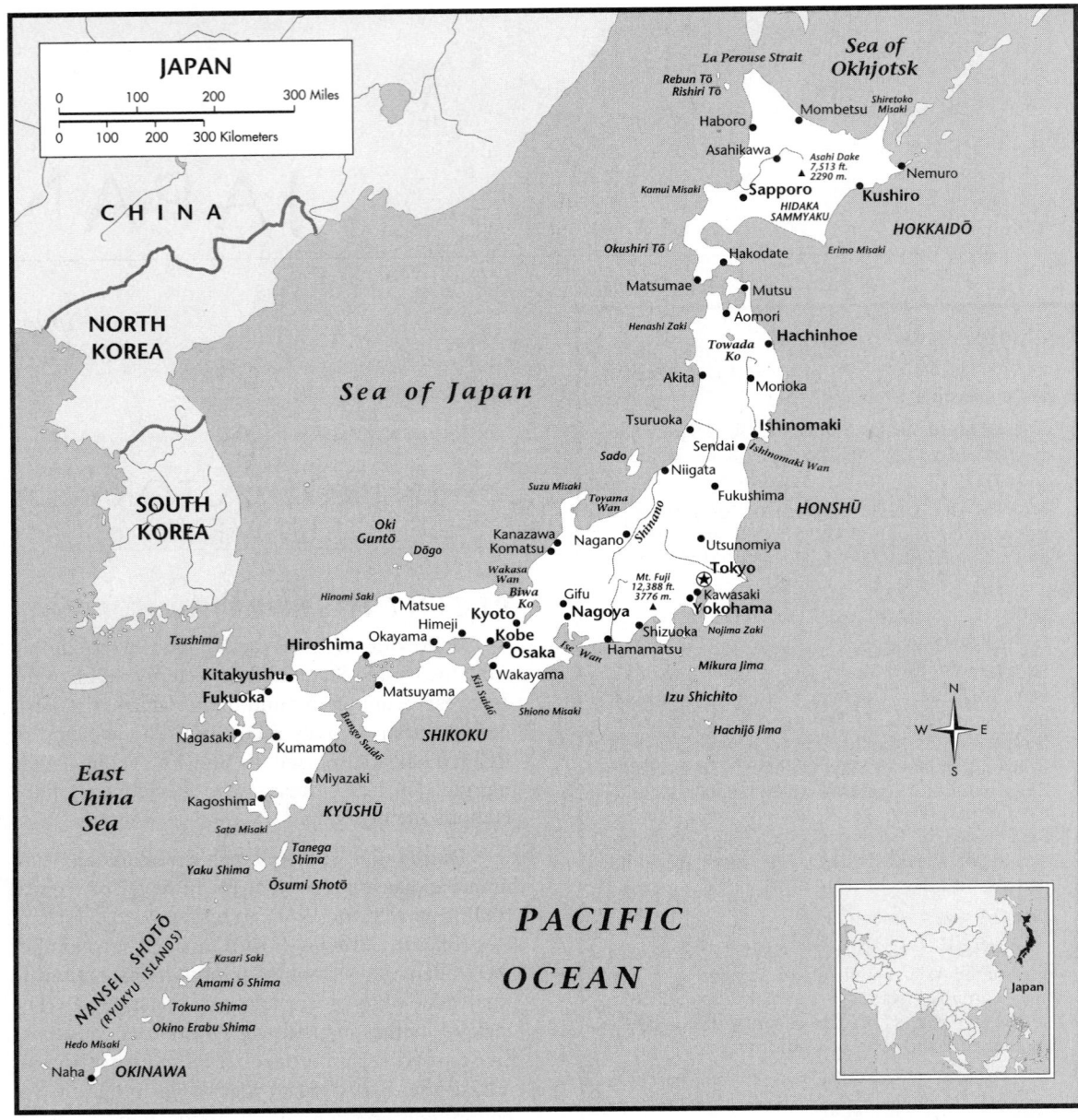

The 1980s ended with a major scandal involving illegal stock trading. Scandals continued into the 1990s with stock dealings and, in 1992, contributions to politicians from a trucking company linked to organized crime. The stock market started falling in 1990. By the summer of 1992, it was at its lowest point in six years, 62% below the record high of 1989. By the end of 1993, Japan was amid its worst economic downturn in at least twenty years.

Against the background of scandals and economic recession, the political landscape began a major change. After the resignation of prime minister Noboru Takeshita in April 1989, the ruling Liberal Democratic Party (LDP) lost its majority in the upper house of the Diet (parliament), its worst defeat in thirty-four years. The new prime minister, Mirihiro Hosokawa (JNP), was chosen in July 1993, by a seven-party coalition of LDP defectors, Socialists, and conservatives. In April 1994, the LDP and the Socialist Party, traditionally opponents, allied to form a new coalition. They selected as prime minister Tomiichi Murayama, the head of the Socialist Party and the first Socialist prime minister since 1948. Ryutaro Hashimoto of the

LDP became prime minister in 1996. During his administration, Japan fell into its worst recession since World War II.

In July 1998, the LDP was defeated in elections for half the seats in the upper house of the Diet (although it still held more than any other party), and Hashimoto resigned. Keizo Obuchi of the LDP was confirmed as new prime minister.

GOVERNMENT

Japan follows a parliamentary system in accordance with the constitution of 1947. The most significant change from the previous constitution of 1889 was the transfer of power from the emperor to the people. The emperor is now defined as "the symbol of the state and of the unity of the people." The constitution provides for the supremacy of the National Diet (parliament) as the legislative branch of the government; upholds the separation of legislative, executive, and judicial powers; and guarantees civil liberties.

The executive branch is headed by a prime minister selected from the Diet by its membership. The cabinet consists of the prime minister and twenty state ministers (as of January 1988), each heading a government ministry or agency.

The National Diet is bicameral (consisting of two chambers). The House of Representatives (the lower house) has a membership of 512; the House of Councillors (the upper house) has 252 members. Anyone age 20 or older can vote.

Judiciary

The system consists of the Supreme Court, eight regional higher courts, district courts, and a number of summary courts. In addition, there are family courts, on the same level as the district courts, to rule on family conflicts and complaints such as divisions of estates, marriage annulments, and juvenile protection cases.

The Supreme Court determines the constitutionality of any law, order, regulation, or official act that is challenged during the regular hearing of a lawsuit. The Constitution affords criminal defendants a right to a speedy and public trial by an impartial judge. There is no right to a trial by jury.

Political Parties

The Liberal Democratic Party (LDP) represents much of Japanese society, but most especially the conservative elements. Formed in 1955, this party held the reins of government from its formation until July 1993. The Japan Socialist Party (JSP), Japan's principal opposition party, draws its support mainly from the working class.

In the summer of 1993, amid economic recession and scandals involving corruption, sex, and organized crime, the old political order disintegrated as dozens of younger LDP members defected to form new parties. Chief among these were the Japan New Party (JNP), the Sakigake (Harbinger Party), and the Shinseito (Renewal Party). In the 1996 parliamentary elections, the LDP won 38.6% of the vote.

DEFENSE

There has been a heated debate over the reestablishment of Japanese defense forces since Japan's participation in World War II. Laws establishing a Defense Agency and a Self-Defense Force became effective on 1 July 1954, both under firm civilian control.

The strength of Japan's armed forces in 1995 was 235,500. The Ground Self-Defense Force had 148,000 personnel. There were also 46,000 men in the reserves. The Maritime Self-Defense Force consisted of 43,000 personnel. Air Self-Defense Force personnel numbered 44,500.

Although Japan's defense budgets—about $45.1 billion in 1996—rank high by world standards, they are small in relation to the size of the nation's economy. Japan relies for its military security on U.S. conventional and nuclear forces, and the United States has repeatedly urged Japan to shoulder more of its own conventional defense burden. The United States maintains extensive military facilities and 40,000 troops in Japan.

ECONOMIC AFFAIRS

Japan's economy is the most advanced in Asia and the second largest in the world, behind that of the United States. According to Japan's Economic Planning Agency, the total gross domestic product (GDP) in 1996 was $4.6 trillion (up 3.6% from 1995). Japan was the first Asian country to develop a large urban middle-class industrial society.

Public Finance

Plans for the national budget usually begin in August, when various agencies submit their budget requests to the Ministry of Finance. On the basis of such requests, the ministry, other government agencies, and the ruling party start negotiations. The government budget plan usually is approved by the Diet without difficulty, and the budget goes into effect in April. Deficits, financed by public bond sales, have steadily increased in size since the 1973 oil crisis. In recent years, however, fiscal stimulus policies have contributed to an increasing budget deficit. Japan's government deficit was 3% of GDP in 1994 and reached 4.3% of GDP in 1995, due to ongoing high levels of public sector borrowing. The government's focus on fiscal policy to compensate for a tight monetary policy has restricted spending on infrastructure.

The U.S. CIA estimates that, in 1995, Japanese government revenues totaled approximately $595 billion and expenditures $829 billion.

Income

In 1998, Japan's GNP was $4.09 trillion, or about $32,380 per person. For the period 1985–95, the average inflation rate was 1.4%, resulting in a real growth rate in GNP per person of 2.9%.

Industry

During the 1970s and early 1980s, the rate of Japan's industrial growth surpassed that of any other non-communist industrialized country. Of the 26 largest industrial companies in the world in the mid-1980s, four were Japanese: Toyota Motor, Matsushita Electric, Hitachi, and Nissan Motor. Despite declining profits with the economic downturn of the early 1990s, Japanese companies have continued to make large investments in new plants and equipment. Japanese industry is characterized by a complex system of exclusive buyer-supplier networks and alliances. The relationships are maintained by companies belonging to the same business grouping, called *keiretsu.*

The electronics industry grew with extraordinary speed in the 1980s and now leads the world. Japan plays an increasingly important role in the computer industry. Japan is the world's leading shipbuilder. More than half the ships built are exported, including some of the world's largest oil tankers. In the early 1980s, Japan became the world's leading automobile producer, topping the United States for the first time in the history of the industry. Japan's superior technology in the design of bicycles, motorcycles, buses, and high-speed trains has been another major factor in the growth of the transport industry. The chemical and petrochemicals industry has been another of the economy's key growth areas since the late 1960s.

Banking and Finance

Japan's highly sophisticated banking system continues to play a dominant role in financing the country's and the world's economic development. In the mid-1980s, while the U.S. was becoming a debtor nation, Japan became the world's largest creditor.

The controlling national monetary institutions are the Bank of Japan and the Ministry of Finance. The Bank of Japan, as central bank, has power over note issue and audits financial institutions to provide guidance for improving banking and management practices. At the end of 1995, the money supply, as measured by M2. totaled 548,986 billion. Total foreign exchange reserves (including gold) held by the Bank of Japan amounted to $208.4 billion at the end of May 1996, the highest in the world.

Major securities exchanges are in Tokyo, Hiroshima, Fukuoka, Nagoya, and Osaka. The Tokyo Securities and Stock Exchange became the largest in the world in 1988, in terms of combined market value of outstanding shares and capitalization, while the Osaka Stock Exchange ranked third after those of Tokyo and New York.

Economic Development

Japan's phenomenal economic growth since the 1950s has been based on an efficient blend of two economic tendencies. First is government activism in national planning and implementation, with guidance of the largely free economy via sophisticated and powerful monetary and fiscal policies. Second is the distinctively Japanese way of coupling largely private ownership of assets with conservative, public-spirited management. Especially significant is the role of the Ministry of International Trade and Industry (MITI), which coordinates national industrial policies consistent with economic and social growth.

In 1988, a five-year plan was adopted to sustain real GNP growth at 3.75% per year, maintain low unemployment (2.5% per year), contain inflation, reduce the country's trade surplus, and improve the quality of life through a shorter work week and stabilized property prices. Many of these objectives were achieved or surpassed in the closing years of the decade. Since 1992, however, the economy's downturn has been likened by some analysts to the 1974 recession in its severity and length. Economic indicators have included steep declines and sluggish recovery in the stock market index since 1989, falling real estate prices, as well as a shrunken rate of GNP growth, despite surging exports. To prompt a recovery, the Ministry of Finance approved large stimulus packages for 1992 and 1993, totaling $85.6 billion and $119 billion in expenditures, respectively. Real growth during the 1990s has hovered around 1% a year. Since Japanese wages have been rising, wage pressures are creating a higher cost for business, which would tend to make Japan less competitive in a world that is becoming increasingly more competitive.

SOCIAL WELFARE

The social stability of Japan is due largely to the strong sense of family solidarity among the Japanese. Virtually every home has its *butsudan*, or altar of the ancestors, and most elderly people are cared for in the homes of their grown children.

The social insurance system includes national health insurance, maternity coverage, unemployment insurance, and workers' accident compensation insurance. It also provides pension plans designed to maintain living standards for the elderly and for families of deceased workers.

Nearly the entire population receives benefits in one form or another from the health insurance system. Those not covered at work are insured through the National Health Insurance program.

Change is evident in the fact that women now make up 40% of Japan's employed workers. Marriages arranged by a go-between, or *o-miai* (half of all marriages in 1966), had declined dramatically by the 1990s.

Healthcare

Death rates from cancer and heart disease have risen considerably and now rank among the leading causes of death, trailing cerebrovascular diseases (high blood pressure and strokes). In 1993, there were 300,000 deaths due to cardiovascular disease. Average life expectancy was estimated to be about 80 years for the period 1990–95, among the highest rates in the world.

About 66% of Japanese men and 14% of Japanese women smoke. In 1995, it was estimated that smoking was the underlying cause for 12% of all deaths.

Housing

Construction of new housing slowed down in the 1980s, falling to between 1.1 million and 1.5 million units. This is due to a rapid rise in land and construction costs, which has put new housing out of the reach of many potential buyers. Condominiums and prefabricated homes provided much of the nation's new housing in the 1980s.

EDUCATION

Japan's entire educational system was reorganized and made similar to the United States system after World War II, with six years of primary school, three years of lower secondary school, three years of upper secondary school—full-time, part-time or correspondence—and four years of college. Education is available to both males and females. Virtually the entire adult population is literate.

Enrollment at the compulsory elementary and junior high school levels is very high, approaching 100%. In 1994, 8.6 million students were enrolled in the 24,635 elementary schools, and 10.2 million students in the 695,707 lower and upper secondary schools. In 1991, there were 2.9 million students enrolled in all higher educational institutions.

1999 KEY EVENTS TIMELINE

January
- The ruling Liberal Democratic Party agrees to form a coalition government with the opposition Liberal Party.

February
- A massive deposit of gold and silver is found in an underwater volcano south of Japan.

March
- Japanese sea and air forces chase suspected North Korean boats out of Japanese waters.
- The Japanese Diet passes a record ¥82 trillion budget.

April
- Kiyoshi Kurosawa wins recognition at Hong Kong film festival.
- The Liberal Democratic Party suffers losses in local elections held in over 2,000 towns and cities.

May
- Prime Minister Obuchi meets with President Clinton in Washington, D.C.

June
- Obuchi moves to draw the New Komeito religious opposition party into his coalition government.

- Japan's economy begins to grow for the first time in two years.

August

- The Japanese parliament makes Japan's national anthem and flag official for the first time, despite discomfort over World War II associations.

September

- Japan promises G7 leaders it will take further measures to boost its ailing economy.

- Japan's cigarette industry protests health ministry plan to cut smoking.

- An incident at the Tokaimura nuclear processing plant releases dangerous radiation and raises questions about the safety of Japan's nuclear power industry.

November

- Japan considers a new measure for national accounts that would more accurately portray the country's huge, semi-hidden debts and assets.

- The Japanese government unveils its economic stimulus package worth over $169 billion.

- Japanese officials attend the Association of South-East Asian Nations (ASEAN) summit meeting in Manila; Japan asks the members to support Eisuke Sakakibara, a former Japanese minister, to head the International Monetary Fund.

December

- The Aum Shinrikyo doomsday cult apologizes for a series of poison gas attacks, including the deadly assault on the Tokyo subway in 1995, and offers compensation to survivors.

- Crown Prince Naruhiot and Princess Masako raise the nation's spirits with an announcement that they are expecting a baby, but she experiences a miscarriage before the end of December.

ANALYSIS OF EVENTS: 1999

BUSINESS AND THE ECONOMY

In 1999 Japan began a tentative recovery from its longest and most severe recession since the end of World War II. The OECD expected Japan's economy to grow by a slight 0.2 percent for the year, revised from an earlier forecast of a 1.4 percent decline. In August, industrial production posted its largest gain in three years. However, Japan's economic recovery was expected to be gradual; capital spending by corporations and personal income and demand remained depressed, and unemployment remained high. Another cause for concern was the rapid rise in the strength of the Japanese yen since the first signs of economic growth in June, a leap of 15 percent over the summer alone, which could hurt manufacturers by making their exports more expensive abroad, thus destabilizing the nation's position in international trade. In September the Group of Seven (G7) members expressed concern over the effect of the rising yen on the world economy and issued a statement asking Japan to implement stimulus measures to boost growth and take steps to control the strength of the yen.

Toward the end of August, Japan became a major player in the realm of bank megamergers when three of its leading financial institutions—Dai-Ichi Kangyo Bank, Fuji Bank, and the Industrial Bank of Japan (IBJ)—announced formation of a joint holding company that would constitute the world's first trillion-dollar financial entity. Assets of the new financial group were expected to total $1.3 trillion.

Earlier in the year, gigantic wealth in a very different form had been highlighted when Japanese geologists announced the discovery of an enormous deposit of gold and other minerals in an underwater volcano at the bottom of the sea, some 250 miles south of Tokyo. The collapsed center of the volcano was thought to contain as much as 200 tons of gold and 12,000 tons of silver. However, prospects for a ''gold rush'' by private speculators were deemed remote due to the heavy equipment outlays that would be necessary to mine the site.

GOVERNMENT AND POLITICS

Prime Minister Keizo Obuchi began the year by forming a coalition government with the opposition right-wing Liberal Party under the leadership of political rival Ichiro Ozawa. The coalition plan was reached following agreement between the Liberals and Obuchi's Liberal Democratic Party on the issue of expanding the Japanese international military presence by reinterpreting provisions of the pacifist constitution drafted following World War II. Specifically, the two sides agreed on allowing the Japanese military to play a more active role in

NATO peacekeeping forces. In July Obuchi launched an initiative to bring the New Komeito, the political arm of the Soka Gakkai lay Buddhist group, into the governing coalition as well.

The Liberal Democratic Party suffered a setback in local elections held in over 2,000 cities and towns throughout Japan in April, when it lost 197 seats in local legislatures and 24 seats in city assemblies, as well as the Tokyo gubernatorial race, which was won by independent candidate Shintaro Ishihara.

In international politics, tensions raised between Japan and North Korea in 1998 by Korea's test-firing of a ballistic missile over Japan continued to grow when Japan ejected two disguised North Korean boats from Japanese waters in March. By fall, however, Japanese officials were considering retracting some of the retaliatory measures it had imposed on Korea the previous year, including an embargo on chartered flights between the two countries, suspension of food aid, and the halting of negotiations on restoring diplomatic ties between the two nations.

International diplomacy took Prime Minister Obuchi to both Washington, D.C. and Beijing, China, in the course of the year. Obuchi's six-day American tour made him the first Japanese prime minister to visit the U.S. in twelve years.

CULTURE AND SOCIETY

On September 30, Japan suffered the worst nuclear accident in its history when workers at a nuclear processing plant in Tokaimura, 85 miles northeast of Tokyo, mistakenly fed nearly eight times the normal amount of uranium into a tank. The uranium combined with nitric acid to start a nuclear fission reaction, releasing potentially lethal radiation within the plant itself and into the surrounding area. Plant employees, three of them in serious condition, and rescue personnel were treated for radiation exposure, nearby residents were evacuated, and some 300,000 people in Tokaimura and surrounding towns were ordered to stay indoors and seal their houses until the disaster was contained 20 hours later.

The accident, rated as a Level Four disaster (more serious than Three Mile Island but less severe than Chernobyl), raised renewed concerns about the unsatisfactory safety record of Japan's nuclear power industry, which supplies roughly one-third of the nation's power at 52 power plants throughout the country. Implementation of safety standards within the industry was criticized as inadequate, as was the lack of an automatic backup response to the disaster and the length of time it took for plant operators and local authorities to notify local residents and contain the accident.

The Tokaimura accident brought back memories of the massive radiation exposure following the bombing of Hiroshima and Nagasaki at the end of World War II. Memories of the war were also raised by the enactment of a controversial law according official legal status to the Japanese flag and national anthem, both of which were commonly perceived as having associations with Japanese militarism and expansionism in World War II.

In the arts, the focus was on the Japanese film industry at the Hong Kong film festival in April. Five films by up-and-coming director Kiyoshi Kurosawa—no relation to film legend Akira Kurosawa—were shown. Spanning the period from 1985 to 1998, they revealed the director's range and originality. Other respected Japanese directors whose work was shown at the festival included Hirokazu Kore-Eda and Yoshimitsu Morita.

DIRECTORY

CENTRAL GOVERNMENT
Head of State

Emperor
Akihito, Office of the Emperor, Imperial Household Agency, 11 Chiyoda, Chiyoda-ku, Tokyo 100, Japan

Prime Minister
Keizo Obuchi, Office of the Prime Minister, 1-6-1 Nagata-cho, Chiyoda-ku, Tokyo 100, Japan
PHONE: +81 (33) 5812361

Ministers

Minister of Agriculture, Forestry, and Fisheries
Tokuichiro Tamazawa, Ministry of Agriculture, Forestry, and Fisheries, 1-2-1 Kasumigaseki, Chiyoda-ku, Tokyo 100, Japan
PHONE: +81 (33) 5028111

Minister of Construction
Masaaki Nakayama, Ministry of Construction, 1-2-2 Kasumigaseki, Chiyoda-ku, Tokyo 100-8972, Japan

Minister of Education

Hirofumi Nakasone, Ministry of Education, 3-2-2 Kasumigaseki, Chiyoda-ku, Tokyo 100, Japan
PHONE: +81 (3) 581-4211

Minister of Finance

Kiichi Miyazawa, Ministry of Finance, 3-1-1 Kasumigaseki, Chiyoda-ku, Tokyo 100, Japan
PHONE: +81 (3) 5814111

Minister of Home Affairs

Ministry of Home Affairs, 2-2-1 Toranomon, Minato-ku, Tokyo 105, Japan
PHONE: +81 (3) 55747111

Minister of Foreign Affairs

Yohei Kono, Ministry of Foreign Affairs, 2-2-1 Kasumigaseki, Chiyoda-ku, Tokyo 100, Japan
PHONE: +81 (3) 5803311

Minister of Health and Welfare

Yuya Niwa, Ministry of Health and Welfare, 1-2-2 Kasumigaseki, Chiyoda-ku, Tokyo 100, Japan
PHONE: +81 (3) 5031711

Minister of International Trade and Industry

Takashi Fukaya, Ministry of International Trade and Industry, 1-3-1 Kasumigaseki, Chiyoda-ku, Tokyo 100, Japan
PHONE: +81 (3) 5011511

Minister of Justice

Hideo Usui, Ministry of Justice, 1-1-1 Kasumigaseki, Chiyoda-ku, Tokyo 100, Japan
PHONE: +81 (3) 5804111

Minister of Labor

Takamori Makino, Ministry of Labor, 1-2-2 Kasumigaseki, Chiyoda-ku, Tokyo 100, Japan
PHONE: +81 (3) 2117451

Minister of Education

Hirofumi Nakasone, Ministry of Education, 2-2-1 Kasumigaseki, Chiyoda-ku, Tokyo 100, Japan
PHONE: +81 (3) 5815271
FAX: +81 (3) 5950567

Minister of Posts and Telecommunications

Eita Yashiro, Ministry of Posts and Telecommunications, 1-3-2 Kasumigaseki, Chiyoda-ku, Tokyo 100, Japan
PHONE: +81 (3) 5044798

Minister of Transport

Toshihiro Nikai, Ministry of Transport, 2-1-3 Kasumigaseki, Chiyoda-ku, Tokyo 100, Japan
PHONE: +81 (3) 5803111

POLITICAL ORGANIZATIONS

Liberal Democratic Party (LDP)

TITLE: Secretary General
NAME: Yoshiro Mori

Shinseito-JRP (Japan Renewal Party)

Minshuto (Democratic Party)

Liberal Party

TITLE: President
NAME: Ichiro Ozawa

Komeito-CGP (Clean Government Party)

17 Minamimotomachi, Shinjuku-ku, Tokyo 151-8586, Japan
TITLE: Secretary-General
NAME: Tetsuzo Fuyushiba

Japanese Communist Party

4-26-7 Sendagaya, Shibuya-ku, Tokyo 160, Japan
TITLE: Secretariat Head
NAME: Kazuo Shii

Minshu Shakaito (Democratic Socialist Party)

Shakai Minshuto (Social Democratic Party)

8-1 Nagatacyo 1, Chiyodaku, Tokyo 100-8909, Japan
PHONE: +81 (3) 35801171
TITLE: Secretariat Head
NAME: Tomiichi Murayama

New Party Sakigake (New Harbinger Party)

TITLE: President
NAME: Masayoshi Takemura

Japan Labor Party

PHONE: +81 (3) 32951011
FAX: +81 (3) 32951004

Kaikaku Kurabu-RC (Reform Club)

Zenkokushakensha (Socialist Workers Party)

Okiyama Building, 1-17-11 Minami Ikebukuro, Toshima-ku, Tokyo, Japan
PHONE: +81 (3) 39710622
E-MAIL: swp@aqu.bekkoame.ne.jp

Niigata (New Party for People)

Jiyu Rengo (Liberal League)

PHONE: +81 (3) 35513980
FAX: +81 (3) 35516406

The Japan Wellbeing Party

PHONE: +81 (3) 59826855
FAX: +81 (3) 59826853
E-MAIL: jwp@t3.rim.or.jp

Japan Revolutionary Communist League

525-3 Waseda-tsurumaki-cho, Shinjuku-ku,
Tokyo 162-0041, Japan
PHONE: +81 (3) 32071261
E-MAIL: jrcl@pop21.odn.ne.jp

DIPLOMATIC REPRESENTATION

Embassies in Japan

Afghanistan
Olympia Annex Apt. 503, 6-31-21 Jingumae,
Shibuya-ku, Toyko 150, Japan
PHONE: +81 34077900
FAX: +81 34007912

Algeria
2-10-67 Mita, Meguro-ku, Toyko 153, Japan
PHONE: +81 37112661
FAX: +81 37106534

Argentina
2-14-14 Moto-Azabu, Minato-ku, Toyko 106,
Japan
PHONE: +81 54207101
FAX: +81 54207109

Australia
2-1-14 Mita, Minato-ku, Toyko 108, Japan
PHONE: +81 52324111
FAX: +81 52324149

Austria
1-1-20 Moto-Azabu, Minato-ku, Toyko 106,
Japan
PHONE: +81 34518281
FAX: +81 34518283

Bangladesh
4-15-15, Megro-ku, Toyko 153, Japan
PHONE: +81 57040216
FAX: +81 57041696

Belarus
Royal Court 603, 23-2 Ichiban-cho, Chiyoda-ku,
Toyko 102, Japan

Belgium
5 Niban-cho, Chiyoda-ku, Toyko 102, Japan

PHONE: +81 32620191
FAX: +81 32620651

Bolivia
No. 38 Kowa Building, 8th Floor, Room 804, 4-
12-24, Nishi-Azabu, Minato-ku, Toyko 106,
Japan
PHONE: +81 34995441
FAX: +81 34995443

Brazil
2-11-12 Kita-Aoyama, Minato-ku, Toyko 107,
Japan
PHONE: +81 34045211
FAX: +81 34055846

Brunei
6-5-2 Kitashinagawa, Shinagawa-ku, Toyko 141,
Japan
PHONE: +81 34477997
FAX: +81 34479260

Bulgaria
5-36-3 Yoyogi, Shibuya-ku, Toyko 151, Japan
PHONE: +81 34651021; 34651026
FAX: +81 34651031

Burkina Faso
Hiroo Glisten Hills 3F, 3-1-17 Hiroo, Shibuya-
ku, Toyko, Japan
PHONE: +81 34007919
FAX: +81 34006945

Burundi
6-5-3, Kita-Shinagawa, Shinagawa-ku, Toyko
141, Japan
PHONE: +81 34437321
FAX: +81 34437720

Cambodia
8-6-9 Akasaka, Minato-ku, Toyko 107, Japan
PHONE: +81 34780861
FAX: +81 34780865

Cameroon
3-27-16 Nozawa, Setagaya-ku, Toyko 154, Japan
PHONE: +81 54304381
FAX: +81 54306489

Canada
7-3-38 Akasaka, Minato-ku, Toyko 107, Japan
PHONE: +81 34082101; 834039176
FAX: +81 34795320

Chile
Nihon Seimei Akabanebashi Bldg., 8F, 3-1-14
Shiba, Minato-ku, Toyko 105, Japan
PHONE: +81 34527561
FAX: +81 34524457

China
3-4-33 Moto-Azabu, Minato-ku, Toyko 106,
Japan
PHONE: +81 34033380
FAX: +81 34033345

Colombia
3-10-53 Kami-Osaki, Shinagawa-ku, Toyko 141,
Japan
PHONE: +81 34406451
FAX: +81 34406724

Costa Rica
4-12-24 Nishi-Azabu, Minato-ku, Toyko 106,
Japan
PHONE: +81 34861812
FAX: +81 34861813

Côte d'Ivoire
2-19-12 Uehara, Shibuya-ku, Toyko 151, Japan
PHONE: +81 54541401
FAX: +81 54541405

Croatia
2-8-1 Tomigaya, Shibuya-ku, Toyko 151, Japan
PHONE: +81 54788481; 54788542; 54788549
FAX: +81 54788491; 54788564

Cuba
4-11-12 Shimomeguro, Meguro-ku, Toyko 153,
Japan
PHONE: +81 37163112
FAX: +81 37164334

Czech Republic
2-16-14 Hiroo, Shibuya-ku, Toyko 150, Japan
PHONE: +81 34008122
FAX: +81 34008124

Denmark
29-6, Sarugaku-cho, Shibuya-ku, Toyko 150,
Japan
PHONE: +81 34963001
FAX: +81 34963440

Djibouti
9-12 Nanpeidai-cho, Shibuya-ku, Toyko 150,
Japan
PHONE: +81 34966135; 34965629
FAX: +81 34968335

Dominican Republic
No. 38 Kowa Building, Room 904, 4-12-24
Nishi-Azabu, Minato-ku, Toyko 106, Japan
PHONE: +81 34996020
FAX: +81 34992627

Ecuador
No. 38 Kowa Building, Room 806, 12-24 Nishi-
Azabu, Minato-ku, Toyko 106, Japan

PHONE: +81 34992800; 34983984
FAX: +81 34994400

Egypt
1-5-4, Aobadai, Meguro-ku, Toyko 153, Japan
PHONE: +81 37708022
FAX: +81 37708021

El Salvador
No. 38 Kowa Building, 8th floor, Room 803, 4-
12-24 Nishi-Azabu, Minato-ku, Toyko 106,
Japan
PHONE: +81 34994461
FAX: +81 34867022

Ethiopia
1-14-15, Midorigaoka, Meguro-ku, Toyko 152,
Japan
PHONE: +81 37181003
FAX: +81 37180978

European Union
Europa House, 9-15 Sanban-cho, Chiyoda-ku,
Toyko 102, Japan
PHONE: +81 32390441
FAX: +81 32615194

Fiji
Noa Building 14th Floor, 2-3-5 Azabudai,
Minato-ku, Toyko 106, Japan
PHONE: +81 35872038
FAX: +81 35872563

Finland
3-5-39 Minami-Azabu, Minato-ku, Toyko 106,
Japan
PHONE: +81 34422231
FAX: +81 34422175

France
4-11-44 Minami-Azabu, Minato-ku, Toyko 106,
Japan
PHONE: +81 54208800
FAX: +81 54208847; 54208917

Gabon
1-12-11 Kami-Osaki, Shinagawa-ku, Toyko 141,
Japan
PHONE: +81 34489540
FAX: +81 34481596

Germany
4-5-10 Minami-Azabu, Minato-ku, Toyko 106,
Japan
PHONE: +81 3473151
FAX: +81 34734243

Ghana
6-2-4 Fukazawa, Setagaya-ku, Toyko, Japan
PHONE: +81 57063201

FAX: +81 57063205

Greece
3-16-30 Nishi-Azabu, Minato-ku, Toyko 106, Japan
PHONE: +81 34030871
FAX: +81 34024642

Guatemala
No. 38 Kowa Building, 9F, Room 905, 4-12-24 Nishi-Azabu, Minato-ku, Toyko 106, Japan
PHONE: +81 34001830
FAX: +81 34001820

Guinea
2-7-43 Shirogane, Minato-ku, Toyko 108, Japan
PHONE: +81 34438211
FAX: +81 34438213

Haiti
No. 38 Kowa Building, #906, 4-12-24 Nishi-Azabu, Minato-ku, Toyko 106, Japan
PHONE: +81 34867070; 34867096
FAX: +81 34867070

Honduras
No. 38 Kowa Building, 8F, Room 802, 4-12-24 Nishi-Azabu, Minato-ku, Toyko, Japan
PHONE: +81 34091150
FAX: +81 34090305

Hungary
2-17-14 Mita, Minato-ku, Toyko 108, Japan
PHONE: +81 37988801
FAX: +81 37988812

India
2-2-11 Kudan-Minami, Chiyoda-ku, Toyko 102, Japan
PHONE: +81 32622391
FAX: +81 32344866

Indonesia
5-2-9 Higashi-Gotanda, Shinagawa-ku, Toyko 141, Japan
PHONE: +81 34414201
FAX: +81 34471687

Iran
3-10-32 Minami-Azabu, Minato-ku, Toyko 106, Japan
PHONE: +81 34468011
FAX: +81 34469002

Iraq
8-4-7 Akasaka, Minato-ku, Toyko 107, Japan
PHONE: +81 34231727
FAX: +81 34028636

Ireland
2-10-7 Kojimachi, Ireland House, Chiyoda-ku, Toyko 102, Japan
PHONE: +81 32630695
FAX: +81 32652275

Israel
3 Niban-cho, Chiyoda-ku, Toyko 102, Japan
PHONE: +81 32640911
FAX: +81 32640832

Italy
2-5-4 Mita, Minato-ku, Toyko 108, Japan
PHONE: +81 34535291
FAX: +81 34562319

Jamaica
Daiwa Nakameguro Bldg. 7F, 4-6-1 Nakameguro, Meguro-ku, Toyko 153, Japan
PHONE: +81 57214114
FAX: +81 57214118

Jordan
Chiyoda House 4F, 2-17-8 Nagata-cho, Chiyoda-ku, Toyko, 100 Japan
PHONE: +81 35805856
FAX: +81 35939385

Kenya
3-24-3 Yakumo, Meguro-ku, Toyko 152, Japan
PHONE: +81 37234006
FAX: +81 37234488

South Korea
1-2-5 Minami-Azabu,, Minato-ku, Toyko 106, Japan
PHONE: +81 34527611
FAX: +81 52326911

Kuwait
4-13-12 Mita, Minato-ku, Toyko 108, Japan
PHONE: +81 34550361
FAX: +81 34566290

Laos
3-3-22 Nishi-Azabu, Minato-ku, Toyko 106, Japan
PHONE: +81 54112291
FAX: +81 54112293

Lebanon
Chiyoda House, 5th floor, 2-17-8 Nagata-cho, Chiyoda-ku, Toyko 103, Japan
PHONE: +81 35801227; 35801206
FAX: +81 35802281

Liberia
Sugi Terrace 201, 3-13-11 Okusawa, Setagaya-ku, Toyko 158, Japan
PHONE: +81 37265711

FAX: +81 37265712

Libya
10-14 Daikanyama-cho, Shibuya-ku, Toyko 150, Japan
PHONE: +81 34770701
FAX: +81 34640420

Luxembourg
Niban-cho TS Building, 4F, 2-1 Niban-cho, Chiyoda-ku, Toyko 102, Japan
PHONE: +81 32659621
FAX: +81 32659624

Madagascar
2-3-23 Moto-Azabu, Minato-ku, Toyko 106, Japan
PHONE: +81 34467252
FAX: +81 34467078

Malawi
3-12-9 Kami-Osaki, Shinagawa-ku, Toyko 141, Japan
PHONE: +81 34493010
FAX: +81 34493220

Malaysia
20-16 Nanpeidai-cho, Shibuya-ku, Toyko 150, Japan
PHONE: +81 34763840
FAX: +81 34764971

Marshall Islands
Meiji Park Height 1F, 9-9 Minamimoto-machi, Shinjuku-ku, Toyko 106, Japan
PHONE: +81 53791701
FAX: +81 53791810

Mauritania
5-17-5 Kita-Shinagawa, Shinagawa-ku, Toyko 141, Japan
PHONE: +81 34493810
FAX: +81 34493822

Mexico
2-15-1 Nagata-cho, Chiyoda-ku, Toyko 100, Japan
PHONE: +81 35811131
FAX: +81 35814058

Micronesia
Reinanzaka Building, 2nd floor, 1-14-2 Akasaka, Minato-ku, Toyko 107, Japan
PHONE: +81 35855456
FAX: +81 35855348

Mongolia
21-4 Kamiyama-cho, Shibuya-ku, Toyko 150, Japan
PHONE: +81 34692088; 34692091

FAX: +81 34692216

Morocco
Silva Kingdom Bldg., 5th and 6th Floor, 3-16-3 Sendagaya, Shibuya-ku, Toyko 151, Japan
PHONE: +81 34783271
FAX: +81 34020898

Mozambique
33-3 Ohyama-cho, Shibuya-ku, Toyko 151, Japan
PHONE: +81 34857621
FAX: +81 34857622

Myanmar
4-8-26 Kita-Shinagawa, Shinagawa-ku, Toyko 140, Japan
PHONE: +81 34419291
FAX: +81 34477394

Nepal
7-14-9 Todoroki, Setagaya-ku, Toyko 158, Japan
PHONE: +81 37055558
FAX: +81 37058264

Netherlands
3-6-3 Shibakoen, Minato-ku, Toyko 105, Japan
PHONE: +81 54010411
FAX: +81 54010420

New Zealand
20-40 Kamiyama-cho, Shibuya-ku, Toyko 150, Japan
PHONE: +81 34672271
FAX: +81 34676843; 34672278

Nicaragua
No. 38 Kowa Building, 9th Floor, Room 903, 4-12-24 Nishi-Azabu, Minato-ku, Toyko 106, Japan
PHONE: +81 34990400
FAX: +81 34993800

Nigeria
5-11-17, Shimo-Meguro, Meguro-ku, Toyko 153, Japan
PHONE: +81 57215391
FAX: +81 57215342

Norway
5-12-2 Minami-Azabu, Minato-ku, Toyko 106, Japan
PHONE: +81 34402611
FAX: +81 34402620

Oman
2-28-11 Sendagaya, Shibuya-ku, Toyko 151, Japan
PHONE: +81 34020877; 34022122
FAX: +81 34041334

Pakistan
2-14-9 Moto-Azabu, Minato-ku, Toyko 106,
Japan
PHONE: +81 34544861
FAX: +81 34570341

Panama
No. 38 Kowa Building, 9th Floor, Room 902, 4-
12-24 Nishi-Azabu, Minato-ku, Toyko 106,
Japan
PHONE: +81 34993741
FAX: +81 54853548

Papua New Guinea
Mita Kokusai Bldg., 3rd floor Room 313, 1-4-28
Mita, Minato-ku, Toyko 108, Japan
PHONE: +81 34547801
FAX: +81 34547275

Paraguay
Kowa 38 Bldg., 7F, Room 701, 4-12-24 Nishi-
Azabu, Minato-ku, Toyko 106, Japan
PHONE: +81 54853101
FAX: +81 54853103

Peru
4-4-27 Higashi, Shibuya-ku, Toyko 150, Japan
PHONE: +81 34064240
FAX: +81 34097589

Portugal
Olympia Annex, Apt. 303, 6-31-21 Jingumae,
Shibuya-ku, Toyko 150, Japan
PHONE: +81 34007907
FAX: +81 34007909

Qatar
6-8-7 Akasaka, Minato-ku, Toyko 107, Japan
PHONE: +81 32243911
FAX: +81 32243917

Romania
3-16-19 Nishi-Azabu, Minato-ku, Toyko 106,
Japan
PHONE: +81 34790311
FAX: +81 34790312

Russia
2-1-1 Azabudai, Minato-ku, Toyko 106, Japan
PHONE: +81 35834224; 35828751
FAX: +81 35050593

Rwanda
No. 38, Kowa Building, Room 702, 4-12-24
Nishi-Azabu, Minato-ku, Toyko 106, Japan
PHONE: +81 34867801
FAX: +81 34092434

Saudi Arabia
1-53 Azabu Nagasaka-cho, Minato-ku, Toyko
106, Japan
PHONE: +81 35895241
FAX: +81 35895200

Senegal
1-3-4 Aobadai, Meguro-ku, Toyko 153, Japan
PHONE: +81 34648451
FAX: +81 34648452

Serbia
4-7-24 Kita-Shinagawa, Shinagawa-ku, Toyko
140, Japan
PHONE: +81 34473571
FAX: +81 34473573

Singapore
5-12-3 Roppongi, Minato-ku, Toyko 106, Japan
PHONE: +81 35869111
FAX: +81 35821085

Slovakia
2-16-14 Hiroo, Shibuya-ku, Toyko 150, Japan
PHONE: +81 34008122; 34008328
FAX: +81 34066215

Slovenia
7-5-15 Akasaka, Minato-ku, Toyko 107, Japan
PHONE: +81 55706275
FAX: +81 55706075

South Africa
4F, Zenkyoren Building, 2-7-9 Hirakawa-cho,
Chiyoda-ku, Toyko 102, Japan
PHONE: +81 32653366
FAX: +81 32651108

Spain
1-3-29 Roppongi, Minato-ku, Toyko 106, Japan
PHONE: +81 35838531
FAX: +81 35828627

Sri Lanka
1-14-1 Akasaka, Minato-ku, Toyko 107, Japan
PHONE: +81 35857431
FAX: +81 35869307

Sudan
Kindai-Shisetsu Bldg., 2F and 3F, 1-13-4
Aobadai, Meguro-ku, Toyko 153, Japan
PHONE: +81 34760811
FAX: +81 34760814

Sweden
1-10-3-100 Roppongi, Minato-ku, Toyko 106,
Japan
PHONE: +81 55625050
FAX: +81 55629095

Switzerland
5-9-12 Minami-Azabu, Minato-ku, Toyko 106,
Japan
PHONE: +81 34730121
FAX: +81 34736090

Syria
Homat-Jade, 6-19-45 Akasaka, Minato-ku,
Toyko 107, Japan
PHONE: +81 35868977
FAX: +81 35868979

Tanzania
4-21-9 Kamiyoga, Setagaya-ku, Toyko 158,
Japan
PHONE: +81 34254531
FAX: +81 34257844

Thailand
3-14-6 Kami-Osaki, Shinagawa-ku, Toyko 141,
Japan
PHONE: +81 34411387; 34417352
FAX: +81 34426750

Tunisia
1-18-8 Wakaba, Shinjuku-ku, Toyko 160, Japan
PHONE: +81 33534111
FAX: +81 32254387

Turkey
2-33-6, Jingumae, Shibuya-ku, 150, Toyko,
Japan
PHONE: +81 34705131
FAX: +81 34705136

Uganda
39-15 Oyama-cho, Shibuya-ku, Toyko 151,
Japan
PHONE: +81 34654552
FAX: +81 34654970

Ukraine
5-31-7 Shinbashi, Minato-ku, Toyko 105, Japan
PHONE: +81 34320917
FAX: +81 34320970

United Arab Emirates
9-10 Nanpeidai-cho, Shibuya-ku, Toyko 150,
Japan
PHONE: +81 54890804
FAX: +81 54890813

United Kingdom
1 Ichiban-cho, Chiyoda-ku, Toyko 102, Japan
PHONE: +81 32655511
FAX: +81 52753164

Embassies in Kazakstan

United States
1-10-5, Akasaka, Minato-ku, Toyko 107, Japan
PHONE: +81 32245000
FAX: +81 35051862

United States
1-10-5, Akasaka, Minato-ku, Toyko 107, Japan
PHONE: +81 32245000
FAX: +81 35051862

Uruguay
No. 38 Kowa Building, Room 908, 4-12-24
Nishi-Azabu, Minato-ku., Toyko 106, Japan
PHONE: +81 34861888
FAX: +81 34869872

Vatican City
9-2 Sanban-cho, Chiyoda-ku, Toyko 102, Japan
PHONE: +81 32636851
FAX: +81 32636060

Venezuela
No. 38 Kowa Building, 7th Floor, Room 703, 4-
12-24 Nishi-Azabu, Minato-ku, Toyko 106,
Japan
PHONE: +81 34091501
FAX: +81 34091505

Vietnam
50-11, Moto-yoyogi-cho, Shibuya-ku, Toyko
151, Japan
PHONE: +81 34663311; 34663313
FAX: +81 34663312; 34663391

Yemen
No. 38 Kowa Building, 8th Floor, Room 807, 4-
12-24 Nishi-Azabu, Minato-ku, Toyko 106,
Japan
PHONE: +81 34997151
FAX: +81 34994577

Zambia
Harajuku Green Heights, Rm. 701, Toyko 142,
Japan
PHONE: +81 34910121
FAX: +81 34910123

Zimbabwe
5-9-10 Shiroganedaiu, Minato-ku, Toyko 108,
Japan
PHONE: +81 32800331
FAX: +81 32800466

JUDICIAL SYSTEM
Supreme Court

FURTHER READING
Articles
"Japan's Tender Spring." *The Economist* (March 27, 1999): 41.

"The Japan Syndrome." *Time* (October 11, 1999): 50.

"Nuclear Peril is Over but Japanese Anger Isn't." *The New York Times,* 2 October 1999, p. A1.

"Obuchi Rallies His Troops." *The Economist* (January 9, 1999): 35.

"Praise Clinton and Pass More Bills to Stir Japan's Economy." *The Economist* (May 8, 1999): 31.

"Reform in Japan: Maybe This Time." *Business Week* (September 27, 1999): 45.

"Support, at a Price." *The Economist* (July 3, 1999): 32.

"A Weakened Trust in Government." *The Christian Science Monitor*, 4 October 1999, p. 7.

"Yen's Rise Dampens a Nation's Rally." *The Christian Science Monitor*, 4 October 1999, p. 20.

Books
Cortazzi, Hugh. *Modern Japan: A Concise Survey*. New York: St. Martin's Press, 1993.

Dolan, Ronald E., and Robert L. Worden. *Japan, A Country Study*. Federal Research Division, Library of Congress. Washington, D.C.: U.S. Govt. Printing Office, 1992.

Morris-Suzuki, Tessa. *Re-inventing Japan: Time, Space, Nation*. Armonk, N.Y.: M. E. Sharpe, 1998.

Okuizumi, Hikaru. *The Stones Cry Out*. Trans. by James Westerhoven. New York: Harcourt Brace, 1998.

Reischauer, Edwin O., and Marius B. Jansen. *The Japanese Today: Change and Continuity*. Cambridge, Mass.: Belknap Press of Harvard University, 1995.

JAPAN: STATISTICAL DATA

For sources and notes see "Sources of Statistics" in the front of each volume.

GEOGRAPHY

Geography (1)

Area:

Total: 377,835 sq km.

Land: 374,744 sq km.

Water: 3,091 sq km.

Note: includes Bonin Islands (Ogasawara-gunto), Daito-shoto, Minami-jima, Okino-tori-shima, Ryukyu Islands (Nansei-shoto), and Volcano Islands (Kazan-retto).

Area—comparative: slightly smaller than California.

Land boundaries: 0 km.

Coastline: 29,751 km.

Climate: varies from tropical in south to cool temperate in north.

Terrain: mostly rugged and mountainous.

Natural resources: negligible mineral resources, fish.

Land use:

Arable land: 11%

Permanent crops: 1%

Permanent pastures: 2%

Forests and woodland: 67%

Other: 19% (1993 est.).

HUMAN FACTORS

Demographics (2A)

	1990	1995	1998	2000	2010	2020	2030	2040	2050
Population	123,537.4	125,233.4	125,931.5	126,434.5	127,142.2	123,076.2	116,468.0	109,296.5	101,333.7
Net migration rate (per 1,000 population)	NA	NA	NA	NA	NA	NA	NA	NA	NA
Births	NA	NA	NA	NA	NA	NA	NA	NA	NA
Deaths	820.3	NA	NA	NA	NA	NA	NA	NA	NA
Life expectancy - males	76.0	76.6	76.9	77.1	78.0	78.7	79.3	79.7	80.0
Life expectancy - females	82.0	83.0	83.3	83.5	84.2	84.9	85.3	85.7	86.0
Birth rate (per 1,000)	9.9	9.5	10.3	10.6	9.3	7.9	8.6	8.5	8.1
Death rate (per 1,000)	6.7	7.4	7.9	8.3	10.4	12.7	14.5	15.6	16.1
Women of reproductive age (15-49 yrs.)	31,466.2	31,027.4	30,248.9	29,350.2	26,878.7	24,811.7	21,565.2	19,571.2	18,466.9
of which are currently married	49,852.8	NA	NA	NA	NA	NA	NA	NA	NA
Fertility rate	1.5	1.4	1.5	1.5	1.5	1.6	1.6	1.7	1.7

Except as noted, values for vital statistics are in thousands; life expectancy is in years.

Health Personnel (3)

Total health expenditure as a percentage of GDP, 1990-1997[a]

Public sector 5.7

Private sector 1.7

Total[b] 7.3

Health expenditure per capita in U.S. dollars, 1990-1997[a]

Purchasing power parity 1,670

Total 2,442

Availability of health care facilities per 100,000 people

Hospital beds 1990-1997[a] 1620

Doctors 1993[c] 177

Nurses 1993[c] 641

Health Indicators (4)

Life expectancy at birth

1980 76

1997 80

Daily per capita supply of calories (1996) 2,905

Total fertility rate births per woman (1997) 1.4

Maternal mortality ratio per 100,000 live births (1990-97) . . . . .18[b]

Safe water % of population with access (1995) 96

Sanitation % of population with access (1995) 100

Consumption of iodized salt % of households (1992-98)[a] . . . .

Smoking prevalence

Male % of adults (1985-95)[a] 59

Female % of adults (1985-95)[a] 15

Tuberculosis incidence per 100,000 people (1997) 29

Adult HIV prevalence % of population ages 15-49 (1997) 0.01

Infants and Malnutrition (5)

Under-5 mortality rate (1997) 6

% of infants with low birthweight (1990-97) 7

Births attended by skilled health staff % of total[a] . . .NA

% fully immunized (1995-97)

TB 91x

DPT 100

Polio 98

Measles 94

Prevalence of child malnutrition under age 5 (1992-97)[b] . . . . .NA

Ethnic Division (6)

Japanese 99.4%

Other (mostly Korean) 0.6%

Religions (7)

Observe both Shinto and Buddhist 84%

Other 16%

Other includes Christian 0.7%.

Languages (8)

Japanese.

EDUCATION

Public Education Expenditures (9)

Public expenditure on education (% of GNP)

1980 . . . . .5.8

1996 . . . . .3.6[1]

Expenditure per student

Primary % of GNP per capita

1980 . . . . .14.8

1996 . . . . .19.3[1]

Secondary % of GNP per capita

1980 . . . . .16.6

1996 . . . . .19.0[1]

Tertiary % of GNP per capita

1980 . . . . .21.0

1996 . . . . .13.9[1]

Expenditure on teaching materials

Primary % of total for level (1996) 4.9

Secondary % of total for level (1996) . . . .

Primary pupil-teacher ratio per teacher (1996) . . . . .19[1]

Duration of primary education years (1995) 6

Educational Attainment (10)

Age group (1990)[18] . . . . .25+

Total population 81,991,363

Highest level attained (%)

No schooling 0.3

First level

Not completed 33.6

Completed . . . . .NA

Entered second level

S-1 . . . . .43.7

S-2 . . . . .NA

Postsecondary 20.7

Literacy Rates (11B)

Adult literacy rate

1980

  Male 100%

  Female 99%

1995

  Male . . . .-

  Female . . . .-

GOVERNMENT & LAW

Political Parties (12)

House of Representatives	No. of seats
Liberal Democratic Party (LDP)	.240
New Frontier Party (NFP)	.142
Democratic Party of Japan (DPJ)	.52
Japan Communist Party (JCP)	.26
Social Democratic Party (SDP)	.15
Sun Party	.10
Others	.15

Subsequent to the last legislative elections, the New Frontier Party (NFP) disbanded; the Sun Party was formed by former NFP members, but later disbanded; the DPJ was formed by former members of the SDP and Sakigake and, in April 1998, was joined by three additional parties which had formed after the NFP disbanded; Reform Club, New Peace Party, and Liberal Party were formed in January 1998 after the NFP disbanded.

Government Budget (13A)

Year: 1993

Total Expenditures: 112,478 Billions of Yen

Expenditures as a percentage of the total by function:

  General public services and public order . . . . . .3.63[p]

  Defense . . . . .4.11[p]

  Education . . . . .6.03[p]

  Health . . . . .1.60[p]

  Social Security and Welfare . . . . .36.80[p]

  Housing and community amenities . . . . .13.76[p]

  Recreational, cultural, and religious affairs . . . . . . .14[p]

  Fuel and energy . . . .-[p]

  Agriculture, forestry, fishing, and hunting . . . . .1.09[p]

  Mining, manufacturing, and construction . . . . . .1.64[p]

  Transportation and communication . . . . .30[p]

  Other economic affairs and services . . . . .32[p]

Crime (15)

Crime rate (for 1997)

  Crimes reported .1,980,900

  Total persons convicted 841,900

  Crimes per 100,000 population 1,550

Persons responsible for offenses

  Total number of suspects 383,500

  Total number of female suspects 81,700

  Total number of juvenile suspects 161,800

LABOR FORCE

Labor Force (16)

Total (million) 67.23

Trade and services 50%

Manufacturing, mining, and construction 33%

Utilities and communication 7%

Agriculture, forestry, ...

  and fishing 6%

Government 3%

Distribution data for 1994. Total for March 1997.

Unemployment Rate (17)

3.4% (1997)

PRODUCTION SECTOR

Electric Energy (18)

Capacity . . . . .199.878 million kW (1995)

Production . . . . .930.55 billion kWh (1995)

Consumption per capita . . . . .7,414 kWh (1995)

Transportation (19)

Highways:

total: 1.16 million km

paved: 859,560 km (including 6,070 km of expressways)

unpaved: 300,440 km (1996 est.)

Waterways: about 1,770 km; seagoing craft ply all coastal inland seas

Pipelines: crude oil 84 km; petroleum products 322 km; natural gas 1,800 km

Merchant marine:

total: 738 ships (1,000 GRT or over) totaling 14,323,766 GRT/20,709,738 DWT

Airports: 167 (1997 est.)

Airports—with paved runways:

total: 137

over 3,047 m: 7

2,438 to 3,047 m: 32

1,524 to 2,437 m: 38

914 to 1,523 m: 29

under 914 m: 31 (1997 est.)

Airports—with unpaved runways:

total: 30

914 to 1,523 m: 2

under 914 m: 28 (1997 est.)

Top Agricultural Products (20)

Rice, sugar beets, vegetables, fruit; pork, poultry, dairy products, eggs; world's largest fish catch of 10 million metric tons in 1991.

GOVERNMENT & LAW

Military Affairs (14B)

	1990	1991	1992	1993	1994	1995
Military expenditures						
Current dollars (mil.)	40,740	43,820	46,030	47,760	49,300	50,240
1995 constant dollars (mil.)	46,820	48,430	49,510	50,070	50,540	50,240
Armed forces (000)	250	250	242	242	233	240
Gross national product (GNP)						
Current dollars (bil.)	4,187,000	4,541,000	4,727,000	4,841,000	4,981,000	5,153,000[e]
1995 constant dollars (bil.)	4,811,000	5,018,000	5,084,000	5,076,000	5,106,000	5,153,000[e]
Central government expenditures (CGE)						
1995 constant dollars (bil.)	777,700	1,100,000	1,101,000	1,194,000	NA	NA
People (mil.)	123.5	124.0	124.4	124.7	125.0	125.2
Military expenditure as % of GNP	1.0	1.0	1.0	1.0	1.0	1.0
Military expenditure as % of CGE	6.0	4.4	4.5	4.2	NA	NA
Military expenditure per capita (1995 $)	379	391	398	402	404	401
Armed forces per 1,000 people (soldiers)	2.0	2.0	1.9	1.9	1.9	1.9
GNP per capita (1995 $)	38,950	40,480	40,880	40,700	40,860	41,160
Arms imports[6]						
Current dollars (mil.)	1,100	1,100	1,200	575	700	625
1995 constant dollars (mil.)	1,264	1,216	1,291	603	718	625
Arms exports[6]						
Current dollars (mil.)	70	10	10	10	10	20
1995 constant dollars (mil.)	80	11	11	10	10	20
Total imports[7]						
Current dollars (mil.)	235,400	237,000	233,200	241,600	275,200	335,900
1995 constant dollars (mil.)	270,500	261,900	250,900	253,300	282,100	335,900
Total exports[7]						
Current dollars (mil.)	287,600	314,800	339,900	362,200	397,000	443,100
1995 constant dollars (mil.)	330,500	347,800	365,600	379,800	407,000	443,100
Arms as percent of total imports[8]	.5	.5	.5	.2	.3	.2
Arms as percent of total exports[8]	0	0	0	0	0	0

MANUFACTURING SECTOR

GDP & Manufacturing Summary (21)

Detailed value added figures are listed by both International Standard Industry Code (ISIC) and product title.

	1980	1985	1990	1994
GDP ($-1990 mil.)[1]	1,959,820	2,354,213	2,932,088	3,098,620
Per capita ($-1990)[1]	16,778	19,483	23,734	24,826
Manufacturing share (%) (current prices)[1]	28.2	28.4	27.5	25.7

Manufacturing

	1980	1985	1990	1994
Value added ($-1990 mil.)[1]	485,633	643,188	852,566	853,531
Industrial production index	100	120	150	140
Value added ($ mil.)	339,234	412,505	891,767	1,257,761
Gross output ($ mil.)	970,567	1,114,671	2,245,766	3,062,847
Employment (000)	10,253	10,652	11,172	10,853

Profitability (% of gross output)

	1980	1985	1990	1994
Intermediate input (%)	65	63	60	59
Wages and salaries inc. supplements (%)	12	13	13	15
Gross operating surplus	23	24	27	26

Productivity ($)

	1980	1985	1990	1994
Gross output per worker	88,443	102,310	201,017	278,841
Value added per worker	30,912	37,862	79,822	117,764
Average wage (inc. supplements)	11,522	13,644	26,368	41,297

Value added ($ mil.)

	1980	1985	1990	1994
311/2 Food products	25,889	32,041	66,676	108,436
313 Beverages	5,015	5,303	10,305	15,450
314 Tobacco products	1,888	700	2,003	4,138
321 Textiles	15,436	15,259	27,046	32,752
322 Wearing apparel	5,156	5,622	11,921	16,605
323 Leather and fur products	886	977	1,865	2,350
324 Footwear	697	658	1,478	1,873
331 Wood and wood products	8,997	6,888	14,006	18,111
332 Furniture and fixtures	3,788	3,798	8,730	11,047
341 Paper and paper products	9,310	9,759	22,287	32,558
342 Printing and publishing	17,099	20,789	47,938	71,862
351 Industrial chemicals	13,809	16,811	38,076	54,911
352 Other chemical products	15,471	19,758	46,764	72,650
353 Petroleum refineries	6,620	4,595	4,841	15,270
354 Miscellaneous petroleum and coal products	1,063	713	1,540	2,266
355 Rubber products	4,150	5,077	11,403	16,198
356 Plastic products	9,478	13,570	30,796	47,093
361 Pottery, china and earthenware	1,623	6,127	2,984	4,899
362 Glass and glass products	2,876	4,029	8,467	11,431
369 Other non-metal mineral products	12,565	12,321	26,652	43,689
371 Iron and steel	26,444	25,224	48,539	59,300
372 Non-ferrous metals	7,458	5,236	11,976	15,460
381 Metal products	22,409	26,356	62,905	92,613
382 Non-electrical machinery	39,270	53,576	126,563	152,326
383 Electrical machinery	38,868	63,180	133,884	184,888
384 Transport equipment	32,107	45,158	95,594	133,377
385 Professional and scientific equipment	5,685	6,972	12,798	15,807
390 Other manufacturing industries	5,178	6,510	13,730	20,405

FINANCE, ECONOMICS, & TRADE

Economic Indicators (22)

National product: GDP—purchasing power parity—$3.08 trillion (1997 est.)

National product real growth rate: 0.9% (1997 est.)

National product per capita: $24,500 (1997 est.)

Inflation rate—consumer price index: 1.7% (1997)

Exchange Rates (24)

Exchange rates:

Yen (¥) per US$1

January 1998	129.45
1997	120.99
1996	108.78
1995	94.06
1994	102.21
1993	111.20

Top Import Origins (25)

$339 billion (c.i.f., 1997) Data are for 1996.

Origins	%
France	NA
Turkey	NA
Jordan	NA
Vietnam	NA
Australia	NA

NA stands for not available.

Top Export Destinations (26)

$421 billion (f.o.b., 1997).

Destinations	%
United States	27
Southeast Asia	17
European Union	15
China	5

Economic Aid (27)

Donor: ODA, $8.3 billion (1998 est.). Note: ODA and OOF commitments (1970-94), $174 billion.

Import Export Commodities (28)

Import Commodities	Export Commodities
Manufactures 54%	Manufactures 96% (including machinery 50%, Motor vehicles 19%, Consumer electronics 3%)
Foodstuffs and raw materials 28%	
Fossil fuels 16%	

Balance of Payments (23)

	1992	1993	1994	1995	1996
Exports of goods (f.o.b.)	332,560	352,660	385,700	428,720	400,280
Imports of goods (f.o.b.)	−207,790	−213,240	−241,510	−296,930	−316,720
Trade balance	124,760	139,420	144,190	131,790	83,560
Services - debits	−200,300	−203,720	−221,320	−270,790	−301,510
Services - credits	191,940	201,050	213,490	257,720	292,820
Private transfers (net)	−2,070	−2,400	−2,820	−3,280	−1,970
Government transfers (net)	−1,770	−2,700	−3,290	−4,400	−7,030
Overall balance	112,570	131,650	130,250	111,050	65,870

JERSEY

CAPITAL: Saint Helier.

FLAG: White with a diagonal red cross of Saint Patrick (patron saint of Ireland) extending to the corners of the flag. In the top triangular field is the seal of Jersey—a red shield with three gold lions, topped by a gold crown.

ANTHEM: God Save the Queen.

MONETARY UNIT: 1 Jersey pound (£J) = 100 pence.

WEIGHTS AND MEASURES: The imperial system is standard, but the metric and historic local measurement units are used as well.

HOLIDAYS: Liberation Day, 9 May.

TIME: Noon = noon GMT.

LOCATION AND SIZE: Jersey, a territory of England, lies about 32 km (20 miles) off the coast of France in the English Channel. 49°15′N, 2°10′W. Total area: 117 sq. km.

CLIMATE: Jersey has a mild, maritime climate, with an average rainfall of 84 cm (33 inches). February temperatures average 6°C (43°F) and August temperatures range between 16–17°C (60–63°F). The most southerly of the Channel Islands, Jersey has one of the best sunshine records in the British Isles.

INTRODUCTORY SURVEY

RECENT HISTORY

Jersey is one of a group of islands known as the Channel Islands lying from 10 to 30 miles off the northwest coast of France. Once a part of the Duchy of Normandy, the islands have belonged to the Crown of England since the twelfth century. Although belonging to the Crown, they are not part of the United Kingdom which includes England, Wales, Scotland, and Northern Ireland. The islands, including Jersey, maintain their own legislative, legal, and administrative systems.

By the fifteenth century, Jersey had its own administrator called captain. The captain's position evolved into the governor and, in 1854, into the lieutenant governorship. Jersey's Royal Court was created in the seventeenth century and the legislative body, the States of Jersey, in the eighteenth century. The lieutenant governorship, Royal Court, and States of Jersey continue into the twenty-first century. Although plagued by family wars through the eighteenth and nineteenth centuries, the Jersey population grew economically from fisheries, smuggling, and later from cattle, potatoes, and tourism. Jersey has long been famous for the Jersey milk cattle, a pure breed exported worldwide. Jersey, just as all of the Channel Islands, was left undefended from 1940 to 1945 during World War II and fell briefly to the Germans.

GOVERNMENT

Jersey, along with the Isle of Man and Guernsey, have unique relations with the United Kingdom. Neither sovereign states nor part of the United Kingdom, they are dependencies on the Crown. The chief of state is the British monarch. The monarch's personal representative and channel for communication between the Crown and island government is the lieutenant-governor which also serves as commander-in-chief of Jersey. Appointed by the Crown, the lieutenant-governor may attend and speak in the legislative body, the States of Jersey, but has no vote. He holds veto power over specific forms of legislation.

Jersey's unicameral legislative branch, the Assembly of the States of Jersey, is composed of the bailiff, the lieutenant-governor, the Dean of Jersey, the attorney-general, the solicitor-general, and

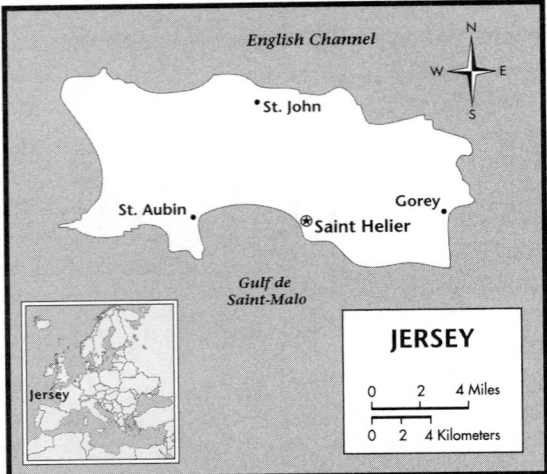

English Channel

•St. John

St. Aubin •
Gorey •
⊗Saint Helier

Gulf de
Saint-Malo

Jersey

JERSEY

0   2   4 Miles

0   2   4 Kilometers

fifty-three members elected by universal suffrage. Appointed by the Crown, the bailiff is President of the States, has the right of dissent and one casting vote. Also appointed by the Crown, the dean, attorney-general, and solicitor-general may sit and speak in the States but not vote. The fifty-three elected seats include twelve senators popularly elected for six-year terms with half retiring every third year, twelve constables of the twelve parishes popularly elected triennially, and twenty-nine deputies popularly elected triennially. Except in certain instances, permanent laws passed by the States require the sanction of the Queen-in-Council.

The Committees of the States, whose members are appointed by the Assembly of States of Jersey, serves as the administrative cabinet.

Judiciary

Jersey's justice system is administered by the Royal Court. The Royal Court is comprised of the bailiff or deputy bailiff when authorized to act for the bailiff, and twelve jurats or magistrates. Appeals proceed to the Court of Appeal consisting of the bailiff and two judges selected from a Crown-appointed panel. In specific cases, final appeal may be made to the Judicial Committee of the Privy Council in England. Minor civil and criminal cases fall within the jurisdiction of a Stipendiary Magistrate.

Political Parties

No political parties exist. All elected officials are independents.

DEFENSE

Jersey maintains its own form of self-government but the British government remains responsible for Jersey's international relations and for its defense.

ECONOMIC AFFAIRS

Financial services, tourism and agriculture are the key sectors of Jersey's economy. Of the Channel Islands, Jersey maintains the largest offshore financial centers. Jersey's commercial laws encourage merchant banks, especially subsidiaries of London banks, to locate on the island due to Jersey's ability to set low taxation rates. The finance sector contributed approximately 55% of Jersey's gross domestic product (GDP) in 1996 compared to only 26% in 1980 when the banking interests first began to expand. Tourism, with a long history as an economic mainstay, accounts for 24% of the GDP.

The agriculture sector concentrates on dairying and breeding of the Jersey milk cattle, which are exported worldwide. Milk products are exported chiefly to the United Kingdom and other European markets. Many small farms grow potatoes, tomatoes, cauliflower, and flowers for export primarily to the United Kingdom. Greenhouse production of flowers and vegetables contributes significantly to the total crop output.

In the 1990s the government successfully encouraged light industry to locate in Jersey. An electronics industry developed alongside the traditional manufacturing of knitted woolen jerseys.

Jersey's chief exports include light industrial and electrical goods, foodstuffs, and textiles. Exports are protected by British tariff barriers. Major imports include machinery and transport equipment, manufactured goods, foodstuffs, mineral fuels, and chemicals. Imports are free of British purchase tax. The inflation rate for 1998 was 4.3%.

Public Finance

In 1997 revenue amounted to 291 million pounds and expenditures were 245 million pounds. The chief revenue source is taxation.

Income

In 1995 the composition of the GDP by sector was 93% services, 5% agriculture, and 2% industry.

Industry

Principle industrial activities concentrate in light industries such as electrical goods and the traditional knitted textiles and clothing. Financial services is the largest employer, followed by distributive trades, construction, and hotels and restaurants.

Banking and Finance

The Jersey Financial Services Commission serves as the financial services regulator. In 1998 seventy-nine banks were licensed in Jersey as the island maintained the largest offshore financial district of the Channel Islands. The range of financial services provided include fund management, corporate banking, and company and trust formation. Concerns over investment fraud and tax evasion under the lax enforcement of banking regulations drew considerable attention of the British government through the 1990s.

SOCIAL WELFARE

The Jersey's Social Security Department administers a contributory Health Insurance Scheme. Benefits paid out by the Department were in the areas of long-term benefits, sickness, invalidity, and family allowances.

Healthcare

In 1995, five hospitals with 651 beds were located on Jersey. Ninety-five doctors practiced on Jersey. Life expectancy for the total population is 78.8 years, with males 76 years and females 82 years.

EDUCATION

In 1996 Jersey had twenty-four public primary schools and five public secondary schools. Eight private primary schools and eight private secondary schools were also available. Jersey had one higher education college.

1999 KEY EVENTS TIMELINE

January

- The launch of the new single currency, the euro, sparks controversy in the Channel Islands. Several prominent European politicians, including the commissioner for the single market, Mario Monti, call for the banking business of the Channel Islands to be closed down, and for the islands' status as a tax haven to end.

February

- The former head of the Russian Central Bank, Sergei Dubinin, defends his role in hiding state funds in the accounts of a company called Financial Management Company (FIMACO), based in Jersey.

March

- Special anniversary Channel Island stamps are issued to celebrate the United Kingdom's Royal National Lifeboat Institution's 175 years of saving lives at sea.

- Computer millionaire Christopher Dawes is one of three people killed in a car crash. Dawes, arrested in December 1998 in the first ever crack cocaine seizure in the Channel Islands, was due to appear in court later this year charged with possession of a Class A drug.

May

- U.K. Tory leader William Hague attacks Prime Minister Tony Blair over a proposal for a European withholding tax aimed at stopping EU citizens from using tax havens such as the Channel Islands.

- While the Marine Conservation Society reports sewage problems on the U.K.'s northern beaches are becoming worse, its Good Beach Guide 1999 praises the south of England and Channel Island beaches for clean up efforts.

August

- Authorities suspect Russian mobsters may have been involved in the diversion of International Monetary Fund (IMF) loans made to Russia; investigators focus on $200 million that ended up in an account held by a Russian commercial bank at a bank on Jersey.

September

- Jersey politician John Rothwell asks the States of Jersey to offer 20,000 pounds compensation to Alphonse Le Gastelois. In 1960, Le Gastelois was questioned by the police in an investigation in a serial sex offense case. Although he was never charged, his name was linked to the investigation in the press and he was driven to live in vitual exile on the tiny Channel Islands reef of Ecrehous for fourteen years, until the real offender was caught and prosecuted.

- Jersey declares its agriculture free of genetic modification, halting research into a new strain of potatoes.

October

- Britain's Treasury and Internal Revenue announces it will take immediate action to crack down on companies' use of special tax regimes in its dependent territories. The tax legislation, to be officially introduced in the government's next finance bill, is expected to affect the economies of the Channel Islands of Jersey and Guernsey.

- European Union talks stall over proposals for a minimum EU-wide withholding tax and how such a tax would apply to nations like Luxembourg, and dependent territories like the Channel Islands. EU finance ministers meet to seek a compromise over controversial measures designed to eliminate tax evasion in the EU.

December

- The European Union's tax commission wants regulations to extend to associated and dependent territories like Jersey so that savers can no longer avoid taxes by banking "offshore."

- A new British Irish Council is formed to provide a forum for regional debate. The Council includes representatives from the U.K., Ireland, Northern Ireland, Jersey, Guernsey, and the Isle of Man.

ANALYSIS OF EVENTS: 1999

BUSINESS AND THE ECONOMY

The launch of the euro and the issue of standardizing tax rates within the European Union sparked controversy as 1999 began. Several prominent European politicians, including then-commissioner of the EU, Mario Monti, called for the Channel Islands' banking business to be closed down and its status as a tax haven to end. In response, British foreign secretary Robin Cook called upon the islands to police banking activity, however, chief executive of the Channel Islands Stock Exchange, Tamara Mentashvili, claimed that island regulation is already comparable to British mainland banking law. Focus on a proposal for a European withholding tax designed to stop EU citizens from using banks in the Channel Islands as tax havens caused year-long strife within the British government. While the Islands are territories of the United Kingdom, they have been self-governing for 800 years, and any attempt at control by the UK could potentially incite rebellion. Nonetheless, by October, Britain's Treasury and Inland Revenue announced it was cracking down on special tax structures in its dependent territories, with legislation aimed at the Channel Islands of Jersey and Guernsey. The territories claimed that Gordon Brown, Chancellor of the Exchequer, was responding to pressure from the EU, where there is considerable debate over a controversial package of measures to eliminate tax evasion across the eurozone (zone of countries using the euro).

Channel Island banks were also involved in another international scandal in 1999. The Russian prosecutor's office accused its own bank officials of hiding over $50 billion in the offshore accounts of the little-known Financial Management Company (FIMACO), registered in the Channel Islands. Former head of the Russian Central Bank, Sergei Dubinin, defended his role in hiding state funds in the tax haven, claiming it was necessary to keep it away from foreign creditors trying to seize it.

CULTURE AND SOCIETY

Jersey ended research into a new strain of potatoes in response to consumer demand to discontinue genetically modified foods. The States of Jersey Department of Agriculture and Fisheries declared its agriculture free of genetic modification. The Jersey parliament approved two propositions related to genetically modified agricultural products: the first, to stop research work into a potential variant of its premium Jersey Royal potato intended to make it resistant to the potato cyst eel worm; the second, to ban the future cultivation of genetically modified crops, should any suitable for Jersey's agricultural conditions become available.

Channel Island beaches were praised in the Marine Conservation Society's Good Beach Guide 1999 for improved sewage treatment. Other causes for celebration included the 175th anniversary of the Royal National Lifeboat Institution in March, for which the Channel Islands issued special anniversary stamps. The British Royal Mint also issued special gold and silver proof coins for the Channel Island of Alderney, which scientists declared as one of the best places in the world to observe August's total eclipse of the Sun.

DIRECTORY

CENTRAL GOVERNMENT

Head of State

Lieutenant-Governor
Michael Wilkes

Bailiff of Jersey
Sir Phillip Ballhache, Bailiff's Chambers, Royal
Court House, St. Heller JE1 1DD, Jersey
PHONE: (1534) 502100
FAX: (1534) 502199

Cabinet

Controller of the Social Security Department
A. Esterson, Social Security Department, St.
Heller JE4 8PE, Jersey
PHONE: (1534) 280000

**Chief Executive Officer of Financial Services
Department**
C.A. Syvret, Financial Services Department, PO
Box 267, St. Heller JE4 8TP, Jersey
PHONE: (1534) 603000
FAX: (1534) 89155

**Chief Administrator of Health and Social
Services**
G. Jennings, Office of Health and Social
Services, 4th Floor, Peter Crill House, St. Heller
JE2 3QS, Jersey
PHONE: (1534) 622291
FAX: (1534) 37050

Director of Tourism
S.P. Henwood, Office of Tourism, Liberation
Square, St. Heller JE1 1BB, Jersey
PHONE: (1534) 507000
FAX: (1534) 500899

Head of Housing Department
E.H. Le Ruez, Housing Department, PO Box
587, Hilgrove House, Hilgrove St., St. Helier
JE4 8XT, Jersey
PHONE: (1534) 884422
FAX: (1534) 884488

Director of Education
T.W. McKeon, Office of Education, PO Box
142, St. Seviour JE4 8QJ, Jersey
PHONE: (1534) 509500
FAX: (1534) 509800

**Chief Executive Officer of the Planning and
Building Services Department**
J. Young, Planning and Building Services
Department, 8A South Hill, St Heller JE2 4US,
Jersey
PHONE: (1534) 25511
FAX: (1534) 68952

Chief Officer of Agriculture and Fisheries
P. Bastion, Office of Agriculture and Fisheries,
Trinity JE4 8UF, Jersey
PHONE: (1534) 866200
FAX: (1534) 866201

**Chief Executive Officer of Public Services
Department**
C.J. Swinnerton, Public Services Department, PO
Box 412, South Hill, St. Heller JE4 8UY, Jersey
PHONE: (1534) 601690
FAX: (1534) 68950

POLITICAL ORGANIZATIONS

None

DIPLOMATIC REPRESENTATION

None, British crown dependency

JUDICIAL SYSTEM

Royal Court

Royal Court House, St. Heller JE1 1DD, Jersey
PHONE: (1534) 502100
FAX: (1534) 502199

FURTHER READING

Articles

Barraclough, Colin. ''Taxing Times for Money
Havens,'' *Institutional Investor,* 33 (May
1999): 137.

''Hapoalim Opens Jersey Trust Company.''
Israel Business Today, 11 (July 15, 1997): 12.

Books

Channel Islands in Your Pocket. Clermont-
Ferrand, France: Manufacture Francaise des
Pneumatiques Michelin, 1999.

Internet

Jersey Island. Available Online @ http://
www.jerseyisland.com (October 25, 1999).

A Pictorial Guide to Jersey. Available Online @
http://www.jtourism.com (October 25, 1999).

The States of Jersey. Available Online @ http://
www.jersey.gov.uk (October 25, 1999).

JERSEY: STATISTICAL DATA

For sources and notes see "Sources of Statistics" in the front of each volume.

GEOGRAPHY

Geography (1)

Area:

Total: 116 sq km.

Land: 116 sq km.

Water: 0 sq km.

Area—comparative: about 0.7 times the size of Washington, DC.

Land boundaries: 0 km.

Coastline: 70 km.

Climate: temperate; mild winters and cool summers.

Terrain: gently rolling plain with low, rugged hills along north coast.

Natural resources: agricultural land.

Land use:

Arable land: 66%

Permanent crops: NA%

Permanent pastures: NA%

Forests and woodland: NA%

Other: 34%

HUMAN FACTORS

Ethnic Division (6)

UK and Norman-French descent.

Religions (7)

Anglican, Roman Catholic, Baptist, Congregational New Church, Methodist, Presbyterian.

Demographics (2A)

	1990	1995	1998	2000	2010	2020	2030	2040	2050
Population	NA	87.2	89.1	90.3	93.7	94.4	92.2	86.8	79.4
Net migration rate (per 1,000 population)	NA	NA	NA	NA	NA	NA	NA	NA	NA
Births	NA	NA	NA	NA	NA	NA	NA	NA	NA
Deaths	NA	NA	NA	NA	NA	NA	NA	NA	NA
Life expectancy - males	NA	75.5	75.9	76.2	77.5	78.4	79.1	79.6	80.0
Life expectancy - females	NA	81.2	81.7	82.0	83.4	84.3	85.1	85.6	86.0
Birth rate (per 1,000)	NA	13.1	12.3	11.5	8.4	8.9	8.4	7.1	7.3
Death rate (per 1,000)	NA	9.2	9.1	9.1	9.4	10.5	12.4	14.9	17.0
Women of reproductive age (15-49 yrs.)	NA	23.4	23.1	22.9	22.2	19.1	17.6	16.2	13.9
of which are currently married	NA	NA	NA	NA	NA	NA	NA	NA	NA
Fertility rate	NA	1.5	1.5	1.5	1.5	1.5	1.5	1.5	1.5

Except as noted, values for vital statistics are in thousands; life expectancy is in years.

Languages (8)

English (official), French (official), Norman-French dialect spoken in country districts.

GOVERNMENT & LAW

Political Parties (12)

The legislative branch is a unicameral Assembly of the States (57 seats, 53 elected including 12 senators popularly elected for six-year terms, half retiring every third year, 12 constables popularly elected triennially, and 29 deputies popularly elected triennially). There are no parties.

Government Budget (13B)

Revenues . . . .$643.7 million

Expenditures . . . .$597.2 million

  Capital expenditures . . . . .NA

Data for 1995 est. NA stands for not available.

Military Affairs (14A)

Defense is the responsibility of the UK.

LABOR FORCE

Unemployment Rate (17)

Rate not available.

PRODUCTION SECTOR

Electric Energy (18)

Some standby capacity. Electricity supplied by France.

Transportation (19)

Highways:

total: NA km

paved: NA km

unpaved: NA km

Merchant marine: none

Airports: 1 (1997 est.)

Airports—with paved runways:

total: 1

1,524 to 2,437 m: 1 (1997 est.)

Top Agricultural Products (20)

Potatoes, cauliflowers, tomatoes; meat, dairy products.

FINANCE, ECONOMICS, & TRADE

Economic Indicators (22)

No data available.

Exchange Rates (24)

Exchange rates:

Jersey pounds (£) per US$1

January 1998	.0.6115
1997	.0.6106
1996	.0.6403
1995	.0.6335
1994	.0.6529
1993	.0.6658

The Jersey pound is at par with the British pound

Economic Aid (27)

None.

Import Export Commodities (28)

Import Commodities	Export Commodities
Machinery and transport equipment	Light industrial and electrical goods
Manufactured goods	Foodstuffs
Foodstuffs	Textiles
Mineral fuels	
Chemicals	

JORDAN

The Hashemite Kingdom of Jordan
Al-Mamlaka al-Urdunniyya al-Hashimiyya

INTRODUCTORY SURVEY

CAPITAL: ʿAmman.

FLAG: The national flag is a tricolor of black, white, and green horizontal stripes with a seven-pointed white star on a red triangle at the hoist.

ANTHEM: *As-Salam al-Maliki (Long Live the King).*

MONETARY UNIT: The Jordanian dinar (JD) is a paper currency of 1,000 fils. There are coins of 1, 5, 10, 20, 25, 50, 100, and 250 fils and notes of 1, 5, 10, and 20 dinars. JD1 = $1.41044 (or $1 = JD0.709).

WEIGHTS AND MEASURES: The metric system is the legal standard, but some local and Syrian units are still widely used, especially in the villages.

HOLIDAYS: Arbor Day, 15 January; Independence Day, 25 May; Accession of King Hussein, 11 August; King Hussein's Birthday, 14 November. Muslim religious holidays include the 1st of Muharram (Islamic New Year), ʿId al-Fitr, ʿId al-ʿAdha', and Milad an-Nabi. Christmas and Easter are observed by sizable Christian minorities.

TIME: 2 PM = noon GMT.

LOCATION AND SIZE: Situated in southwest Asia, Jordan has an area of 83,335 square kilometers (32,175 square miles), slightly smaller than the state of Indiana. It has a total boundary length of 1,645 kilometers (1,022 miles), not including the West Bank.

Jordan's capital city, ʿAmman, is located in the northwestern part of the country.

CLIMATE: The Jordan Valley has little rainfall, intense summer heat, and mild, pleasant winters. The desert regions are subject to great extremes of temperature and receive rainfall of less than 20 centimeters (8 inches) annually, while the rest of the country has an average rainfall of up to 58 centimeters (23 inches) a year.

Temperatures at ʿAmman range from about −4°C (25°F) in winter to more than 38°C (100°F) in summer.

RECENT HISTORY

After the Arab-Israeli war of 1948, King ʿAbdallah annexed the area of Palestine now known as the West Bank. It was incorporated into the Hashemite Kingdom of Jordan in 1950. Meanwhile, since the 1948 war, Jordan had absorbed about 500,000 of some 1 million Palestinian Arab refugees, mostly sheltered in UN-administered camps. On 20 July 1951, ʿAbdallah was assassinated in Jerusalem by a Palestinian Arab, and the throne passed to his grandson Hussein I, who was formally enthroned on 2 May 1953.

Following the overthrow of Egypt's King Faruk in July 1952, the Arab countries were strongly influenced by the movement for Arab unity. Jordan, however, maintained a close association with Britain in an effort to preserve the kingdom as a separate, independent country. British intervention during the 1956 war in the Suez hurt their relations with Jordan. But Hussein turned again to the West for support after his cousin King Faisal II (Faysal) of Iraq was assassinated in a July 1958 coup. British troops were flown to Jordan from Cyprus.

Hussein, while retaining Jordan's Western ties, gradually steadied his relations with other Arab states (except Syria). But even in years of comparative peace, relations with Israel remained the focus of tensions in the region. Terrorist raids launched from within Jordan drew strong Israeli reprisals. In addition, the activities of the Palestine Liberation Organization (PLO) often violated Jor-

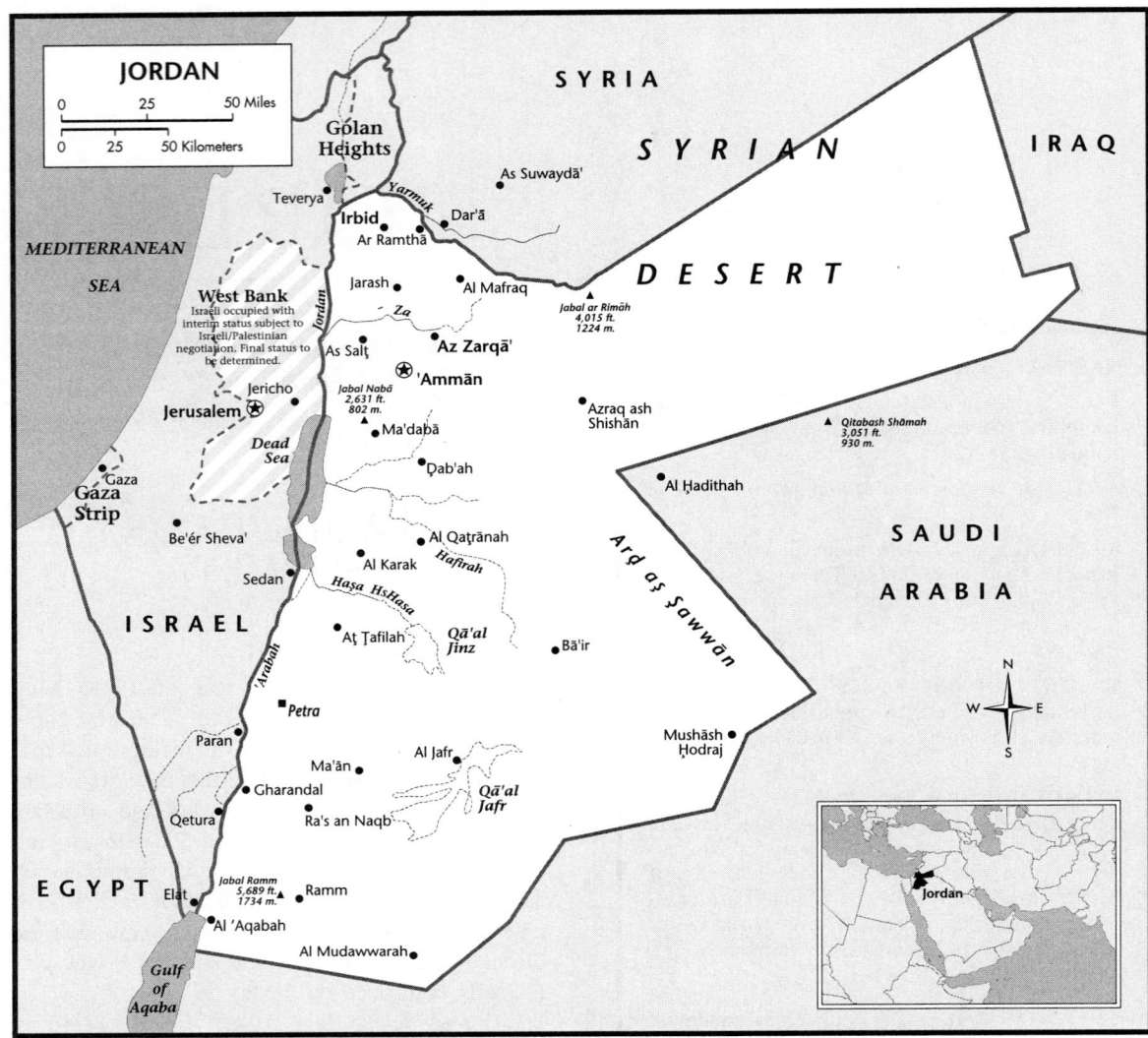

dan's borders, leading Hussein in July 1966, and again in early 1967, to withdraw support for the PLO, again angering the Arab world.

In the 1967 Six-Day War with Israel, Israel took over the Jordanian West Bank (including all of Jerusalem). Jordan suffered heavy casualties, and over 300,000 Palestinians fled across the Jordan River to the East Bank. Jordan's refugee population swelled from 700,000 in 1966 to over 1 million, adding to the severe economic problems caused by the war.

After Hussein's acceptance of a cease-fire with Israel in August 1970, he tried to suppress various Palestinian guerrilla organizations, finally driving them out in July 1971. In the following September, Premier Wasfi al-Tal was assassinated by guerrilla commandos. Coup attempts, in which Libya was said to have been involved, were defeated in November 1972 and February 1973.

Jordan did not actively participate in the "Yom Kippur War" against Israel in October 1973, but it sent an armored brigade of about 2,500 men to assist Syria. After the Egyptian-Israeli Peace Treaty of 1979, Jordan joined other Arab states in trying to isolate Egypt diplomatically. Hussein refused to join further Egyptian-Israeli talks on the future of the West Bank.

In the 1980s, Hussein followed policies of gradually liberalized internal politics. In 1988, Jordan cut its ties with the Israeli occupied West Bank. In 1989, for the first time since 1956, Jordan held relatively free parliamentary elections. New parliamentary elections were held in 1993.

In 1990, Jordan was critical of the Gulf War led by the United States. This hurt Jordan's relations with the United States and the Gulf states. Jordan lost its subsidies from the latter while having to support hundreds of thousands of refugees from the war and its aftermath.

Jordan's willingness to participate in peace talks with Israel in late 1991 helped repair relations with Western countries. In June 1994, Jordan and Israel began meetings to work out practical steps on water, borders, and energy that would lead to normal relations. In July 1994, Jordan and Israel signed a peace treaty that officially ended their state of war. In September 1995, Israel agreed to give administrative control of the West Bank to the Palestinians.

On February 7, 1999 King Hussein died of cancer after a reign of forty-six years. He was succeeded by his oldest son, Abdullah.

GOVERNMENT

Jordan is a constitutional monarchy. The king has wide powers over all branches of government. The constitution gives legislative power to the National Assembly, comprising a forty-member Senate and an eighty-member lower house, the Chamber of Deputies. There is universal suffrage at age 18, women having received the right to vote in April 1973.

Judiciary

There are four levels of civil and criminal courts, religious courts, and tribal courts. The Supreme Court and the courts of appeals deal with appeals from lower courts. Courts of First Instance hear major civil and criminal cases. Religious courts, such as the Muslim Shari'ah courts, have authority over matters such as marriage, divorce, wills and testaments, and orphans.

Political Parties

Political parties were abolished on 25 April 1957, following an alleged attempted coup by Arab militants. In 1992, parties were again permitted and twenty were allowed to take part in elections. The main opposition group has been the Islamic Action Front, the political arm of the Moslem (Muslim) Brotherhood. In the parliamentary elections of 1993, the Islamic Action Front took sixteen of eighty seats.

DEFENSE

In 1995, the Jordanian army had some 90,000 men. The air force had 8,000 men, and the navy had only about 650 men. Reserve manpower was estimated at 35,000. Defense expenditures for 1995 were $440 million.

ECONOMIC AFFAIRS

Jordan's economy has been greatly affected by the Arab-Israeli conflict. The loss of the West Bank in 1967 resulted in the loss of most of Jordan's richest agricultural land and a decline in the growing tourist industry. Western economic aid, notably from the United States, Britain, and Germany, has also been important to the economy.

The start of a recession in Jordan in the mid-1980s followed by the economic collapse of 1988–89 and the Gulf War in 1991 left the country with an unemployment rate of approximately 30–35% and high inflation. About 25–30% of the population fell below the poverty line. The international embargo against Iraq caused Jordan to lose a major market for its exports and re-exports.

In 1995, the government began a program of economic reforms, which included market-oriented policies, commitment to international investment, and the signing of trade and transportation agreements with Israel.

Public Finance

Jordan has had to rely on foreign assistance for support of its budget, which has increased rapidly since the 1967 war. During the late 1980s, Jordan incurred large fiscal deficits, which led to a heavy burden of external debt. In 1992, expenditures exceeded revenues by $600 million. By 1993, the current account deficit stood at 11.4% of GDP. By 1994, the government's austerity measures reduced this figure to 6.7%, and in 1995 it had come into line with targets at 3.7% of GDP.

The U.S. CIA estimates that, in 1995, government revenues totaled approximately $2.5 billion and expenditures $2.5 billion. External debt totaled $6.9 billion, approximately 78% of which was financed abroad.

Income

In 1998, Jordan's gross national product (GNP) was $6.93 billion or about $1,520 per person. For the period 1985–95, the average inflation rate was 7.1%, resulting in a decline in per person GNP of 2.8%.

Industry

Most industrial income comes from four industries: cement, oil refining, phosphates, and potash. Manufacturing output fell by 2.9% in 1991 due to the impact of the Gulf War. It grew again by 6.2% in 1992.

Banking and Finance

The Central Bank of Jordan, founded in 1964 with a capital of JD 2 million and reorganized in 1971, is in charge of note issue, foreign exchange control, and supervision of commercial banks, in cooperation with the Economic Security Council. Its total foreign reserves, excluding gold, in 1995 amounted to $1,972.9 million. Money supply, measured by M2, at that time totaled JD 5,159.8 million.

Loans are extended by the Jordan Industrial Bank, Agricultural Credit Corp., Jordan Co-operative Organization, and other credit institutions.

The Amman Financial Market (AFM) has been in existence since the late 1970s.

Economic Development

In 1988, Jordan began working with the IMF on restructuring its economy. These plans were thrown into considerable disarray by political events in the Gulf (most notably Jordan's ill-conceived support of Iraq in the face of global opposition to that country's 1990 invasion of Kuwait), but new agreements were concluded in 1991, as Jordan began to institute democratic reforms. Foremost in the IMF plan are reductions in government spending, taming of inflation, increasing foreign exchange, and decreasing government ownership of economic enterprises. In the economic plan of 1996–98, Jordan is expected to decrease its ownership of enterprises from 1994's level of 64% to 55% by 1998.

SOCIAL WELFARE

The social insurance system provides old-age, disability, and survivor benefits, as well as workers' compensation. The UN Relief and Works Agency conducts an extensive welfare program for Palestinian refugees.

Women experience legal discrimination regarding pension and social security benefits, inheritance, and divorce. Under Islamic law, a female heir's inheritance is half that of a male, and in court, a woman's testimony has only half the value of a man's. However, in 1992, Parliament effectively blocked Islamists from enacting further legislation discriminating against women.

Healthcare

In 1995, Jordan had 6,839 physicians, 3,118 pharmacists, 2,015 dentists, and 4,304 nurses. Total health care expenditures for 1995 were $347 million. In 1992, 97% of the population had access to health care services. Trachoma, hepatitis, typhoid fever, intestinal parasites, acute skin inflammations, and some other conditions remain common, however. In 1990–95, 89% of the population had access to safe water, and 95% of the population had adequate sanitation. The average life expectancy is 71 years.

Housing

Jordan still lacked adequate housing in the early 1980s. During 1981–86, some 42,300 new residential building permits were issued. According to the latest available information for 1980–88, the total number of dwellings was 660,000 with 4.1 people per dwelling.

EDUCATION

The illiteracy rate declined from 68% of the population in 1961 to 13% in 1995, with male illiteracy estimated at 6.6% and female at 20.6%. Education is compulsory for nine years. A further three years prepares students for university education. In 1993, Jordan had 2,479 primary schools with 48,150 teachers and 1 million pupils. Secondary schools had a total of 123,825 pupils the same year.

In 1993, a total of 85,936 students were enrolled at all higher level institutions. Higher education teaching staff numbered 4,280.

1999 KEY EVENTS TIMELINE

January

• An ailing King Hussein shakes up the line of succession by replacing his brother, Hassan, with his son, Abdullah, as crown prince.

February

• On February 5, Abdullah is sworn in as regent. King Hussein succumbs to his illness the next day and Abdullah becomes the new monarch. Amid heavy security, dignitaries from all over the world attend King Hussein's funeral on February 8.

March

- In his first address to the nation as king, Abdullah thanks Jordanians for their sympathy and promises to build upon his father's legacy.

- The Muslim Brotherhood pledges allegiance to Abdullah.

April

- King Abdullah caps off a tour of several Arab capitals with a trip to Damascus where he holds talks with Syrian President Assad.

May

- Abdullah hosts visits by Israeli opposition leaders Barak and Mordechai before traveling to Western Europe, the United States and Canada.

June

- Jordanians celebrate the official coronation of King Abdullah.

July

- Newly elected Israeli prime minister, Ehud Barak, and King Abdullah hold talks in Aqaba, July 14, to discuss ways of reviving the stalled Israeli-Palestinian peace process.

August

- Arrest warrants are issued for four prominent, Amman-based Hamas leaders.

- Jordan and Kuwait re-establish diplomatic relations ruptured during the 1990 Gulf War.

September

- King Abdullah and Queen Rania visit Kuwait and Lebanon.

- Hamas leaders appeal to Abdullah to end the government's crackdown on the group.

November

- U.S. First Lady Hillary Clinton launches a $5 million aid program to provide economic opportunities to young Jordanians in a ceremony sponsored by Jordan's Queen Rania.

- Jordanian officials claim to have found the actual site—in what is modern-day Jordan—where John the Baptist anointed Jesus. Biblical scholars in Israel do not dispute the claim.

December

- Cancellations of sessions due to protests at the meeting of the World Trade Organization in Seattle, Washington prevent Jordan from being elected to membership.

- More than 1,000 Jordanian pilgrims were not allowed to leave the country for a trip to Muslim holy sites in Saudi Arabia. The pilgrims were traveling on 23 Saudi Arabian buses, which are banned in Jordan.

ANALYSIS OF EVENTS: 1999

BUSINESS AND THE ECONOMY

Jordan has few natural resources. Phosphates and agricultural produce are its main exports and the country is entirely dependent on imported oil. Unofficial estimates place Jordan's unemployment rate at around 15 percent and inflation at 6 percent. Foreign debt is a crippling $6.8 billion. Thirty percent of the population lives below the poverty line. Estimated GDP growth for the year is 2.2 percent. Economic reforms, trade and debt relief are high on the government's agenda. In meetings with Western leaders, Abdullah won promises for further economic assistance and Jordan's inclusion in the group of poor developing countries eligible for debt relief.

A major privatization deal was signed in August with a consortium of foreign investors to take over the expansion and modernization of the state-run freight railway line. Trade agreements were also reached with Syria and Iraq. Jordan is unhappy that peace with Israel has not boosted trade between the two neighbors. Israeli protectionism aimed at preserving domination of West Bank markets is cited as an obstacle to freer trade. Jordan is unlikely to become a member of the World Trade Organization this year. Even though the country has met some of the requirements, all the necessary economic reforms have not yet been implemented.

GOVERNMENT AND POLITICS

King Hussein's death and the succession of his eldest son, Abdullah to the Hashemite throne were the most significant events in Jordan in 1999. The transition of power, the first in 47 years, occurred early in the year. In January,

King Hussein returned to Jordan after months of treatment for non-Hodgkins lymphoma at the Mayo Clinic in the United States. He then abruptly dismissed his brother, Hassan, as crown prince and named Abdullah, his new heir. Speculation has it that the King was unhappy with Hassan's leadership style and desired one of his sons to inherit the throne. King Hussein died on February 6 and Abdullah was sworn in as monarch. In his first official act, the new king made his younger half-brother, Hamza, the crown prince, reportedly complying with Hussein's dying wishes.

Jordan has a parliamentary form of government but the monarch enjoys virtually undisputed powers as the head of state. The executive functions of government are conducted by a council of ministers headed by a prime minister appointed by the king. Most of the members of parliament are popularly elected. The last parliamentary elections were held in 1997, but were boycotted by the main opposition groups, protesting electoral laws that favored pro-monarchy candidates. Jordan's parliament rarely takes any legislative initiatives without the king's consent and, during King Hussein's reign, served as little more than a ''rubber stamp'' for royal decisions. East Bank Jordanians and the Bedouin desert tribes dominate the ruling establishment and are the monarchy's firmest supporters. Though Palestinians and Jordanians of Palestinian origins comprise nearly half the population, they are not well represented in the power structure. Islamist groups like the Muslim Brotherhood are a well-organized opposition. Though they oppose peace with Israel, they maintained good relations with King Hussein and have pledged allegiance to Abdullah. King Hussein made the kingdom's stability a priority and, consequently, the military and security establishments, instead of political institutions, prospered as bulwarks of the state. In the early 1990s the king took tentative steps towards political liberalization but, concerned with the possibility of unrest over a peace treaty with Israel and a deteriorating economy, he soon reversed course, imposing new restrictions on the media and on political freedoms.

Abdullah's March appointment of a seasoned politician, Abdul-Raouf Rawabdeh, as prime minister, signaled the king's intent for continuity in the country's policies; especially a commitment to maintaining Hussein's legacy of peace with Israel. Rawabdeh is a strong advocate of Jordan's 1994 peace treaty with Israel, which remains unpopular with many Jordanians. Slow progress is being made in tackling bureaucratic reform, fighting pervasive corruption, and quickening the pace of privatization and other languishing economic reforms. Following in his father's footsteps, Abdullah appears in no hurry to carry out the democratic reforms demanded by the political opposition. He has, however, promised to restore some press freedoms and make the political process more open and inclusive. In midsummer, the country held municipal elections, which opposition groups described as a test of the government's sincerity in providing freer balloting. Abdullah also recalled parliament from its summer recess to consider new legislation. In September, parliament amended press laws, lifting restrictions on certain forms of expression.

On the diplomatic front, Abdullah reaffirmed his government's commitment to Palestinian statehood. He traveled extensively, visiting other Arab states, Western Europe and the United States. Significant achievements included a warming in Jordan-Syria relations and the restoration of diplomatic ties with Kuwait. Jordan continued to play a vital role in the Middle East peace process. Addressing parliament on November 1, Abdullah called for lifting international economic sanctions against the Iraqi and Sudanese people.

CULTURE AND SOCIETY

The population of 4.5 million is almost evenly divided between native or East Bank Jordanians and Palestinians. The latter are mainly refugees from Israeli-held territory west of the River Jordan. The people are overwhelmingly Sunni Muslims and Arabic is the official language. The large Palestinian population is under represented in government and public life. Although the Palestinians have thrived in the country's commercial establishment, their exclusion from corridors of power has led to resentment over perceived ''second class-citizen'' status. Abdullah, whose wife is of Palestinian descent, has called for an end to institutionalized bias against Palestinians. The status of women in Jordanian society drew attention in the summer when Human Rights Watch charged the government with failing to protect women from ''honor killings.'' In September, the government, in a step towards greater cultural openness, lifted a ban on literature considered offensive to Islamic and Arab sensitivities.

DIRECTORY

CENTRAL GOVERNMENT

Head of State

King
Abdallah ibn al-Hussein al-Hashimi, Monarch
E-MAIL: info@nic.gov.jo

Prime Minister
Abd al-Raouf al-Rawabdeh, Office of the Prime Minister, PO Box 80, 352 Amman, Jordan

Ministers

Minister of Agriculture
Hashem Shboul, Ministry of Agriculture, PO Box 2099, Amman, Jordan
PHONE: +962 686431
FAX: +962 686310

Minister of Awqaf and Islamic Affairs
Abdul Salam al-Abbadi, Ministry of Awqaf and Islamic Affairs

Minister of Culture
Faisal al-Rafua, Ministry of Culture

Minister of Communications
Ministry of Communications, PO Box 71, Amman, Jordan
PHONE: +962 624301
FAX: +962 825262

Minister of Defense
Abdur-Rauf Rawabdeh, Ministry of Defense

Minister of Education
Izzat Jaradat, Ministry of Education, PO Box 1646, Amman, Jordan
PHONE: +962 669181; 667182
FAX: +962 666019

Minister of Energy and Mineral Resources
Suleiman Abu-Alam, Ministry of Energy and Mineral Resources, PO Box 140027, Amman, Jordan
PHONE: +962 863326
FAX: +962 666019

Minister of Finance
Michel Marto, Ministry of Finance

Minister of Foreign Affairs
Abdel-Elah al-Khatib, Ministry of Foreign Affairs, PO Box 1577, Amman 11511, Jordan
PHONE: +962 6644361
FAX: +962 6648825

Minister of Health
Ishaq Maraqa, Ministry of Health, PO Box 86, Amman, Jordan
PHONE: +962 5665131
FAX: +962 5688373

Minister of Justice
Hamzeh Haddad, Ministry of Justice, PO Box 6040, Amman, Jordan
PHONE: +962 663103
FAX: +962 680238

Minister of Transport
Nasir al-Lawzi, Ministry of Transport, PO Box 35214, Amman, Jordan

Minister of Higher Education
Ministry of Higher Education, PO Box 138, Amman, Jordan
PHONE: +962 847671
FAX: +962 837616

Minister of Industry and Trade
Muhammad Asfour, Ministry of Industry and Trade, PO Box 2019, Amman, Jordan
PHONE: +962 663191
FAX: +962 603721

Minister of Information
Ayman al-Majali, Ministry of Information, PO Box 1845, Amman, Jordan
PHONE: +962 642311
FAX: +962 648895

Minister of Interior
Nayif al-Qadi, Ministry of Interior

Minister of Labor
Aid al-Fayez, Ministry of Labor, PO Box 8160, Amman, Jordan
PHONE: +962 663945; 663186; 667161
FAX: +962 667193

Minister of Municipal, Rural Affairs and Environment
Tawfiq Khreishan, Ministry of Municipal, Rural Affairs and Environment, PO Box 1799, Amman, Jordan
PHONE: +962 4641393
FAX: +962 4640404

Minister of Planning
Rima Khalaf, Ministry of Planning, PO Box 555, Amman, Jordan
PHONE: +962 644466
FAX: +962 649341

Minister of Post and Telecommunications
Jamal Sarayrah, Ministry of Post and Telecommunications

Minister of Public Works and Housing
Husni Abu Ghida, Ministry of Public Works and Housing

Minister of Religious Affairs
Abdelsalam Abbadi, Mininstry of Religious Affairs

Minister of Social Development
Ministry of Social Development, PO Box 1310, Amman, Jordan
PHONE: +962 5931391
FAX: +962 5607391

Minister of Transport
Nasir al-Lawzi, Ministry of Transport, PO Box 35214, Amman, Jordan
PHONE: +962 641461
FAX: +962 649428

Minister of Tourism
Aqel Biltaji, Ministry of Tourism, PO Box 224, Amman, Jordan
PHONE: +962 642311
FAX: +962 648465

Minister of Youth and Sports
Said Shuqum, Ministry of Youth and Sports

Minister of Water and Irrigation
Kamal Mahadin, Ministry of Water and Irrigation, PO Box 2769, Amman, Jordan
PHONE: +962 689400; 689410
FAX: +962 689916

POLITICAL ORGANIZATIONS

Al-Ahrar (Freedom Party)

TITLE: Secretary General
NAME: Ahmad Zo'bi

Arab Ba'th (Progressive Party)

TITLE: Secretary General
NAME: Mahmoud al-Ma'aytah

Doa'a (Arab Islamic Democratic Party)

TITLE: Secretary General
NAME: Yousif Abu Bakr

Arab Land Party

TITLE: Secretary General
NAME: Muhammad al-'Oran

Arab Jordanian Ansar Party

TITLE: Secretary General
NAME: Mahummad Majali

Democratic Party of the Left

TITLE: Secretary General
NAME: Musa Ma'aitah

Islamic Action Front

TITLE: Secretary General
NAME: Ishaq al-Farhan

Jordanian Arab Constitutional Front Party

TITLE: Secretary General
NAME: Milhem Tell

Jordanian Ba'th Arab Socialist Party

TITLE: Secretary General
NAME: Tayseer al-Homsi

Jordanian Communist Party

TITLE: Secretary General
NAME: Ya'acoub Zayadin

Jordanian Democratic Popular Unity Party

TITLE: Secretary General
NAME: Sa'eed Mustapha

Jordanian Labor Party

TITLE: Secretary General
NAME: Muhammad Khatayibah

Jordanian Peace Party

TITLE: Secretary General
NAME: Shaher Khreis

Jordanian People's Democratic Party

TITLE: Secretary General
NAME: Salem Nahhas

Al-Mustaqbal (Future Party)

TITLE: Secretary General
NAME: Suleiman 'Arar

Haqq (National Action Party)

TITLE: Secretary General
NAME: Muhammad Zo'bi

National Constitutional Party

TITLE: Secretary General
NAME: Abdul Hadi Majali

National Democratic Public Movement Party

TITLE: Secretary General
NAME: Muhammad al-'Amer

Progressive Party

TITLE: Secretary General
NAME: Na'el Barakat

Al-Umma (Nation Party)

TITLE: Secretary General
NAME: Ahmad Hneidi

DIPLOMATIC REPRESENTATION

Embassies in Jordan

Australia
PHONE: +962 5930246

Austria
PHONE: +962 4644635

Belgium
PHONE: +962 5675683

Brazil
PHONE: +962 4642169

Canada
PO Box 815403, Amman 11180, Jordan
PHONE: +962 6666124
FAX: +962 6689227

Chile
PHONE: +962 5924097

China
PHONE: +962 5699137

Denmark
PHONE: +962 5603703

Egypt
PHONE: +962 5605202

France
PHONE: +962 4641273

Germany
PHONE: +962 5930351

Greece
PHONE: +962 5672331

Hungary
PHONE: +962 5930836

India
PHONE: +962 4637262

Iraq
PHONE: +962 4623175

Israel
PHONE: +962 5524680

Italy
PHONE: +962 4638185

Japan
PHONE: +962 5923005

South Korea
PHONE: +962 5660745

Netherlands
PHONE: +962 4619693

Pakistan
PHONE: +962 4622787

Poland
PHONE: +962 4637153

Russia
PHONE: +962 4641158

Saudi Arabia
PHONE: +962 5924154

South Africa
PHONE: +962 5812288

Spain
PHONE: +962 4614167

Turkey
PHONE: +962 4641251

United Kingdom
PHONE: +962 5923100

United States
PO Box 354, Amman 11118, Jordan
PHONE: +962 6820101
NAME: William Joseph Burns

JUDICIAL SYSTEM
Court of Cassation

FURTHER READING
Articles

"Jordan." *Middle East Economic Digest* 43 (September 3, 1999): 20.

"Jordan's King Visits Kuwait as Tensions Ease." *The New York Times,* 7 September 1999, p. A10.

Morris, Nomi. "Lebanon: Abdullah's historic visit." *The New York Times,* 15 September 1999, p. A16.

Orme, William A. Jr. ''Jordan's New King Assuming Key Role In Mideast Talks.'' *The New York Times,* 7 October 1999, p. A4.

Books

Mannheim, Ivan. *Jordan, Syria and Lebanon Handbook.* Lincolnwood, Ill.: Passport Books, 1998.

Rollin, Sue. *Jordan.* 2nd ed. New York: WW Norton, 1998.

Wilson, Rodney. *Politics and the Economy in Jordan.* New York: Routledge, 1991.

Internet

ArabNet. ''Jordan.'' Available Online @ http://www.arab.net/jordan/jordan_contents.html (November 12, 1999).

JORDAN: STATISTICAL DATA

For sources and notes see "Sources of Statistics" in the front of each volume.

GEOGRAPHY

Geography (1)

Area:

Total: 89,213 sq km.

Land: 88,884 sq km.

Water: 329 sq km.

Area—comparative: slightly smaller than Indiana.

Land boundaries:

Total: 1,619 km.

Border countries: Iraq 181 km, Israel 238 km, Saudi Arabia 728 km, Syria 375 km, West Bank 97 km.

Coastline: 26 km.

Climate: mostly arid desert; rainy season in west (November to April).

Terrain: mostly desert plateau in east, highland area in west; Great Rift Valley separates East and West Banks of the Jordan River.

Natural resources: phosphates, potash, shale oil.

Land use:

Arable land: 4%

Permanent crops: 1%

Permanent pastures: 9%

Forests and woodland: 1%

Other: 85% (1993 est.).

HUMAN FACTORS

Demographics (2A)

	1990	1995	1998	2000	2010	2020	2030	2040	2050
Population	3,276.7	4,099.0	4,435.0	4,700.8	6,102.7	7,510.7	8,919.4	10,207.0	11,303.3
Net migration rate (per 1,000 population)	NA	NA	NA	NA	NA	NA	NA	NA	NA
Births	NA	NA	NA	NA	NA	NA	NA	NA	NA
Deaths	NA	NA	NA	NA	NA	NA	NA	NA	NA
Life expectancy - males	69.4	70.4	71.0	71.3	73.0	74.5	75.7	76.6	77.4
Life expectancy - females	72.9	74.2	74.8	75.3	77.4	79.2	80.7	82.0	83.0
Birth rate (per 1,000)	39.6	37.3	35.2	33.5	26.3	22.5	19.1	16.3	14.8
Death rate (per 1,000)	4.6	4.1	3.9	3.8	3.5	3.6	3.8	4.6	6.0
Women of reproductive age (15-49 yrs.)	717.5	927.5	1,017.8	1,092.9	1,549.2	1,992.8	2,344.7	2,617.2	2,740.0
of which are currently married	NA	NA	NA	NA	NA	NA	NA	NA	NA
Fertility rate	6.1	5.3	4.8	4.5	3.3	2.7	2.3	2.2	2.1

Except as noted, values for vital statistics are in thousands; life expectancy is in years.

Health Personnel (3)

Total health expenditure as a percentage of GDP, 1990-1997[a]

Public sector 3.7

Private sector 4.2

Total[b] 7.9

Health expenditure per capita in U.S. dollars, 1990-1997[a]

Purchasing power parity 261

Total 117

Availability of health care facilities per 100,000 people

Hospital beds 1990-1997[a] 160

Doctors 1993[c] 158

Nurses 1993[c] 224

Health Indicators (4)

Life expectancy at birth

1980 64

1997 71

Daily per capita supply of calories (1996) 2,681

Total fertility rate births per woman (1997) 4.2

Maternal mortality ratio per 100,000 live births (1990-97) . . . . .150[c]

Safe water % of population with access (1995) 98

Sanitation % of population with access (1995) 98

Consumption of iodized salt % of households (1992-98)[a] 75

Smoking prevalence

Male % of adults (1985-95)[a] . . . .

Female % of adults (1985-95)[a] . . . .

Tuberculosis incidence per 100,000 people (1997) 11

Adult HIV prevalence % of population ages 15-49 (1997) 0.02

Infants and Malnutrition (5)

Under-5 mortality rate (1997) 24

% of infants with low birthweight (1990-97) 7

Births attended by skilled health staff % of total[a] . . .97

% fully immunized (1995-97)

TB 24

DPT 96

Polio 96

Measles 90

Prevalence of child malnutrition under age 5 (1992-97)[b] 10

Ethnic Division (6)

Arab 98%

Circassian 1%

Armenian 1%

Religions (7)

Sunni Muslim 96%

Christian . . . . .4% (1997 est.)

Languages (8)

Arabic (official), English widely understood among upper and middle classes.

EDUCATION

Public Education Expenditures (9)

Public expenditure on education (% of GNP)

1980 . . . . .6.6

1996 . . . . .7.3

Expenditure per student

Primary % of GNP per capita

1980 . . . .

1996 . . . .

Secondary % of GNP per capita

1980 . . . .

1996 . . . . .90.5[1]

Tertiary % of GNP per capita

1980 . . . . .60.1

1996 . . . . .74.7

Expenditure on teaching materials

Primary % of total for level (1996) . . . .

Secondary % of total for level (1996) 4.6

Primary pupil-teacher ratio per teacher (1996) . . . . .21[1]

Duration of primary education years (1995) 10

Literacy Rates (11A)

In thousands and percent[1]	1990	1995	2000	2010
Illiterate population (15+ yrs.)	425	414	370	267
Literacy rate - total adult pop. (%)	82.1	86.6	89.8	94.8
Literacy rate - males (%)	90.9	93.4	95.1	97.5
Literacy rate - females (%)	72.7	79.4	84.2	91.9

GOVERNMENT & LAW

Political Parties (12)

House of Representatives	No. of seats
National Constitutional Party	.2
Arab Land Party	.1
independents	.75
Other	.2

Government Budget (13A)

Year: 1996

Total Expenditures: 1,666.9 Millions of Dinars

Expenditures as a percentage of the total by function:

General public services and public order	13.73
Defense	17.00
Education	14.31
Health	9.04
Social Security and Welfare	18.38
Housing and community amenities	2.58
Recreational, cultural, and religious affairs	2.36
Fuel and energy	3.25
Agriculture, forestry, fishing, and hunting	4.28
Mining, manufacturing, and construction	.08
Transportation and communication	4.27
Other economic affairs and services	1.18

Military Affairs (14B)

	1990	1991	1992	1993	1994	1995
Military expenditures						
Current dollars (mil.)	397	422	429[e]	447	437	481[e]
1995 constant dollars (mil.)	456	466	461[e]	469	448	481[e]
Armed forces (000)	100	100	100	100	100	112
Gross national product (GNP)						
Current dollars (mil.)	3,613	3,893	4,811	5,294	5,735	6,280
1995 constant dollars (mil.)	4,152	4,302	5,175	5,550	5,879	6,280
Central government expenditures (CGE)						
1995 constant dollars (mil.)	1,654	1,766	1,690	1,871	2,037	2,219
People (mil.)	3.3	3.6	3.8	3.9	4.0	4.1
Military expenditure as % of GNP	11.0	10.8	8.9	8.4	7.6	7.7
Military expenditure as % of CGE	27.5	26.4	27.3	25.0	22.0	21.7
Military expenditure per capita (1995 $)	139	131	123	120	112	117
Armed forces per 1,000 people (soldiers)	30.5	28.1	26.6	25.7	25.0	27.3
GNP per capita (1995 $)	1,267	1,208	1,376	1,427	1,470	1,532
Arms imports[6]						
Current dollars (mil.)	130	60	20	30	40	70
1995 constant dollars (mil.)	149	66	22	31	41	70
Arms exports[6]						
Current dollars (mil.)	0	0	0	0	30	0
1995 constant dollars (mil.)	0	0	0	0	31	0
Total imports[7]						
Current dollars (mil.)	2,601	2,508	3,255	3,540	3,382	3,698
1995 constant dollars (mil.)	2,989	2,771	3,501	3,711	3,467	3,698
Total exports[7]						
Current dollars (mil.)	1,064	1,130	1,215	1,232	1,424	1,760
1995 constant dollars (mil.)	1,223	1,249	1,307	1,292	1,460	1,769
Arms as percent of total imports[8]	5.0	2.4	.6	.8	1.2	1.9
Arms as percent of total exports[8]	0	0	0	0	2.1	0

Crime (15)

Crime rate (for 1997)

Crimes reported 21,800

Total persons convicted 16,400

Crimes per 100,000 population 475

Persons responsible for offenses

Total number of suspects 26,500

Total number of female suspects 9,150

Total number of juvenile suspects 44,800

LABOR FORCE

Labor Force (16)

Total (million) . . . . .1.15 plus 300,000 foreign workers

Industry 11.4%

Commerce, restaurants, ...

and hotels 10.5%

Construction 10.0%

Transport and communications 8.7%

Agriculture 7.4%

Other services 52.0%

Data for 1997 est. Percent distribution for 1992.

Unemployment Rate (17)

15% official rate; actual rate is 20%-25% (1997 est.)

PRODUCTION SECTOR

Electric Energy (18)

Capacity . . . . .1.066 million kW (1995)

Production . . . . .5.02 billion kWh (1995)

Consumption per capita . . . . .1,259 kWh (1995)

Transportation (19)

Highways:

total: 6,640 km

paved: 6,640 km

unpaved: 0 km (1996 est.)

Pipelines: crude oil 209 km

Merchant marine:

total: 4 ships (1,000 GRT or over) totaling 43,759 GRT/69,795 DWT ships by type: bulk 3, cargo 1 (1997 est.)

Airports: 17 (1997 est.)

Airports—with paved runways:

total: 14

over 3,047 m: 9

2,438 to 3,047 m: 4

914 to 1,523 m: 1 (1997 est.)

Airports—with unpaved runways:

total: 3

914 to 1,523 m: 1

under 914 m: 2 (1997 est.)

Top Agricultural Products (20)

Wheat, barley, citrus, tomatoes, melons, olives; sheep, goats, poultry.

MANUFACTURING SECTOR

GDP & Manufacturing Summary (21)

Detailed value added figures are listed by both International Standard Industry Code (ISIC) and product title.

	1980	1985	1990	1994
GDP ($-1990 mil.)[1]	3,057	3,940	3,934	5,143
Per capita ($-1990)[1]	1,046	1,028	924	989
Manufacturing share (%) (current prices)[1]	10.1	11.6	14.9	*13.2*
Manufacturing				
Value added ($-1990 mil.)[1]	441	603	520	620
Industrial production index	100	157	204	245
Value added ($ mil.)	406	581	583	862[1]
Gross output ($ mil.)	917	1,997	1,846	*2,966*
Employment (000)	25	42	44	*68*
Profitability (% of gross output)				
Intermediate input (%)	56	71	68	*71*
Wages and salaries inc. supplements (%)	12	9	8	*7*
Gross operating surplus	32	20	24	*22*
Productivity ($)				
Gross output per worker	26,708	38,671	33,085	*36,466*
Value added per worker	11,819	11,243	10,443	*10,603*
Average wage (inc. supplements)	4,418	4,326	3,175	*2,974*
Value added ($ mil.)				
311/2 Food products	24	48	58	*78*
313 Beverages	20	27	28	*53*

	1980	1985	1990	1994
314 Tobacco products	50	92	75	110
321 Textiles	10	14	20	18
322 Wearing apparel	8	10	13	16
323 Leather and fur products	2	2	4	4
324 Footwear	8	8	3	7
331 Wood and wood products	7	7	4	6
332 Furniture and fixtures	11	11	14	31
341 Paper and paper products	9	9	20	22
342 Printing and publishing	7	11	12	32
351 Industrial chemicals	10	14	44	28
352 Other chemical products	20	28	42	91
353 Petroleum refineries	53	87	55	55
354 Miscellaneous petroleum and coal products	—	—	—	—
355 Rubber products	—	—	1	1
356 Plastic products	12	13	17	25
361 Pottery, china and earthenware	2	3	3	7
362 Glass and glass products	2	3	3	3
369 Other non-metal mineral products	98	123	85	161
371 Iron and steel	11	8	24	32
372 Non-ferrous metals	5	4	9	13
381 Metal products	27	31	23	36
382 Non-electrical machinery	2	4	9	14
383 Electrical machinery	2	2	11	9
384 Transport equipment	—	1	1	9
385 Professional and scientific equipment	—	—	2	1
390 Other manufacturing industries	7	23	2	—

FINANCE, ECONOMICS, & TRADE

Economic Indicators (22)

National product: GDP—purchasing power parity—$20.7 billion (1997 est.)

National product real growth rate: 5.3% (1997 est.)

National product per capita: $4,800 (1997 est.)

Inflation rate—consumer price index: 3% (1997 est.)

Exchange Rates (24)

Exchange rates:

Jordanian dinars (JD) per US$1

January 1998-1996	.0.7090
1995	.0.7005
1994	.0.6987
1993	.0.6928

Since May 1989, the dinar has been pegged to a basket of currencies

Balance of Payments (23)

	1992	1993	1994	1995	1996
Exports of goods (f.o.b.)	1,219	1,246	1,424	1,770	1,817
Imports of goods (f.o.b.)	−2,999	−3,145	−3,004	−3,288	−3,818
Trade balance	−1,780	−1,899	−1,579	−1,518	−2,001
Services - debits	−1,785	−1,757	−1,780	−2,009	−2,010
Services - credits	1,562	1,673	1,635	1,825	1,958
Private transfers (net)	386	357	324	326	408
Government transfers (net)	781	997	1,003	1,118	1,424
Overall balance	−835	−629	−398	−259	−222

Top Import Origins (25)

$3.7 billion (c.i.f., 1997).

Origins	%
European Union	NA
Iraq	NA
United States	NA
Japan	NA
Turkey	NA

NA stands for not available.

Top Export Destinations (26)

$1.53 billion (f.o.b., 1997).

Destinations	%
United States	37
United Kingdom	13
Canada	12
Netherlands	9
Norway	7

Economic Aid (27)

Recipient: ODA, $424 million (1996).

Import Export Commodities (28)

Import Commodities	Export Commodities
Crude oil	Phosphates
Machinery	Fertilizers
Transport equipment	Potash
Food	Agricultural products
Live animals	Manufactures
Manufactured goods	

KAZAKSTAN

Republic of Kazakstan
Kazakstan Respublikasy

INTRODUCTORY SURVEY

RECENT HISTORY

In World War II, much Russian industry was moved to Kazakstan. This was followed in 1953–65 by the so-called Virgin Lands campaign, which converted huge tracts of Kazak grazing land to wheat and other grain production. This brought thousands more Russians and other non-Kazaks to Kazakstan. As a result, Kazakstan became the only Soviet republic in which the native people were not a majority of the population.

The first public nationalist protest in the Soviet Union before its breakup occurred in Kazakstan in 1986. In June 1989, more civil disturbances brought about the appointment of Nursultan Nazarbaev as republic leader. Nazarbaev, who later became president, strongly promoted Kazak participation in the formation of the Commonwealth of Independent States. Kazakstan declared its independence on 16 December 1991.

In November 1994, Kazakstan agreed to transfer bomb-grade uranium to the United States (with Russia's approval). The nuclear material was poorly protected and could have been a possible source of nuclear material for other countries or arms dealers.

On June 10, 1998 the Kazak government officially transferred the country's capital from Alomaty in the south to Astana (formerly Akmola, or Tselinograd) in the north. Astana, which means ''capital,'' is a rapidly growing city of 300,000.

In elections held on January 10, 1999, President Nazarbaev received 82% of the vote. However, foreign observers characterized the elections as unfair.

GOVERNMENT

The constitution of the Republic of Kazakstan, adopted 28 January 1993 and amended in 1995, mandates three separate branches of government: a president and vice-president; a legislative branch, consisting of a parliament called the Majlis and a senate; and a judiciary, appointed by the president. The president's executive powers also include appointment of a prime minister and cabinet.

Judiciary

The Constitutional Court established in 1992 to interpret the constitution was dissolved in 1995 and replaced by a seven-member Constitutional Council. The courts are arranged in three tiers: local level, province (oblys) level, and Supreme Court. Local level courts provide initial hearings for less serious crimes. Oblys level courts hear more serious criminal cases and also hear cases in rural areas where no local courts have been established. Judgment of local courts may be appealed to the oblys level. The Supreme Court hears appeals from the oblys courts. The judiciary is under the control of the president and the executive branch.

Political Parties

The Socialist Party is the successor to the Communist Party. The People's Congress, or Social-Democratic Party, has both Kazak and Russian members. A third party, the Party for National Unity (SNEK), was registered in October 1992. There are four large Kazak nationalist movements and four Russian nationalist organizations.

DEFENSE

Kazakstan's armed forces are estimated at 40,000, with approximately 25,000 in the army.

There is no navy, and the air force has 15,000 personnel. Paramilitary forces consist of 2,500 republican guards, 20,000 security troops, and 12,000 border guards. The defense budget in 1995 was estimated at $316 million, but actual expenditures were around $425 million.

ECONOMIC AFFAIRS

Like other countries of the former Soviet Union, Kazakstan has faced serious economic adjustments since 1991, resulting from the disruption of trade with other post-Soviet republics, an end to the flow of money from the Soviet central government, the decline in state production orders, and the need for sudden currency adjustments.

Legislation adopted since 1992 has promoted the spread of private ownership in business and housing, and the inflow of large foreign investments.

Public Finance

The consolidated state budget ran a deficit of 6% of GDP in 1992, causing the government to maintain relatively restricted fiscal policies. But due to these tight fiscal conditions and lack of financing, however, 1992 government investment shrank to half its 1991 level. In 1996, the government's deficit as a share of GDP stood at 3.1%, and was projected at 3.2% in 1997.

Income

In 1998, Kazakstan's gross national product (GNP) was $20.5 billion or about $1,310 per person. During 1985–95, the average annual decline of the GNP per person was 8.6%.

Industry

Kazakstan's industrial sector is slowly being converted toward market-driven production. The government has required that nearly all state-owned enterprises must be sold to private companies by 2000.

Processing of agricultural products and metallurgy and mining are important industries. In 1995, industry accounted for 30% of the gross domestic product (GDP), while agricultural production accounted for about 12% and services made up 58%.

Textile and leather production is well-developed because Kazakstan produces its own wool and hides and imports cotton from other former Soviet republics nearby. Machine-building is also among the largest of Kazakstan's industries.

Banking and Finance

In December 1990, the Alma-Ata branch of Gosbank (the former Soviet State Bank) was made into the Independent Kazak (National Bank of Kazakstan-NBK). In 1991, the existence of private and public financial institutions was legalized. In 1993, the parliament approved a new banking law that separated the National Bank of Kazakstan from the government, and gave the central bank the power to conduct monetary and credit policies and regulate the commercial banking sector. Until November 1993, the currency unit in the country was the ruble. On 15 November 1993, Kazakstan established its own currency, the tenge. In November 1996, money supply, as measured by M2, was T 121.9 billion.

Economic Development

Since sovereignty was declared in 1990, Kazakstan has embarked on a process of economic restructuring, aimed at establishing a market economy. Gradual privatization of most state enterprises has been the focal point of the restructuring program and the centralized state ordering system was abolished in 1992.

In addition to price liberalization, government decrees since 1991 have mandated the gradual elimination of various subsidies to industry and other sectors, further reductions in state expenditures, and the development of a social safety net to assist households at high poverty risk. The government is also placing great emphasis on realizing the infusion of foreign capital both to the oil and gas industry as well as various other industrial subsectors, such as agro-processing, light industry and ferrous metals.

SOCIAL WELFARE

Social security programs provide for old-age, disability, and survivorship pensions. The government, however, is often unable to pay out benefits to citizens.

Women generally have access to higher education but are still channeled into mostly low-level, low-paid jobs. The constitution provides for the upkeep and education of orphans.

There is some tension between ethnic Kazaks and Russians. Kazaks receive preferential treatment in housing, education, and employment.

Healthcare

The average life expectancy is 65 years. In 1992, there was 1 doctor for every 254 people.

There were 13.6 hospital beds per 1,000 inhabitants.

Housing

In 1990, Kazakstan had 14.2 square meters (107 square feet) of housing space per person. As of 1 January 1991, 520,000 households were on waiting lists for housing in urban areas.

EDUCATION

The adult illiteracy rate is estimated at 2%. There are 1.2 million primary school students and 2 million secondary school students. Institutions of higher education had 482,690 students in 1994.

1999 KEY EVENTS TIMELINE

January

- President Nursultan Nazarbaev promises, if elected, to spend $100 million to support domestic manufacturing and urge consumers to buy Kazak products.

- The International Monetary Fund will extend $217 million and the World Bank $75 million in loans to Kazakstan. Kazakstan and Ukraine sign a joint communique regarding trade, economic cooperation, transportation of Kazak crude oil to the West via Ukraine, and purchase by Kazakstan of Ukrainian agricultural machinery.

- Nazarbaev, monopolizing advertising and banning two opponents, wins a resounding presidential victory with 81% of the vote.

- Two former generals of the Kazak National Security Committee are charged with selling alcohol and classified information.

- Russia releases four SU-27 fighter aircraft to Kazakstan. Whether these are a partial payment of the rent for the Baikonur Space Complex or of Soviet military equipment withdrawn in 1993 is unclear.

February

- In order to protect domestic producers, Kazakstan imposes limits on imports from Kyrgyzstan and Uzbekistan and, in order to stop dumping of goods, duties of 100–200% are imposed.

- Leaders of the Kazak Republican People's Party and of the Orleu movement complain that the Justice Ministry delays registration of their parties to prevent their participation in the upcoming parliamentary elections.

- International organizations have promised $43 million for the victims of the 473 nuclear explosions conducted in the area around Semipalatinsk between 1949 and 1989.

March

- Kazakstan moves to protect the northern Caspian littoral against environmental disaster. Under the 1997 Law on Specially Protected Territories, the northern section of the Caspian Sea and the Ural River have the status of nature preserve, which gives fishing priority over oil extraction.

- Nazarbaev criticizes the work of the courts stating that citizens should not have to write the president, the government, and the local authorities to find a resolution to legal problems.

- Akezhan Kazhegeldin, who was barred from participating in the January 1999 presidential elections and who was shot at last fall is again the target of assassination.

- The Kazak opposition movement, Azamat, criticizes the government, calling its Kazak-Chinese border treaty, which cedes lead and gold deposits to China, a "criminal" act.

- The appearance of anti-Nazarbaev slogans on fences and buildings in Almaty and Astana prompts the formation of a group to investigate the background of criminal groups involved.

April

- Kazakstan and China explore rules for equal exploitation of the Irtysh and Ili rivers. Beijing's building new dams and power stations on the Irtysh complicates the negotiations.

- The devaluation of the Russian ruble forces Kazakstan to free the exchange rate for the national currency, the official exchange rate for which fell from 88 to 100 to the dollar.

- Kazakstan authorities recognize the Czech Republic as one of their key partners in central Europe, noting that trade turnover has doubled from $50 million in 1997 to $100 million last year.

- Found guilty of spying for a foreign power, the former deputy head of Kazakstan's security service was sentenced to 10 years in prison.

May

- Armial Tasymbekov, suspected of daubing slogans on buildings and fences in Astana that denounced Nazarbaev, is found dead in his apartment in Almaty.

- Journalists subject Kazakstan's new draft law on mass media to harsh criticism, and charge that freedom of speech and the press in Kazakstan will be restricted unless certain amendments are included in the law.

- Uzbek and Kazak rail transit, halted due to non-payment of debts (Uzbekistan owes $8 million and Kyrgyzstan $3.8), is resumed.

- In an attempt to protect domestic manufacturers from an influx of cheap foreign goods, imported goods must bear labels in both Kazak and Russian detailing their country of origin, date of manufacture, and expiration date.

- In an effort to pave the way for a more democratic 1999 election, several opposition parties and movements including Azat, Azamat, Orleu, and the Communist Party have signed a memorandum against the existing political system.

- While Nazarbaev views the new draft law for the media empowering, his opponents see nothing but restriction on freedom of speech. Any one of 43 minor offenses in the new election law has the potential to disqualify candidates from participation at any level.

- Kazakstan is scheduled to receive more than $50 million in U.S. aid in 1999.

- Nazarbaev criticizes the government for its lack of concrete ideas for the economy and the ministers for interfering in the work of other agencies.

June

- Kazakstan plans to maintain the 1998 level of $1.2 billion in direct foreign investment and $2.1 billion in domestic investment.

- Of the 67 deputies in the lower house of the Kazak parliament, 44 have joined OTAN.

- Kazakstanis are requested to donate gold and silver jewelry to help shore up the country's gold and hard currency reserves.

- Nazarbaev criticizes the government, and Prime Minister Nurlan Balghymbaev personally, for the lack of a coherent program for the next three to five years. The Federation of Trade Unions of Kazakstan joined the OTAN party in calling for the government's replacement.

- OTAN succeeds in registering branches in only three of Kazakstan's fourteen oblasts. Seven oblasts are needed to contend in the parliamentary elections.

- The government of Kazakstan signed a memorandum of intent with British Gas, Italy's Agip, Texaco, and Russia's Lukoil on construction of a 460 kilometer, $440 million pipeline from the Karachaganak field to Atyrau.

- Talks between Russia and Kazakstan continue on the delimitation of the Russian and Kazak sectors of the Caspian Sea on the basis of an agreement signed by both presidents. Under that agreement, the seabed is divided into national sectors while the waters remain the common property of all littoral states.

July

- Engine problems cause Russian Proton rocket, launched from the Baikonur cosmodrome, to explode. 5,000 square meters of land in Kazakstan's central Karaganda Oblast are contaminated with highly toxic heptil rocket fuel.

- President Nazarbaev schedules elections to the upper and lower chambers of Kazakstan's new parliament for September 17 and October 10 respectively.

- Kazak experts are concerned that deadly anthrax bacteria buried in Vozrozhdeniye island might contaminate the region once the island loses its surrounding water.

- Almaty's main airport is almost entirely destroyed by a fire caused by faulty electrical wiring.

- Ten of the Kazakstan's fourteen oblasts register a decline in output, compared with the same period in 1998.

- Budget revenues amount to 86% of the planned amount, and the total taxes collected are inadequate to fund all state programs. Kazakstan earned almost $190 million from privatization during the first half of the year and oil production during the first six months totaled 14.2 million tons, which was 5.5% above the figure for 1998 but still short of the planned 14.27 million tons. BP Amoco may sell its 9.5% stake in the Offshore Kazakstan International Operating Company (OKIOC).

August

- Nazarbaev grants amnesties to 13,000 prisoners, most of whom are suffering from tuberculosis.

- State funding for 23 publications is abolished, forcing the editors to secure new sources of funding.

- Six opposition parties and the ''Respublika,'' demanding unspecified amendments that would make the present election law more democratic, request the president to postpone the elections to the upper chamber of parliament until December.

- Criminal suspects are being released from jail without trial because of an on-going strike by Kazakstan's lawyers. Under Kazakstan's constitution, suspects can be detained without trial for no longer than six months.

- After six frustrating years, a OKIOC drill pierces the seabed of the Caspian and kicks off a project that is likely to shape the future of the Kazak oil industry.

- BP Amoco rethinks the sale of its 9.5% stake in the OKIOC for an asking price of $440 million. Kazakstan and the American International Petroleum Corporation sign a contract for the development of the 700 BCF Shagyrly-Shomyshty gas field.

- Kazakstan plans to shed a portion of its 25% ($2.5 billion) share in the Tengizchevroil to cover this year's expected $560 million budget deficit and pay off state debts of $630 million.

September

- Eleven political parties register to contend in the October 10 elections to the lower house of the parliament. Ten of the 77 seats in the lower house will be allocated under the proportional (party list) system. An average of nine candidates will compete for each seat in the lower house, while 35 candidates will contest the 16 seats in the 17 September Senate elections.

- The first round of Kazak-Russian talks on delineating their state frontiers opens in Moscow.

- Kazakstan commemorates the centenary of the start of drilling near Atyrau, on the east coast of the Caspian Sea.

- Kazakstan plans to harvest 10 million tons of grain this year and export 3 million tons to Russia, Iran, and Uzbekistan.

- Desperately raising revenue to plug its budget deficit, Kazakstan plans to sell 20% of the state-controlled savings institution Halyk Bank which, at the end of June had a total assets of 45 billion tenge ($333 million).

- Reacting to events in southern Kyrgyzstan, Nazarbaev creates a commission to counter religious extremism.

- Citing 25% reduction of trade between the CIS countries and Kazakstan, Nazarbaev characterizes the CIS as an institution in the process of disintegration.

- Kazak parliament passes the 2000 draft budget in its first reading with the stipulation of reconsidering parts thereof.

October

- Kazakstani Prime Minister resigns but the cabinet continues its work until after October 10, when a new appointment is made.

- Parliament confirms Foreign Minister Kasymzhomart Tokayev as the new Prime Minister.

- Devaluation of the tenge, designed to protect domestic industry from cheap imports, affects people's wages and living standards.

- Commission admits the existence of violations but downplays their overall impact on the election process.

November

- A Russian proton rocket launched from Baikonur station in Kazakstan crashes. It is the second rocket crash this year. After the first crash in July, Russians paid the Kazak government $270,000 to get them to lift a ban on further launches.

- The Caspian Pipeline Consortium begins work on a 1,580-kilometer pipeline from Kazakstan to the Russian port of Novorossiisk.

- The United States levies sanctions against companies in Kazakstan and the Czech Republic for selling fighter planes to North Korea.

December

- The International Monetary Fund approves a $453 million, three-year loan to Kazakstan. The World Bank also announces a $140 million, 20-year loan to improve the country's power supply systems.

- President Nursultan Nazarbayev arrives on an official visit to the United States to meet with

American political leaders and Kofi Annan, secretary-general of the United Nations.

ANALYSIS OF EVENTS: 1999

BUSINESS AND THE ECONOMY

Since the 1991 dissolution of the U.S.S.R. and its planned economic coordination of production, the traditional high demand for Kazakstan's heavy equipment production had been in a state of collapse. The year 1999 may, however, prove to be the turnaround point for Kazakstan. Largely because of its rich natural endowment in fossil fuels as well as grain and livestock production, there was some reason for optimism regarding Kazakstan's economic development. In addition, the privatization of formerly state enterprises pleased the main capitalist lending institutions. The International Monetary Fund (IMF) announced that it would extend Kazakstan $217 million in loans. The World Bank promised $75 million. Ukraine was scheduled to import 5 million tons of oil from Kazakstan. Russia released four SU-27 fighter aircraft to Kazakstan. ''Dumping'' (selling below cost) by strong trade competitors was a problem in 1999. Thus, import agreements with Britain's Trans-World Group (BTWG) are termed invalid. The BTWG is responsible for losses totaling $145 million at Aksu Ferroalloy Works, $102 million at Aluminum of Kazakstan, $86 million at Ferrokhrom ferroalloy works, and $40 million at the Sokolov-Sarbai Mining Production Association.

The year 1999 also brought disruptive changes in the monetary situation. Devaluation of Russian ruble forced Kazakstan to free its exchange rate. Kazakstanis were requested to donate gold and silver jewelry to shore up gold and hard currency reserves. Trade with some former socialist countries, however, was improving. Kazak-Czech bilateral trade doubled to $100 million. Imported goods had to bear Kazak and Russian labels detailing country of origin, date of manufacture, and expiration date.

Oil continued to be the most enticing aspect of the Kazak economy, from the standpoint of foreign investors. In the short run, the sale and lease of these formerly state enterprises bring in a substantial amount of money. Kazakstan earned almost $190 million from privatization during the first half of the year. This was so even though the production of oil was uneven. Ten of Kazakstan's 14 oblasts registered a decline in output.

Construction commenced on the $2.2 billion marine terminal for the planned 1,580 kilometer oil export pipeline from Kazakstan's Tengiz field. Kazakstan will receive $50 million in U.S. aid. Kazakstan plans to maintain its $1.2 billion in direct foreign investment and $2.1 billion in domestic investment. Kazakstan signed a memorandum of intent with British Gas, Italy's Agip, Texaco, and Russia's Lukoil for the construction of a 460 kilometer, $440 million pipeline from the Karachaganak field to Atyrau. BP Amoco threatened to sell its 9.5% stake in the OKIOC. After six frustrating years, OKIOC pierced the Caspian seabed.

Amoco rethought the sale of its 9.5 percent stake in the OKIOC. Kazakstan and the AIPC sign a contract for the development of the 700 BCF Shagyrly-Shomyshty gas field. Kazakstan plans to shed a portion of its 25 percent ($2.5 billion) share in the Tengizchevroil to cover this year's expected $560 million budget deficit and $630 million in state debts. Kazakstan planned to harvest 10 million tons of grain and export 3 million tons. Kazakstan planned to sell 20 percent of the state-controlled Halyk Bank with a total assets of 45 billion tenge ($333 million). Kazak parliament passed the 2000 draft budget. Devaluation of the tenge, designed to protect domestic industry, results in the Prime Minister's resignation. IMF considers the draft budget's tax revenue target unrealistic.

GOVERNMENT AND POLITICS

President Nazarbaev promised to spend $100 million to support domestic manufacturing. Nazarbaev won a resounding presidential victory (81 percent of the vote). Azamat criticized the government's Kazak-Chinese border treaty. Kazakstan and China explored the possibility of equal exploitation of the Irtysh and Ili rivers. Opposition parties and movements signed a memorandum against the existing political system. Nazarbaev's opponents considered the new draft law opposed to freedom of speech. Meanwhile relations between Russia and Kazakstan were constructive. The two nations divided the Caspian seabed into national sectors looking towards oil exploration. The relations between Russia and

Kazakstan ran into difficulties when engine problems caused Russian Proton rocket launched from the Baikonur to explode. Five thousand square meters in Karaganda were contaminated with toxic heptil rocket fuel. Kazakstan suspended launches, including a supply craft bound for the ''Mir'' space station. Moscow agreed to pay $115 million annually for the use of the Baikonur complex. Kazak authorities permitted Russia to launch the Mir-bound rocket.

Elections to Kazakstan's new parliament were set for 17 September and 10 October. Eleven political parties registered to contend the 10 October elections. Citing 25 percent reduction in trade, Nazarbaev characterizes the formerly Soviet Commonwealth of Independent States (CIS) as an institution in the process of disintegration. OSCE criticized Kazakstan's senate elections.

CULTURE AND SOCIETY

The fundamental conservatism of Kazakstan's people (as well as the undemocratic nature of the political system) was reflected in numerous ways. Caspian fishing was given priority over oil extraction. Nazarbaev unconsciously reflected the underdevelopment of citizens' rights in Kazakstan when he declared that citizens should not have to write the president for legal problems. Meanwhile, anti-Nazarbaev slogans in Astana prompted a police investigation. Kazak Demography fund offered 100,000 tenge ($1,150) to the first 2,000 babies born in 2000. Kazakstan formed a commission to counter the threat of religious extremism (Moslem fundamentalism).

Nazarbaev criticized the government for a lack of coherent programs for the next three to five years. Seventy ethnic Kazak academics, writers and artists demanded that 70-80 percent of broadcasts should be in Kazak. Kazak journalists called for increased Kazak-language broadcasting. Kazak experts worried that deadly anthrax bacteria buried in Vozrozhdeniye Island might contaminate the region. Meanwhile, market forces pressed on the Kazak producers of the supposedly aphrodisiac stag antlers. Thirteen thousand prisoners, most of them suffering from Tuberculosis, were released from prison. State funding for 23 publications ended. A 46-year old woman became the seventh to contract bubonic plague. Kazakstan commemorated the centenary of drilling near Atyrau. Nazarbaev visited Bulgaria.

DIRECTORY

CENTRAL GOVERNMENT

Head of State

President
Nursultan Nazarbayev, Office of the President, Republic Square, 480091 Almaty, Kazakstan
PHONE: +7 (3272) 623016

Prime Minister
Kasymzhomart Tokayev, Office of the Prime Minister, Republic Square, 480091 Almaty, Kazakstan
PHONE: +7 (3272) 623097

Ministers

First Deputy Prime Minister
Pavlov Alexander Sergeyevich, Office of the First Deputy Prime Minister

Deputy Prime Minister
Akhmetov Danial Kenzhetayevich, Office of the Deputy Prime Minister

Deputy Prime Minister
Utembayev Erzhan Abulkhairovich, Office of the Deputy Prime Minister

Minister of Finance
Esenbayev Mazhit Tuleubekovich, Ministry of Finance

Minister of Foreign Affairs
Idrisov Erlan Abilphaziyevich, Ministry of Foreign Affairs

Minister of Defense
Kulekeyev Zhaksybek Abdrakhmanovich, Ministry of Defense

Minister of Economy
Tokpakbayev Sat Besimbayevich, Ministry of Economy

Minister of Labor and Social Protection
Radostovets Nickolai Vladimirovich, Ministry of Labor and Social Protection

Minister of Education and Science
Kusherbayev Krymbek Eleuovich, Ministry of Education and Science

Minister of Power Engineering, Industry and Trade
Shkolnik Vladimir Sergeyevich, Ministry of Power Engineering, Industry and Trade

Minister of Interior Affairs

Suleimenov Kairbek Shoshanovich, Ministry of
Interior Affairs

Minister of State Incomes

Kakimzhanov Zeinulla Khalidollovich, Ministry
of State Incomes

Minister of Justice

Mukhamedzhanov Baurzhan Alimovich, Ministry
of Justice

**Minister of Culture, Information and Public
Accord**

Sarsenbayev Altynbek Sarsenbayevich, Ministry
of Culture, Information and Public Accord

Minister of Agriculture

Mynbayev Sauat Mukhametbayevich, Ministry of
Agriculture

**Minister of Natural Resources and
Environmental Protection**

Daukeyev Serikbek Zhusupbekovich, Ministry of
Natural Resources and Environmental Protection

POLITICAL ORGANIZATIONS

People's Unity Party (PUP)

TITLE: Chairman
NAME: Akhan Bizhanov

People's Congress of Kazakhstan (NKK)

TITLE: Chairman
NAME: Anuar Ismailov

Azamat Movement

NAME: Petr Svoik

Communist Party (KPK)

TITLE: First secretary
NAME: Serikbolsyn Abdildin

December National Democratic Party

TITLE: Chairman
NAME: Hasen Kozhakhmetov

Labor and Workers Movement

TITLE: Chairman

NAME: Madel Ismailov

Republican People's Slavic Movement

TITLE: Chairman
NAME: Aleksander Samarkin

Russian Center (RT)

TITLE: Chairwoman
NAME: Nina Sidorova

DIPLOMATIC REPRESENTATION

Embassies in Kazakhstan

United States
99/97A Furmanova St., Almaty, Republic of
Kazakstan 49009
PHONE: +7 (3272) 6333921; 631375; 507623
FAX: +7 (3272) 633883
TITLE: Ambassador
NAME: Richard H. Jones

JUDICIAL SYSTEM

Supreme Court

Constitutional Council

FURTHER READING

Government Publications

U.S. Department of State. *Country Reports on
Human Rights Practices for 1998: Europe,
Canada, and the New Independent States.*

World Trade Organization. *World in Brief*, 14
October 1998.

Books

Central Intelligence Agency. *World Factbook,
1998.* Washington, D.C.: Government Printing
Office, 1999.

*Conflict in the Soviet Union: the Untold Story of
the Clashes in Kazakstan.* New York: Human
Rights Watch, 1990.

Kalyuzhnova, Yelena. *Kazakstani Economy:
Independence and Transition.* New York: St.
Martin's Press, 1998.

KAZAKSTAN: STATISTICAL DATA

For sources and notes see "Sources of Statistics" in the front of each volume.

GEOGRAPHY

Geography (1)

Area:

Total: 2,717,300 sq km.

Land: 2,669,800 sq km.

Water: 47,500 sq km.

Area—comparative: slightly less than four times the size of Texas.

Land boundaries:

Total: 12,012 km.

Border countries: China 1,533 km, Kyrgyzstan 1,051 km, Russia 6,846 km, Turkmenistan 379 km, Uzbekistan 2,203 km.

Coastline: 0 km (landlocked).

Note: Kazakstan borders the Aral Sea (1,015 km) and the Caspian Sea (1,894 km).

Climate: continental, cold winters and hot summers, arid and semiarid.

Terrain: extends from the Volga to the Altai Mountains and from the plains in western Siberia to oasis and desert in Central Asia.

Natural resources: major deposits of petroleum, natural gas, coal, iron ore, manganese, chrome ore, nickel, cobalt, copper, molybdenum, lead, zinc, bauxite, gold, uranium.

Land use:

Arable land: 12%

Permanent crops: 11%

Permanent pastures: 57%

Forests and woodland: 4%

Other: 16% (1996 est.).

Demographics (2A)

	1990	1995	1998	2000	2010	2020	2030	2040	2050
Population	16,708.3	16,961.4	16,846.8	16,816.2	17,231.9	18,127.5	19,030.2	19,898.6	20,426.4
Net migration rate (per 1,000 population)	NA	NA	NA	NA	NA	NA	NA	NA	NA
Births	NA	NA	NA	NA	NA	NA	NA	NA	NA
Deaths	NA	NA	NA	NA	NA	NA	NA	NA	NA
Life expectancy - males	62.2	58.9	58.1	57.7	60.6	64.7	68.3	71.3	73.8
Life expectancy - females	71.7	70.1	69.3	68.9	71.1	74.6	77.6	80.0	81.9
Birth rate (per 1,000)	22.8	19.3	17.2	17.1	19.4	15.3	14.1	13.4	12.0
Death rate (per 1,000)	8.2	9.6	10.1	10.5	10.3	9.3	9.2	9.7	10.2
Women of reproductive age (15-49 yrs.)	4,175.4	4,424.8	4,510.0	4,570.6	4,722.2	4,701.9	4,853.0	4,633.2	4,626.0
of which are currently married	NA	NA	NA	NA	NA	NA	NA	NA	NA
Fertility rate	2.8	2.4	2.1	2.1	2.2	2.1	2.0	1.9	1.9

Except as noted, values for vital statistics are in thousands; life expectancy is in years.

Health Personnel (3)

Total health expenditure as a percentage of GDP, 1990-1997[a]

Public sector 2.5

Private sector 0.8

Total[b] 3.3

Health expenditure per capita in U.S. dollars, 1990-1997[a]

Purchasing power parity 107

Total 42

Availability of health care facilities per 100,000 people

Hospital beds 1990-1997[a] 1030

Doctors 1993[c] 360

Nurses 1993[c] 874

Health Indicators (4)

Life expectancy at birth

1980 67

1997 65

Daily per capita supply of calories (1996) 3,007

Total fertility rate births per woman (1997) 2.0

Maternal mortality ratio per 100,000 live births (1990-97) . . . . .53[b]

Safe water % of population with access (1995) . . . .

Sanitation % of population with access (1995) . . . .

Consumption of iodized salt % of households (1992-98)[a] 53

Smoking prevalence

Male % of adults (1985-95)[a] . . . .

Female % of adults (1985-95)[a] . . . .

Tuberculosis incidence per 100,000 people (1997) 104

Adult HIV prevalence % of population ages 15-49 (1997) 0.03

Infants and Malnutrition (5)

Under-5 mortality rate (1997) 44

% of infants with low birthweight (1990-97) . . . . . .NA

Births attended by skilled health staff % of total[a] . . .99

% fully immunized (1995-97)

TB 99

DPT 97

Polio 100

Measles 92

Prevalence of child malnutrition under age 5 (1992-97)[b] 8

Ethnic Division (6)

Kazakh (Qazaq) 46%

Russian 34.7%

Ukrainian 4.9%

German 3.1%

Uzbek 2.3%

Tatar 1.9%

Other 7.1% (1996)

Religions (7)

Muslim 47%

Russian Orthodox 44%

Protestant 2%

Other 7%

Languages (8)

Kazakh (Qazaq) official language spoken by over 40% of population, Russian official language spoken by two-thirds of population and used in everyday business.

EDUCATION

Public Education Expenditures (9)

Public expenditure on education (% of GNP)

1980 . . . .

1996 . . . . .4.7

Expenditure per student

Primary % of GNP per capita

1980 . . . .

1996 . . . .

Secondary % of GNP per capita

1980 . . . .

1996 . . . .

Tertiary % of GNP per capita

1980 . . . .

1996 . . . . .22.0[1]

Expenditure on teaching materials

Primary % of total for level (1996) . . . .

Secondary % of total for level (1996) . . . .

Primary pupil-teacher ratio per teacher (1996) . . . . .18[1]

Duration of primary education years (1995) 4

Educational Attainment (10)

Age group (1989) . . . . .25+

Total population 8,414,539

Highest level attained (%)

No schooling 7.7

First level

Not completed 29.2

Completed . . . . .NA

Entered second level

S-1 . . . . .50.7

S-2 . . . . .NA

Postsecondary 12.4

Literacy Rates (11B)

Adult literacy rate

1980

Male . . . .-

Female . . . .-

1995

Male 100%

Female 99%

GOVERNMENT & LAW

Political Parties (12)

Majilis (Lower House)	No. of seats
People's Unity Party (UP)	24
December National Democratic Party	12
Kazakh Agrarian Union	5
Confederation of Kazakh Trade Unions	5
Communist Party (KPK)	2
Independents and others	19

Government Budget (13B)

Revenues . . . .$3 billion

Expenditures . . . .$4.6 billion

Capital expenditures . . . .$40 million

Data for 1996 est.

Military Affairs (14A)

Military age . . . . .18 years of age

Availability of manpower

Males age 15-49 (1998 est.) 4,429,484

Fit for military service

Males (1998 est.) 3,534,839

Reaching military age annually

Males (1998 est.) .154,218

Total expenditures (1995) . . . . .18.9 billion tenges

Expenditures as % of GDP . . . . .NA%

Conversion of defense expenditures into US dollars using the current exchange rate could produce misleading results. NA stands for not available.

Crime (15)

Crime rate (for 1997)

Crimes reported 162,500

Total persons convicted 101,200

Crimes per 100,000 population 1,300

Persons responsible for offenses

Total number of suspects 97,500

Total number of female suspects 13,600

Total number of juvenile suspects 6,950

LABOR FORCE

Labor Force (16)

Total (million) 6.9

Industry 27%

Agriculture and forestry 23%

Other 50%

Data for 1996.

Unemployment Rate (17)

2.6% includes only officially registered unemployed; also large additional numbers of unemployed and underemployed workers (December 1996 est).

PRODUCTION SECTOR

Electric Energy (18)

Capacity . . . . .18.9 million kW (1995)

Production . . . . .61.7 billion kWh (1995)

Consumption per capita . . . . . . .3,800 kWh (1996 est.)

Transportation (19)

Highways:

total: 141,076 km

paved: 113,566 km

unpaved: 27,510 km (1996 est.)

Waterways: 4,002 km on the Syr Darya and Ertis Darya

Pipelines: crude oil 2,850 km; refined products 1,500 km; natural gas 3,480 km (1992)

Airports: 10 (1997 est.)

Airports—with paved runways:

total: 9

over 3,047 m: 4

2,438 to 3,047 m: 3

1,524 to 2,437 m: 2 (1997 est.)

Airports—with unpaved runways:

total: 1

914 to 1,523 m: 1 (1997 est.)

Top Agricultural Products (20)

Grain, mostly spring wheat, cotton; wool, meat.

FINANCE, ECONOMICS, & TRADE

Economic Indicators (22)

National product: GDP—purchasing power parity—$50 billion (1997 est.)

National product real growth rate: 2.1% (1997 est.)

National product per capita: $3,000 (1997 est.)

Inflation rate—consumer price index: 12% (1997 est.)

Exchange Rates (24)

Exchange rates:

Tenges per US$1

February 1998	.76.4
January 1998	.75.55
1997	.75.44
1996	.67.30
1995	.60.95
1994	.35.54

Top Import Origins (25)

$6 billion (1996)

Origins	%
Russia	.NA
Ukraine	.NA
Uzbekistan	.NA
Turkey	.NA
Germany	.NA

NA stands for not available.

Balance of Payments (23)

	1995	1996
Exports of goods (f.o.b.)	5,164	6,292
Imports of goods (f.o.b.)	−5,387	−6,618
Trade balance	−223	−326
Services - debits	−934	−1,207
Services - credits	580	731
Private transfers (net)	73	52
Government transfers (net)	−14	−2
Overall balance	−518	−752

MANUFACTURING SECTOR

GDP & Manufacturing Summary (21)

	1980	1985	1990	1992	1993	1994
Gross Domestic Product						
Millions of 1990 dollars	21,683	28,636	39,831	31,678	27,591	20,694
Growth rate in percent	3.76	6.16	15.54	−13.00	−12.90	−25.00
Per capita (in 1990 dollars)	1,454.5	1,814.7	2,389.4	1,877.0	1,627.6	1,215.3
Manufacturing Value Added						
Millions of 1990 dollars	NA	NA	5,497	7,290	6,210	4,472
Growth rate in percent	NA	NA	NA	−14.24	-14.80	-28.00
Manufacturing share in percent of current prices	18.9	19.2	13.8	17.0	17.0	NA

FINANCE, ECONOMICS, & TRADE

Top Export Destinations (26)

$5.6 billion (1996) Data are for 1996 est.

Destinations	%
Japan	.29
United States	.16
Netherlands	.13
Singapore	.12

Economic Aid (27)

Recipient: ODA, $10 million (1993). Note: commitments, 1992- 95, $4,780 million ($1,795 million disbursements).

Import Export Commodities (28)

Import Commodities	Export Commodities
Machinery and parts	Oil
Industrial materials	Ferrous and nonferrous metals
Oil and gas	Chemicals
	Grain
	Wool
	Meat
	Coal

KENYA

Republic of Kenya
Jamhuri ya Kenya

INTRODUCTORY SURVEY

RECENT HISTORY

The region that would become Kenya was ruled by Great Britain as a colony in the first half of the twentieth century. Many Kenyans were unhappy with British rule and struggled against it. The Mau Mau revolutionary movement led to the declaration of a state of emergency in October 1952 that lasted until late 1959. The 1960 "Macleod" constitution mandated an African-elected majority in Kenya's Legislative Council. This marked a decisive shift in the direction of African control.

On 12 December 1963, Kenya became independent. Exactly one year later, it became a republic within the Commonwealth of Nations, with Jomo Kenyatta as the country's first president. His political party, the Kenya African National Union (KANU), dominated the government. Leaders of a rival party, banned in 1969, were arrested.

Kenyatta died on 22 August 1978 and was succeeded by his vice-president, Daniel arap Moi, who was elected president without opposition a month later. In June 1982, the National Assembly voted unanimously to make Kenya formally a one-party state. President Moi ran unopposed in the elections of September 1983. In 1986, Moi declared that KANU was above government, the parliament, and the judiciary. Critics of Moi were expelled from KANU, and government repression increased. In July 1990, clashes between pro-democracy demonstrators and police left five dead. In 1991, riot police dispersed thousands of protesters.

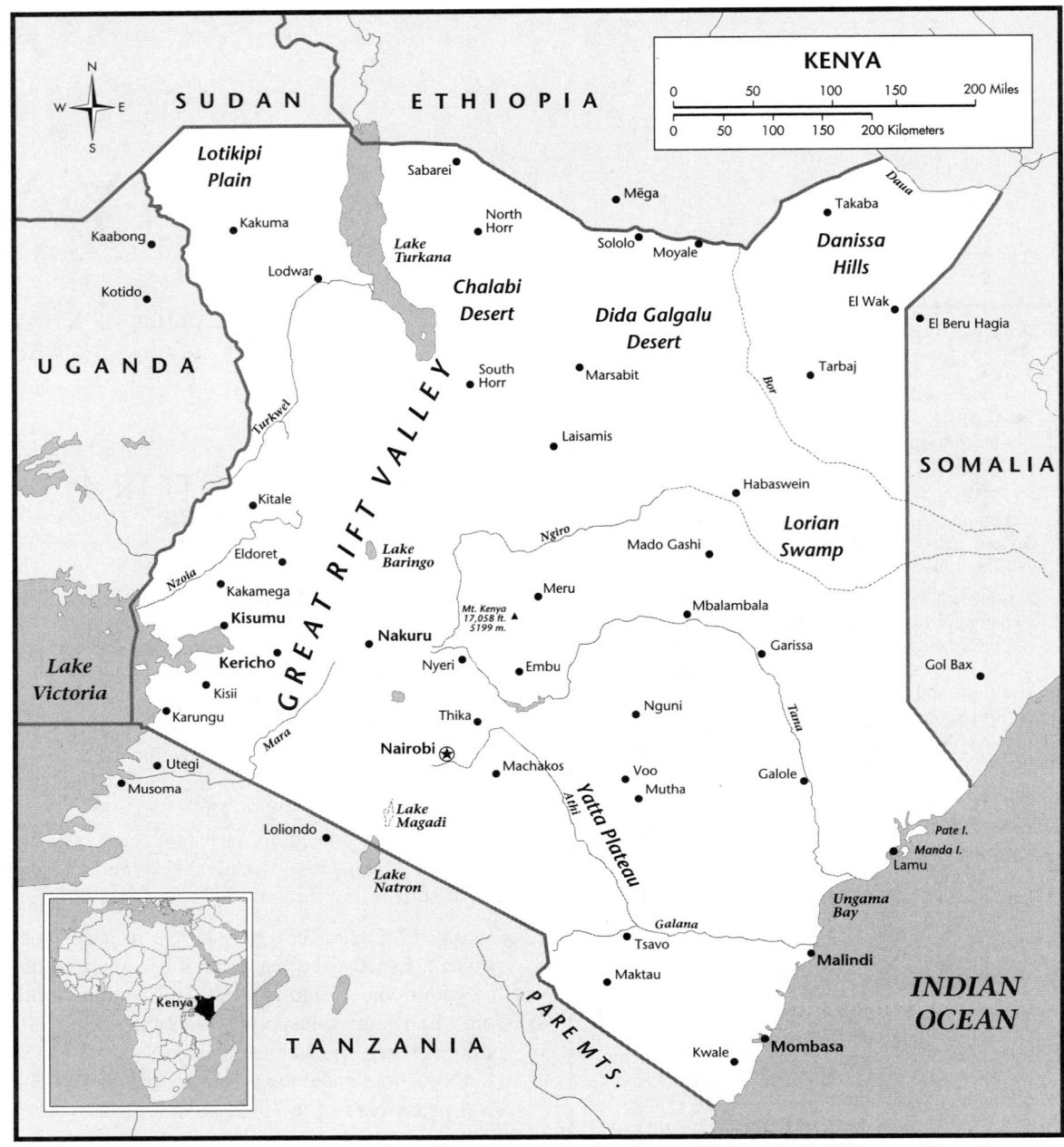

In December 1991, in response to growing pressure by the United States and other donors of foreign aid, Moi proposed dropping the 1982 constitutional amendment legalizing one-party rule. KANU agreed to it, but opposition to Moi and civil unrest continued. In Nairobi in January 1992, more than 100,000 attended the first legal antigovernment rally in 22 years. The following year Moi delayed elections until his opposition, divided into eight parties, fell apart. In the late December elections, Moi was reelected with 37%

of the vote. Foreign aid has been reduced as Moi continues to pressure the opposition in and out of parliament. In 1993, Africa Watch, a U.S.-based human rights group, reported that as many as 1,500 Kenyans have been killed and over 300,000 displaced as a result of ethnic violence triggered by Moi's regime. The government's security forces increased oppression of the opposition in 1994 and 1995. Civil unrest escalated through 1997 and international donors have become reluctant to offer assistance.

On 7 August 1998, U.S. embassies in Nairobi and Dar es Salaam, Tanzania were bombed, killing over 200 people. It was believed that Islamist terrorists were responsible.

GOVERNMENT

According to the constitution of 1963, as later amended, the government of Kenya is led by a president who is chief of state, head of government, and commander-in-chief of the armed forces. The president appoints the members of the cabinet from among members of the National Assembly. The unicameral National Assembly was established when the Senate and House of Representatives were merged by constitutional amendment in 1967. A constitutional amendment in 1986 increased the number of elected seats to 188.

Judiciary

The judicial system consists of the Court of Appeal and subordinate courts. The High Court consists of a chief justice and twenty-four associate judges, who are appointed by the president of the republic. Lower courts are presided over by resident magistrates and district magistrates. Questions of Islamic law are determined by *qadis'* courts. Military courts handle courts marital of military personnel.

Political Parties

Since 1964, the Kenya African National Union (KANU) has dominated Kenyan politics. All parliamentary candidates also were KANU members in 1974 and 1979. On 9 June 1982, following reports that former vice-president Oginga Odinga was planning to form a new, Socialist-oriented party, the National Assembly declared Kenya a one-party state.

A clandestine dissident group known as Mwakenya was founded in 1981. Other underground opposition groups emerged in the 1980s. In 1987, many of them joined to form the United Movement for Democracy (UMOJA, Swahili for unity).

In December 1991, the Moi government decided to end KANU's monopoly on legal political activity. A grand coalition known as the Forum for the Restoration of Democracy (FORD) was formed. Before the December 1992 election, it fragmented into two factions—FORD-Kenya and FORD-Asili.

DEFENSE

Military service is voluntary. In 1995, the army had 20,500 men; the navy, 1,200 men; and the air force, 2,500 men. The 5,000-member national police has general service, air, and naval paramilitary units.

ECONOMIC AFFAIRS

Kenya's is an agricultural economy supported by a manufacturing sector and a tourism sector, which is an important foreign exchange earner. Financial difficulties and disagreements over the direction of future investments led to a withholding of foreign aid in 1992. Kenya then strengthened its free market by reducing the government's role in the economy. The economy expanded by 3% in 1994, 5% in 1995, and 4% in 1996.

Public Finance

The fiscal year extends from 1 July to 30 June. The U.S. CIA estimates that, in 1994, government revenues totaled approximately $2.4 billion and expenditures $2.8 billion. External debt totaled $7 billion.

Progress in reducing the deficit was substantial between 1993–94 and 1994–95 as the deficit fell from 6.5% of GDP to 0.7%.

Income

In 1998, Kenya's gross national product (GNP) was $9.66 million, or about $330 per person. During 1985–95, the average annual real growth rate of the GNP per person was 0.1%. During that same period, the average annual inflation rate was 13%.

Industry

The transformation of agricultural raw materials, particularly of coffee and tea, remains the principal industrial activity. Meat and fruit canning, wheat flour and cornmeal milling, and sugar refining are also important. Electronics production, vehicle assembly, publishing, and soda ash processing are all significant parts of the sector. Assembly of computer components began in 1987.

Banking and Finance

Kenya acquired its first separate currency on 14 September 1966, when the initial par value for the Kenya shilling was announced by the IMF. The new coin replaced, at par value, the East African shilling, previously issued for Kenya, Tanzania, and Uganda by the East African Currency Board, whose assets were divided by those nations following a June 1965 agreement.

The Central Bank of Kenya (CBK) was established in May 1966, taking over the administration of exchange control. The money supply in December 1995 as measured by M2, was k 9,649 million.

The reputation of the banking sector has suffered from a series of scandals. The largest financial scandal in Kenyan history broke in 1993 when the CBK closed down Exchange Bank and a related company, Goldenberg International, a gold and jewelry firm. Exchange Bank has been accused of failing to honor foreign exchange contracts totaling Sh15.8 billion and Goldenberg of securing privileged access to the now-scrapped export compensation scheme.

Economic Development

Central to Kenyan government planning is a continuing expansion of the level of exports and diversification of cash crops. Moreover, Kenya has sought the orderly introduction of large numbers of African farmers into former European agricultural areas. With the goal of full economic independence, the government continues to pursue Africanization of the private sector, particularly in commerce.

Development in Kenya now depends on the private sector and on foreign and domestic investment as the parastatal sector is dismantled. Foreign exchange earnings are key to the sixth development plan (1989–1993). Increased agricultural and industrial productivity, job creation, and diversification are also goals of current development policy.

SOCIAL WELFARE

The National Social Security Fund operates a limited pension for employed persons. Private and voluntary agencies are highly developed. There are societies that care for the blind, the deaf and mute, and the physically disabled, and voluntary organizations that care for the poor and destitute. Homes and hostels have been established throughout the country for the care of orphans, young offenders, and juvenile prostitutes. Women must obtain written permission from their husbands or fathers to acquire a passport. Intertribal violence is a recurring problem.

Healthcare

Among Kenya's major health problems are tuberculosis and protein deficiency. Although the incidence of malaria has been reduced, it still accounted for over 20% of outpatient deaths in 1990. Water supply, sanitation, and sleeping sickness also pose major problems. Diseases caused by parasites are widespread in some areas. In 1994–95, only 49% of the population had access to safe water, and only 43% had adequate sanitation. There was an average life expectancy of 58 years in 1995.

Housing

Housing in rural areas is privately owned. Most of these homes, built with traditional materials, fall apart in a relatively short time. An increasing number of people now build their homes with more permanent materials. The central government is responsible for all housing projects and works closely with local authorities.

EDUCATION

Primary education is free and compulsory for eight years. Children start school at the age of 5 or 6 and spend eight years at primary school, five years at secondary school, and a further four years at the university. In 1993, there were 15,804 primary schools with 5.6 million students. In general secondary schools, there were 616,200 students, and teacher training programs had 18,992 students. In 1995, the adult illiteracy rate was 22%, an estimated 13.7% for men and 30% for women.

1999 TIMELINE OF EVENTS

February

- Finance Minister Simeon Nyachae is relieved of his position.

May

- Kenya's fourth-largest bank restructures to avoid collapse.

- The trial of Simon ole Makallah, accused of killing tourist Julie Ward, opens.

July

- Richard Leakey named Head of Civil Service and Secretary to the Cabinet.

August

- New hominoid genus found in Kenya.

October

- U.S. Secretary of State Madeline Albright visits Kenya and meets with AIDS activists and survivors of the 1998 bombing of the U.S. embassy there.

November

- Hundreds of Kenyan refugees hoping to return home from Ethiopia under a program sponsored by the United Nations High Commission for Refugees (UNHCR) are turned back at the border because they have no identification papers. An estimated 8,000 refugees fled to Ethiopia in 1993 to escape ethnic violence, and Ethiopian officials allegedly confiscated their identification papers.

- Parliament votes to cancel the president's right to appoint the clerk of the house of parliament, paving the way for parliament to appoint its own clerk.

- President Daniel arap Moi, citing the deaths of more that 700,000 from AIDS, declares AIDS a national disaster.

December

- Worsening drought in the northwest of the country results in twenty deaths from starvation. Churches make an urgent appeal for famine relief.

- The Kenya Human Rights Commissions issues a report alleging that women's prison conditions are overcrowded, unsanitary, and that inmates are routinely beaten and sexually abused by wardens. They further allege that prisoners, many of whom were arrested for illegally brewing alcohol or for working in the commercial sex industry, do not have access to medical care.

- The International Monetary Fund (IMF) agrees to open discussions with Kenya about future lending and investment.

- A bridge over the River Ndii on the only road linking Nairobi and the port city of Mombasa collapses when the river floods, stranding thousands of holiday travelers.

ANALYSIS OF EVENTS: 1999

BUSINESS AND THE ECONOMY

On July 23, Richard Leakey was named Head of Civil Service and Secretary to the Cabinet. On July 30, he was also named Director of the Central Bank of Kenya. Leakey had been a political opponent of President Daniel arap Moi, though the two had worked together in the past. Leakey's political rise was largely due to World Bank pressure. The World Bank is funding Leakey's position, and the fact that Leakey will be paid by an out-of-country institute should help him sidestep the rampant corruption that derailed past reformers.

The World Bank's actions are unprecedented. Never before has the World Bank stepped in and directly influenced a country's governance. Bank member nations, however, were outraged by Kenya's corruption, and they took this move to protect their financial interests.

In May the National Bank of Kenya fired its board of directors and announced major restructuring. Kenya's fourth-largest bank, the National Bank was in danger of collapse following a string of bad loans issued in 1998. The bank fired its former general manager, Ahmed Hashi, for allegedly handing out unsecured loans. The bank's financial troubles surfaced soon after the fall of other major Kenyan banks, including Trust Bank, Reliance Bank, Prudential Bank and Bullion Bank.

In September the Kenyan government announced plans to reform the country's pension system. The new law would limit foreign investments, mandate audits, and require independent managers for all classes of pension funds.

GOVERNMENT AND POLITICS

In February, Finance Minister Simeon Nyachae, began speaking out against government corruption. "The country is adrift, politics is sterile and the economy is indeed in tatters," Nyachae said. This led to Nyache being fired in February, however, he immediately began positioning himself as a future presidential candidate.

The tempestuous relationship between Kenyan President Daniel arap Moi and famous paleontologist Richard Leakey took a surprising twist this year. In July Moi appointed Leakey, a former political opponent, Head of Kenya's Civil Service, Secretary to the Cabinet, and Director of the Central Bank of Kenya. The move made Leakey the second most powerful figure in Kenyan politics, behind the president.

Leakey and Moi have a long history together. After meeting in 1968, Leakey occasionally advised Moi, and in 1989, Moi named Leakey Director of the Kenya Wildlife Service. However,

Leakey soon quit and formed an anticorruption opposition party, leading Moi to brand Leakey as neocolonial and racist.

Leakey's ascension was largely triggered by outside pressure. The World Bank, troubled by unpaid loans, demanded reform. Leakey, who is a white third-generation Kenyan and son of famous paleontologists Louis and Mary Leakey, will be responsible for cleaning up Kenya's scandal-plagued government. Moi also hopes that Leakey will lure back foreign investment and loans. Leakey, in turn, has promised to better public services, fight corruption, and balance the nation's books.

In March tribal violence broke out in the Kenyan bush country. Ethnic fighting between Pokot and Turkana herdsmen killed over 100 people. Although Kenya is generally seen as peaceful and stable, neighboring wars in Sudan, Uganda, and Ethiopia have made automatic weapons cheap and readily available in parts of Kenya; thus ethnic squabbles have escalated into bloody battles.

CULTURE AND SOCIETY

Simon ole Makallah's trial began on March 1. The trial will presumably be a long one, due to the controversy surrounding this case. Makallah, Assistant Director of the Kenya Wildlife Service, is accused of murdering British tourist Julie Ward in the Masai Mara game park in 1988. Ward's death had initially been blamed on wild animals. However, Julie Ward's father, John Ward, launched an investigation that uncovered inconsistencies in the official account of Julie Ward's death. Makallah was the chief warden of Masai Mara reserve in 1998.

In late 1999 or early 2000, Martha Karua, a Member of Parliament, plans to introduce a bill combating abuse against women. Much of Kenya's population believes that men have the right to use force to control their wives. Wives are blamed for bringing beatings on themselves, and some tribes view women as property. A women's rights movement has been growing, though, and M.P. Martha Karua hopes that legislation will protect women from abuse and provide them with greater equality.

In August a partial hominoid skeleton was found in northern Kenya. The skeleton, named Equatorius, is approximately 15 million years old. Equatorius may force scientists to rethink the family tree of great apes. Originally thought to be an ancestor of living apes, Equatorius is now considered a separate genus.

In October, U.S. Secretary of State Madeline Albright visited Kenya to meet with survivors and orphans of those killed in the 1998 bombing of the U.S. Embassy in Nairobi. In addition, she was given a presentation by a dance troupe whose goal it is to raise awareness of the devastating effects of AIDS in Kenya. An estimated eighteen percent of the adult population is infected with HIV, the virus that causes AIDS. Five hundred Kenyans die each day from AIDS.

DIRECTORY

CENTRAL GOVERNMENT

Head of State

President and Commander-in-Chief of the Armed Forces
D. T. Arap Moi, Office of the President, Harambee House, Harambee Ave., P.O. Box 30510, Nairobi, Kenya
PHONE: +254 (2) 227411

Vice President
George Saitoti, Office of the Vice President, Jogoo House, Harambee Ave., P.O. Box 30520, Nairobi, Kenya
PHONE: +254 (2) 228411

Ministers

Minister of State
Julius Sunkuli, Ministry of State, Harambee House, Harambee Ave., P.O. Box 30510, Nairobi, Kenya
PHONE: +254 (2) 227411

Minister of State
Marsden H. Madoka, Ministry of State, Harambee House, Harambee Ave., P.O. Box 30510, Nairobi, Kenya
PHONE: +254 (2) 227411

Minister of State
Shariff Nasir Taib, Ministry of State, Harambee House, Harambee Ave., P.O. Box 30510, Nairobi, Kenya
PHONE: +254 (2) 227411

Minister of State
William ole Ntimama, Ministry of State, Harambee House, Harambee Ave., P.O. Box 30510, Nairobi, Kenya
PHONE: +254 (2) 227411

Minister of Home Affairs, Heritage, Culture and Sport
Noah Katana Ngala, Ministry of Home Affairs, Heritage, Culture and Sport, Jogoo House, Harambee Ave., P.O. Box 30520, Nairobi, Kenya
PHONE: +254 (2) 228411

Minister of Agriculture
Chris Mogere Obure, Ministry of Agriculture, Kilimo House, Cathedral Rd., P.O. Box 30028, Nairobi, Kenya
PHONE: +254 (2) 718870

Minister of Rural Development
Hussein Maalim Mohammed, Ministry of Rural Development, Kilimo House, Cathedral Rd., P.O. Box 30028, Nairobi, Kenya
PHONE: +254 (2) 718870

Minister of Education
Stephen Kalonzo Musyoka, Ministry of Education, Jogoo House ''B,'' Harambee Ave., P.O. Box 30040, Nairobi, Kenya
PHONE: +254 (2) 334411
E-MAIL: elimu1@africaonline.co.ke

Minister of Science and Technology
Henry Kosgey, Ministry of Science and Technology, Jogoo House ''B,'' Harambee Ave., P.O. Box 30040, Nairobi, Kenya
PHONE: +254 (2) 334411
E-MAIL: elimu1@africaonline.co.ke

Minister of Labor
Joseph Ngutu, Ministry of Labor, Jogoo House ''B,'' Harambee Ave., P.O. Box 30040, Nairobi, Kenya
PHONE: +254 (2) 334411
E-MAIL: elimu1@africaonline.co.ke

Minister of Energy
Yekoyada Francis Masakhalia, Ministry of Energy, Nyayo House, Kenyatta Ave., P.O. Box 30582, Nairobi, Kenya
PHONE: +254 (2) 333551

Minister of Environment and Natural Resources
Kipng'eno arap Ng'eny, Ministry of Environment and Natural Resources, Kencom House, Moi Ave., P.O. Box 30126, Nairobi, Kenya
PHONE: +254 (2) 229261

Minister of Environment
Francis Nyenz, Ministry of Environment, Kencom House, Moi Ave., P.O. Box 30126, Nairobi, Kenya
PHONE: +254 (2) 229261

Minister of Mineral Exploitation
Jackson Kalweo, Ministry of Mineral Exploitation, Kencom House, Moi Ave., P.O. Box 30126, Nairobi, Kenya
PHONE: +254 (2) 229261

Minister of Finance
Chrysanthus Okemo, Ministry of Finance, Treasury Building, Harambee Ave., P.O. Box 30007, Nairobi, Kenya
PHONE: +254 (2) 338111
E-MAIL: mof@form-net.com

Minister of Planning
Gideon Ndambuki, Ministry of Planning, Treasury Building, Harambee Ave., P.O. Box 30007, Nairobi, Kenya
PHONE: +254 (2) 338111
E-MAIL: mof@form-net.com

Minister of Foreign Affairs and International Co-operation
Bonaya Godana, Ministry of Foreign Affairs and International Co-operation, Old Treasury Building, Harambee Ave., P.O. Box 30551, Nairobi, Kenya
PHONE: +254 (2) 334433

Minister of Transport and Communications
W. Musalia Mudavadi, Ministry of Transport and Communications, Telecom House, Ngong Rd., P.O. Box 52692, Nairobi, Kenya
PHONE: +254 (2) 729200

Minister of Lands and Settlement
Joseph Nyagah, Ministry of Lands and Settlement, Ardhi House, Ngong Rd., P.O. Box 30450, Nairobi, Kenya
PHONE: +254 (2) 718050

Minister of Local Government
Joseph J. Kamotho, Ministry of Local Government, Jogoo House ''A,'' Taifa Rd., P.O. Box 30004, Nairobi, Kenya
PHONE: +254 (2) 217475
E-MAIL: mlog@form-net.com

Minister of Public Works and Housing
Andrew C. Kiptoon, Ministry of Public Works and Housing, Ngong Rd., P.O. Box 30260, Nairobi, Kenya
PHONE: +254 (2) 723101

Minister of Tourism, Trade and Industry
Kipyator Nicholas K. Biwott, Ministry of
Tourism, Trade and Industry, Utalii House,
Uhuru Highway, P.O. Box 331030, Nairobi,
Kenya
PHONE: +254 (2) 723101

POLITICAL ORGANIZATIONS

Kenya African National Union (KANU)

TITLE: President
NAME: Daniel Toroitich arap Moi

Democratic Party of Kenya (DP)

NAME: Mwai Kibaki

Forum for the Restoration of Democracy-Asili (FORD-A)

TITLE: Chairman
NAME: Martin Shikuku

Forum for the Restoration of Democracy-Kenya (FORD-K)

NAME: Michael Kijana Wamalwa

Forum for the Restoration of Democracy-People (FORD-People)

NAME: Raymond Matiba

National Development Party (NDP)

TITLE: President
NAME: Raila Odinga

DIPLOMATIC REPRESENTATION

Embassies in Kenya

Algeria
4th. Floor, Comcraft House, Haile Selassie Ave.,
P.O. Box 53902, Nairobi, Kenya
PHONE: +254 (2) 213864
FAX: +254 (2) 337286; 217477
E-MAIL: algerianembassy@form-net.com

Argentina
7th Floor, Town House, Kaunda Street, P.O.
Box 30283, Nairobi, Kenya
PHONE: +254 (2) 335242; 339949
E-MAIL: argentina@form-net.com

Australia
ICIPE House, River Side Drive, P.O. Box
39341, Nairobi, Kenya
PHONE: +254 (2) 445034
FAX: +254 (2) 444617

Austria
6th Floor, Posta Sacco Plaza, P.O. Box 30560,
Nairobi, Kenya
PHONE: +254 (2) 228281
FAX: +254 (2) 331972

Bangladesh
Ole Odume Rd., P.O. Box 41645, Nairobi,
Kenya
PHONE: +254 (2) 562815
FAX: +254 (2) 562817

Belgium
Muthaiga, Limuru Rd., P.O. Box 30461, Nairobi,
Kenya
PHONE: +254 (2) 741564
FAX: +254 (2) 741568
E-MAIL: belgianemb_ke@form-net.com

Brazil
4th Floor, Jeevan Bharati Building, Harambee
Ave., P.O. Box 30754, Nairobi, Kenya
PHONE: +254 (2) 332649; 215755
FAX: +254 (2) 336245

Burundi
14th Floor, Development House, Moi Ave., P.O.
Box 44439, Nairobi, Kenya
PHONE: +254 (2) 218458
FAX: +254 (2) 219005

Canada
6th Floor, Comcraft House, Haile Selassie Ave.,
P.O. Box 30481, Nairobi, Kenya
PHONE: +254 (2) 214804
FAX: +254 (2) 226987
E-MAIL: kenyapsudir@form-net.com

Chile
5th Floor, International House, Mama Ngina St.,
P.O. Box 45554, Nairobi, Kenya
PHONE: +254 (2) 337934; 331320
FAX: +254 (2) 215648
E-MAIL: echileke@form-net.com

China
Woodlands Rd., Hurlingham, P.O. Box 30508,
Nairobi, Kenya
PHONE: +254 (2) 722559
FAX: +254 (2) 746402

Colombia
Muthaiga Rd., House No. 3, P.O. Box 48494,
Nairobi, Kenya
PHONE: +254 (2) 765927
FAX: +254 (2) 765911
E-MAIL: embcol@form-net.com

Comoros
Nation Centre, Kimathi Street, P.O. Box 43912,
Nairobi, Kenya
PHONE: +254 (2) 222964
FAX: +254 (2) 222564
E-MAIL: embcol@form-net.com

Democratic Republic of Congo
12th Fl., Electricity House, Harambee Ave., P.O.
Box 48106, Nairobi, Kenya
PHONE: +254 (2) 229771-2
FAX: +254 (2) 564394

Costa Rica
Geosurvey Building, Wilson Airport, Langata
Rd., P.O. Box 30750, Nairobi, Kenya
PHONE: +254 (2) 500226; 721845
FAX: +254 (2) 222564
E-MAIL: aranibarmkt@form-net.com

Côte d'Ivoire
Lonrho House, Standard Street, P.O. Box 22683,
Nairobi, Kenya
PHONE: +254 (2) 220179
FAX: +254 (2) 211677; 228427

Cyprus
5th Floor, Eagle House, Kimathi Street, P.O.
Box 30739, Nairobi, Kenya
PHONE: +254 (2) 220881; 441954
FAX: +254 (2) 331232

Czech Republic
Embassy House, Harambee Rd., P.O. Box
48785, Nairobi, Kenya
PHONE: +254 (2) 210494

Denmark
11th Floor, HFCK Building, Kenyatta Ave., P.O.
Box 40412, Nairobi, Kenya
PHONE: +254 (2) 331088
FAX: +254 (2) 331492

Djibouti
2nd Floor, Comcraft House, Haile Selassie Ave.,
P.O. Box 59528, Nairobi, Kenya
PHONE: +254 (2) 339640; 336433

Egypt
7th Floor, Harambee Plaza, Haile Selassie Ave.,
P.O. Box 30285, Nairobi, Kenya
PHONE: +254 (2) 570360
FAX: +254 (2) 211560

Eritrea
2nd Floor, New Rehema House, Raphta Rd.,
P.O. Box 38651, Nairobi, Kenya
PHONE: +254 (2) 444316
FAX: +254 (2) 443165

Ethiopia
State House Ave., P.O. Box 45198, Nairobi,
Kenya
PHONE: +254 (2) 723027
FAX: +254 (2) 723401

Finland
2nd Floor, International House, Mama Ngina St.,
P.O. Box 30379, Nairobi, Kenya
PHONE: +254 (2) 334777; 334408
FAX: +254 (2) 335986

France
9th Floor, Barclays Plaza, Loita Street, P.O. Box
41784, Nairobi, Kenya
PHONE: +254 (2) 339783; 339978
FAX: +254 (2) 339421
E-MAIL: maisonfrance@form-net.com

Gabon
Hotel Intercontinental, City Hall Way, P.O. Box
30353, Nairobi, Kenya
PHONE: +254 (2) 335550
FAX: +254 (2) 337854

Germany
4th Floor, Williamson House, Ngong Rd., P.O.
Box 30180, Nairobi, Kenya
PHONE: +254 (2) 712527
FAX: +254 (2) 714886
E-MAIL: bavaria@form-net.com

Greece
13th Floor, Nation Centre, Kimathi Street, P.O.
Box 30543, Nairobi, Kenya
PHONE: +254 (2) 340722
FAX: +254 (2) 216044

Hungary
Ole Odume Rd., P.O. Box 61146, Nairobi,
Kenya
PHONE: +254 (2) 560060; 560453
FAX: +254 (2) 560114

Iceland
Ruaka Rd., Runda, P.O. Box 45000, Nairobi,
Kenya
PHONE: +254 (2) 521487
FAX: +254 (2) 521487

India
2nd Floor, Jeevan Bharati Building, Harambee
Ave., P.O. Box 30074, Nairobi, Kenya
PHONE: +254 (2) 225104; 225180
FAX: +254 (2) 334167
E-MAIL: hcindia@form-net.com

Indonesia
3rd Floor, Utalii House, Uhuru Highway, P.O.
Box 48868, Nairobi, Kenya
PHONE: +254 (2) 215848
FAX: +254 (2) 340721
E-MAIL: hcindia@form-net.com

Iran
Dennis Pritt Rd., P.O. Box 49170, Nairobi,
Kenya
PHONE: +254 (2) 720343; 720796
FAX: +254 (2) 339936

Iraq
Loresho Rd., P.O. Box 49213, Nairobi, Kenya
PHONE: +254 (2) 580262; 581073
FAX: +254 (2) 582880

Ireland
5th Floor, Waumini House, Chiromo Rd., P.O.
Box 30659, Nairobi, Kenya
PHONE: +254 (2) 444367
FAX: +254 (2) 440897

Israel
Bishops Rd., P.O. Box 30354, Nairobi, Kenya
PHONE: +254 (2) 722182
FAX: +254 (2) 715966

Italy
9th Floor, International House, Mama Ngina
Street, P.O. Box 30107, Nairobi, Kenya
PHONE: +254 (2) 337356
FAX: +254 (2) 337056
E-MAIL: afra@form-net.com

Japan
15th Floor, ICEA Building, Kenyatta Ave., P.O.
Box 60202, Nairobi, Kenya
PHONE: +254 (2) 332955
FAX: +254 (2) 332955

South Korea
Anniversary Towers, University Way, P.O. Box
30455, Nairobi, Kenya
PHONE: +254 (2) 333581
FAX: +254 (2) 332839
E-MAIL: koremb@form-net.com

Kuwait
Muthaiga Rd., House No. 38, P.O. Box 42353,
Nairobi, Kenya
PHONE: +254 (2) 761614
FAX: +254 (2) 762837
E-MAIL: kuwaitembassy@form-net.com

Lebanon
9th Floor, Maendeleo House, Monrovia Street,
P.O. Box 30074, Nairobi, Kenya

PHONE: +254 (2) 223708; 229981
FAX: +254 (2) 340944

Lesotho
4th Floor, International House, Mama Ngina St.,
P.O. Box 44096, Nairobi, Kenya
PHONE: +254 (2) 224876; 217785
FAX: +254 (2) 337493

Luxembourg
8th Floor, International House, Mama Ngina St.,
P.O. Box 30610, Nairobi, Kenya
PHONE: +254 (2) 224318
FAX: +254 (2) 229938

Madagascar
1st Floor, Hilton Hotel, Mama Ngina Street,
P.O. Box 41723, Nairobi, Kenya
PHONE: +254 (2) 226494; 225286

Malawi
Mvuli, Church Rd., Westlands, P.O. Box 30453,
Nairobi, Kenya
PHONE: +254 (2) 440569
FAX: +254 (2) 440568

Malaysia
4th Floor, Eagle House, Kimathi Street, P.O.
Box 45000, Nairobi, Kenya
PHONE: +254 (2) 229724
FAX: +254 (2) 521487

Mauritius
1st Floor, Union Towers, Moi Ave., P.O. Box
49326, Nairobi, Kenya
PHONE: +254 (2) 330215
FAX: +254 (2) 221006

Mexico
Kibagare Way off Loresho Ridge, P.O. Box
14145, Nairobi, Kenya
PHONE: +254 (2) 582850; 582579
FAX: +254 (2) 581500
E-MAIL: embmexke@form-net.com

Morocco
3rd Floor, Diamond Trust House, Moi Ave.,
P.O. Box 61093, Nairobi, Kenya
PHONE: +254 (2) 222361; 222364
FAX: +254 (2) 222364
E-MAIL: embassymorocco@form-net.com

Mozambique
4th Floor, Hughes Building, Kenyatta Ave., P.O.
Box 66923, Nairobi, Kenya
PHONE: +254 (2) 221979
FAX: +254 (2) 222446

Netherlands
6th Floor, Uchumi House, Nkrumah Ave., P.O. Box 41537, Nairobi, Kenya
PHONE: +254 (2) 227111
FAX: +254 (2) 339155
E-MAIL: holland@form-net.com

Nigeria
Lenana Rd. Hurlingham, P.O. Box 30516, Nairobi, Kenya
PHONE: +254 (2) 564116
FAX: +254 (2) 564117; 562776

Norway
8th Floor, Rehani House, Kenyatta Ave., P.O. Box 46363, Nairobi, Kenya
PHONE: +254 (2) 337121
FAX: +254 (2) 216009

Pakistan
St. Michael's Rd., Westlands Ave., P.O. Box 30045, Nairobi, Kenya
PHONE: +254 (2) 443911
FAX: +254 (2) 446507

Peru
Lagutrop House, Enterprise Rd., P.O. Box 59446, Nairobi, Kenya
PHONE: +254 (2) 530156
FAX: +254 (2) 524114

Philippines
State House Rd., P.O. Box 47941, Nairobi, Kenya
PHONE: +254 (2) 721791
FAX: +254 (2) 725897

Poland
Kabarnet Rd., Woodley, P.O. Box 30086, Nairobi, Kenya
PHONE: +254 (2) 566288
FAX: +254 (2) 727701
E-MAIL: polambnairobi@form-net.com

Portugal
10th Floor, Reinsurance Plaza, Aga Khan Walk, P.O. Box 34020, Nairobi, Kenya
PHONE: +254 (2) 338990; 339853
FAX: +254 (2) 214711

Russia
Lenana Rd., P.O. Box 30049, Nairobi, Kenya
PHONE: +254 (2) 722462; 728700
FAX: +254 (2) 721888

Saudi Arabia
Muthaiga Rd., P.O. Box 58297, Nairobi, Kenya
PHONE: +254 (2) 762781

Seychelles
7th Floor, Agip House, Waiyaki Way, P.O. Box 20400, Nairobi, Kenya
PHONE: +254 (2) 440552
FAX: +254 (2) 441150

Slovakia
Milimani Rd., P.O. Box 30204, Nairobi, Kenya
PHONE: +254 (2) 721896
FAX: +254 (2) 721898

South Africa
Lonrho House, Standard Street, P.O. Box 42441, Nairobi, Kenya
PHONE: +254 (2) 215616
FAX: +254 (2) 223687

Spain
5th Floor, Bruce House, Standard Street, P.O. Box 45503, Nairobi, Kenya
PHONE: +254 (2) 335711
FAX: +254 (2) 332858

Sri Lanka
8th Floor, International House, Mama Ngina St., P.O. Box 48145, Nairobi, Kenya
PHONE: +254 (2) 227577; 227878
FAX: +254 (2) 225391

Sudan
Minet-ICDC Building, Mamlaka Rd., P.O. Box 48784, Nairobi, Kenya
PHONE: +254 (2) 720853; 721704
FAX: +254 (2) 721015

Swaziland
3rd Floor, Transnational Plaza, Mama Ngina St., P.O. Box 41887, Nairobi, Kenya
PHONE: +254 (2) 339231; 222817
FAX: +254 (2) 330540

Sweden
10th Floor, International House, Mama Ngina St., P.O. Box 30060, Nairobi, Kenya
PHONE: +254 (2) 229042
FAX: +254 (2) 218908; 220863

Switzerland
7th Floor, International House, Mama Ngina St., P.O. Box 30752, Nairobi, Kenya
PHONE: +254 (2) 228735
FAX: +254 (2) 217388
E-MAIL: sdckenya@form-net.com

Tanzania
Continental House, Uhuru Highway, P.O. Box 47790, Nairobi, Kenya
PHONE: +254 (2) 331056
FAX: +254 (2) 218269

Thailand
Ground Floor, Ambassadeur House, Rose Ave.,
P.O. Box 58349, Nairobi, Kenya
PHONE: +254 (2) 715800
FAX: +254 (2) 715801
E-MAIL: thainbi@form-net.com

Turkey
Gigiri Rd., P.O. Box 30785, Nairobi, Kenya
PHONE: +254 (2) 520404
FAX: +254 (2) 521237

Uganda
5th Floor, Uganda House, Kenyatta Ave., P.O.
Box 60853, Nairobi, Kenya
PHONE: +254 (2) 330801; 330814
FAX: +254 (2) 330970

United Kingdom
Bruce House, Standard Street, P.O. Box 48868,
Nairobi, Kenya
PHONE: +254 (2) 335944
FAX: +254 (2) 333196

United States
Moi Ave./Haile Selassie Ave., P.O. Box 30137,
Nairobi, Kenya
PHONE: +254 (2) 334141
FAX: +254 (2) 340838; 340835

Vatican City
Apostolic Nuciature, Manyani Rd., Waiyaki
Way, P.O. Box 14326, Nairobi, Kenya
PHONE: +254 (2) 442975
FAX: +254 (2) 446789
E-MAIL: nunciokenya@form-net.com

Venezuela
International House, Mama Ngina Street, P.O.
Box 34477, Nairobi, Kenya
PHONE: +254 (2) 340134
FAX: +254 (2) 337487
E-MAIL: embavenez@form-net.com

Yemen
Ngong, Kabarnet Rd., P.O. Box 44642, Nairobi,
Kenya
PHONE: +254 (2) 564379; 564517
FAX: +254 (2) 564394

Zambia
Nyerere Rd., P.O. Box 48741, Nairobi, Kenya

PHONE: +254 (2) 724850; 724796
FAX: +254 (2) 718494

Zimbabwe
6th Floor, Minet-ICDC Building, Mamlaka Rd,
P.O. Box 30806, Nairobi, Kenya
PHONE: +254 (2) 721071
FAX: +254 (2) 726503

JUDICIAL SYSTEM
Court of Appeal

High Court

FURTHER READING
Articles
Gedda, George. "Albright: AIDS Steals Kenya Future." Associated Press, 22 October 1999.

"Kenya's New Fireman: Richard Leakey Spent Years Trying to Save Africa's Animals. Now He's Trying to Save a Nation." *Time* 154 (September 20, 1999): 30.

Otieno, Barrack. "Bad Loans Threaten National Bank." *African Business* (May 1999): 32.

Vesely, Milan. "'Sheriff' Leakey to Clean Up Kenya." *African Business* (September 1999): 8.

Voller, Mary Anne. "Who Killed Julie Ward?" *Harper's Bazaar* (September 1999): 405.

Books
Nowrojee, Binaifer. *Divide and Rule: State-Sponsored Ethnic Violence in Kenya.* New York: Human Rights Watch, 1993.

United Nations Industrial Development Organization. *Kenya: Paving the Road to Newly Industrialized Countries Status.* New York: United Nations, 1996.

Internet
Embassy of Kenya. Available Online @ http://www.kenyaembassy.com/ (October 28, 1999).

Kenya Government. Available Online @ http://www.kenyaweb.com/kenyagov/index.html (October 18, 1999).

KENYA: STATISTICAL DATA

For sources and notes see "Sources of Statistics" in the front of each volume.

GEOGRAPHY

Geography (1)

Area:

Total: 582,650 sq km.

Land: 569,250 sq km.

Water: 13,400 sq km.

Area—comparative: slightly more than twice the size of Nevada.

Land boundaries:

Total: 3,446 km.

Border countries: Ethiopia 830 km, Somalia 682 km, Sudan 232 km, Tanzania 769 km, Uganda 933 km.

Coastline: 536 km.

Climate: varies from tropical along coast to arid in interior.

Terrain: low plains rise to central highlands bisected by Great Rift Valley; fertile plateau in west.

Natural resources: gold, limestone, soda ash, salt barytes, rubies, fluorspar, garnets, wildlife.

Land use:

Arable land: 7%

Permanent crops: 1%

Permanent pastures: 37%

Forests and woodland: 30%

Other: 25% (1993 est.).

HUMAN FACTORS

Demographics (2A)

	1990	1995	1998	2000	2010	2020	2030	2040	2050
Population	23,674.1	26,864.4	28,337.1	29,250.5	32,442.8	33,935.9	36,026.7	39,755.3	43,852.0
Net migration rate (per 1,000 population)	NA	NA	NA	NA	NA	NA	NA	NA	NA
Births	NA	NA	NA	NA	NA	NA	NA	NA	NA
Deaths	NA	NA	NA	NA	NA	NA	NA	NA	NA
Life expectancy - males	52.1	48.5	47.0	46.1	43.5	47.5	59.2	70.8	74.8
Life expectancy - females	53.2	50.1	48.1	46.9	43.9	48.3	62.0	75.7	80.1
Birth rate (per 1,000)	39.0	34.2	31.7	29.9	24.4	21.1	18.9	16.5	14.6
Death rate (per 1,000)	11.8	13.1	14.2	15.0	18.6	17.2	10.5	5.9	5.8
Women of reproductive age (15-49 yrs.)	5,175.0	6,186.1	6,763.8	7,164.0	8,717.1	9,544.3	10,266.3	10,947.2	11,231.3
of which are currently married	NA	NA	NA	NA	NA	NA	NA	NA	NA
Fertility rate	5.7	4.6	4.1	3.7	2.6	2.2	2.0	2.0	2.0

Except as noted, values for vital statistics are in thousands; life expectancy is in years.

Health Personnel (3)

Total health expenditure as a percentage of GDP, 1990-1997[a]

Public sector 1.9

Private sector 1.0

Total[b] 2.6

Health expenditure per capita in U.S. dollars, 1990-1997[a]

Purchasing power parity 28

Total 8

Availability of health care facilities per 100,000 people

Hospital beds 1990-1997[a] 1.60

Doctors 1993[c] 15

Nurses 1993[c] 23

Health Indicators (4)

Life expectancy at birth

1980 55

1997 52

Daily per capita supply of calories (1996) 1,971

Total fertility rate births per woman (1997) 4.7

Maternal mortality ratio per 100,000 live births (1990-97) . . . . .650[c]

Safe water % of population with access (1995) 45

Sanitation % of population with access (1995) 45

Consumption of iodized salt % of households (1992-98)[a] 100

Smoking prevalence

Male % of adults (1985-95)[a] . . . .

Female % of adults (1985-95)[a] . . . .

Tuberculosis incidence per 100,000 people (1997) 297

Adult HIV prevalence % of population ages 15-49 (1997) 11.64

Infants and Malnutrition (5)

Under-5 mortality rate (1997) 87

% of infants with low birthweight (1990-97) 16

Births attended by skilled health staff % of total[a] . . .45

% fully immunized (1995-97)

TB 42

DPT 36

Polio 36

Measles 32

Prevalence of child malnutrition under age 5 (1992-97)[b] 23

Ethnic Division (6)

Kikuyu 22%

Luhya 14%

Luo 13%

Kalenjin 12%

Kamba 11%

Kisii 6%

Meru 6%

Other African 15%

Non-African 1%

Non-African includes Asian, European, and Arab.

Religions (7)

Protestant (including Anglican) 38%

Roman Catholic 28%

Indigenous beliefs 26%

Muslim 6%

Other 2%

Languages (8)

English (official), Swahili (official), numerous indigenous languages.

EDUCATION

Public Education Expenditures (9)

Public expenditure on education (% of GNP)

1980 . . . . .6.8

1996 . . . . .6.6

Expenditure per student

Primary % of GNP per capita

1980 . . . . .15.7

1996 . . . . .17.0[1]

Secondary % of GNP per capita

1980 . . . .

1996 . . . .

Tertiary % of GNP per capita

1980 . . . . .928.7

1996 . . . .

Expenditure on teaching materials

Primary % of total for level (1996) . . . .

Secondary % of total for level (1996) . . . .

Primary pupil-teacher ratio per teacher (1996) . . . . .30[1]

Duration of primary education years (1995) 8

Educational Attainment (10)

Age group (1979)[25] . . . . .25+

Total population 4,818,310

Highest level attained (%)

No schooling 58.6

First level

Not completed 32.2

Completed . . . . .NA

Entered second level

S-1 . . . . .7.9

S-2 . . . . .1.3

Postsecondary . . . . .NA

Literacy Rates (11A)

In thousands and percent[1]	1990	1995	2000	2010
Illiterate population (15+ yrs.)	3,357	3,237	2,934	2,397
Literacy rate - total adult pop. (%)	72.0	78.1	83.1	90.1
Literacy rate - males (%)	82.2	86.3	89.5	93.7
Literacy rate - females (%)	62.0	70.0	76.7	86.6

GOVERNMENT & LAW

Political Parties (12)

National Assembly	No. of seats
Kenya African National Union (KANU) 107	
Forum for the Restoration of Democracy-Asili (FORD-Asili) 1	
Forum for the Restoration of Democracy-Kenya (FORD-Kenya) 17	
Forum for the Restoration of Democracy-People (FORD-People) 3	
Democratic Party of Kenya (DP) 39	
National Development Party (NDP) 21	
Social Democratic Party (SDP) 15	
SAFINA 5	
Smaller parties 2	

Government Budget (13A)

Year: 1996

Total Expenditures: 152,832 Millions of Shillings

Expenditures as a percentage of the total by function:

General public services and public order 18.61

Defense 5.91

Education 20.24

Health 5.96

Social Security and Welfare 03

Housing and community amenities 3.43

Recreational, cultural, and religious affairs 1.97

Fuel and energy . . . .-

Agriculture, forestry, fishing, and hunting 5.00

Mining, manufacturing, and construction 1.06

Transportation and communication 7.60

Other economic affairs and services 2.20

LABOR FORCE

Labor Force (16)

Total (million) 8.78

Agriculture 75%-80%

Non-agriculture 20%-25%

Data for 1993 est.

Unemployment Rate (17)

35% urban (1994 est.)

PRODUCTION SECTOR

Electric Energy (18)

Capacity .808,000 kW (1995)

Production . . . . .3.59 billion kWh (1995)

Consumption per capita . . . . .134 kWh (1995)

Transportation (19)

Highways:

total: 63,800 km

paved: 8,868 km

unpaved: 54,932 km (1996 est.)

Waterways: part of Lake Victoria system is within boundaries of Kenya

Pipelines: petroleum products 483 km

Merchant marine:

total: 2 ships (1,000 GRT or over) totaling 4,883 GRT/6,255 DWT ships by type: oil tanker 1, roll on/roll off 1 (1997 est.)

Airports: 240 (1997 est.)

Airports—with paved runways:

total: 29

over 3,047 m: 3

2,438 to 3,047 m: 1

1,524 to 2,437 m: 2

914 to 1,523 m: 22

under 914 m: 1 (1997 est.)

Airports—with unpaved runways:

total: 211

2,438 to 3,047 m: 1

1,524 to 2,437 m: 13

914 to 1,523 m: 114

under 914 m: 83 (1997 est.)

Top Agricultural Products (20)

Coffee, tea, corn, wheat, sugarcane, fruit, vegetables; dairy products, beef, pork, poultry, eggs.

GOVERNMENT & LAW

Military Affairs (14B)

	1990	1991	1992	1993	1994	1995
Military expenditures						
Current dollars (mil.)	173	176	195	171	147	173[e]
1995 constant dollars (mil.)	198	195	209	179	151	173[e]
Armed forces (000)	20	20	24	24	22	22
Gross national product (GNP)						
Current dollars (mil.)	5,942	6,230	6,406	6,403	6,930	7,557
1995 constant dollars (mil.)	6,828	6,884	6,891	6,713	7,104	7,557
Central government expenditures (CGE)						
1995 constant dollars (mil.)	2,024	2,158	1,818	2,000	2,249	2,797[e]
People (mil.)	23.9	24.8	25.8	26.6	27.1	27.6
Military expenditure as % of GNP	2.9	2.8	3.0	2.7	2.1	2.3
Military expenditure as % of CGE	9.8	9.0	11.5	8.9	6.7	6.2
Military expenditure per capita (1995 $)	9.0	8	8	7	6	6
Armed forces per 1,000 people (soldiers)	.8	.8	.9	.9	.8	.8
GNP per capita (1995 $)	286	277	267	252	262	274
Arms imports[6]						
Current dollars (mil.)	70	10	20	0	10	10
1995 constant dollars (mil.)	80	11	22	0	10	10
Arms exports[6]						
Current dollars (mil.)	0	0	0	0	0	0
1995 constant dollars (mil.)	0	0	0	0	0	0
Total imports[7]						
Current dollars (mil.)	2,124	1,798	1,713	1,711	2,156	2,948
1995 constant dollars (mil.)	2,441	1,987	1,843	1,794	2,210	2,948
Total exports[7]						
Current dollars (mil.)	1,031	1,107	1,339	1,336	1,609	1,883
1995 constant dollars (mil.)	1,185	1,223	1,440	1,401	1,649	1,883
Arms as percent of total imports[8]	3.3	.6	1.2	.0	.5	.3
Arms as percent of total imports[8]	0	0	0	0	0	0

MANUFACTURING SECTOR

GDP & Manufacturing Summary (21)

Detailed value added figures are listed by both International Standard Industry Code (ISIC) and product title.

	1980	1985	1990	1994
GDP ($-1990 mil.)[1]	5,605	6,485	8,532	8,974
Per capita ($-1990)[1]	337	326	361	328
Manufacturing share (%) (current prices)[1]	12.9	11.4	11.4	10.9
Manufacturing				
Value added ($-1990 mil.)[1]	540	652	862	976
Industrial production index	100	111	141	151
Value added ($ mil.)	744	670	921	715
Gross output ($ mil.)	3,656	4,301	7,975	8,260
Employment (000)	143	163	188	196
Profitability (% of gross output)				
Intermediate input (%)	80	84	88	91
Wages and salaries inc. supplements (%)	9	7	4	3
Gross operating surplus	11	9	8	6
Productivity ($)				
Gross output per worker	25,544	26,428	42,491	42,133
Value added per worker	5,197	4,115	4,907	3,592
Average wage (inc. supplements)	2,269	1,795	1,605	1,113
Value added ($ mil.)				
311/2 Food products	177	185	252	228
313 Beverages	65	72	90	68
314 Tobacco products	10	13	12	11
321 Textiles	59	40	55	40
322 Wearing apparel	17	19	16	12
323 Leather and fur products	6	3	4	3
324 Footwear	9	6	13	7
331 Wood and wood products	20	17	17	12
332 Furniture and fixtures	9	8	11	6
341 Paper and paper products	34	23	42	31
342 Printing and publishing	22	19	27	18
351 Industrial chemicals	25	16	17	14
352 Other chemical products	39	50	67	46
353 Petroleum refineries	15	6	7	6
354 Miscellaneous petroleum and coal products	—	—	—	—
355 Rubber products	25	27	33	21
356 Plastic products	14	13	24	23
361 Pottery, china and earthenware	1	—	1	1
362 Glass and glass products	3	4	5	3
369 Other non-metal mineral products	20	17	42	26
371 Iron and steel	12	6	12	11
372 Non-ferrous metals	—	—	—	—
381 Metal products	44	31	64	45
382 Non-electrical machinery	6	4	5	4
383 Electrical machinery	40	36	44	40
384 Transport equipment	64	43	39	26
385 Professional and scientific equipment	1	1	2	1
390 Other manufacturing industries	6	8	18	13

FINANCE, ECONOMICS, & TRADE

Economic Indicators (22)

National product: GDP—purchasing power parity—$45.3 billion (1997 est.)

National product real growth rate: 2.9% (1997 est.)

National product per capita: $1,600 (1997 est.)

Inflation rate—consumer price index: 8.8% (1996)

Exchange Rates (24)

Exchange rates:

Kenyan shillings (KSh) per US$1

January 1998	.61.164
1997	.58.732
1996	.57.115
1995	.51.430
1994	.56.051
1993	.58.001

Top Import Origins (25)

$2.9 billion (f.o.b., 1996)

Origins	%
United Kingdom	.21.3
UAE	.18
Japan	.14
Germany	.NA
United States	.NA

NA stands for not available.

Top Export Destinations (26)

$2.1 billion (f.o.b., 1996).

Destinations	%
Uganda	.22.8
United Kingdom	.20.1
Tanzania	.19.1
Germany	.14.0
Netherlands	.7.6
United States	.6.1

Economic Aid (27)

NA. NA stands for not available.

Import Export Commodities (28)

Import Commodities	Export Commodities
Machinery and transportation equipment 31%	Tea 18%
	Coffee 15%
Consumer goods 13%	Petroleum products
Petroleum products 12%	

Balance of Payments (23)

	1992	1993	1994	1995	1996
Exports of goods (f.o.b.)	1,108	1,263	1,537	1,914	2,071
Imports of goods (f.o.b.)	−1,609	−1,510	−1,775	−2,652	−2,581
Trade balance	−500	−247	−238	−738	−510
Services - debits	−923	−962	−1,072	−1,222	−1,102
Services - credits	1,044	1,067	1,138	1,060	977
Private transfers (net)	214	94	123	91	128
Government transfers (net)	−15	119	148	409	433
Overall balance	−180	71	98	−400	−74

KIRIBATI

Republic of Kiribati

CAPITAL: Tarawa.

FLAG: Above a blue and white heraldic representation of Pacific waters, a golden sun rises against a red background, with a golden frigate bird at the top.

ANTHEM: *Troika kain Kiribati (Stand Kiribati).*

MONETARY UNIT: The Australian dollar is the national currency. A $1 = US $0.79177 (or US $1 = A $1.263).

WEIGHTS AND MEASURES: Kiribati is in transition from imperial to metric standards.

HOLIDAYS: New Year's Day, 1 January; Independence Day, 12 July; Youth Day, 4 August; Christmas Day, 25 December; Boxing Day, 26 December. Movable holidays include Good Friday, Easter Monday, Queen's Birthday (June), Bank Holiday (August), and Prince of Wales's Birthday (November).

TIME: Midnight = noon GMT.

LOCATION AND SIZE: Kiribati (pronounced ''Kiribass'') consists of 33 islands in the central Pacific, situated around the point where the International Date Line intersects the equator. Scattered over more than 5 million square kilometers (2 million square miles) of ocean, Kiribati's total land area is 717 square kilometers (277 square miles), and its total coastline is 1,143 kilometers (710 miles).

Kiribati's capital city, Tarawa, is located on the small island of Tarawa (between Abaiang and Maiana).

CLIMATE: Rainfall varies from an average of 102 centimeters (40 inches) near the equator to 305 centimeters (120 inches) in the extreme north and south. Daily temperatures range from 25°C (77°F) to 32°C (90°F), with an annual mean temperature of 27°C (81°F).

INTRODUCTORY SURVEY

RECENT HISTORY

During World War II (1939–45), Ocean Island, Ellice Island (now Tuvalu), and Kiritimati (Christmas Island) were occupied by Japanese forces. In 1943, the Japanese were driven out by United States forces, with heavy casualties on both sides. Ocean Island was liberated by the Australians in 1945.

In a 1974 referendum, the Ellice Islands voted for separation, becoming the independent nation of Tuvalu. The Gilbert Islands became the independent Republic of Kiribati on 12 July 1979. Ieremia Tabai, chief minister at the time of independence, became president of the new republic in 1979 and was reelected in May 1982 and February 1983.

The Banabans, who had been resettled in 1946 on Rabi (Fiji) so that strip mining could be pursued on their native island, sued for damages in 1975. After a lengthy legal battle, a settlement was reached in 1981, providing for creation of a trust fund of nearly US $10.5 million for Banaban development.

Kiribati began resettling more than 4,700 people on outlying atolls in August 1988 to relieve overcrowded conditions on the Tarawa atolls. In September 1988, Kiribati ratified the South Pacific Regional Fisheries Treaty, which permits U.S. tuna ships to operate within its 200-mile exclusive zone. In early 1992, the House of Assembly told the government to seek payment from the United

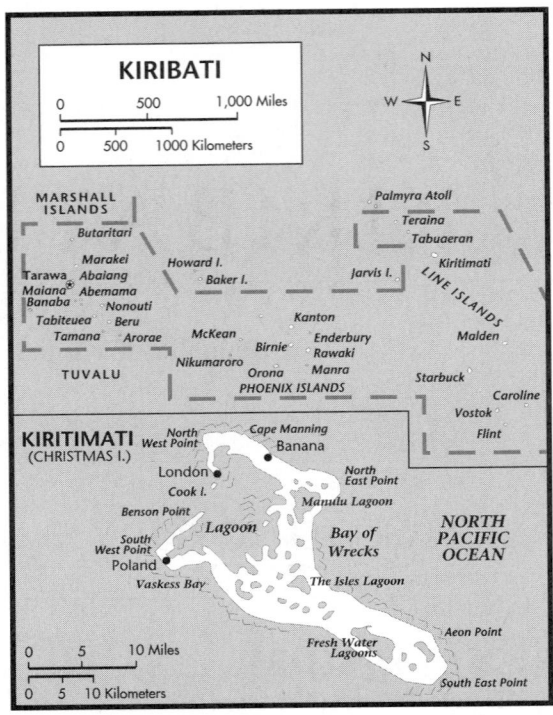

States for damage done to the country during World War II.

GOVERNMENT

Kiribati is a democratic republic within the Commonwealth of Nations. It has a single-chamber legislature, the House of Assembly (Maneaba ni Maungatabu). The *beretitenti* (president), who is both head of state and head of government, is elected directly by popular vote from among members of the Assembly.

Judiciary

The 1979 constitution provides for a High Court to act as the supreme court and court of appeal. Island courts were established in 1965 to deal with civil and criminal offenses. Native land courts handle property claims.

Political Parties

In 1985, opponents of a Soviet fishing agreement founded the Christian Democratic party. Since 1991, the Liberal Party, the Maneaba Party, the New Movement Party, and the Health Peace and Honour Party have been formed.

DEFENSE

There have been no armed forces in Kiribati since legislation providing for the establishment of a defense force of 170 men was repealed in 1978.

ECONOMIC AFFAIRS

The nation relies on fishing, subsistence agriculture, and exports of copra (dried coconut meat) and is heavily dependent on aid from the United Kingdom, New Zealand, Japan, and investment from Australia.

Public Finance

Local revenues are derived mainly from import duties, philately, fishing fees, and investment income from the phosphate fund. The country has been running a capital account deficit since independence. Overall, budgetary deficits have appeared in recent years, growing substantially in the mid-1990s.

The U.S. CIA estimates that, in 1995, government revenues totaled approximately U.S. $32.5 million and expenditures U.S. $54.3 million. External debt totaled U.S. $2 million.

Income

In 1998, Kiribati's gross national product (GNP) was US $101 million, or about US $1,180 per person. For the period 1985–95, the average inflation rate was 3.8%, resulting in a decline in per person GNP of about 0.3%.

Industry

Several small industries have been established, including a soft-drink plant, a biscuit factory, boat-building shops, construction companies, furniture plants, repair garages, and bakeries. The government also promotes local handicrafts.

Banking and Finance

The Bank of Kiribati in Tarawa is jointly owned by the Westpac Banking Corp. (Australia) and the government of Kiribati (49%). In 1992, it had total assets of $34.7 million. The Kiribati Development Bank, opened in 1987, was to take over the assets of the National Loans Board when it became fully operational.

Economic Development

The economic development plan for 1987–91 was economic self-reliance through gradual and sustainable development, with particular emphasis on the subsistence lifestyle of the outer islands. The UN Development Program is implementing an economic development plan for the northern Line Islands focusing on infrastructure, agriculture, and tourism. For the years 1990–92, the average yearly receipt of development aid from all sources was U.S. $99.7 million.

SOCIAL WELFARE

The majority of the population still lives a traditional village life with an extended family system. This makes state welfare largely unnecessary. Problems exist mainly in the south Tarawa Island area, where cities have grown rapidly. Some juvenile delinquency has developed there.

Healthcare

Tuberculosis remains the most serious public health problem. Other widespread diseases are leprosy, filariasis, and dysentery. Average life expectancy is about 60 years.

All health services are free. Each inhabited island has a health clinic, and there is a medical radio network linking all the islands.

Housing

Most Kiribatians live in small villages of 10 to 150 houses. They construct their own dwellings from local materials. The use of more permanent building materials, such as concrete with corrugated aluminum roofing, is becoming common in urban areas.

EDUCATION

In 1993, Kiribati had 95 primary schools with 16,316 students enrolled. At the secondary level, there were 179 teachers and 3,152 students. Kiribati has a teacher-training college, a technical institute, and a marine training school. Higher education courses are available at the Kiribati Extension Centre of the University of the South Pacific (Fiji) in Tarawa.

1999 KEY EVENTS TIMELINE

March

- Kiribati appeals for international help as the tiny island nation faces a critical situation with an ongoing drought. President Teburoro Tito says the country needs desalination plants and water trucks to help resolve the crisis.

April

- Micronesian countries support Kiribati's claim that it will be the first nation in the world to see the dawn of the new millennium.
- Kiribati has spent more than $100,000 to promote Christmas Island and Millennium Island (formerly Caroline Island) as millennium tourist destinations.

May

- Government officials say the islands are still suffering from drought.
- Kiribati residents have problems controlling rodent problem.

June

- Two islands in the Tarawa Lagoon may be among the first casualties of global warming and rising sea levels; both islands are submerged, according to some press reports.

July

- Kiribati celebrates its 20th anniversary of independence from Britain on July 12.
- The Government of India offers Kiribati a desalination plant to deal with the drought; Australia, China, New Zealand, Nauru, South Korea and the United States offer help.
- A member of the Kiribati Parliament says one of the country's uninhabited islands should become a detention center for people who have been tested positive for HIV and AIDS.

September

- Kiribati, along with Tonga and Nauru, becomes a member of the United Nations.

November

- Leaders of various Pacific island nations travel to Europe to ask developed nations to reduce greenhouse gases. Kiribati representative says some villages were being forced to move inland because of worsening coastal erosion.

December

- A December 31 beach ceremony including dancing, singing, and fireworks marks the first nation in the world where midnight launched a new millennium. The uninhabited island, called Millennium Island, is in a remote location. Dancers traveled by boat for three weeks from the capital, Tarawa, to reach the island.

ANALYSIS OF EVENTS: 1999

BUSINESS AND THE ECONOMY

The Asian Development Bank praised Kiribati for its economic management, saying Kiribati was one of only three Pacific Island nations that had economic growth in 1998. Kiribati's economy grew by 1.5 percent during that year, and expected a similar growth rate in 1999. Part of the healthy economic picture is the country's trust fund, established before independence, when phosphate mining was bringing in money. Based on its record, the Asian Development Bank approved a $10.4 million loan so Kiribati can overhaul and upgrade a sewage and water facility on South Tarawa.

GOVERNMENT AND POLITICS

In 1999, with the country suffering severe drought, Kiribati sought closer ties to the international community, first by appealing for help, and later by joining the United Nations. Kiribati became a powerful symbol for Pacific Island nations attempting to convince developed countries to curtail greenhouse gases. Kiribati, which reportedly lost two small islands to rising waters during 1999, also wanted wealthier nations to share their new technologies to help the islands cope with climactic changes. Kiribati officials said some villages were being forced to move inland because of worsening coastal erosion.

In April, Kiribati President Teburoro Tito said his country would pursue the annexation of three islands currently under U.S. jurisdiction. The islands of Howland, Baker, and Jarvis have been U.S. possessions since 1856, when they were annexed under the Guano Mining Act. The act said a country could take possession of an uninhabited island by mining its guano (natural phosphate fertilizers from bird droppings). But Kiribati is not interested in the guano. It may want to have access to potential natural resources on the sea bottom. Kiribati officials were expected to bring up the issue sometime in 2000, when island nations in the Pacific meet to discuss regional issues.

Several nations assisted Kiribati during its drought, but island officials said more needed to be done by developed nations. Kiribati and neighboring island nations began to pressure the developed world during 1999. Kiribati representatives said they needed more technology to ensure a stable water supply, and more sophisticated technologies, such as coral re-growth, to help the islands protect themselves from rising sea waters.

In November, Kiribati joined seven other Pacific Island nations to criticize worldwide lack of action to reduce greenhouse gas emissions. The eight nations held a press conference in Bonn, Germany, and described damages already being felt in their nations.

In September, Kiribati and two other Pacific Island nations joined the United Nations, and Kiribati President Teburoro Tito said admission would help his nation. As a new member, the president said, Kiribati would actively participate to raise concerns about global warming and the threats on some of the Pacific atolls.

CULTURE AND SOCIETY

A World Health Organization and United Nations Children's Fund survey found that Kiribati men and women were among the heaviest smokers in the Asia-Pacific region. The survey said 80 percent of men, and 70 percent of women age 15 and up were active smokers. Kiribati officials said smoking was prevalent among I-Kiribati, the indigenous population, because tobacco was widely accepted in traditional exchange of gifts. During 1999, Kiribati health officials said more islanders between 20 and 40 years were becoming more vulnerable to stroke because of lifestyle changes. I-Kiribati, health officials said, had become more dependent on imported foods, which were causing high blood pressure and diabetes, diseases that can lead to stroke. Officials did not release statistics, but said I-Kiribati should return to traditional lifestyles, and diet, which include outdoor activities and fishing.

Underscoring the concerns on HIV and AIDS in the Pacific, a Kiribati member of Parliament said the government should set aside one of the country's uninhabited islands as a detention center for all people who have tested positive for the virus. According to press reports, Baitong Taburimai, who represents Abemama Island, wanted all I-Kiribati to take a blood test. A detention center would act as a warning, the representative said. The press report said 28 people in Kiribati have the HIV virus, and four have AIDS, according to international organizations.

DIRECTORY

CENTRAL GOVERNMENT

Head of State

President
Teburoro Tito, Office of the President
PHONE: +686 21183; 21342
FAX: +686 21466

Ministers

Minister of Commerce, Industry and Tourism
Teaiwa Tenieu, Ministry of Commerce, Industry
and Tourism
PHONE: +686 21342
FAX: +686 21466

Minister of Education, Training and Technology
Teambo Keariki, Ministry of Education, Training
and Technology
PHONE: +686 21342
FAX: +686 21466

Minister of Environment and Social Development
Kataotiko Tekee, Ministry of Environment and
Social Development
PHONE: +686 21342
FAX: +686 21466

Minister of Finance and Economic Planning
Beniamina Tinga, Ministry of Finance and
Economic Planning
PHONE: +686 21343
FAX: +686 21466

Minister of Foreign Affairs
Teburoro Tito, Ministry of Foreign Affairs
PHONE: +686 21183; 21342
FAX: +686 21466

Minister of Health and Family Planning
Baraniko Mooa, Ministry of Health and Family
Planning
PHONE: +686 21342
FAX: +686 21466

Minister of Home Affairs and Rural Development
Tewareka Tentoa, Ministry of Home Affairs and
Rural Development
PHONE: +686 21342
FAX: +686 21466

Minister of Information, Communication and Transport
Willie Tokataake, Ministry of Information,
Communication and Transport
PHONE: +686 21342
FAX: +686 21466

Minister of Labor Employment and Cooperative
Teiraoi Tetabea, Ministry of Labor Employment
and Cooperative
PHONE: +686 21342
FAX: +686 21466

Minister of Line and Phoenix Development
Tim Taekiti, Ministry of Line and Phoenix
Development
PHONE: +686 21342
FAX: +686 21466

Minister of Natural Resources and Development
Emile Schutz, Ministry of Natural Resources and
Development
PHONE: +686 21342
FAX: +686 21466

Minister of Works and Energy
Manraoi Kaiea, Ministry of Works and Energy
PHONE: +686 21342
FAX: +686 21466

POLITICAL ORGANIZATIONS

Liberal Party
NAME: Tewareka Tenota

Maneaban Te Mauri Party
NAME: Teburoro Tito

National Progressive Party
NAME: Teatao Teannaki

New Movement Party

DIPLOMATIC REPRESENTATION

Embassies in Kiribati

Australia
PO Box 77, Bairiki, Tarawa, Kiribati
PHONE: +686 21184
FAX: +686 21440

New Zealand
P.O. Box 53, Tarawa, Kiribati
PHONE: +686 21400

FAX: +686 21402

JUDICIAL SYSTEM
High Court
Court of Appeal

FURTHER READING
Articles

"Kiribati Appeals for International Drought Aid," Pacific Islands Development Program/East-West Center, Center for Pacific Islands Studies/University of Hawai'i at Manoa. March 7, 1999.

"Kiribati Celebrates a Birthday," *Pacific Magazine* (September/October 1999): 39.

"Kiribati MP Wants Detention Center for AIDS Patients," Pacific Islands Development Program/East-West Center, Center for Pacific Islands Studies/University of Hawai'i at Manoa. July 1, 1999.

"Pacific Island Countries Criticize Inaction Over Climate Change," Pacific Islands Development Program/East-West Center, Center for Pacific Islands Studies/University of Hawai'i at Manoa. November 3, 1999.

"UN Admits Three New Members, New General Assembly Session Opens," The Associated Press. September 15, 1999.

"U.S. Not Likely to Part with Central Pacific Islands," Pacific Magazine (September/October 1999): 36.

KIRIBATI: STATISTICAL DATA

For sources and notes see "Sources of Statistics" in the front of each volume.

GEOGRAPHY

Geography (1)

Area:

Total: 717 sq km.

Land: 717 sq km.

Water: 0 sq km.

Note: includes three island groups—Gilbert Islands, Line Islands, Phoenix Islands.

Area—comparative: four times the size of Washington, DC.

Land boundaries: 0 km.

Coastline: 1,143 km.

Climate: tropical; marine, hot and humid, moderated by trade winds.

Terrain: mostly low-lying coral atolls surrounded by extensive reefs.

Natural resources: phosphate (production discontinued in 1979).

Land use:

Arable land: NA%

Permanent crops: 51%

Permanent pastures: NA%

Forests and woodland: 3%

Other: 46% (1993 est.).

HUMAN FACTORS

Demographics (2B)

Population (July 1998 est.) 83,976

Age structure:

  0-14 years . . . . .NA

  15-64 years . . . . .NA

65 years and over . . . . .NA

Population growth rate (1998 est.) 1.82%

Birth rate, 1998 est. (births/1,000 population) 26.46

Death rate, 1998 est. (deaths/1,000 population) . . .7.62

Net migration rate, 1998 est. (migrant(s)/1,000 population) . . . .-0.66

Infant mortality rate, 1998 est. (deaths/1,000 live births) 49.69

Life expectancy at birth (years):

  Total population 62.61

  Male 60.79

  Female (1998 est.) 64.68

Total fertility rate, 1998 est. (children born/woman) .3.13

Infants and Malnutrition (5)

Under-5 mortality rate (1997) 75

% of infants with low birthweight (1990-97) 3

Births attended by skilled health staff % of total[a] . . .NA

% fully immunized (1995-97)

  TB 100

  DPT 91

  Polio 93

  Measles 82

Prevalence of child malnutrition under age 5 (1992-97)[b] . . . . .NA

Ethnic Division (6)

Micronesian.

Religions (7)

Roman Catholic 53%

Protestant (Congregational) 41%

Seventh-Day Adventist, ...

  Baha'i, Church of God, Mormon . . . . .6% (1985 est.)

Languages (8)

English (official), Gilbertese.

EDUCATION

Literacy Rates (11B)

Adult literacy rate

1980

  Male . . . .-

  Female . . . .-

1995

  Male . . . .-

  Female 92x

GOVERNMENT & LAW

Political Parties (12)

House of Assembly	No. of seats
Maneaban Te Mauri Party	13
National Progressive Party	7
Independents	19

Government Budget (13B)

Revenues . . . .$33.3 million

Expenditures . . . .$47.7 million

  Capital expenditures . . . . .NA million

Data for 1996 est. NA stands for not available.

Military Affairs (14A)

Total expenditures . . . .$NA

Expenditures as % of GDP . . . . .NA%

NA stands for not available.

LABOR FORCE

Labor Force (16)

Total 7,870 economically active, not including subsistence farmers. Data for 1985 est.

Unemployment Rate (17)

2%; underemployment 70% (1992 est.)

PRODUCTION SECTOR

Electric Energy (18)

Capacity . . . . .2,000 kW (1995)

Production . . . . .7 million kWh (1995)

Consumption per capita . . . . .88 kWh (1995)

Transportation (19)

Highways:

total: 670 km (1996 est.)

paved: NA km

unpaved: NA km

Waterways: small network of canals, totaling 5 km, in Line Islands.

Merchant marine:

total: 2 ships (1,000 GRT or over) totaling 3,248 GRT/4,496 DWT ships by type: oil tanker 1, passenger-cargo 1 (1997 est.)

Airports: 21 (1997 est.)

Airports—with paved runways:

total: 4

1,524 to 2,437 m: 4 (1997 est.)

Airports—with unpaved runways:

total: 17

914 to 1,523 m: 12

under 914 m: 5 (1997 est.)

Top Agricultural Products (20)

Copra, taro, breadfruit, sweet potatoes, vegetables; fish.

FINANCE, ECONOMICS, & TRADE

Economic Indicators (22)

National product: GDP—purchasing power parity—$62 million (1996 est.)

National product real growth rate: 1.9% (1996 est.)

National product per capita: $800 (1996 est.)

Inflation rate—consumer price index: -0.6% (1996 est.)

Exchange Rates (24)

Exchange rates:

Australian dollars ($A) per US$1

January 1998	1.5281
1997	1.3439
1996	1.2773
1995	1.3486
1994	1.3667
1993	1.4704

Top Import Origins (25)

$37.4 million (c.i.f., 1996 est.) Data are for 1996.

Origins	%
Australia	.46
Fiji	.NA
Japan	.NA
NZ	.NA
United States	.NA

NA stands for not available.

Top Export Destinations (26)

$6.7 million (f.o.b., 1996 est.) Data are for 1996.

Destinations	%
United States	.NA
Australia	.NA
NZ	.NA

NA stands for not available.

Economic Aid (27)

Recipient: ODA, $4.725 million from Australia (FY96/97 est.); $2.175 million from NZ (FY95/96).

Import Export Commodities (28)

Import Commodities	Export Commodities
Foodstuffs	Copra 62%
Machinery and equipment	Seaweed
Miscellaneous manufactured goods	Fish
Fuel	

Balance of Payments (23)

	1990	1991	1992	1993	1994
Exports of goods (f.o.b.)	3	4	6	4	6
Imports of goods (f.o.b.)	−28	−26	−37	−29	−27
Trade balance	−24	−23	−32	−25	−21
Services - debits	−21	−19	−20	−21	−19
Services - credits	27	33	33	31	35
Private transfers (net)	8	11	9	9	5
Government transfers (net)	2	2	1	2	2
Overall balance	−9	4	−9	−4	1

NORTH KOREA (DPRK)

CAPITAL: P'yŏngyang.

FLAG: A wide horizontal red stripe is bordered on top and bottom by narrow blue stripes, separated from the red by thin white stripes. The left half of the red stripe contains a red five-pointed star on a circular white field.

ANTHEM: *The Song of General Kim Il-sung.*

MONETARY UNIT: The won (w) of 100 ch'on (or jeon) is the national currency. There are coins of 1, 5, 10, and 50 ch'on, and 1 won, and notes of 1, 5, 10, 50, and 100 won. w1 = $0.4561 (or $1 = w2.15).

WEIGHTS AND MEASURES: The metric system and native Korean units of measurement are used.

HOLIDAYS: New Year's Day, 1 January; Kim Jong Il's Birthday, 16 February; International Women's Day, 8 March; Kim Il-sung's Birthday, 15 April; May Day, 1 May; Liberation Day, 15 August; National Foundation Day, 9 September; Founding of the Korean Workers' Party, 10 October; Anniversary of the Constitution, 27 December.

TIME: 9 PM = noon GMT.

LOCATION AND SIZE: The Democratic People's Republic of Korea (DPRK), often called North Korea, occupies the northern 55% of the Korean Peninsula in East Asia. It has an area of 120,540 square kilometers (46,541 square miles), slightly smaller than the state of Mississippi. It has a total boundary length of 2,309 kilometers (1,435 miles).

The DPRK's capital city, P'yŏngyang, is located in the southwestern part of the country.

CLIMATE: The climate ranges widely on the small peninsula. The average January temperature is −17°C (1°F) on the north-central border and −8°C (18°F) at P'yŏngyang. In the hottest part of the summer, temperatures range only from 24°C (75°F) in P'yŏngyang to 21°C (70°F) along the northeast coast. Precipitation is around 50 centimeters (20 inches) along the upper reaches of the Tumen, but more than half of the peninsula receives 75–100 centimeters (30–40 inches) per year.

Democratic People's Republic of Korea
Choson Minjujuui Inmin Konghwa-guk

INTRODUCTORY SURVEY

RECENT HISTORY

After Japan surrendered on 14 August 1945, the 38th parallel was chosen as a line of demarcation between Soviet occupation forces in the North and American occupation forces in the South. The Americans set up a military government allied with conservative Korean political forces. The Soviets allied their government with leftist and communist Korean forces led by Kim Il-sung, who had been an anti-Japanese guerrilla leader in Manchuria. The two governments were unable to agree on terms for the reunification of the country. They proclaimed two separate republics in 1948: the Republic of Korea (ROK) in the South and the Democratic People's Republic of Korea (DPRK) in the North.

On 25 June 1950, the People's Army of the DPRK invaded the ROK to unify the country under communist control. The DPRK forces advanced rapidly, and the destruction of the ROK seemed near. However, U.S. and UN multinational forces came to the aid of the South Koreans. A military campaign led by U.S. General Douglas MacArthur brought about the total defeat of the DPRK's forces.

MacArthur then made a fateful decision to attack the North. China entered the fighting, forcing MacArthur into a costly retreat. The battle line stabilized near the 38th parallel, where it remained for two years. On 27 July 1953, a peace agreement finally was signed by all parties. The war killed an estimated 415,000 South Koreans, 23,300 Americans, 3,100 UN allies, and, according to official

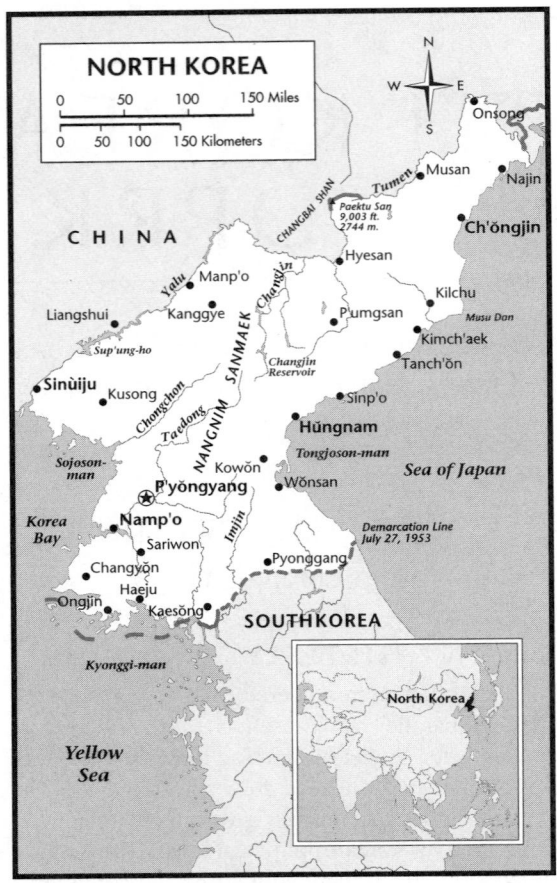

NORTH KOREA

numbers, 50,000 North Koreans and Chinese (although this number is thought to be as high as 2 million).

The DPRK, with the aid of China and the former Soviet Union, began to restore its war-damaged economy. By the end of the 1950s, Kim Il-sung had emerged as the unchallenged leader of the DPRK. Throughout the 1970s and 1980s, the DPRK extended its diplomatic relations to over 100 countries. In the 1980s, Korea's basic divisions remained unresolved, but there was some improvement in relations between the North and South. The DPRK provided aid to the ROK after a flood in 1984. Talks under Red Cross sponsorship led to a brief reunion of separated families in 1985. The DPRK did not participate, however, in the 1988 summer Olympic Games, officially hosted by the ROK, since it was not named as co-host.

The collapse of the Soviet Union cut off an important source of economic and political support for the DPRK. In 1990, China and the ROK began to encourage mutual trade and in 1992 established

formal diplomatic relations. Beginning in 1993, China demanded that all its exports to the DPRK be paid for with cash instead of through barter. The DPRK found itself increasingly isolated and in severe economic difficulty.

In the first half of the 1990s, the DPRK's foreign relations revolved around the issue of nuclear capabilities. It was suspected that the DPRK was developing the technology to build nuclear weapons. Tensions were defused with an agreement for high-level talks between the United States and the DPRK. These talks were to be followed by a summit in P'yŏngyang between the presidents of the two Koreas, the first such summit since Korea was divided in 1945.

On 8 July 1994, just as the United States-DPRK talks were beginning, President Kim Il-sung died. The talks were held off until after Kim's funeral on 17 July. Kim Jong-il replaced his father as president following an election by the Supreme People's Assembly on 11 July 1994.

Widespread flooding, due in part to massive deforestation, has led to a national famine. Relief efforts have not been able to provide enough food to feed the starving population. The government's own strict authoritarian policies have made it difficult for other nations to donate food aid. By late 1997, an estimated 2 million North Koreans were starving.

GOVERNMENT

In theory, the highest state power is the Supreme People's Assembly (SPA), with 687 members in 1993. In practice, however, governmental control rests with the leadership of the Korean Workers' (Communist) Party. The SPA elects the president of the DPRK, the Central People's Committee, and the Administrative Council (cabinet). The state ideology is self-reliance (*Chuch'e* or *Juch'e*), the Korean version of Marxism-Leninism. Suffrage extends to all men and women 17 years of age or older. Elections are on a single slate of communist-approved candidates, on a yes or no basis.

Judiciary

The DPRK's judicial system consists of the Central Court, formerly called the Supreme Court; the courts of provinces, cities, and counties; and special courts (courts-martial and transport courts). Most cases are first tried by people's courts at the city or county level. Provincial courts try important cases and examine appeals of lower court judgments. Prosecution of alleged crimes against the state is conducted in secret outside the judicial system.

Political Parties

On 10 October 1945, the Communist Party merged with the New Democratic Party to form the Korean Workers' (Communist) Party, now the ruling party of the DPRK. The National Party Congress adopts the party program and approves the political line set by its Central People's Committee. Officially, there are two non-communist political parties: the Korean Social Democratic Party, and the Friends Party, founded in 1946 for adherents of the Ch'ondogyo faith.

DEFENSE

The DPRK has one of the world's largest and best-equipped armed forces. Out of an estimated 1 million personnel on active duty in 1995, 923,000 were in the army, 46,000 in the navy, and 85,000 in the air force. An additional 790,000 were in the reserves, and there was a civilian militia of 3–5 million. Defense expenditures in 1995 totaled about $5.2 billion, or 20% of gross domestic product (GDP).

ECONOMIC AFFAIRS

The Korean War devastated much of the DPRK's economy, but postwar reconstruction helped repair it rapidly. The communist regime has used its rich mineral resources to promote industry, especially heavy industry. Available information suggests that since the early 1990s, the country has suffered serious economic problems.

Public Finance

The annual state budget, the leading element of the command economy, is approved at regular sessions of the SPA. In April 1995, the government failed to announce its 1995–96 budget at the annual meeting of the Supreme People's Assembly, which exacerbated the economic stagnation. Foreign aid, important after the Korean War, has not appeared as budgetary income since 1961. External debt in 1995 was about $10.6 billion, 75% of it owed to OECD countries.

The U.S. CIA estimates that, in 1992, government revenues totaled approximately $19.3 billion and expenditures $19.3 billion.

Income

The U.S. government estimated the DPRK's gross domestic product (GDP) at $21.5 billion in 1995, or $920 per person. The rate of decline for the GDP was 5% in 1995.

Industry

The communist regime has emphasized the development of manufacturing. By the late 1980s, heavy industry accounted for 50% of total industrial production. About 90% of all industry is state-owned.

Banking and Finance

The Central Bank, established in 1946, is the sole recipient of national revenues and the repository for all precious metals. It supplies basic operating funds to various sectors of the economy and is subordinate to the Ministry of Finance. The Central Bank is also an administrative organ that executes the fiscal policies of the State Planning Commission.

There are no securities exchanges in the DPRK.

A consortium of sixty Western banks filed suit in 1996 in a U.S. district court against the DPRK's Foreign Trade Bank for a total of $1.4 billion in principal and accumulated interest. For the first time, the plaintiffs included Russia's Bank for Foreign Economic Affairs.

Economic Development

The economy is operated on a planned basis, with priority given to the development of industry, particularly heavy industry. Statements released by the Korean Workers' Party Central Committee in late 1993 confirmed the overall failure of the last seven-year plan and announced a two to three year period of economic adjustment during which investments in agriculture, light industry and foreign trade would be prioritized.

In the past, the DPRK's principal economic benefactors were the USSR and China. However, following a developing rapprochement between the former USSR and South Korea in 1990, with the latter now offering badly needed economic aid to the Soviet government, Soviet assistance to the North was curtailed in 1991.

SOCIAL WELFARE

All citizens are entitled to free medical care, disability benefits, and retirement allowances. There are also programs allowing paid vacations and paid maternity leaves, with the state making up the rest of the cost. Retirement pensions are roughly one-half of the annual average wage. Those who continue working after retirement age receive both their salary and their pension.

The constitution guarantees equal rights for women. The state provides nurseries and day-care centers, and large families are encouraged.

Human rights organizations are not allowed to operate. An estimated 150,000 political prisoners are held in rural camps.

The government classifies all citizens (most recently in 1996) into three groups: core, wavering, and hostile. The security rating is a mark of how much loyalty the government expects that the individual will give. The rating may be considered when the government allocates housing, employment, medical, and other benefits. Travel abroad is prohibited; travel within the country is also strictly controlled.

Healthcare

For the period 1990–94, there were 2.72 doctors and 13.5 hospital beds per 1,000 people.

Western medicine is used alongside traditional Eastern medicine (*tonguihak*). Cancer is now the leading cause of death, followed by heart disease and high blood pressure. Average life expectancy is 63 years.

Housing

The Korean War (1950–53) destroyed about one-third of the country's housing. A construction level of 150,000–200,000 units a year was projected for 1987–93. Available figures for 1980–88 show a total housing stock of 4.6 million with 4.5 people per dwelling. The government reported that heavy floods in 1995 caused 500,000 residents to become homeless.

EDUCATION

Both primary and secondary education are free and compulsory for eleven years, beginning at age 6. The adult literacy rate was estimated to be over 99% in 1991. In 1987, there were an estimated 4,813 primary institutions with 1.5 million students enrolled. An additional 2.5 million students were enrolled in secondary schools. Kim Il-sung University is the only university, with about 12,000 students and 2,000 teachers.

1999 KEY EVENTS TIMELINE

January

- North Korean actress Kim Hae-young defects to South Korea; about 200 North Koreans have defected to the south in the past three years due to severe food and fuel shortages.

- North Korea and the United States engage in nuclear weapons reduction talks in Geneva.

- North Korea accuses the U.S. and South Korea of preparing for nuclear war; if attacked, it will "turn both countries into a 'sea of fire'."

February

- Geneva talks continue between North Korea and the United States.

March

- U.S. and North Korea reach a pact that will allow U.S. inspection of underground nuclear development site; North Korea will receive food aid in return.

April

- The second session of the tenth Supreme People's Assembly (parliament) meets to sum up the 1998 and 1999 state budget and to adopt laws regarding the national economy.

May

- Inspection of suspected North Korean nuclear-weapons site reports no evidence of nuclear development.

- U.S. President Clinton sends his Secretary of Defense, William J. Perry, to North Korea with a proposal to gradually lift economic sanctions in return for North Korea's end to missile testing and selling of missile technology, and to freeze nuclear weapons development.

June

- After nine days of mounting tensions and confrontation between North and South Korean military vessels in the Yellow Sea, South Korean naval forces sink a North Korean torpedo boat in an exchange of fire lasting 30 minutes.

- North Korea and the United States meet to report on the May 1999 inspection of suspected nuclear development site.

- North Korea makes initial preparations to test its longer-range ballistic missiles, the Taepo Dong 2.

July

- Unofficial talks in Beijing between North Korea and South Korea, focusing on reuniting families divided by the Korean War 50 years ago, ended without progress.

- Mass rallies, seminars, and parades are held to mark the fifth anniversary of the death of North Korea's founder, Kim Il-sung.

- Despite warnings from the United States, Japan, and South Korea, North Korea proceeds with plans to test-fire missiles.

August

- The United Nations reports the North Korean famine easing as a result of international food aid, but years of prolonged hunger have cost millions of lives.

- Chung Seong-wook wins a gold medal in the woman's marathon of the seventh World Track and Field Championships in Seville, Spain; she is the first Korean woman to win in a world marathon.

- Japan threatens to suspend all cash remittances to North Korea if it proceeds with plans to test-fire missiles.

- The missile-testing crisis eases when North Korean officials offer to negotiate with the U.S., Japan, and South Korea.

September

- North Korea and the United States begin five days of talks in Berlin on suppressing the North Korean missile program.

- North Korea celebrates its 51st birthday by issuing a hostile statement to the United States, Japan, and South Korea, warning them to "stop their dangerous war moves" or face "corresponding counter-measures."

- North Korea agrees to end missile testing so long as talks with United States continue and they receive economic aid from the U.S. and Japan.

- President Clinton broadly relaxes economic embargo on North Korea.

- First inter-Korean basketball matches were held at the Pyongyang Indoor Stadium; arrangements were made between DPRK's Asia-Pacific Peace Committee and ROK's Hyundai Group.

October

- DPRK begins a satellite telecast, Korean Central TV, which can be viewed in all areas of Asia and most of European and African regions.

- The Hyundai Group is granted approval to begin construction on a $10 billion industrial complex near the border of North and South Korea.

December

- The Korean Peninsula Energy Organization, a consortium formed by the United States, Japan, South Korea, and the European Union, agrees to build two nuclear reactors at a cost of $3.2 billion. The countries act in response to North Korea's promise to freeze the country's nuclear program.

ANALYSIS OF EVENTS: 1999

BUSINESS AND THE ECONOMY

The economy of isolationist North Korea, based on self-reliant socialism, continues on a steady decline. Its industries and collective agricultural system are nearly nonexistent, and disastrous harvests and economic collapse since the mid-1990s has plagued the Hermit Kingdom, forcing it to depend solely on charity to feed its 22 million people. Without a functioning economy, it is difficult for North Korea to engage in international trade. North Korea's sales of missiles in the Middle East and to Pakistan have constituted its only lucrative export in recent years. Last year it brought in $1 billion in arms trade—the only source of revenue. However, South Korea's "sunshine" policy toward North Korea promotes business transactions with the North, and recent agreements with the North Korean government and South Korea's largest chaebol, Hyundai Group, have increased the country's revenue. The tourism deal that the North made with Hyundai becomes more favorable as the country receives millions of dollars each month from South Korean tourists. In addition, Hyundai's plan to construct a $10 billion industrial complex on the border of North and South Korea may encourage isolated North Korea to open its doors to the world. The most recent development between the United States and North Korea is significant to improving North Korea's economy in that lifting economic sanctions promotes trade between the Stalinist state and the west.

A shift in economic policy of this degree is risky to the communist state. The Supreme People's Assembly (DPRK's parliament) convened earlier this year to discuss policies of the national economy. If the Kim Jong-Il regime implements policies with a market-oriented twist, it threatens what little socioeconomic stability it has and becomes a challenge to its political legitimacy. Ultimately, the economy will decline further, weakening political control and threatening national sovereignty. But for now, its recent economic adjustments promise some improvement without requiring major internal changes.

GOVERNMENT AND POLITICS

A series of talks at the beginning of 1999 showed no progress in easing tensions on the Korean peninsula. However, the Communist nation made waves when it agreed to allow U.S. officials to inspect a suspected nuclear weapons development site near Kumchangni in exchange for more economic and food relief. But North Korea remains a classic example of brinkmanship. Just when it appears ready to compromise, it intrudes into South Korean waters opening a fierce gun battle, and threatens its neighbors and the international community with plans to test longer-range ballistic missiles. These incidents cause serious setbacks in negotiations. South Korea, Japan, and the United States respond with warnings of retaliation-sanctions that would cut off all foreign aid, including food and agricultural products that have become vital to the reclusive country.

North Korean officials have become masters of toying with their counterparts by using the missile program as a bargaining tool. Communist officials hope to gain a degree of leverage and bargaining power in obtaining more foreign aid and in dealing with South Korea, and also as an attempt to raise national morale and protect the sovereignty of its people. However, the North Korean missile crisis eased once again when the communist regime said it was ready to negotiate. Having met to discuss a possible solution to the problem, the United States broadly relaxed the economic embargo so long as North Korea agreed to curb its missile program.

CULTURE AND SOCIETY

Apart from years of floods and droughts leading to widespread famine and a tattered economy, millions of won are spent on mass rallies, seminars and parades marking the fifth anniversary of the death of North Korea's founder, Kim Il-sung. The celebration of the personality cult reminds North Koreans of the importance of pledging loyalty and filial piety towards the Great Leader for his revolutionary exploits and theory of self-reliance, or *juche* idea. Korean nationalism is continuously demonstrated with North Korea's reunification rallies, sporting events, and ceremonies. A deep sense of pride encompassed its people when North Korean marathoner Chung Seong-wook won the gold in Spain.

DIRECTORY

CENTRAL GOVERNMENT
Head of State
Chairman of the National Defense
Kim Jong-il, Office of the President

Eternal President
Kim Il-sung (b. 1912–1994)

Premier
Hong Song-nam, Office of the Premier

Ministers

Minister of Agriculture
Yi Ha-sop, Ministry of Agriculture

Minister of Chemical Industry
Pak Pong-chu, Ministry of Chemical Industry

Minister of City Management
Ch'oe Chong-kon, Ministry of City Management

Minister of Commerce
Yi Yong-son, Ministry of Commerce

Minister of Construction and Building-Materials Industries
Cho Yun-hui, Ministry of Construction and Building-Materials Industries

Minister of Culture
Ch'oe Chae-hyon, Ministry of Culture

Minister of Education
Pyon Yong-rip, Ministry of Education

Minister of Extractive Industries
Son Chong-ho, Ministry of Extractive Industries

Minister of Finance
Yim Kyong-suk, Ministry of Finance

Minister of Fisheries
Yi Song-un, Ministry of Fisheries

Minister of Foreign Affairs
Paek Nam-sun, Ministry of Foreign Affairs

Minister of Foreign Trade
Kang Chong-mo, Ministry of Foreign Trade

Minister of Forestry
Yi Sang-mu, Ministry of Forestry

Minister of Labor
Yi Won-il, Ministry of Labor

Minister of Land and Environment Protection
Il-Son Chang, Ministry of Land and
Environment Protection

Minister of Land and Marine Transport
Kim Yong-il, Ministry of Land and Marine
Transport

Minister of Light Industry
Yi Yon-su, Ministry of Light Industry

Minister of Metal and Machine-Building Industries
Chong Sung-hun, Ministry of Metal and
Machine-Building Industries

Minister of Physical Culture and Sports
Pak Myong-ch'ol, Ministry of Physical Culture
and Sports

Minister of Post and Telecommunications
Yi Kum-pom, Ministry of Post and
Telecommunications

Minister of Power and Coal Industries
Sin T'ae-nok, Ministry of Power and Coal
Industries

Minister of Procurement and Food Administration
Paek Ch'ang-yong, Ministry of Procurement and
Food Administration

Minister of Public Health
Kim Su-hak, Ministry of Public Health

Minister of Public Security
Vice Marshall Paek Hak-nim, Ministry of Public
Security

Minister of Railways
Kim Yong-sam, Ministry of Railways

Minister of State Construction Control
Pae Tal-chun, Ministry of State Construction
Control

Minister of State Inspection
Kim Ui-sun, Ministry of State Inspection

Minister of People's Armed Forces
Vice Marshal Kim Il-ch'ol, Ministry of People's
Armed Forces

POLITICAL ORGANIZATIONS
Democratic Front for the Reunification of the Fatherland (DF)

Korean Workers' Party (KWP)

TITLE: General Secretary
NAME: Kim Chong-il

Korean Social Democratic Party

TITLE: Chairwoman
NAME: Kim Pyong-sik

Chondoist Chongu Party

TITLE: Chairwoman
NAME: Yu Mi-yong

JUDICIAL SYSTEM
Supreme Court

FURTHER READING
Articles

''Closer Encounter.'' *The Economist* (June 12,
1999): 37.

''Echoes from the Hermit Kingdom.'' *The
Economist* (May 22, 1999): 47.

''Famine in North Korea: A Glimpse.'' *The
Economist* (August 7, 1999): 32.

''Golden Potatoes.'' *The Economist* (March 22,
1999): 45–6.

''Just Testing, Again.'' *The Economist*
(September 18, 1999): 45–6.

''The Month in Review: North Korea.'' *Current
History* 98 (February 1999): 94.

''The Month in Review: North Korea.'' *Current
History* 98 (May 1999): 238.

''North Korea Throws a Party.'' *The Economist*
(February 20, 1999): 38.

''A Survey of the Koreas: Yesterday's War,
Tomorrow's Peace.'' *The Economist* (July 10,
1999): 1–16.

Books

Eckert, Carter J. et al. *Korea Old and New: A
History*. Seoul: Ilchokak Publishers, 1990.

Lee, Ki-Baek. *A New History of Korea*. Edward
W. Wagner, trans. Cambridge, Mass.: Harvard
University Press, 1984.

McDonald, Donald Stone. *The Koreans: Contemporary Politics and Society.* 3rd ed. Boulder, Col.: Westview Press, 1992.

Oberdorser, Don. *The Two Koreas.* Reading, Mass.: Addison-Wesley, 1992.

Internet

The Korea Herald. Available Online @ www.koreaherald.co.kr/ (October 13, 1999).

Korea Times. Available Online @ www.koreatimes.co.kr (October 20, 1999).

Korea Webweekly. Available Online @ www.kimsoft.com/korea.htm (October 22, 1999).

Information Please. ''North Korea.'' Available Online @ www.infoplease.com/ipa/A0107686.html (October 13, 1999).

The Republic of Korea. Available Online @ www.korea.go.kr/index19990820.html (October 20, 1999).

NORTH KOREA: STATISTICAL DATA

For sources and notes see "Sources of Statistics" in the front of each volume.

GEOGRAPHY

Geography (1)

Area:

Total: 120,540 sq km.

Land: 120,410 sq km.

Water: 130 sq km.

Area—comparative: slightly smaller than Mississippi.

Land boundaries:

Total: 1,673 km.

Border countries: China 1,416 km, South Korea 238 km, Russia 19 km.

Coastline: 2,495 km.

Climate: temperate with rainfall concentrated in summer.

Terrain: mostly hills and mountains separated by deep, narrow valleys; coastal plains wide in west, discontinuous in east.

Natural resources: coal, lead, tungsten, zinc, graphite, magnesite, iron ore, copper, gold, pyrites, salt, fluorspar, hydropower.

Land use:

Arable land: 14%

Permanent crops: 2%

Permanent pastures: 0%

Forests and woodland: 61%

Other: 23% (1993 est.).

HUMAN FACTORS

Ethnic Division (6)

Racially homogeneous; there is a small Chinese community and a few ethnic Japanese.

Demographics (2A)

	1990	1995	1998	2000	2010	2020	2030	2040	2050
Population	NA	21,551.4	21,234.4	21,687.6	23,504.8	24,936.9	25,955.8	26,238.3	25,930.4
Net migration rate (per 1,000 population)	NA	NA	NA	NA	NA	NA	NA	NA	NA
Births	NA	NA	NA	NA	NA	NA	NA	NA	NA
Deaths	NA	NA	NA	NA	NA	NA	NA	NA	NA
Life expectancy - males	NA	48.9	48.9	67.8	72.1	75.2	77.3	78.7	79.6
Life expectancy - females	NA	53.9	53.9	73.9	78.4	81.5	83.6	84.9	85.7
Birth rate (per 1,000)	NA	20.1	15.3	20.4	13.1	12.9	11.3	9.9	9.8
Death rate (per 1,000)	NA	16.1	15.6	6.9	6.9	7.6	8.4	10.1	12.0
Women of reproductive age (15-49 yrs.)	NA	5,664.2	5,716.8	5,847.6	6,399.1	6,144.2	5,866.7	5,604.5	5,249.0
of which are currently married	NA	NA	NA	NA	NA	NA	NA	NA	NA
Fertility rate	NA	2.1	1.6	2.3	1.8	1.8	1.7	1.7	1.7

Except as noted, values for vital statistics are in thousands; life expectancy is in years.

Religions (7)

Buddhism and Confucianism, some Christianity and syncretic Chondogyo.

Languages (8)

Korean.

GOVERNMENT & LAW

Political Parties (12)

The legislative branch is a unicameral Supreme People's Assembly (687 seats; members elected by popular vote to serve five-year terms). The term of the Assembly expired in April 1995 without a new election. and it has not been convened since the death of KIM Il-song in July 1994.

Military Affairs (14B)

Government Budget (13B)

Revenues . . . .$19.3 billion
Expenditures . . . .$19.3 billion
  Capital expenditures . . . . .NA

Data for 1992 est. NA stands for not available.

Crime (15)

Crime rate (for 1994)
  Crimes reported 1,309,326
  Total persons convicted 129,259
  Crimes per 100,000 population 2,945
Persons responsible for offenses
  Total number of suspects 1,423,618
  Total number of female suspects 183,027
  Total number of juvenile suspects 6,514

	1990	1991	1992	1993	1994	1995
Military expenditures						
Current dollars (mil.)	5,940	5,000	5,500	5,300	5,500	6,000
1995 constant dollars (mil.)	6,827	5,525	5,916	5,556	5,638	6,000
Armed forces (000)	1,200	1,200	1,200	1,200	1,200	1,040
Gross national product (GNP)						
Current dollars (mil.)	NA	23,300	22,000	21,300	21,300	21,000
1995 constant dollars (mil.)	NA	25,750	23,660	22,330	21,830	21,000
Central government expenditures (CGE)						
1995 constant dollars (mil.)	NA	NA	NA	NA	NA	NA
People (mil.)	21.4	21.8	22.2	22.6	23.1	23.5
Military expenditure as % of GNP	NA	21.5	25.0	24.9	25.8	28.6
Military expenditure as % of CGE	NA	NA	NA	NA	NA	NA
Military expenditure per capita (1995 $)	319	253	266	245	244	255
Armed forces per 1,000 people (soldiers)	56.0	55.0	54.0	53.0	52.0	44.3
GNP per capita (1995 $)	NA	1,180	1,065	986	947	894
Arms imports[6]						
Current dollars (mil.)	200	90	30	5	90	100
1995 constant dollars (mil.)	230	99	32	5	92	100
Arms exports[6]						
Current dollars (mil.)	210	220	160	180	60	40
1995 constant dollars (mil.)	241	243	172	189	62	40
Total imports[7]						
Current dollars (mil.)	2,620[e]	NA	1,900[e]	1,930	1,440[e]	1,710[e]
1995 constant dollars (mil.)	3,011[e]	NA	2,044	2,023[e]	1,476[e]	1,710[e]
Total exports[7]						
Current dollars (mil.)	2,020	1,025[e]	1,300[e]	1,220	1,240[e]	1,100[e]
1995 constant dollars (mil.)	2,321	1,133[e]	1,398[e]	1,279	1,271[e]	1,100[e]
Arms as percent of total imports[8]	7.6	NA	1.6	.3	6.3	5.8
Arms as percent of total exports[8]	10.4	21.5	12.3	14.8	4.8	3.6

LABOR FORCE

Labor Force (16)

Total (million) 9.615

Agricultural 36%

Nonagricultural 64%

Unemployment Rate (17)

Rate not available.

PRODUCTION SECTOR

Electric Energy (18)

Capacity . . . . .9.5 million kW (1995)

Production . . . . .35.2 billion kWh (1995)

Consumption per capita . . . . .1,499 kWh (1995)

Transportation (19)

Highways:

total: 31,200 km

paved: 1,997 km

unpaved: 29,203 km (1996 est.)

Waterways: 2,253 km; mostly navigable by small craft only.

Pipelines: crude oil 37 km

Merchant marine:

total: 105 ships (1,000 GRT or over) totaling 663,527 GRT/930,587 DWT ships by type: bulk 7, cargo 87, combination bulk 1, multifunction large-load carrier 1, oil tanker 3, passenger 3, passenger-cargo 1, short-sea passenger 2 note: North Korea owns an additional 1 ship (1,000 GRT or over) totaling 15,143 DWT operating under the registry of Honduras (1997 est.)

Airports: 49 (1994 est.)

Airports—with paved runways:

total: 22

over 3,047 m: 2

2,438 to 3,047 m: 15

1,524 to 2,437 m: 2

914 to 1,523 m: 1

under 914 m: 2 (1994 est.)

Airports—with unpaved runways:

total: 27

2,438 to 3,047 m: 4

1,524 to 2,437 m: 5

914 to 1,523 m: 12

under 914 m: 6 (1994 est.)

Top Agricultural Products (20)

Rice, corn, potatoes, soybeans, pulses; cattle, pigs, pork, eggs.

FINANCE, ECONOMICS, & TRADE

Economic Indicators (22)

National product: GDP—purchasing power parity—$21.8 billion (1997 est.)

National product real growth rate: -3.7% (1997 est.)

National product per capita: $900 (1997 est.)

Inflation rate—consumer price index: NA%

Exchange Rates (24)

Exchange rates:

North Korean won (Wn) per US$1

May 1994 . . . . .2.15

May 1992 . . . . .2.13

September 1991 . . . . .2.14

January 1990 . . . . .2.1

December 1989 . . . . .2.3

MANUFACTURING SECTOR

GDP & Manufacturing Summary (21)

	1980	1985	1990	1992	1993	1994
Gross Domestic Product						
Millions of 1990 dollars	11,014	17,622	21,000	19,950	19,252	18,674
Growth rate in percent	9.89	9.59	−3.70	−5.00	−3.50	−3.00
Per capita (in 1990 dollars)	603.2	886.0	964.5	882.2	835.3	795.2
Manufacturing Value Added						
Millions of 1990 dollars	NA	NA	NA	NA	NA	NA
Growth rate in percent	NA	NA	NA	NA	NA	NA
Manufacturing share in percent of current prices	NA	NA	NA	NA	NA	NA

Top Import Origins (25)

$1.95 billion (c.i.f., 1996 est.)

Origins	%
Turkey	NA
Cuba	NA
United States	NA
Germany	NA

NA stands for not available.

Top Export Destinations (26)

$912 million (f.o.b., 1996 est.)

Destinations	%
China	NA
Japan	NA
South Korea	NA

Germany	NA
Hong Kong	NA
Russia	NA

NA stands for not available.

Economic Aid (27)

Recipient: an estimated $200 million to $300 million in aid from US, South Korea, Japan, and EU in 1997.

Import Export Commodities (28)

Import Commodities	Export Commodities
Petroleum	Minerals
Grain	Metallurgical products
Coking coal	Agricultural and fishery products
Machinery and equipment	Manufactures (including armaments)
Consumer goods	

SOUTH KOREA (ROK)

Republic of Korea
Taehan Min-guk

INTRODUCTORY SURVEY

RECENT HISTORY

The Republic of Korea, headed by President Syngman Rhee, was proclaimed on 15 August 1948 in the southern portion of the Korean Peninsula, which had been under U.S. military administration since 1945. Like the Democratic People's Republic of Korea (DPRK), established in the north with backing from the Soviet Union, the ROK claimed to be the legitimate government of all Korea. The ROK was recognized as the legitimate government by the UN General Assembly.

On 25 June 1950, the People's Army of the DPRK invaded the ROK to unify the country under communist control. The DPRK forces advanced rapidly, and the destruction of the ROK seemed near. However, U.S. and UN multinational forces came to the aid of the South Koreans. A military campaign led by U.S. General Douglas MacArthur brought about the total defeat of the DPRK's forces.

MacArthur then made a fateful decision to attack North Korea. China entered the fighting, forcing MacArthur into a costly retreat. The battle line stabilized near the 38th parallel, where it remained for two years. On 27 July 1953, a peace agreement finally was signed by all parties. The war killed an estimated 415,000 South Koreans, 23,300 Americans, 3,100 United Nations allies, and, according to official numbers, 50,000 North Koreans and Chinese (although this number is thought to be as high as two million).

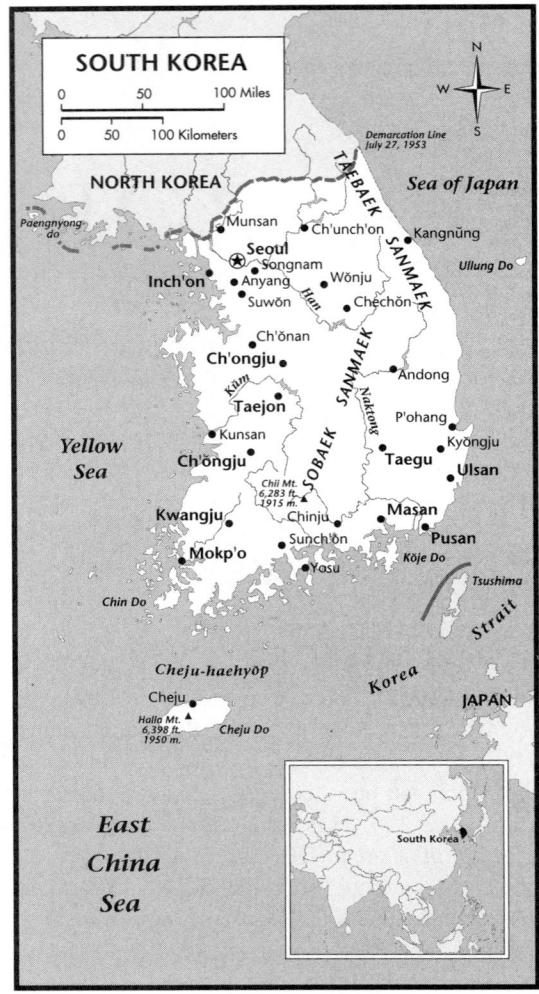

SOUTH KOREA

0   50   100 Miles

0   50   100 Kilometers

NORTH KOREA

Demarcation Line July 27, 1953

Sea of Japan

Paengnyong-do

Munsan
Ch'unch'on
Kangnŭng

Seoul
Songnam
Anyang   Wŏnju   *Ullung Do*
Inch'on   Suwŏn   Chechŏn

Han

Ch'ŏnan

Ch'ongju

TAEBAEK SANMAEK

Andong

Kŭm   Taejon   Naktong   P'ohang

Yellow Sea   Kunsan   Kyŏngju
Ch'ŏngju   SOBAEK SANMAEK   Taegu   Ulsan

Chil Mt. 6,283 ft. 1915 m.   Masan

Kwangju   Chinju   Pusan
Mokp'o   Sunch'ŏn   *Kŏje Do*
Yŏsu

Tsushima

Chin Do   *Korea Strait*

Cheju-haehyŏp

JAPAN

Cheju
Halla Mt. 6,398 ft. 1950 m.   Cheju Do

East China Sea

South Korea

In 1954, the United States and the ROK signed a mutual defense treaty, under which United States troops remained in the country. Financial assistance throughout the 1950s was provided by the United States, averaging $270 million annually between 1953 and 1958. Syngman Rhee ran the government until 1960, when his authoritarian rule provoked violent student demonstrations that finally brought about his downfall. In May 1961, the Second Korean Republic was overthrown in a military coup headed by Major General Park Chunghee.

For the next eighteen years, Park ruled South Korea, periodically resorting to martial law in response to student demonstrations and other forms of opposition. On 26 October 1979, Park was assassinated by the director of the Korean intelligence agency (KCIA), Kim Jae-gyu, who was later executed.

In December 1979, Major General Chun Doo Hwan led a coup against Park's successor. Demonstrations by university students spread through the spring of 1980, and by mid-May the government once more declared martial law. In the 1981 elections, Chun was elected to a seven-year presidential term by a new electoral college. His Democratic Justice Party (DJP) secured a majority in the reorganized National Assembly. In June 1987, the DJP nominated its chairman, Roh Tae Woo, a former general and a close friend of Chun, as its candidate for his successor. Roh defeated the two major opposition candidates, Kim Young Sam and Kim Dae Jung, and was inaugurated as president in February 1988.

Following a revision of the constitution in 1987, South Koreans enjoyed greater freedoms of expression and assembly and freedom of the press. In 1988, several hundred political dissidents were released from prison. The United States agreed to withdraw its nuclear weapons from the ROK in November 1991. And, on the last day of the year, the ROK and the DPRK signed an agreement to ban nuclear weapons from the entire Korean peninsula.

In the presidential election on 19 December 1992, Kim Young Sam, now leader of the majority DLP, was elected president. President Kim granted amnesty to 41,000 prisoners and fired many high-ranking military officials. Kim also cleaned up the government and business sector by arresting, firing, or publicly scolding several thousand government officials and business people.

In April 1996, North Korean troops violated the armistice and entered Panmunjom for training exercises. In September 1996, a small North Korean submarine was grounded off the eastern coast of the ROK. The boat appeared to be carrying a team of North Koreans who intended to spy in the ROK. The North Korean government apologized for the incident in February 1997.

In late 1996, former President Chun Doo Hwan and his successor Roh Tae Woo were tried and found guilty of treason and mutiny. They were held responsible for the Kwangju massacre of 1980. Chun was sentenced to life in prison, while Roh's term was seventeen years.

In late 1997, Korea's debts became more than its economy could handle. The government requested the help of the International Monetary Fund, which authorized loans totaling $55 billion, the largest assistance package ever made by the institution.

GOVERNMENT

Under the new constitution, which took effect in February 1988, the president is elected by direct popular vote for a single term of five years. There are also a prime minister and two deputy prime ministers, who head the State Council (the cabinet). The ROK legislature is the 299-seat National Assembly (Kuk Hoe). Suffrage is universal at age 20.

Judiciary

The legal system combines elements of European civil law, Anglo-American law, and classical Chinese philosophies. The highest judicial court is the Supreme Court. Under the Supreme Court are three intermediate appeals courts, located in Seoul, Taegu, and Kwangju. Lower courts include district and family courts. The constitution provides for a presumption of innocence, protection from self-incrimination, the right to a speedy trial, protection from double jeopardy, and other due process safeguards. There are no jury trials.

Political Parties

Since the revised 1987 constitution took effect, political parties have had a greater governmental role. In 1996, the majority party was the New Korea Party (NKP). The opposition parties were the National Congress for New Politics (NCNP), the United Liberal Democratic Party (ULDP), and the Democratic Party (DP).

DEFENSE

The ROK has one of the world's largest and best-equipped armed forces. Defense spending accounted for $14.4 billion in 1995, or 4.5% of gross domestic product (GDP). Of a total of 660,000 personnel on active duty, 548,000 were in the army; 60,000 in the navy and marines; and 52,000 in the air force. An additional 4.5 million were in the reserves. All males age 19 must serve twenty-six to thirty months in the military.

ECONOMIC AFFAIRS

The ROK has been one of the fastest-developing countries in the post-war period, shifting from an agricultural to an industrial economy in the course of only a few decades. Much of this industrialization involves heavy industry, notably steel, construction, shipbuilding, and technologically advanced goods such as electronics. The domestic economy grew by an annual average of 9.6% dur-

ing 1985–90, but slowed to about 8.4% during the early 1990s. However, the economy grew by 9% in 1995 and by 7.1% in 1996. Services account for 47% of the gross domestic product (GDP), while industry contributes 45% and agriculture makes up 8%.

Public Finance

The U.S. CIA estimates that, in 1995, government revenues totaled approximately $69 billion and expenditures $67 billion. External debt totaled $77 billion.

Income

In 1998, Korea's gross national product (GNP) was $370 billion or about $7,970 per person. For the period 1985–95, the average inflation rate was 6.8%, resulting in a real growth rate in per person GNP of 7.6%.

Industry

The ROK ranks as a major Asian producer of steel, chemicals, ships, machinery, nonferrous metals, and electronic equipment. In the 1980s, the manufacture of metals, machinery, electronic, and other equipment overtook textile production as the country's leading industry.

Output from the steel industry in 1995 included 22.3 million tons of pig iron and 36.8 million tons of crude steel. The production of passenger cars was 2 million in 1995. Total vehicle output that year was 2.5 million, or 5% of the world's production. Hyundai is the leading automotive manufacturer, followed by Kia and Daewoo.

Samsung Electronics, LG, and Daewoo Electronics dominate in the production of consumer electronics.

Banking and Finance

The Bank of Korea serves as the central bank, the bank of issue, and the depository for government funds. It was established in 12 June 1950.

Money supply, as measured by M2, totaled won $153,945 billion at the end of 1995. M2 at the end of the second quarter of 1996 was won 1,597.54 trillion.

The Korean Stock Exchange, a share-issuing private corporation, functions as the country's only stock exchange.

Economic Development

The ROK has a market economy in which both private enterprise and foreign investors play an important role. Overall economic development is guided, however, by the Economic Planning Board and, since 1962, by a series of five-year plans. A revised Seventh Five-Year Economic and Social Development Plan for 1992–96 aims at establishing the ROK as an advanced industrialized economy by the year 2000.

SOCIAL WELFARE

The government passed legislation in 1988 that included old-age, disability, and survivors' pensions. It passed health insurance legislation in 1989.

The wage of the average female worker is roughly half of that of the average male worker. The Amended Family Law of 1991 recognizes women as heads of households.

Healthcare

Health care has improved greatly owing to improvement of diet, the rise in living standards, and the development of health and medical programs. During 1985–95, 100% of the population had access to health care services. Life expectancy is 72 years. In 1992, there were 236 general hospitals. There was 1 hospital bed for every 300 people and 1 physician for every 951 people in 1993.

Housing

A housing shortage continues to plague the nation, especially in large cities. As of 1992, the per person housing space was 9.6 square meters (103 square feet).

EDUCATION

Six-year elementary schools are free and compulsory for children between 6 and 12 years of age. Secondary education begins at 12 years of age and lasts for up to six years. Nearly 95% of children in this age group were enrolled in the secondary schools in 1995. That year, there were 3.9 million students in primary schools, 4.6 million in secondary schools, and 2.3 million in colleges and universities.

1999 KEY EVENTS TIMELINE

January

- Scientists in Seoul clone a human cell from a woman and create an embryo; the experiment is ceased for ethical reasons.

- The National Assembly passes 66 bills unilaterally despite the clamoring of the opposition Grand National Party; the bills focused primarily on economic reform.

- Foreign-exchange reserves increased from $4 billion to $50 billion and real GDP is forecast to grow 2% in 1999.

- The Hyundai Group's plan to remit cash to North Korea under the tourism project is approved.

February

- South Korea, the United States, and Japan meet to discuss security issues including North Korea's suspected nuclear development project; this is the seventh meeting between the three countries since 1994.

- The National Workplace Medical Insurance Association goes on strike as a result of government's proposed wage cut of 4.5%.

- Amnesty is granted to 8,182 inmates and ex-convicts.

- Two million people are reported jobless, sending the unemployment rate up to 9%.

- Samsung employees return to work ending a two-month long strike over job security issues.

March

- Hyundai Asan Corporation officially launches investment projects in North Korea.

April

- A Korea Air cargo jet crashes shortly after take-off in Shanghai killing 5, and injuring 40.

- Employees of Daewoo, one of Korea's largest companies, join a labor strike to protest nationwide job losses.

- Queen Elizabeth II visits South Korea, marking the first state visit to Korea by a British monarch.

May

- The South Korean government frees 1,240 prisoners in celebration of Buddha's birthday.

- President Kim Dae-jung reorganizes the Korean cabinet as part of the campaign to reform the family-run conglomerates, the *chaebol*, which dominate the South Korean economy.

- Kim Dae-jung arrives in Russia for a state visit to gain support for his policy of engagement with North Korea.

- The Korean national women's basketball team defeats their Japanese counterparts in the Asia Women's Basketball Championship final to win the right to represent the entire Asian region in the 2000 Sydney Olympics.

June

- After nine days of mounting tensions and confrontation between North and South Korean military vessels in the Yellow Sea, South Korean naval forces sink a North Korean torpedo boat in an exchange of fire lasting 30 minutes.

- Former president Kim Young-sam is attacked at Kimpo International Airport as punishment for ''economic devastation during his tenure.''

- Minister of Agriculture and Forestry Kim Sung-hoo bans the domestic sale and use of pork imported from Belgium, France, and the Netherlands due to dioxin contamination; sales will resume once the safety of imported pork is ensured.

- The ''Michael Jackson and Friends—what more can I give?'' charity concert is held at the Olympic Stadium on the anniversary of the commencement of the Korean War; the purpose of the concert was to promote peace and to aid suffering children worldwide.

July

- President Kim Dae-jung meets with President Clinton in the United States to discuss economic and security issues.

- President Kim Dae-jung and Canadian Prime Minister Jean Chrétien sign the Agreement on the Procurement of Telecommunications Equipment which opens the respective communications markets to each other and guarantees ''transparency and an end discrimination in their markets.''

- Governor Lim Chang-yuel is arrested for taking bribes of 100 million won prior to the June 4 local elections from a former bank president.

- Lee Seung-yup of the Samsung Lions is voted ''Best Baseball Player'' for 1999 by the Korean National Baseball Organization.

- South Korean Foreign Minister, Hong Soon-young, Japanese Foreign Minister, Masahiko Komura, and U.S. Secretary of State Madeleine Albright issue a joint statement directed to North Korea, urging it to abort its plans to test long-range missiles in exchange for improved rela-

tions in the international community and promises of aid and development.

August

- Typhoon Olga hits the Korean peninsula causing flash-floods and mud-slides; at least 69 people are reported dead or missing, and the damage is projected to cost 400 billion won ($332 million).

- Over 3,000 convicts, including 56 political prisoners and 7 North Korean spies, are granted amnesty as part of celebrations marking 54 years of independence from Japan's colonial rule.

September

- Rep. Suh Sang-mok of the opposition Grand National Party, who was indicted on suspicion of the illegal collection of the presidential campaign fund in 1997, resigned his post in the National Assembly after denouncing the legal action as a ''political vendetta'' against the opposition.

- The first ''total-duty'' female police squad is formed to focus on sexual assault crimes, homicides, and violent cases involving female victims.

- Former Supreme Court Justice Choi Jong-young is appointed as the Chief Supreme Court Justice.

- ''Kazoku Cinema,'' ''Fly Low,'' and ''The Harmonium in my Memory,'' three Korean films, are invited to compete in the 35th Chicago International Film Festival in the United States.

October

- Uzbekistan president Islam Karimov and president Kim Dae-jung hold a summit meeting to seek ways of promoting bilateral cooperation in investment and trade as well as promoting the status of Koreans in the central Asian nation.

- Twenty-two employees of the Wolsung nuclear power plant are exposed to radiation from a heavy water leak during maintenance of the plant's cooling pump.

- The Korean Language Academy completes the most comprehensive Korean language dictionary. Available in three volumes, the Standard Korean Language Dictionary contains the largest collection of Korean words with over 500,000 entries.

- The Grand Peace Palace, Asia's largest concert hall, opens at Kyung Hee University.

December

- Hundred of protestors battle police when a labor rally, attended by an estimated 20,000, gets out of control. The rally is staged to demand a shorter work week and an increase in government subsidies.

ANALYSIS OF EVENTS: 1999

BUSINESS AND THE ECONOMY

Economic prospects improve after two years of trying to recover from the Asian economic crisis. Out of all the Southeast Asian countries, South Korea appears to be making the most progress in rebuilding its economy. Industrial output and the stock market have created a sound economic base, and the currency is healthy enough to be competitive without threatening savings. Falling interest rates in the stock market are encouraging investors to use their money in shares rather than bank deposits. Foreign exchange reserves have increased from less than $4 billion a year ago to $50 billion at the beginning of 1999. Real GDP is forecast to grow by at least 2% this year, after decreasing by an estimated 5.5% in 1998.

This rapid economic recovery is not entirely optimistic. Unemployment, which has risen to nearly 9% from below 3% in 1998, is still a major concern. With the restructuring of South Korea's largest conglomerates, the *chaebol*, there has been a series of lay-offs and labor strikes. The Korean government is determined to slim down the conglomerates which have been running its economy for decades, but the more they force the companies to restructure, the more people they have to lay off. The government is fearful that so many strikes will drive away foreign investors and has taken serious measures to ensure this stability.

Another threat to the stability of South Korea's economy is the banking system. In 1998, the government allocated $41 trillion won into the financial system to recapitalize weak banks, buy non-performing loans and protect investors. It is estimated that the government will spend another 21 trillion won this year. In order for the banking system to be fully recovered, it will require more reforms and more public money, leaving less to spend on social welfare.

Nonetheless, Kim Dae-jung's first year in office has been successful considering the predicament that awaited him when he took office. Great strides have been made by making businesses more open, and giving investors and shareholders more say in corporate affairs. Small businesses that used to contribute a significant percentage to bankruptcies now furnish nearly half of South Korea's gross domestic product (GDP) and employ a third of its workers. Foreign investment is even more welcome, and on the rise. Foreign direct investment is predicted to double from 1998's $8.9 billion.

The general consensus across East Asia is that the economies are on the mend. But many companies are still burdened with bad debt, and it appears that despite recent recovery, South Korea still has a long way to go before its economy can perform up to par.

GOVERNMENT AND POLITICS

Kim Dae-jung is approaching the second year in his presidential term, and yet, power politics and scandals prevail in South Korea's National Assembly. So far, it is evident that President Kim has been successful with economic reform as he slims down Korea's largest conglomerates. And he decreed an amnesty to 5 million prisoners. His position on North Korea and reuniting the peninsula is favorable and is sticking to his "sunshine" policy. But these are not the only issues that need his attention. The political sphere in South Korea has a bad reputation of being laden with corruption, scandals and power politics, and so far, no attempt has been made to fix this.

Within 15 minutes the ruling coalition (National Congress for New Politics) unilaterally passed 66 bills in January. In May it dished out 6 bills in 8 minutes. Many of them were designed to restructure the economy and bring in reforms requested by the International Monetary Fund (IMF). The citizens became tired of the contention between the ruling coalition and opposition party (United Liberal Democrats), and feel that their political games are an obstacle to improving society as a whole. Scandals are another weak spot in the Assembly. Both the justice minister and the senior prosecutor were removed for allegedly abusing their authority.

On the northern frontier, little progress has been made between North and South Korea in terms of opening the Stalinist country and bringing peace to the Korean peninsula. But South Korea remains hopeful as Kim Dae-jung sticks to his "sunshine" policy toward North Korea, concentrating on issues which it hopes the North will accept such as holding peace talks regularly. President Kim has agreed to supply fertilizer to the North in exchange for direct talks with the communist regime and trying to reunite families that were separated during the Korean War (1950–53). However, the naval shoot-out that lasted 30 minutes in the Yellow Sea earlier this summer caused some setback in North-South relations. North Korea's refusal to discuss reuniting families and its demand for an apology from South Korea for sinking one of its war ships halted talks that were supposed to take place in Beijing shortly after the naval skirmish. South Korea's national security was put on the line as well when North Korea announced it was going to proceed with test-firing ballistic missiles.

CULTURE AND SOCIETY

South Koreans demonstrated their discontent with restructuring of the economy with strikes and labor movements. Big companies like Daewoo witnessed union leaders organizing strikes because of lay-offs across the nation. In response, the government has been using not only threats of dismissal from jobs but also forceful tactics to break up labor movements.

Also devastating to the country in 1999 was typhoon Olga, which disrupted life in August. As the tropical storm swept across the nation, it caused floods and landslides destroying over 20,000 ha of farmland and 6,677 homes in her path. Although disaster relief plans went into effect shortly thereafter, citizens were discontent with the government's lack of readiness for a natural disaster.

On the brighter side, South Korean women are making great strides in society. The creation of a "total-duty" female police squad has set a new trend in Korea. These women will be responsible for homicides and sexual assault crimes involving female victims. Even more heartening were the exploits of the Korean national women's basketball team. In defeating their Japanese counterparts they won the right to represent the entire Asian region in the 2000 Sydney Olympics.

The year 1999 presented South Korea with a busy social calendar for hosting the international community. In June it held the 109th International Olympic Committee session to select the host for the 2006 Olympics, and also accommodated "Michael Jackson and Friends-What more can I give?"

charity concert promoting peace and aid to suffering children worldwide. In September, three Korean films, "Kazoku Cinema," "Fly Low," and "The Harmonium in my Memory" were invited to compete in the 35th Chicago International Film Festival. Adding to the success was the completion of the most comprehensive Korean language dictionary, the Standard Korean Language Dictionary, by the Korean Language Academy. Lastly, Asia's largest concert hall, the Grand Peace Palace, opened at Kyung Hee University. These accomplishments add to the great sense of national pride, as well as create a positive image in the eyes of the global community.

DIRECTORY

CENTRAL GOVERNMENT
Head of State

President
Kim Dae-jung, Office of the President, 1 Sejong-no, Chongno-ku, Seoul, South Korea
FAX: +82 (02) 5037727

Ministers

Prime Minister
Kim Chong-pil, Office of the Prime Minister, 77 Sejong-ro, Chongno-gu, Seoul 110–050, South Korea
PHONE: +82 (02) 7370094
FAX: +82 (02) 7370109
E-MAIL: m_opm@opm.go.kr

Minister of Agriculture and Forestry
Kim Song-hoo, Ministry of Agriculture and Forestry, 1 Chungang-dong, Kwachon, Kyonggi-do 427–010, South Korea
PHONE: +82 (02) 5037200
FAX: +82 (02) 5037238

Minister of Budget and Planning
Chin Nyom, Ministry of Budget and Planning

Minister of Commerce, Industry and Energy
Chung Tok-ku, Ministry of Commerce, Industry and Energy, 1 Chungang-dong, Kwachon, Kyonggi-do 427–010, South Korea
PHONE: +82 (02) 5037171
FAX: +82 (02) 5033142

Minister of Construction and Transportation
Yi Kun-chun, Ministry of Construction and Transportation, 1 Chungang-dong, Kwachon, Kyonggi-do 427–010, South Korea

PHONE: +82 (02) 5049031
FAX: +82 (02) 5046825

Minister of Culture and Tourism

Pak Chi-won, Ministry of Culture and Tourism, 82–1 Sejong-ro, Chongno-gu, Seoul 110–050, South Korea
PHONE: +82 (02) 7367946
FAX: +82 (02) 7368513

Minister of Education

Kim Tok-chung, Ministry of Education, 77 Sejong-ro, Chongro-ku, Seoul 110–760, South Korea
PHONE: +82 (02) 7203400
FAX: +82 (02)7235656

Minister of Environment

Kim Myong Cha, Ministry of Environment, 1 Chungang-dong, Kwachon, Kyonggi-do 427–010, South Korea
PHONE: +82 (02) 5037171
FAX: +82 (02) 5049277

Minister of Finance and Economy

Kang Pong-kyun, Ministry of Finance and Economy, 1 Chungang-dong, Kwachon, Kyonggi-do 427–010, South Korea
PHONE: +82 (02) 5037171
FAX: +82 (02) 5020193

Minister of Foreign Affairs and Trade

Hong Soon-young, Ministry of Foreign Affairs and Trade, 77–6 Sejongro, Chongno-gu, Seoul, South Korea
PHONE: +82 (02) 7032114
FAX: +82 (02) 7202686

Minister of Government Administration and Local Autonomy

Kim Ki-chae, Ministry of Government Administration and Local Autonomy, 77–6 Sejong-ro, Chongno-gu, Seoul 110–050, South Korea
PHONE: +82 (02) 7357401
FAX: +82 (02) 7208681

Minister of Health and Welfare

Cha Hung-pong, Ministry of Health and Welfare, 1 Chungang-dong, Kwachon, Kyonggi-do 427–010, South Korea
PHONE: +82 (02) 5037505
FAX: +82 (02) 5037568

Minister of Information and Communication

Namgung Suk, Ministry of Information and Communication, 116 1-ga Shinmun-ro, Chongno-gu Seoul 110–061, South Korea

PHONE: +82 (02) 7502000
FAX: +82 (02) 7502915

Minister of Justice

Kim Chung-kil, Ministry of Justice, 1 Chungang-dong, Kwachon Kyonggi-do 427–010, South Korea
PHONE: +82 (02) 5037012
FAX: +82 (02) 5043337

Minister of Labor Affairs

Yi Sang-yong, Ministry of Labor Affairs, 1 Chungang-dong, Kwachon Kyonggi-do 427–010, South Korea
PHONE: +82 (02) 5039713
FAX: +82 (02) 5038862

Minister of Maritime Affairs and Fisheries

Chong Sang-chun, Ministry of Maritime Affairs and Fisheries, 826–14 Yoksam-dong, Kangnam-gu Seoul 135–080, South Korea
PHONE: +82 (02) 5542095
FAX: +82 (02) 5542096

Minister of National Defense

Cho Song-tae, Ministry of National Defense, 1 3-ga Yongsan-dong, Yongsan-gu, Seoul 140–023, South Korea
PHONE: +82 (02) 7950071
FAX: +82 (02) 7960369

Minister of Science and Technology

So Chong-ok, Ministry of Science and Technology, 1 Chungang-dong, Kwachon Kyonggi-do 427-010, South Korea
PHONE: +82 (02) 5037171
FAX: +82 (02) 5037673
E-MAIL: depta3@mostws.most.go.kr

Minister of Unification

Yim Tong-won, Ministry of Unification, 77-6 Sejong-ro, Chongno-gu Seoul 110-050, South Korea
PHONE: +82 (02) 7202431
FAX: +82 (02) 7202432
E-MAIL: m_unikorea@unikorea.go.kr

POLITICAL ORGANIZATIONS

National Congress for New Politics (NCNP)

14-31 Youido-dong, Yongdungpo-gu, Seoul 150-010, South Korea
PHONE: +82 (02) 7847007
FAX: +82 (02) 7846070
NAME: Dae Jung Kim

United Liberal Democratic Party (ULD)

103-4 Shinsu-dong, Mapo-gu, Seoul 121-110,
South Korea
PHONE: +82 (02) 7013355
FAX: +82 (02) 7071637
NAME: Jong Pil Kim

New People's Party (NPP)

TITLE: President
NAME: Yi In-che

Grand National Party (GNP)

14-8 Youido-dong, Yongdungop-gu, Seoul 150-010, South Korea
PHONE: +82 (02) 7839811
FAX: +82 (02) 7804687
TITLE: President
NAME: Cho Sun

DIPLOMATIC REPRESENTATION

Embassies in South Korea

Algeria
2-6 Itaewon 2-dong, Yongsan-ku, Seoul, South Korea
PHONE: +82 (02) 7945034
FAX: +82 (02) 7927845
TITLE: Ambassador
NAME: Ahmed Boutache

Argentina
733-73 Hannam-dong, Yongsan-ku, Seoul 140-210, South Korea
PHONE: +82 (02) 7934062; 7970636
FAX: +82 (02) 7925820
TITLE: Ambassador
NAME: Jorge T. Lapsenson

Australia
11th Floor, Kyobo Bldg., Chongro-1-Ka, Chongro-Ku, South Korea
PHONE: +82 (02) 7306490
FAX: +82 (02) 7356601
TITLE: Ambassador
NAME: Anthony John Hely

Austria
1913 19th Fl. Kyobo Bldg., Chongro 1-Ka, Chongro-ku C.P.O. Box 10099, Seoul, South Korea
PHONE: +82 (02) 7329071
FAX: +82 (02) 7329486
TITLE: Ambassador
NAME: Ewald Jaeger

Bangladesh
1-67 1-92 Dongbinggo-dong, Yongsan-ku, Seoul, South Korea
PHONE: +82 (02) 7964056; 7956535
FAX: +82 (02) 7905313
E-MAIL: dootrok@soback.kornet21.net
TITLE: Charge d'Affaires
NAME: Nazrul Islam

Belarus
5-1005 Chunghwa Apt. 22-2, Itaewon-dong, Yongsan-Ku, Seoul 140-200, South Korea
PHONE: +82 (02) 7989004
FAX: +82 (02) 7989360
TITLE: Charge d'Affaires
NAME: Igor A. Malevich

Belguim
1-94 Dongbinggo-dong, Yongsan-ku, Seoul 140-230 P.O. Box 4406, South Korea
PHONE: +82 (02) 7490381
FAX: +82 (02) 7971688
E-MAIL: Seoul@Diplobel.org
TITLE: Ambassador
NAME: Renier Nijskens

Brazil
3rd Fl., Keumjung Bldg., 192-11 Uljiro 1-ka, Chung-ku, Seoul 100-191, South Korea
PHONE: +82 (02) 7563170
FAX: +82 (02) 7522180
E-MAIL: braseul@soback.kornet21.net
TITLE: Ambassador
NAME: Sergio Serra

Brunei
1-97 Dongbinggo-dong, Yongsan-ku, Seoul 140-230, South Korea
PHONE: +82 (02) 7977679; 7985565
FAX: +82 (02) 7985564
E-MAIL: kbrunei@chollian.net
TITLE: Ambassador
NAME: Dato A. Aziz Mohammad

Bulgaria
723-42 Hannam 2-dong, Yongsan-ku, Seoul 140-212, South Korea
PHONE: +82 (02) 7948625
FAX: +82 (02) 7948627
TITLE: Ambassador
NAME: Dimiter Ikonomov

Canada
10th and 11th Fl., Kolon Bldg., 45 Mugyo-dong, Chung-ku, Seoul, South Korea
PHONE: +82 (02) 34556000
FAX: +82 (02) 7550686

TITLE: Ambassador
NAME: Arthur Perron

Chile
9th Fl., Youngpoong Bldg., 142 Nonhyun-dong,
Kangnam-ku, Seoul, South Korea
PHONE: +82 (02) 5491654
FAX: +82 (02) 5491656
E-MAIL: echilekr@soback.kornet.nm.kr
TITLE: Ambassador
NAME: Ignacio Gonzalez Serrano

China
83 Myund-dong 2-ka, Chung-ku, Seoul, South
Korea
PHONE: +82 (02) 3195101
FAX: +82 (02) 3195103
TITLE: Ambassador
NAME: Dawei WU

Colombia
13th Fl., Kyobo Bldg., 1 Chongro 1-ka,
Chongro-ku, P.O. Box 1175, Seoul, South Korea
PHONE: +82 (02) 7201369
FAX: +82 (02) 7256959
TITLE: Ambassador
NAME: Miguel Duran

Côte d'Ivoire
2nd Fl., Chungam Bldg., 794-4 Hannam-dong,
Yongsan-ku, Seoul, South Korea
PHONE: +82 (02) 37850561
FAX: +82 (02) 37850564
TITLE: Ambassador
NAME: Charles D. A. Atchimon

Czech Republic
1-121 Shinmoonro 2-ka, Chongro-ku, Seoul,
South Korea
PHONE: +82 (02) 7256765; 7206453
FAX: +82 (02) 7346452
TITLE: Charge d'Affaires
NAME: Milan Hupcej

Denmark
5th Fl., Namsong Bldg., 260-199 Itaewon-dong,
Yongsan-ku, Seoul 140-200, South Korea
PHONE: +82 (02) 7954187
FAX: +82 (02) 7960986
TITLE: Charge d'Affaires
NAME: Hans Jorgen Ipland

Domican Republic
1601 Garden Tower Bldg., 98-78 Woonni-dong,
Chongro-ku, Seoul, South Korea
PHONE: +82 (02) 7426867
FAX: +82 (02) 7441803
TITLE: Charge d'Affaires

NAME: Juan Dominguez

Ecuador
330-275 Sungbuk-dong, Sungbuk-ku, Seoul 136-
020, South Korea
PHONE: +82 (02) 7431617
FAX: +82 (02) 7456963
E-MAIL: e26258@nuri.net
TITLE: Ambassador
NAME: Patricio Zuquilanda-Duque

Egypt
744-4 Hannam-dong, Yongsan-ku, Seoul 140-
210, South Korea
PHONE: +82 (02) 7490787
FAX: +82 (02) 7952588
TITLE: Ambassador
NAME: Hussein Elfarouk Derar

El Salvador
701 Garden Tower Bldg., 98-78 Wooni-dong
Chongro-ku, Seoul, South Korea
PHONE: +82 (02) 7417527; 7659726
FAX: +82 (02) 7417528
TITLE: Ambassador
NAME: Alfredo Francisco Ungo

Ethiopia
657-26 Hannam-dong, Yongsan-ku, Seoul 140-
210, South Korea
PHONE: +82 (02) 7908927
FAX: +82 (02) 7908929
TITLE: Ambassador
NAME: Fekade Workneh

Finland
1602 Kyobo Bldg., Chongro 1-ka, Chongro-ku,
Seoul, South Korea
PHONE: +82 (02) 7326737
FAX: +82 (02) 7234969
TITLE: Ambassador
NAME: Unto Turunen

France
30 Hap-dong, Sodaemun-ku, South Korea
PHONE: +82 (02) 3123272
FAX: +82 (02) 3936108
TITLE: Ambassador
NAME: Jean-Paul Reau

Gabon
4th Fl., Yoosung Bldg., 738-20 Hannam-dong,
Yongsan-ku, Seoul, South Korea
PHONE: +82 (02) 7939575
FAX: +82 (02) 7939574
E-MAIL: amgabsel@unitel.co.kr
TITLE: Ambassador
NAME: Joseph Mamboungou

Germany
308-5 dongbinggo-dong, Yongsan-ku, Seoul 140-230, South Korea
PHONE: +82 (02) 7484114
FAX: +82 (02) 7484161
E-MAIL: GERMANY@SHINBIRO.COM
TITLE: Ambassador
NAME: Claus Vollers

Greece
27th Fl., Hanwha Bldg., 1 Janggyo-dong, Chung-ku, Seoul 100-797, South Korea
PHONE: +82 (02) 7291400
FAX: +82 (02) 7291402
TITLE: Ambassador
NAME: Ioannis Vavvas

Guatemala
602 Garden Tower Bldg., 98-78 Wooni-dong, Chongro-ku, Seoul I, South Korea
PHONE: +82 (02) 7653265
FAX: +82 (02) 7636010
TITLE: Ambassador
NAME: Giovanni R. Castillo Polanco

Honduras
802 Garden Tower Bldg., Woonni-dong Chongro-ku, Seoul, South Korea
PHONE: +82 (02) 7447563; 7417677
FAX: +82 (02) 7447564
TITLE: Ambassador
NAME: Gustavo E. Gamero Rosales

Hungary
1-103 Dongbinggo-dong, Yongsan-ku, Seoul 140-230, South Korea
PHONE: +82 (02) 7922103
FAX: +82 (02) 7922109
E-MAIL: HUEMBSEL@shinbiron.com
TITLE: Charge d'Affaires
NAME: Istavan Perosa

India
37-3 Hannam-dong, Yongsan-ku, Seoul, South Korea
PHONE: +82 (02) 7984257
FAX: +82 (02) 7969534
E-MAIL: eoiseoul@soback.kornet.nm.kr
TITLE: Ambassador
NAME: Santosh Kumar

Indonesia
55 Yoido-dong, Youngdeungpo-ku, Seoul, South Korea
PHONE: +82 (02) 7835675; 7835371
FAX: +82 (02) 7804280
TITLE: Ambassador
NAME: Jauhari Nataatmaja

Israel
823-21 Yeoksam-dong, Kangnam-ku, Seoul, South Korea
PHONE: +82 (02) 5643448
FAX: +82 (02) 5643449
TITLE: Ambassador
NAME: Arie Arazi

Iran
726-126 Hannam-dong, Yongsan-ku, Seoul, South Korea
PHONE: +82 (02) 7937751
FAX: +82 (02) 7927052
E-MAIL: Matbuat@MFA.GOV.Ir
TITLE: Ambassador
NAME: Mohsen Talaei

Ireland
15th Fl., Daehan Fire and Marine Insurance Bldg., 51-1 Namchang-dong, Chung-ku, Seoul 100-060, South Korea
PHONE: +82 (02) 7746455
FAX: +82 (02) 7746458
E-MAIL: hibernia@bora.dacom.co.kr
TITLE: Charge d'Affaires
NAME: Paul Barnwell

Italy
1-398 Hannam-dong, Yongsan-ku, South Korea
PHONE: +82 (02) 7960491
FAX: +82 (02) 7975560
TITLE: Ambassador
NAME: Carlo Trezza

Japan
18-11 Choonghak-dong, Chongro-ku, Seoul, South Korea
PHONE: +82 (02) 7335626
FAX: +82 (02) 7344528
TITLE: Ambassador
NAME: Kazuo Ogura

Kazakstan
32-15 Nonhyun-dong, Kangnam-ku, Seoul, South Korea
PHONE: +82 (02) 5481415; 5161440
FAX: +82 (02) 5481416
TITLE: Ambassador
NAME: Tulegen Zhukeyev

Kuwait
309-15 Dongbinggo-dong, Yongsan-ku, Seoul, South Korea
PHONE: +82 (02) 7493688
FAX: +82 (02) 7493687
TITLE: Ambassador

NAME: Salem Abdullah Jaber Al-Sabah

Lebanon
1-48 Dongbinggo-dong, Yongsan-lu, Seoul,
South Korea
PHONE: +82 (02) 7946482
FAX: +82 (02) 7946485
TITLE: Charge d'Affaires
NAME: Salim Baddoura

Malaysia
4-1 Hannam-dong, Yongsan-ku, South Korea
PHONE: +82 (02) 7940349; 7953032
FAX: +82 (02) 7945488
TITLE: Ambassador
NAME: Dato Vyramuttu Yoogalingam

Mexico
33-6 Hannam-dong, Yongsan-ku, Seoul 140-210,
South Korea
PHONE: +82 (02) 7981694
FAX: +82 (02) 7900939
TITLE: Charge d'Affaires
NAME: Armando Alvarez Reina

Mongolia
33-5 Hannam-dong, Yongsan-ku, Seoul, South
Korea
PHONE: +82 (02) 7941350
FAX: +82 (02) 7947605
E-MAIL: monemb@uriel.net
TITLE: Ambassador
NAME: Lodoidamba Galbadrah

Morocco
S-15 U.N. Village, 270-3, Hannam-Dong,
Yongsan-Ku, Seoul, South Korea
PHONE: +82 (02) 7936249
FAX: +82 (02) 7928178
E-MAIL: sifamase@bora.dacom.co
TITLE: Ambassador
NAME: Mohamed Bennani-Smires

Myanmar
723-1 Hannam-dong, Yongsan-ku, Seoul 140-
210, South Korea
PHONE: +82 (02) 7923341; 7969858
FAX: +82 (02) 7965570
TITLE: Ambassador
NAME: U Nyi Nyi Than

Netherlands
14th Fl., Kyobo Bldg., . 1 Chongro 1-ka,
Chongro-ku, P.O. Box 509, Seoul 110-714,
South Korea
PHONE: +82 (02) 7379514
FAX: +82 (02) 7351321
E-MAIL: nlgovseo@bora.dacom.co.kr

TITLE: Charge d'Affaires
NAME: Gert Heijkoop

New Zealand
18th Fl., Kyobo Bldg., 1 Chongro 1-ka Chongro-
ku, Seoul, South Korea
PHONE: +82 (02) 7307794
FAX: +82 (02) 7374861
TITLE: Ambassador
NAME: Roy Neil Ferguson

Nigeria
724-5 Hannam-dong, Yongsan-ku, Seoul, South
Korea
PHONE: +82 (02) 7972370
FAX: +82 (02) 7961848
TITLE: Ambassador
NAME: Olanrewaju Falola

Norway
258-8 Itaewon-dong, Yongsan-ku, Seoul 140-
200, South Korea
PHONE: +82 (02) 7956850
FAX: +82 (02) 7986072
E-MAIL: noram@bora.dacom.co.kr
TITLE: Ambassador
NAME: Torolf Raa

Oman
309-3, Dongbinggo-dong, Yongsan-ku, Seoul,
South Korea
PHONE: +82 (02) 7902431
FAX: +82 (02) 7902430
TITLE: Ambassador
NAME: Yahya Salim Al-Wahaibi

Pakistan
258-13 Itaewon-dong, Yongsan-ku, Seoul 140-
230, South Korea
PHONE: +82 (02) 7968252; 7960312
FAX: +82 (02) 7960313
TITLE: Ambassado
NAME: Tariq Osman Hyder

Panama
1101 Garden Tower Bldg., 98-78, Wooni-dong,
Chongro-ku, Seoul, South Korea
PHONE: +82 (02) 7450720; 7640363
FAX: +82 (02) 7425874
TITLE: Ambassador
NAME: Alfredo Zebede Macharaviaya

Papua New Guinea
5th Fl., 36-1 Hannam 1-dong, Yongsan-ku,
Seoul, South Korea
PHONE: +82 (02) 7989854
FAX: +82 (02) 7989856
TITLE: Ambassador

NAME: David Anggo

Paraguay
603 Garden Tower Bldg., 98-78 Woonni-dong Chongro-ku, Seoul, South Korea
PHONE: +82 (02) 7422190
FAX: +82 (02) 7422191
E-MAIL: pyemc@nuri.net
TITLE: Charge d'Affaires
NAME: Nilda Acosta

Peru
6th Fl., Namhan Bldg., 76-42 Hannam-dong, Yongsan-ku, Seoul 140-210, South Korea
PHONE: +82 (02) 7935810; 7905758
FAX: +82 (02) 7973736
E-MAIL: Ipruseul@uriel.net
TITLE: Ambassador
NAME: Luis Felipe Galvez Villarroel

Philippines
9th Fl. Diplomatic Center 1376-1, Seocho-dong, Seocho-ku, Seoul, South Korea
PHONE: +82 (02) 5776147; 5716147
FAX: +82 (02) 5744286
E-MAIL: Phsk@soback.Kornet.nm.kr
TITLE: Ambassador
NAME: Juanito P. Jarasa

Poland
1-72 Dongbinggo-dong, Yongsan-ku, Seoul, South Korea
PHONE: +82 (02) 7499681
FAX: +82 (02) 7499680
TITLE: Ambassador
NAME: Janusz Switkowski

Portugal
2nd Fl., Wonseo Bldg., 171 Wonseo-dong, Chongro-ku, Seoul 110-280, South Korea
PHONE: +82 (02) 36752251
FAX: +82 (02) 36752250
E-MAIL: embport@chollian.net
TITLE: Ambassador
NAME: Fernando R. Machado

Qatar
1-44 Dongbinggo-dong, Yongsan-ku, Seoul, South Korea
PHONE: +82 (02) 7901308
FAX: +82 (02) 7901027
TITLE: Ambassador
NAME: Ali Abdullateef Ahmed al-Muslemani

Romania
UN Village, 1-42 Hannam-dong, Yongsan-ku, Seoul, South Korea
PHONE: +82 (02) 7974924

FAX: +82 (02) 7943114
TITLE: Ambassador
NAME: Nicolae Ropotean

Russia
1001-13, 14 Daechi-dong, Kangnam-ku, Seoul, South Korea
PHONE: +82 (02) 5527096; 5388896
FAX: +82 (02) 5527098
TITLE: Ambassador
NAME: Evgeny V. Afannasiev

Saudi Arabia
1-112, Shinmoonro 2-ka, Chongro-ku, P.O. Box 108, Seoul, South Korea
PHONE: +82 (02) 7391631
FAX: +82 (02) 7323110
TITLE: Ambassador
NAME: Saleh Bin Mansour Al-Rajhy

Singapore
19th Fl., Taepyungno Building, 310 Taepyungno 2ka Chung-ku, Seoul 100-102, South Korea
E-MAIL: singemb@unitel.co.kr
TITLE: Ambassador
NAME: Teo Eng Cheng

Slovakia
389-1 Hannam-dong, Yongsan-ku, Seoul, South Korea
PHONE: +82 (02) 7943981
FAX: +82 (02) 7943982
TITLE: Ambassador
NAME: Peter Sopko

South Africa
1-37 Hannam-dong, Yongsan-ku, Seoul, South Korea
PHONE: +82 (02) 7924855
FAX: +82 (02) 7924856
TITLE: Ambassador
NAME: Johannes J. Spies

Spain
726-52 Hannam-dong, Yongsan-ku, Seoul, South Korea
PHONE: +82 (02) 7943581
FAX: +82 (02) 7968207
TITLE: Ambassador
NAME: Enrique Romeu

Sri Lanka
2002 Kyobo Bldg., Chongro 1-ka, Chongro-ku, Seoul 110-714, South Korea
PHONE: +82 (02) 7352966; 7222681
FAX: +82 (02) 7379577
E-MAIL: lankaemb@ktnet.co.kr
TITLE: Charge d'Affairs

NAME: Shanthi Sudusinghe Fernando

Sudan

653-24 Hannam-dong, Yongsan-ku, Seoul, South Korea
PHONE: +82 (02) 7938692; 7491090
FAX: +82 (02) 7938693
E-MAIL: sudansol/@ppp.kornet.nm.kr
TITLE: Ambassador
NAME: Abdel-Hamied Ibrahim Gibreel

Sweden

12th Fl., Hanhyo Bldg., 136 Seorin-dong, Chongro-ku, Seoul, South Korea
PHONE: +82 (02) 7380846; 7381149; 7394767
FAX: +82 (02) 7331317
E-MAIL: swedemb@sobadk.kornet.nm.kr
TITLE: Ambassador
NAME: Sture T. Stiernlof

Switzerland

32-10 Songwol-dong, Chongro-ku, Seoul 100-101, South Korea
PHONE: +82 (02) 7399511
FAX: +82 (02) 7379392
E-MAIL: swissemb@elim.net
TITLE: Ambassador
NAME: Eric N. Pfister

Thailand

653-7 Hannam-dong, Yongsan-ku, South Korea
PHONE: +82 (02) 7953098
FAX: +82 (02) 7983448
E-MAIL: rteseoul@elim.net
TITLE: Ambassador
NAME: Vichai Vannasin

Tunisia

7-13 Dongbinggo-dong, Yongsan-ku, Seoul 140-230, South Korea
PHONE: +82 (02) 7904334
FAX: +82 (02) 7904333
E-MAIL: tunseoul@att.co.kr
TITLE: Ambassador
NAME: Mondher Jemail

Turkey

4th Fl., Vivien Corporation Bldg., 4-52 Subinggo-dong, Yongsan-ku, Seoul, South Korea
PHONE: +82 (02) 7940255
FAX: +82 (02) 7978546
E-MAIL: seulbe@soback.korne21.net
TITLE: Ambassador
NAME: Halil Dag

Ukraine

901 Diplomatic Center, 1376-1 Seoch 2-dong, Seocho-ku, Seoul, South Korea
PHONE: +82 (02) 5786910; 5786911
FAX: +82 (02) 5785514
E-MAIL: ukremb@chollian.dacom.co.kr
TITLE: Ambassador
NAME: Mykhailo B. Reznik

United Arab Emirates

5-5 Hannam-Dong, Yongsan-Ku, Seoul, South Korea
PHONE: +82 (02) 7903235
FAX: +82 (02) 7903238
TITLE: Ambassador
NAME: Abdulla Mohamed Ali al-Shurafa al-Hammady

United Kingdom

PHONE: +82 (02) 7357341
FAX: +82 (02) 7251738
E-MAIL: postmaster@seoul.mail.fco.gov.uk
TITLE: Ambassador
NAME: Stephen D.R. Brown

United States

82 Sejong-ro, Chongro-ku, South Korea
PHONE: +82 (02) 3974114
TITLE: Ambassador
NAME: Stephen W. Bosworth

Uruguay

Daewoo Center Bldg., Rm. 1802 541, Namdaemoon-ro 5-ka, Chung-ku, South Korea
PHONE: +82 (02) 7537893; 7540720
FAX: +82 (02) 7774129
E-MAIL: uruseul.nuri.net
TITLE: Ambassador
NAME: Julio Giambruno

Uzbekistan

Room 701, Diplomatic Center 1376-1 Seocho 2-dong, Seocho-ku, Seoul, South Korea
PHONE: +82 (02) 5746554; 5773660
FAX: +82 (02) 5780576
TITLE: Charge d'Affaires
NAME: Vitali V. Fen

Venezuela

1801 Garden Tower Bldg., 98-78, Wooni-dong, Chongro-ku, South Korea
PHONE: +82 (02) 7410036
FAX: +82 (02) 7410046
E-MAIL: emvesel@soback.koret.nm.kr
TITLE: Charge d'Affaires
NAME: Alberto Murrillo

Vietnam

28-58 Samcheong-dong, Chongro-ku, Seoul, South Korea
PHONE: +82 (02) 7392065; 7382318

FAX: +82 (02) 7392064
TITLE: Ambassador
NAME: Nguyen Van Xuong

Yemen
657-40 Hannam-dong, Yongsan-ku, Seoul, South Korea
PHONE: +82 (02) 7929883
FAX: +82 (02) 7929885
E-MAIL: yemensel@ppp.hornet21.net
TITLE: Charge d'Affaires
NAME: Yahya A. al-Wazir

JUDICIAL SYSTEM
Supreme Court
967 Socho-dong, Socho-gu, Seoul 137-070, South Korea
PHONE: +82 (02) 34801100
FAX: +82 (02) 5331911

FURTHER READING
Articles
"Across the Divide." *The Economist* (January 23, 1999): 37–8.

"Gunboat Diplomacy." *The Economist* (June 19, 1999): 33.

"Making a Comeback." *The Economist* (February 20, 1999): 38–9.

"The Month in Review: South Korea." *Current History* 98 (February 1999): 94.

"The Month in Review: South Korea." *Current History* 98 (September 1999): 302.

"The Month in Review: South Korea." *Current History* 98 (April 1999): 189.

"More Pain, Please." *The Economist* (April 7, 1999): 67–8.

"Power Politics, Korean-Style." *The Economist* (May 8, 1999): 33.

"South Korea's Alarming Recovery." *The Economist* (July 31, 1999): 61–2.

"South Korea's Workers Return to the Street." *The Economist* (May 1, 1999): 37–8.

"The Secret in Room 529." *The Economist* (January 9, 1999): 37.

"Toughing It Out." *The Economist* (September 4, 1999): 43–4.

"Worker Bosses." *The Economist* (March 6, 1999): 61–2.

Books
Eckert, Carter J., et al. *Korea Old and New: A History.* Seoul: Ilchokak Publishers, 1990.

Lee, Ki-Baek. *A New History of Korea.* Edward W. Wagner, trans. Cambridge, Mass.: Harvard University Press, 1984.

McDonald, Donald Stone. *The Koreans: Contemporary Politics and Society.* 3rd ed. Boulder, Colo.: Westview Press, 1992.

Oberdorser, Don. *The Two Koreas.* Reading, Mass.: Addison-Wesley, 1992.

Internet
Chosun Ilbo. Available Online @ www.chosun.com (October 12, 1999).

The Korea Herald. Available Online @ www.koreaherald.co.kr (October 12, 1999).

Korea Times. Available Online @ www.koreatimes.co.kr (October 12, 1999).

Korea Webweekly. Available Online @ www.kimsoft.com/korea.htm (October 12, 1999).

SOUTH KOREA: STATISTICAL DATA

For sources and notes see "Sources of Statistics" in the front of each volume.

GEOGRAPHY

Geography (1)

Area:

Total: 98,480 sq km.

Land: 98,190 sq km.

Water: 290 sq km.

Area—comparative: slightly larger than Indiana.

Land boundaries:

Total: 238 km.

Border countries: North Korea 238 km.

Coastline: 2,413 km.

Climate: temperate, with rainfall heavier in summer than winter.

Terrain: mostly hills and mountains; wide coastal plains in west and south.

Natural resources: coal, tungsten, graphite, molybdenum, lead, hydropower.

Land use:

Arable land: 19%

Permanent crops: 2%

Permanent pastures: 1%

Forests and woodland: 65%

Other: 13% (1993 est.).

HUMAN FACTORS

Demographics (2A)

	1990	1995	1998	2000	2010	2020	2030	2040	2050
Population	42,869.0	45,017.8	46,416.8	47,350.5	51,235.2	53,450.9	54,825.6	54,577.1	52,624.7
Net migration rate (per 1,000 population)	NA	NA	NA	NA	NA	NA	NA	NA	NA
Births	NA	NA	NA	NA	NA	NA	NA	NA	NA
Deaths	NA	NA	NA	NA	NA	NA	NA	NA	NA
Life expectancy - males	67.1	69.3	70.4	71.1	74.1	76.3	77.8	78.9	79.6
Life expectancy - females	75.2	77.1	78.0	78.7	81.2	83.0	84.2	85.1	85.7
Birth rate (per 1,000)	15.0	16.3	16.1	15.8	12.4	10.9	10.7	9.3	9.2
Death rate (per 1,000)	5.9	5.7	5.7	5.7	6.3	7.7	9.3	11.7	13.5
Women of reproductive age (15-49 yrs.)	12,115.0	12,853.7	13,229.4	13,414.3	13,040.1	12,302.3	11,297.3	10,758.1	10,249.3
of which are currently married	17,208.0	18,375.0	NA	NA	NA	NA	NA	NA	NA
Fertility rate	1.6	1.8	1.8	1.8	1.8	1.8	1.8	1.7	1.7

Except as noted, values for vital statistics are in thousands; life expectancy is in years.

Health Personnel (3)

Total health expenditure as a percentage of GDP,
1990-1997[a]

Public sector 2.3

Private sector 1.7

Total[b] 4.0

Health expenditure per capita in U.S. dollars,
1990-1997[a]

Purchasing power parity 522

Total 397

Availability of health care facilities per 100,000 people

Hospital beds 1990-1997[a] 440

Doctors 1993[c] 127

Nurses 1993[c] 232

Ethnic Division (6)

Homogeneous (except for about 20,000 Chinese).

Religions (7)

Christianity 49%

Buddhism 47%

Confucianism 3%

Other 1%

Other includes pervasive folk religion (shamanism),
Chondogyo (Religion of the Heavenly Way), and other.

Languages (8)

Korean.

EDUCATION

Educational Attainment (10)

Age group (1995) . . . . .25+

Total population 26,217,862

Highest level attained (%)

No schooling 8.7

First level

Not completed 0.9

Completed 17.3

Entered second level

S-1 . . . . .15.7

S-2 . . . . .36.2

Postsecondary 21.1

Literacy Rates (11A)

In thousands and percent[1]	1990	1995	2000	2010
Illiterate population (15+ yrs.)	937	697	493	224
Literacy rate - total adult pop. (%)	97.1	98.0	98.7	99.4
Literacy rate - males (%)	99.0	99.3	99.5	99.7
Literacy rate - females (%)	95.2	96.7	97.9	99.2

GOVERNMENT & LAW

Political Parties (12)

National Assembly	No. of seats
New Korea Party (NKP)	139
National Congress for New Politics (NCNP)	79
United Liberal Democrats (ULD)	50
Democratic Party (DP)	15
Independents	16

Government Budget (13B)

Revenues . . . .$101 billion

Expenditures . . . .$101 billion

Capital expenditures . . . .$20 billion

Data for 1996 est.

Crime (15)

Crime rate (for 1997)

Crimes reported 553,300

Total persons convicted 465,900

Crimes per 100,000 population 1,200

Persons responsible for offenses

Total number of suspects 710,300

Total number of female suspects 114,600

Total number of juvenile suspects 99,500

LABOR FORCE

Labor Force (16)

Total (million) 20

Services and other 52%

Mining and manufacturing 27%

Agriculture, fishing, forestry 21%

Data for 1991.

Unemployment Rate (17)

2% (1996)

PRODUCTION SECTOR

Electric Energy (18)

Capacity . . . . .31.665 million kW (1995)

Production . . . . .174.52 billion kWh (1995)

Consumption per capita . . . . .3,831 kWh (1995)

GOVERNMENT & LAW

Military Affairs (14B)

	1990	1991	1992	1993	1994	1995
Military expenditures						
Current dollars (mil.)	10,780	10,820	11,840	12,450	13,930	14,410
1995 constant dollars (mil.)	12,390	11,950	12,740	13,050	14,280	14,410
Armed forces (000)	650	750	750	750	750	655
Gross national product (GNP)						
Current dollars (mil.)	258,700	293,700	316,700	343,300	380,400	424,800e
1995 constant dollars (mil.)	297,300	324,500	340,700	359,900	389,900	424,800e
Central government expenditures (CGE)						
1995 constant dollars (mil.)	55,530	61,060	64,210	66,890	82,040	106,100
People (mil.)	42.9	43.2	43.7	44.1	44.6	45.0
Military expenditure as % of GNP	4.2	3.7	3.7	3.6	3.7	3.4
Military expenditure as % of CGE	22.3	19.6	19.8	19.5	17.4	13.6
Military expenditure per capita (1995 $)	289	276	292	296	321	320
Armed forces per 1,000 people (soldiers)	15.2	17.3	17.2	17.0	16.8	14.5
GNP per capita (1995 $)	6,935	7,504	7,803	8,161	8,751	9,437
Arms imports[6]						
Current dollars (mil.)	650	1,100	490	1,100	1,400	1,100
1995 constant dollars (mil.)	747	1,216	527	1,153	1,435	1,100
Arms exports[6]						
Current dollars (mil.)	130	40	30	50	40	60
1995 constant dollars (mil.)	149	44	32	52	41	60
Total imports[7]						
Current dollars (mil.)	69,840	81,520	81,770	83,800	102,300	135,100
1995 constant dollars (mil.)	80,270	90,090	87,960	87,850	104,900	135,100
Total exports[7]						
Current dollars (mil.)	65,020	71,870	76,630	82,240	96,010	125,100
1995 constant dollars (mil.)	74,720	79,420	82,430	86,210	98,420	125,100
Arms as percent of total imports[8]	.9	1.3	.6	1.3	1.4	.8
Arms as percent of total exports[8]	.2	.1	0	.1	0	0

PRODUCTION SECTOR

Transportation (19)

Highways:
total: 83,400 km
paved: 63,467 km (including 1,920 km of expressways)
unpaved: 19,933 km (1996 est.)
Waterways: 1,609 km; use restricted to small native craft
Pipelines: petroleum products 455 km; note—additionally, there is a parallel petroleum, oils, and lubricants (POL) pipeline being completed
Merchant marine:
total: 474 ships (1,000 GRT or over) totaling 6,749,052 GRT/10,447,597 DWT
Airports: 103 (1997 est.)
Airports—with paved runways:
total: 67
over 3,047 m: 1
2,438 to 3,047 m: 18
1,524 to 2,437 m: 15
914 to 1,523 m: 14
under 914 m: 19 (1997 est.)
Airports—with unpaved runways:
total: 36
914 to 1,523 m: 4
under 914 m: 32 (1997 est.)

Top Agricultural Products (20)

Rice, root crops, barley, vegetables, fruit; cattle, pigs, chickens, milk, eggs; fish catch of 2.9 million metric tons, seventh largest in world.

FINANCE, ECONOMICS, & TRADE

Economic Indicators (22)

National product: GDP—purchasing power parity—$631.2 billion (1997 est.)
National product real growth rate: 6% (1997 est.)
National product per capita: $13,700 (1997 est.)
Inflation rate—consumer price index: 5% (1996)

Exchange Rates (24)

Exchange rates:

South Korean won (W) per US$1
January 1998	1,706.80
1997	.951.29
1996	.804.45
1995	.771.27
1994	.803.45
1993	.802.67

Top Import Origins (25)

$150.2 billion (c.i.f., 1996) Data are for 1995.

Origins	%
United States	.22
Japan	.21
European Union	.13

Top Export Destinations (26)

$129.8 billion (f.o.b., 1996) Data are for 1995.

Destinations	%
United States	.17
European Union	.13
Japan	.12

Economic Aid (27)

$NA. NA stands for not available.

Import Export Commodities (28)

Import Commodities	Export Commodities
Machinery	Electronic and electrical equipment
Electronics and electronic equipment	Machinery
Oil	Steel
Steel	Automobiles
Transport equipment	Ships; textiles
Textiles	Clothing
Organic chemicals	Footwear; fish
Grains	

Balance of Payments (23)

	1992	1993	1994	1995	1996
Exports of goods (f.o.b.)	75,169	80,950	93,676	123,203	128,303
Imports of goods (f.o.b.)	−77,315	−79,090	−96,822	−127,949	−143,609
Trade balance	−2,146	1,860	−3,146	−4,746	−15,306
Services - debits	−17,600	−19,524	−23,754	−32,540	−37,454
Services - credits	14,532	17,109	21,485	28,623	29,580
Private transfers (net)	−25	−142	−228	−258	−370
Government transfers (net)	1,300	1,713	1,788	671	489
Overall balance	−3,939	1,016	−3,855	−8,250	−23,061

KUWAIT

State of Kuwait
Dawlat al-Kuwayt

INTRODUCTORY SURVEY

RECENT HISTORY

At the end of the nineteenth century, Sheikh Mubarak as-Sabah, fearing the territorial ambitions of the Ottoman Turks, asked to be taken under British protection. The British, in turn, were concerned not only by Turkish claims but also by the activities of Russia and Germany in the area. In 1899, Sheikh Mubarak agreed not to open any of his territory to foreign control. In return, the British offered their services as well as an annual subsidy to support the sheikh and his heirs.

On 19 June 1961, the protective treaty with the United Kingdom was terminated by mutual consent, and Kuwait declared itself fully independent. By this time, the sheikhdom had already become a major oil producer. Iraq refused to recognize Kuwait's independence, asserting it had inherited the Ottoman claim to the territory. Baghdad's threat of an invasion was foiled by British troops and later by the support of the Arab League. Iraq then appeared to agree to Kuwait's sovereignty, although border issues were never definitely resolved. During the next two decades, Kuwait succeeded in establishing an open and prosperous economy, based in large part on foreign, especially Palestinian and Egyptian, labor.

During the Iran-Iraq War (1980–88), Kuwait, although technically neutral, provided important aid to Baghdad, including shipment of goods and over $6 billion in loans. In 1987, Iranian attacks on Persian Gulf shipping led Kuwait to request U.S. protection for its supertankers.

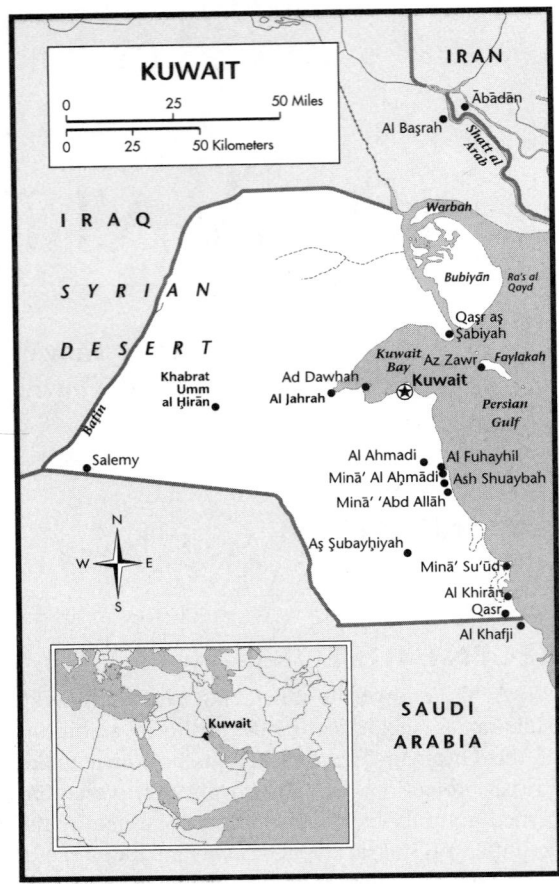

KUWAIT

0   25   50 Miles

0   25   50 Kilometers

IRAN

Ābādān

Al Başrah

Shaṭṭ al ʿArab

IRAQ

SYRIAN

DESERT

Warbah

Bubiyān   Ra's al Qayd

Qaşr aş Şabiyah

Kuwait Bay   Az Zawr   Faylakah

Khabrat Umm al Ḥirān

Ad Dawhah   Kuwait

Al Jahrah

Persian Gulf

Salemy

Al Ahmadi   Al Fuhayhil

Minā' Al Aḥmādi   Ash Shuaybah

Minā' 'Abd Allāh

Aş Şubayḥiyah

Minā' Su'ūd

Al Khirān

Qasr

Al Khafji

SAUDI ARABIA

Kuwait

With the end of the war, Iraq-Kuwait relations were stable until 1990 when Saddam Hussein, president of Iraq, accused his neighbor of illegally pumping oil from the shared Rumailia field. On 2 August 1990, Iraqi forces invaded Kuwait, asserting that they were rightfully reclaiming their own territory. Kuwaiti defense forces offered little resistance and most senior officials fled the country.

The United States led an international coalition of Arab and other nations to demand the withdrawal of Iraqi forces. After a lengthy buildup of forces, Iraq was assaulted by massive air and land forces; after six weeks, its defenses collapsed and Kuwait was liberated in February 1991. Kuwait's leaders returned to find a hostile population that resented their abandonment and demanded greater political participation. Enormous physical damage had been inflicted on the country, including over 700 oil well fires that did serious ecological damage before being extinguished after almost nine months' effort.

The regime and many Kuwaitis turned harshly against those suspected of collaboration with Iraq, and much of the large Palestinian community was ejected from the country. Relations with Iraq remained tense. Kuwait's vulnerability to possible attack from Iraq or Iran drew the nation closer to the United States, which has been willing to offer enhanced security collaboration.

In October 1994, Iraq began moving 60,000 troops to within 32 kilometers (20 miles) of the Kuwaiti border. The United Nations Security Council condemned Iraq's actions. Kuwait then agreed to let the United States station a squadron of warplanes there. On 10 November 1994 Iraq agreed to recognize the independence and borders of Kuwait. In April 1996 an international military exercise was held in Kuwait by some of its Gulf War allies. The United Nations also renewed its multinational force of border observers to oversee the demilitarized zone that separates Kuwait from Iraq.

GOVERNMENT

Kuwait is an independent, sovereign Arab state, under a constitutional monarch. Executive power is vested in the emir, who exercises it through a Council of Ministers. The National Assembly (*Majlis*) consists of 50 elected representatives and 25 appointed members. There are five governorates, but political authority is highly centralized in the capital.

Judiciary

A Tribunal of First Instance has jurisdiction over matters involving personal status, civil and commercial cases, and criminal cases, except those of a religious nature. The Court of Appeals, the highest in the land, has jurisdiction over appeals involving personal status and civil cases, as well as those involving commercial and criminal cases. Ordinary criminal cases may be appealed to the High Court of Appeals. A military court handles offenses committed by members of the security forces. Religious courts, Sunni and Shi'ite, decide family law matters according to Muslim law.

Political Parties

Political parties are prohibited, but opposition groups are active in the nation's political life. Muslim fundamentalists held 17 of 50 seats in the National Assembly in 1996.

DEFENSE

Kuwait's rebuilt armed forces totaled 15,300 volunteers in 1995. The army had 11,000 men and 200 tanks; the air force, 2,500 men and 76 combat aircrafts; and the navy, 1,800 men and 2 patrol crafts. There is a 5,000-member National Guard. United Nations observers and advisors number 400. Estimated defense expenditures in 1995 were $3.1 billion.

ECONOMIC AFFAIRS

The Kuwaiti standard of living was among the highest in the Middle East and in the world by the early 1980s. The government has used its oil revenues to build ports, roads, an international airport, a seawater distillation plant, and modern government and office buildings.

Kuwait's economy suffered enormously from the effects of the Gulf War and the Iraqi occupation, which ended in February 1991 with the destruction of much of Kuwait's oil production capacity and other economic resources. The damage inflicted on the economy is estimated at $20 billion. After the war, the gross domestic product (GDP) increased by 40.2% in 1993, 1.3% in 1994, and 2.9% in 1995.

Public Finance

In 1994/95, the Kuwaiti government reported revenues of KD2,637.2 million and expenditures of KD4,140 million. The U.S. Central Intelligence Agency estimates that, in 1994, government revenues totaled approximately $9.7 billion and expenditures $14.2 billion. For 1995/96, revenues and expenditures were targeted at $10 billion and $13.8 billion, respectively, leaving an anticipated $3.8 billion deficit.

Much of the recent improvement in public finances is the result of higher oil prices and production, rather than government reforms. In 1994, the Kuwaiti government began to consider various austerity measures, which became a source of debate in parliament. Several plans in discussion call for reductions in government subsidies and welfare benefits, increases in taxes, privatization of state-owned businesses, and banking sector reforms. Subsidies are one of the most contentious and politicized austerity measures; in 1995, the Ministry of Finance stated that the country annually spends $1.8 billion on utility subsidies and free health care.

Income

In 1997, the gross domestic product (GDP) was $46.3 billion or about $22,300 per person. During 1985–95, the average annual growth rate of the per person GNP was 0.9%.

Industry

Although oil extraction continues to be the economic mainstay, Kuwait has diversified its industry to give manufacturing a larger role. Small-scale manufacturing plants produce ammonia, fertilizer, paper products, processed foods, and other consumer goods. Major refinery products were fuel oil, gas oil, naphtha, kerosene, and diesel fuel. Manufacturing all but stopped during the Iraqi invasion due to shortages of raw material and looting of equipment. After liberation, industry was hard-hit by the departure of Palestinian skilled labor.

Banking and Finance

The Central Bank of Kuwait, established in 1969, formulates and implements the nation's monetary policy, regulates the currency, and controls the banking system. The Central Bank's foreign assets totaled KD1,151.4 million at the end of 1993. As of December 1995, the total money supply, as measured by M2, was KD7,317 million. There are seven commercial banks with 96 branches in Kuwait, of which one is a single-branch operation belonging to a joint-venture bank (the Bank of Bahrain and Kuwait). Apart from this special case, foreign banks are not permitted to operate within Kuwait or to own shares in Kuwaiti banks. Kuwaiti bank shares are typically closely held, either by the government and its agencies or by the merchant families who founded them. The pre-eminent bank is the National Bank of Kuwait, which at the end of 1995 accounted for one-third of all Kuwaiti bank branches.

The Central Bank of Kuwait only took on a serious regulatory role in 1984, after a debt crisis engulfed commercial banks, all of which had exposure to the collapsed informal stock market. However, the Central Bank's powers are limited, and, although it considers some of the banks to be too weak to be competitive, it has so far been unable to force mergers.

There are three specialized banks, one of which, Kuwait Finance House, operates as a commercial bank restricted to Islamic financial transactions. The other two, Industrial Bank of Kuwait and Kuwait Real Estate Bank, were created to provide long-term credit at a time when the supply of fresh capital from the public sector was not constrained. In the more austere environment since the war, they function like a U.S. investment bank. The idea of establishing more Islamic banks has been welcomed. Total reserves, excluding gold, totaled $3,515 million at the end of 1996.

Kuwait's official securities exchange, the Kuwait Stock Exchange (KSE), was founded in 1977 and handles only government bonds and securities of Kuwaiti companies. An unofficial and unregulated securities exchange, the Souk al-Manakh, listing the stocks of 45 Gulf companies outside Kuwait and considered highly speculative, collapsed suddenly in August 1982. At the time of the crash, some 6,000 investors and $94 billion in postdated checks drawn in anticipation of future stock price increases were said to be involved. In order to limit the effect of the collapse on the Kuwaiti economy, the government created a special rescue fund to pay compensation to small investors for validated claims. All trading operations of the KSE were suspended on the Iraqi invasion of Kuwait on 2 August 1990. The KSE recommenced trading on 28 September 1992. On the exchange, 1995 was a banner year. The combined effect of rapidly expanding credit and privatization resulted in a 36% increase in the stock price index and a 226% increase in trading volume. At the end of 1995, 51 companies were listed with a total capitalization of KD 3.33 billion ($11.2 billion). Only Gulf Cooperation Council (GCC) citizens are permitted to buy shares in Kuwaiti companies.

Economic Development

Since the mid-1970s, Kuwait has restrained its spending on economic development and has fostered a policy of controlled growth. From 1977 to 1982, allocations for development projects remained steady at $1.7–2.5 billion annually, of which 76% was spent on public works, electric power plants, and desalination and irrigation projects. Development plans for the 1980s, stressing industrial diversification, included the expansion of local oil refineries and major projects in petrochemicals, electricity, water supply, highway construction, and telecommunications. Overseas, refining and marketing operations were stepped up.

Post-war economic planning was hampered by the expulsion of the mainly Palestinian middle-ranking civil servants in various government departments. The Industrial Bank of Kuwait has played a major role in the industrial redevelopment of the emirate following the war. In 1994, the

World Bank urged Kuwait to begin privatization (including the oil industry). The Kuwait Investment Authority sold nearly $1 billion of its foreign assets in 1995. In March 1996, Kuwait National Petroleum Co. announced that it would sell off one-third of its 90 gasoline stations as a preliminary move in divesting 80% of its retail assets.

In December 1961, Kuwait established the Kuwait Fund for Arab Economic Development, patterned after Western and international lending agencies, to issue loans at low rates of interest for Arab economic development. By the end of 1985, Kuwait had extended loans to developing countries amounting to $4.3 billion. The Kuwait-based Arab Fund for Economic and Social Development also has contributed to various development institutions. However, in 1990 the AFESD transferred its operations to Bahrain. Since Iraq's invasion most of Kuwait's aid commitments have taken the form of government-to-government agreements. Within the Arab world, the overwhelming share of Kuwaiti aid goes to Egypt and Syria.

SOCIAL WELFARE

Kuwait has a widespread system of social welfare, financed by government oil revenues. It offers welfare services for the poor, provides free medical service and education to all residents, and spends heavily for waterworks, public gardens, and other public facilities. Social insurance legislation provides for old age, disability, and survivor pensions.

Women have the same property rights as men, although they are not permitted to vote. Kuwaiti women married to foreign men suffer legal discrimination. The government began a counseling service in 1995 for women suffering from male violence.

Abusive treatment of foreign domestic servants is also an ongoing social problem. Bedouins (Bedu) are not entitled to citizenship and are unable to legally work or enroll their children in schools.

Healthcare

In 1993, 100% of the population had access to health care services. Influenza is common, and measles has resulted in a high fatality rate among children up to age five. The urban population has access to safe water and adequate sanitation. In 1994 there were 2,717 doctors.

Housing

According to the 1995 census, there were 255,477 households in Kuwait. About 50% of all housing units were apartments, 19% were detached homes, and 15% were traditional dwellings (mostly small cottages and mud huts).

EDUCATION

Kuwait offers its students free education, including free food, clothing, books, stationery, and transportation, from kindergarten through the fourth year of college. In 1995, Kuwait had 576 public schools with 274,665 students, and 258 private schools with 97,853 students.

In 1994, Kuwait University had a student enrollment of 12,712. All higher-level institutions had 14,027 students in 1994.

1999 KEY EVENTS TIMELINE

January

- Kuwait invites the Jordanian foreign minister for a visit that would officially end an eight-year freeze in relations between the two countries.

- The Kuwaiti Minister of State for Cabinet Affairs, Abdul-Aziz al-Dakhil, visits Jordan in the first high-level Kuwaiti visit since the Gulf crisis of 1990–91.

- A meeting between Iraqi and Kuwaiti officials to discuss the disappearance of hundreds of people during the Gulf crisis of 1990–91 is postponed indefinitely because the Iraqis decline to attend.

- British Prime Minister Tony Blair arrives in Kuwait for a one-day visit, where he will meet with pilots and ground crew from the Royal Air Force involved in the air strikes against Iraq in December.

- The state-influenced media in Kuwait and Saudi Arabia launch fierce personal attacks against the Iraqi president, Saddam Hussein, and his government.

- The Iraqi National Assembly votes to suspend all cooperation with the United Nations and declares Kuwait and Saudi Arabia fully responsible for the consequences of air attacks by the United States and United Kingdom.

- Kuwait places military units on full alert in response to threats from Iraq.

- The Kuwait Red Crescent Society claims to receive an invitation from its Iraqi counterpart to

attend a meeting in Baghdad next month; Kuwait declines.

- An Islamic human rights group says that Kuwait has handed over fifteen Egyptians to the authorities in Cairo after accusing them of being Iraqi spies; the Islamic Observation Centre, based in London, denies any links with Iraq, fears torture, and calls on the international community to secure their release.

February

- The Gulf states unite in mourning over the death of Jordan's King Hussein.

- Iraqi President Saddam Hussein warns the rulers of Kuwait and Saudi Arabia to stop cooperating with the United States against Iraq, as Iraq can target military bases in their nations.

- The secretary-general of the Arab League, Esmat Abdel-Meguid, condemns Iraq's threats against Kuwait and Saudi Arabia.

- Iraq repeats its threats against Kuwait and Saudi Arabia despite a warning from the American secretary of state, Madeleine Albright, that Baghdad would face a swift response if it attacked any bases in any neighboring countries used to launch air raids on Iraq.

- Kuwait's ambassador to the United States attends a ceremony in Arlington National Cemetery with former United States General Norman Schwarzkopf, commemorating the 400 American soldiers who died in the Gulf War and marking the eighth anniversary of its end.

- The Emir of Kuwait, Jaber al-Ahmed al-Sabah, marks the state's national day by pardoning more than 300 prisoners, including eight Jordanians still jailed for collaborating with Iraq during the 1990–91 Gulf crisis.

- Stateless Arabs, deported from Kuwait after the 1991 Gulf War, stage a protest outside the United Nations Development Program offices in the Iraqi capital, demanding to be allowed to return to Kuwait.

March

- Foreign minister of Jordan, Abdel-Ilah Khatib, visits Kuwait and opens a temporary embassy in an attempt to normalize diplomatic ties damaged by the 1990 Gulf crisis.

- Members of OPEC (Organization of Petroleum Exporting Countries), including Kuwait, reach an agreement to make substantial cuts in oil production in an effort to boost depressed prices.

April

- Iraqi authorities report incursions by Western planes from Kuwaiti and Saudi Arabian airspace.

May

- Emir Sheik Jaber al-Ahmad al-Sabah dissolves parliament after lawmakers threaten to oust his Islamic affairs minister, Ahmed al-Kulaib, because of errors and omissions in a government-funded printing of the Koran.

- The emir calls for parliamentary elections to be held July 3, nearly a year-and-a-half ahead of schedule.

- The cabinet issues a decree that gives women the right to vote and run for parliament.

- The foreign minister of Yemen, Abdel Kader Bajammal, visits Kuwait and reopens the Yemeni embassy in Kuwait City as part of an effort to improve relations between the two countries, which have been on hold since the 1991 Gulf War when Kuwait accused Sanaa of siding with Iraq.

June

- The Kuwaiti government says it is taking steps to prosecute those who are disregarding the nation's electoral laws in order to gain an advantage for their tribal groups. Names of some of the candidates in the upcoming parliamentary elections are turned in to the public prosecutor on suspicion that they took part in outlawed primary elections to improve the prospects of certain individuals, fostering tribalism and factionalism.

- Iraq accuses Kuwaiti patrols of carrying out unjustified acts of provocation and aggression along their land and sea borders and calls on the United Nations to stop it; Kuwait denies the charge.

- The interior ministry announces a change in policy allowing women to attain status of military personnel and become fully-fledged police officers for the first time.

- Jordanian authorities appeal to Kuwait to end its boycott of the upcoming Pan-Arab games in Amman; Kuwait maintains its refusal to participate unless Iraq releases hundreds of Kuwaiti prisoners authorities say have been held since the Gulf War.

- The Kuwaiti government shuts down the bureau of the al-Jazeera satellite channel, charging that the station had broadcast unacceptable remarks about the Emir.

- The Kuwaiti government detains an Islamist opposition candidate in the upcoming elections, Khalaf al-Arbeed, for defamation of senior government officials.

July

- Results from elections held July 3 award pro-government legislators 14 seats (down from 30), liberals 16 seats, and Islamists 20 seats.

- Sheik Jaber calls on the newly elected parliament to approve sixty laws passed by decree after the last parliament's dissolution.

- Saudi Defense Minister Prince Sultan bin Abdel Aziz visits Kuwait on a tour of the Gulf states designed to help Iran improve relations with the other states in the region.

- Kuwaiti defense minister Sheikh Salem al Sabah announces that the government is preparing to train women soldiers to fight in the front line in the event of a war.

- Sudanese foreign minister Mustafa Osman Ismail arrives in Kuwait and reopens the Sudanese embassy in Kuwait City, nine years after relations between the two countries were frozen due to the Gulf crisis.

August

- Iraq marks the ninth anniversary of its invasion of Kuwait with a defiant defense of its actions.

- Kuwait impounds an Indian boat, which had left Iraq loaded with goods, in opposition to international sanctions against Baghdad.

- A Syrian delegation led by the son of President Hafez al-Assad pays an official visit to Kuwait.

- Iraqi President Saddam Hussein condemns the governments of Kuwait, Saudi Arabia, and Turkey for allowing their bases to be used by Western aircraft carrying out attacks against Iraq.

September

- King Abdullah II of Jordan begins a two-day visit to Kuwait—the first by a Jordanian monarch since the 1990–91 Iraqi occupation.

- Kuwait charges that two guards were shot dead by gunfire from inside Iraq while patrolling the Iraqi border.

- Members of OPEC, including Kuwait, announce that the price of oil is to be kept high for at least six months.

- Nearly 150 Asian and Arab prostitutes are arrested in Kuwait as part of a widespread crackdown by the powerful Islamist movement in its drive to ban what it sees as all forms of immoral behavior.

October

- A Kuwaiti court sentences a university professor, Dr. Ahmad al-Baghdadi of Kuwait University, to one month in prison for defaming Islam; several days later, he is hospitalized for an irregular heartbeat after starting a hunger strike. Later in the month, the Emir, Sheikh Jaber al-Ahmad al-Sabah, pardons him, and Dr. Baghdadi responds by expressing his gratitude to the Emir.

- Kuwaiti authorities suspend a newspaper for five days for publishing an article considered to be offensive to the Emir.

- The United States Defense department announces that the U.S. will upgrade its airforce and army bases in Kuwait with the goal of increasing pressure on Iraqi President Saddam Hussein; Kuwaiti Defense Minister Sheikh Salem al-Sabah praises the U.S. for its decision.

- The National Assembly in Kuwait, the only elected law-making body on the Gulf Arab states, is formally opened by the Emir; the last National Assembly had been dissolved in May.

- Kuwaiti security forces use tear gas and live bullets to regain control in a residential area of Kuwait City after two days of rioting by Egyptian workers frustrated at not getting promised work; the unrest began when a fight broke out between Egyptian and Bangladeshi residents over a broken plate in a supermarket.

November

- A high-level Egyptian delegation led by the employment minister, Ahmed el-Amawi, visits Kuwait to discuss recent riots involving Egyptian workers.

- Kuwait's parliament, all of whose members are men, votes down the ruler's decree that would have granted women political rights.

December

- Rasha al-Sabah, a woman and member of Kuwait's ruling party, is appointed undersecretary of education.

ANALYSIS OF EVENTS: 1999

BUSINESS AND THE ECONOMY

Kuwait, along with other members of the Organization of Petroleum Exporting Countries (OPEC), announced that it planned to cut production and maintain higher prices for oil through early 2000.

Kuwait is a small and relatively open economy with proved crude oil reserves of about 94 billion barrels—10% of world reserves. Petroleum accounts for nearly half of Kuwait's GDP, 90% of export revenues, and 75% of government income. Kuwait lacks water and has practically no arable land, thus preventing the development of agriculture. With the exception of fish, it depends almost wholly on food imports. About 75% of potable water must be distilled or imported. The economy improved moderately from 1994–97, but suffered from the large decline in world oil prices in 1998. The Kuwaiti cabinet approved a reform package in January 1999, including reducing subsidies and increasing taxes on large consumer goods. Nevertheless, Kuwait anticipates continuing budget deficits for the next few years. Kuwait is attracting foreign oil companies to develop fields in the northern part of the country.

GOVERNMENT AND POLITICS

After nearly a decade has passed since Iraq invaded Kuwait and triggered the Gulf War (1990–91), relations between the two nations have not yet stabilized. The year began with heightened tensions between Iraq and its neighbors, Kuwait and Saudi Arabia. The Kuwaiti military was on full alert, in response to Iraqi threats: Iraqi leader Saddam Hussein justified his threats by contending that Kuwait and Saudi Arabia were responsible for the air attacks on Iraq that were mounted by NATO allies, the United States and United Kingdom. Relations with Sudan and Jordan were returning to normal, however, with Sudan reopening its embassy in July after nine years, and King Abdullah II of Jordan visiting Kuwait in September.

In May, Emir Sheik Jaber al-Ahmad al-Sabah dissolved the National Assembly in response to protests by Assembly members over errors in a government-funded printing of the Islamic holy book, the Koran. Elections were held in July, with the Islamists gaining significant representation in the National Assembly and the pro-government legislators representation dropping from thirty seats to just fourteen.

CULTURE AND SOCIETY

For the first time, Kuwait announced that it would train female soldiers to fight in front-line combat if war breaks out in the region. Islamic influences were bringing pressure on Kuwait society to eliminate immoral influences, such as prostitution and anti-Islamic journalism. Citizens who left Kuwait during the 1990–91 Gulf War continue to return to their homeland, a fact reflected in the projected population growth of almost four percent in 1999.

DIRECTORY

CENTRAL GOVERNMENT

Head of State

Amir
Jabir al-Ahmad al-Jabir al-Sabah, Monarch

Crown Prince and Prime Minister
Sheikh Saad al-Abdullah al-Salem al-Sabah, Office of the Prime Minister, Amir Sheikh, Amiri Diwan, P.O. Box 799, 13008 Safat, Kuwait
PHONE: +965 5398888
FAX: +965 5393069

Ministers

Minister of Foreign Affairs
Sabah al-Ahmed al-Jaber al-Sabah, Ministry of Foreign Affairs, P.O. Box 3, Safat 13001, Kuwait
PHONE: +965 2425141
FAX: +965 2412169

Minister of Defense
Sheikh Salem al-Sabah, P.O. Box 1170, Safat 13012, Kuwait
PHONE: +965 48483009
FAX: +965 4837244

Minister of Cabinet Affairs
Abdul-Aziz al-Dakhil, Ministry of Cabinet Affairs

Minister of Finance and Communication
Sheik Ahmed Abdallah al-Ahmed al-Sabah, Ministry of Finance and Communication

Minister of Justice
Saad Jassem Youssef al-Hashel, Ministry of Justice, Ministries Complex, Block 4, Safat, Kuwait
PHONE: +965 2486232
FAX: +965 2460290
E-MAIL: webmaster@mail.moj.gov.kw

Minister of Information
Saad Mohammed bin Teflah al-Ajmi, Ministry of Information, P.O. Box 193, Safat 13002, Kuwait
PHONE: +965 2415301
FAX: +965 2419642

Minister of Oil
Saud Nasser al-Sabah, Ministry of Oil

Minister of Foreign Affairs
Suleiman Majed al-Shaheen, Ministry of Foreign Affairs

Minister of State Housing Affairs and Minister of Awqaf and Islamic Affairs
Adel Khaled al-Sebeih, Ministry of State Housing Affairs and Ministry of Awqaf and Islamic Affairs

Minister of Trade and Industry and Minister of Labour and Societal Affairs
Abdel Wahab Mohammed al-Wazzan, Ministry of Trade and Industry and Ministry of Labour and Societal Affairs, P.O. Box 2944, Safat 13030, Kuwait
PHONE: +965 2463600
FAX: +965 2436832; 2411089

Minister of Public Works
Eid Hathal Saud al-Rashidi, Ministry of Public Works

Minister of Planning and Administrative Development Affairs
Mohammed Bteihan al-Dweihees, Ministry of Planning and Administrative Development Affairs

Minister of Health
Mohammed Ahmed al-Jarallah, Ministry of Health

Minister of the Interior
Sheik Mohammed Khaled al-Hamad al-Sabah, Ministry of the Interior

Minister of Education and Higher Education
Youssef Hamad al-Ibrahim, P.O. Box 7, Safat 13001, Kuwait
PHONE: +965 4836800
FAX: +965 4837829

POLITICAL ORGANIZATIONS
None.

DIPLOMATIC REPRESENTATION
Embassies in Kuwait

Austria
P.O. Box 33259, Rawdha 73453, Kuwait
PHONE: +965 2552532; 2532761
FAX: +965 2563052

Brazil
P.O. Box 21370, Safat 13074, Kuwait
PHONE: +965 2561029
FAX: +965 2562153

Canada
P.O. Box 25281, Safat 13113, Kuwait
PHONE: +965 2563025; 2561456
FAX: +965 2564167

China
P.O. Box 2346, Safat 13024, Kuwait
PHONE: +965 5333340
FAX: +965 5333341

France
P.O. Box 1037, Safat 13011, Kuwait
PHONE: +965 2571062
FAX: +965 2571058

Germany
P.O. Box 805, Safat 13009, Kuwait
PHONE: +965 2520857
FAX: +965 2520763

India
P.O. Box 1450, Safat 13015, Kuwait
PHONE: +965 2530600
FAX: +965 2525811

Italy
P.O. Box 4453, Safat 13043, Kuwait
PHONE: +965 4817400
FAX: +965 4817244

Japan
P.O. Box 2304, Safat 13024, Kuwait
PHONE: +965 5312870
FAX: +965 5326168

Russia
P.O. Box 1765, Safat 13018, Kuwait
PHONE: +965 2560427
FAX: +965 2524969

Spain
P.O. Box 22207, Safat 13083, Kuwait
PHONE: +965 5325827
FAX: +965 5325826

Turkey
P.O. Box 20627, Safat 13067, Kuwait
PHONE: +965 2531785; 2531466
FAX: +965 2560673

United Kingdom
P.O. Box 2, Safat 13001, Kuwait
PHONE: +965 2403336
FAX: +965 2407395; 2426799

United States
P.O. Box 77, Safat 13001, Kuwait
PHONE: +965 2424151
FAX: +965 2442855

JUDICIAL SYSTEM
High Court of Appeal

FURTHER READING
Articles
"A Bolder Kuwait." *The Economist* (July 10, 1999): 39.

"Kuwait: An Unholy Row." *The Economist* (May 8, 1999): 48.

"Women's Day in Kuwait." *The Economist* (May 22, 1999): 50.

Books
Cordesman, Anthony H. *Kuwait: Recovery and Security after the Gulf War.* Boulder, Colo.: Westview Press, 1997.

Longva, Anh Nga. *Walls Built on Sand: Migration, Exclusion, and Society in Kuwait.* Boulder, Colo.: Westview Press, 1997.

Al Yahya, Mohammad Abdul Rahman. *Kuwait: Fall and Rebirth.* New York: Kegan Paul International, 1993.

Internet
"Egyptians Riot in Kuwait." BBC World Service, 31 October 1999. Available Online @ news2.thls.bbc.co.uk/hi/english/world/middle%5Feast/newsid%5F500000/500708.stm (December 13, 1999).

"Iraq Accuses Kuwait and Saudi of Treachery." BBC World Service, 10 January 1999. Available Online @ news2.thls.bbc.co.uk/hi/english/events/crisis%5Fin%5Fthe%5Fgulf/latest%5Fnews/newsid%5F252000/252353.stm (December 13, 1999).

"King Abdullah Historic Visit Begins." BBC World Service, 6 September 1999. Available

Online @ news2.thls.bbc.co.uk/hi/english/
world/middle%5Feast/newsid%5F439000/
439920.stm (December 13, 1999).

''Kuwait Arrests 150 Prostitutes.'' BBC World
Service, 26 September 1999. Available Online
@ news2.thls.bbc.co.uk/hi/english/world/
middle%5Feast/newsid%5F458000/458103.stm
(December 13, 1999).

''Kuwait Swings Towards Liberals.'' BBC
World Service, 4 July 1999. Available Online
@ news2.thls.bbc.co.uk/hi/english/world/
middle%5Feast/newsid%5F384000/384731.stm
(December 13, 1999).

*Official Web Site for Kuwait Government,
Ministry of Information.* Available Online @
www.moinfo.gov.kw (December 3, 1999).

''Oil Prices Kept High.'' BBC World Service,
22 September 1999. Available Online @
news2.thls.bbc.co.uk/hi/english/business/
the%5Feconomy/newsid%5F454000/
454849.stm (December 13, 1999).

''Oil Production Cuts Agreed.'' BBC World
Service, 12 March 1999. Available Online @
news2.thls.bbc.co.uk/hi/english/business/
the%5Feconomy/newsid%5F294000/
294843.stm (December 13, 1999).

Welcome to Kuwait. Available Online @
www.aiwakuwait.com/ (December 3, 1999).

KUWAIT: STATISTICAL DATA

For sources and notes see "Sources of Statistics" in the front of each volume.

GEOGRAPHY

Geography (1)
Area:

Total: 17,820 sq km.

Land: 17,820 sq km.

Water: 0 sq km.

Area—comparative: slightly smaller than New Jersey.

Land boundaries:

Total: 464 km.

Border countries: Iraq 242 km, Saudi Arabia 222 km.

Coastline: 499 km.

Climate: dry desert; intensely hot summers; short, cool winters.

Terrain: flat to slightly undulating desert plain.

Natural resources: petroleum, fish, shrimp, natural gas.

Land use:

Arable land: 0%

Permanent crops: 0%

Permanent pastures: 8%

Forests and woodland: 0%

Other: 92% (1993 est.).

HUMAN FACTORS

Demographics (2A)

	1990	1995	1998	2000	2010	2020	2030	2040	2050
Population	2,130.9	1,672.8	1,913.3	2,067.7	2,780.1	3,351.1	3,724.8	3,983.5	4,158.6
Net migration rate (per 1,000 population)	NA	NA	NA	NA	NA	NA	NA	NA	NA
Births	NA	NA	NA	NA	NA	NA	NA	NA	NA
Deaths	NA	NA	NA	NA	NA	NA	NA	NA	NA
Life expectancy - males	72.1	73.8	74.8	75.4	77.9	79.3	80.0	80.4	80.6
Life expectancy - females	76.5	77.8	78.9	79.7	82.3	84.1	85.2	85.8	86.2
Birth rate (per 1,000)	24.5	22.8	21.0	20.0	18.1	16.0	14.5	13.6	12.8
Death rate (per 1,000)	2.2	2.3	2.3	2.3	3.0	4.3	6.3	8.3	9.3
Women of reproductive age (15-49 yrs.)	480.4	335.2	391.0	429.1	589.0	717.7	814.3	864.6	898.8
of which are currently married	NA	NA	NA	NA	NA	NA	NA	NA	NA
Fertility rate	3.4	3.8	3.4	3.2	2.7	2.4	2.2	2.1	2.0

Except as noted, values for vital statistics are in thousands; life expectancy is in years.

Health Personnel (3)

Total health expenditure as a percentage of GDP, 1990-1997[a]

Public sector 3.5

Private sector . . . . .NA

Total[b] . . . . .NA

Health expenditure per capita in U.S. dollars, 1990-1997[a]

Purchasing power parity . . . . .NA

Total . . . . .NA

Availability of health care facilities per 100,000 people

Hospital beds 1990-1997[a] . . . . .NA

Doctors 1993[c] 178

Nurses 1993[c] 468

Health Indicators (4)

Life expectancy at birth

1980 71

1997 76

Daily per capita supply of calories (1996) 3,075

Total fertility rate births per woman (1997) 2.9

Maternal mortality ratio per 100,000 live births (1990-97) . . . . .20[b]

Safe water % of population with access (1995) 100

Sanitation % of population with access (1995) 100

Consumption of iodized salt % of households (1992-98)[a] . . . .

Smoking prevalence

Male % of adults (1985-95)[a] 52

Female % of adults (1985-95)[a] 12

Tuberculosis incidence per 100,000 people (1997) 81

Adult HIV prevalence % of population ages 15-49 (1997) 0.12

Infants and Malnutrition (5)

Under-5 mortality rate (1997) 13

% of infants with low birthweight (1990-97) 7

Births attended by skilled health staff % of total[a] . . .98

% fully immunized (1995-97)

TB . . . . .NA

DPT 96

Polio 100

Measles 95

Prevalence of child malnutrition under age 5 (1992-97)[b] 11

Ethnic Division (6)

Kuwaiti 45%

Other Arab 35%

South Asian 9%

Iranian 4%

Other 7%

Religions (7)

Muslim 85%

Sunni 45%

Shi'a 40%

Christian, Hindu, Parsi, ...

and other 15%

Languages (8)

Arabic (official), English widely spoken.

EDUCATION

Public Education Expenditures (9)

Public expenditure on education (% of GNP)

1980 . . . . .2.4

1996 . . . . .5.7[1]

Expenditure per student

Primary % of GNP per capita

1980 . . . . .14.8

1996 . . . . .21.8[1]

Secondary % of GNP per capita

1980 . . . . .12.4[1]

1996 . . . . .14.6[1]

Tertiary % of GNP per capita

1980 . . . . .37.5

1996 . . . . .89.5[1]

Expenditure on teaching materials

Primary % of total for level (1996) 6.3

Secondary % of total for level (1996) . . . .

Primary pupil-teacher ratio per teacher (1996) 15

Duration of primary education years (1995) 4

Educational Attainment (10)

Age group (1988) . . . . .10+

Total population 1,409,065

Highest level attained (%)

No schooling 17.6

First level

Not completed 18.4

Completed . . . . .NA

Entered second level

S-1 .... .22.7

S-2 .... .14.6

Postsecondary 11.1

Literacy Rates (11A)

In thousands and percent[1]	1990	1995	2000	2010
Illiterate population (15+ yrs.)	330	200	222	231
Literacy rate - total adult pop. (%)	75.7	78.6	81.5	86.0

Literacy rate - males (%)	78.5	82.2	84.1	87.4
Literacy rate - females (%)	71.6	74.9	78.6	84.4

GOVERNMENT & LAW

Political Parties (12)

Legislative branch is a unicameral National Assembly (50 seats; members elected by popular vote to serve four-year terms). There are no political parties.

Military Affairs (14B)

	1990	1991	1992	1993	1994	1995
Military expenditures						
Current dollars (mil.)	13,170[e]	15,950[e]	18,990[e]	3,585[e]	3,069	3,488
1995 constant dollars (mil.)	15,130[e]	17,620[e]	20,430[e]	3,759[e]	3,146	3,488
Armed forces (000)	7	10	12	12	15	20
Gross national product (GNP)						
Current dollars (mil.)	24,820	15,660	24,680	27,750	27,720	29,990
1995 constant dollars (mil.)	28,520	17,300	26,540	29,090	28,410	29,990
Central government expenditures (CGE)						
1995 constant dollars (mil.)	11,290	24,580	21,210	15,380	14,190	13,700
People (mil.)	2.1	.9	1.4	1.5	1.7	1.8
Military expenditure as % of GNP	53.1	101.8	77.0	12.9	11.1	11.6
Military expenditure as % of CGE	134.0	71.7	96.3	24.4	22.2	25.5
Military expenditure per capita (1995 $)	7,111	18,610	14,630	2,445	1,874	1,919
Armed forces per 1,000 people (soldiers)	3.3	10.6	8.6	7.8	8.9	11.0
GNP per capita (1995 $)	13,400	18,270	19,010	18,930	16,920	16,500
Arms imports[6]						
Current dollars (mil.)	320	290	975	925	220	900
1995 constant dollars (mil.)	368	320	1,049	970	226	900
Arms exports[6]						
Current dollars (mil.)	0	0	10	0	0	0
1995 constant dollars (mil.)	0	0	11	0	0	0
Total imports[7]						
Current dollars (mil.)	3,972	4,761	7,261	7,036	6,697	7,784
1995 constant dollars (mil.)	4,565	5,261	7,810	7,376	6,865	7,784
Total exports[7]						
Current dollars (mil.)	7,042	1,088	6,660	10,250	11,610	12,980
1995 constant dollars (mil.)	8,093	1,202	7,164	10,740	11,910	12,980
Arms as percent of total imports[8]	8.1	6.1	13.4	13.1	3.3	11.6
Arms as percent of total exports[8]	0	0	.2	0	0	0

Government Budget (13A)

Year: 1997

Total Expenditures: 3,453 Millions of Dinars

Expenditures as a percentage of the total by function:

General public services and public order 16.94

Defense 22.53

Education 10.86

Health 7.62

Social Security and Welfare 17.29

Housing and community amenities 1.88

Recreational, cultural, and religious affairs 2.84

Fuel and energy 8.49

Agriculture, forestry, fishing, and hunting . . . .-

Mining, manufacturing, and construction 38

Transportation and communication 2.46

Other economic affairs and services . . . .-

Crime (15)

Crime rate (for 1997)

Crimes reported 27,100

Total persons convicted . . . . .NA

Crimes per 100,000 population 1,350

Persons responsible for offenses

Total number of suspects 18,100

Total number of female suspects 2,000

Total number of juvenile suspects . . . . .NA

LABOR FORCE

Labor Force (16)

Total (million) 1.1

Government and social services 50%

Services 40%

Industry and agriculture .10%

Data for 1996 est. Percent distribution for 1996 est. 68% of the population in the 15-64 age group is non-national (July 1998 est.)

Unemployment Rate (17)

1.8% (official 1996 est.)

PRODUCTION SECTOR

Electric Energy (18)

Capacity . . . . .6.988 million kW (1995)

Production . . . . .25 billion kWh (1995)

Consumption per capita . . . . .13,756 kWh (1995)

Transportation (19)

Highways:

total: 4,450 km

paved: 3,587 km

unpaved: 863 km (1996 est.)

Pipelines: crude oil 877 km; petroleum products 40 km; natural gas 165 km

Merchant marine:

total: 42 ships (1,000 GRT or over) totaling 1,965,633 GRT/3,109,720 DWT ships by type: cargo 10, container 3, liquefied gas tanker 7, livestock carrier 3, oil tanker 19 (1997 est.)

Airports: 8 (1997 est.)

Airports—with paved runways:

total: 4

over 3,047 m: 2

2,438 to 3,047 m: 2 (1997 est.)

Airports—with unpaved runways:

total: 4

1,524 to 2,437 m: 1

914 to 1,523 m: 1

under 914 m: 2 (1997 est.)

Top Agricultural Products (20)

Practically no crops; extensive fishing in territorial waters.

MANUFACTURING SECTOR

GDP & Manufacturing Summary (21)

Detailed value added figures are listed by both International Standard Industry Code (ISIC) and product title.

	1980	1985	1990	1994
GDP ($-1990 mil.)[1]	20,913	16,270	17,969	23,841
Per capita ($-1990)[1]	15,209	9,459	8,385	14,600
Manufacturing share (%) (current prices)[1]	5.6	5.9	11.9	*9.0*
Manufacturing				
Value added ($-1990 mil.)[1]	1,607	1,717	2,151	*4,398*
Industrial production index	100	138	136	*136*
Value added ($ mil.)	1,752	1,275	2,179	*2,436*
Gross output ($ mil.)	6,218	7,435	5,531	*5,629*
Employment (000)	43	46	56	*61*
Profitability (% of gross output)				

	1980	1985	1990	1994
Intermediate input (%)	72	83	61	57
Wages and salaries inc. supplements (%)	7	8	8	13
Gross operating surplus	21	9	31	30
Productivity ($)				
Gross output per worker	144,813	151,542	94,963	88,969
Value added per worker	40,798	25,988	37,394	38,604
Average wage (inc. supplements)	9,789	13,000	8,062	12,286
Value added ($ mil.)				
311/2 Food products	96	101	69	140
313 Beverages	20	31	21	40
314 Tobacco products	—	—	—	—
321 Textiles	7	8	16	32
322 Wearing apparel	84	75	54	134
323 Leather and fur products	—	—	—	—
324 Footwear	—	—	—	—
331 Wood and wood products	40	14	10	20
332 Furniture and fixtures	41	31	30	60
341 Paper and paper products	5	12	31	22
342 Printing and publishing	40	52	5	49
351 Industrial chemicals	118	56	43	37
352 Other chemical products	13	16	15	23
353 Petroleum refineries	915	561	1,652	1,385
354 Miscellaneous petroleum and coal products	1	1	—	4
355 Rubber products	5	7	2	1
356 Plastic products	24	24	16	39
361 Pottery, china and earthenware	2	—	—	1
362 Glass and glass products	2	4	12	15
369 Other non-metal mineral products	143	115	72	102
371 Iron and steel	7	14	11	23
372 Non-ferrous metals	—	—	—	—
381 Metal products	99	88	54	130
382 Non-electrical machinery	10	30	19	59
383 Electrical machinery	22	15	27	27
384 Transport equipment	45	12	2	67
385 Professional and scientific equipment	5	2	1	2
390 Other manufacturing industries	7	5	17	25

FINANCE, ECONOMICS, & TRADE

Economic Indicators (22)

National product: GDP—purchasing power parity—$46.3 billion (1997 est.)

National product real growth rate: 1% (1997 est.)

National product per capita: $22,300 (1997 est.)

Inflation rate—consumer price index: 3.2% (1996)

Exchange Rates (24)

Exchange rates:

Kuwaiti dinars (KD) per US$1

January 1998	.0.3055
1997	.0.3033
1996	.0.2994
1995	.0.2984
1994	.0.2976
1993	.0.3017

Top Import Origins (25)

$7.7 billion (f.o.b., 1996) Data are for 1996 est.

Origins	%
United States	.31
United Kingdom	.14
Japan	.13
Germany	.8
Italy	.7

Top Export Destinations (26)

$14.7 billion (f.o.b., 1996) Data are for 1996 est.

Destinations	%
Japan	.29
United States	.16
Netherlands	.13
Singapore	.12

Economic Aid (27)

$NA. NA stands for not available.

Import Export Commodities (28)

Import Commodities	Export Commodities
Food	Oil and refined products
Construction materials	Fertilizers
Vehicles and parts	
Clothing	

Balance of Payments (23)

	1992	1993	1994	1995	1996
Exports of goods (f.o.b.)	6,548	10,141	11,129	12,632	14,696
Imports of goods (f.o.b.)	−7,237	−6,954	−6,670	−7,154	−7,662
Trade balance	−689	−3,187	4,460	5,478	7,034
Services - debits	−5,252	−5,526	−5,453	−6,538	−6,156
Services - credits	7,401	5,788	5,187	7,295	7,578
Private transfers (net)	−1,081	−282	−374	−308	−307
Government transfers (net)	−829	−1,229	−1,331	−1,354	−1,376
Overall balance	−451	1,938	2,489	4,573	6,773

KYRGYZSTAN

Kyrgyz Republic
Kyrgyz Respublikasy

CAPITAL: Bishkek.·

FLAG: Red field with a yellow sun in the center; in the center of the sun is a red ring crossed by two sets of three lines, a stylized representation of the vent in a Kyrgyz yurt.

ANTHEM: *Kyrgyz National Anthem.*

MONETARY UNIT: The som was established in May 1993; som1 = $0.08264 (or $1 = som12.1).

WEIGHTS AND MEASURES: The metric system is in force.

HOLIDAYS: Constitution Day, 5 May; Independence Day, 31 August; National Day, 2 December.

TIME: 5 PM = noon GMT.

LOCATION AND SIZE: Kyrgyzstan is located in southern Asia, between China and Kazakstan. Comparatively, it is slightly smaller than the state of South Dakota, with a total area of 198,500 square kilometers (76,641 square miles). The country's boundary length totals 3,878 kilometers (2,410 miles), and its capital city, Bishkek, is located in the north central part of the country.

CLIMATE: The country's climate ranges from continental to polar in the Tian Shan Mountains. In the valley the average temperature is 28°C (82°F) in July and in January is −21°C (−5°F).

INTRODUCTORY SURVEY

RECENT HISTORY

By 1916, Russia's livestock and land-use policies had left the Kyrgyz badly impoverished. Hostility to the Russian tsars, or emperors, meant that there was some support for the Bolshevik revolution, at least until it became clear that it would not lead to regional independence.

As Bolshevik power was consolidated, Kyrgyzstan was first made an autonomous province (*oblast*) of the Russian Federation in 1924, then upgraded in 1926 to an autonomous republic, but still within Russia. It did not become a full Soviet Republic until 1936.

The republic was regarded as one of the least developed of the Soviet states, politically and economically, making it a great surprise when, in October 1990, Kyrgyzstan became the first Soviet republic to select its own non-communist leader, Askar Akaev. Akaev and his supporters began an ambitious program of disengaging the republic from the Communist Party, which was interrupted by the attempted coup in Moscow of August 1991. Afterwards, Kyrgyzstan declared its independence on 31 August.

On 12 October 1991, Akaev's presidency was confirmed by direct popular election. A constitution was adopted in May 1993. Akaev's presidency was reaffirmed by a popular referendum of support conducted in January 1994. Akaev was reelected to the presidency in December 1995 in the first official elections held by Kyrgyzstan.

GOVERNMENT

Kyrgyzstan's new constitution, ratified 5 May 1993 and amended in February 1996, calls for three branches of government: the Jogorku Kenesh (Supreme Council), which has legislative responsibility; the ministries, appointed by the president to oversee executive responsibilities, but subject to ratification by the parliament; and a judiciary, appointed by the president. The republic is divided into six *oblasttar,* or administrative regions, plus the capital city of Bishkek.

Judiciary

The 1993 constitution instituted a Western-type judicial system. However, the judicial system still operates mostly under former-Soviet laws and procedures. Criminal cases are heard by a judge and two people's assessors. Appeals are possible. There is a Supreme Court, which includes a Constitutional Court authorized to review legislation and administrative acts for consistency with the constitution. It also considers cases on appeal involving individual rights and liberties of citizens. Constitutional Court decisions are final.

Political Parties

The Communist Party of Kyrgyzia, which was the only legal political party during the Soviet years, was abolished at the time of independence. A successor, the Kyrgyz Communist Party, was allowed to register in September 1992. Other communist parties include the Republican People's Party, the Social-Democrats of Kyrgyzstan, and the People's Party of Kyrgyzstan.

Other parties began as unofficial civic movements. The first was Ashar, begun in 1989 to take over unused land for housing. A number of different parties and groups are joined under the umbrella of the Democratic Movement of Kyrgyzstan (DDK). Another democratically inclined party is Asaba (Banner).

DEFENSE

One Russian division occupies Kyrgyzstan, supported by 55 air defense missiles and around 200 combat aircraft, all under dual control of Commonwealth of Independent States (CIS) military authorities. The new republic plans a national army of 20,000 (half active, half reserve) based on 18 months' conscription (military service by draft).

ECONOMIC AFFAIRS

Kyrgyzstan is among the poorest of the post-Soviet countries with a per person income estimated to be roughly half that of Russia. Although coal, gold, mercury, and uranium deposits are considerable, the country boasts few of the oil and gas reserves that promise a badly needed economic windfall to other Central Asian republics. The country's post-Soviet economy remains dominated by agriculture.

Under the presidency of Askar Akaev, the transition to a free market economy has outpaced that of most other post-Soviet republics. By 1995, 60% of all state-owned enterprises had been privatized or converted to joint stock company. The government began a tight monetary policy that reduced inflation from 23% per month in 1993 to 2.3% by 1995.

Public Finance

Since 1991, economic output has been declining. As a result, the proportion of public revenues in GDP has plummeted. Transfers from the former Soviet Union amounting to over 11% of GDP largely created an overall budget surplus equivalent to 4.1% of GDP in 1991.

In 1992, parliament agreed to a further tightening of fiscal policy (including decreased expenditures and the elimination of transfers to inefficient state enterprises) due to the virtual termination of in-flowing subsidies caused by the demise of the Soviet Union. The som, currency introduced by the government in May 1993, has proven fairly stable, and monthly inflation has slowed from 40% to about 10%.

Income

In 1997, Kyrgyzstan's gross national product (GNP) was $9.7 billion, or about $2,100 per person. For the period 1985–95 the average inflation rate was 172.3%, resulting in a decline in GNP of 6.9% per person.

Industry

Nearly all of Kyrgyzstan's industrial output comes from Bishkek and surrounding areas. Mechanical and electrical engineering (vehicle assembly, washing machines, electrical appliances, electronics), light industry (mainly textiles and wool processing), and food processing make up close to 75% of the country's industrial production and 80% of its industrial exports. Other important industries include chemicals, leather goods, and construction materials.

Banking and Finance

The central bank of Kyrgyzstan is the National Bank of the Kyrgyz Republic. It heads all 18 banks in the system, the savings bank, three former specialized state banks that have been converted into joint-stock commercial banks, two foreign joint-venture banks, and newly established, and, as of 1996, still very small, commercial banks. The specialized banks still dominate the allocation of credit and the taking of deposits, although some smaller banks are starting to challenge the major banks. However, nine of the country's commercial banks had only one office at the beginning of 1995. The larger banks have large bad loan portfolios; Promstroybank (Construction Bank) had 80% of its loans overdue at the end of 1994. Bank failures and bank consolidation are expected.

The NBK, formerly the local branch of Gosbank (the State Bank of the former Soviet Union), began to operate independently in December 1991 and is intended to perform all the functions of a central bank.

Although broad money (M2) grew by 212.8% in nominal terms from end-June 1993 to end-1994, it lagged prices by 43.9%. The government has stuck with a tight monetary policy since then. The currency unit was initially the ruble following independence; however, with IMF support, the government introduced a new currency, the som, in May 1993 in order to stabilize the economy, avoid the inflation of the ruble, and attract foreign investment.

The country has a small stock exchange, opened in May 1995. As of January 1996, 298 companies issued securities, with 7 trading on the stock exchange.

Economic Development

Under the Soviet system, economic planning efforts in Kyrgyzstan focused on increasing agricultural production (particularly in the meat and dairy subsectors during the 1980s) and specialized development of industrial sectors in line with the wider Soviet economy. Transfer payments from the central government as well as capital inflows into state enterprises covered the republic's modest balance of trade deficit with its Soviet trading partners and countries beyond. With this support, GDP growth was sustained at moderately high levels in the late 1980s, averaging 5.1% in 1985–89.

Kyrgyzstan declared its independence in 1991. Since then, the Kyrgyzstan government faced the task of sustaining a viable national economy despite the sudden cessation of transfers from the central government, the country's critical dependence on oil and gas imports, and its landlocked geographic position that has hampered development of trading ties outside the economically troubled former Soviet Union. Reforms have aimed at making the transition to a market-oriented economy.

Kyrgyzstan experienced declines in gross domestic product (GDP) from 1991–94. Both per capita income and overall output fell to well below the 1990 level. Agricultural output fell by an estimated 20%, and industrial output, by 42%. By 1996, however, Kyrgyzstan had begun to show progress, especially when compared to the other former Soviet republics, in the areas of privatizing state enterprises, ending the state ordering system, lifting price controls, and converting military enterprises to civilian uses. Prime Minister Apas Jumagulov reported in 1995 that the economic crises had eased, and the rates of decline were slowing.

A value-added tax was introduced in 1992 to help strengthen the government revenue base. Expected state revenues however, have fallen short due to steeply declining consumption and collection difficulties within the new tax system. With seriously declining revenues since 1991, the government's ability to make new development investments in either the productive sectors or physical and social infrastructure has been severely constrained. Capital expenditures as a percentage of total budgetary expenditures declined from 15% in 1990 to only 7% in 1992. Because of its commitment to democracy, Kyrgyzstan has received favorable treatment from international economic aid agencies. In 1992, the government signed a formal agreement with Russia transferring its share of the former Soviet Union's external debt to the latter in return for relinquishing most claims to the financial and other assets of the former USSR.

In May 1996, President Akayev negotiated an aid package from the Asian Development Bank that included $60 million in loans to finance privatization of agriculture and to renovate power and heating facilities in Bishkek. In support of the government's efforts to evolve the country's agriculture from large communes to private farms, the Asian Development Bank also offered loans to small farmers. In July 1996, the International Finance Corporation promised $40 million to finance a project to mine for gold near Issy-Kul', a large lake in the northeast. In November 1996, the World Bank moved to support programs to reform the Kyrgyzstan banking system and to modernize the electric power generating system.

SOCIAL WELFARE

Social security laws were introduced in 1990, and amended in 1992 and 1994. All employees and members of cooperatives and collective farms are eligible for pensions. The government, however, is often unable to pay pension benefits.

Women have equal status under the law and are well represented in the work force in urban areas.

In 1993, parliament narrowly rejected a law to legalize polygamy (having multiple spouses). Polygyny (one man with multiple wives) is most common, and each wife must be provided with her own household. In order for a woman to have multiple husbands (polyandry), she must have substantial wealth or influence.

Healthcare

Kyrgyzstan has one physician per 303 people, and one hospital bed per 92 people. Life expectancy is 67 years. The incidence of tuberculosis and diphtheria increased in the early 1990s, reflecting economic hardship and the deterioration of health care.

Housing

In 1989, 42.7% of all privately owned urban housing had running water, 32.4% had sewer lines, 14% had central heating, and 1.4% had hot water. In 1990, Kyrgyzstan had 12.1 square meters (130 square feet) of housing space per person.

EDUCATION

The adult illiteracy rate was estimated at 3%. During the 1994 school year, secondary schools had 606,381 students enrolled. During 1993, 55,229 students were enrolled at institutions of higher learning, including the State University of Kyrgyzstan.

1999 KEY EVENTS TIMELINE

January

- Osh oblast plans to build a monument to "red terror victims."

- President Askar Akaev demands that enterprises in Bishkek pay the state their $26 million debt.

- Russia postpones the repayment of Kyrgyzstan's $132 million debt.

- The director-general of the Kyrgyzgazmunizat company is dismissed.

- There are currently 14,500 registered refugees in Kyrgyzstan, most of whom are ethnic Kyrgyz who have fled the civil war in Tajikistan.

- Kyrgyzstan considers purchasing Belarusian farm machinery in payment for deliveries of Kyrgyz wool and agricultural products.

- Akaev visits Austria.

February

- An austerity program is announced to offset a $167,000 shortfall; even the use of telephones is limited.

- Kyrgyzstan secures its border with Uzbekistan.

- Akaev's mandate for economic stability includes: improving tax legislation for both local and foreign businesses; establishing a special board at the Tax Inspectorate to concentrate on deals with foreign companies; liberalizing legislation on foreign investment; reforming the judicial system to ensure the legality of deals between state agencies and foreign producers; limiting the interference of administrative bodies in the activities of foreign companies; setting up free trade zones.

- Kyrgyzstan recalls its battalion from CIS peace-keeping troops in Tajikistan.

March

- Uzbekistan may have moved some of its border posts into Kyrgyz territory by as much as 24 kilometers.

- Uzbekistan threatens to stop delivery of natural gas if Kyrgyzstan does not pay its $3.3 million debt.

- Akaev introduces the "diplomacy of the Silk Road" centered on Kyrgyzstan.

- Kyrgyzstan's som, at 32.7 to $1, is decreasing in value.

- A Kyrgyz government study claims that Uzbekistan has been advancing its borders into Kyrgyz territory and building new fortified border posts. Kyrgyzstan strengthens its border with numbers withdrawn from the Tajik/Afghan border.

- Kyrgyzstan owes Uzbekistan more than $6 million for gas supplies.

- Eighty people die as a direct consequence of the spill of sodium cyanide into the Barskoon River. Neither the Kyrgyzaltyn state gold company nor the Canadian Kumtor Operating Company (KOC) provides compensation for damages.

- Kyrgyzstan's loss as a result of Kazakstan's custom's tariff totals $1.5 million.

April

- Akaev is accused of entrusting senior posts to politicians from his (Kemin) district of Chu oblast.

- Akaev visits India.

- Kyrgyzstan cannot pay Uzbekistan $4.5 million for gas deliveries because enterprises in Kyrgyzstan owe Kyrgyzgaz 6.5 million.

- Parliament approves the candidacy of Amangeldi Muraliev as prime minister.

- The lower chamber of parliament passes the government's new election code.

May

- Kazak and Uzbek authorities agree on the resumption of rail traffic from Kyrgyzstan across Kazak territory.

- Twelve people are arrested for an alleged attempt to assassinate Akaev.

- The Kyrgyz cabinet is unable to pay $14 million in back payments.

- An Uzbek citizen transporting a canister of radioactive plutonium to the United Arab Emirates for $16,000 is arrested in Bishkek.

- Residents of the Issyk Kul region block roads to the Kumtor gold mine.

- $22,000 allocated by Kumtor for victims of the toxic chemical spill disappears.

- The Kyrgyz government agrees to IMF conditions for resumption of financing under a three-year Economic Structural Adjustment Facility program.

- Kyrgyzstan will receive more Uzbek gas once the Uzbek gas pipeline crosses Kyrgyz territory.

June

- The Ministry of Justice refuses to re-register the Kyrgyz Committee for Human Rights.

- Between 1,500-2,000 pensioners picket the government building in Bishkek to protest deteriorating living conditions.

- Prime Minister Muraliev expresses concern at the decline in value of the som, rising unemployment, and the government's failure to meet targets for tax collection. The Kyrgyz government owes $4.5 million in overdue wages.

- Intergaz, the Kazak company which supplies gas from Uzbekistan to Kyrgyzstan, cuts supplies to northern regions of Kyrgyzstan, including Bishkek, to force the Kyrgyz government to pay $3.2 million for past deliveries.

- As a result of the shipment of needed Kyrgyz flour in the republic to Uzbekistan as payment for gas, flour prices in Kyrgyzstan have risen by 30–40%.

- Akaev proposes a reduction from twelve to six months the minimum registration period prior for parliamentary elections.

- Kyrgyz authorities arrest Marat Kalmurzaev, who is suspected of embezzling $200,000.

July

- The People's Party of Kyrgyzstan views the rapidly deteriorating social and economic situation in the republic as an indicator for the return to power of the Communist Party in the parliamentary elections due early next year.

- Akaev regards Russia as Kyrgyzstan's present and future ''main [economic] strategic partner.''

- Unless Kyrgyzstan pays the United Nations $1 million in membership fees, the U.N. will discontinue the republic's membership and right to vote.

- Losses to Kyrgyzstan from economic crimes is estimated at $15 million.

- Kyrgyzstan will not be able to meet the planned 10% increase in agricultural output for 1999.

August

- Kyrgyzgaz announces the purchase of natural gas from Kazakhstan at a price lower than Uzbekistan prices.

- New legislation enhances the role of the state language (Kyrgyz), which would have to be used for all official documentation.

- Citizens of World Trade Organization member states will no longer need a visa to enter Kyrgyzstan.

- Tajik militants take four hostages in the Batken district of southern Kyrgyzstan. Kyrgyz authorities pay $50,000 in cash to obtain the release of the four.

- Tajikistan protests Uzbekistan's bombing of its Jirgatal district.

- The ethnic Uzbek guerrilla band of a thousand headed by Juma Namangani aims to create an Islamic state in the Fergana Valley that would include the Andijan, Fergana, and Namangan oblasts of Uzbekistan and the Leninabad oblast of Tajikistan.

- The Justice Ministry re-registers Kyrgyzstan's Human Rights Committee.

- Tajik authorities attribute the guerrillas' loyalty to ethnic Uzbek field commander Juma Namangani, who has refused to comply with Tajikistan's disarmament law.

- Alexandr Kim, editor of the independent and outspoken daily ''Vechernii Bishkek'' is arrested on charges of tax evasion.

- Kyrgyz and Tajik presidents agree to close border crossing between their countries.

- Twenty Kyrgyz troops sent to locate the guerrillas are abducted themselves.

- China's Jiang Zemin visits Kyrgyzstan. Akaev and Zemin settle their countries' border disputes.

- Kyrgyz government asks Russia for military and technical assistance to locate and disarm the militant groups.

- Hostages released by Islamic militants confirm that the Kyrgyz Interior Ministry general and the four Japanese geologists taken hostage are still alive.

- The New York-based Committee to Protect Journalists protests the Kyrgyz Tax Police's harassment of Alexandr Kim.

- In Chon-Alai, Kyrgyz forces halt the guerrillas' movement north.

September

- The BBC announces that Muslim militants would exchange hostages for members of the Uzbek Islamic Movement imprisoned in Uzbekistan. Akaev insists that hostages must be freed unharmed.

- The United States announces that in 2000, Kyrgyzstan will have to meet foreign debt repayments equal to 40% of the annual budget. The lion's share consists of a $130 million Russian loan.

- Zubair ibn Abdurrakim, chairman of the political council of the Islamic Movement of Uzbekistan, makes his declaration of ''Holy War'' against Uzbekistan with the aim of releasing 50,000 Muslims held in Uzbek prisons.

- The estimated 400–500 ethnic Uzbek militants holding 12 hostages are willing to negotiate but Kyrgyzstan rejects the militants' demand.

- Parliament votes to provide economic aid to victims of the conflict.

- Akaev recognizes Russian air support as the most effective weapon against the guerrillas.

- The draft budget for 2000 envisages a budget surplus equal to 2.5% of GDP. It is the first deficit-free budget ever proposed by the government. Revenues are predicted to rise by 12% compared with 1999, and spending will be cut by 17%. Industrial output should grow by 2%, and agricultural production by 5%. The inflation rate is estimated at 12%.

- No firm date is set for talks on the release of the twelve hostages. The Uzbek official media identifies the militants as members of the United Tajik Opposition rather than of the Islamic Movement of Uzbekistan.

- Akaev meets in Berlin with Chancellor Gerhard Schroeder for German financial support for construction of a new hydro-power station and for exporting electricity to neighboring China. Akaev also requests a DM 75 million ($40 million) loan to support small business in Kyrgyzstan and an additional DM 20 million in technical help.

- Alexandr Kim resigns following dispute with Kyrgyz Tax Police.

October

- Uzbek special forces clear the rebels from Zardaly. Inflation reaches 32.5%. Food prices rise by 39.7%, consumer goods by 6.8%, and gasoline by 2.1%.

December

- On December 13, Uzbekistan resumes gas shipments that had been stopped in November. Kyrgyzstan is indebted to Uzbekistan for about $4 million for gas, and the two countries are negotiating a settlement. Thousands in Bishkek, the capital, and surrounding areas were without gas after Uzbekistan cut off supplies to the country.

ANALYSIS OF EVENTS: 1999

BUSINESS AND THE ECONOMY

Kyrgyzstan, one of the most under-developed republics of the Union of Soviet Socialist Republics (USSR), proved to be one of the most compliant members of the post-USSR Commonwealth of Independent States (CIS) with regard to free market economic reforms. Still, the economic and credit crisis of its neighboring states, plus Kyrgyzstan's own economic underdevelopment posed a limit to what could immediately be done to simultaneously increase the national wealth and to facilitate the introduction of a free market economy in Kyrgyzstan.

Kyrgyzstan's foreign and domestic creditors extended the repayment dates of loans to the small republic. The initial loans in the mid-1990s had briefly improved the quality of life of the people of Kyrgyzstan. But now the loans were coming due. The Kyrgyz National Bank and Turkey's Ex-Im Bank postponed the repayment of a $75 million credit. Russia also postponed repayment of Kyrgyzstan's $132 million debt. Kyrgyzstan considered a barter deal with Belarus. Kyrgyzstan would purchase Belarusian farm machinery in return for wool and agricultural products. Gross domestic product (GDP) in 1998 increased by 1.8 percent; industrial output amounted to $700 million. But agricultural output remains at the 1997 level.

The economic climate was too chaotic for the economy to sustain many of its gains. The effects of this chaotic economic situation upon the Kyrgyz standard of living were sobering. The annual inflation rate fluctuated wildly. The average monthly salary was only $28. The foreign trade deficit increased to $290 million.

GOVERNMENT AND POLITICS

The political leadership of the country announced an austerity program. But Kyrgyzstan's neighbors balked at a trade war with the little nation. Kazakhstan imposed a 200 percent tariff on foodstuffs and goods imported from Kyrgyzstan. Kyrgyzstan's lost $1.5 million to Kazakhstan in the tariff wars. Kyrgyzstan owed Uzbekistan $6 million for gas supplies. Uzbekistan threatened to stop delivery of natural gas if Kyrgyzstan failed to pay its debts.

The government stabilized the currency at 36–38.5 soms to the dollar. But Kyrgyzstan was still suffering inflation and found itself unable to pay Uzbekistan until Kyrgyz enterprises had paid the state $6.5 million in taxes. Kyrgyzstan could not even pay the $14 million in back wages to government employees. On top of this was graft and embezzlement. Twenty-two thousand dollars allocated by the Kumtor Operating Company as compensation for toxic spill victims disappeared. The government agreed to IMF austerity conditions for resumption of financing. But this program of belt-tightening damaged the credibility of the government in the eyes of its people. Between 1,500-2,000 pensioners protested deteriorating living conditions. Kyrgyz government owed $4.5 million that it could not pay in overdue wages. Intergaz cut supplies to northern Kyrgyzstan, including Bishkek, to force the Kyrgyz to pay $3.2 million for past deliveries.

President Askar Akaev announced that Russia would be Kyrgyzstan's present and future "main [economic] strategic partner." To stimulate trade the government of Kyrgyzstan loosened visa restrictions. Akaev asked Germany for a $40 million loan to support small businesses and for funds to build a hydro-power station. Food prices rose by 39.7 percent, consumer goods by 6.8 percent, and gasoline by 2.1 percent.

Probably because of the intense strains that the transition to capitalism imposed on the people of Kyrgyzstan, the Communist Party remained the most popular among Kyrgyzstan's 22 registered political parties. In the new, post-Soviet period, Kyrgyzstan had to deal with the threatening moves of former fraternal states in the USSR. Uzbekistan moved its border posts into Kyrgyz territory. The reflex of relying on Russia to protect Kyrgyzstan continued to affect the small republic's foreign policy.

In the midst of this extremely volatile foreign and domestic situation, the country's parliamentarians attempted to bring order into governmental procedure. A new election code passed in the first reading. More direct threats to the stability of the republic were apparent in the arrest of a dozen conspirators in an assassination plot against President Akaev. The People's Party of Kyrgyzstan viewed the rapidly deteriorating socio-economic situation as an argument for the return of the Communist Party.

Inter-state warfare, civil war, clan blood feuds, and random banditry made travel and trade all the more risky. The government of Uzbekistan proved to be the most aggressive of the former USSR. Simultaneous nomadic uprisings against Kyrgyzstan challenged the very governability of the small state. Uzbek guerrilla bands set out to create an Islamic state in the Fergana Valley. Kyrgyz military helicopters bombed southern Kyrgyzstan, near the valleys, but the guerrilla uprising proved hard to extinguish. Twenty Kyrgyz troops were sent to locate and subdue the guerrillas, but they were abducted themselves.

The Kyrgyz government asked Russia for military and technical assistance. Meanwhile, the BBC announced that the Muslim militants were willing to exchange hostages for jailed comrades. One Muslim guerrilla leader, Zubair ibn Abdurrakim, declared a "Holy War" against Uzbekistan with the aim of releasing 50,000 Muslims from Uzbek prisons. Kyrgyzstan rejected all of the militants' demands. President Akaev declared that Russian air support was the most effective weapon against the guerrillas.

CULTURE AND SOCIETY

Kyrgyzstan emerged from the USSR as a polyglot society. Russian officials formerly posted in the country made up 18 percent of the population. The Kyrgyz accounted for 52 percent. Uzbeks, Ukrainians, and Germans filled in most of the balance. Another cause of ethnic confusion was the problem of refugees. There were 14,500 registered refugees who fled the civil war in Tajikistan. New legislation sought to enhance the role of the state language (Kyrgyz) for all official documentation. However, the primitive economic life, the diversity of language and culture, and the predatory instincts of its neighbors make Kyrgyzstan a questionable candidate for nationhood. The UN threatened to discontinue Kyrgyzstan's membership unless back dues of $1 million were paid.

DIRECTORY

CENTRAL GOVERNMENT
Head of State

President
Askar Akaev, Office of the President, Ulitsa Kirova 205, Bishkek, Kyrgyzstan

Ministers

Prime Minister
Amangeldi Muraliev, Office of the Prime Minister, Zhorgorku Kenesh, Bishkek, Kyrgyzstan

First Deputy Prime Minister
Boris Silaev, Office of the First Deputy Prime Minister

Deputy Prime Minister, Minister of Industry and Foreign Trade
Esengul Omuraliev, Ministry of of Industry and Foreign Trade

Minister of Foreign Affairs
Muratbek Imanaliyev, Ministry of Foreign Affairs

Minister of Economics and Finance
Sultan Mederov, Ministry of Economics and Finance

Minister for Social Welfare
Imankadyr Rysaliev, Ministry of Social Welfare

Minister of Agriculture and Water Resources
Emil Uzakbayev, Ministry of Agriculture and Water Resources

Minister of Environmental Protection
Tynybek Alykulov, Ministry of Environmental Protection

Minister of National Security
Misir Ashirkulov, Ministry of National Security

Minister of the Interior
Omurbek Kutuyev, Ministry of the Interior

Minister of Defense
Myrzakan Subanov, Ministry of Defense

Minister of Health
Naken Kasiyev, Ministry of Health

Minister of Justice
Nellya Beyshenaliyeva, Ministry of Justice

Minister of Communications and Transportation
Jantoro Satybaldiyev, Ministry of Communications and Transportation

Minister of Emergencies and Civil Defense
Sultan Urmanayev, Ministry of Emergencies and Civil Defense

Minister of Education, Science and Culture
Tursunbek Bekbolotov, Ministry of Education, Science and Culture

POLITICAL ORGANIZATIONS
Alta Mekel (Fatherland)
NAME: Omurbek Tekebayev

Argrarian Party of Kyrgyzstan
NAME: A. Aliyev

Ashar (Mutual Help Movement)
NAME: Zhumagazy Usupov

Banner National Revival Party (ASABA)
NAME: Chaprashty Bazarbay

Democratic Movement of Kyrgyzstan (DDK)
TITLE: Chairman
NAME: Jypar Jeksheyev

Communist Party of Kyrgyzstan (PKK)
TITLE: Chairman
NAME: Absamat Masaliyev

Kyrgyzstan Erkin-ErK (Democratic Movement of Free Kyrgyzstan)
NAME: Tursunbay Bakir Uulu

Movement for the People's Salvation
NAME: Djumgalbek Amambayev

Republican Popular Party of Kyrgyzstan
NAME: Zh. Sharshenaliyev

Social Democratic Party (PSD)

JUDICIAL SYSTEM
Supreme Court
Constitutional Court
Higher Court of Arbitration

FURTHER READING
Articles
World Trade Organization. *News in Brief* (October 14, 1998).

Books
Central Intelligence Agency. *World Factbook, 1998.* Washington, D.C.: Government Printing Office, 1999.

U.S. Department of State. *Country Reports on Human Rights Practices for 1998.* Washington, D.C.: Government Printing Office, 1999.

KYRGYZSTAN: STATISTICAL DATA

For sources and notes see "Sources of Statistics" in the front of each volume.

GEOGRAPHY

Geography (1)

Area:

Total: 198,500 sq km.

Land: 191,300 sq km.

Water: 7,200 sq km.

Area—comparative: slightly smaller than South Dakota.

Land boundaries:

Total: 3,878 km.

Border countries: China 858 km, Kazakhstan 1,051 km, Tajikistan 870 km, Uzbekistan 1,099 km.

Coastline: 0 km (landlocked).

Climate: dry continental to polar in high Tien Shan; subtropical in southwest (Fergana Valley); temperate in northern foothill zone.

Terrain: peaks of Tien Shan and associated valleys and basins encompass entire nation.

Natural resources: abundant hydroelectric potential; significant deposits of gold and rare earth metals; locally exploitable coal, oil, and natural gas; other deposits of nepheline, mercury, bismuth, lead, and zinc.

Land use:

Arable land: 7%

Permanent crops: 0%

Permanent pastures: 44%

Forests and woodland: 4%

Other: 45% (1993 est.).

Note: Kyrgyzstan has the world's largest natural growth walnut forest.

HUMAN FACTORS

Demographics (2A)

	1990	1995	1998	2000	2010	2020	2030	2040	2050
Population	4,389.7	4,528.5	4,522.3	4,584.3	5,118.6	5,764.3	6,359.3	6,925.7	7,394.2
Net migration rate (per 1,000 population)	NA	NA	NA	NA	NA	NA	NA	NA	NA
Births	NA	NA	NA	NA	NA	NA	NA	NA	NA
Deaths	NA	NA	NA	NA	NA	NA	NA	NA	NA
Life expectancy - males	62.2	60.3	59.4	59.1	61.8	65.6	68.9	71.7	74.1
Life expectancy - females	70.9	69.1	68.3	67.9	70.2	74.0	77.1	79.7	81.7
Birth rate (per 1,000)	30.5	24.5	22.0	21.7	22.2	18.5	16.2	15.4	13.9
Death rate (per 1,000)	8.1	8.5	8.6	8.8	8.6	7.3	7.0	7.7	8.4
Women of reproductive age (15-49 yrs.)	1,027.7	1,108.8	1,150.6	1,199.3	1,452.2	1,571.3	1,692.8	1,688.2	1,707.7
of which are currently married	NA	NA	NA	NA	NA	NA	NA	NA	NA
Fertility rate	3.8	3.0	2.7	2.6	2.3	2.2	2.2	2.1	2.1

Except as noted, values for vital statistics are in thousands; life expectancy is in years.

Health Indicators (4)

Life expectancy at birth

1980 65

1997 67

Daily per capita supply of calories (1996) 2,489

Total fertility rate births per woman (1997) 2.8

Maternal mortality ratio per 100,000 live births
(1990-97) . . . . .32[b]

Safe water % of population with access (1995) 81

Sanitation % of population with access (1995) . . . .

Consumption of iodized salt % of households
(1992-98)[a] . . . .

Smoking prevalence

Male % of adults (1985-95)[a] . . . .

Female % of adults (1985-95)[a] . . . .

Tuberculosis incidence per 100,000 people
(1997) 99

Adult HIV prevalence % of population ages
15-49 (1997) . . . .<0.005

Infants and Malnutrition (5)

Under-5 mortality rate (1997) 48

% of infants with low birthweight (1990-97) . . . . . .NA

Births attended by skilled health staff % of total[a] . . .98

% fully immunized (1995-97)

TB 99

DPT 95

Polio 95

Measles 85

Prevalence of child malnutrition under age 5
(1992-97)[b] 11

Ethnic Division (6)

Kirghiz 52.4%

Russian 18%

Uzbek 12.9%

Ukrainian 2.5%

German 2.4%

Other 11.8%

Religions (7)

Muslim 75%

Russian Orthodox 20%

Other 5%

Languages (8)

Kirghiz (Kyrgyz)—official language, Russian—official
language. In March 1996, the Kyrgyzstani legislature
amended the constitution to make Russian an official
language, along with Kirghiz, in territories and work
places where Russian-speaking citizens predominate.

EDUCATION

Public Education Expenditures (9)

Public expenditure on education (% of GNP)

1980 . . . .

1996 . . . . .5.7

Expenditure per student

Primary % of GNP per capita

1980 . . . .

1996 . . . .

Secondary % of GNP per capita

1980 . . . .

1996 . . . . .36.4[1]

Tertiary % of GNP per capita

1980 . . . .

1996 . . . . .50.5[1]

Expenditure on teaching materials

Primary % of total for level (1996) . . . .

Secondary % of total for level (1996) . . . . .0.6[1]

Primary pupil-teacher ratio per teacher (1996) . . . . .20[1]

Duration of primary education years (1995) 4

Literacy Rates (11B)

Adult literacy rate

1980

Male . . . .-

Female . . . .-

1995

Male 99

Female 95

GOVERNMENT & LAW

Political Parties (12)

The legislative branch is a bicameral Supreme Council.
It consists of the Assembly of People's Representatives
(70 seats; members are elected by popular vote to serve
five-year terms) and the Legislative Assembly (35 seats;
members are elected by popular vote to serve five-year
terms). Data on election results are not available.

Government Budget (13B)

Revenues . . . .$225 million
Expenditures . . . .$308 million
  Capital expenditures . . . .$11 million

Data for 1996 est.

Crime (15)

Crime rate (for 1997)
  Crimes reported 39,600
  Total persons convicted 22,700
  Crimes per 100,000 population 850
Persons responsible for offenses
  Total number of suspects 23,400

Total number of female suspects 2,600
Total number of juvenile suspects 1,650

LABOR FORCE

Labor Force (16)

Total (million) 1.7
Agriculture and forestry 40%
Industry and construction 19%
Other 41%

Data for 1995 est.

GOVERNMENT & LAW

Military Affairs (14B)

	1992	1993	1994	1995
Military expenditures				
Current dollars (mil.)	47	51	57	NA
1995 constant dollars (mil.)	51	53	58	NA
Armed forces (000)	12	12	9	13
Gross national product (GNP)				
Current dollars (mil.)	12,120	10,920	7,980	8,127
1995 constant dollars (mil.)	13,040	11,450	8,180	8,127
Central government expenditures (CGE)				
1995 constant dollars (mil.)	4,421	NA	NA	NA
People (mil.)	4.5	4.6	4.5	4.5
Military expenditure as % of GNP	0.4	.5	.7	NA
Military expenditure as % of CGE	1.1	NA	NA	NA
Military expenditure per capita (1995 $)	11	12	13	NA
Armed forces per 1,000 people (soldiers)	2.6	2.6	2.0	2.9
GNP per capita (1995 $)	2,878	2,515	1,800	1,793
Arms imports[6]				
Current dollars (mil.)	0	0	0	0
1995 constant dollars (mil.)	0	0	0	0
Arms exports[6]				
Current dollars (mil.)	0	10	10	10
1995 constant dollars (mil.)	0	10	10	10
Total imports[7]				
Current dollars (mil.)	419	418	459	508
1995 constant dollars (mil.)	451	438	471	508
Total exports[7]				
Current dollars (mil.)	316	268	339	408
1995 constant dollars (mil.)	340	281	347	408
Arms as percent of total imports[8]	0	0	0	0
Arms as percent of total exports[8]	0	3.7	2.9	2.5

LABOR FORCE

Unemployment Rate (17)

8% (December 1996 est.)

PRODUCTION SECTOR

Electric Energy (18)

Capacity . . . . .3.632 million kW (1995)

Production . . . . .13.7 billion kWh (1996 est.)

Consumption per capita . . . . .2,090 kWh (1995)

Transportation (19)

Highways:

total: 18,500 km

paved: 16,854 km (including 140 km of expressways)

unpaved: 1,646 km (1996 est.)

Waterways: 600 km (1990)

Pipelines: natural gas 200 km

Airports: 54 (1994 est.)

Airports—with paved runways:

total: 14

over 3,047 m: 1

2,438 to 3,047 m: 3

1,524 to 2,437 m: 9

under 914 m: 1 (1994 est.)

Airports—with unpaved runways:

total: 40

1,524 to 2,437 m: 4

914 to 1,523 m: 4

under 914 m: 32 (1994 est.)

Top Agricultural Products (20)

Wool, tobacco, cotton, potatoes, vegetables, grapes, fruits and berries; sheep, goats, cattle.

FINANCE, ECONOMICS, & TRADE

Economic Indicators (22)

National product: GDP—purchasing power parity—$9.7 billion (1997 est.)

National product real growth rate: 10% (1997 est.)

National product per capita: $2,100 (1997 est.)

Inflation rate—consumer price index: 15% (1997 est.)

Exchange Rates (24)

Exchange rates:

Soms (KGS) per US$1

January 1997 . . . . .14.6

Yearend 1995 . . . . .11.2

Yearend 1994 . . . . .10.6

Top Import Origins (25)

$890 million (1996)

Origins	%
Turkey	NA
Cuba	NA
United States	NA
Germany	NA

NA stands for not available.

Balance of Payments (23)

	1993	1994	1995	1996
Exports of goods (f.o.b.)	340	340	409	531
Imports of goods (f.o.b.)	−447	−426	−531	−783
Trade balance	−107	−86	−122	−252
Services - debits	−56	−92	−233	−291
Services - credits	9	33	43	36
Private transfers (net)	66	62	78	82
Government transfers (net)	1	1	1	2
Overall balance	−88	−83	−233	−423

Top Export Destinations (26)

$506 million (1996).

Destinations	%
China	NA
United Kingdom	NA
FSU	NA

NA stands for not available.

Economic Aid (27)

Recipient: ODA, $56 million (1993). Note: commitments, 1992- 95, $1,695 million ($390 million disbursements).

Import Export Commodities (28)

Import Commodities	Export Commodities
Grain	Cotton
Lumber	Wool
Industrial products	Meat
Ferrous metals	Tobacco; gold
Fuel	Mercury
Machinery	Uranium
Textiles	Hydropower; machinery;
Footwear	shoes

LAOS

Lao People's Democratic Republic
Sathalanalat Paxathipatai Paxaxon Lao

INTRODUCTORY SURVEY

RECENT HISTORY

During World War II (1939–45), Laos was occupied by Japan. After the war, French forces reoccupied Laos and established Sisavang Vong, the king of Louangphrabang, as king of Laos under French domination. In May 1947, the king established a constitution providing for a democratic government, and by 1953 Laos had achieved full sovereignty.

In the meantime, Vietnamese communist (Viet-Minh) forces had invaded Laos in the spring of 1953. A Laotian communist movement, the Pathet Lao (Lao State), collaborated with the Viet-Minh during its Laotian offensive. Under the terms of a 1954 cease-fire, the Pathet Lao pulled back to two northern provinces, but the group was to continue fighting for control of Laos until it finally prevailed some 20 years later.

In the 1960s, Laos was steadily drawn into the role of a main theater in the escalating Vietnam war. The Laotian segment of the so-called Ho Chi Minh trail was the target for heavy United States bombing raids. While the Vientiane government was heavily bolstered by United States military and economic support, the Pathet Lao received key support from the Democratic Republic of Vietnam in the north.

By the end of the war, the Pathet Lao controlled over three-fourths of Laos. Following the fall of the U.S.-backed regimes in Vietnam and Cambodia in April 1975, the Laotian communists

embarked on a campaign to achieve complete military and political supremacy in Laos. On 23 August, Vientiane was declared "liberated," and on 2 December 1975, the Lao People's Democratic Republic (LPDR) was established, with Prince Souphanouvong as president. King Savang Vatthana abdicated his throne, ending the monarchy that had survived in Laos for 622 years.

During the late 1970s, the communists moved to consolidate their control and socialize the economy. Private trade was banned, factories were nationalized, and forcible collectivization of agriculture was initiated. "Reeducation" camps for an estimated 40,000 former royalists and military leaders were established in remote areas.

However, with the economy near collapse in 1979, in part because of severe drought followed by flooding, the Laotian government slowed the process of socialization and announced a return to private enterprise and a readiness to accept aid from the non-communist world.

In April 1994 the first international bridge, the Mittaphap (Friendship) Bridge, linking Laos and Thailand across the Mekong River, was opened. The 1,174-meter (3,852-foot) bridge, built and paid for by Australia, is part of a plan for an Asian super-highway to facilitate travel from Singapore to Shanghai. The most immediate benefits are anticipated by the tourism industry and as a spur to real estate investment.

The U.S. Department of State notes that despite constitutional guarantees, freedom of speech, assembly, and religion are restricted, and political killings have accompanied continued rebellion, primarily among Hmong tribesmen.

GOVERNMENT

Under a new constitution adopted in 1991, the executive branch consists of the president, prime minister and two deputy prime ministers, and the Council of Ministers (cabinet) who are appointed by the president with the approval of the National Assembly. The legislative branch is the National Assembly, which is elected by universal suffrage for a period of five years. The judicial branch is the Supreme People's Court Leaders. The constitution calls for a strong legislature elected by secret ballot, but most political power continues to rest with the party-dominated council of ministers.

Laos consists of 16 provinces (khoueng), each subdivided into districts (muong), townships (tasseng), and villages (ban).

Judiciary

The government is now in the process of developing a codified body of laws. The constitution contains provisions designed to guarantee the independence of judges and prosecutors, but in practice the courts appear to be subject to influence of other government agencies. There is a Central Supreme Court in Vientiane. In 1993 the government began publishing an official gazette in which all laws and regulations are disseminated.

Political Parties

The only legal political party was the communist Lao People's Revolutionary Party (LPRP) which includes the Lao Front for National Construction (LFNC).

DEFENSE

In 1995 the armed forces in Laos numbered 37,000, with 18 months of military service compulsory for all males. A total of 33,000 Laotians served in the army. The navy, equipped with 84 patrol craft and boats, enlisted 500. The air force, with 3,500 men, was equipped with antiaircraft missiles and 31 combat aircraft. The village self-defense force numbers 100,000. There are also about 2,000 rebels in Laos ready to confront the armed forces.

ECONOMIC AFFAIRS

One of the world's poorest and least-developed nations, Laos is overwhelmingly agricultural, with about 80% of the population engaged in farming, which accounts for about 56% of the gross domestic product (GDP). Because industrialization is minimal, Laos imports nearly all the manufactured products it requires.

The hostilities of the 1960s and 1970s badly disrupted the economy, forcing the country to depend on imports from Thailand to supplement its daily rice requirements. The third five-year plan (1991–95) emphasized improvement of communications and transportation networks, export growth, and development of domestic industry to decrease reliance on imports.

By 1997, there was more than $5 billion in foreign investment, as Laos had opened up its economy. However, inflations and problems with tax collection have contributed to increasing budget deficits.

Public Finance

The civil war rendered normal budgetary procedures impossible, the budget being covered largely by U.S. aid and monetary inflation. Deficit financing continued in the 1970s and 1980s, covered mostly by foreign aid from communist nations. With the collapse of this support, however, Laos has increasingly looked to foreign investment capital and Western lending agencies for financial support. Beginning in 1994, the IMF initiated an annual program of loans to assist the country with a structural adjustment program. It lent Laos $17 million in 1995. Still, 31% of the 1995 budget was international aid.

The U.S. Central Intelligence Agency estimates that, in 1995, government revenues totaled approximately $198 million and expenditures $351 million. External debt totaled $2 billion.

Income

In 1997, Laos's gross national product (GNP) was $5.9 billion, or about $1,150 per person.

Industry

Manufacturing is largely confined to the processing of agricultural and forestry products. There are some small mining operations, charcoal ovens, a cement plant, a few brick works, carpenter shops, a tobacco factory, rice mills, some furniture factories, and more than two dozen sawmills.

Handicrafts account for an important part of the income of many Laotians. Some villages or areas specialize in certain types of products: silk fabrics, baskets, lacquerware, and gold and silver jewelry and ornaments. Bricks, pottery, iron products, and distilled beverages are made in individual villages.

Banking and Finance

The central bank, the Bank of the Laotian People's Democratic Republic, regulates a rapidly expanding sector comprising 13 national and foreign-owned banks under the terms of the Commercial Bank and Financial Institutions Act of January 1992. Most of the wholly foreign-owned banks are Thai (such as the Thai Military Bank and Siam Commercial) and many of the joint-venture banks are backed by Thai financiers (such as the Joint Development Bank). The central bank continues to receive technical assistance from multilateral lending agencies, and is gradually strengthening the potential framework. The banks are now believed to be more efficient. The largest commercial bank, established in 1953, is the Bank of Indochina.

The large-scale flight of foreign currency that accompanied the Pathet Lao's ascendancy to power led the new government to shut down Vientiane's banks in September 1975. Officials subsequently announced the expropriation of most private accounts, claiming they were the property of former rightists and "traitors."

Banking reforms of the 1988–89 period opened Laos to foreign banks. Banks in Laos include: Banque Pour le Commerce Exterieur Lao, Joint Development Bank, Nakhonelouang Bank, and the Vientiane Commercial Bank.

All banks now provide basic business services and offer a range of deposit and credit facilities. Interest rates are increasingly responsive to market conditions but tend to remain close to rates set by the central bank. Public confidence in the banking system as measured by the level of domestic capital mobilization is still low. Until 1988 the wholly state-controlled system serviced the needs of the command economy, offering uncompetitive rates of interest to savers or producers in need of regular credit. Most families continued to save by investing in gold and jewelry. The system suffered severe liquidity problems in 1990–91 when the "privatization'' of former state-owned enterprises was at its peak: old debts were not repaid and new capital arriving as a result of the opening of the economy to foreign investors was coming in too slowly. The ADB supplied sdr 17.42 million ($25 million) to recapitalize the system in 1991.

Economic Development

The National Plan and Foreign Aid Council was established in June 1956 to prepare a general plan for the development of Laos and to set up a series of five-year plans. In view of its limited capital resources, the government sought increased private foreign investment, continued U.S. governmental economic assistance, and help from international monetary bodies and the Colombo Plan organization. An economic plan drafted by the Laotian government in 1962 was never fully implemented, however, owing to internal instability. Little of the infrastructure for public works, industry, and mining that was abandoned in 1961 has been resumed. Although a major goal of the 1969–74 economic and social development plan, completion of the Nam Ngum Dam, was fulfilled, a host of other targets had to be abandoned because of disruption stemming from the war. Following the Pathet Lao takeover in 1975, efforts were made to restructure the Laotian economy along socialist lines. By 1979, with the economy reduced to a virtual standstill because of poor harvests, rapid inflation, and the absence of any private incentive, the government abandoned centralized planning as the sole route to economic development. Instead, a centrally coordinated amalgam of state-run enterprises, cooperatives, and private ventures was pursued. Laos' first five-year plan (1981–85) envisioned increases of 65–68% in the gross social product, 23–24% in agricultural production, and 100–120% in industrial production, as well as completion of repairs on major highways and waterways. These goals were not met because of managerial inefficiency and waste. The second five-year plan (1986–90) emphasized export of food products, strengthening of economic management, rehabilitation of routes to seaports and rural feeder roads, reform of general education and training, and development of small- and medium-scale projects.

U.S. aid to Laos began in 1955 and continued until the U.S. pullout in 1975. During this period, the Laotian economy became almost totally dependent on U.S. aid, which amounted to over $900 million in nonmilitary loans and grants and $1.6 billion in military assistance. After the Pathet Lao took power, China supplied much of the needed assistance between 1975 and 1979. Since 1979, Laos has received direct aid mainly from the former USSR, Viet Nam, and their allies. Aid from Council for Mutual Economic Assistance (CMEA) countries totaled $90 million in 1985. Among non-Communist nations, Japan, Australia, Sweden, and the Netherlands have also furnished assistance. In 1985, the U.S. ban on aid to Laos was lifted, largely because of Laotian cooperation in accounting for U.S. military personnel missing in action in Laos during the Viet Nam war. Aid from international agencies totaled $183.1 million between 1946 and 1986. In the 1990s the U.S. suspended aid and preferential treatment based on Laos' failure to assist the suppression of drug traffic, but reversed this decision following renewed co-operation by Laos.

The New Economic Mechanism (NEM) approved in 1986 (based on *chin tanakan may*, ''new thinking,'') introduced free enterprise initiatives including decentralized decision making, deregulation of pricing and financial systems, and promotion of domestic and international trade and foreign investment. Reforms have been introduced in phases. In 1988 land use reforms and market determined prices were introduced. In 1989 the tax system was modified, the Foreign Investment Code and Decree was implemented, the banking system was restructured, and the privatization of state enterprises commenced. Creation of a taxation system and a customs administration are aimed at increasing government revenue. The Ministry of Industry and Primary Resources, the Economic Planning Unit, which monitors existing and new businesses, and the Economic Development Board (EDB), which assists in the establishment of new industries, facilitate foreign investment in most sectors of the economy. Incentives offered to encourage the development of industrial and commercial enterprises include allowing 100% foreign ownership.

The third Five Year Plan (1991–95) continued previous policies of infrastructure improvement, export growth, and import substitution. Four sectors are considered as areas of future income for Laos: mining and energy; agriculture and forestry; tourism; and service, as a way-station and service center between China, Viet Nam, and Cambodia. Laos has untapped mineral resources and proven reserves of gold, gemstones and iron ore. Pulp and paper tree plantations would be substituted for the export of timber and agricultural products to serve the Thai market. Based on Thailand's experience, the government recognizes that mass tourism involves environmental degradation, yet the opening of the Mittaphap (Friendship) Bridge over the Mekong between Laos and Thailand (1994) is an opportunity for both trade and tourism which is readily exploited. (A second bridge was approved in 1996.) In 1993 three western oil companies, Enterprise Oil and Monument Oil, both from the UK, and Hunt Oil of Dallas, engaged in exploration for oil and gas in Laos. The potential for finding hydrocarbons in Laos is largely unknown and exploration risks are considerable, including inadequate geological maps, unexploded ordinance, tough terrain, encounters with the remnants of the anti-communist insurgency movement, tropical and dietary illness, and the expense of drilling and pipeline construction for transport to the Vietnamese coast. Two major hydroelectric projects, the Nam Thuen Dam on a tributary of the Mekong in Khammouan province, and the Xeset dam in southern Laos produce electricity sold to Thailand.

At the sixth party congress, held in March 1996, Laotian officials debated the country's slow pace of opening up to the international investment community. By that year, the country had allowed more than 500 foreign investors, in a variety of sectors, to either establish or buy (in whole or in part) Laotian businesses. The majority of $5 billion (75%) was invested in hydroelectric power.

SOCIAL WELFARE

Laos is one of the world's most impoverished nations. Food intake does not meet basic requirements, and contamination of drinking water is widespread. In 1980, the government indicated that it regarded the nation's population as too low. Family planning programs were disbanded and the use of contraceptives banned. The Laotian population increased by 2.4% per year during 1980–90.

Almost no families own cars, and bicycles and radios are considered luxuries. In general, the lowland Lao have the highest living standards, with lower standards prevailing among the upland tribes.

Women in Laos have traditionally been subservient to men and have generally been discouraged from obtaining an education.

Healthcare

In 1990–95, only 45% of the population had access to safe water, and only 27% had adequate sanitation. In parts of Laos, malaria—the most serious health threat—is known to affect the majority of children. Other health problems are acute upper respiratory infections (including pneumonia and influenza), diarrhea and dysentery, parasites, yaws, skin ailments, various childhood diseases, hepatitis, venereal disease, and tuberculosis.

Housing

The traditional Laotian dwelling is rectangular, built entirely of wooden planks and bamboo, with a thatched roof, and raised off the ground on wooden pilings 1–2 meters (3–6 feet) high. There is a critical housing shortage in the towns, and many dwellings are substandard. As of 1990, 47% of urban and 25% of rural dwellers had access to a public water supply, while 30% of urban and 8% of rural dwellers had access to sanitation services.

EDUCATION

Education in Laos is compulsory for eight years. In 1993, there were 8,361 primary schools with 22,649 teachers and 681,044 students. In all secondary schools, there were 12,713 teachers and 155,366 students. Sisavongvong University is located in Vientiane. In 1993 there were 998 teaching faculty and 6,179 students enrolled at all higher-level institutions. The illiteracy rate is 43%.

1999 KEY EVENTS TIMELINE

January

- The first gambling casino begins operating in Laos, a joint venture between the military and a Malaysian company in a resort area.

- An unknown soldier's monument is established in a celebration of the 50th anniversary of the founding of the Pathet Lao, the Laotian army.

March

- A huge, environmentally controversial hydroelectric project, the Nam Theun II dam, is stalled for lack of World Bank guaranteed loans, due to Laos' weak economy.

April

- The building of a $33 million railway line between Laos and Thailand is announced.

May

- The Laotian government and United Nations Development Program (UNDP) officials sign economic agreements preliminary to the eventual acceptance of Laos in the World Trade Organization (WTO).

June

- Eight Laotian Christians who had been arrested because of their Bible class membership are released after serving one year jail terms for disruptive activities.

July

- H'mong hill tribe guerrillas skirmish with government troops near Laos' border with Vietnam.

August

- British scientists, following DNA analysis, announce that striped rabbits found in Laotian forests are a previously unknown species.

- As Laos' economy continues to weaken, the government's two highest economic officials, Kamphoui Keoboulap (Finance Minister) and Cheuang Sombounkham (Central Bank Governor), lose their government posts.

- Deputy Prime Minister Bounyang Vorachit becomes Finance Minister, and Soukanh Maharath takes over the Central Bank administration.

September

- The government artificially boosts the value of the Laotian currency, the kip, from 9,400 to the dollar to 5,800 to the dollar.

November

- At an informal meeting in Manila, Philippines, six members of the Association of Southeast Asian Nations (ASEAN)—Brunei, Indonesia, Malaysia, Philippines, Singapore, and Thailand—agree to establish a free-trade zone by eliminating duties on most goods traded in the region by 2010. The remaining four newer and less-developed nation members—Cambodia, Laos, Myanmar (Burma), and Vietnam—will eliminate duties by 2015. Rice will be excluded from trade agreements, however.

ANALYSIS OF EVENTS: 1999

BUSINESS AND THE ECONOMY

Laos began 1999 with an alarming set of statistics indicating its on-going economic crisis. Its currency, the kip, plunged into apparent free-fall during 1999 and then was artificially strengthened by the government late in the year. The Laotian currency's value decreased from 4,500 kip to the dollar to 9,500 to the dollar during the first half of 1999. Virulent inflation took hold at a rate of as much as 200 percent annually, the highest rate in the region, as the state-controlled economy of Laos failed to recover from the Asian economic crisis. In August, two key economic policy makers, the Finance Minister and the Central Bank Governor, were replaced. Then, on September 23, the government took the step of "correcting" the valuation of the kip to 5,800 to the dollar.

International lending institutions, frustrated by lack of meaningful economic reform by the Laotian government, continued to withhold credit to Laos. An enormous hydroelectric project, the Nam Theun II dam was in jeopardy due to lack of confidence on the part of the World Bank, which delayed guaranteed loans. The dam project was controversial because of its environmental effects and the relocation of indigenous people to make way for it. Laos remained extremely dependent on foreign aid donations. Foreign currency reserves were estimated at below $200 million at mid-year. What foreign exchange came in was mainly through aid and tourism.

International travelers provided one of the few economic bright spots as Visit Laos Year was promoted. Laos' first gambling casino opened, the city of Luang Prabang was a popular cultural attraction, and eco-tourism began to emerge. But late in the year tourism was threatened by the kip revaluation, as were exports. The garment and textile export sector also suffered from delay of a trade agreement with the United States on human rights grounds.

Overall, Laos' economy remained mainly agricultural, but the nation had to import rice from Vietnam to feed its population. Transport improvements were underway with the construction of railway lines within Laos and from the capital, Vientiane to the Thai border. Hours were lengthened for border crossings on the Mekong River bridge between Laos and Thailand.

Uncontrolled logging continued to ravage Laos' forests in 1999, with the military heavily involved in the timber business. The illicit trade in heroin from neighboring Burma, and domestic opium production continued, and the smuggling of consumer goods (mainly trans-shipment between Thailand, China and other neighboring countries) remained rampant.

GOVERNMENT AND POLITICS

The Laotian government continued to be firmly controlled by the Lao People's Revolutionary Party, the only party tolerated. The upper echelon of the government consisted largely of military men, veterans of the Pathet Lao, which in 1999 celebrated the 50th anniversary of its founding. Opposition groups were not tolerated, but within the elite tension appeared to exist between the old guard of the ''party faithful'' and younger technocrats in favor of further free market reforms. The August purge of finance officials revealed confusion within the government about how to handle the ailing economy. The public remained apparently politically inactive, enduring economic hardship without significant protests.

The sporadic insurgency of H'mong hill tribe people flared anew in 1999 reviving animosity from the Indochina war of the 1970s. The H'mong raids in the Laos/Vietnam border region, were probably provoked by government plans to relocate highland people to plains areas, as well as the H'mongs' belief in 2000 as a year of liberation.

Laos began the process of agreements aimed at eventual acceptance into the World Trade Organization. Laotian delegations participated in Association of Southeast Asian Nations (ASEAN) conferences and United Nations events. Laos also joined a new organization, the Association of Asian Parliamentarians for Peace, at its inaugural conference in Bangladesh. Laotian foreign policy continued to be strongly influenced by Vietnam, along with some influence by major trading partners China and Thailand. Rumored discontent within the ruling party about Vietnam's overwhelming influence failed to bring about any changes.

CULTURE AND SOCIETY

Laos remained far below the poverty line in 1999. Health care was dependent on foreign aid donations, and education still failed to reach many areas, especially in the mountainous north.

The government released several members of Laos' Christian minority who had served sentences imposed in 1998 for conducting Bible study classes, an activity perceived as a threat to State authority in the predominantly Buddhist, Communist-ruled country.

Large numbers of workers from China involved in infrastructure projects were residing in northern Laos. Thai investors continued to change the face of Laotian towns and cities with new buildings, and the media of Thailand ruled Laotian airwaves, influencing national culture. Still, daily life in Laos continued at a quieter, slower pace than in the neighboring countries.

DIRECTORY

CENTRAL GOVERNMENT

Head of State

President
Khamtay Siphandone, Office of the President

Prime Minister
Sisavath Keobounphanh, Office of the Prime Minister

Ministers

Minister of Foreign Affairs
Somsavat Lengsavad, Ministry of Foreign Affairs, Thatluang Road, Vientiane, Laos
PHONE: +856 414031

Minister of Interior
Asang Laoly, Ministry of Interior

Minister of Education
Phimmasone Leuangkhamma, Ministry of Education

Minister of Information and Culture
Sileua Bounkham, Ministry of Information and Culture

Minister of Labor and Social Welfare
Somphanh Phengkhammy, Ministry of Labor and Social Welfare

Minister of Commerce
Phoumy Thipphavone, Ministry of Commerce

Minister of Industry and Handicrafts
Soulivong Daravong, Ministry of Industry and Handicrafts

Minister of Communications, Transport, Posts and Construction
Phao Bounnaphol, Ministry of Communications, Transport, Posts and Construction

Minister of Public Health
Ponemek Daraloy, Ministry of Public Health

Minister of Justice
Kham Ouane Boupha, Ministry of Justice

Minister of Agriculture and Forestry
Siene Saphangthong, Ministry of Agriculture and Forestry

POLITICAL ORGANIZATIONS

Laos People's Revolutionary Party (LPRP)

TITLE: President
NAME: Khamtai Siphandon

DIPLOMATIC REPRESENTATION

Embassies in Laos

Australia
Nehru St., Vientiane, Laos
PHONE: +856 413610; 413805; 413602

Bulgaria
Sisangvonh area, Vientiane, Laos
PHONE: +856 412110

Cambodia
Thanon Saphan Thong Neua, Vientiane, Laos
PHONE: +856 314952; 312584

Czech Republic
The Deua Rd, Km 4, Vientiane, Laos
PHONE: +856 315291; 215899

China
Wat Nak St., Vientiane, Laos
PHONE: +856 315100; 315101; 315103

Cuba
Ban Saphanthong Nua, Vientiane, Laos
PHONE: +856 314902

France
Sethathirath St., Vientiane, Laos
PHONE: +856 215258; 215259
FAX: +856 215255

Germany
26 Thanon Sok Pa Luang, Vientiane, Laos
PHONE: +856 312110; 312111

India
That Luang Road, Vientiane, Laos
PHONE: +856 413802

Indonesia
Phon Kheng Road, P.O. Box 277, Vientiane, Laos
PHONE: +856 413907; 413909; 413910

Japan
Sisangvone Road, Vientiane, Laos
PHONE: +856 212623; 414400; 414406
FAX: +856 414403

North Korea
Wat Nak Road, Sisattanak, Vientiane, Laos
PHONE: +856 315260; 351261

Malaysia
That Luang Road, Vientiane, Laos
PHONE: +856 414205

Mongolia
Tha Deua Road Km 2, Vientiane, Laos
PHONE: +856 315220

Myanmar
Sokphaluand Road, Vientiane, Laos
PHONE: +856 312439; 314910

Palestine
The Deua Road Km 2.5, Vientiane, Laos
PHONE: +856 315252

Poland
The Deua Road, Km 3, Vientiane, Laos
PHONE: +856 313940; 312085

Russia
Thaphalanxay area, Vientiane, Laos
PHONE: +856 312219; 212222

Slovakia
Tha Deua Rd., Km 4, Vientiane, Laos
PHONE: +856 315291; 215899

Sweden
Wat Nak, Vientiane, Laos
PHONE: +856 313772; 315000; 315018

Thailand
Thanon Phon Kheng, Vientiane, Laos
PHONE: +856 214582; 214583; 214585

United States
Thanon Bartholomie, Vientiane, Laos
PHONE: +856 212580; 312609
FAX: +856 212584

JUDICIAL SYSTEM
Supreme People's Court

FURTHER READING
Books

Butler-Diaz, Jacqueline, ed. *New Laos, New Challenge.* Tempe, AZ: Arizona State University, 1998.

Kremmer, Christopher *Stalking the Elephant King: In Search of Laos.* Honolulu: University of Hawaii, 1998.

Stuart-Fox, Martin *A History of Laos.* New York: Cambridge University Press, 1997.

LAOS: STATISTICAL DATA

For sources and notes see "Sources of Statistics" in the front of each volume.

GEOGRAPHY

Geography (1)

Area:

Total: 236,800 sq km.

Land: 230,800 sq km.

Water: 6,000 sq km.

Areaócomparative: slightly larger than Utah.

Land boundaries:

Total: 5,083 km.

Border countries: Burma 235 km, Cambodia 541 km, China 423 km, Thailand 1,754 km, Vietnam 2,130 km.

Coastline: 0 km (landlocked).

Climate: tropical monsoon; rainy season (May to November); dry season (December to April).

Terrain: mostly rugged mountains; some plains and plateaus.

Natural resources: timber, hydropower, gypsum, tin, gold, gemstones.

Land use:

Arable land: 3%

Permanent crops: 0%

Permanent pastures: 3%

Forests and woodland: 54%

Other: 40% (1993 est.).

HUMAN FACTORS

Demographics (2A)

	1990	1995	1998	2000	2010	2020	2030	2040	2050
Population	4,191.3	4,837.2	5,260.8	5,556.8	7,168.5	8,922.7	10,669.3	12,325.6	13,843.9
Net migration rate (per 1,000 population)	NA	NA	NA	NA	NA	NA	NA	NA	NA
Births	NA	NA	NA	NA	NA	NA	NA	NA	NA
Deaths	NA	NA	NA	NA	NA	NA	NA	NA	NA
Life expectancy - males	48.2	50.7	52.1	53.1	58.1	62.7	66.7	70.2	72.9
Life expectancy - females	51.3	53.8	55.3	56.4	61.5	66.4	70.7	74.4	77.4
Birth rate (per 1,000)	45.7	42.6	40.6	39.3	32.7	26.8	21.9	18.7	16.4
Death rate (per 1,000)	16.7	14.3	13.0	12.2	9.0	7.0	6.0	5.8	6.1
Women of reproductive age (15-49 yrs.)	955.6	1,108.5	1,212.5	1,289.0	1,768.6	2,329.0	2,896.9	3,356.9	3,627.6
of which are currently married	NA	NA	NA	NA	NA	NA	NA	NA	NA
Fertility rate	6.4	6.0	5.7	5.4	4.2	3.2	2.5	2.2	2.1

Except as noted, values for vital statistics are in thousands; life expectancy is in years.

Health Personnel (3)

Total health expenditure as a percentage of GDP,
1990-1997[a]

Public sector 1.3

Private sector 1.3

Total[b] 2.6

Health expenditure per capita in U.S. dollars,
1990-1997[a]

Purchasing power parity 31

Total 10

Availability of health care facilities per 100,000 people

Hospital beds 1990-1997[a] 260

Doctors 1993[c] ....NA

Nurses 1993[c] ....NA

Ethnic Division (6)

Lao Loum (lowland) 68%

Lao Theung (upland) 22%

Lao Soung (highland) including

the Hmong ("Meo") and

the Yao (Mien) 9%

Ethnic Vietnamese/Chinese 1%

Religions (7)

Buddhist 60%

Animist and other 40%

Languages (8)

Lao (official), French, English, and various ethnic
languages.

EDUCATION

Literacy Rates (11A)

In thousands and percent[1]	1990	1995	2000	2010
Illiterate population (15+ yrs.)	1,149	1,170	1,190	1,225
Literacy rate - total adult pop. (%)	51.5	56.6	61.7	71.3
Literacy rate - males (%)	65.1	69.4	73.5	80.7
Literacy rate - females (%)	38.6	44.4	50.4	62.2

GOVERNMENT & LAW

Political Parties (12)

National Assembly	No. of seats
Lao People's Revolutionary Party (LPRP)	98
Independents	1

All parties other than the LPRP are proscribed.

Government Budget (13B)

Revenues ....$230.2 million

Expenditures ....$365.9 million

Capital expenditures ....$317 million

Data for 1996.

LABOR FORCE

Labor Force (16)

Agriculture 80%. Data for 1997 est.

Unemployment Rate (17)

1.7% overall; 4.5% in urban areas (1995 est.)

PRODUCTION SECTOR

Electric Energy (18)

Capacity ....217,000 kW (1997)

Production ....1.2 billion kWh (1996)

Consumption per capita ....60 kWh (1995)

Transportation (19)

Highways:

total: 22,321 km

paved: 3,502 km

unpaved: 18,819 km (1997 est.)

Waterways: about 4,587 km, primarily Mekong and
tributaries; 2,897 additional kilometers are sectionally
navigable by craft drawing less than 0.5 m

Pipelines: petroleum products 136 km

Merchant marine:

total: 1 cargo ship (1,000 GRT or over) totaling 2,370
GRT/3,000 DWT (1997 est.)

Airports: 52 (1997 est.)

Airports—with paved runways:

total: 9

over 3,047 m: 1

1,524 to 2,437 m: 5

914 to 1,523 m: 3 (1997 est.)

Airports—with unpaved runways:

total: 43

1,524 to 2,437 m: 1

914 to 1,523 m: 17

under 914 m: 25 (1997 est.)

Top Agricultural Products (20)

Sweet potatoes, vegetables, corn, coffee, sugarcane, cotton; water buffalo, pigs, cattle, poultry; tobacco.

FINANCE, ECONOMICS, & TRADE

Economic Indicators (22)

National product: GDPópurchasing power parityó$5.9 billion (1997 est.)

National product real growth rate: 1.5% (1997 est.)

National product per capita: $1,150 (1997 est.)

Inflation rateóconsumer price index: 16% (1997 est.)

GOVERNMENT & LAW

Military Affairs (14B)

	1990	1991	1992	1993	1994	1995
Military expenditures						
Current dollars (mil.)	NA	NA	110	110	78[e]	72[e]
1995 constant dollars (mil.)	NA	NA	118	115	80[e]	72[e]
Armed forces (000)	55	53	37	37	45	50
Gross national product (GNP)						
Current dollars (mil.)	1,087	1,169	1,287	1,392	1,539	1,734
1995 constant dollars (mil.)	1,249	1,292	1,384	1,459	1,578	1,734
Central government expenditures (CGE)						
1995 constant dollars (mil.)	NA	NA	NA	NA	359	NA
People (mil.)	4.2	4.3	4.4	4.6	4.7	4.8
Military expenditure as % of GNP	NA	NA	8.5	7.9	5.1	4.2
Military expenditure as % of CGE	NA	NA	NA	NA	22.3	NA
Military expenditure per capita (1995 $)	NA	NA	27	25	17	15
Armed forces per 1,000 people (soldiers)	13.1	12.3	8.3	8.1	9.6	10.3
GNP per capita (1995 $)	298	299	312	319	336	358
Arms imports[6]						
Current dollars (mil.)	40	10	10	30	90	0
1995 constant dollars (mil.)	46	11	11	31	92	0
Arms exports[6]						
Current dollars (mil.)	0	0	0	0	0	0
1995 constant dollars (mil.)	0	0	0	0	0	0
Total imports[7]						
Current dollars (mil.)	238[e]	215	253	432	564	587
1995 constant dollars (mil.)	274[e]	238	272	453	578	587
Total exports[7]						
Current dollars (mil.)	61[e]	97	133	241	300	348
1995 constant dollars (mil.)	70[e]	107	143	253	308	348
Arms as percent of total imports[8]	16.8	4.7	4.0	6.9	16.0	0
Arms as percent of total exports[8]	0	0	0	0	0	0

FINANCE, ECONOMICS, & TRADE

Exchange Rates (24)

Exchange rates:

New kips (NK) per US$1

January 1998	2,500
1997	1,256.73
1996	921.14
1995	804.69
1994	717.67
1993	716.25

As of September 1995, a floating exchange rate policy was adopted

Top Import Origins (25)

$678 million (c.i.f., 1996)

Origins	%
Thailand	NA
Japan	NA
Vietnam	NA
China	NA
Singapore	NA

NA stands for not available.

Top Export Destinations (26)

$313.1 million (f.o.b., 1996).

Destinations	%
Vietnam	NA
Thailand	NA
Germany	NA
France	NA

NA stands for not available.

Economic Aid (27)

Recipient: ODA, $212.2 million.

Import Export Commodities (28)

Import Commodities	Export Commodities
Machinery and equipment	Wood products
	Garments
Vehicles	Electricity
Fuel	Coffee
	Tin

Balance of Payments (23)

	1992	1993	1994	1995	1996
Exports of goods (f.o.b.)	133	248	305	311	323
Imports of goods (f.o.b.)	−233	−397	−519	−627	−644
Trade balance	−100	−150	−214	−316	−321
Services - debits	−76	−82	−161	−135	−157
Services - credits	67	94	94	104	114
Private transfers (net)	61	102	121	110	82
Government transfers (net)	...	...	...	...	...
Overall balance	−48	−36	−160	−237	−283

MANUFACTURING SECTOR

GDP & Manufacturing Summary (21)

	1980	1985	1990	1992	1993	1994
Gross Domestic Product						
Millions of 1990 dollars	515	704	868	975	1,014	1,099
Growth rate in percent	1.70	5.06	7.61	7.00	4.00	8.40
Per capita (in 1990 dollars)	160.6	195.9	206.6	218.2	220.2	231.8
Manufacturing Value Added						
Millions of 1990 dollars	23	31	38	46	*50*	*54*
Growth rate in percent	7.94	3.84	10.87	8.00	*8.10*	*8.50*
Manufacturing share in percent of current prices	NA	NA	NA	12.6	13.4	NA

LATVIA

Republic of Latvia
Latvijas Republika

CAPITAL: Riga

FLAG: The flag consists of a single white horizontal stripe on a maroon field.

ANTHEM: *Dievs, svēti Latviju! (God bless Latvia!)*

MONETARY UNIT: The lat was introduced as the official currency in May 1993; $1 = Ls0.55.

WEIGHTS AND MEASURES: The metric system is in force.

HOLIDAYS: New Year's Day, 1 January; Good Friday (movable); Midsummer Festival, 23–24 June; National Day, Proclamation of the Republic, 18 November; Christmas, 25–26 December; New Year's Eve, 31 December.

TIME: 2 PM = noon GMT.

LOCATION AND SIZE: Latvia is located in northeastern Europe, bordering the Baltic Sea, between Sweden and Russia. Comparatively, Latvia is slightly larger than the state of West Virginia, with a total area of 64,100 square kilometers (24,749 square miles). Latvia's boundary length totals 1,150 kilometers (715 miles). Latvia's capital city, Riga, is located in the northern part of the country along the Baltic Sea coast.

CLIMATE: The mean temperature is between 16.8° and 17.6°C (62–64°F) in July and between −6.6° and 2.6 °C (20–27 °F) in January. Mean annual rainfall is between 60–65 centimeters (24–26 inches).

INTRODUCTORY SURVEY

RECENT HISTORY

Germans, Poles, Swedes, and Russians competed for influence in what is now Latvia from the Middle Ages until the eighteenth century, when it was incorporated into the Russian Empire. During the 19th century, a Latvian nationalist movement occurred and on 18 November 1918, the independent Republic of Latvia was proclaimed. It was recognized by Moscow ten years later. However, the 1939 Nazi-Soviet pact placed Latvia under Soviet influence. Soviet forces invaded Latvia on 17 June 1940 and incorporated it into the Soviet Union. Latvia was seized by the Germans in July 1941, when Hitler launched his attack on the Soviet Union, but was recaptured by Soviet forces in 1944.

In the 1980s, Soviet President Mikhail Gorbachev's liberal policies allowed Latvians to voice their long-suppressed desire for national self-determination. The Latvian Popular Front (LPF) gained a majority in the elections for the Latvian Supreme Council in the spring of 1990. On 21 August 1991—shortly after the failed coup against Gorbachev—Latvia once again proclaimed its independence.

In April 1994 the Latvian and Russian governments agreed to a schedule that withdrew all Russian troops from Latvia by 31 August 1994. The agreement did not include 599 soldiers at the Skrunda Radar Station, which Russia may operate until 31 August 1998 and must dismantle by 29 February 2000. In June 1995, Latvia signed an accord with the European Union that may eventually lead to full membership.

GOVERNMENT

The new parliament (Saeima) elected in June 1993 consists of a single chamber with 100 deputies. The executive branch of government is made up of the president, prime minister, and the cabinet. Latvia's territory is divided into four historical districts.

Judiciary

The courts are being reorganized along democratic lines. Regional courts were added in 1995 to hear appeals of lower court decisions. There is also a Supreme Court and a Constitutional Court.

Political Parties

In the October 1995 elections, nine parties gained representation in the parliament (Saeima). The Democratic Party won the most seats, at 18.

DEFENSE

The Latvian armed forces total 8,000, including 1,500 National Guard personnel for border and coastal defense with only one battalion ready for mobile warfare. The 16,500-man militia serves as a reserve.

ECONOMIC AFFAIRS

Latvia has a relatively well-developed transport and communications network and a variety of industries. Agriculture makes up approximately 20% of national income and centers around the cultivation of potatoes, cereals, fodder (animal feed), and other crops, as well as dairy farming. The growth rate of the gross domestic product (GDP) increased from -33.5% in 1992 to 2.1% in 1996. During that time, the inflation rate declined from 960% to 16%.

Public Finance

A stabilization program was commenced in 1992 (with IMF support), and a new currency (the lat) was issued in May 1993. Tight fiscal and monetary policy helped minimize public finance deterioration and curb inflation in 1992/93. In the second half of 1992, the Latvian budget deficit stood at $16 million. Internal and external loans were taken to alleviate the budget deficit. In November 1992, public debt stood at $159.6 million, including $45 million owed to the World Bank and $76.8 million to the IMF. Internal debt came to $12 million. As of 1995, external public debt was $414.4 million.

Income

In 1997 the gross national product (GNP) was $10.4 billion at current prices, or $4,260 per person. During 1985–95, the average annual decline in the real growth rate of the GNP per person was 6.6%.

Industry

Latvia has mainly heavy industries such as chemicals and petrochemicals, metal working, and machine building. Major manufactured items include railway carriages, buses, mopeds, washing machines, and telephone systems.

Banking and Finance

In 1991 banking matters were transferred to the Bank of Latvia from Soviet bank officials. Previously, Latvia had its branch of the Soviet State Bank (Gosbank). The central bank had the authority to issue Latvian rubles and regulate the commercial banking sector. There are many banks in Latvia, including the Baltic Transit Bank, Banka Atmoda, Latgale Stocj Commercial Bank, Latvian Credit Bank, Investment Bank of Latvia, and the Latvian Land Bank.

Latvia effectively exited the ruble zone on 20 July 1992. By early 1993 the Bank of Latvia introduced a national currency, the lat. The lat is now fully convertible for capital- and current-account purposes.

Latvia's banking sector has proved one of the country's most successful industries and also its most controversial. Riga has developed into an offshore financial center, offering numbered accounts and related services, and drawing in a substantial chunk of flight capital from other former Soviet republics. Owing to fairly liberal banking laws in the early 1990s, a large number of banks (54 as of May 1995) had been established. Subsequently, capital and other requirements have been progressively tightened. For existing banks, the minimum reserve requirements have been raised from Ls100,000 as of 1995 to Ls1.0 million by 31 March 1998. As of April 1995 all banks had to be audited by one of the recognized international accounting firms. The stricter capital regime has lead to an inevitable attrition, with 11 banks losing their licenses between 1992 and 1995. Only some 15 banks made profits in 1994 and had adequate reserves. The audits also revealed huge losses at Baltija Bank (Latvia's largest institution, with some 200,000 private depositors), which had been incurred as a result of systematic fraud.

In February 1997, the Bank of Latvia gave its approval to the proposed merger between the Latvian Savings Bank and the United Baltic Bank

of Riga. As a result of the merger, the state now owns 75% of shares in the Latvian Savings Bank. The government's plans are to privatize the newly merged entity. Money supply, as measured by M1, totaled Ls403.7 million at the end of January 1997. There is a stock exchange in Riga.

Economic Development

The government began introducing economic reforms in 1990 to effect the transition to a market-driven economy. Individual and family-owned businesses, cooperatives, and privately- and publicly-held companies are now permitted. The privatization process was simplified with a 1994 law that created the Privatization Agency (PA) and the State Property Fund. Distribution of privatization vouchers was completed by March 1995, with certificates valued at Ls2.8 billion distributed to 2.2 million Latvians.

The privatization program focuses on international tenders and public offerings of shares. By mid-1994, 450 state enterprises had been transferred for privatization. The first international tender of 45 enterprises came in November 1994, followed by 80 more in 1995. Large-scale privatization began in 1996.

SOCIAL WELFARE

The 1990 law on social insurance established old age, disability, and survivorship pensions for all wage and salary earners.

Although employment discrimination based on sex is illegal, women are barred from certain occupations considered dangerous. Some employers hesitate to hire women because they are legally required to pay childbirth benefits to female employees.

Healthcare

Life expectancy in 1995 was 69 years. In 1993, there was one physician for every 278 people. Heart disease is the cause of death for 40% of all Latvians over age 65.

Housing

Housing construction lags behind demand. At the beginning of 1990, 165,000 families (one out of five) were registered for new housing.

EDUCATION

Compulsory education lasts for nine years beginning at the age of six. Secondary education generally lasts for three years. In the 1996, there were 1,066 public schools with 345,214 students and 24 private schools with 1,655 students. Latvia has two major universities: the University of Latvia and the Riga Technical University. In 1995, there were 45,828 students at 17 state institutions and 3,112 students at 10 private institutions of higher learning.

1999 KEY EVENTS TIMELINE

February

• Bombings plague the capital city of Riga.

March

• Controversy erupts when veterans of a Latvian Nazi SS legion march in Riga on the occasion of soldiers' remembrance day.

April

• Latvian parliament abolishes the death penalty.

May

• Latvian farmers protest cheap pork imported from European Union (EU).

June

• Latvia's first woman president is elected.

July

• Parliament passes legislation mandating the use of Latvian language; the law is vetoed by the president.

• Prime Minister Vilis Kristopans resigns.

• NATO's supreme commander in Europe visits Latvia.

October

• EU announces Latvia's candidacy for membership in 2003.

ANALYSIS OF EVENTS- 1999

BUSINESS AND THE ECONOMY

The Latvian banking industry was dealt a blow by economic problems in Russia. With 8% of their total assets invested in Russia, and 40% of that amount in Russian short-term government bonds (GKO treasury bills), Latvian banks suffered when

Moscow defaulted on its GKO bills and when the Russian ruble was consequently devalued. The difficulties incurred by Latvian banks will make it that much more difficult for them to bring their operations into conformity with the specifications of the Basle Committee, a necessary prerequisite for Latvia's entry into the European Union (EU).

In May, farmers by the hundreds blocked border crossings between Latvia and the neighboring countries of Lithuania and Estonia to protest cheap pork imported into Latvia through those countries from the European Union. In response, the Latvian parliament levied a temporary tariff of 70% on imported pork.

The EU announced in October that Latvia was one of six nations newly added to the EU's list of candidates for membership. Latvia could join the EU as early as 2003.

GOVERNMENT AND POLITICS

In February, the Latvian parliament overwhelmingly approved a provision of the European Convention on Human Rights that mandates the abolition of the death penalty. Doing away with capital punishment will facilitate Latvia's eventual entry into the European Union (EU). In April, the parliament passed legislation abolishing the death penalty in Latvia, the last of the Baltic states to do so.

Latvians were fearful that their country's membership in the EU might be hampered or delayed by disputes over reform of the EU budget. Discussions of budget reform resulted in deadlock in March, with France insisting on retaining the current system of agricultural and other subsidies, and Germany advocating the reduction of subsidies in order to promote enlargement of the EU.

At a congress in Riga in May, Latvia's three social democratic parties—the Social Democratic Party, the Social Democratic Workers' Party, and the Democratic Party of Latgale—voted to combine into a single party in hopes of increasing their chances of victory in local elections in 2001.

In June, the Latvian parliament elected independent Latvia's first woman president, Vaira Vike-Freiborga, defeating her opponent, Latvian Foreign Minister Valdis Birkas, 53 to 20. In her first official act, Vike-Freiborga appointed Andris Skele as prime minister. Skele had served as prime minister twice before, from December 1995 to July 1997. He replaces Vilis Kristopans, who resigned in July after the publication of figures indicating an economic recession. Kristopans' three-party minority government had also been plagued by disputes.

The Latvian parliament in July passed legislation that makes the Latvian language mandatory at most public events and in private commercial transactions, despite the fact that one third of the country's population is Russian-speaking. Russia denounced the law as discriminatory. Latvian President Vike-Freiborga vetoed the law a week later.

NATO's supreme commander in Europe, General Wesley Clark, visited Latvia in July in order to strengthen ties between NATO and Latvia. Clark also discussed NATO operations in the Balkans and expressed gratitude for Latvian participation in NATO efforts in Kosovo.

CULTURE AND SOCIETY

In January 1999 about 150 citizens of Riga participated in a telephone poll to determine what area of the city should be set aside for prostitution, which is legal in Latvia. Callers were also able to register their preference for a ban on prostitution. Latvian law requires health checks for prostitutes. Previous efforts to regulate prostitution, including a prostitute passport, have proved ineffective.

Four bombing incidents occurred in Riga in early February. Bomb explosions damaged a military plane and two offices and a grenade missile was launched at a businessman. In 1998, bombings occurred in Riga's only synagogue and at the Russian embassy.

In other criminal activity, ten Latvian sailors were arrested in France in February when French customs officials found cannabis resin worth $230 million hidden in a cargo of fish on the Estonian trawler that employed the sailors. A 21-year-old man used a meat cleaver to kill three young girls and a teacher at a nursery school in the town of Gulbene near Latvia's border with Russia. The man told police he had planned the killings so as to become a famous serial killer.

The Latvian government also participated in a modest way in the international arms race. Pilots from Latvia joined pilots from the Ukraine and Russia in manning Sukhoi 27 fighter planes and MiG-29 interceptors purchased in late 1998 by Ethiopia and Eritrea respectively. Neither country has pilots qualified to fly the high-tech planes, and

they have also had to employ Russian technicians to maintain them.

Issues arose concerning Latvia's history during World War II. In March authorities in Riga allowed hundreds of veterans of a Latvian Nazi SS legion to march in the capital on the occasion of soldiers' Remembrance Day. The march was condemned by both the Latvian and Russian foreign ministers, and ethnic Russians living in Latvia also protested. Also, on June 14 a minute of silence was observed at railway stations to commemorate some 14,000 Latvians who were deported by rail to Siberia in 1941. Latvia came under Stalin's rule in 1940 under the Ribbentrop-Molotov Pact with Nazi Germany.

During 1999, Latvians suffered the random misfortunes of life that make up the grist of journalism. The World Health Organization reported in June that incidents of cholera had been reported in Latvia due to inadequate water treatment facilities. In June, seven people were killed and twenty-five injured at an automobile race at a track in Lazdona, in the Madona district, when two cars collided, a third left the track, and a fourth rolled into the crowd of spectators.

DIRECTORY

CENTRAL GOVERNMENT
Head of State

President
Vaira Vike-Freiberga, Office of the President, Pils Laukums 3, LV-1900 Riga, Latvia
PHONE: +371 7377548
FAX: +371 7325800
E-MAIL: chancery@president.lv

Ministers

Prime Minister
Andris Ðíçle, Office of the Prime Minister, Brîvîbas Blvd. 36, LV-1395 Riga, Latvia
PHONE: +371 7332232
FAX: +371 7286598

Minister of Defense
Ìirts Valdis Kristovskis, Ministry of Defense

Minister of Foreign Affairs
Indulis Bçrziòð, Ministry of Foreign Affairs, Brivibas Blvd. 36, LV-1395 Riga, Latvia
PHONE: +371 7016210
FAX: +371 7828121; 7282882
E-MAIL: info@mfa.gov.lv

Minister of Finance
Vladimirs Makarovs, Ministry of Finance

Minister of Economy
Edmunds Krastiòð, Ministry of Economy

Minister of Interior
Mareks Segliòð, Ministry of Interior

Minister of Education and Science
Silva Golde, Ministry of Education and Science, Vaïòu Iela 2, LV-1050 Rîga, Latvia
PHONE: +371 7222415
FAX: +371 7213992
E-MAIL: izm@izm.gov.lv

Minister of Special Assignments for Public and Municipal Reform Affairs
Jânis Bunkðs, Ministry of Special Assignments for Public and Municipal Reform Affairs

Minister of Co-Operation with International Financial Institutions
Roberts Zîle, Ministry of Co-Operation with International Financial Institutions

Minister of Culture
Karina Pçtersone, Ministry of Culture

Minister of Welfare
Roberts Jurdþs, Ministry of Welfare

Minister of Transport
Anatolijs Gorbunovs, Ministry of Transport

Minister of Justice
Valdis Birkavs, Ministry of Justice

Minister of Environmental Protection and Regional Development
Vents Balodis, Ministry of Environmental Protection and Regional Development, Peldu iela 25, LV-1494 Riga, Latvia
PHONE: +371 7026470
FAX: +371 7820442

Minister of Agriculture
Aigars Kalvîtis, Ministry of Agriculture

POLITICAL ORGANIZATIONS
Demokratiska Partija Saimnieks-DPS (Democratic Party Master)
TITLE: Chairman
NAME: Ziedonis Cevers

Latvijas Zemnieku Savienîba (Latvian Farmer's Union)
Jçkaba 16-309, LV-1001 Rîga, Latvia
PHONE: +371 7087270
FAX: +371 7087262
E-MAIL: lzs@lzs.lv

TITLE: Chairman
NAME: Laimonis Strujevics

Latvijas Zemnieku Savieniba-LZS (Latvian Farmers Union)
TITLE: Chairmen
NAME: Laimonis Strujevics; Talavs Jundzis

Savieniba Latvijas Celš-LC (Latvia's Way)
TITLE: Chairman
NAME: Valdis Birkavs

Latvian Social-Democratic Workers Party (LSDA)
NAME: Janis Dinevics

Latvijas Socialistiska Partija-LSP (Latvian Socialist Party)
NAME: Sergejs Diamanis

Latvijas Vienibas Partija-LVP (Latvian Unity Party)
NAME: A. Kauls

Tautas Saskadias Partija (National Harmony Party)
NAME: Janis Jurkans

Jauna Partija (New Party)
Tautas Kustibas Latvijai-TKL (People's Movement for Latvia)
NAME: Joachim Siegerist

Tautas Partija-TP (People's Party)
Dzirnavu iela 68, LV-1050 Rîga, Latvia
PHONE: +371 7286441
FAX: +371 7286405
E-MAIL: koord1@tautaspartija.lv
TITLE: Chairman
NAME: Andris Ðíçle

Tevzemei un Brivibai-TB (Fatherland and Freedom)
NAME: Maris Grinblats; Anna Seile; Andrejs Krastins

Latvian Green Party (LSZ)
NAME: Olegs Batarevsk

Savienîba "Latvijas cels" (LC)

DIPLOMATIC REPRESENTATION
Embassies in Latvia

Austria
Basteja bulvaris 14, LV-1050 Riga, Latvia
PHONE: +371 7216125
FAX: +371 7216126
TITLE: Ambassador
NAME: Anton Kozusnik

Canada
Doma laukums 4, LV-1977 Riga, Latvia
PHONE: +371 7226315; 7221822; 7830141
FAX: +371 7830140
TITLE: Ambassador
NAME: Peter P.L. McKellar

China
Ganibu dambis 5, LV-1045 Riga, Latvia
PHONE: +371 7357023; 7357024
FAX: +371 7357025; 9350502
TITLE: Ambassador
NAME: Yao Peisheng

France
Raina bulvaris 9, LV-1050 Riga, Latvia
PHONE: +371 7820135; 7213972
FAX: +371 7820131
TITLE: Ambassador
NAME: Louise Avon

Germany
Raina bulvaris 13, LV-1050 Riga, Latvia
PHONE: +371 7229096
FAX: +371 7820223
TITLE: Ambassador
NAME: Reinhart Kraus

Italy
Teatra iela 9, 4th floor, LV-1050 Riga, Latvia
PHONE: +371 7216069; 7211507; 7211517
FAX: +371 7216084
E-MAIL: ambitalia.riga@apollo.lv
TITLE: Ambassador
NAME: Alessandro Pietromarchi

Russia
Antonijas iela 2, LV-1010 Riga, Latvia
PHONE: +371 7220693; 7332151
FAX: +371 7830209
E-MAIL: rusembas@junik.lv
TITLE: Ambassador
NAME: Alexander Udaltsov

United Kingdom
J. Alunana iela 5, LV-1010 Riga, Latvia
PHONE: +371 7338126
FAX: +371 7338132
E-MAIL: british.embassy@apollo.lv
TITLE: Ambassador
NAME: Stephen Thomas Nash

United States
Raina bulvaris 7, LV-1510 Riga, Latvia
PHONE: +371 7210005; 7222349
FAX: +371 7820047
TITLE: Ambassador
NAME: James H. Holmes

JUDICIAL SYSTEM
Supreme Court

FURTHER READING
Articles

Bambarger, Bradley. "Composer Peteris Vasks: the Art of Emotion." *Billboard* (July 31, 1999): 45.

"Diphtheria Rise in Riga." *Geographical Magazine* (August 1999): 87.

"Four Parties Back Latvian Language Law." *New York Times,* 8 July 1997, p. A3.

Ishiyama, John T. "Representational Mechanisms and Ethnopolitics: Evidence from Transitional Democracies in Eastern Europe." *East European Quarterly* (Summer 1999): 251.

Jones, Colin. "Losing their Independence." *The Banker* (October 1999): 65.

———. "Starting from Scratch." *The Banker* (October 1999): 55.

Lieven, Anatol. "No Russian Spoken Here." *New York Times,* 16 July 1999, p. A19.

"Russian, Nordics, and Balts: Cosy up." *The Economist* (June 12, 1999): 45.

"Vaira Vike-Freiborga, a Canadian-European." *The Economist* (August 21, 1999): 43.

Books

Dreifelds, Juris. *Latvia in Transition.* New York: Cambridge University Press, 1996.

Plakans, Andrejs. *Historical Dictionary of Latvia.* Lanham, Md.: Scarecrow Press, 1997.

Internet

Embassy of Latvia. Available Online @ www.latvia-usa.org (November 5, 1999).

News from Latvia. Available Online @ www.mfa-org.lv/efram.htm (November 5, 1999).

LATVIA: STATISTICAL DATA

For sources and notes see "Sources of Statistics" in the front of each volume.

GEOGRAPHY

Geography (1)

Area:

Total: 64,100 sq km.

Land: 64,100 sq km.

Water: 0 sq km.

Areaócomparative: slightly larger than West Virginia.

Land boundaries:

Total: 1,150 km.

Border countries: Belarus 141 km, Estonia 339 km, Lithuania 453 km, Russia 217 km.

Coastline: 531 km.

Climate: maritime; wet, moderate winters.

Terrain: low plain.

Natural resources: minimal amber, peat, limestone, dolomite.

Land use:

Arable land: 27%

Permanent crops: 0%

Permanent pastures: 13%

Forests and woodland: 46%

Other: 14% (1993 est.).

HUMAN FACTORS

Demographics (2A)

	1990	1995	1998	2000	2010	2020	2030	2040	2050
Population	2,671.7	2,504.5	2,385.4	2,326.7	2,152.2	2,029.9	1,906.6	1,795.7	1,658.6
Net migration rate (per 1,000 population)	NA	NA	NA	NA	NA	NA	NA	NA	NA
Births	NA	NA	NA	NA	NA	NA	NA	NA	NA
Deaths	NA	NA	NA	NA	NA	NA	NA	NA	NA
Life expectancy - males	64.0	60.8	61.0	61.5	65.0	69.2	72.5	75.2	77.1
Life expectancy - females	74.2	73.1	73.5	73.8	75.7	78.4	80.7	82.4	83.8
Birth rate (per 1,000)	14.2	8.5	8.1	8.1	12.0	8.3	8.1	7.7	6.5
Death rate (per 1,000)	13.1	15.4	15.8	15.8	15.4	14.2	13.9	14.4	15.4
Women of reproductive age (15-49 yrs.)	648.4	605.5	589.6	583.5	536.6	460.9	426.9	345.1	319.7
of which are currently married	NA	NA	NA	NA	NA	NA	NA	NA	NA
Fertility rate	2.0	1.3	1.2	1.2	1.6	1.5	1.4	1.4	1.4

Except as noted, values for vital statistics are in thousands; life expectancy is in years.

Health Personnel (3)

Total health expenditure as a percentage of GDP, 1990-1997[a]

Public sector 3.5

Private sector . . . . .NA

Total[b] . . . . .NA

Health expenditure per capita in U.S. dollars, 1990-1997[a]

Purchasing power parity . . . . .NA

Total . . . . .NA

Availability of health care facilities per 100,000 people

Hospital beds 1990-1997[a] 1030

Doctors 1993[c] 303

Nurses 1993[c] 628

Health Indicators (4)

Life expectancy at birth

1980 69

1997 69

Daily per capita supply of calories (1996) 2,861

Total fertility rate births per woman (1997) 1.1

Maternal mortality ratio per 100,000 live births (1990-97) . . . . .15[b]

Safe water % of population with access (1995) . . . .

Sanitation % of population with access (1995) . . . .

Consumption of iodized salt % of households (1992-98)[a] . . . .

Smoking prevalence

Male % of adults (1985-95)[a] 67

Female % of adults (1985-95)[a] 12

Tuberculosis incidence per 100,000 people (1997) 82

Adult HIV prevalence % of population ages 15-49 (1997) 0.01

Infants and Malnutrition (5)

Under-5 mortality rate (1997) 20

% of infants with low birthweight (1990-97) . . . . . .NA

Births attended by skilled health staff % of total[a] . .100

% fully immunized (1995-97)

TB 100

DPT 75

Polio 76

Measles 97

Prevalence of child malnutrition under age 5 (1992-97)[b] . . . . .NA

Ethnic Division (6)

Latvian 56.5%

Russian 30.4%

Byelorussian 4.3%

Ukrainian 2.8%

Polish 2.6%

Other 3.4%

Religions (7)

Lutheran, Roman Catholic, Russian Orthodox.

Languages (8)

Lettish (official), Lithuanian, Russian, other.

EDUCATION

Public Education Expenditures (9)

Public expenditure on education (% of GNP)

1980 . . . . .3.3

1996 . . . . .6.5

Expenditure per student

Primary % of GNP per capita

1980 . . . .

1996 . . . .

Secondary % of GNP per capita

1980 . . . .

1996 . . . . .38.2

Tertiary % of GNP per capita

1980 . . . . .19.1

1996 . . . . .33.8

Expenditure on teaching materials

Primary % of total for level (1996) . . . .

Secondary % of total for level (1996) 0.7

Primary pupil-teacher ratio per teacher (1996) 13

Duration of primary education years (1995) 4

Educational Attainment (10)

Age group (1989) . . . . .25+

Total population 1,725,639

Highest level attained (%)

No schooling 0.6

First level

Not completed 18.5

Completed 21.2

Entered second level

S-1 . . . . .46.3

S-2 . . . . .NA

Postsecondary 13.4

Literacy Rates (11B)

Adult literacy rate

1980

Male ....–

Female ....–

1995

Male 100

Female 100

GOVERNMENT & LAW

Political Parties (12)

Parliament	% of seats
Saimnieks 18
Latvia's Way (LC) 17
For Latvia 16
For Fatherland and Freedom (TVB) 14
Latvian National Conservative Party (LNNK) 8
Unity 8
Latvian Farmers Union (LZS) / Christian Democrat Union (LKDS) 7
Harmony...................................6
Socialist 6

Government Budget (13A)

Year: 1997

Total Expenditures: 1,028.38 Millions of Lats

Expenditures as a percentage of the total by function:

General public services and public order 13.89

Defense 2.21

Education 5.50

Health 11.43

Social Security and Welfare 42.14

Housing and community amenities 1.07

Recreational, cultural, and religious affairs 1.80

Fuel and energy 03

Agriculture, forestry, fishing, and hunting 4.49

Mining, manufacturing, and construction 05

Transportation and communication 5.52

Other economic affairs and services 52

Military Affairs (14B)

	1992	1993	1994	1995
Military expenditures				
Current dollars (mil.)	NA	73	112	74
1995 constant dollars (mil.)	NA	76	114	74
Armed forces (000)	5	5	6	7

Gross national product (GNP)

Current dollars (mil.)	9,920	8,445	8,479	8,479
1995 constant dollars (mil.)	10,670	8,853	8,692	8,479

Central government expenditures (CGE)

1995 constant dollars (mil.)	3,403	NA	NA	NA
People (mil.)	2.6	2.6	2.5	2.5
Military expenditure as % of GNP	NA	.9	1.3	.9
Military expenditure as % of CGE	NA	NA	NA	NA
Military expenditure per capita (1995 $)	NA	29	45	29
Armed forces per 1,000 people (soldiers)	1.9	1.9	2.4	2.8
GNP per capita (1995 $)	4,054	3,423	3,413	3,383

Arms imports[6]

Current dollars (mil.)	0	0	0	0
1995 constant dollars (mil.)	0	0	0	0

Arms exports[6]

Current dollars (mil.)	0	0	0	0
1995 constant dollars (mil.)	0	0	0	0

Total imports[7]

Current dollars (mil.)	944	872	1,251	1,810
1995 constant dollars (mil.)	1,015	914	1,282	1,810

Total exports[7]

Current dollars (mil.)	825	963	962	1,283
1995 constant dollars (mil.)	887	1,010	986	1,283
Arms as percent of total imports[8]	0.0	0	0	.3
Arms as percent of total exports[8]	0.0	0	0	0

Crime (15)

Crime rate (for 1997)

Crimes reported 36,900

Total persons convicted 18,900

Crimes per 100,000 population 1,500

Persons responsible for offenses

Total number of suspects 17,500

Total number of female suspects 1,800

Total number of juvenile suspects 2,800

LABOR FORCE

Labor Force (16)

Total (million) 1.4

Industry 41%

Agriculture and forestry .16%

Services 43%

Data for 1997. Percent distribution for 1990.

Unemployment Rate (17)

7% (1996)

PRODUCTION SECTOR

Electric Energy (18)

Capacity . . . . .2.035 million kW (1995)

Production . . . . .4.095 billion kWh (1995)

Consumption per capita . . . . .2,300 kWh (1995)

Transportation (19)

Highways:

total: 60,046 km

paved: 22,998 km

unpaved: 37,048 km (1995 est.)

Waterways: 300 km perennially navigable

Pipelines: crude oil 750 km; refined products 780 km; natural gas 560 km (1992)

Merchant marine:

total: 24 ships (1,000 GRT or over) totaling 293,799 GRT/440,575 DWT ships by type: cargo 2, oil tanker 18, refrigerated cargo 4 (1997 est.)

Airports: 50 (1994 est.)

Airports—with paved runways:

total: 36

2,438 to 3,047 m: 6

1,524 to 2,437 m: 2

914 to 1,523 m: 1

under 914 m: 27 (1994 est.)

Airports—with unpaved runways:

total: 14

2,438 to 3,047 m: 2

914 to 1,523 m: 2

under 914 m: 10 (1994 est.)

Top Agricultural Products (20)

Grain, sugar beets, potatoes, vegetables; meat, milk, eggs; fish.

MANUFACTURING SECTOR

GDP & Manufacturing Summary (21)

Detailed value added figures are listed by both International Standard Industry Code (ISIC) and product title.

	1980	1985	1990	1994
GDP ($-1990 mil.)[1]	5,551	6,540	7,805	4,057
Per capita ($-1990)[1]	2,191	2,503	2,922	1,570
Manufacturing share (%) (current prices)[1]	45.7	37.1	31.4	*19.7*
Manufacturing				
Value added ($-1990 mil.)[1]	NA	NA	2,690	NA
Industrial production index	NA	NA	NA	NA
Value added ($ mil.)	NA	NA	NA	706
Gross output ($ mil.)	*87*	*55*	6,362	1,520
Employment (000)	*522*	*385*	*346*	*164*
Profitability (% of gross output)				
Intermediate input (%)	NA	NA	NA	54
Wages and salaries inc. supplements (%)	NA	NA	NA	*11*
Gross operating surplus	NA	NA	NA	*35*
Productivity ($)				
Gross output per worker	*161*	*136*	18,413	*9,279*
Value added per worker	NA	NA	NA	4,307
Average wage (inc. supplements)	*12*	*15*	2,396	*1,055*
Value added ($ mil.)				
311/2 Food products	NA	NA	NA	193
313 Beverages	NA	NA	NA	76
314 Tobacco products	NA	NA	NA	4
321 Textiles	NA	NA	NA	41
322 Wearing apparel	NA	NA	NA	23
323 Leather and fur products	NA	NA	NA	3
324 Footwear	NA	NA	NA	9
331 Wood and wood products	NA	NA	NA	56
332 Furniture and fixtures	NA	NA	NA	21
341 Paper and paper products	NA	NA	NA	4

	1980	1985	1990	1994
342 Printing and publishing	NA	NA	NA	24
351 Industrial chemicals	NA	NA	NA	13
352 Other chemical products	NA	NA	NA	21
353 Petroleum refineries	NA	NA	NA	1
354 Miscellaneous petroleum and coal products	NA	NA	NA	NA
355 Rubber products	NA	NA	NA	6
356 Plastic products	NA	NA	NA	6
361 Pottery, china and earthenware	NA	NA	NA	5
362 Glass and glass products	NA	NA	NA	4
369 Other non-metal mineral products	NA	NA	NA	17
371 Iron and steel	NA	NA	NA	19
372 Non-ferrous metals	NA	NA	NA	6
381 Metal products	NA	NA	NA	13
382 Non-electrical machinery	NA	NA	NA	39
383 Electrical machinery	NA	NA	NA	42
384 Transport equipment	NA	NA	NA	59
385 Professional and scientific equipment	NA	NA	NA	3
390 Other manufacturing industries	NA	NA	NA	10

FINANCE, ECONOMICS, & TRADE

Economic Indicators (22)

National product: GDP purchasing power parity $10.4 billion (1997 est.)

National product real growth rate: 6% (1997 est.)

National product per capita: $4,260 (1997 est.)

Inflation rateóconsumer price index: 7.4% (1997 est.)

Exchange Rates (24)

Exchange rates:

Lats (LVL) per US$1

January 1998	0.595
1997	0.581
1996	0.551
1995	0.528
1994	0.560
1993	0.675

Top Import Origins (25)

$2.3 billion (c.i.f., 1996)

Origins	%
Russia	NA
other CIS	NA
Germany	NA
Sweden	NA
United Kingdom	NA
Finland	NA

NA stands for not available.

Balance of Payments (23)

	1992	1993	1994	1995	1996
Exports of goods (f.o.b.)	800	1,054	1,022	1,368	1,488
Imports of goods (f.o.b.)	−840	−1,051	−1,322	−1,947	−2,286
Trade balance	−40	3	−301	−580	−798
Services - debits	−157	−215	−339	−299	−841
Services - credits	294	550	708	791	1,267
Private transfers (net)	90	47	107	35	51
Government transfers (net)	6	31	26	36	42
Overall balance	192	417	201	−16	−280

Top Export Destinations (26)

$1.4 billion (f.o.b., 1996).

Destinations	%
Russia	NA
other CIS	NA
Germany	NA
Sweden	NA
United Kingdom	NA

NA stands for not available.

Economic Aid (27)

Recipient: ODA, $122 million (1993). Note: commitments from the West and international institutions, $525 million (1992-95).

Import Export Commodities (28)

Import Commodities	Export Commodities
Fuels	Wood and wood products
Machinery and equipment	Textiles
Chemicals	Foodstuffs

LEBANON

Republic of Lebanon
Al-Jumhuriyah al-Lubnaniyah

INTRODUCTORY SURVEY

RECENT HISTORY

The entry of the Ottoman Empire into World War I (1914–18) led to the destruction of Lebanese prosperity. In 1920, an Allied conference gave France a mandate (authorization to govern) over Syria, in which Mount Lebanon was included. The mandate years were a time of material growth and little political development.

Lebanon came under control of the French Vichy (Nazi-ruled) government in 1940. However, in 1941, Lebanon and Syria were taken by a combined Anglo–Free French force. After growing conflicts between the Lebanese nationalists and the French, Lebanon gained complete independence in 1946.

The 1950s and 1960s were generally characterized by economic and political stability. Beginning in 1952, Lebanon received increased United States aid. It also benefited from an influx of Western commercial personnel and from growing oil royalties. During this time, Lebanon seemed the calmest part of the Middle East. It took little part in the Arab-Israeli war of 1948, and no action in the wars of 1967 and 1973.

However, in the late 1960s and early 1970s Lebanon's role began to change. This was due to the presence of the Palestinian Liberation Organization (the PLO). The PLO was a terrorist organization fighting for an independent homeland within the borders of Israel. Well-armed members of the PLO had moved into the area of Lebanon that

---

CAPITAL: Beirut (Bayrut).

FLAG: The national flag, introduced in 1943, consists of two horizontal red stripes separated by a white stripe which is twice as wide; at the center, in green and brown, is a cedar tree.

ANTHEM: *Kulluna lil watan lil`ula lil`alam (All of Us for the Country, Glory, Flag).*

MONETARY UNIT: The Lebanese pound, or livre libanaise (LL), is a paper currency of 100 piasters. There are coins of 1, 2, 5, 10, 25, and 50 piasters and 1 Lebanese pound, and notes of 1, 5, 10, 25, 50, 100, 250, 1,000 and 10,000 Lebanese pounds. LL1 = $0.00064 (or $1 = LL1,556.0).

WEIGHTS AND MEASURES: The metric system is the legal standard, but traditional weights and measures are still used.

HOLIDAYS: New Year's Day, 1 January; Arab League Day, 22 March; Independence Day, 22 November; Evacuation Day, 31 December. Christian religious holidays include Feast of St. Maron, 9 February; Good Friday; Easter Monday; Ascension; Assumption, 15 August; All Saints' Day, 1 November; and Christmas, 25 December. Muslim religious holidays include `Id al-Fitr, `Id al-`Adha`, and Milad an-Nabi.

TIME: 2 PM = noon GMT.

LOCATION AND SIZE: Situated on the eastern coast of the Mediterranean Sea, Lebanon has an area of 10,400 square kilometers (4,015 square miles), about three-fourths the size of the state of Connecticut, and a total boundary length of 656 kilometers (407 miles). Lebanon's capital city, Beirut, is located on the Mediterranean coast.

CLIMATE: Lebanon has an extraordinarily varied climate: within 45 minutes' drive in winter, spring, and fall, both skiing and swimming are possible. Rainfall averages about 90 centimeters (35 inches) yearly along the coast, about 125 centimeters (50 inches) on the western slopes of the mountains, and less than 38 centimeters (15 inches) in the Bekaa Valley. The average annual temperature in Beirut is 21°C (70°F), with a range from 13°C (55°F) in winter to 28°C (82°F) in summer.

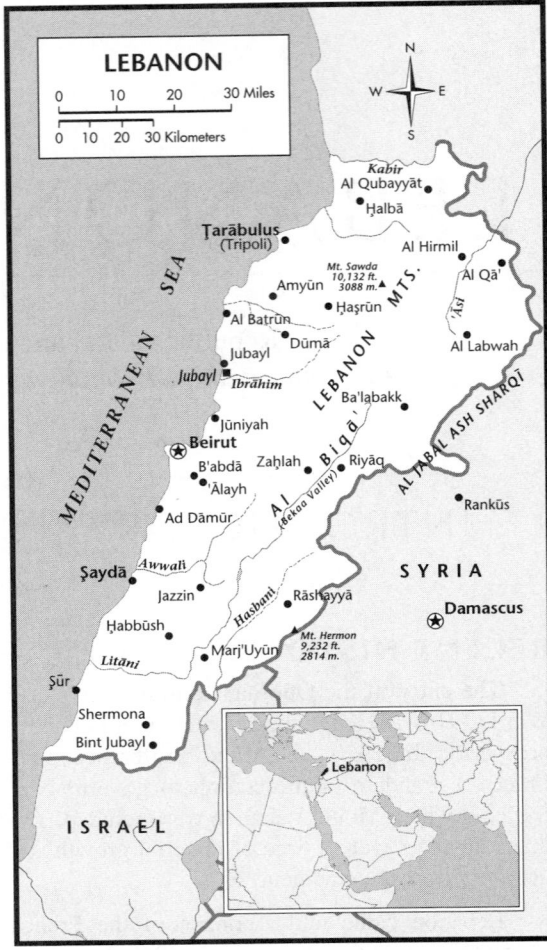

borders with Israel. This led to clashes between the PLO and Lebanon's army. In 1969, Jordan's government, fearing a civil war, signed the so-called Cairo Accord with the PLO. This agreement made the terrorist organization practically a separate state within Lebanon, with the right to establish military bases and launch cross-border raids into Israel.

The PLO presence inflamed tensions between Christians and Muslims and, by 1975, led to a civil war. The war pitted Maronite Christians against Muslims and against other Christian sects. It also pitted rightist militants against Palestinian guerrillas and other leftist Arab forces. At least 100,000 people on all sides were killed. In addition, some 600,000 persons were displaced during the 18 months of fighting. A cease-fire arranged through the mediation of Sa'udi Arabia and other Arab countries enabled a peacekeeping force (including Syrian troops) to separate the combatants and end the war in October 1976.

The conflict devastated Lebanon economically. It also weakened the central government to the point where different parts of the country were under the control of the Syrians, the Palestinians, and the militias of some 30 factions.

In March 1978, the Israeli army invaded southern Lebanon, destroying PLO bases. It withdrew, and a United Nations (UN) force was assigned to keep the peace.

However, the PLO continued rocket attacks on northern Israel. In addition, the Syrian military remained in Lebanon. Israel saw the Syrian military presence in Lebanon as a threat to its security. These factors prompted Israel to launch a full-scale invasion of Lebanon in June 1982. Following a two-month Israeli siege of West Beirut, where the Palestinians were encamped, a truce was agreed to by Israel, the PLO, and Syria. A multinational peacekeeping force, composed of British, French, and Italian soldiers and U.S. marines, was stationed in the Beirut area in early September.

Despite the truce, the violence continued. On 14 September 1982, Bashir Gemayel, a Christian Phalangist leader who in August had been elected president by the Lebanese parliament, was assassinated. He was succeeded by his brother Amin Gemayel. The Phalangists blamed the PLO and soon afterwards, Israel allowed Christian Phalangist forces into the refugee camps. In the fighting that followed, at least 600 Palestinians, many of them civilians, were massacred. In 1983, Israeli and Syrian troops still occupied large portions of Lebanon, and they became targets of attack by Muslim and Druze forces.

The American embassy in Beirut was bombed in April 1983, and U.S. marines were harassed by sniper fire. On 23 October, 241 marines were killed by a truck-bomb explosion in the U.S. barracks at Beirut airport. Israel's withdrawal of its troops from most of Lebanon in early 1985 left in its wake renewed fighting for the evacuated territory.

The badly divided factions could not agree on a successor to president Amin Gemayel when his term expired in September 1988. Christian Army Commander Michel Aoun asserted himself as prime minister, giving Lebanon two governments, a Muslim one in West Beirut and a Christian one in East Beirut. Aoun was opposed by the Syrians and Muslims and by rival Christian factions.

In September 1989, a committee appointed by the Arab League arrived at a seven-point ceasefire, called the Taif Accord.

In 1991–92, the government gradually began to reassert its authority. Almost all militias were dissolved, and Palestinian militants were repressed in Sayda (Sidon). Internally, the poor economy aggravated political instability, but the appointment of Prime Minister Rafiq al-Hariri in November 1992 promised a serious effort at reconstruction.

Al-Hariri, who became a self-made billionaire in Sa'udi Arabia, had a long history of making charitable donations to help rebuild Beirut. As prime minister, however, he has been frequently accused of corruption. His efforts to reunite the country have generally won the people's approval, and al-Hariri was reelected in 1996.

Southern Lebanon, occupied by Israeli forces, is still subject to political violence. In 1996, 255 people (including 27 Israeli soldiers) were killed in violence.

GOVERNMENT

As defined by the constitution of 1926 and subsequent amendments, Lebanon is an independent republic. Executive power is vested in a president (elected by the legislature for six years) and a prime minister and cabinet, chosen by the president but responsible to the legislature. Legislative power is exercised by a 128-member National Assembly elected for a four-year term by universal adult suffrage. The Taif Accord of 1989 set the Christian-Muslim balance in parliament at 50–50, but the failure of Christians to participate in the elections of 1992 and 1996 gave Muslim groups the largest number of seats in the Chamber.

Lebanon is divided into five provinces (muhafazat), which are subdivided into districts (aqdiya), municipalities, and villages.

Judiciary

Ultimate supervisory power rests with the minister of justice, who appoints the magistrates. Courts of first instance, of which there are 56, give cases their first hearing; they are presided over by a single judge and deal with both civil and criminal cases. Appeals may be taken to 11 courts of appeal, each made up of three judges.

Religious courts—Islamic, Christian, and Jewish—deal with marriages, deaths, inheritances, and other matters of personal status in their respec-

tive faiths. In the Palestinian refugee camps, rival factions try opponents without any semblance of due process.

Political Parties

Principal political groups, with mainly Christian membership, are the National Liberal Party and the Phalangist Party. There are various parties of the left, including the Progressive Socialist Party (of mostly Druze membership), the Ba'th Party, and the Lebanese Communist Party.

The various Palestinian groups have played an important role in the political life of Lebanon since the late 1960s. Amal, a conservative grouping, and Hezbollah, more militant, represent the Shi'ite Muslim community.

DEFENSE

In 1995, the regular Lebanese army numbered 47,500 men. There was a small navy of 600 and an air force of 800 personnel, neither well-armed.

Although many of the militias have disbanded, the Muslim Hezbollah (3,000) is the only significant communal army remaining. The South Lebanese Army, mostly Christian, numbers 2,500 and receives Israeli support for its border patrol duties.

ECONOMIC AFFAIRS

Lebanon is traditionally a trading country, with a relatively large agricultural sector and small but well-developed industry. Until the 1975–76 civil war, it had always figured prominently as a center of tourist trade. The war caused an estimated $5 billion in property damage and reduced economic activities to about 50% of the prewar level.

After the 1989 Taif Accord for National Reconciliation ended hostilities, the economy began to recover. Economic activity surged in 1991, and in 1993 the al-Hariri government was able to stabilize the economy and launch a program to reconstruct the country's transportation and communication networks. Since 1992, annual economic growth has averaged about 7%, but a rising budget deficit may threaten further reforms.

Public Finance

The annual budget of the central government must be approved by the National Assembly. The Lebanese government annually faces the formidable problem of financing a massive deficit resulting from heavy financial obligations and huge shortfalls in revenues. To reduce the deficit, the government has tried to increase revenues by raising taxes and tightening the budget. The government relies heavily on grants and loans from multilateral agencies, Arab governments, and the French to cover the deficit.

In 1995, government revenues totaled approximately $1.4 billion and expenditures $3.2 billion. External debt totaled $1.3 billion in 1996, approximately 12% of which was financed abroad. Total debt stands at about 70% of GDP.

Income

In 1997 the gross national product (GNP) was $15.2 billion, or $4,400 per person.

Industry

The civil war caused tremendous damage to the industrial sector. By 1993, it was estimated that the Lebanese industry suffered losses of $1.5 billion. Inadequate transport and communications networks and a shortage of skilled labor are major obstacles in the process of rehabilitation. In 1995, industry accounted for 28% of the gross domestic product. Major industrial products are clothing, metal, food, marble and sanitary equipment, cement, jewelry, furniture, paper, beverages, and plastic.

Banking and Finance

The Bank of Lebanon, established on 1 April 1964, is now the sole bank of issue. Its powers to regulate and control commercial banks and other institutions and to implement monetary policy were expanded by amendments to the Code of Money and Credit promulgated in October 1973. Before the civil war, Lebanon was an important banking center. Many organizations moved their headquarters from Cairo to Beirut after the 1952 Egyptian revolution. After 1973, additional oil revenue from the Gulf was handled by Lebanese banks. The system of free exchange and strict secrecy laws attracted money from across the world.

Financing foreign trade and discounting trade bills make up most banking transactions; exchange and transfer of capital in the international market are substantial. To encourage the movement and deposit of foreign capital in Lebanon, a bank secrecy law of 1956 forbids banks to disclose details of a client's business even to judicial authorities. Legislation to permit a banking free zone in Beirut to encourage foreign banks became effective in 1977.

In 1968, several banks were seized, liquidated, or merged; as a result, the number of commercial banks operating in Lebanon was reduced from 93 to 74. The banking sector was an early casualty of the civil war, with money and institutions leaving the capital. In the 1980s, banks grew more reliant on lending to the government, either directly or via three-month Treasury bills. Government borrowing, necessitated by successive budget deficits, led to a rise in its debt to local banks from LL14 billion at the end of 1982 to LL10.2 trillion in the first quarter of 1996.

In the latter half of the 1980s, the Banque du Liban issued a series of regulations aimed at reducing liquidity and controlling speculation against the Lebanese pound. In 1986, the statutory reserve requirement by commercial banks was raised from 18% to 22% of deposits, but was later reduced to 10%. Then, under a 1994 government decree, banks were obliged to invest only 40% of new deposits in T-bills, compared with 60% in 1987. In 1994, the central bank constructed commercial banks to expand their capital bases and reduce their hard-currency loan exposures by limiting lending to 60% of hard-currency deposits.

At the end of 1994, 12 of the 82 banks in the country were foreign. The banks are required to keep 10% of their profits inside the country to strengthen reserves; Lebanese banks are required to do the same with both domestic and foreign profits.

The Beirut Stock Exchange was officially opened in 1952 as a center in which the few available company shares could be traded. The exchange closed during the civil war but reopened in 1979; however, there was little trading in stock during 1980–81. In 1982, Beirut was chosen as the headquarters of the Arab Stock Exchange Union, reflecting Lebanon's continuing importance as financial center of the Middle East.

In September 1995, the Beirut Stock Exchange reopened after a 12-year closure. Trading began in January 1996, but with just three compnaies listed, all of them producers of cement or construction material. A fourth company joined in mid-1996. A secondary market was opened to trade shares in the private property company, Solidere. Solidere is developing the destroyed business heart of Beirut. With the secondary market considerably more successful than the stock exchange, plans to list Solidere on the latter have, for the moment, been shelved. In 1997, however, Solidere moved its shares from the secondary market to the Beirut Stock Exchange. An important reason for the move was a plant to cross-list Solidere shares on the Kuwait Stock Exchange. Kuwait said it would do so only if shares were traded on the official bourse rather than on the secondary market. The Lebanese Stock Exchange authority signed an agreement to cross-list shares not only with Kuwait but also with Egypt from early in 1997. Solidere has a 115–125 million GDR (global depository receipt) to be listed on the London Stock Exchange.

In 1995, a private Lebanese institution, Banque Audi, was the first Lebanse bank to issue GDRs which are listed on the Luxembourg Stock Exchange.

Money supply, as measured by M2, was LL22,858.4 billion at the end of 1995.

Economic Development

Since World War II, Lebanon has followed free-enterprise and free-trade policies. The country's favorable geographical position as a transit point and the traditional importance of the trading and banking sectors of the economy helped make Lebanon prosperous by the early 1970s. Lebanon became a center of trade, finance, and tourism by means of a stable currency backed largely with gold, by a conservative fiscal policy, by various incentives for foreign investors, and by minimization of banking regulations.

Lebanon's development went awry in the mid-1970s, as factional conflict, always present in Lebanese society, erupted into open warfare. The loss to the economy was enormous, particularly in Beirut. The reconstruction plan submitted in 1979 by the Council for Development and Reconstruction (CDR) envisaged total expenditures of LL 22 billion for rebuilding, including LL10 billion in the public sector and LL12 billion in the private sector. The cost of new housing and repair of damaged homes was estimated at LL4.5 billion, and of major road construction at LL1.5 billion. Redevelopment of the port of Beirut and reconstruction of Beirut airport were begun under the program.

In November 1979, Sa'udi Arabia and six other oil-producing Arab countries promised to contribute $2 billion for Lebanon's reconstruction effort over a five-year period, but only $381 million had been provided by October 1987. (After Israel invaded Lebanon in June 1982, the Arab countries decided to withhold future funds until Israeli forces had withdrawn completely.)

Under the leadership of Prime Minister Rafiq al-Hariri, Lebanon embarked on the Horizon 2000 program in 1993. Areas of major activity targeted by the plan are the rehabilitation of telecommunications, electricity grids, highways, sewage, waste management, water networks, renovation of the Beirut International Airport, harbor, education, and housing. The plan also calls for investment in commercial facilities that will reestablish Beirut as an international business center in competition with Hong Kong and Singapore. Although in 1997 the government reset the target date to 2007, the plan had been scheduled for completion by 2000. The total cost is estimated at over $18 billion.

SOCIAL WELFARE

A government social security plan, not fully implemented, is intended to provide sickness and maternity insurance, accident and disability insurance, and family allowances.

Women must obtain permission from their husbands in order to engage in trade. Many of the religious laws governing family and personal status discriminate against women.

Healthcare

In 1991, there were 6,638 physicians. Average life expectancy is 70 years. In 1994, 100% of the population had access to safe water and 95% had access to health care services.

Housing

A housing shortage in the early 1970s was aggravated by the civil war and subsequent fighting, in which half of the country's real estate was severely damaged or destroyed. According to the latest available information for 1980–88, total housing units numbered 820,000 with 3.3 people per dwelling. Housing needs until 2000 have been estimated at 400,000 units. With the return of stability, a boom in construction is underway in Beirut.

EDUCATION

Lebanon's illiteracy rate is relatively low for the Middle East; an estimated 8% (5.3% of adult males and 9.7% of adult females) cannot read and write. In 1994 there were 365,174 primary school pupils and 277,646 general secondary school students. In 1991, the total enrollment for all higher level institutions was 85,495. Leading universities include the American University in Beirut, St. Joseph University, and the Lebanese (State) University.

1999 KEY EVENTS TIMELINE

January

- Fighting in southern Lebanon escalates as Hezbollah stages attacks on Israeli forces and the Israeli-backed South Lebanon Army (SLA). Israel retaliates with air raids on Hezbollah strongholds.

February

- Guerrillas in the "security zone" kill several Israelis, including a general; Israel responds with air strikes in northern and southern Lebanon and threatens a wider war.

April

- Trade unions call for mass demonstrations against government plans to raise taxes in the 1999 budget.

June

- SLA militiamen withdraw from the town of Jezzine, which it has occupied since 1985.

- Syrian and Lebanese prime ministers meet in Damascus, Syria, to discuss closer ties between the two countries.

- On June 6 unknown assailants kill four Lebanese judges in a courtroom in the town of Sidon.

- On June 24 Israeli warplanes carry out the heaviest air raids in three years, destroying bridges and power stations in Lebanon in retaliation for a deadly rocket attack on northern Israel.

July

- The United Nations Security Council renews the mandate for UNIFIL, the U.N. Interim Force in Lebanon, for six months; it also reiterates support for Lebanon's territorial integrity and sovereignty.

August

- Fatah, the Palestinian organization loyal to Yasser Arafat, increases its military presence in refugee camps; some observers believe the move is intended to strengthen Arafat's hand in final status negotiations with Israel.

September

- U.S. Secretary of State Madeline Albright visits Beirut for talks with Lebanese authorities. Albright and Lebanon's Prime Minister Salim al-Hoss disagree over the issue of Palestinian refugees in Lebanon. Hoss insists that Lebanon be a party to any talks concerning the refugees' fate.

December

- Fifteen Lebanese school children are seriously injured when Israeli militia forces fire missiles at a village Israelis believe to be a stronghold of Hezbollah militia.

ANALYSIS OF EVENTS: 1999

BUSINESS AND THE ECONOMY

The government of Prime Minister Salim al-Hoss took office promising economic reforms and fiscal austerity aimed at reducing Lebanon's mushrooming fiscal deficit. The country's financial problems were blamed on mismanagement and corruption under the previous Hariri government, which embarked on an ambitious $20 billion infrastructure reconstruction program financed by foreign borrowing. Lebanon now owes $18.6 billion—113% of its GDP—in foreign debt.

The Hoss government's 1999 budget unveiled in April projects increased spending of $5.5 billion and revenues of $3.4 billion. Higher taxes, privatization of loss-making public enterprises, and improved revenue collection are measures proposed to combat the deficit. Analysts, however, view the budget as accomplishing little to ease the fiscal deficit, which has grown to 15% of GDP. In November the government admitted it would not meet its deficit reduction target. Lebanon's largest company, Solidere, responsible for rebuilding Beirut's business district, registered a loss for the first half of 1999. A depressed economy, a real estate crisis, and bureaucratic inertia are blamed.

GOVERNMENT AND POLITICS

Traditionally government and politics in Lebanon are divided along sectarian lines. A power-sharing formula, drawn in 1943, stipulates that the president is always a Maronite Christian, the prime minister a Sunni Muslim, and the Speaker of the Assembly a Shia Muslim. In the mid-1970s the delicate political and religious equilibrium disintegrated into civil war as armed militias, representing contending sectarian factions, fought for control. Problems created by the presence of a sizable Palestinian refugee population contributed to the collapse of civil order. Lebanon's turmoil prompted the Arab League to mandate Syrian intervention. Syrian troops entered the country while Israel, motivated by its own security concerns, occupied parts of southern Lebanon. After nearly two decades of civil war, Lebanon began a process of national reconstruction and reconciliation in the 1990s.

The Ta'if Accord of 1989 laid the blueprint for a new Lebanese order that grants the country's Muslim majority greater political power by increasing their representation in the Assembly and making the prime minister the head of the government. The president's powers have been reduced, but the office wields influence as a symbol of national unity above partisan party politics. The new arrangement has created what is dubbed a semi-official ruling "troika."

Most militias have disbanded and a reorganized Lebanese army has helped the government reassert its authority. In southern Lebanon, however, militias led by the Shia Muslim Hezbollah movement remain active, organizing armed resistance against Israeli occupation of a 15 km strip in southern Lebanon. Israel considers this territory a "security zone" intended to protect its northern border from guerrilla attacks. Israel and its ally, the SLA, a mostly Christian militia, patrol this zone.

Syria, which retains a strong military presence in Lebanon, enjoys considerable clout in the country's affairs. Some observers credit Syrian influence as a stabilizing force against Lebanon's descent into fresh sectarianism. Others, mainly among Maronites, are less sanguine about Syria's role and perceive it as a continuing threat to Lebanon's sovereignty.

In November 1998 Emile Lahoud was sworn in as president. Lahoud asked Rafik Hariri, prime minister since 1992, to continue in office. A dispute between the two men, however, caused Hariri to reject the offer. On December 1 Lahoud appointed a veteran politician, Salim al-Hoss, prime minister. Lebanon's security and stability highlighted problems facing the new government in 1999. Despite a consensus within Israel favored an Israeli withdrawal from the security zone, a cycle of attacks and reprisals continued in the area throughout the year. Early in 1999 retaliatory Israeli air strikes against Hezbollah strongholds occurred. The clashes escalated after a guerrilla ambush killed an Israeli general. The Lebanese government rejected an Israeli demand to disarm the guerrillas.

Prime Minister Hoss also denied reports alleging secret peace talks with Israel, which has sought security guarantees from Lebanon in exchange for withdrawal from the security zone. Aware of Syrian interests, the Hoss government has insisted that it will not strike a separate deal, and that the Israeli withdrawal should occur only within the framework of a comprehensive peace settlement involving Syria. The new Barak government in Israel has committed to pull out of this zone by July 2000, indicating it will do so even if no agreement is reached.

Bickering between the Hoss government and opposition forces allied with Hariri stalled legislative attempts for electoral law and administrative reforms. Critics of the government's anti-corruption drive described it as a witch-hunt against Hariri and his loyalists. As the year wound down Lahoud held talks with Hariri and other prominent opposition leaders. Commentators hope these talks clear the air for a constructive dialogue between the government and its opponents.

CULTURE AND SOCIETY

The self-proclaimed cultural capital of the Arab world in 1999 Lebanon has long enjoyed a reputation for cultural and artistic freedom. The government launched a campaign in 1999 to recover some of the cultural antiquities looted from its museums during the war. Despite these efforts, there is concern that Lebanon today may be less tolerant of free expression. Authorities have begun to routinely ban books and censor other media. In October 1999 a judge requested prosecution of renowned musician, Marcel Khalife, for allegedly insulting Islam by setting a Koranic verse to music. Clerical opinion is divided. Sunni clergy back the judge's decision, but Shia religious leaders find it unfounded. Khalife, a Christian, has drawn widespread support, including that of Prime Minister Hoss. The trial is scheduled to begin in 2000.

As preparations unfold for final status negotiations between Israel and the Palestinians the eventual fate of Lebanon's Palestinian refugees looms as a major concern. More than 350,000 Palestinians live in squalid refugee camps and have limited education or employment opportunities. Lebanon sees these refugees as a threat to the country's social and political balance and wants their repatriation part of any peace settlement.

DIRECTORY

CENTRAL GOVERNMENT

Head of State

President
Emile Lahoud, Office of the President

Prime Minister
Selim al-Hoss, Office of the Prime Minister

Ministers

Minister of Agriculture
Suleiman Franjieh, Ministry of Agriculture
PHONE: +961 (1) 423525; 455630; 455631

Minister of Cultural and Higher Education Affairs
Mohammed Yousef Beydoun, Ministry of Cultural and Higher Education Affairs

Minister of Displaced Persons
Khalil al-Anwar, Ministry of Displaced Persons

Minister of Economy and Trade
Ministry of Economy and Trade, Artois Street, Hamra, Beirut, Lebanon
PHONE: +961 (1) 340503
FAX: +961 (1) 354640
E-MAIL: PostMaster@Economy.gov.lb

Minister of Environment
Artur Nazarian, Ministry of Environment
PHONE: +961 (1) 522222
E-MAIL: info@moe.gov.lb

Minister of Finance
George Kurum, Ministry of Finance

Minister of Foreign Affairs
Selim al-Hoss, Ministry of Foreign Affairs

Minister of Housing and Cooperatives
Mahmud Abu Hamdan, Ministry of Housing and Cooperatives

Minister of Industry and Oil
Sulayman Trablousi, Ministry of Industry and Oil

Minister of Information
Anwar al-Khalil, Ministry of Information

Minister of Interior
Michel al-Murr, Ministry of Interior

Minister of Justice
Joseph Shaoul, Ministry of Justice

Minister of Labor
Michel Moussa, Ministry of Labor

Minister of Municipal and Rural Affairs
Michel al-Murr, Ministry of Municipal and Rural Affairs

Minister of National Defense
Ghazi Zaytar, Ministry of National Defense

Minister of National Economy and Trade
Nasser Saidi, Ministry of National Economy and Trade

Minister of National Education, Youth, and Sports
Mohammed Yousef Beydoun, Ministry of National Education, Youth, and Sports

Minister of Post and Telecommunications
Issam Naaman, Ministry of Post and Telecommunications, Badaro, Sami El-Solh Street, 3rd Floor, Beirut, Lebanon
PHONE: +961 (1) 424400; 422404
FAX: +961 (1) 888310
E-MAIL: PK@mpt.gov.lb

Minister of Public Health
Karam Karam, Ministry of Public Health

Minister of Public Works
Najib Mikati, Ministry of Public Works, Damascus Road, Beirut, Lebanon
PHONE: +961 (1) 458975; 458980

Minister of Social Affairs
Michel Moussa, Ministry of Social Affairs

Minister of State
Michel Edde, Ministry of State

Minister of State
Ilyas Hanna, Ministry of State

Minister of State
Ghazi Sayf al-Din, Ministry of State

Minister of Administrative Reform Affairs
Hassan Shalaq, Ministry of Administrative Reform Affairs

Minister of Tourism
Artur Nazarian, Ministry of Tourism
E-MAIL: mot@lebanon-tourism.gov.lb

Minister of Transportation
Najib Mikati, Ministry of Transportation

Minister of Vocational and Technical Education
Mohammed Yousef Beydoun, Ministry of Vocational and Technical Education

POLITICAL ORGANIZATIONS

Amal Movement

TITLE: President
NAME: Nabih Berri

Arab Democratic Party

TITLE: President
NAME: Ali Eid

Baath Arab Socialist Party

TITLE: Regional Secretary
NAME: Ghazi Seifeddin

Christian Democratic Party

TITLE: President
NAME: George Jabre

Communist Party

TITLE: General Secretary
NAME: Farouk Dahrouj

Congress Party

TITLE: President
NAME: Hassan Hachem

Democratic Socialist Party

TITLE: President
NAME: Kamel al-Assaad

Federation of Popular Leagues and Committees

TITLE: General Coordinator
NAME: Maan Bashour

Guardians of the Cedars

TITLE: President
NAME: Etienne Sakr

Henchak Party

TITLE: President
NAME: Vahrij Jerijian

Hizbollah

E-MAIL: hizbollahmedia@hizbollah.org
TITLE: General Secretary
NAME: Hassan Nasrallah

Islamic Amal Movement

TITLE: President
NAME: Hussein Moussawi

Islamic Charitable Projects Association

TITLE: President
NAME: Hussam Karakira

Islamic Group

TITLE: General Secretary
NAME: Faysal Mawlawi

Kataeb Party

TITLE: President
NAME: George Saadeh

Lebanese Democratic Movement

TITLE: President
NAME: Jacques Tamer

Lebanese Movement

TITLE: President
NAME: Nabil Mchantaf

Lebanese People's Front

TITLE: President
NAME: Joseph Haddad

Lebanese Popular Congress

TITLE: President
NAME: Kamal Shatila

Lebanese Republican Party

TITLE: President
NAME: Imad Jaara

Marada Institution

TITLE: President
NAME: Sleiman Frangieh

Maronite League

TITLE: President
NAME: Pierre Helou

Movement of Change

TITLE: President
NAME: Elie Mahfoud

Najjadeh Party

TITLE: President
NAME: Mostafa Al-Hakim

Nasserite Unification Movement

NAME: Samir Sabbagh

National Bloc

TITLE: General Secretary
NAME: Ibrahim Estefan

National Liberal Party

TITLE: President
NAME: Dory Chamoun

Popular Nasserite Organization

TITLE: President
NAME: Mustafa Saad

Progressive Socialist Party

TITLE: President
NAME: Walid Joumblatt

Ramgavar Party

TITLE: President
NAME: Hovsep Amirian

Socialist Arab Union

TITLE: President
NAME: Mounir As-Sayyad

Solidarity Party

TITLE: President
NAME: Emile Rahmeh

Syrian National Social Party

TITLE: President
NAME: Inaam Raad

Tahcnak Party

TITLE: General Secretary
NAME: Sebouh Hovnanian

Union Party

TITLE: President
NAME: Omar Harb

Waad Party

TITLE: President
NAME: Elias Hobeika

Workers League

TITLE: President
NAME: Zaher al-Khatib

DIPLOMATIC REPRESENTATION
Embassies in Lebanon

Italy
Rue de Rome Immobiliere 209, Hamra, BP 11–4128, Beirut, Lebanon
PHONE: +961 (1) 749801
FAX: +961 (1) 749804
E-MAIL: istitlib@inco.com.lb

United States
Awkar, P.O. Box 70–840, Beirut, Lebanon
PHONE: +961 (1) 542600; 543600
FAX: +961 (1) 544136

JUDICIAL SYSTEM
Courts of Cassation
Constitutional Council
Supreme Council

FURTHER READING
Articles

Boukhari, Sophie. ''Tug-of-War in Beirut and Cairo.'' *UNESCO Courier* (September 1999): 42.

''Exit, in Disorder.'' *The Economist* (June 5, 1999): 45.

''Israel's Mess in Lebanon.'' *The Economist* (March 6, 1999): 41.

''Laziza Rises Again.'' *The Economist* (June 26, 1999): 75.

''Lebanese Films: Blame Others.'' *The Economist* (October 30, 1999): 96.

''Palestinian Refugees: Losers, Always.'' *The Economist* (August 28, 1999): 35.

''Silent Clapping.'' *The Economist* (August 14, 1999): 37.

''Time to Leave the Insecurity Zone.'' *The Economist* (May 29, 1999): 42.

Internet

An-Nahar. Available Online @ www.annahar.com.lb/ (November 29, 1999).

Lebanon Daily Star. Available Online @ www.dailystar.com.lb/Welcome.html (November 29, 1999).

LEBANON: STATISTICAL DATA

For sources and notes see "Sources of Statistics" in the front of each volume.

GEOGRAPHY

Geography (1)

Area:

Total: 10,400 sq km.

Land: 10,230 sq km.

Water: 170 sq km.

Areaócomparative: about 0.7 times the size of Connecticut.

Land boundaries:

Total: 454 km.

Border countries: Israel 79 km, Syria 375 km.

Coastline: 225 km.

Climate: Mediterranean; mild to cool, wet winters with hot, dry summers; Lebanon mountains experience heavy winter snows.

Terrain: narrow coastal plain; Al Biqa' (Bekaa Valley) separates Lebanon and Anti-Lebanon Mountains.

Natural resources: limestone, iron ore, salt, water-surplus state in a water-deficit region.

Land use:

Arable land: 21%

Permanent crops: 9%

Permanent pastures: 1%

Forests and woodland: 8%

Other: 61% (1993 est.).

HUMAN FACTORS

Demographics (2A)

	1990	1995	1998	2000	2010	2020	2030	2040	2050
Population	3,130.3	3,340.5	3,505.8	3,620.0	4,163.9	4,613.0	5,045.8	5,396.9	5,598.5
Net migration rate (per 1,000 population)	NA	NA	NA	NA	NA	NA	NA	NA	NA
Births	NA	NA	NA	NA	NA	NA	NA	NA	NA
Deaths	NA	NA	NA	NA	NA	NA	NA	NA	NA
Life expectancy - males	65.9	67.3	68.1	68.6	70.9	72.9	74.5	75.9	77.0
Life expectancy - females	70.6	72.4	73.3	74.0	76.9	79.2	81.1	82.5	83.6
Birth rate (per 1,000)	22.5	22.6	22.7	22.2	17.6	15.2	14.5	12.8	12.3
Death rate (per 1,000)	7.1	6.7	6.5	6.4	5.9	5.8	6.3	7.6	9.9
Women of reproductive age (15-49 yrs.)	810.7	940.4	1,008.6	1,044.9	1,183.1	1,276.7	1,226.0	1,225.9	1,224.1
of which are currently married	NA	NA	NA	NA	NA	NA	NA	NA	NA
Fertility rate	2.7	2.4	2.3	2.2	2.1	2.0	2.0	2.0	2.0

Except as noted, values for vital statistics are in thousands; life expectancy is in years.

Health Personnel (3)

Total health expenditure as a percentage of GDP, 1990-1997[a]

Public sector 3.0

Private sector 7.0

Total[b] 10.0

Health expenditure per capita in U.S. dollars, 1990-1997[a]

Purchasing power parity . . . . .NA

Total 87

Availability of health care facilities per 100,000 people

Hospital beds 1990-1997[a] 310

Doctors 1993[c] 191

Nurses 1993[c] 122

Health Indicators (4)

Life expectancy at birth

1980 65

1997 70

Daily per capita supply of calories (1996) 3,279

Total fertility rate births per woman (1997) 2.5

Maternal mortality ratio per 100,000 live births (1990-97) . . . . .300[c]

Safe water % of population with access (1995) 94

Sanitation % of population with access (1995) 97

Consumption of iodized salt % of households (1992-98)[a] 92

Smoking prevalence

Male % of adults (1985-95)[a] . . . .

Female % of adults (1985-95)[a] . . . .

Tuberculosis incidence per 100,000 people (1997) 26

Adult HIV prevalence % of population ages 15-49 (1997) 0.09

Infants and Malnutrition (5)

Under-5 mortality rate (1997) 37

% of infants with low birthweight (1990-97) 10

Births attended by skilled health staff % of total[a] . . .89

% fully immunized (1995-97)

TB . . . . .NA

DPT 92

Polio 92

Measles 89

Prevalence of child malnutrition under age 5 (1992-97)[b] 3

Ethnic Division (6)

Arab 95%

Armenian 4%

Other 1%

Religions (7)

Islam 70% (5 legally recognized Islamic groups—Alawite or Nusayri Druze, Isma'ilite, Shi'a, Sunni), Christian 30% (11 legally recognized Christian Groups—4 Orthodox Christian, 6 Catholic, 1 Protestant), Judaism.

Languages (8)

Arabic (official), French, English, Armenian widely understood.

EDUCATION

Public Education Expenditures (9)

Public expenditure on education (% of GNP)

1980 . . . .

1996 . . . . .2.5

Expenditure per student

Primary % of GNP per capita

1980 . . . .

1996 . . . . .18.5

Secondary % of GNP per capita

1980 . . . .

1996 . . . .

Tertiary % of GNP per capita

1980 . . . .

1996 . . . . .22.3[1]

Expenditure on teaching materials

Primary % of total for level (1996) . . . .

Secondary % of total for level (1996) . . . .

Primary pupil-teacher ratio per teacher (1996) . . . .

Duration of primary education years (1995) 5

Literacy Rates (11A)

In thousands and percent[1]	1990	1995	2000	2010
Illiterate population (15+ yrs.)	154	151	138	115
Literacy rate - total adult pop. (%)	90.8	92.4	93.7	95.8
Literacy rate - males (%)	93.6	94.7	95.6	96.9
Literacy rate - females (%)	88.2	90.3	92.0	94.7

GOVERNMENT & LAW

Political Parties (12)

The legislative branch is a unicameral National Assembly (128 seats; members elected by popular vote on the basis of sectarian proportional representation to serve four-year terms). Seats are allocated one-half to Christian and one-half to Muslim groups.

Government Budget (13A)

Year: 1996

Total Expenditures: 7,732 Billions of Pounds

Expenditures as a percentage of the total by function:

General public services and public order 15.83
Defense 10.31
Education 6.17
Health 2.16
Social Security and Welfare 7.71
Housing and community amenities 1.13
Recreational, cultural, and religious affairs 87
Fuel and energy 1.58
Agriculture, forestry, fishing, and hunting 55
Mining, manufacturing, and construction 6.58
Transportation and communication 7.53
Other economic affairs and services 5.25

Military Affairs (14B)

	1990	1991	1992	1993	1994	1995
Military expenditures						
Current dollars (mil.)	262[e]	289[e]	347	328	332[e]	410
1995 constant dollars (mil.)	301[e]	319[e]	373	344	340[e]	410
Armed forces (000)	36	36	37	37	50	55
Gross national product (GNP)						
Current dollars (mil.)	6,598	8,478	8,606	9,262	10,230	11,160[e]
1995 constant dollars (mil.)	7,583	9,368	9,257	9,710	10,480	11,160[e]
Central government expenditures (CGE)						
1995 constant dollars (mil.)	2,147[e]	2,471[e]	2,016	2,236	3,518	NA
People (mil.)	3.4	3.4	3.5	3.6	3.6	3.7
Military expenditure as % of GNP	4.0	3.4	4.0	3.5	3.2	3.7
Military expenditure as % of CGE	14.0	12.9	18.5	15.4	9.7	NA
Military expenditure per capita (1995 $)	89	93	107	97	94	111
Armed forces per 1,000 people (soldiers)	10.7	10.5	10.6	10.4	13.8	14.9
GNP per capita (1995 $)	2,252	2,725	2,651	2,733	2,895	3,020
Arms imports[6]						
Current dollars (mil.)	0	5	0	10	5	40
1995 constant dollars (mil.)	0	6	0	10	5	40
Arms exports[6]						
Current dollars (mil.)	0	0	0	0	0	0
1995 constant dollars (mil.)	0	0	0	0	0	0
Total imports[7]						
Current dollars (mil.)	2,521	3,729	4,075	4,371	6,000	7,300[e]
1995 constant dollars (mil.)	2,897	4,120	4,383	4,583	6,150	7,300[e]
Total exports[7]						
Current dollars (mil.)	489	547	450	517	500	1,000[e]
1995 constant dollars (mil.)	562	605	484	542	513	1,000[e]
Arms as percent of total imports[8]	0	.1	0	.2	.1	.5
Arms as percent of total exports[8]	0	0	0	0	0	0

LABOR FORCE

Labor Force (16)
Total (million) 1.0
Services 62%
Industry 31%
Agriculture 7%

Data for 1996 est. Percent distribution for 1997 est. Total does not include 1 million foreign workers.

Unemployment Rate (17)
18% (1997 est.)

PRODUCTION SECTOR

Electric Energy (18)
Capacity . . . . .1.35 million kW (1997)
Production . . . . .5 billion kWh (1995)
Consumption per capita . . . . .1,380 kWh (1995)

Transportation (19)
Highways:
total: 6,350 km
paved: 6,032 km
unpaved: 318 km (1996 est.)

Pipelines: crude oil 72 km (none in operation)

Merchant marine:
total: 62 ships (1,000 GRT or over) totaling 258,383 GRT/392,087 DWT ships by type: bulk 5, cargo 40, chemical tanker 1, combination bulk 1, combination ore/oil 1, container 2, livestock carrier 5, oil tanker 1, roll-on/roll-off cargo 2, specialized tanker 1, vehicle carrier 3 (1997 est.)

Airports: 9 (1997 est.)

Airports—with paved runways:
total: 7
over 3,047 m: 1
2,438 to 3,047 m: 2
1,524 to 2,437 m: 2
914 to 1,523 m: 1
under 914 m: 1 (1997 est.)

Airports—with unpaved runways:
total: 2
914 to 1,523 m: 1
under 914 m: 1 (1997 est.)

Top Agricultural Products (20)
Citrus, vegetables, potatoes, olives, tobacco, hemp (hashish); sheep, goats.

FINANCE, ECONOMICS, & TRADE

Economic Indicators (22)
National product: GDP purchasing power parity $15.2 billion (1997 est.)
National product real growth rate: 4% (1997 est.)
National product per capita: $4,400 (1997 est.)
Inflation rate consumer price index: 9% (1997 est.)

Exchange Rates (24)
Exchange rates:
Lebanese pounds (£) per US$1
January 1998 . . . . .1,526.1
1997 . . . . .1,539.5
1996 . . . . .1,571.4
1995 . . . . .1,621.4
1994 . . . . .1,680.1
1993 . . . . .1,741.4

Top Import Origins (25)
$7.559 billion (c.i.f., 1996) Data are for 1996.

Origins	%
Italy	12
United States	11
Germany	9
France	8
Syria	4
United Kingdom	4
Japan	4

Top Export Destinations (26)
$1.018 billion (f.o.b., 1996) Data are for 1996.

Destinations	%
UAE	23
Saudi Arabia	14
Kuwait	8
Syria	7
Jordan	5
France	5
Italy	4
United States	3

Economic Aid (27)

Recipient: aid pledges of $3.5 billion for 1997-2001.

Import Export Commodities (28)

Import Commodities	Export Commodities
Machinery and transport equipment 28%	Paper and pape products 26%
Foodstuffs 20%	Food stuffs 16%

Consumer goods 19%

Chemicals 9%

Textiles 5%

Metals 5%

Fuels 3%

Textiles and textile products 10%

Jewelry 8%

Metals and metal products 8%

Electrical equipment and products 8%

Chemical products 6%

Transport vehicles 4%

LESOTHO

Kingdom of Lesotho
Muso oa Lesotho

INTRODUCTORY SURVEY

RECENT HISTORY

In 1880, the so-called Gun War broke out between the Basotho and the Boers over the attempt to disarm the Basotho. A high point in Basotho history was the successful resistance waged against the Cape's forces.

In 1884, Basutoland was returned to British administration under a policy of indirect rule. Local government was introduced in 1910 which in effect allowed the chiefs to govern for the next 50 years. Under a new constitution that became effective in 1960, an indirectly elected legislative body, the Basutoland National Council, was created. A pre-independence constitution went into effect on 30 April 1965.

The United Kingdom granted independence to the newly named Kingdom of Lesotho on 4 October 1966; Moshoeshoe II was proclaimed king. The first general election was held in January 1970. As the election progressed, it appeared that the ruling party, the Basotho National Party (BNP), would be defeated by the Basotho Congress Party (BCP). Fearing defeat, Prime Minister Leabua Jonathan, the leader of the BNP, declared a state of emergency and suspended the constitution. King Moshoeshoe II was placed under house arrest.

Through the late 1970s and early 1980s the BCP's military arm, the Lesotho Liberation Army (LLA), continued to struggle against the Jonathan government. They claimed responsibility for periodic bombings in Maseru, ambushes of govern-

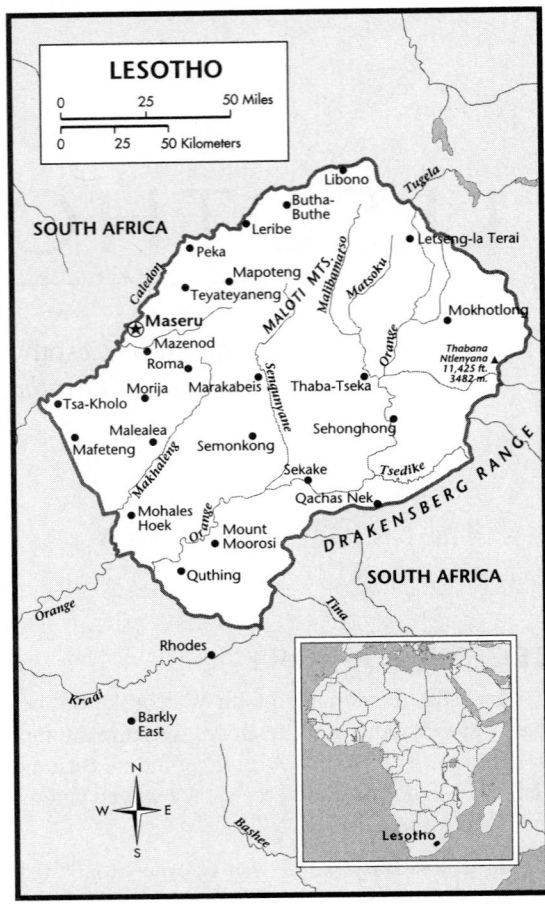

LESOTHO

0   25   50 Miles

0   25   50 Kilometers

ment officials, and attacks on police stations. The Lesotho government charged that South Africa was allowing the LLA to use its territory as a base of operations.

Relations with South Africa deteriorated and on 1 January 1986, South Africa imposed a near-total blockade of Lesotho. The blockade resulted in severe shortages of food and essential supplies. Within the month, a military coup led by Major General Justin Metsing Lekhanya overthrew the government. All political activity was banned. There was widespread skepticism about the military government and its links to South Africa.

Many groups within the country called for a return to civilian rule. In November 1990, a new law was announced providing for a constitutional monarchy, but barring Moshoeshoe II from the throne. However, in April 1991, rebel army officers staged a bloodless coup, forcing Lekhanya to resign. He was succeeded by Colonel Elias Ramaema as leader of a military junta.

Finally, on 27 March 1993, in the first democratic elections in 23 years, the BCP won all 65 seats in the Assembly. The BCP formed a new government under Prime Minister Dr. Ntsu Mokhehle. However, on 25 January 1994, army troops mutinied after the government refused their demands for a 100% pay increase. Prime Minister Mokhehle requested military assistance from South Africa, but that request was denied. After three weeks of sporadic fighting, opposing factions within the military agreed to new negotiations.

In September 1994, the king and Prime Minister Mokhehle signed an agreement reestablishing democratic rule and removing King Letsie from the throne and returning his father, the exiled King Moshoeshoe II. In 1996, King Moshoeshoe II was killed in a car crash and his son was returned to power. The move alarmed supporters of democracy because Letsie had suspended parliament when he earlier held power.

GOVERNMENT

According to the 1965 constitution and its 1993 replacement, the Kingdom of Lesotho is a monarchy with a bicameral parliament. The parliament consists of a National Assembly of 65 members, and a Senate with 33 members. Until 1993 the king was official chief of state *(motlotlehi)*. The 1993 constitution, however, clearly defines the king's role as ceremonial.

Judiciary

The judicial system consists of the High Court, the Court of Appeal, subordinate courts, and the Judicial Service Commission (JSC). The High Court hears appeals from subordinate courts. There is no trial by jury.

Political Parties

Lesotho's government party, the Basotho National Party (BNP), formerly the Basutoland National Party, was founded in 1959 and was in the forefront of Lesotho's independence drive. Also active in the independence drive was the Basotho Congress Party (BCP), founded in 1952. The third major party is the Marematlou Freedom Party (MFP), formed in 1965. The BCP holds all the seats in the National Assembly, although it won just over half the vote in 1993.

DEFENSE

A 2,000-member army has eight combat companies (with United States and United Kingdom weapons) and one air squadron.

ECONOMIC AFFAIRS

Lesotho is an agricultural country, with modest incomes from industry and tourism. Political reforms in South Africa and the involvement of the International Monetary Fund (IMF) have created new opportunities for the Lesotho economy.

Public Finance

The government has posted budget surpluses since 1992. The U.S. Central Intelligence Agency estimates that, in 1995, government revenues totaled approximately $445 million and expenditures $400 million, including capital expenditures of $128 million. The 1996 surplus was expected to be about 1% of GNP. External debt totaled $512 million which is equal to about 33% of GNP.

Income

In 1997 Lesotho's gross national product (GNP) was $1.1 billion, or about $2,500 per person. Taxes from Lesotho's migrant labor force working in South Africa constitute a key source of income. In 1996, 60% of Lesotho's male work force worked in South African coal and gold mines, and their tax payments accounted for 45% of the gross domestic product (GDP).

Industry

Lesotho has a wide variety of light industries, which include, among others, tire retreading, tapestry weaving, diamond processing, and the production of textiles, electric lighting, candles, and ceramics.

Banking and Finance

Lesotho is a member of the Common Monetary Area. The 1974 agreement, which was revised in 1986, provides access to the South African capital market for the Lesotho banking system. Lesotho is now responsible for its own monetary policy and controls its own financial institutions, but management of the rand currency and the gold and foreign exchange reserves of the rand area remains the sole responsibility of South Africa.

In 1980, the newly established Lesotho Monetary Authority (now the Central Bank of Lesotho) began issuing maloti as the national currency, but the South African rand remained legal tender and the loti was pegged at par with the rand.

Demand for credit to the private sector has been strong in the 1990s in response to growth in the manufacturing, services and construction sectors. In contrast, claims on central government have been sharply reduced as a result of the IMF-supported Structural Adjustment Program; in fact, the government has been a net saver with the domestic banking system since 1992. In the 1990s interest rates have remained positive in real terms and generally slightly higher than in South Africa due to higher margins. By the end of June 1996, the discount rate was 15.7%, and the Treasury-bill rate was 15.48%.

The commercial bank sector is dominated by the government-owned Lesotho Bank and the South African-owned Stambic Bank which has recently acquired Barclays Bank's interest in Lesotho. The Lesotho Building Finance Corporation merged with Lesotho Bank in April 1993 to facilitate an increase in the scale of domestic mortgage lending. At the end of December 1995, mortgage loans outstanding were only m 82 million in a total of m 612 million for all commercial loans. The Lesotho Agricultural Development Bank (LADB) serves to mobilize rural savings and provide agricultural credit. Monetary supply, as measured by m2, totaled m 1,121.8 million in 1995. Total reserves (excluding gold) were $456.7 million at the end of 1995.

No securities exchange was in operation in Lesotho as of 1997.

Economic Development

The Lesotho government's development objectives are based on a food-security policy approach, built around small-scale irrigated agriculture projects and improved rural water supplies. Donors supported the fourth five-year plan (1988–91) with pledges of $390 million. Lesotho receives development assistance from the United Kingdom, South Africa, Canada, Taiwan, the World Bank, and various United Nations agencies. Political reforms in South Africa in 1994 should have a beneficial impact on the Lesotho economy.

SOCIAL WELFARE

The Social Welfare Department is administered by the Ministry of Health. The Homemakers' Association, an organization long active in social welfare, has given family-management courses in remote areas under a grant from the Oxford Committee for Famine Relief (Oxfam).

The roles of women are limited by law and tradition, although a few women serve in important government roles.

Healthcare

Major health problems include pellagra, kwashiorkor, and other diseases that stem from poor nutrition and inadequate hygiene. In 1989–95, 21% of children under five years of age were considered malnourished. Famines have resulted from periodic droughts.

Tuberculosis and venereal diseases are also serious problems. In 1995, approximately 80% of the population had access to health care service. Estimated life expectancy in 1995 was 58 years.

Housing

The Lesotho Housing Corp. builds new housing for sale and rent, and a government-supported development program is building low-cost housing.

EDUCATION

In 1994, Lesotho had 1,234 primary schools. That year, there were 366,935 primary school pupils taught by 7,433 teachers, and 61,615 general secondary school students taught by 2,597 teachers. In 1992, 1,590 students were enrolled in vocational training. Education is compulsory between the ages of 6 and 13.

The University of Lesotho, at Botswana and Swaziland, was renamed the National University of Lesotho in 1975 by Prime Minister Leabua Jonathan. In 1993, all higher level institutions totaled 4,001 pupils and 492 teaching staff.

1999 KEY EVENTS TIMELINE

January

- Lesotho's former prime minister, Dr. Ntsu Mokhehle, dies in Maseru at age 80 after a long illness.

- Lesotho's national air service, Air Lesotho, to close down on February 6 due to "heavy losses."

- About 50 alleged mutineers who overpowered prison wardens and Lesotho Defence Force (LDF) members and took over the Maseru prison go back to their cells as the standoff is defused.

- Amnesty International expresses concern at the failure of Lesotho authorities to improve the "inhumane" conditions at the prison in Maseru where 50 soldiers charged in connection with the September 1998 mutiny have been held for months.

- Troops from South Africa and Botswana to remain in Lesotho until asked by Lesotho to leave.

February

- The South African Home Affairs department places notices at border posts between Lesotho and South Africa informing the public that the issuing of travel concessions granted to people who traveled regularly for business or study had been suspended until further notice.

- An arms cache is discovered by Southern African Development Community (SADC) soldiers in Maseru following an intensive search of a dam outside the capital.

- The prime minister addresses the National Assembly on the security situation in Lesotho.

March

- Metsing Lekhanya, who was Lesotho's military ruler from 1986 to 1991, is elected new leader of the opposition Basotho National Party (BNP).

- The Irish government gives Lesotho development aid totaling R45m (Rands) for Lesotho this year.

- Prime Minister Pakalitha Mosisili announces a plan to rid government and the armed forces of "troublemakers."

- Lesotho's opposition alliance announces that they would seek United Nations intervention to get the Southern African Development Community (SADC) troops out of Lesotho.

April

- The United States Embassy in Maseru pledges M15, 640 as a contribution to support the National University of Lesotho Drama Group in its campaign against HIV/AIDS in Lesotho.

- Prime Minister Pakalitha Mosisili announces the withdrawal of the Southern African Development Community, SADC, forces from the country.

- South African Water Affairs and Forestry Minister Kader Asmal holds talks with Lesotho Prime Minister Pakalitha Mosisili in Maseru on the revision of a water treaty between the two countries.

- The Lesotho Government kicks out the Lesotho Red Cross Society (LRCS) from the drought relief program.

May

- The 35-year old King of Lesotho, King Letsie III, chooses a bride.

- A third force emerges in Lesotho politics, with the establishment of a new opposition grouping committed to the denunciation of violent and unconstitutional methods in resolving political disputes.

- Large convoys of the Southern African Development Community, SADC, forces in Lesotho have start moving out of the country for Botswana and South Africa respectively.

- South Africa's military intelligence and other foreign soldiers in Lesotho are warned to leave the country by the end of July or face "elimination".

- Five more members of the Lesotho Defense Force (LDF) are arrested in connection with the death of former Deputy Prime Minister Selubetsi Baholo, bringing the number of suspects in his death to fourteen.

June

- South Africa and Lesotho sign two agreements to regulate the development and management of the Lesotho Highlands Water Project.

- The Lesotho parliament approves a budget exceeding 2 billion Rands for the 1999/2000 financial year.

- Lesotho faces a domestic cereal shortage of more than 162,000 tons in the year 1999–2000 to feed its population.

July

- The Lesotho government complains it was snubbed by the organizers of the World Economic Forum (WEF), which failed to invite it to the region's premier economic summit in Durban.

- Prime Minister Pakalitha Mosisili calls for African states to consciously formulate and implement programs of poverty eradication as a means of minimizing internal dissatisfaction and conflict.

August

- Lesotho agrees to sponsor a two-day National Dialogue on privatization and restructuring of the economy.

September

- Bristol-Myers Squibb pledges to provide $100 million over five years to assist South Africa, Botswana, Namibia, Lesotho, and Swaziland in their attempts to find sustainable solutions for communities to combat HIV/AIDS.

- Lesotho's Interim Political Authority (IPA) announces that the number of seats in the kingdom's parliament will be increased by 50 to 130 for the elections scheduled for April 2000.

- 170,000 miners return to Lesotho, jobless.

October

- A number of South African-based credit card providers complain about Lesotho's nationals who overspend and disappear without paying.

- United Nations Development Program Administrator Mark Mallock Brown encourages Lesotho to deal with the political process in a timely fashion.

- Two hundred and seventy-six passports mysteriously disappear before they are brought into use; this leaves unanswered questions concerning those who had custody over them.

December

- The head of the billion-dollar Lesotho Highlands Water Project is found guilty of accepting an estimated $2 million in bribes, and charges of bribery are levied against eight construction companies that won contracts for work on the project, which is partially funded by the World Bank. The government is investigating allegations that companies from France, Italy, the U.K., Canada, and South Africa attempted to bribe the manager of the construction project.

ANALYSIS OF EVENTS: 1999

BUSINESS AND THE ECONOMY

Lesotho, a small, landlocked, and mountainous country completely surrounded by South Africa, entered 1999 at the mercy of its powerful neighbor,

South Africa. Lesotho's economy was based on subsistence agriculture, livestock, and remittances from miners employed in South Africa. The number of the migratory mine workers declined during the 1990s. In 1990 the remittances of these workers to their families of a portion of their wages added about 67 percent to Lesotho's gross domestic product (GDP) compared with the addition of roughly 33 percent in 1996. With the unprecedented political changes in South Africa, labor migration to South African was no longer a viable option for most Lesotho workers. In 1999 over 170,000 miners in South Africa were laid off and sent home to Lesotho to become jobless. Early in 1999 the South African Home Affairs department placed notices at the border posts between the two countries informing the public that the issuing of travel concessions to people who traveled regularly to South Africa for business or study had been suspended until further notice.

The only other major resource that draws significant revenues for the country was water. Although a drought decreased agricultural activity over several years, the January 1998 completion of a major hydroelectric facility in Lesotho permitted the sale of water to South Africa. This generated important and steady revenue to Lesotho. The Lesotho Government received a total of M391.32 million in royalties from the sales of water to South Africa. (The Lesotho currency is the *loti*,—plural, *maloti*—which equals less than 20 cents U.S.) For most of 1999 South African Water Affairs and Forestry Minister Kader Asmal held talks with Lesotho Prime Minister Pakalitha Mosisili in Maseru (Lesotho's capital city) on revising a water treaty between the two countries. The talks led to two agreements to regulate the development and management of the Lesotho Highlands Water Project.

Other economic news included the approval by the Lesotho Parliament of a budget exceeding 2 billion Rands for the 1999/2000 financial year to be financed partly by local resources and foreign aid. The debilitated state of Lesotho's economy brought down the national air service, Air Lesotho, which folded due to heavy losses. A number of South African based credit card providers were swindled by a substantial number of Lesotho's nationals who have the habit of overspending and disappearing without paying.

GOVERNMENT AND POLITICS

The government of Lesotho is a parliamentary constitutional monarchy with King Letsie III as chief of state. He ascended to the throne on February 7, 1996 following the death of his father, King Moshoeshoe II. In the autumn of 1998 an uprising led by a disgruntled faction of the Lesotho Defense forces was quelled by a peace keeping force of soldiers brought in from Botswana and South Africa. Over fifty Lesotho soldiers were taken into custody and charged with the September 1998 mutiny. Amnesty International expressed concern at the failure of Lesotho authorities to improve the ''inhumane'' conditions at the prison in Maseru where the 50 soldiers were held for months. In protest against the inhumane conditions, the 50 alleged mutineers overpowered prison wardens and Lesotho Defense Force (LDF) members and temporarily took over the Maseru prison.

As the year progressed, Lesotho's opposition alliance grew unhappy with the reluctance of the peace keeping forces to vacate the country. The country's political opposition appealed to the United Nations to get the South African and Botswana troops out of Lesotho. South Africa's military intelligence and other foreign soldiers in Lesotho were openly warned to leave the country by the end of July or face ''elimination''. These warnings appear to have been heeded by South Africa and Botswana as they began to withdraw their forces in April. Another important political development included the announcement of parliamentary elections set for April 2000.

CULTURE AND SOCIETY

Although the inflation rate was estimated at eight percent, one of the lowest in the region, the population living below the poverty line was almost fifty percent and there was substantial unemployment and underemployment affecting more than half of the labor force. Poverty was a major national issue discussed widely in the media. Alongside poverty was the issue of AIDS. Lesotho is one of the countries in the Southern African subregion hardest hit by the AIDS epidemic. This crisis contributed to a low life expectancy at birth. For men born in 1999, the life expectancy was only 51 years. For women it was 55 years. The United States Embassy and Bristol-Myers Squibb (BMS) pledged substantial amounts of money to alleviate the suffering caused by AIDs. The Embassy gave money to support the National University of

Lesotho Drama Group in its campaign to heighten awareness of HIV/AIDS in Lesotho. Bristol-Myers Squibb (BMS) pledged 100 million dollars over five years to assist Lesotho and other countries in South Africa in finding sustainable solutions for communities to combat HIV/AIDS.

Other noteworthy news concerning culture and society included the finding of a bride for the King. The 35 year old King of Lesotho, King Letsie III, finally chose his wife after five years of searching. Lesotho's former prime minister, Dr. Ntsu Mokhehle, died in Maseru at age 80 after a long illness.

DIRECTORY

CENTRAL GOVERNMENT
Head of State

King
Letsie III, Monarch, Royal Palace, Maseru, Lesotho

Ministers

Prime Minister
Pakalitha Mosisili, Office of the Prime Minister, c/o The Government Secretary, PO Box 527, Maseru 100, Lesotho

Deputy Prime Minister and Minister of Finance and Development Planning
Kelebone Albert Maope, Ministry of Finance and Development Planning

Minister of Agriculture, Cooperatives, and Land Reclamation
Vova Bulane, Ministry of Agriculture, Cooperatives, and Land Reclamation

Minister of Communications Information, Broadcasting, Posts and Telecommunications
Qnyane Mphafi, Ministry of Communications Information, Broadcasting, Posts and Telecommunications

Minister of Defense
Pakalitha Mosisili, Ministry of Defense

Minister of Education
Lesao Archibald Lehohla, Ministry of Education

Minister of Employment and Labor
Nots'i Victor Molopo, Ministry of Employment and Labor

Minister of Environment, Gender, and Youth Affairs
Mathabiso Lepono, Ministry of Environment, Gender, and Youth Affairs

Minister of Foreign Affairs
Motsoahae Thomas Thabane, Ministry of Foreign Affairs

Minister of Health and Social Welfare
Tefo Mabote, Ministry of Health and Social Welfare

Minister of Industry, Trade, and Marketing
Mpho Meli Malie, Ministry of Industry, Trade, and Marketing

Minister of Justice, Human Rights, Law and Constitutional Affairs
Shakane Mokhehle, Ministry of Justice, Human Rights, Law and Constitutional Affairs

Minister of Local Government and Home Affairs
Mopshatla Mabitle, Ministry of Local Government and Home Affairs

Minister of Natural Resources
Monyane Moleleki, Ministry of Natural Resources

Minister of Public Works and Transport
Mofelehetsi Moerane, Ministry of Public Works and Transport

Minister of Tourism, Sports, and Culture
Mlalele Motaung, Ministry of Tourism, Sports, and Culture

POLITICAL ORGANIZATIONS
Basotho Congress Party (BCP)
NAME: Molapo Qhobela

Basotho National Party (BNP)
NAME: Evaristus Sekhonyana

DIPLOMATIC REPRESENTATION
Embassies in Lesotho

United States
254 Kingsway, PO Box 333, Maseru 100, Lesotho
PHONE: +266 312666
FAX: +266 310116

JUDICIAL SYSTEM
High Court

Court of Appeal

Magistrate's Court

FURTHER READING
Government Publications

Central Intelligence Agency. *CIA World Factbook, 1998.* Washington, DC: Government Printing Office, 1999.

Gay, John, et al. *Health in Lesotho: 1993 Profile.* Maseru, Lesotho: Ministry of Health, Government of Lesotho in collaboration with the European Community, World Bank, and World Organization, 1993.

Lesotho Bureau of Statistics. *1996 Lesotho Population Census Village List.* Maseru, Lesotho: Lesotho Bureau of Statistics, 1997.

Lesotho Bureau of Statistics. *Basotho Women and Their Men: Statistics on Women and Men in Lesotho.* Maseru, Lesotho: Lesotho Bureau of Statistics, 1993.

Lesotho Bureau of Statistics. *Household Budget Survey 1994/1995.* Maseru, Lesotho: Lesotho Bureau of Statistics, 1995.

Lesotho Bureau of Statistics. *Lesotho National Accounts, 1980–1990.* Maseru, Lesotho: Lesotho Bureau of Statistics, 1992.

Lesotho Bureau of Statistics. *The Agricultural Census in Lesotho, 1989/90: Analytical Report.* Maseru, Lesotho: Lesotho Bureau of Statistics, 1994.

Population—a Strategic Programme of Action. *Lesotho Sectoral Round Table Consultations: Population—a Strategic Programme of Action.* Maseru: Government of the Kingdom of Lesotho, Ministry of Economic Planning, 1996.

Sebatane, E. Molapi and Mabud, Mohammed A. *Implications of Lesotho's Population Growth for Education.* Maseru, Lesotho: Dept. of Population and Manpower, Ministry of Economic Planning, Government of Lesotho, 1995.

U.S. Department of State. *Country Reports on Human Rights Practices for 1997.* Washington, DC: Government Printing Office, 1998.

Sources of Statistical Information

Africa South of the Sahara, 1999. London: Europa Publications Ltd., 1998.

Center for International Health Information. *Lesotho: Health Situation and Statistics Report, 1994.* Arlington, VA: Center for International Health Information, 1994.

Economist Intelligence Unit. *Country Report: Lesotho, 2nd Quarter.* London: The Economist Intelligence Unit, 1999.

Ribe, F. et al. *Lesotho, Recent Economic Developments.* Washington, D.C.: International Monetary Fund, 1996.

Articles

"170,000 Miners Go Home to Become Jobless." *Mopheme/The Survivor*, 28 September 1999.

"Credit Card Providers Cry Foul of Basotho Citizens." *Mopheme/The Survivor*, 19 October 1999.

"Deal With the Political Processes, the Sooner, the Better." *Mopheme/The Survivor*, 19 October 1999.

"Five Southern Africa Countries to Get 100m Dollars to Fight AIDS." South African News Agency-SAPA, Johannesburg, BBC Monitoring International Reports, 1 September 1999.

"Government Shaken by Political Purges." *Africa Information Afrique*, 18 March 1999.

"Government Terminates Partnership with Red Cross." *Mopheme/The Survivor*, 27 April 1999.

"Ireland Grants Lesotho 45m Rands in Aid." South African News Agency-SAPA, Johannesburg, BBC Monitoring International Reports, 17 March 1999.

"King Finds Lady of his Dreams." *Afrika News Network*, 11 May 1999.

"Lesotho: Alleged Mutineers Return to Their Cells." South African News Agency-SAPA, Johannesburg, BBC Monitoring International Reports, 18 January 1999.

Keketso, Lawrence. "Highlands Water Project a Major Factor in National Economic Growth." *Mopheme/The Survivor*, 8 June 1999.

"Lesotho: Amnesty Protests 'Inhumane' Conditions for Jailed Mutinous Soldiers." South African News Agency-SAPA, Johannesburg, BBC Monitoring International Reports, 21 January 1999.

"Lesotho 'Angered' by South African Suspension of Travel Concessions." South African News Agency-SAPA, Johannesburg,

BBC Monitoring International Reports, 11 February 1999.

"Lesotho: Arms Cache Found in Dam by South African Divers." South African News Agency-SAPA, Johannesburg, BBC Monitoring International Reports, 23 February 1999.

"Lesotho: Country Facing 162,000-Tonnes Cereal Shortfall." South African News Agency-SAPA, Johannesburg, BBC Monitoring International Reports, 22 June 1999.

"Lesotho: Five More Soldiers Held for 1994 Death of Deputy Premier." Radio Lesotho, Maseru, BBC Monitoring International Reports, 31 May 1999.

"Lesotho: Former Military Ruler Elected New BNP Leader." South African News Agency-SAPA, Johannesburg, BBC Monitoring International Reports, 14 March 1999.

"Lesotho: Former Premier Ntsu Mokhehle Dies." South African News Agency-SAPA, Johannesburg, BBC Monitoring International Reports, 7 January 1999.

"Lesotho: New 'Third Force' Political Alliance Formed; Opposition Party Splits." South African News Agency-SAPA, Johannesburg, BBC Monitoring International Reports, 11 May 1999.

"Lesotho: Opposition Wants Southern African Development Community Troops Out." South African News Agency-SAPA, Johannesburg, BBC Monitoring International Reports, 22 March 1999.

"Lesotho PM Says Regional Intervention Force to Withdraw." Radio Lesotho, Maseru, BBC Monitoring International Reports, 9 April 1999.

"Lesotho: Prime Minister Addresses National Assembly on Security Situation." Radio Lesotho, Maseru, BBC Monitoring International Reports, 26 February 1999.

"Lesotho: Parliament Passes 2 Billion Rands Budget." South African News Agency-SAPA, Johannesburg, BBC Monitoring International Reports, 18 June 1999.

"National Dialogue to be Held on Privatisation." Mopheme/The Survivor, 23 August 1999.

"South Africa Says Troops to Remain in Lesotho Until Asked to Leave." South African News Agency-SAPA, Johannesburg, BBC Monitoring International Reports, 22 January 1999.

"U.S. Ambassador Pledges Aid for HIV/AIDS Campaign." Mopheme/The Survivor, 20 April 1999.

Books

Hope, Kempe R. AIDS and Development in Africa: A Social Science Perspective. New York: Haworth Press, 1999.

Murray, Jon. South Africa, Lesotho and Swaziland. Hawthorn, Australia: Lonely Planet, 1998.

Nthunya, Mpho 'M'atsepo. Singing Away the Hunger: Stories of a Life in Lesotho. London: Souvenir, 1999.

O'Malley, Padraig. Southern Africa: The People's Voices-Perspectives on Democracy. Bellville, South Africa: School of Government, University of the Western Cape, 1999.

Internet

Africa Information Afrique (AIA). Available Online @ csf.colorado.edu/ipe/africa.html (October 28, 1999).

Africa Inter Mennonite Mission. Available Online @ home.sprynet.com/~aimm/ (October 28, 1999).

LESOTHO: STATISTICAL DATA

For sources and notes see "Sources of Statistics" in the front of each volume.

GEOGRAPHY

Geography (1)

Area:

Total: 30,350 sq km.

Land: 30,350 sq km.

Water: 0 sq km.

Area—comparative: slightly smaller than Maryland.

Land boundaries:

Total: 909 km.

Border countries: South Africa 909 km.

Coastline: 0 km (landlocked).

Climate: temperate; cool to cold, dry winters; hot, wet summers.

Terrain: mostly highland with plateaus, hills, and mountains.

Natural resources: water, agricultural and grazing land, some diamonds and other minerals.

Land use:

Arable land: 11%

Permanent crops: NA%

Permanent pastures: 66%

Forests and woodland: NA%

Other: 23% (1993 est.).

HUMAN FACTORS

Demographics (2A)

	1990	1995	1998	2000	2010	2020	2030	2040	2050
Population	1,743.9	1,964.4	2,089.8	2,166.5	2,444.9	2,624.6	2,849.4	3,177.8	3,532.8
Net migration rate (per 1,000 population)	NA	NA	NA	NA	NA	NA	NA	NA	NA
Births	NA	NA	NA	NA	NA	NA	NA	NA	NA
Deaths	NA	NA	NA	NA	NA	NA	NA	NA	NA
Life expectancy - males	55.3	54.8	52.2	50.6	43.9	47.5	57.6	67.6	71.3
Life expectancy - females	61.4	59.6	55.8	53.5	45.4	49.7	62.7	75.7	79.9
Birth rate (per 1,000)	36.8	33.6	31.8	30.7	26.5	23.4	20.8	18.1	15.9
Death rate (per 1,000)	11.3	11.4	12.8	13.7	18.7	16.6	10.9	6.8	6.3
Women of reproductive age (15-49 yrs.)	410.4	476.8	515.8	539.7	629.1	693.5	783.7	878.6	936.0
of which are currently married	NA	NA	NA	NA	NA	NA	NA	NA	NA
Fertility rate	4.9	4.4	4.1	3.9	3.1	2.6	2.3	2.1	2.1

Except as noted, values for vital statistics are in thousands; life expectancy is in years.

Health Personnel (3)

Total health expenditure as a percentage of GDP, 1990-1997[a]

Public sector 3.7

Private sector ....NA

Total[b] ....NA

Health expenditure per capita in U.S. dollars, 1990-1997[a]

Purchasing power parity ....NA

Total ....NA

Availability of health care facilities per 100,000 people

Hospital beds 1990-1997[a] ....NA

Doctors 1993[c] 5

Nurses 1993[c] 33

Health Indicators (4)

Life expectancy at birth

1980 53

1997 56

Daily per capita supply of calories (1996) 2,209

Total fertility rate births per woman (1997) 4.8

Maternal mortality ratio per 100,000 live births (1990-97) ....610[c]

Safe water % of population with access (1995) 62

Sanitation % of population with access (1995) ....

Consumption of iodized salt % of households (1992-98)[a] 73

Smoking prevalence

Male % of adults (1985-95)[a] 38

Female % of adults (1985-95)[a] 1

Tuberculosis incidence per 100,000 people (1997) 407

Adult HIV prevalence % of population ages 15-49 (1997) 8.35

Infants and Malnutrition (5)

Under-5 mortality rate (1997) 137

% of infants with low birthweight (1990-97) 11

Births attended by skilled health staff % of total[a] ...50

% fully immunized (1995-97)

TB 46

DPT 50

Polio 48

Measles 43

Prevalence of child malnutrition under age 5 (1992-97)[b] 16

Ethnic Division (6)

Sotho 99.7%

Europeans 1,600,

Asians 800

Religions (7)

Christian 80%, rest indigenous beliefs.

Languages (8)

Sesotho (southern Sotho), English (official), Zulu, Xhosa.

EDUCATION

Public Education Expenditures (9)

Public expenditure on education (% of GNP)

1980 ....5.1

1996 ....7.0[1]

Expenditure per student

Primary % of GNP per capita

1980 ....8.6

1996 ....16.2[1]

Secondary % of GNP per capita

1980 ....72.2

1996 ....62.0[1]

Tertiary % of GNP per capita

1980 ....999.7

1996 ....397.6[1]

Expenditure on teaching materials

Primary % of total for level (1996) ....0.4[1]

Secondary % of total for level (1996) ....

Primary pupil-teacher ratio per teacher (1996) 47

Duration of primary education years (1995) 7

Literacy Rates (11A)

In thousands and percent[1]	1990	1995	2000	2010
Illiterate population (15+ yrs.)	341	340	338	326
Literacy rate - total adult pop. (%)	66.7	71.3	75.5	82.4
Literacy rate - males (%)	77.7	81.1	83.9	88.4
Literacy rate - females (%)	56.6	62.3	67.6	76.6

GOVERNMENT & LAW

Political Parties (12)

The legislative branch is a bicameral Parliament consisting of the Senate (33 members—22 principal chiefs and 11 other members appointed by the ruling party) and the Assembly (65 seats; members elected for a five-year term by popular vote). Note: Due to a schism in the Basotholand Congress Pary, Prime Minister Ntsu Mokhehle formed the new Lesotho Congress for Democracy (LCD) in June 1997, taking 42 seats away from the BCP, reducing it to 23 seats and the role of an opposition party.

Government Budget (13B)

Revenues . . . .$507 million

Expenditures . . . .$487 million

  Capital expenditures . . . .$170 million

Data for FY96/97 est.

Military Affairs (14B)

	1990	1991	1992	1993	1994	1995
Military expenditures						
Current dollars (mil.)	55[e]	NA	35	31[e]	26[e]	28
1995 constant dollars (mil.)	64[e]	NA	38	32[e]	27[e]	28
Armed forces (000)	2	2	2	2	2	2
Gross national product (GNP)						
Current dollars (mil.)	1,052	1,089	1,103	1,202	1,315	1,478
1995 constant dollars (mil.)	1,209	1,203	1,187	1,260	1,348	1,478
Central government expenditures (CGE)						
1995 constant dollars (mil.)	373	389	364	394	1,011	1,131
People (mil.)	1.7	1.8	1.8	1.9	1.9	1.9
Military expenditure as % of GNP	5.3	NA	3.2	2.6	2.0	1.9
Military expenditure as % of CGE	17.1	NA	10.5	8.2	2.7	2.5
Military expenditure per capita (1995 $)	37	NA	21	17	14	15
Armed forces per 1,000 people (soldiers)	1.2	1.1	1.1	1.1	1.1	1.0
GNP per capita (1995 $)	697	677	653	653	711	765
Arms imports[6]						
Current dollars (mil.)	0	0	0	0	0	0
1995 constant dollars (mil.)	0	0	0	0	0	0
Arms exports[6]						
Current dollars (mil.)	0	0	0	0	0	0
1995 constant dollars (mil.)	0	0	0	0	0	0
Total imports[7]						
Current dollars (mil.)	640	820	900[e]	869[e]	843[e]	986[e]
1995 constant dollars (mil.)	736	906	968[e]	911[e]	864[e]	986[e]
Total exports[7]						
Current dollars (mil.)	59	68	109[e]	134[e]	143[e]	160[e]
1995 constant dollars (mil.)	68	75	117[e]	141[e]	147[e]	160[e]
Arms as percent of total imports[8]	0	0	0	0	0	0
Arms as percent of total exports[8]	0	0	0	0	0	0

Crime (15)

Crime rate (for 1997)

Crimes reported 445,000

Total persons convicted 93,500

Crimes per 100,000 population 26,200

Persons responsible for offenses

Total number of suspects 26,900

Total number of female suspects 17,000

Total number of juvenile suspects 18,000

LABOR FORCE

Labor Force (16)

Total 689,000; economically active 86% of resident population engaged in subsistence agriculture; roughly 35% of the active male wage earners work in South Africa.

Unemployment Rate (17)

Substantial unemployment and underemployment affecting more than half of the labor force (1996 est.)

PRODUCTION SECTOR

Electric Energy (18)

Electricity supplied by South Africa. Consumption per capita is 163 kWh (1995).

Transportation (19)

Highways:

total: 4,955 km

paved: 887 km

unpaved: 4,068 km (1996 est.)

Airports: 29 (1997 est.)

Airports—with paved runways:

total: 3

over 3,047 m: 1

914 to 1,523 m: 1

under 914 m: 1 (1997 est.)

Airports —with unpaved runways:

total: 26

914 to 1,523 m: 4

under 914 m: 22 (1997 est.)

Top Agricultural Products (20)

Corn, wheat, pulses, sorghum, barley; livestock.

MANUFACTURING SECTOR

GDP & Manufacturing Summary (21)

Detailed value added figures are listed by both International Standard Industry Code (ISIC) and product title.

	1980	1985	1990	1994
GDP ($-1990 mil.)[1]	389	417	584	676
Per capita ($-1990)[1]	290	267	326	338
Manufacturing share (%) (current prices)[1]	6.3	10.4	13.1	NA
Manufacturing				
Value added ($-1990 mil.)[1]	20	36	64	95
Industrial production index	100	177	315	466
Value added ($ mil.)	*14*	*22*	*67*	*121*
Gross output ($ mil.)	*57*	*66*	*189*	*332*
Employment (000)	*4*	*7*	*19*	*14*
Profitability (% of gross output)				
Intermediate input (%)	75	67	65	63
Wages and salaries inc. supplements (%)	*6*	*9*	*11*	*8*
Gross operating surplus	*18*	*24*	*25*	*29*
Productivity ($)				
Gross output per worker	*14,314*	*9,778*	*10,138*	*23,364*
Value added per worker	*3,535*	*3,234*	*3,588*	*8,829*
Average wage (inc. supplements)	*1,032*	*941*	*1,103*	*1,838*
Value added ($ mil.)				
311/2 Food products	*6*	*9*	*28*	*51*
313 Beverages	*5*	*7*	*21*	*38*
314 Tobacco products	NA	NA	NA	NA
321 Textiles	*1*	*2*	*6*	*12*
322 Wearing apparel	—	*1*	*2*	*3*
323 Leather and fur products	—	—	—	*1*

	1980	1985	1990	1994
324 Footwear	—	—	*1*	*2*
331 Wood and wood products	NA	NA	NA	NA
332 Furniture and fixtures	—	—	*1*	*1*
341 Paper and paper products	NA	NA	NA	NA
342 Printing and publishing	—	—	—	—
351 Industrial chemicals	NA	NA	NA	NA
352 Other chemical products	1	1	*4*	*8*
353 Petroleum refineries	NA	NA	NA	NA
354 Miscellaneous petroleum and coal products	NA	NA	NA	NA
355 Rubber products	NA	NA	NA	NA
356 Plastic products	NA	NA	NA	NA
361 Pottery, china and earthenware	NA	NA	NA	NA
362 Glass and glass products	NA	NA	NA	NA
369 Other non-metal mineral products	—	—	*1*	*1*
371 Iron and steel	NA	NA	NA	NA
372 Non-ferrous metals	NA	NA	NA	NA
381 Metal products	1	1	*2*	*4*
382 Non-electrical machinery	NA	NA	NA	NA
383 Electrical machinery	NA	NA	NA	NA
384 Transport equipment	NA	NA	NA	NA
385 Professional and scientific equipment	NA	NA	NA	NA
390 Other manufacturing industries	—	—	—	—

FINANCE, ECONOMICS, & TRADE

Economic Indicators (22)

National product: GDP —purchasing power parity — $5.1 billion (1997 est.)

National product real growth rate: 9% (1997 est.)

National product per capita: $2,500 (1997 est.)

Inflation rate —consumer price index: 8.7% (1996 est.)

Exchange Rates (24)

Exchange rates:

Maloti (M) per US$1

January 1998	4.94193
1997	4.60796
1996	4.29935
1995	3.62709
1994	3.55080
1993	3.26774

The Basotho loti is at par with the South African rand.

Balance of Payments (23)

	1990	1991	1992	1993	1994
Exports of goods (f.o.b.)	60	67	109	134	144
Imports of goods (f.o.b.)	−673	−803	−933	−868	−810
Trade balance	−613	−736	−823	−734	−667
Services - debits	−103	−104	−115	−93	−104
Services - credits	496	518	538	481	407
Private transfers (net)	267	392	422	362	458
Government transfers (net)	19	14	16	13	13
Overall balance	65	83	38	29	108

Top Import Origins (25)

$1.1 billion (c.i.f., 1996 est.) Data are for 1995.

Origins	%
South African Customs Union	.90
Asia	.6
European Union	.2

Top Export Destinations (26)

$218 million (f.o.b., 1996 est.) Data are for 1995.

Destinations	%
South African Customs Union	.52
North America	.38
European Union	.9

Economic Aid (27)

Recipient: ODA, $NA. NA stands for not available.

Import Export Commodities (28)

Import Commodities	Export Commodities
Corn	Clothing
Clothing	Wool
Building materials	Footwear
Vehicles	Road vehicles
Machinery	Mohair
Medicines	
Petroleum products	

LIBERIA

CAPITAL: Monrovia.

FLAG: The national flag, dating from 1847, consists of 11 horizontal stripes, alternately red (6) and white (5), with a single five-pointed white star on a square blue field 5 stripes deep in the upper left corner.

ANTHEM: *All Hail, Liberia, Hail.*

MONETARY UNIT: The Liberian dollar (L $) of 100 cents is established by law as equivalent to the U.S. dollar. There are no Liberian notes. U.S. notes in the denominations of 5, 10, 20, 50, and 100 dollars are in circulation and are legal tender. Both U.S. and Liberian coins of 1, 5, 10, 25, and 50 cents, and 1 dollar are in circulation; in 1982, a $5 Liberian coin was issued.

WEIGHTS AND MEASURES: U.S. and UK weights and measures are used.

HOLIDAYS: New Year's Day, 1 January; Armed Forces Day, 11 February; Decoration Day, 2d Wednesday in March; Birthday of J. J. Roberts (first president), 15 March; Fast and Prayer Day, 2d Friday in April; National Redemption Day, 12 April; Unification Day, 14 May; Independence Day, 26 July; Flag Day, 24 August; Thanksgiving Day, 1st Thursday in November; Anniversary of 1985 Coup Attempt, 12 November; President Tubman's Birthday, 29 November; Christmas, 25 December. Good Friday and Easter Monday are movable religioU.S.holidays.

TIME: GMT.

LOCATION AND SIZE: Located on the west coast of Africa, Liberia has an area of about 111,370 square kilometers (43,000 square miles), slightly larger than the state of Tennessee. Liberia's capital city, Monrovia, is located on the Atlantic coast.

CLIMATE: The climate is tropical with a mean temperature of 27°c (81°F). Yearly rainfall is as high as 510 centimeters (200 inches) on the coast. Most of the rainfall occurs between late April and mid-November. Between December and March, a dust-laden wind known as the harmattan blows from the Sahara Desert.

INTRODUCTORY SURVEY

RECENT HISTORY

The establishment of a United States air base in Liberia during World War II (1939–45) and the building of an artificial harbor at Monrovia stimulated the country's development. William V. S. Tubman, elected president in 1944 and reelected for five additional terms, sought to unify the descendants of the original American ex-slaves and the tribal peoples of the interior. Upon Tubman's death in 1971, Vice-President William R. Tolbert, Jr., succeeded to the presidency. Having been elected without opposition in October 1975, Tolbert was inaugurated for an eight-year term in January 1976.

Tolbert and at least 26 supporters were killed in the fighting during a military coup on 12 April 1980; 13 officials were publicly executed ten days later. The People's Redemption Council (PRC), formed to rule the country, was led by Sergeant Samuel K. Doe, who became head of state. The constitution was suspended, but a return to civilian rule was promised for 1985. In the elections held on 15 October 1985, Doe was elected president with 51% of the vote. Foreign observers declared that the elections were rigged, and most of the opposition candidates who were elected refused to take their seats.

Since late December 1989, Liberia has fallen into chaos. Insurgents (people who revolt against authority) led by Charles Taylor began a campaign to overthrow the Doe regime. Thousands of civilians were massacred by gunmen on both sides.

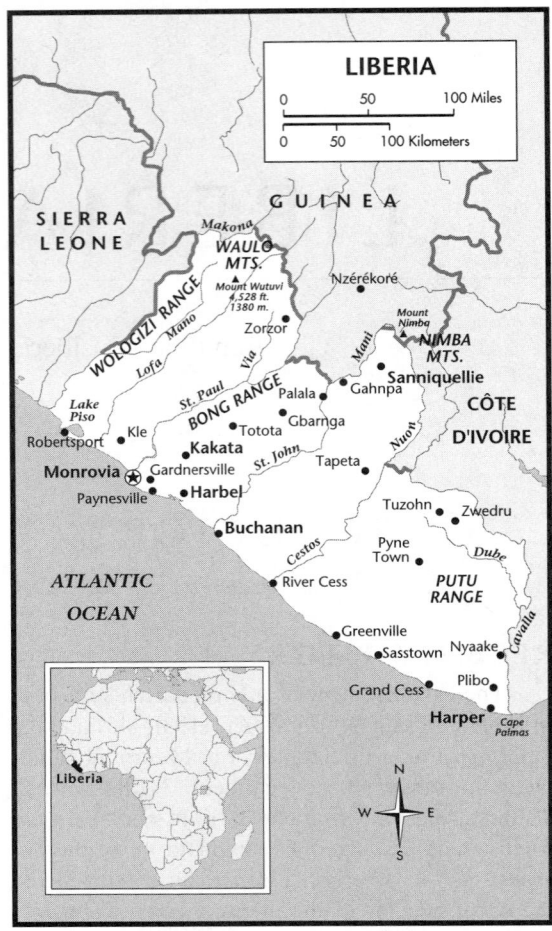

LIBERIA

0   50   100 Miles

0   50   100 Kilometers

SIERRA LEONE

GUINEA

Makona

WAULO MTS.

Mount Wutuvi 4,528 ft. 1380 m.

Nzérékoré

Zorzor

Mount Nimba

NIMBA MTS.

Sanniquellie

WOLOGIZI RANGE

Mano

Lofa

Via

Mani

BONG RANGE

St. Paul

Palala

Gahnpa

CÔTE D'IVOIRE

Lake Piso

Kle

Gbarnga

Totota

Robertsport

Kakata

St. John

Tapeta

Nuoh

Monrovia

Gardnersville

Harbel

Paynesville

Tuzohn

Zwedru

Dube

Buchanan

Cestos

Pyne Town

PUTU RANGE

River Cess

Cavalla

ATLANTIC OCEAN

Greenville

Sasstown

Nyaake

Grand Cess

Plibo

Harper

Cape Palmas

Liberia

N
W   E
S

Hundreds of thousands fled their homes. By June 1990, Doe was besieged in Monrovia. In an effort to stop the killing, a regional peacekeeping force, known as ECOMOG, entered the country and installed an interim government. Most of the ECOMOG force was supplied by Nigeria. However, on 9 September 1990, rebel forces shot their way into ECOMOG's headquarters and captured Doe, videotaping his torture and execution. On two occasions since entering the country, the ECOMOG forces prevented Charles Taylor's forces from capturing the capital, Monrovia.

The interim government was able to establish authority over most of Monrovia, but the rest of Liberia was in the hands of various factions. Despite three major peace agreements since 1990, fighting continued. Finally, in August 1995 all sides agreed to a ceasefire and set up a council of state to govern the country until elections could be held. The ceasefire only held until the year's end, when fighting resumed. In early 1996, roving gangs

of heavily armed teenagers recklessly shot up Monrovia. International relief organizations became the targets of looting, since seven years of war had left the country empty of anything worth stealing.

Liberia's four main militias approved a peace plan on 8 May 1996. In August 1996 West African leaders put together a new ceasefire agreement between the warring factions and selected an interim government. Elections were finally held in July 1997 and were overseen by ECOMOG forces. ECOMOG's presence in Liberia was an important factor in ending the civil war that had killed more than 150,000 people over seven years. Charles Taylor, the man who had initially started the uprising, was elected with 66% of the vote.

GOVERNMENT

Under the constitution approved on 3 July 1984, Liberia is a republic modeled after the United States. Its constitution provides for a president and vice-president elected jointly by universal vote for a four-year term with a limit of two consecutive terms. The legislature is divided into a 26-member Senate and a 64-member House of Representatives.

Judiciary

Most cases originate in magistrates' courts and may be taken for appeal to one of ten circuit courts or to the highest court. More serious cases originate in the circuit courts. Traditional courts are presided over by tribal chiefs. The 1984 constitution provides for the establishment of a Supreme Court consisting of a chief justice and four associate justices. Due to the war, the judiciary did not function in most areas as of early 1997.

Political Parties

Charles Taylor's National Patriotic Front of Liberia (NPFL) has gained influence since his election to the presidency in 1997. The United Liberation Movement of Liberia (ULIMO) has been identified with former Doe supporters.

DEFENSE

The regular armed forces (5,000) and police are active only in parts of Monrovia. Liberia no longer has air or naval capabilities. The rebel National Patriotic Forces of Liberia number 15,000. A six-nation African peacekeeping force numbers around 6,000.

ECONOMIC AFFAIRS

Liberia's economy, which is primarily agricultural, is in turmoil as a result of financial mismanagement and the civil war which has divided the country into two economic zones, one centered in and around the major urban centers, the other in the countryside. Even prior to the civil war, however, Liberia faced serious financial problems. In 1988 the World Bank closed its offices in Monrovia. In March of 1990, the International Monetary Fund (IMF) threatened to expel Liberia for nonpayment of its debt.

Public Finance

Government budgets, roughly in balance up to the mid-1970s, have since run heavily into deficit. Since civil war erupted in 1989, Liberia's fiscal management has collapsed. The U.S. Central Intelligence Agency estimates that, in 1994, government revenues totaled approximately $225 million and expenditures $285 million. External debt totaled $1.9 billion.

Income

Liberia's gross domestic product (GDP) in 1997 was $2.6 billion, or about $1,000 per person.

Industry

Before the civil war, Liberia's industrial sector was dominated by processing plants associated with its key agricultural outputs: rubber, palm oil, and lumber. Liberia also produced cement, plastics, shoes, recycled steel, and refined petroleum products.

During 1990–96, faction leaders and traders exploited the industrial wealth of Liberia. They used forced labor and stolen goods and fuel. The method of manufacture often harmed the environment or the ability to produce in the future. Profits from these enterprises were used to buy more weapons.

Banking and Finance

In 1974, the government established the National Bank of Liberia. It became the exclusive banker and fiscal agent of the government, introduced reserve requirements for commercial banks, and undertook their supervision. Liberia's commercial banks have their main offices in Monrovia. They offer a normal range of commercial and international banking services. The Liberian Bank for Development and Investment was established in November 1965 to provide additional medium- and long-term financial aid to worthwhile industrial

projects. A National Housing and Savings Bank was established in 1972, with priority given to low-cost public housing. An Agricultural and Cooperative Development Bank provides credit to facilitate capital investment in agriculture.

In the 1980s, Liberia was plagued by the outflow and hoarding of U.S.dollars, the only legal notes. The government minted a $5 coin to restore liquidity, but this action only led to more hoarding of U.S.bills, which traded informally at a premium compared to similarly denominated Liberian coins.

In November, 1996, the Chairwoman of the ruling Council of State, Ruth Perry, imposed a freeze on all government spending. She said the step was necessary to stabilize state finances and provide for civil service salaries, many of which had not been paid for months.

Economic Development

The civil war and international financial obligations dim the prospects of economic development. While refugee resettlement looms as an early postwar priority, future economic development depends on reestablishing international confidence in Liberia's financial management.

SOCIAL WELFARE

In 1976, the National Social Security and Welfare Corp. was established to administer pensions, sickness benefits, and welfare funds. Before the civil war, the Liberian Red Cross was active in child care and welfare, as were the Antoinette Tubman Welfare Foundation and the Catherine Mills Rehabilitation Center. Today, however, virtually no social services are functioning within the country.

An estimated 10% of those who fought in the civil war were under 15 years of age. Massacres of civilians were carried out by all the major fighting factions. Many children were wounded, killed, orphaned, or abandoned.

Healthcare

Liberia has an average life expectancy of only 49 years. In 1992 there were an estimated 11 doctors per 100,000 people, and only about 39% of the population had access to health care services. The major causes of death are malaria and gastrointestinal disease. The World Health Organization (WHO) estimates that about 1 million people in sub-Saharan Africa are HIV positive.

Housing

The typical dwelling of the tribal people in the Liberian interior is the rondavel, a circular, one-room mud-and-wattle thatch-roofed hut, windowless and with a single low door. These rondavels are being replaced by large rectangular huts, also of mud and wattle, subdivided into two or more rooms and equipped with windows. Many of the older corrugated-iron structures in Monrovia have also been replaced with more modern dwellings.

EDUCATION

Although education is compulsory from ages 6 to 16, probably fewer than half of all children are in school. The adult illiteracy rate was 62%. There are three institutions of higher learning: the government-operated University of Liberia in Monrovia (established in 1862); Cuttington University College at Monrovia, an Episcopalian institution; and a three-year engineering school, the William V. S. Tubman College of Technology.

1999 KEY EVENTS TIMELINE

January

- Some 400,000 Liberian refugees remain in Guinea and Côte d'Ivoire, waiting for conditions making it safe for them to return home.

February

- Despite signs that Monrovia is returning to peace, theft and breaches of security are commonplace suggesting that the country is still in a state of war.

March

- A noted Liberian conservationist expresses fear that massive logging as well as hunting and farming in protected areas threaten species and sustainable use of forests in Liberia.

April

- A criminal court sentences 13 persons accused of plotting a coup last September 18 and 19 to 10 years in prison.

- A group of armed bandits loots 13 vehicles belonging to the UNHCR and other international aid agencies near Voinjama in Lofa County. The death toll is placed at around 20 persons.

May

- President Taylor makes a tour of four West African states.

- Taylor signs a contract with Freedom Gold, a mining company founded by Evangelist Pat Robertson, and registered in the Cayman Islands.

- Jean-Marie Doré, a leading Guinean opposition figure, visits Monrovia on a fact-finding mission to help resolve disputes between Liberia and Guinea over dissidents operating across their common border.

- Taylor sacks the majority of his cabinet for failing to attend a prayer service. They are later reinstated.

June

- Nine soldiers are refused trial based on American law, and instead a sedition trial is set for them governed by Liberian laws.

- President Taylor announces that arms collected from former factions will be destroyed July 26.

- The Liberian government and Firestone/Bridgestone Rubber Plantation Companies sign a new concession agreement.

- An investigation committee is established in response to complaints of harassment of Mandingoes in Bong County.

- Graduating seniors of A.M.E. Zion University College, unable to pay a little over $100 for graduation, offer to work on President Taylor's farm in return for financial assistance.

July

- After 41 years, Bong Mining Company formally ceases operations. The company had been inactive for nearly a decade due to civil war.

- The Liberian Peace Forum (LPF), a project of the UN Program for Coordination and Assistance for Security and Development (PCASED), is launched in Monrovia.

- Liberian women petition for sweeping constitutional rights.

- A huge weapons stockpile is destroyed at a special ceremony on Liberia's independence day, July 26th.

August

- Armed dissidents reportedly occupy five localities in northwestern Liberia.

- Ivorian President, Henri Konan Bédié, visits Monrovia. Before leaving he announces that legal procedures must be taken to repatriate Liberians imprisoned in Côte d'Ivoire.

- The government of Liberia campaigns to have UN arms embargo lifted.

- Western aid workers are abducted in the border region with Sierra Leone.

- Joe Tate, chief of the country's national police force, is killed in a plane crash.

September

- USAID reports that basic services are still lacking and that a climate of insecurity hangs over Liberia. It also reports that it gave $32.98 million in humanitarian aid in fiscal 1999.

October

- Last ECOMOG troops begin leaving the country.

- President Taylor warns public officials against harassing investors.

- Ethnic animosity is reported in the southern county of Sinoe.

- United Nations reports that Liberia has completed the destruction of the 20,000 weapons and three million rounds of ammunition confiscated in 1997 at the end of the country's civil war.

December

- Police demolition teams begin removing army checkpoints in Monrovia that had been installed during the country's seven-year civil war that ended in 1997.

- Freedom Gold, a mining company headed by U.S. businessman and evangelist Pat Robertson, begins mining for gold in southeast Liberia under terms of a May agreement.

- Troops are posted along the southeast border with Côte d'Ivoire after that country's leader is ousted in a coup.

- President Taylor and the Liberia Electricity Corporation (LEC) are unable to restore power to homes of Monrovia by the end of 1999 as they had hoped. Residents of the capital lost power during the country's seven-year civil war.

ANALYSIS OF EVENTS: 1999

BUSINESS AND THE ECONOMY

Two years into the first elected term of President Charles Taylor, the conventional economy had virtually ceased to function, making Liberia's financial outlook dim indeed. Mismanagement of the Liberian shipping registry, which generated substantial revenue even during the war years, cost the government millions of dollars.

After 41 years of nominal operations, the Bong Mining Company, located about 50 miles north of Monrovia, officially closed down. This was the fourth time that the company had shut down since it opened in 1954. The German company had provided 2,000 jobs for Liberians and expatriates. While the loss of jobs, tax revenues, and foreign exchange earnings hurt the Liberian government, the Bong closure was painful also as a symptom of the larger practice of looting and depreciating the physical infrastructure of the country. One example of this was that the government had planned to privatize the airport, but the facility was totally destroyed during the civil war.

Some positive news was received when a U.S. firm announced it would invest in the mineral sector. The minerals company, Freedom Gold, planned to invest between $1 million and $15 million in exploration and development of a 900 square kilometer concession in the southeast part of the country. Despite Liberia's vast wealth in iron, zinc, copper, rutile, tin, lead, and nickel, only gold and diamonds are being mined, and these mining operations are mostly artisanal, small-scale alluvial extraction. Actual production figures are hard to obtain given the large volume of smuggling.

The agricultural sector showed signs of recovery, albeit from a very low base. Exploitation of rubber was targeted to expand from 400,000 acres to 1 million acres. Rubber production in 1999 was only 5% lower than in the early 1980s. The recovery has been sparked by a new contract between the Firestone/Bridgestone Rubber Plantation Company and the government. The Firestone agreement provides for investments in schools, living quarters, medical facilities and other infrastructure in the concession area. Other sectors such as cocoa and forestry would require substantial investment in roads, fertilizers, seeds, and micro-credit before they reached their former capacities. Ironically, forests and wildlife, which benefited from neglect during the war, now are being subjected to massive harvesting, despite their protected status.

GOVERNMENT AND POLITICS

Although Liberia is nominally at peace, a state of insecurity prevails, and a total cessation of hostilities has not yet taken place. Dissidents control areas of the Forest Region, and incidents of violence have occurred. Several Western aid workers were abducted in August. The state security service (SSS) has a reputation for harassing and intimidating press critics, and political opponents.

Restoration of public services has yet to be achieved by the government. A US-AID report notes that potable water and electricity, shelter, and health care are insufficient. Indeed, observers widely believe that the Taylor government has shown itself incapable of restoring the conditions necessary for rebuilding the country. Local elections were delayed, officials claimed, because of insufficient funds needed to hold elections. Having co-opted or eliminated the opposition, Liberia looked like a one party-state.

President Taylor was sensitive to criticism. To shore up the government's image, he has retained the services of Cohen and Woods, International, a Washington-based public relations firm run by former Assistant Secretary of State for Africa, Herman (Hank) Cohen. Critics charged that since the 1997 election the government had substituted political image for substance. But the firm may have helped to persuade a U.S. court in Massachusetts to drop criminal charges against Taylor, and to allow him to address the UN General Assembly when he visited the U.S. in September. In spite of these efforts, a political force to unseat Taylor, the New Democratic Alternative of Liberia, was launched both in Liberia and in the U.S.

CULTURE AND SOCIETY

Liberian society was still recovering from the effects of a decade of civil war. Some 700,000 persons were estimated living across the borders in Guinea and Côte d'Ivoire or were internally displaced within the country. It would take years to rehabilitate child soldiers and maimed war veterans. The war was particularly hard on women who had not been able to tend the fields, feed or care for children, and send them to school. The African Development Bank had granted $500,000 to the health sector, but many donors and humanitarian agencies were withholding assistance, citing difficulties with the Taylor government. In two separate incidents, Lutheran World Services lost more than 30 tons of rice seed, and 11,000 agricultural tools in well-organized looting.

Despite survival concerns, Liberian women took action to improve their inheritance rights in both statutory and customary marriages. They petitioned the legislature to pass into law a draft bill based on provisions in the 1986 constitution. Their action coincided with similar activity in eight West African states simultaneously as part of the ''Day of Action for Women's Inheritance Rights'' in July. The Liberia Peace Forum (LPF) launched its campaign to prepare peace curricula for schools, colleges, and universities in Liberia. The program was part of the implementation of the Moratorium on the Importation, Exportation, and Manufacture of Light Weapons in West Africa, signed in October 1998.

DIRECTORY

CENTRAL GOVERNMENT
Head of State

President
Charles Ghanky Taylor, Office of the President, PO Box 10-9001, Capitol Hill, 1000 Monrovia 10, Liberia
PHONE: +231 226737; 224467

Vice President
Enoch Dogolea, Jr., Office of the Vice President, Executive Mansion, PO Box 10-9001, Capitol Hill 1000 Monrovia 10, Liberia
E-MAIL: EMansion@liberia.net

Ministers

Minister of Agriculture
Roland Massaquoi, Ministry of Agriculture, Tubmand Blvd, PO Box 10-9010, 1000 Monrovia 10, Liberia

Minister of Commerce and Industry
Brahima Kaba, Ministry of Commerce and Industry, Ashmun Street, PO Box 10-9014, 1000 Monrovia 10, Liberia

Minister of Information, Culture and Tourism
Joe Mulbah, Ministry of Information, Culture and Tourism, PO Box 10-9021, Capitol Hill, 1000 Monrovia 10, Liberia

Minister of Defense
Peter D. Chea, Ministry of Defense, Benson Street, PO Box 10-9007, 1000 Monrovia 10, Liberia

Minister of Education
Evelyn White Kandakai, Ministry of Education, Broad Street, PO Box 10-1545, 1000 Monrovia 10, Liberia

Minister of Finance
Elie Saleeby, Ministry of Finance, Broad Street, PO Box 10-9013, 1000 Monrovia 10, Liberia

Minister of Foreign Affairs
Monie Captan, Ministry of Foreign Affairs, PO Box 10-9002, Mamba Point, 1000 Monrovia 10, Liberia
PHONE: +231 227857
FAX: +231 226076

Minister of Health and Social Welfare
Gbatokai Darkinah, Ministry of Health and Social Welfare, PO Box 10-9004, Sinkor, 1000 Monrovia 10, Liberia

Minister of Internal Affairs
Edward Komo Sackor, Ministry of Internal Affairs, Corner of Warren and Benson Streets, PO Box 10-9008, 1000 Monrovia 10, Liberia

Minister of Justice
Eddington Vamah, Ministry of Justice, Ashmun Street, PO Box 10-9006, 1000 Monrovia 10, Liberia

Minister of Labour
Tom Woewiyu, Ministry of Labour, Mechlin Street, PO Box 10-9040, 1000 Monrovia 10, Liberia

Minister of Lands, Mines and Energy
Jenkins Dunbar, Ministry of Lands, Mines and Energy, Capitol Hill, PO Box 10-9024, 1000 Monrovia 10, Liberia

Minister of National Security
Philip Kamah, Ministry of National Security

Minister of Planning and Economic Affairs
Amelia Ward, Ministry of Planning and Economic Affairs, Broad Street, PO Box 10-9016, 1000 Monrovia 10, Liberia

Minister of Posts and Telecommunications
D. Maxwell Kaba, Ministry of Posts and Telecommunications, Carey Street, Monrovia, Liberia

Minister of State for Presidential Affairs
T. Ernest Eastman, Ministry of State for Presidential Affairs, Executive Mansion, Capitol Hill, Monrovia, Liberia

Minister of Public Works
John T. Richardson, Ministry of Public Works, Lynch Street, PO Box 10-9011, 1000 Monrovia 10, Liberia

Minister of Rural Development
Roosevelt Johnson, Ministry of Rural Development, PO Box 10-9030, 1000 Monrovia 10, Liberia

Minister of Transport
Lami Kawah, Ministry of Transport

Minister of Youth and Sports
Francois Massaquoi, Ministry of Youth and Sports, Sinkor, PO Box 10-9040, 1000 Monrovia 10, Liberia

POLITICAL ORGANIZATIONS
National Patriotic Party (NPP)
TITLE: Leader
NAME: Charles Ghankay Taylor

All Liberia Coalition Party (ALCOP)
TITLE: Chairman
NAME: Alhaji Kromah

Free Democratic Party (FDP)
TITLE: Chairman
NAME: Fayah Gbollie

Liberian Action Party (LAP)
TITLE: Chairman
NAME: Cletis Wotorson

Liberian National Union (LINU)
TITLE: Chairman
NAME: Harry Moniba

Liberian Peoples Party (LPP)
TITLE: Chairman
NAME: Togba-Nah Tipoteh

Liberian Unification Party (LUP)
TITLE: Chairman
NAME: Laveli Supuwood

National Democratic Party of Liberia (NDPL)

TITLE: Chairman
NAME: George E. Saigbe Boley

National Reformation Party (NRP)

TITLE: Chairman
NAME: Martin Sherif

People's Democratic Party of Liberia (PDPL)

TITLE: Chairman
NAME: George Toe Washington

People's Progressive Party (PPP)

TITLE: Chairman
NAME: Chea Cheapoo

Reformation Alliance Party (RAP)

TITLE: Chairman
NAME: Henry Boimah Fahnbulleh

True Whig Party (TWP)

TITLE: Chairman
NAME: Rudolph Sherman

Unity Party (UP)

TITLE: Chairman
NAME: Ellen Johnson-Sirleaf

United People's Party (UPP)

TITLE: Chairman
NAME: Gabriel BaccU.S.Matthews

DIPLOMATIC REPRESENTATION

Embassies in Liberia

Nigeria
Box 366, Monrovia, Liberia

Poland
PO Box 860, Gardener Avenue, Monrovia, Liberia

PHONE: +231 261113

United States
111 United Nations Drive, PO Box 100098, Mamba Point, Monrovia, Liberia
PHONE: +231 226370
FAX: +231 226148
NAME: Bismarck Myrick

JUDICIAL SYSTEM
Supreme Court

FURTHER READING
Articles

Cain, Kenneth L. ''The Rape of Dinah: Human Rights, Civil War in Liberia, and Evil Triumphant.'' *Human Rights Quarterly* (May 1999): 265+.

''Liberia: Appeal for Aid.'' *The New York Times,* 20 August 1999, p. A4.

''Liberia: Intervention Force Slows Departure.'' *The New York Times,* 29 July 1999, p. A6.

''Liberia: Security Chief Dies in Crash.'' *The New York Times,* 12 August 1999, p. A4.

''Liberia: Sierra Leone Border Reopened.'' *The New York Times,* 6 October 1999, p. A10.

''Liberia: Weapons Set Ablaze.'' *The New York Times,* 27 July 1999, p. A10.

Books

Liebenow, J. Gus. *Liberia: The Quest for Democracy.* Bloomington: Indiana University Press, 1985.

Internet

Africaonline. Available Online @ www.africaonline.com (October 28, 1999).

Africa News Online. Available Online @ www.africanews.org/west/stories/1999_feat1.html (October 28, 1999).

Integrated Regional Information Network (IRIN). Available Online @ www.reliefweb.int/IRIN (October 28, 1999).

LIBERIA: STATISTICAL DATA

For sources and notes see "Sources of Statistics" in the front of each volume.

GEOGRAPHY

Geography (1)

Area:

Total: 111,370 sq km.

Land: 96,320 sq km.

Water: 15,050 sq km.

Area—comparative: slightly larger than Tennessee.

Land boundaries:

Total: 1,585 km.

Border countries: Guinea 563 km, Cote d'Ivoire 716 km, Sierra Leone 306 km.

Coastline: 579 km.

Climate: tropical; hot, humid; dry winters with hot days and cool to cold nights; wet, cloudy summers with frequent heavy showers.

Terrain: mostly flat to rolling coastal plains rising to rolling plateau and low mountains in northeast.

Natural resources: iron ore, timber, diamonds, gold.

Land use:

Arable land: 1%

Permanent crops: 3%

Permanent pastures: 59%

Forests and woodland: 18%

Other: 19% (1993 est.).

HUMAN FACTORS

Demographics (2A)

	1990	1995	1998	2000	2010	2020	2030	2040	2050
Population	2,264.9	2,281.9	2,771.9	3,090.0	4,341.7	5,737.2	7,357.0	9,125.6	10,992.1
Net migration rate (per 1,000 population)	NA	NA	NA	NA	NA	NA	NA	NA	NA
Births	NA	NA	NA	NA	NA	NA	NA	NA	NA
Deaths	NA	NA	NA	NA	NA	NA	NA	NA	NA
Life expectancy - males	53.7	55.7	56.8	57.6	61.3	64.7	67.7	70.3	72.6
Life expectancy - females	58.3	60.7	62.2	63.1	67.6	71.6	75.0	77.7	80.0
Birth rate (per 1,000)	45.4	43.3	41.9	41.1	37.5	33.5	29.1	25.3	22.9
Death rate (per 1,000)	13.2	12.2	11.3	10.8	8.6	7.1	6.0	5.4	5.2
Women of reproductive age (15-49 yrs.)	497.6	501.6	608.7	680.5	1,001.1	1,379.0	1,848.0	2,370.9	2,872.0
of which are currently married	NA	NA	NA	NA	NA	NA	NA	NA	NA
Fertility rate	6.6	6.3	6.1	5.9	5.2	4.4	3.6	3.1	2.8

Except as noted, values for vital statistics are in thousands; life expectancy is in years.

Infants and Malnutrition (5)

Under-5 mortality rate (1997) 235
% of infants with low birthweight (1990-97) . . . . . .NA
Births attended by skilled health staff % of total[a] . . .NA
% fully immunized (1995-97)
   TB 38
   DPT 26
   Polio 25
   Measles 28
Prevalence of child malnutrition under age 5
   (1992-97)[b] . . . . .NA

Ethnic Division (6)

Indigenous African tribes 95% (including Kpelle Bassa,
Gio, Kru, Grebo, Mano, Krahn, Gola, Gbandi, Loma,
Kissi, Vai, and Bella), Americo-Liberians 2.5%
(descendants of immigrants from the US who had been
slaves).

Religions (7)

Traditional 70%
Muslim 20%
Christian 10%

Languages (8)

English 20% (official), about 20 tribal languages, of
which a few can be written and are used in
correspondence.

GOVERNMENT & LAW

Military Affairs (14B)

	1990[12]	1991	1992	1993	1994	1995
Military expenditures						
Current dollars (mil.)	NA	NA	NA	35[e]	29[e]	45[e]
1995 constant dollars (mil.)	NA	NA	NA	37[e]	30[e]	45[e]
Armed forces (000)	8	5	2	NA	NA	NA
Gross national product (GNP)						
Current dollars (mil.)	NA	NA	NA	NA	NA	NA
1995 constant dollars (mil.)	NA	NA	NA	NA	NA	NA
Central government expenditures (CGE)						
1995 constant dollars (mil.)	NA	NA	NA	NA	285[e]	NA
People (mil.)	2.3	2.0	2.1	2.3	2.3	2.2
Military expenditure as % of GNP	NA	NA	NA	NA	NA	NA
Military expenditure as % of CGE	NA	NA	NA	NA	10.5	NA
Military expenditure per capita (1995 $)	NA	NA	NA	16	13	21
Armed forces per 1,000 people (soldiers)	3.5	2.5	.9	NA	NA	NA
GNP per capita (1995 $)	NA	NA	NA	NA	NA	NA
Arms imports[6]						
Current dollars (mil.)	10	0	0	0	0	0
1995 constant dollars (mil.)	11	0	0	0	0	0
Arms exports[6]						
Current dollars (mil.)	0	0	0	0	0	0
1995 constant dollars (mil.)	0	0	0	0	0	0
Total imports[7]						
Current dollars (mil.)	NA	NA	NA	NA	NA	NA
1995 constant dollars (mil.)	NA	NA	NA	NA	NA	NA
Total exports[7]						
Current dollars (mil.)	1,941[e]	482[e]	771[e]	615[e]	530[e]	NA
1995 constant dollars (mil.)	2,231[e]	533[e]	829[e]	645[e]	543[e]	NA
Arms as percent of total imports[8]	NA	NA	NA	NA	NA	NA
Arms as percent of total exports[8]	0	0	0	0	0	NA

EDUCATION

Literacy Rates (11A)

In thousands and percent[1]	1990	1995	2000	2010
Illiterate population (15+ yrs.)	937	1,104	1,094	1,255
Literacy rate - total adult pop. (%)	33.5	38.3	43.2	53.7
Literacy rate - males (%)	48.7	53.9	58.8	68.2
Literacy rate - females (%)	18.1	22.4	27.4	39.0

GOVERNMENT & LAW

Political Parties (12)

House of Representatives	No. of seats
National Patriotic Party (NPP)	49
Unity Party (UP)	7
All Liberia Coalition Party (ALCOP)	3
Alliance of Political Parties	2
United People's Party (UPP)	2
Liberian Peoples Party (LPP)	1

Government Budget (13B)

Revenues . . . . .NA
Expenditures . . . . .NA

NA stands for not available.

LABOR FORCE

Labor Force (16)

Agriculture 70%.

Unemployment Rate (17)

Rate not available.

PRODUCTION SECTOR

Electric Energy (18)

Capacity .332,000 kW (1995)
Production . . . . .472 million kWh (1995)
Consumption per capita . . . . .154 kWh (1995)

Transportation (19)

Highways:
total: 10,600 km
paved: 657 km
unpaved: 9,943 km (1996 est.)
Merchant marine:
total: 1,620 ships (1,000 GRT or over) totaling 59,521,524 GRT/97,187,450 DWT
Airports: 46 (1997 est.)
Airports—with paved runways:
total: 2
over 3,047 m: 1
1,524 to 2,437 m: 1 (1997 est.)
Airports—with unpaved runways:
total: 44
1,524 to 2,437 m: 3
914 to 1,523 m: 6
under 914 m: 35 (1997 est.)

Top Agricultural Products (20)

Rubber, coffee, cocoa, rice, cassava (tapioca), palm oil, sugarcane, bananas; sheep, goats; timber.

MANUFACTURING SECTOR

GDP & Manufacturing Summary (21)

	1980	1985	1990	1992	1993	1994
Gross Domestic Product						
Millions of 1990 dollars	915	841	805	725	725	725
Growth rate in percent	−6.29	−2.02	−10.00	0.00	0.00	0.00
Per capita (in 1990 dollars)	487.5	382.6	312.6	263.4	254.7	246.4
Manufacturing Value Added						
Millions of 1990 dollars	82	80	59	60	*60*	*61*
Growth rate in percent	−21.21	−1.61	−32.51	5.88	*0.54*	*0.82*
Manufacturing share in percent of current prices	9.5	6.6	7.9	NA	NA	NA

FINANCE, ECONOMICS, & TRADE

Economic Indicators (22)

National product: GDP—purchasing power parity—$2.6 billion (1997 est.)

National product real growth rate: NA% (1997 est.)

National product per capita: $1,000 (1997 est.)

Inflation rate—consumer price index: NA%

Exchange Rates (24)

Exchange rates:

Liberian dollars (L$) per US$1

 Officially fixed rate since 1940 . . . . .1.0000

Market exchange rate:

 Liberian dollars (L$) per US$1

  October 1995 50

  January 1992 7

Market rate floats against the US dollar

Top Import Origins (25)

$5.8 billion (f.o.b., 1995 est.)

Origins	%
United States	NA
European Union	NA
Japan	NA

China . . . . .NA
Netherlands . . . . .NA
ECOWAS . . . . .NA
South Korea . . . . .NA

NA stands for not available.

Top Export Destinations (26)

$667 million (f.o.b., 1995 est.).

Destinations	%
United States	NA
European Union	NA
Netherlands	NA
Singapore	NA

NA stands for not available.

Economic Aid (27)

Recipient: ODA, $NA. NA stands for not available.

Import Export Commodities (28)

Import Commodities	Export Commodities
Mineral fuels	Diamonds
Chemicals	Iron ore
Machinery	Rubber
Transportation equipment	Timber
Manufactured goods; rice and other foodstuffs	Coffee

Balance of Payments (23)

	1980	1985
Exports of goods (f.o.b.)	600	430
Imports of goods (f.o.b.)	−478	−264
Trade balance	122	167
Services - debits	−97	−212
Services - credits	13	38
Private transfers (net)	36	92
Government transfers (net)	−29	−28
Overall balance	46	57

LIBYA

Socialist People's Libyan Arab
Jamahiriya
*Al-Jamahiriyah al-`Arabiyah al-Libiyah
ash-Sha`biyah al-Ishtirakiyah*

INTRODUCTORY SURVEY

CAPITAL: Tripoli (Tarabulus).

FLAG: The national flag is plain green.

ANTHEM: *Almighty God.*

MONETARY UNIT: The Libyan dinar (LD) of 1,000 dirhams is a paper currency. There are coins of 1, 5, 10, 20, 50, and 100 dirhams, and notes of 1, 5, and 10 dinars. LD1 = $2.75482 (or $1 = LD0.363).

WEIGHTS AND MEASURES: The metric system is the legal standard, but some local weights and measures are used.

HOLIDAYS: UK Evacuation Day, 28 March; U.S. Evacuation Day, 11 June; Anniversary of the Revolution, 1 September; Constitution Day, 7 October. Muslim religious holidays include `Id al-Fitr, `Id al-`Adha', the 1st of Muharram, and Milad an-Nabi.

TIME: 2 PM = noon GMT.

LOCATION AND SIZE: Situated on the coast of North Africa, Libya is the fourth-largest country on the continent, with an area of 1,759,540 square kilometers (679,362 square miles), slightly larger than the state of Alaska. Libya's capital city, Tripoli, is located on the Mediterranean coast.

CLIMATE: The climate has marked seasonal variations influenced by both the Mediterranean Sea and the desert. Summer temperatures range between 27–46°C (81–115°F). The ghibli, a hot, dry desert wind, can change temperatures by 17–22°C (30–40°F) in both summer and winter. Rain falls generally in a short winter period and frequently causes floods. Evaporation is high, and severe droughts are common. The Sahara Desert has less than 5 centimeters (2 inches) of rain a year.

RECENT HISTORY

In September 1911, the Italians invaded Libya, meeting fierce resistance from both Turks and indigenous Libyans. The Italian struggle for control of the region continued until 1932, when its conquest was completed. In World War II (1939–45), Libya became a main battleground for Allied and Axis forces, until it was occupied by victorious British and Free French troops. The Treaty of 1947 between Italy and the Allies ended Italian rule in Libya. When the Allies could not decide upon the country's future, Libya's fate was left to the United Nations. On 21 November 1949, the United Nations General Assembly voted that Libya should become an independent state. On 24 December 1951, Libya gained independence, with Muhammad Idris al-Mahdi as-Sanusi as king.

On 1 September 1969, a secret army organization, the Free Unionist Officers, deposed the king and proclaimed a republican regime. On 8 September, the Revolutionary Command Council (RCC) announced the formation of a civilian government. This government resigned on 16 January 1970, and a new cabinet was formed under Colonel Mu`ammar al-Qadhafi, chairman of the RCC.

Gaddafi has sought to make Libya the axis of a unified Arab nation, but relations with many Arab nations, including Egypt and Tunisia, have often been tense. Gaddafi has been equally active in Africa, annexing the disputed Aouzou Strip from Chad in 1973, and supporting the failing regimes of Uganda's Idi Amin in 1979, and Chad's Goukouni

Oueddei in 1980. Gaddafi has also been accused of supporting subversive plots in such countries as Morocco, Niger, Sudan, and Egypt. He has also been accused of providing material support to the Irish Republican Army, the Muslim rebels in the Philippines, and to Japanese and German terrorists.

In 1982, the United States charged Gaddafi with supporting international terrorism. In January 1986, the United States ordered all Americans to leave Libya and cut off all economic ties. On 15 April, following a West Berlin bomb attack in which United States servicemen were victims, United States warplanes bombed targets in Tripoli and Banghazi.

Gaddafi has survived several reported assassination and coup attempts (1984 and 1993). Opposition from Islamic groups prompted him to crack down on militants in 1993. His most serious challenge has been the tough sanctions imposed on Libya by the United Nations Security Council. These sanctions were imposed after he refused to surrender two men suspected in the terrorist bombing of a Pan American passenger jet over Lockerbie, Scotland, in 1988.

In September 1995, Libya began deporting thousands of Palestinian, Sudanese, and Egyptian workers. Gaddafi claimed the foreigners were being deported to create jobs for Libyans. However, Gaddafi stated that many of those being deported were Islamic militant ''infiltrators'' pretending to be migrant workers.

In 1996, it was believed that Libya was almost finished building the world's largest underground chemical weapons plant at Tarhunah near Tripoli. Intelligence officials from the United States claimed that the facility is capable of producing tons of poison gas per day. The Libyan government claimed that the building was a water irrigation system.

GOVERNMENT

The people theoretically exercise their authority through a system of people's congresses and committees. Gaddafi, as ''Leader of the Revolution,'' however, is the de facto head of state. He also is the commander of the armed forces and virtually all power is concentrated in him and his close advisers.

Judiciary

Minor civil and commercial cases may be heard by a sitting judge in each village and town. Other cases are heard initially by courts of first instance, and appeals may be taken to provincial courts of appeal. There is also a Supreme Court, consisting of a president and judges appointed by the GPC. In 1981, the private practice of law was abolished and all lawyers became employees of the secretariat of justice. Since 1981, revolutionary committees have been encouraged to conduct public trials without legal safeguards.

Political Parties

Political parties have not played an effective role in Libya's history. In 1971, the RCC (Revolutionary Command Council) founded the Libyan Arab Socialist Union as an alternative to political parties. It was viewed as an organization to promote national unity but has functioned in a minor capacity since 1977.

DEFENSE

In 1995, the army had 3,500 personnel organized into 28 brigades, about half armored, half infantry; armaments included 2,210 tanks, all made in the former Soviet Union. The navy had 8,000 personnel and 65 vessels, including 4 Russian submarines. The air force had 22,000 personnel, with 420 combat aircraft and 52 combat helicopters. The military budget was estimated at $1.4 billion in 1995, or 7% of the gross domestic product (GDP).

ECONOMIC AFFAIRS

Until the late 1950s, Libya was one of the poorest countries in the world. But with the discovery of the Zaltan oil field in 1959, the economic horizons of the country were dramatically enlarged. Production has fallen since 1970, but its value has increased, and Libya remains one of the world's leading oil producers. Until the late 1950s, about 80% of the population was engaged in agriculture and animal farming; in 1989, however, only 19% of the labor force was engaged in agricultural pursuits.

A massive water pipeline project, called the Great Manmade River (GMR) project began in the early 1990s. The GMR will carry water in a huge 267-mile-long pipeline from 225 underground wells to irrigate 1.2 million acres of land used to grow cereal crops. The public works project is expected to cost $25 billion. There is concern among United States intelligence officials that the GMR might be used to shuttle troops or weapons underground in order to avoid detection.

Since the 1992 UN-imposed air embargo, many large projects have been postponed because of budget restrictions. Libya's isolation has slowed the pace of oil exploration through the absence of major foreign oil companies. Lack of outlets is limiting the development of refineries, petrochemicals, and gas facilities.

Public Finance

Since 1974, the fiscal year has followed the calendar year. There are two budgets, one for ordinary expenses, the other (and larger one) for development. By law, 15% of oil revenues is put aside yearly into the country's reserves, while 70% of the remainder goes to development expenditures. All non-oil revenues are assigned to cover ordinary expenditures, and any shortfall is made up by transferring some of the petroleum revenues from the development budget.

If funds from petroleum revenues are not sufficient to cover development expenses, some planned projects are postponed. Although Libya has used part of its oil revenue to finance internal development (new schools, hospitals, roads) much has been wasted. Limited privatization continued in 1993, involving the sale of some parastatal assets. In 1989 revenues were $8.1 billion and expenditures were $9.8 billion, including capital expenditures of $3.1 billion.

The U.S. Central Intelligence Agency estimates that, in 1991, government revenues totaled approximately $8.1 billion and expenditures $9.8 billion, including capital expenditures of $3.1 billion. External debt totaled $3.5 billion.

Income

In 1997 Libya's gross national product (GNP) was 38 billion or $6,700 per person.

Industry

Industry accounts for 55% of the gross domestic product (GDP). Libyan manufacturing industries had been developing significantly since the early 1960s, but have fallen far behind the petroleum sector of the economy. Total refinery capacity in 1996 was about 348,400 barrels per day.

A large methanol, ammonia, and urea plant is at Marsa al-Burayqah, and a major plant producing ethylene, propylene, and butene was opened in 1987. The $6 billion iron and steel complex at Misratah began operations in 1990; crude steel production totaled 874,000 tons in 1994. Libya's other manufacturing industries are small, lightly capitalized, and devoted primarily to the processing of local agricultural products and to textiles, building materials, and basic consumer items.

Banking and Finance

The Central Bank of Libya, established in 1956, supervises the national banking system, regulates credit and interest, and issues bank notes. It also regulates the volume of currency in circulation, acts as a banker to the government, provides clearinghouse facilities for the country's commercial banks, and administers exchange control. Since 5 August 1962, the bank has been vested with a monopoly in the import of fine gold.

Libya formerly had branches of many Arab, Italian, and British commercial banks; they were nationalized in 1969. The government ruled that 51% of the capital of each should be taken over by the government, which paid the value of this share. Thus, the Banco di Roma became Umma Bank, Barclays Bank eventually became Jamahiriya Bank, and the Banco di Sicilia became the Sahara Bank. The commercial department of the Central Bank was merged with two small banks to form the National Commercial Bank. In 1972, a reorganization of the commercial banks left the Jamahiriya and Umma banks owned by the Central Bank of Libya; two other institutions, the Sahara Bank and the Wahda Bank, were jointly owned by the Central Bank and private interests.

The National Agricultural Bank, established in 1957, provides advice and guidance on agricultural problems, advances loans to farm cooperatives, and generally assists the agricultural community. The Industrial and Real Estate Bank, founded in 1965, made loans for building, food-processing, chemical, and traditional industries; later it was divided into the Savings and Real Estate Bank and the Development Bank. A decree in 1966 abolished interest on loans made by the government development banks. In 1972/73, the government created the Libyan Arab Foreign Bank, later renamed Jamahiriya Foreign Bank, owned by the Central Bank of Libya, to invest in foreign countries. In 1981, its role in foreign investment was taken over by the Libyan Arab Foreign Investment Co.

In 1997, in addition to the central bank, there were eight other banks in Libya: the Agricultural Bank, Jamahiriya Bank, Libyan Arab Foreign Bank, National Commercial Bank, Sahara Bank, Savings and Real Estate Investment Bank, Umma Bank, and Wahda Bank. In 1994, Libyan financial assets frozen in the U.S. alone amounted to some $1 billion. Money supply, as measured by M2, totaled LD8,882 million at the end of 1994. Interest rates are fixed by the central bank, which has applied a discount rate of 5% since 1980. The maximum lending rate for secured loans and overdrafts currently stands at 7%.

There are no securities exchanges in Libya.

Economic Development

Under Libya's first five-year development plan (1963–68), several long-run measures were taken to raise industrial production and to expand and improve the quality of agriculture. Of the government's oil revenue, 70% was earmarked for the 1963–68 development plan. Of a total (for the five years) of $473,658,000, 23% was allocated for public works, 17.3% for agriculture, 16.4% for communications, 13.2% for education, 7.4% for public health, 4.1% for industry, and 18.6% for other areas.

The 1972–75 development plan had a total public development budget of LD1,165 million; the budget was subsequently increased to about LD2 billion. Its growth target was a 10.7% annual increase in the GDP. Investment was allocated as follows: industry and mineral resources, 15%; agriculture, 14.2%; communications, 14.1%; housing, 10.7%; petrochemicals, 10.5%; education, 9.3%; and other sectors, 26.2%.

The 1976–80 development plan projected an investment of LD7,500 million, but the actual investment was LD9,250 million, principally in agriculture, 20%; communications, 14%; industry, 13%; and housing, 12%.

The 1981–85 development plan called for investment of LD18.5 billion. It allocated funds principally to industry, 23%; agriculture, 18%; communications, 12%; and electricity, 12%. The average annual growth rate was projected at 9.4%. The drop in oil income caused a contraction in planned projects, however. A third five-year plan, which was due to run from 1986, never materialized.

In 1980, Libyan bilateral aid to developing countries totaled $281.9 million, or 0.92% of GNP. In 1981, however, the total was only $105.4 million, or 0.39% of GNP. In 1981, Libya also contributed $63.8 million to multilateral aid organizations, principally to the Arab agencies and the OPEC Fund. As of 1987, the investments of the Libyan Arab Foreign Investment Co. totaled LD310.2 million, including 30 companies in Arab countries. There are also significant Libyan holdings in African countries.

According to BIS, Libya increased its deposits in foreign banks in 1986, while at the same time reducing its outstanding debt. By 1989 Libya's net creditor position with BIS reporting banks had declined to $2.2 billion, from a high of $6.2 in 1987. However, rising deposits in 1990 reflecting soaring oil revenues because of the Persian Gulf crisis, combined with reduced liabilities, led to a positive net balance of $5.2 billion. Due to the decline in oil export receipts in 1991, this surplus was reduced by 33%, to $3.5 billion.

SOCIAL WELFARE

By law, all employees are entitled to sickness, invalid, disability, death, and maternity benefits, unemployment payments, and pensions. Profit sharing, free medical care and education, and subsidized food are other social welfare benefits.

Women were granted full legal rights in 1969, but few women work outside the home.

Under Libyan law, an individual may be arrested and detained without a specific charge. Political dissenters are imprisoned. Citizens do not have the right to legal counsel or to fair public trials.

Healthcare

In 1993, 100% of Libya's population had access to health care services. Widespread diseases include typhoid, venereal diseases, and infectious hepatitis. With the assistance of the World Health Organization (WHO), Libya has eradicated malaria, once a major problem. The average life expectancy was 68 years.

Housing

Increasing urbanization has created slum conditions in the major cities. There have been slum clearance and building projects since 1954, but the housing deficit has not yet been met. Real estate was the main area of private investment until 1978, when most tenants were made owners of their residences.

EDUCATION

The government has invested heavily in education, which is free at all levels. School is compulsory from the age of 6 until 15. Illiteracy was estimated at 24% in 1995 (males, 12.1% and females, 37%). In 1993, primary schools had 1.4 million pupils. Secondary schools had 310,556 pupils in 1992.

In 1976, the University of Libya at Tripoli was renamed Al-Fatah University, and the University of Libya at Banghazi was renamed the University of Garyounis. The Bright Star University of Technology at Marsa al-Brega was founded in 1981. Total enrollment at all higher level institutions was 72,899 in 1991.

1999 KEY EVENTS TIMELINE

February

- The United Nations says it will allow Libyans to fly from Libya to Saudi Arabia for the annual Muslim pilgrimage to the holy cities of Mecca and Medina. International air travel has been suspended since 1992.

- A Paris court tries six Libyan secret agents in absentia for the September 1989 mid-air bombing of a French UTA flight on its way to Paris from Niger. They are found guilty and sentenced to life in prison.

April

• Two men accused of blowing up a Pan Am flight over Scotland in 1988, killing 270 people, arrive in the Netherlands for trial before a Scottish court. The surrender of both men clears the way for lifting international sanctions against Libya. Trial is scheduled for February 2000. The United States retains its sanctions against Libya.

• Libya resumes international flights, celebrating its first legal flight since 1992 by bringing home about 150 Muslim pilgrims from Saudi Arabia. Egypt, Malta, Tunisia and Jordan announce plans to resume flights to Libya.

May

• Egyptian President Hosni Mubarak flies to Libya to speak with Libyan leader Muammar Gaddafi. He is first head of state to fly to Libya after international sanctions are lifted.

June

• The United States and Libya hold first official talks in 18 years. The United Nations moderates the talks.

July

• Libya pays $31.72 million to compensate the families of victims in the bombing of French airliner that killed 170 people in 1989.

• Britain, Libya agree to resume diplomatic relations after 15 years. Death of London police officer Yvonne Fletcher at a demonstration against Gaddafi. The Libyan government agrees to pay compensation to the family.

August

• The London-based Amnesty International urges Libya to improve its record on human rights violations if it wishes to end international isolation.

• The Clinton administration considers dropping Libya from the U.S. list of alleged state sponsors of terrorism.

• Gaddafi calls for a united Africa. He said the time has come to unite all the countries of Africa into a federation.

September

• Gaddafi rejects charges by international human rights organizations that his government jails cit-izens for political reasons. He claims Libya has no political prisoners.

• British trade mission heads to Libya. The British hope to forge lucrative business deals from renewed political goodwill.

• Gaddafi celebrates 30 years in power. More than two dozen heads of state watch huge military parade. He hosts an extraordinary summit of the Organization of African Unity.

• Libya unveils ''revolutionary'' car. It seats five, and looks like a rocket.

October

• Scottish police send several officers to Libya as part of investigations in the 1988 Lockerbie airliner bombing.

• Three U.S. senators seek assurances that no deals have been made to protect Libyan officials from complicity during the Lockerbie trial.

• Egypt and Libya try to revive Sudanese peace drive. The two countries are trying to arrange a national conference.

December

• Massimo D'Alema, Italy's prime minister, seeks to boost trade links with Libya by becoming the first western leader in seven years to meet with Colonel Muammer Gadaffi in Tripoli.

ANALYSIS OF EVENTS: 1999

BUSINESS AND THE ECONOMY

According to World Bank estimates, economic sanctions cost Libya as much as $18 billion in lost revenue, mostly as a result of underinvestment in oil. A continued high birth rate, and an inefficient state-dominated economy have driven unemployment to about 30 percent. In 1998, and part of 1999, falling world prices for oil cut Libyan revenues by 40 percent. That explains why Gaddafi, who has practiced his own brand of socialist-type economy, said he welcomed foreign investment during a speech at a business symposium in September. More than 60 businessmen from around the world attended the first business meeting of its kind since Gaddafi took power in 1969. The country needs to invest $35 billion between 2001–2005 to average 5 percent growth annually, a Libyan official said. Of that amount, about 60 to 70 percent would come from the government, and the rest from foreign investment. The country needs to invest $6 billion in the hydrocarbons industry, $6 billion for power, and $8 billion for water improvements.

With the suspension of sanctions, several European countries lined up to talk business with Gaddafi. In April, more than 400 industry executives traveled to Geneva to attend a conference on oil and gas investments in Libya. In October, the British sent more than 50 delegates who hope to win contracts in oil, gas, construction and engineering deals. The British were trying to catch up to the Italians, who kept their business contacts during the economic embargo. Also in October, a Libyan official said his country was prepared to purchase 24 Airbus planes valued at $1.5 billion as soon as sanctions were lifted.

GOVERNMENT AND POLITICS

In April, Abdel Basset al-Megrahi and Al-Amin Khalifa arrived in the Netherlands, 11 years after allegedly blowing up a Pan Am flight over Scotland, and killing 270 people. For several years, Libyan leader Moammar Gaddafi refused to turn the two men to British or American authorities, forcing his country to suffer through seven years of debilitating economic sanctions imposed by the United Nations and the United States.

The route to get both men to justice was arduous. Five years ago, Gaddafi appeared ready to allow the two men to go to trial, but the United States and Britain insisted any trial should be held in American or Scottish soil. Unable to get the United Nations Security Council to call for an oil embargo, the U.S. and Britain relented to have the trial in a third country. The two men now will face trial by a panel of Scottish judges in the Netherlands. But opening arguments are not expected until February 2000, to give the defense time to prepare. The trial could last for at least a year.

While Lockerbie victims' families waited for justice, the French found some solace in February, when six Libyan secret agents, including Gaddafi's brother-in-law, were tried for the mid-air bombing of a French UTA airliner over Niger in 1989. The Libyans were found guilty and sentenced to life in prison for the bombing, which killed 170 people. Gaddafi was not expected to turn the men over to French police. Instead, he wired about $31 million to compensate the victims' families, and said sending the money was not an admittance of guilt. But the French said the payment was an acknowledgement of responsibility. So far, Gaddafi has avoided a direct link to the bombing, and France, eager to resume relations, has not tried to place Gaddafi on trial. In August, a French prosecutor recommended against trying to go after Gaddafi, but a French judge demanded the Libyan leader's prosecution, embarrassing the French government. The Americans are trying to avoid the French dilemma.

In October, three U.S. senators sought assurances from Secretary of State Madeleine Albright that no promises had been made to shield Libyan leaders from complicity during the Lockerbie trial. At issue was a letter from United Nations Secretary General Kofi Annan that allegedly included a U.S.-British pledge that the trial was not designed to undermine the Libyan regime. Senators John Kennedy of Massachusetts, and Robert Torricelli and Frank Lautenberg, both from New Jersey, wanted to make clear that no assurances had been made to prevent the pursuit of evidence that could link Gaddafi or other senior Libyan officials to the airliner bombing. The U.N. Security Council, under United States pressure, has not lifted the sanctions against Libya. Sanctions have only been suspended. The United States argued in July that Libya was required to cooperate with the prosecution, and it would be hard to decide if the nation was complying until the trial got under way. Libya continued to press the United Nations to lift sanctions, arguing that to keep them in place would only hurt the credibility of the Security Council.

The British, in the meantime, have softened their stance against Libya. In July, Britain agreed to resume diplomatic relations with the North African country after 15 years. Again, money softened the deal, with Libya agreeing to pay compensation to the family of London police officer Yvonne Fletcher, who was killed outside the Libyan Embassy during a demonstration against Gaddafi. Two months later talks resumed between the two nations, a large British trade mission headed to Libya hoping to strike lucrative business deals from renewed political goodwill.

While Gaddafi maneuvered the best possible deal with the West, he was trying to emerge as a leader in a united Africa. Using the 30th anniversary celebrations of his military coup as a backdrop in September, Gaddafi said it was time for the nations of Africa to unite, citing the success of the European Union. For Gaddafi, it was a big change in rhetoric and direction. For years, he advocated pan-Arabism, seeking to unite the Arab countries of the world into a single federated state. But Gaddafi didn't get the support he expected from his Arab neighbors during the embargo. African countries remained on his side. In 1998, the Organization of African Unity (OAU) did not observe the U.N.'s air embargo. After the embargo was suspended, he changed the name of the national radio station from Voice of the Greater Arab Homeland to the Voice of Africa. In stinging remarks, he declared pan-Arabism ''a mirage.'' To back up the rhetoric, Gaddafi began acting as peacemaker and sought to intervene in peace talks in several African conflicts. A united Africa is not a new dream. As European nations began to leave their African colonies after World War II, many Africans wanted to unite the continent. Gaddafi has found a power vacuum in Africa, and seeks to fill it. In September, during anniversary celebrations, more than two dozen heads of state were in attendance. The huge military parade included soldiers from 20 African nations. Critics said some African leaders have no choice but to show up. Gaddafi has oil money, and the power to help his poorer neighbors. African diplomats said the OAU decided to hold its summit in Libya as a show of respect for Gaddafi and his contributions to the continent. Gaddafi, who has always confounded critics, seems to be doing it again.

CULTURE AND SOCIETY

In its September 20th issue, Sports Illustrated featured a story about Muammar Muhammad Gaddafi, the 27-year-old son of leader Gadaffi. The son is president of the country's Olympic team, and told the magazine he is deeply committed to changing his country's image from one of terrorism to a nation that embraces sports. Gadaffi Jr. said he expects to take a small delegation to the Sydney Summer Olympics in 2000. His country's participation, he said, will be simple and symbolic. Libyan athletes are likely to participate in track and field events and swimming. Libya participated for the first time in the Summer Olympics in 1964. He said sports were neglected in Libya, but that has changed, with corporate sponsorship in the near future.

DIRECTORY

CENTRAL GOVERNMENT

Head of State

Leader of the Revolution, De facto Head of State
Mu'ammar al-Gaddafi, Office of the President

General People's Committee

Secretary of the General People's Congress
Al-Zenati Mohammad al-Zenati, General People's Congress

Assistant Secretary of the General People's Congress
Ali Mursi al-Sha'ri, General People's Congress

Secretary of the General People's Committee
Mohammad Ahmad al-Manqoush, General People's Committee

Secretary of Agriculture
Ali Yousif Juma, Department of Agriculture

Secretary of Animal Wealth
Mas'oud Abul-So'oud, Department of Animal Wealth

Secretary of Communications and Transport
Izz al-Deen al-Hinsheeri, Department of Communications and Transport

Secretary of Culture
Jum'a al-Fazzani, Department of Culture

Secretary of Economy and Trade
Abd al-Hafeedh al-Zleetni, Department of Economy and Trade

Secretary of Education and Vocational Training
Ma'touq Mohammad Ma'touq, Department of Education and Vocational Training

Secretary of Energy
Abdallah Salim al-Badri, Department of Energy

Secretary of Finance
Mohammad Bayt al-Mal, Department of Finance

Secretary of Health and Social Security
Ehtaywish Faraj Ehtaywish, Department of Health and Social Security

Secretary of Housing and Utilities
Embarak el-Shamikh, Department of Housing and Utilities

Secretary of Industry and Mines
Muftah Ezouzah, Department of Industry and Mines

Secretary of Information, Culture, and Mass Mobilization
Fawziyah Shalabi, Department of Information, Culture, and Mass Mobilization

Secretary of Justice and Public Security
Mohammad Bel-Qasim al-Zuwayy, Department of Justice and Public Security

Secretary of Marine Resources
Basheer Ramadan Abu-Jinah, Department of Marine Resources

Secretary of People's Control and Follow-up
Mahmoud Badi, Department of People's Control and Follow-up

Secretary of People's External Liaison and International Cooperation Bureau
Omar Mustafa al-Muntassir, Department of People's External Liaison and International Cooperation Bureau

Secretary of Planning
Jadallah 'Azzouz al-Talhi, Department of Planning

Secretary of Tourism
Al-Bokhari Salem Hauda, Department of Tourism

Secretary of Youth and Sport
Mohammad Mahmoud al-Hijazi, Department of Youth and Sport

Governor of the Central Bank
Tahir al-Jehaimi, Department of the Central Bank

POLITICAL ORGANIZATIONS

Attajamoa al-Watani al-Leebi (Libyan National Group)

Al-Haraka al-Wataniya ad-Dimokratia al-Leebiya (Libyan Democratic National Movement)

At-Tajamoa al-Watani ad-Dimokrati al-Leebi (Libyan Democratic National Group)

Al-Haraka al-Wataniya al-Leebiya (Libyan National Movement)

Aj-Jamaa al-Islamiya "Libya" (Islamic Group Libya)

Al-Haraka al-Islamiya "Libya" (Islamic Movement Libya)

Aj-Jabha al-Leebiya al-Wataniya ad-Dimokratiya (Democratic National Libyan Front)

Aj-Jabha al-Wataniya Li-Inqad Libya (National Front For The Salvation Of Libya)

Jaish al-Inqad al-Watani al-Leebi (Libyan National Salvation Army)

Harakat al-Kifah al-Watani al-Leebi (Libyan National Struggle Movement)

Monathamat Jaish al-Inqad al-Watani al-Leebi (Libyan National Salvation Army Organization)

Al-Haraka al-Leebiya Lil-Taghyieer Wal-Islah (Libyan Movement For Change)

Monathamat Tahreer Libya (Organization For Free Libya)

Attantheem Alwatani Alleebi (Libyan National Group)

Al-Haiaa al-Libiya Lil-Kalas al-Watani (Libyan Authority For National Salvation)

Monathamat al-Burkan al-Leebi (Libyan Volcano Group)

Al-Ittihad ad-Dostouri al-Leebi (Libyan Constitutional Union)

Hizb at-Tahreer (Freedom Party)

Jabhat al-Wataniyeen al-Libi-Yeen (National Libyans Front)

Harakat al-Nidal Ash-Shaabi al-Leebi (Libyan People's Struggle Movement)

Al-Hizb ad-Dimokrati al-Leebi (Libyan Democratic Party)

Hizb al-Umma (Nation's Party)

Attahalof al-Watani al-Leebi (Libyan National Union)

Al-Motamar ad-Dimokrati al-Leebi (Libyan Democratic Conference)

Hai-At at-Tanseeq ad-Dimokratiya al-Leebiya (Libyan Democratic Authority)

Aj-Jamaa al-Islamiya al-Mokatila (Fighting Islamic Group)

Hizb al-Mohafi-Deen al-Leebi (Libyan Conservatives Party)

DIPLOMATIC REPRESENTATION

Embassies in Libya

Brazil

Shara Ben Ashur, PO Box 2270, Tripoli, Libya
PHONE: +218 (21) 3607747
FAX: +218 (21) 607970
E-MAIL: 100125.52@compuserve.com
TITLE: Trade Attache
NAME: Jose Marcos Viana

British Interests Section, c/o Italian Embassy

Sharia Uahran 1, PO Box 4206, Tripoli, Libya
PHONE: +218 (21) 3331191
FAX: +218 (21) 4445753

India

16/18 Shara Mahmoud Shaltout, Garden City,
PO Box 3150, Tripoli, Libya
PHONE: +218 (21) 41835
FAX: +218 (21) 37560

Italy

Shara Uaharan, 1, Tripoli, Libya
PHONE: +218 (21) 3334131
FAX: +218 (21) 3331673

Japan

Organization of African Unity Road, Dhat al-
Imad, Tower No.4, Halls No.13 and 14, PO Box
3265, Tripoli, Libya
PHONE: +218 (21) 3350056; 3350057
FAX: +218 (21) 3350055

Nigeria

PO Box 4417, Tripoli, Libya
PHONE: +218 (21) 43036

Russia

10 Mustafa Kamel Street, Tripoli, Libya
PHONE: +218 (21) 30545; 30546
FAX: +218 (21) 21821

JUDICIAL SYSTEM

Supreme Court

FURTHER READING

Articles

"British Trade Mission Heads for Libya."
Reuters, 22 September 1999.

"Change of Tone and Maybe More in Gaddafi's
Libya." Reuters, 9 September 1999.

"Gaddafi Revives 1960s African Unity Dream."
Reuters, 5 September 1999.

"Libya and the Bombed Airliners." *The
Economist* (March 13, 1999): 55.

"Libya and Lockerbie: Deadlock Broken." *The
Economist* (April 10, 1999): 44.

"Libya: Muddling On." *The Economist*
(September 4, 1999): 47.

"Libya Sets Up Shop Again." *Petroleum
Economist* (June 1999): 10.

"Qaddafi Says Farewell, Arabia, and Sets his
Sights on Africa." *The Economist* (April 24,
1999): 43.

"Gaddafi Says War Over, Calls for United
States of Africa." Reuters, 26 August 1999.

"Scots Police in Libya to Investigate
Lockerbie." Reuters, 19 October 1999.

"Senators ask Albright for UN letter on
Lockerbie." Reuters, 19 October 1999.

"U.S. Congress Report says Libya may Exit
Blacklist." Reuters, 17 August 1999.

Books

*Developments Concerning the National
Emergency with Libya.* Washington, D.C.:
U.S. Government Printing Office, 1998.

St. John, Ronald Bruce. *Historical Dictionary of
Libya.* 3rd ed. Lanham, Md.: Scarecrow Press,
1998.

LIBYA: STATISTICAL DATA

For sources and notes see "Sources of Statistics" in the front of each volume.

GEOGRAPHY

Geography (1)

Area:

Total: 1,759,540 sq km.

Land: 1,759,540 sq km.

Water: 0 sq km.

Area—comparative: slightly larger than Alaska.

Land boundaries:

Total: 4,383 km.

Border countries: Algeria 982 km, Chad 1,055 km, Egypt 1,150 km, Niger 354 km, Sudan 383 km, Tunisia 459 km.

Coastline: 1,770 km.

Climate: Mediterranean along coast; dry, extreme desert interior.

Terrain: mostly barren, flat to undulating plains, plateaus, depressions.

Natural resources: petroleum, natural gas, gypsum.

Land use:

Arable land: 1%

Permanent crops: 0%

Permanent pastures: 8%

Forests and woodland: 0%

Other: 91% (1993 est.).

HUMAN FACTORS

Demographics (2A)

	1990	1995	1998	2000	2010	2020	2030	2040	2050
Population	4,139.7	4,654.5	4,874.7	5,114.0	6,431.4	7,717.7	8,839.3	9,858.9	10,704.4
Net migration rate (per 1,000 population)	NA	NA	NA	NA	NA	NA	NA	NA	NA
Births	NA	NA	NA	NA	NA	NA	NA	NA	NA
Deaths	NA	NA	NA	NA	NA	NA	NA	NA	NA
Life expectancy - males	70.6	72.6	73.5	74.1	76.4	78.0	79.0	79.7	80.2
Life expectancy - females	74.5	76.6	77.4	78.1	80.5	82.3	83.7	84.6	85.3
Birth rate (per 1,000)	31.4	26.2	27.3	27.3	24.2	19.0	16.0	15.1	13.7
Death rate (per 1,000)	4.2	3.5	3.4	3.3	3.2	3.4	4.1	5.3	7.1
Women of reproductive age (15-49 yrs.)	903.7	1,114.6	1,234.9	1,325.7	1,738.7	2,040.2	2,270.2	2,384.4	2,474.0
of which are currently married	NA	NA	NA	NA	NA	NA	NA	NA	NA
Fertility rate	5.0	4.1	3.9	3.7	3.0	2.5	2.2	2.1	2.0

Except as noted, values for vital statistics are in thousands; life expectancy is in years.

Health Personnel (3)

Total health expenditure as a percentage of GDP, 1990-1997[a]

Public sector . . . . .NA

Private sector . . . . .NA

Total[b] . . . . .NA

Health expenditure per capita in U.S. dollars, 1990-1997[a]

Purchasing power parity .NA

Total . . . . .NA

Availability of health care facilities per 100,000 people

Hospital beds 1990-1997[a] 420

Doctors 1993[c] 137

Nurses 1993[c] 366

Health Indicators (4)

Life expectancy at birth

1980 60

1997 70

Daily per capita supply of calories (1996) 3,132

Total fertility rate births per woman (1997) 3.8

Maternal mortality ratio per 100,000 live births (1990-97) . . . . .220[c]

Safe water % of population with access (1995) 95

Sanitation % of population with access (1995) 86

Consumption of iodized salt % of households (1992-98)[a] 90

Smoking prevalence

Male % of adults (1985-95)[a] . . . .

Female % of adults (1985-95)[a] . . . .

Tuberculosis incidence per 100,000 people (1997) 19

Adult HIV prevalence % of population ages 15-49 (1997) 0.05

Infants and Malnutrition (5)

Under-5 mortality rate (1997) 25

% of infants with low birthweight (1990-97) 7

Births attended by skilled health staff % of total[a] . . .94

% fully immunized (1995-97)

TB 99

DPT 96

Polio 96

Measles 92

Prevalence of child malnutrition under age 5 (1992-97)[b] . . . . .NA

Ethnic Division (6)

Berber and Arab 97%; Greeks, Maltese, Italians, Egyptians, Pakistanis, Turks, Indians, Tunisians.

Religions (7)

Sunni Muslim 97%

Languages (8)

Arabic, Italian, English, all are widely understood in the major cities.

EDUCATION

Public Education Expenditures (9)

Public expenditure on education (% of GNP)

1980 . . . . .3.4

1996 . . . .

Expenditure per student

Primary % of GNP per capita

1980 . . . .

1996 . . . .

Secondary % of GNP per capita

1980 . . . .

1996 . . . .

Tertiary % of GNP per capita

1980 . . . . .58.2

1996 . . . .

Expenditure on teaching materials

Primary % of total for level (1996) . . . .

Secondary % of total for level (1996) . . . .

Primary pupil-teacher ratio per teacher (1996) . . . .

Duration of primary education years (1995) 9

Educational Attainment (10)

Age group (1984)[4] . . . . .25+

Total population 996,774

Highest level attained (%)

No schooling 59.7

First level

Not completed 15.4

Completed 8.5

Entered second level

S-1 . . . . .5.2

S-2 . . . . .8.5

Postsecondary 2.7

Literacy Rates (11A)

In thousands and percent[1]	1990	1995	2000	2010
Illiterate population (15+ yrs.)	741	702	649	514
Literacy rate - total adult pop. (%)	69.9	76.2	81.6	89.8
Literacy rate - males (%)	83.9	87.9	91.2	96.0
Literacy rate - females (%)	53.6	63.0	71.0	83.1

GOVERNMENT & LAW

Political Parties (12)

The legislative branch is a unicameral General People's Congress. Members are elected indirectly through a hierarchy of peoples' committees. There are no political parties.

Government Budget (13B)

Revenues . . . .$10.4 billion
Expenditures . . . .$10.3 billion
   Capital expenditures . . . .$2.5 billion

Data for 1995 est.

Military Affairs (14B)

	1990	1991	1992	1993	1994	1995
Military expenditures						
Current dollars (mil.)[3]	NA	2,092	1,999	1,410	1,297	1,999
1995 constant dollars (mil.)[3]	NA	2,311	2,150	1,478	1,330	1,999
Armed forces (000)	86	86	85	85	80	76
Gross national product (GNP)						
Current dollars (mil.)	24,620	28,210	29,000	27,420	30,500	33,220
1995 constant dollars (mil.)	28,300	31,170	31,190	28,750	31,260	33,220
Central government expenditures (CGE)						
1995 constant dollars (mil.)	NA	NA	NA	NA	NA	NA
People (mil.)	4.4	4.5	4.7	4.9	5.1	5.2
Military expenditure as % of GNP	NA	7.4	6.9	5.1	4.3	6.0
Military expenditure as % of CGE	NA	NA	NA	NA	NA	NA
Military expenditure per capita (1995 $)	NA	511	458	303	263	381
Armed forces per 1,000 people (soldiers)	19.7	19.0	18.1	17.4	15.8	14.5
GNP per capita (1995 $)	6,498	6,894	6,644	5,900	6,182	6,329
Arms imports[6]						
Current dollars (mil.)	370	410	80	0	10	0
1995 constant dollars (mil.)	425	453	86	0	10	0
Arms exports[6]						
Current dollars (mil.)	20	20	10	0	0	0
1995 constant dollars (mil.)	69	22	11	0	0	0
Total imports[7]						
Current dollars (mil.)	5,336	5,361	5,161	5,376	4,204	4,903
1995 constant dollars (mil.)	6,133	5,924	5,551	5,636	4,310	4,903
Total exports[7]						
Current dollars (mil.)	13,220	11,230	9,948e	8,047e	7,200e	NA
1995 constant dollars (mil.)	15,200	12,410	10,700e	8,436e	7,381e	NA
Arms as percent of total imports[8]	6.9	7.6	1.6	0	.2	0
Arms as percent of total exports[8]	.5	.2	.1	0	0	NA

LABOR FORCE

Labor Force (16)

Total (million) 1.0
Industry 31%
Services 27%
Government 24%
Agriculture 18%

3% of the population in the 15-64 age group is non-national (July 1998 est.)

Unemployment Rate (17)

25% (1997 est.)

PRODUCTION SECTOR

Electric Energy (18)

Capacity . . . . .4.6 million kW (1995)
Production . . . . .17 billion kWh (1995)
Consumption per capita . . . . .3,239 kWh (1995)

Transportation (19)

Highways:

total: 83,200 km

paved: 47,590 km

unpaved: 35,610 km (1996 est.)

Waterways: none

Pipelines: crude oil 4,383 km; petroleum products 443 km (includes liquefied petroleum gas or LPG 256 km); natural gas 1,947 km

Merchant marine:

total: 30 ships (1,000 GRT or over) totaling 615,505 GRT/1,044,175 DWT ships by type: cargo 9, chemical tanker 1, liquefied gas tanker 3, oil tanker 9, roll-on/roll-off cargo 4, short-sea passenger 4 (1997 est.)

Airports: 145 (1997 est.)

Airports—with paved runways:

total: 60

over 3,047 m: 24

2,438 to 3,047 m: 5

1,524 to 2,437 m: 23

914 to 1,523 m: 5

under 914 m: 3 (1997 est.)

Airports—with unpaved runways:

total: 85

over 3,047 m: 5

2,438 to 3,047 m: 2

1,524 to 2,437 m: 15

914 to 1,523 m: 43

under 914 m: 20 (1997 est.)

Top Agricultural Products (20)

Wheat, barley, olives, dates, citrus, vegetables, peanuts; meat, eggs.

MANUFACTURING SECTOR

GDP & Manufacturing Summary (21)

Detailed value added figures are listed by both International Standard Industry Code (ISIC) and product title.

	1980	1985	1990	1994
GDP ($-1990 mil.)[1]	29,196	24,333	26,078	26,524
Per capita ($-1990)[1]	9,594	6,427	5,738	5,076
Manufacturing share (%) (current prices)[1]	1.9	4.5	8.4	NA
Manufacturing				
Value added ($-1990 mil.)[1]	855	1,662	2,185	3,003
Industrial production index	100	136	177	244
Value added ($ mil.)	358	540	724	784
Gross output ($ mil.)	1,177	1,727	2,392	2,530
Employment (000)	18	23	27	32
Profitability (% of gross output)				
Intermediate input (%)	70	69	70	69
Wages and salaries inc. supplements (%)	13	12	12	12
Gross operating surplus	17	19	19	19
Productivity ($)				
Gross output per worker	64,186	76,077	87,224	77,559
Value added per worker	19,577	24,663	28,543	26,395
Average wage (incl. supplements)	8,327	9,580	10,337	9,369
Value added ($ mil.)				
311/2 Food products	35	37	40	36
313 Beverages	17	18	20	18

GDP & Manufacturing Summary (21)

	1980	1985	1990	1994
314 Tobacco products	55	73	79	77
321 Textiles	14	22	27	30
322 Wearing apparel	5	5	6	5
323 Leather and fur products	7	15	21	27
324 Footwear	14	25	34	42
331 Wood and wood products	3	5	6	7
332 Furniture and fixtures	2	2	2	2
341 Paper and paper products	3	3	3	3
342 Printing and publishing	—	8	9	8
351 Industrial chemicals	35	41	52	54
352 Other chemical products	21	34	43	48
353 Petroleum refineries	81	124	200	204
354 Miscellaneous petroleum and coal products	—	—	—	—
355 Rubber products	—	—	1	—
356 Plastic products	2	4	5	7
361 Pottery, china and earthenware	1	2	2	2
362 Glass and glass products	—	—	—	—
369 Other non-metal mineral products	51	99	142	177
371 Iron and steel	—	—	—	—
372 Non-ferrous metals	—	—	—	—
381 Metal products	3	5	5	4
382 Non-electrical machinery	—	—	—	—
383 Electrical machinery	—	—	—	—
384 Transport equipment	—	—	—	—
385 Professional and scientific equipment	—	—	—	—
390 Other manufacturing industries	9	18	25	32

FINANCE, ECONOMICS, & TRADE

Economic Indicators (22)

National product: GDP—purchasing power parity—$38 billion (1997 est.)

National product real growth rate: 0.5% (1997 est.)

National product per capita: $6,700 (1997 est.)

Inflation rate—consumer price index: 30% (1997 est.)

Exchange Rates (24)

Exchange rates:

Libyan dinars (LD) per US$1

January 1998	0.3902
1997	0.3891
1996	0.3651
1995	0.3532
1994	0.3596
1993	0.3250

Balance of Payments (23)

	1980	1985	1990
Exports of goods (f.o.b.)	21,919	10,353	11,352
Imports of goods (f.o.b.)	−10,368	−5,754	−7,575
Trade balance	15,551	4,599	3,777
Services - debits	−3,650	−2,315	−1,878
Services - credits	1,446	526	783
Private transfers (net)	−46	−45	−35
Government transfers (net)	−1,089	−859	−446
Overall balance	8,213	1,906	2,202

Top Import Origins (25)

$6.2 billion (f.o.b., 1995)

Origins	%
Italy	NA
Germany	NA
United Kingdom	NA
France	NA
Spain	NA
Turkey	NA
Tunisia	NA
Eastern Europe	NA

NA stands for not available.

Top Export Destinations (26)

$9 billion (f.o.b., 1995).

Destinations	%
Italy	NA
Germany	NA
Spain	NA
France	NA
Turkey	NA
Greece	NA
Egypt	NA

NA stands for not available.

Economic Aid (27)

$NA. NA stands for not available.

Import Export Commodities (28)

Import Commodities	Export Commodities
Machinery	Crude oil
Transport equipment	Refined petroleum products
Food	Natural gas
Manufactured goods	

LIECHTENSTEIN

Principality of Liechtenstein
Fürstentum Liechtenstein

Principality of Liechtenstein
Fürstentum Liechtenstein

CAPITAL: Vaduz.

FLAG: The national flag is divided into two horizontal rectangles, blue above red. On the blue rectangle, near the hoist, is the princely crown in gold.

ANTHEM: *Oben am jungen Rhein (On the Banks of the Young Rhine)*.

MONETARY UNIT: The Swiss franc (SwFr) of 100 centimes, or rappen, has been in use since February 1921. There are coins of 1, 5, 10, 20, and 50 centimes and 1, 2, and 5 francs, and notes of 10, 20, 50, 100, 500, and 1,000 francs. SwFr1 = $0.7092 (or $1 = SwFr1.41).

WEIGHTS AND MEASURES: The metric system is the legal standard.

HOLIDAYS: New Year's Day, 1 January; Epiphany, 6 January; Candlemas, 2 February; St. Joseph's Day, 19 March; Labor Day, 1 May; Assumption, 15 August; Nativity of Our Lady, 8 September; All Saints' Day, 1 November; Immaculate Conception, 8 December; Christmas, 25 December; St. Stephen's Day, 26 December. Movable religious holidays include Good Friday, Easter Monday, Ascension, Whitmonday, and Corpus Christi.

TIME: 1 PM = noon GMT.

LOCATION AND SIZE: Liechtenstein is a landlocked country in the Rhine (Rhein) River Valley. The fourth-smallest country in Europe, the principality has an area of 160 square kilometers (61.8 square miles), about 0.9 times the size of Washington, D.C. Liechtenstein's capital city, Vaduz, is located in the western part of the country.

CLIMATE: The annual lowland temperature varies between −4.5°C (24°F) in January and 19.9°C (68°F) in July. Late frost and prolonged dry periods are rare. Average annual precipitation is 105 centimeters (41 inches).

INTRODUCTORY SURVEY

RECENT HISTORY

From 1852 to the end of World War I (1914–18), Liechtenstein was closely tied economically to Austria. After Austria's defeat in the war, Liechtenstein sought closer ties with its other neighbor, Switzerland. A treaty concluded in 1923 provided for a customs union and the use of Swiss currency.

Liechtenstein (like Switzerland) remained neutral in World War II, as it had in World War I. The postwar decades have been marked by political stability and outstanding economic growth. On 26 August 1984, Franz Josef II, who succeeded his granduncle, Franz I, in 1938, handed over executive authority to his eldest son and heir, Crown Prince Hans Adam.

Liechtenstein has sought further integration into the world community. The country was admitted to the United Nations in September 1991. In 1995 Liechtenstein became a member of the European Economic Area (an organization associated with the European Union).

GOVERNMENT

Liechtenstein is a constitutional monarchy ruled by the hereditary princes of the house of Liechtenstein. The constitution provides for a single-chamber parliament (Landtag) of 25 members elected for four years. The prince appoints the prime minister on the recommendation of parliament. Liechtenstein is divided into 11 communes (Gemeinden) for administrative purposes.

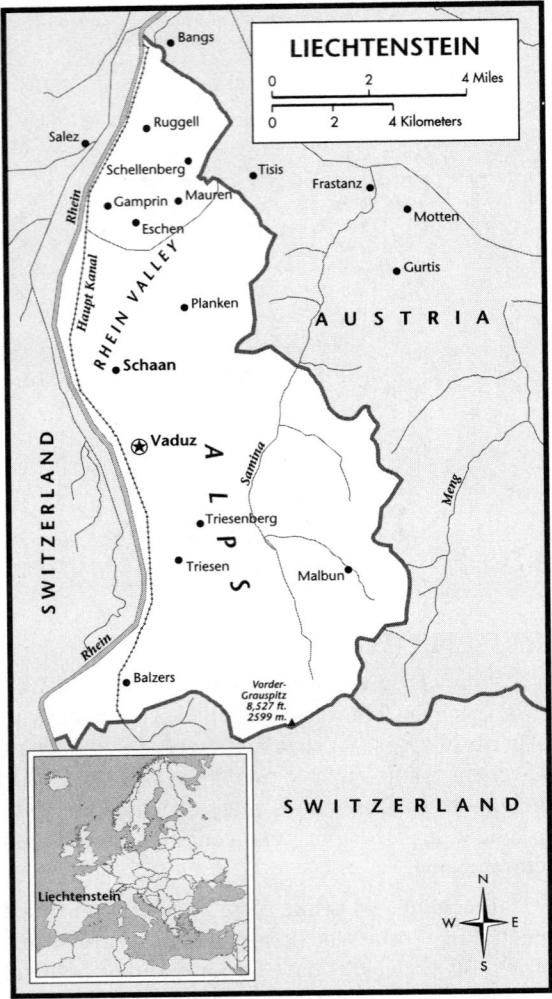

LIECHTENSTEIN

0   2   4 Miles

0   2   4 Kilometers

Judiciary

Courts that function under sole Liechtenstein jurisdiction are the County Court (Landgericht), which decides minor civil cases and criminal offenses; the juvenile court; and the Schöffengericht, a court for misdemeanors.

Political Parties

The two principal parties are the Fatherland Union (Vaterländische Union—VU) and the Progressive Citizens' Party (Fortschrittliche Bürgerpartei—FBP).

DEFENSE

Since 1868, no military forces have been maintained in Liechtenstein.

ECONOMIC AFFAIRS

Despite its small size and limited national resources, Liechtenstein has developed since the 1940s from a mainly agricultural to an industrialized country and a prosperous center of trade and tourism.

Public Finance

The U.S. Central Intelligence Agency estimates that, in 1995, government revenues totaled approximately $455 million and expenditures $442 million.

Income

In 1997, Liechtenstein's gross domestic product (GDP) was $713 million in current U.S. dollars, or $23,000 per person.

Industry

The industry of Liechtenstein, limited by shortages of raw materials, is primarily devoted to small-scale production of precision items. The output includes optical lenses, high-vacuum pumps, heating equipment, electron microscopes, and electronic measuring and control devices.

Banking and Finance

Although there is a national bank, the duties of the central bank are performed by the Swiss National Bank, a consequence of the currency union with Switzerland. Liechtenstein's banks form an important part of the economy, and they have experienced significant growth in the 1990s. As of 1994, the banking sector employs an estimated 4% of the work force.

The National Bank of Liechtenstein (Liechtensteinische Landesbank), founded in 1861, is the state bank of issue; in addition, it deals in real estate mortgages and ordinary banking operations. Liechtenstein Global Trust (LGT), the country's biggest financial institution (owned by the royal family), and the Private Trust Bank Corp., founded in 1956, play an important role in the finance and credit spheres of Liechtenstein's economy. Banking is linked with the Swiss banking system, as is securities trading. In 1945, Liechtenstein's banks had a combined balance sheet of SwFr38 million; at the end of 1996, it was SwFr27.4 billion. Net income from Liechtenstein's banks totaled SwFr232.5 million in 1996, and contributed over 12% to the country's national income in terms of taxes and dividends paid.

Because of Liechtenstein's strict bank secrecy, several thousand foreign businesses are nominally headquartered there. The secrecy laws are, however, waived in the case of criminal intent. There are at present no restrictions on foreign investors' access to financing in Liechtenstein. New laws to combat insider trading and money laundering have recently tightened fiduciary regulations.

Economic Development

The government generally encourages the increasing diversification of industry and the development of tourism. The principality's low taxes and highly secret banking system are attractive to foreign corporations wanting to safeguard patents and trademarks and to individuals who want to protect their wealth for the future. Thousands of corporations have established nominal headquarters in Liechtenstein.

SOCIAL WELFARE

Accident, old age, and survivors' insurance are compulsory, as are unemployment and health insurance. Family allowances have been granted since 1958. A 1992 constitutional amendment guarantees women equality under the law.

Healthcare

Average life expectancy is about 79 years. In 1992, Liechtenstein had an estimated 2.5 physicians per 1,000 population. Regular examinations are provided for children up to the age of 10.

Housing

Liechtenstein does not have a significant housing problem.

EDUCATION

In 1990–91, there were 120 teachers and 1,985 students in the primary schools or about 1 teacher for every 16 students. That same year, there were 112 secondary school teachers, with 1,190 students enrolled. While there are no universities in Liechtenstein, many students continue their studies at universities in Switzerland, Austria, and Germany.

1999 KEY EVENTS TIMELINE

June

- *EuroBusiness* magazine reports that Liechtenstein has world's wealthiest royal family.

July

- Population is officially estimated at 32,057.

September

- Prince Hans-Adam II threatens to move to Austria if parliament reduces his powers.

October

- European Court censures Prince Hans-Adam II for removal of local judge who wanted to curb his powers.

- Government approves financial aid package of 226,000 Swiss francs for Kosovo and other areas of Eastern Europe.

December

- Switzerland has joined in investigations of money laundering in Liechtenstein. An anonymous letter, sent to the Liechtenstein parliament in 1997, alleges that political and business people in Liechtenstein have ties to organized crime.

- Prince Maximilian, the second son of the ruling family of Liechtenstein, becomes engaged to Angela Brown, a fashion designer from Panama, and announces plans to marry in New York in January 2000.

ANALYSIS OF EVENTS: 1999

BUSINESS AND THE ECONOMY

In 1999 the tiny principality of Liechtenstein ranked as one of the world's most prosperous countries, with a per capita GNP on a par with that of Switzerland, a country with which it had strong economic ties: the two nations maintained a customs union, and Liechtenstein used the Swiss franc as its national currency. Liechtenstein had a highly developed industrial sector, and its people enjoyed low unemployment and a high standard of living comparable to those of the major urban areas in Western Europe. Leading industries included machinery, metal, and precision instruments.

The country's financial services sector—which employed roughly half the work force—was also thriving, thanks to low levels of corporate taxation, liberal regulations for incorporation, and a tradition of bank secrecy. It was estimated that between 75,000 and 80,000 foreign corporations, holding companies, and foundations were head-quartered in the principality and accounted for nearly one-third of the government's revenues through an annual tax levied on their capital or net worth. New insurance legislation passed in 1996 had also fueled strong growth in the insurance sector in the late 1990s. A significant traditional source of income was the sale of the principality's limited-edition postage stamps, famed for their beautiful design and sold largely to tourists.

According to 1999 forecasts, the government expected to meet its economic planning objectives over the next five years in spite of significant expenditures on structural engineering projects that would reduce its reserves by 29 million Swiss francs, as well as the anticipated costs of new health insurance legislation and rent subsidies in 2000 and a tax cut in 2001.

GOVERNMENT AND POLITICS

The principality of Liechtenstein, a hereditary constitutional monarchy, was governed by Prince Hans-Adam II, who had been the reigning monarch since 1989. The ruling Vaterländische Union (VU) party held 13 seats in the 25-member Landtag (parliament), the Fortschrittliche Bürgerpartei in Liechtenstein (FBPL) held 10, and the Freie Liste (FL) held 2. VU leader Mario Frick remained Head of Government, a post he had held since 1993. The next legislative elections were scheduled for 2001.

Disagreements between Prince Hans-Adam and parliament, whose relationship had been strained in the past, were in the spotlight in the latter part of 1999. In September, the prince's assertion that he had the right to dissolve the government at his discretion raised tensions to the point where Hans-Adam threatened to go into exile in Austria. October brought a ruling by the European Court of Human Rights on a complaint filed by Dr. Herbert Wille, a senior judge whom the prince had refused to re-appoint because of Wille's assertion that the country's Supreme Court rather than its monarch should be the ultimate authority on constitutional issues. The court ruled that in depriving Wille of his judicial position because of his political views, the prince had violated the judge's freedom of speech. Wille was awarded 10,000 Swiss francs in compensation as well as payment of his legal costs.

The government of Liechtenstein approved the allocation of 226,000 Swiss francs for various foreign aid projects in Eastern Europe, including a joint UNESCO and Council of Europe program to provide social and psychological support to children and their families returning to Kosovo in the aftermath of the fighting and destruction in that region. Other projects were slated for Macedonia, Albania, Bulgaria, and Romania.

CULTURE AND SOCIETY

The population of Liechtenstein—estimated at 32,057 in July—enjoyed one of the world's highest living standards while continuing to pay very low taxes. However, more than one-third were resident foreigners from neighboring countries, who made up a significant portion of Liechtenstein's labor force. Laws governing citizenship in the principality remained highly restrictive, requiring approval by the applicant's local government, parliament, and even the monarch himself.

Liechtenstein garnered international attention in June, when EuroBusiness magazine ranked its royal family as the wealthiest in Europe. With its total wealth estimated at the equivalent of 3.3 billion British pounds, the prince's family came in ahead of Luxembourg's reigning dynasty (3 billion pounds) and Britain's house of Windsor (2.7 billion pounds). Prince Hans-Adam personally was ranked as Europe's third-wealthiest monarch, with a reported worth of 540 million pounds (first and second place were occupied by Queen Beatrix of the Netherlands and Grand Duke Jean of Luxembourg).

Financial support by the royal family and other wealthy patrons helped Liechtenstein maintain a thriving cultural life. The outstanding art collection of its royal family, which was begun in the seventeenth century and included some of the greatest masterpieces by Rubens, was the principality's major tourist attraction. Many of its paintings have been reproduced on Liechtenstein's sought-after stamps.

DIRECTORY

CENTRAL GOVERNMENT

Head of State

Prince
Hans-Adam II, Schloss, FL-9490 Vaduz, Liechtenstein

Head of Government
Mario Frick, Office of the Head of Government, Regierungsgebaeude, FL-9490 Vaduz, Liechtenstein

Ministers

Deputy Head of Government
Michael Ritter, Office of the Deputy Head of Government

Member of the Government in Charge of Foreign Affairs, Family and Equal Rights, Culture and Sports
Andrea Willi, Office of Foreign Affairs, Family and Equal Rights, Culture and Sports

Member of the Government in Charge of Justice
Heinz Frommelt, Office of Justice

POLITICAL ORGANIZATIONS

Vaterlandische Union-VU (Fatherland Union)
NAME: Oswald Krantz

Fortschrittliche Burgerpartei-FBP (Progressive Citizens' Party)
Aeulestrasse 56, FL-9490 Vaduz, Liechtenstein
PHONE: +41 (423) 2377940
FAX: +41 (423) 2377949
TITLE: Party Secretary
NAME: Norbert Seeger

Freie Liste-FL (The Free List)
Im Bretscha 4, Postfach 177, 9494 Schaan, Liechtenstein
PHONE: +41 (423) 2377940
FAX: +41 (423) 2377949
E-MAIL: FListe@lie-net.li
TITLE: Party Secretary
NAME: Norbert Seeger

JUDICIAL SYSTEM
Oberster Gerichtshof (Supreme Court)
Obergericht (Superior Court)

FURTHER READING
Articles
"Liechtenstein: Princely Threat." *The New York Times,* 30 September 1999, p. A6.

Books
Duursma, Jorri. *Self-Determination, Statehood, and International Relations of Micro-states: The Cases of Liechtenstein, San Marino, Monaco, Andorra, and the Vatican City.* New York: Cambridge University Press, 1996.

Meier, Regula A. *Liechtenstein.* Oxford, England: Clio Press, 1993.

Internet
Liechtensteiner Vaterland. Available Online @ www.news.li/news/index.htm (December 8, 1999).

The World Factbook 1998. Available Online @ www.odci.gov/cia/publications/factbooks/ls.html (December 8, 1999).

LIECHTENSTEIN: STATISTICAL DATA

For sources and notes see "Sources of Statistics" in the front of each volume.

GEOGRAPHY

Geography (1)

Area:

Total: 160 sq km.

Land: 160 sq km.

Water: 0 sq km.

Area—comparative: about 0.9 times the size of Washington, DC.

Land boundaries:

Total: 76 km.

Border countries: Austria 35 km, Switzerland 41 km.

Coastline: 0 km (landlocked).

Climate: continental; cold, cloudy winters with frequent snow or rain; cool to moderately warm, cloudy, humid summers.

Terrain: mostly mountainous (Alps) with Rhine Valley in western third.

Natural resources: hydroelectric potential.

Land use:

Arable land: 24%

Permanent crops: 0%

Permanent pastures: 16%

Forests and woodland: 35%

Other: 25% (1993 est.).

HUMAN FACTORS

Demographics (2A)

	1990	1995	1998	2000	2010	2020	2030	2040	2050
Population	NA	30.8	31.7	32.4	35.1	36.2	35.5	33.5	30.7
Net migration rate (per 1,000 population)	NA	NA	NA	NA	NA	NA	NA	NA	NA
Births	NA	NA	NA	NA	NA	NA	NA	NA	NA
Deaths	NA	NA	NA	NA	NA	NA	NA	NA	NA
Life expectancy - males	NA	75.1	75.5	75.8	76.9	77.8	78.6	79.2	79.8
Life expectancy - females	NA	80.0	80.5	80.8	82.3	83.4	84.4	85.1	85.7
Birth rate (per 1,000)	NA	13.8	12.6	11.9	9.7	9.0	7.9	6.9	6.3
Death rate (per 1,000)	NA	7.3	7.3	7.4	8.2	9.5	11.9	14.2	16.3
Women of reproductive age (15-49 yrs.)	NA	8.6	8.6	8.6	8.6	7.9	7.2	6.5	5.7
of which are currently married	NA	NA	NA	NA	NA	NA	NA	NA	NA
Fertility rate	NA	1.6	1.6	1.6	1.5	1.5	1.4	1.3	1.3

Except as noted, values for vital statistics are in thousands; life expectancy is in years.

Infants and Malnutrition (5)

Under-5 mortality rate (1997) 7

% of infants with low birthweight (1990-97) . . . . . .NA

Births attended by skilled health staff % of total[a] . . .NA

% fully immunized (1995-97)

TB . . . . .NA

DPT . . . . .NA

Polio . . . . .NA

Measles . . . . .NA

Prevalence of child malnutrition under age 5
(1992-97)[b] . . . . .NA

Ethnic Division (6)

Alemannic 87.5%

Italian, Turkish, and other 12.5%

Religions (7)

Roman Catholic 80%

Protestant 7.4%

Unknown 7.7%

Other 4.9% (1996)

Languages (8)

German (official), Alemannic dialect.

EDUCATION

Literacy Rates (11B)

Adult literacy rate

1980

Male . . . .-

Female . . . .-

1995

Male 100%

Female 100%

GOVERNMENT & LAW

Political Parties (12)

Diet	% of seats
Fatherland Union (VU)	.50.1
Progressive Citizens' Party (FBPL)	.41.3
The Free List (FL)	.8.5

Government Budget (13B)

Revenues . . . .$455 million

Expenditures . . . .$435 million

Capital expenditures . . . . .NA

Data for 1996 est. NA stands for not available.

Military Affairs (14A)

Defense is the responsibility of Switzerland.

LABOR FORCE

Labor Force (16)

Total 22,891

Industry, trade, and building 46%

Services 52%

Agriculture, fishing, forestry, and

horticulture 2%

Data for 1996 est. Of the total, 13,847 are foreigners; 8,231 commute from Austria and Switzerland to work each day.

Unemployment Rate (17)

1.6% (1997)

PRODUCTION SECTOR

Electric Energy (18)

Capacity .23,000 kW (1995)

Production . . . . .150 million kWh (1995)

Consumption per capita . . . . . . .8,000 kWh (1995 est.)

Transportation (19)

Highways:

total: 250 km

paved: 250 km

unpaved: 0 km

Airports: none

Top Agricultural Products (20)

Wheat, barley, maize, potatoes; livestock, dairy products.

FINANCE, ECONOMICS, & TRADE

Economic Indicators (22)

National product: GDP—purchasing power parity—$713 million (1996 est.)

National product real growth rate: NA%

National product per capita: $23,000 (1996 est.)

Inflation rate—consumer price index: 0.5% (1997 est.)

Exchange Rates (24)

Exchange rates:

Swiss francs, franken, or franchi (SwF) per US$1

January 1998	1.4757
1997	1.4513
1996	1.2360
1995	1.1825
1994	1.3677
1993	1.4776

Top Import Origins (25)

$917.3 million (1996) Data are for 1996.

Origins	%
European Union countries	NA
Switzerland	NA

NA stands for not available.

Top Export Destinations (26)

$2.47 billion (1996) Data are for 1996.

Destinations	%
European Union	41.3
Germany	20.9
Austria	6.0
Czech Republic	30.6
FSU	7.1

Economic Aid (27)

None.

Import Export Commodities (28)

Import Commodities	Export Commodities
Machinery	Small specialty
Metal goods	machinery
Textiles	Dental products
Foodstuffs	Stamps
Motor vehicles	Hardware
	Pottery

LITHUANIA

Republic of Lithuania
Lietuvos Respublika

CAPITAL: Vilnius.

FLAG: Three equal horizontal bands of yellow (top), green, and red.

ANTHEM: *Tautika Giesme (The National Song).*

MONETARY UNIT: The Lithuanian lita of 100 cents has replaced the transitional system of coupons (talonas) which had been in force since October 1992, when the Soviet ruble was demonetized. There are coins of 1, 2, 5, 10, 20, and 50 cents and 1, 2, and 5 litas, and notes of 10, 20, 50, and 100 litas; litas 1 = $0.25 (or $1 = litas 4.0).

WEIGHTS AND MEASURES: The metric system is in force.

HOLIDAYS: New Year's Day, 1 January; Day of the Restoration of the Lithuanian State, 16 February; Good Friday (movable); Anniversary of the Coronation of Grand Duke Mindaugas of Lithuania, 6 July; National Day of Hope and Mourning, 1 November; Christmas, 25–26 December.

TIME: 2 PM = noon GMT.

LOCATION AND SIZE: Lithuania is located in eastern Europe, bordering the Baltic Sea, between Latvia and Russia. With a total area of 65,200 square kilometers (25,174 square miles), it is slightly larger than the state of West Virginia. Lithuania's boundary length totals 1,372 kilometers (853 miles).

Lithuania's capital city, Vilnius, is located in the southeastern part of the country.

CLIMATE: Lithuania's climate is transitional between maritime and continental. Yearly, the mean temperature is 6.1°C (43°F). The mean temperature in July is 17.1°C (63°F). Rainfall averages from 54 centimeters (21 inches) to 93 centimeters (37 inches), depending on location.

INTRODUCTORY SURVEY

RECENT HISTORY

From the fourteenth to the eighteenth centuries, the Grand Duchy of Lithuania was linked to the Kingdom of Poland. What is now Lithuania was annexed to the Russian Empire in 1795. During the nineteenth century, a Lithuanian nationalist movement arose.

On 16 February 1918, Lithuania proclaimed its independence. The new Bolshevik government in Moscow (Russia) attempted to seize power in Lithuania, but failed. In July 1920, Moscow recognized Lithuanian independence. However, the 1939 Nazi-Soviet pact assigned Lithuania to Soviet control, and Soviet forces were stationed on its territory. After proclaiming Lithuania a Soviet Socialist Republic in July 1940, Moscow lost control of the area to Germany in June 1941 but recaptured it in 1944.

Soviet president Mikhail Gorbachev's unrestricted policies allowed Lithuanians to once again seek national self-determination. Lithuanian independence was proclaimed on 11 March 1990 but was not generally recognized until August 1991.

On 14 February 1993, former communist Algirdas Brazauskas was elected president in a general election. In 1997, former U.S. bureaucrat Valdas Adamkus was elected president.

GOVERNMENT

On 25 October 1992, Lithuanian voters approved a new constitution that called for a 141-

member single-chamber legislature (Seimas) and a popularly elected president. Apylinkes (rural settlements) and district towns are the local units.

Judiciary

The legal system is being transformed from that of the old Soviet regime to a democratic model. A newly created Constitutional Court began deliberations in 1993. A new civil and criminal procedure code and a court reform law were enacted in 1995.

Political Parties

The majority party in the Seimas in the 1992 parliamentary elections was the Lithuanian Democratic Labor Party (LDLP). In the elections of 1996, the Homeland Union Party took 70 of 141 seats. The LDLP only won 12 seats.

DEFENSE

The army numbers 5,100, with 11,000 reserves. There is a small navy and an air force with no combat aircraft. The paramilitary has 4,800 border guards.

ECONOMIC AFFAIRS

Agriculture accounts for roughly 13% of the nation's gross domestic product. Services contribute 55%. During the Soviet years, Lithuania built up a large and inefficient industrial sector that in 1996 accounted for 32% of the economy.

Public Finance

During the late 1980s, Lithuania's central and general government budgets typically ran deficits. In 1991, however, the general government budget recorded a surplus equivalent to 3% of GDP, due to new tax reform and collection measures, higher social security revenues, elimination of subsidies, and the end of transfers to the former USSR. In 1992, however, falling tax revenues and increasing expenditures for unemployment and other social benefits caused fiscal tensions. As a former Soviet republic, it is still uncertain how much debt Lithuania will be responsible for paying; Lithuania's official position is that it bears no responsibility for debt incurred during the Soviet period.

Income

In 1997, the gross national product (GNP) was $15.4.1 billion, or about $4,230 per capita.

Industry

Lithuania underwent rapid industrialization during the Soviet era. Major industries include machine building and metalworking, textiles, leather, and agro-processing. About 65% of the industrial sector is privately owned.

Banking and Finance

Since 1991, Lithuania has reorganized its banking sector numerous times. On 3 July 1992 the government adopted a new currency unit, the lita, to replace the ruble. As of April 1996, there were 27 registered banks, of which 11 were fully operational, including one investment bank and three partly state-owned institutions. Lithuania has had its share of banking crises, although not on the level experienced in Estonia and, more recently, Latvia. Between 1992 and 1995, six banks lost their licenses and two were merged; as of mid-1996, 16 were either suspended or facing bankruptcy procedures. The first serious crisis centered on Aurasbankas, the eighth largest bank in the country, and the deposit bank for many ministries. The Bank of Lithuania suspended Aurasbankas's operations in mid-1995 because of liquidity problems caused by bad lending and deposit-taking practices. In July 1995, the minimum capital requirement for existing banks was raised from L5 million to L10 million, the level already established for new banks.

Operations at Lithuania's largest bank, the Joint-Stock Innovation Bank, were suspended on 20 December 1995, and those of the Litimpeks bank, the country's second largest, two days later. The two were in the process of merging to create the Lithuania United Bank and the fraud was uncovered during pre-merger audits. Due to rumors of a devaluation of the currency, a shortage of foreign exchange throughout the whole banking sector was created.

As of the first quarter of 1996, only three banks met all capital adequacy requirements and other prudential ratios laid down by the Bank of Lithuania.

The National Stock Exchange, which opened in September 1993, is the most active in the region, with 245 listed companies. Monthly turnover by the end of 1994 had reached L20.8 million.

In 1997, a key feature of the new economic framework in Lithuania was the pegging of the lita to a currency basket composed of the dollar and the D-mark. Lithuania's two largest commercial banks, Vilniaus and Hermis, announced rises in profits for the 1996 financial year.

State banks in Lithuania include the Savings Bank, the Commercial Bank of Lithuania, and the Agricultural Bank.

Economic Development

In 1990, the Lithuanian government began a comprehensive economic reform program aimed at effecting the transformation to a market-driven economy. Reform measures include price reform, trade reform, and privatization. By mid-1993, 92% of housing and roughly 60% of businesses slated for privatization had been privatized. By 1996, about 36% of state enterprises and about 83% of all state property had been privatized. International aid agencies committed about $765 million of assistance between 1992–95. Most international aid goes either to infrastructure construction or loan credits to business.

SOCIAL WELFARE

A national system of social insurance covers all of Lithuania's residents. Old age, sickness, disability, and unemployment benefits are paid on an earnings-related basis. Women receive maternity and day-care benefits.

Healthcare

Life expectancy was about 70 years in 1995 (75 for females and 63 for males). In 1990, there was 1 physician for every 233 people. There was a 13% increase in diphtheria cases during 1994–95.

Housing

At the end of 1989, housing floor space totaled 70.8 million square meters (761.8 million square feet). A total of 142,000 families (18% of all families) were on waiting lists for housing.

EDUCATION

The adult illiteracy rate is estimated at 2%. Education is free and compulsory for all children between the ages of 6 and 16 years. At the postsecondary level institutions, over 70,863 pupils were enrolled in 1994. Universities include Kaunas University of Technology; Vilnius Technical University; Vilnius University; and Vytautas Magnus University.

1999 KEY EVENTS TIMELINE

February

- A Lithuanian court suspends the trial of two men accused of atrocities during the Second World War.

May

- Prime Minister Gediminas Vagnorius resigns over dispute concerning the sale of Lithuania's sole oil-producing complex to a U.S. company.

July

- NATO's supreme commander in Europe visits Lithuania.

October

- The European Union announces it is considering Lithuania for membership by 2003.

- Prime Minister Rolandas Paksas resigns over disputes with the Lithuanian cabinet.

- Parliament ratifies treaty with Russian demarcating the boundary between Russia and Lithuania.

November

- Irena Degutiene, acting premier, is replaced by Andrius Kubilius, who was appointed on October 29 by President Adamkus and confirmed the Seimas on November 3.

December

- A report is released showing that Lithania's economy has recorded four quarters of recession, as the country suffers repercussion of economic problems of its major trading partner, Russia. The stock market ends the year up a modest 15 percent, although observers are predicting a modest decline in the first quarter 2000 due to weakness in the economy.

- The International Monetary Fund (IMF) and Lithania near agreement over the federal budget. The IMF must approve the country's fiscal standing to clear the way for a structural adjust loan(SAL) of $100 million from the World Bank.

ANALYSIS OF EVENTS: 1999

BUSINESS AND THE ECONOMY

In October, the European Union (EU) added Lithuania to its list of candidates for membership. Lithuania could qualify to join the EU as early as 2003. But Lithuanians had reason to fear their entry into the EU might be impeded by disputes over reform of the EU budget. Discussions of budget reform resulted in deadlock in March, with France insisting on retaining the current system of agricultural and other subsidies, and Germany advocating the reduction of subsidies in order to promote enlargement of the EU. The EU has also made Lithuania's membership contingent on the closure of two aging nuclear reactors in Ignalina, in Lithuania's rural southeast. Officials in Vilnius say the country cannot afford replacement power nor the almost $3 million it would take to close the reactors, which also employ 5,000 workers, most of them ethnic Russians.

Also in October, the Lithuanian cabinet overrode Prime Minister Rolandas Paksas' reservations and agreed to sell the Mazheikiu Nafta oil refinery to the U.S. energy company Williams for $150 million. Williams will have a 33% share and an option to raise its share to 51%. Paksas was doubtful that Lithuania could raise the $350 million in long-term loans to the company required by the agreement. The prime minister and the ministers of finance and economy resigned over the controversy, maintaining that the provisions of the sale would plunge the country into deeper debt—a projected deficit of 9.8% of the Gross Domestic Product (GDP) for 1999 and 12% for 2000—and threaten a new agreement with the International Monetary Fund (IMF), which wants Lithuania to keep its deficit under 2% of the GDP in the coming year before granting the country $100 million in World Bank structural adjustment loans (SALs).

The proposed sale of Mazheikiu Nafta and the political turmoil surrounding it prompted uncertainty about the future that led to the fall of the Lithuanian stock market index, the Litin-10, to its lowest mark for the year. The deal with Williams is pivotal to the Lithuanian economy, as the Mazheikiu Nafta operation, which accounts for 10% of the GDP, may founder if not sold to the U.S. company. Yet, if it is sold, the deficit will increase dramatically.

GOVERNMENT AND POLITICS

To strengthen NATO ties with Lithuania, NATO's supreme commander in Europe, General Wesley Clark, visited the country in July. Clark discussed NATO involvement in the Balkans and expressed gratitude for Lithuanian participation in NATO efforts in Kosovo.

Also in July, the speaker of the Belarus parliament, having been named acting head of state by the Belarus opposition, was granted official protection in Lithuania at the request of the Lithuanian parliamentary speaker. Political upheaval, including mass demonstrations in Minsk, forced the opposition leader to flee Belarus.

In August, a former head of the communist party in Lithuania was sentenced to 15 years in prison for his part in the 1991 storming of the Vilnius television station by Soviet troops. The incident, in which 14 people were killed and hundreds were injured, was one of the most violent attempts made to thwart the independence of a Soviet satellite.

A proposed deal to sell the Mazheikiu Nafta oil production company to a U.S. energy company named Williams aroused public dissatisfaction strong enough to bring down the government of Prime Minister Gediminas Vagnorius in May. His appointed successor, Adamkus Paksas, resigned in October when the cabinet approved the deal despite his misgivings about Lithuania's ability to meet its end of the bargain. The deal has brought to the fore an element of instability in Lithuanian national politics, as the public support for the ruling party erodes and the opposition prepares to hold a public referendum on the sale of the oil works.

To replace Paksas temporarily, President Valdas Adamkus named Labor Minister Irene Degutiene acting premier. The deal has enough political support to go through despite public disapproval, which could be exploited by the popular Paksas to garner yet more public support against the slightly more popular Adamkus.

In October, the Lithuanian parliament ratified a treaty signed by Russian President Boris Yeltsin and Lithuanian President Algirdas Brazauskas in 1997 that agrees on the border between the countries. Parliamentary ratification by both nations is required to put the treaty into effect; the Russian Duma, many of whose members oppose the agreement, is not expected to ratify it until after general elections in December 1999.

CULTURE AND SOCIETY

Viliumas Malinauskas, who has become rich by selling and even exporting mushrooms in different forms, has begun to build a sort of theme park that recreates aspects of Lithuania's Soviet-era past. The park is to feature statues of communist icons that were removed from public spaces in Lithuania after its independence in 1991. Malinauskas has won a government-sponsored competition for having found a use for the relics it houses. However, some of the local people have denounced Malinauskas as a profiteer exploiting Lithuania's painful past as a satellite of the U.S.S.R. and are circulating petitions to halt construction of the park, which is planned to include a replica of the Vilnius railway station from which Lithuanian partisans were sent to Siberia.

The past also haunts newly independent Lithuania in the form of people accused of collaborating with the Nazis during the Second World War. In February, two men who fled to Lithuania from the U.S. after the Justice Department initiated criminal proceedings against them had their trial suspended by a Lithuanian court, which maintained that the men, both over 90 years old and charged with genocide, were too ill to stand trial. The U.S. and Israel protested the suspension. A third man of Lithuanian extraction was deported from the U.S. in April after being similarly accused of genocide.

The question of collaboration is a difficult one in Lithuania, where the Germans were perceived as liberators for driving out the Soviets in 1941, and where the experience of Soviet propaganda makes many people hesitant to believe accusations of treachery. Even in the case of individuals who worked for the KGB, recent legislation (enacted in April) merely bars them from employment in fields where they might possibly be security risks, such as communications and the military. Still, the stated agenda of popular president of Lithuania Valdas Adamkus in this regard is to bring collaborators of the past to justice.

DIRECTORY

CENTRAL GOVERNMENT
Head of State

President
Valdas Adamkus, Office of the President, Simono Daukanto a. 3, LT-2008 Vilnius, Lithuania
PHONE: +370 (2) 625542
FAX: +370 (2) 225382
E-MAIL: info@president.lt

Prime Minister
Andrius Kubilius, Office of the Prime Minister, Gedimino ave. 11, 2039 Vilnius, Lithuania
PHONE: +370 (2) 622101
FAX: +370 (2) 225382
E-MAIL: info@president.lt

Ministers

Minister of Agriculture
Edvardas Makelis, Ministry of Agriculture, Gedimino 19 (Lelevelio 6), LT-2025 Vilnius, Lithuania
PHONE: +370 (2) 621681
FAX: +370 (2) 619953
E-MAIL: zum@zum.lt

Minister of Culture
Arûnas Bekdta, Ministry of Culture, Basanavièiaus g. 5, LT-2600 Vilnius, Lithuania
PHONE: +370 (2) 619486
FAX: +370 (2) 623120
E-MAIL: el.paðtas culture@muza.lt

Minister of Economy
Ministry of Economy, Gedimino av. 38/2, 2600 Vilnius, Lithuania
PHONE: +370 (2) 622416
FAX: +370 (2) 623974

Minister of Education and Science
Kornelijus Platelis, Ministry of Education and Science, A. Volano g. 2/7, LT-2600 Vilnius, Lithuania
PHONE: +370 (2) 622483
FAX: +370 (2) 612077
E-MAIL: smmin@smm.lt

Minister of Environment
Danius Lygis, Ministry of Environment, A. Jaksto 4/9, 2694 Vilnius, Lithuania
PHONE: +370 (2) 610558
FAX: +370 (2) 616515; 220847
E-MAIL: Danius.Lygis@aplinkuma.lt

Minister of Finance
Sigitas Kaktys, Ministry of Finance, J. Tumo-Vaizganto 8a/2, 2600 Vilnius, Lithuania
PHONE: +370 (2) 390005; 390100
FAX: +370 (2) 226387
E-MAIL: finmin@finmin.lt

Minister of Foreign Affairs
Algirdas Saudargas, Ministry of Foreign Affairs, J.Tumo-Vaiþganto g. 2, 2600 Vilnius, Lithuania
PHONE: +370 (2) 390005; 390100
FAX: +370 (2)620752; 618689; 221287

Minister of Justice
Gintaras Baleiunas, Ministry of Justice, Gedimino pr. 30/1, LT-2600 Vilnius, Lithuania
PHONE: +370 (2) 226615
FAX: +370 (2) 625940

Minister of Defense
Èeslovas Vytautas Stankevieius, Ministry of Defense, Totoriø 25/3, 2001 Vilnius, Lithuania
PHONE: +370 (2) 618700
FAX: +370 (2) 226082

Minister of Public Administration Reforms and Local Authorities
Sigitas Kaktys, Ministry of Public Administration Reforms and Local Authorities, Gedimino av. 11, LT-2039 Vilnius, Lithuania
PHONE: +370 (2) 628518
FAX: +370 (2) 226935
E-MAIL: administ@vrsrm.lt

Minister of Social Security and Labor
Ministry of Social Security and Labor, A. Vivulskio 11, 2693 Vilnius, Lithuania
PHONE: +370 (2) 652283
FAX: +370 (2) 652463
E-MAIL: post@socmin.lt

Minister of Transport and Communications
R. Didziokas, Ministry of Transport and Communications, Gedimino av. 17, 2679 Vilnius, Lithuania
PHONE: +370 (2) 393911
FAX: +370 (2) 224335
E-MAIL: transp@transp.lt

POLITICAL ORGANIZATIONS

Lietuvos Centro Sajunga-LCJ (Center Union of Lithuania)

TITLE: Chairman
NAME: Romualdas Ozolas

Lietuvos Demokratine Darbo Partija-LDDP (Democratic Labor Party of Lithuania)

TITLE: Chairman
NAME: Ceslovas Jursenas

Lietuvos Lenku Rinkimu Akcija-LLRA (Election Action of Lithuania's Poles)

TITLE: Chairman
NAME: Rinkimu Akcija

Tevynes sajunga/Lietuvos konservatoriai-TS-LK (Homeland Union/Conservative Party)

TITLE: Chairman
NAME: Vytautas Landsbergis

Lietuviu Krikšsioniu Demokratu Partija-LKDP (Lithuanian Christian Democratic Party)

TITLE: Chairman
NAME: Algirdas Saudargas

Lietuvos Demokratu Partija-LDP (Lithuanian Democratic Party)

TITLE: President
NAME: Lydie Wurth-Polfer

Lietuvos Tautininku Sajunga-LTS (Lithuanian Nationalist Union)

TITLE: Chairman
NAME: Rimantas Smetona

Lietuvos Socialdemokratu Partija-LSDP (Lithuanian Social Democratic Party)

TITLE: Chairman
NAME: Aloyzas Sakalas

DIPLOMATIC REPRESENTATION

Embassies in Lithuania

Canada
Gedimino pr. 64, 2001 Vilnius, Lithuania
PHONE: +370 (2) 220898
FAX: +370 (2) 220884

China
Algirdo 36, 2006 Vilnius, Lithuania
PHONE: +370 (2) 262861; 262862
FAX: +370 (2) 262682; 290237

France
Didzioji 1, 2600 Vilnius, Lithuania

PHONE: +370 (2) 222858; 222979; 222484
FAX: +370 (2) 223530

Germany
Sierakausko 24/8, 2600 Vilnius, Lithuania
PHONE: +370 (2) 650272; 263627; 650182
FAX: +370 (2) 231813

Italy
Tauro g. 12, Vilnius, Lithuania
PHONE: +370 (2) 220620; 220621; 220622
FAX: +370 (2) 220405

Russia
Latviu 53, 2600 Vilnius, Lithuania
PHONE: +370 (2) 721763
FAX: +370 (2) 723877

JUDICIAL SYSTEM

Supreme Court

Constitutional Court

Gedimino av. 36, 2600 Vilnius, Lithuania
PHONE: +370 (2) 226043
FAX: +370 (2) 227975
E-MAIL: mailbox@ConstCourtLt.omnitel.net

Court of Appeals

FURTHER READING

Articles

Civic, Christopher. "Look West . . . and East." *World Today,* March 1999, p. 25.

Edwards, Rob. "No Entry." *New Scientist* (April 17, 1999): 20.

Jones, Colin. "Losing their Independence." *The Banker* (October 1999): 65.

Kurzinsky, Robert S. and George W. Maxim. "Journey to Freedom—The Long Road to Lithuanian Independence." *Social Studies* (March-April 1999): 72.

"Lithuania's Largest Private Banks to Merge." *The Banker* (August 1999): 40.

Margolick, David. "Bordering on Obsession." *New York Times*, 13 June 1999.

Meier, Andrew. "Yankees Come Home: Americans are Returning to Lithuania to do Business—and Run the Country." *Time International*, 8 February 1999, p. 30.

"A Standoff over Aging Nukes . . . Has a lot of Workers Shook Up." *Business Week*, 15 July 1999, p. 4.

LITHUANIA: STATISTICAL DATA

For sources and notes see "Sources of Statistics" in the front of each volume.

GEOGRAPHY

Geography (1)

Area:

Total: 65,200 sq km.

Land: 65,200 sq km.

Water: 0 sq km.

Area—comparative: slightly larger than West Virginia.

Land boundaries:

Total: 1,273 km.

Border countries: Belarus 502 km, Latvia 453 km, Poland 91 km, Russia (Kaliningrad) 227 km.

Coastline: 99 km.

Climate: transitional, between maritime and continental; wet, moderate winters and summers.

Terrain: lowland, many scattered small lakes, fertile soil.

Natural resources: peat.

Land use:

Arable land: 35%

Permanent crops: 12%

Permanent pastures: 7%

Forests and woodland: 31%

Other: 15% (1993 est.).

Demographics (2A)

	1990	1995	1998	2000	2010	2020	2030	2040	2050
Population	3,702.5	3,656.7	3,600.2	3,571.6	3,510.6	3,464.1	3,368.2	3,250.5	3,062.9
Net migration rate (per 1,000 population)	NA	NA	NA	NA	NA	NA	NA	NA	NA
Births	NA	NA	NA	NA	NA	NA	NA	NA	NA
Deaths	NA	NA	NA	NA	NA	NA	NA	NA	NA
Life expectancy - males	66.4	61.9	62.8	63.1	66.4	70.1	73.2	75.5	77.3
Life expectancy - females	76.2	74.8	75.2	75.4	77.2	79.5	81.4	82.9	84.1
Birth rate (per 1,000)	15.3	10.9	10.6	10.5	13.0	9.8	9.1	8.4	7.2
Death rate (per 1,000)	10.8	13.3	12.9	12.9	12.7	12.0	12.1	13.0	14.2
Women of reproductive age (15-49 yrs.)	923.2	912.9	914.7	916.6	889.3	801.9	760.2	665.3	615.6
of which are currently married	NA	NA	NA	NA	NA	NA	NA	NA	NA
Fertility rate	2.0	1.5	1.5	1.4	1.8	1.6	1.5	1.5	1.4

Except as noted, values for vital statistics are in thousands; life expectancy is in years.

HUMAN FACTORS

Health Personnel (3)

Total health expenditure as a percentage of GDP,
1990-1997[a]

Public sector 5.0

Private sector . . . . .NA

Total[b] . . . . .NA

Health expenditure per capita in U.S. dollars,
1990-1997[a]

Purchasing power parity . . . . .NA

Total . . . . .NA

Availability of health care facilities per 100,000 people

Hospital beds 1990-1997[a] 1060

Doctors 1993[c] 399

Nurses 1993[c] 977

Health Indicators (4)

Life expectancy at birth

1980 71

1997 71

Daily per capita supply of calories (1996) 2,805

Total fertility rate births per woman (1997) 1.4

Maternal mortality ratio per 100,000 live births
(1990-97) . . . . .13[b]

Safe water % of population with access (1995) . . . .

Sanitation % of population with access (1995) . . . .

Consumption of iodized salt % of households
(1992-98)[a] . . . .

Smoking prevalence

Male % of adults (1985-95)[a] 52

Female % of adults (1985-95)[a] 10

Tuberculosis incidence per 100,000 people
(1997) 80

Adult HIV prevalence % of population ages
15-49 (1997) 0.01

Infants and Malnutrition (5)

Under-5 mortality rate (1997) 15

% of infants with low birthweight (1990-97) . . . . . .NA

Births attended by skilled health staff % of total[a] . .100

% fully immunized (1995-97)

TB 98

DPT 90

Polio 95

Measles 96

Prevalence of child malnutrition under age 5
(1992-97)[b] . . . . .NA

Ethnic Division (6)

Lithuanian 80.6%

Russian 8.7%

Polish 7%

Byelorussian 1.6%

Other 2.1%

Religions (7)

Primarily Roman Catholic, others include Lutheran,
Russian Orthodox, Protestant, evangelical Christian
Baptist, Islam, Judaism.

Languages (8)

Lithuanian (official), Polish, Russian.

EDUCATION

Public Education Expenditures (9)

Public expenditure on education (% of GNP)

1980 . . . .

1996 . . . . .5.6

Expenditure per student

Primary % of GNP per capita

1980 . . . .

1996 . . . .

Secondary % of GNP per capita

1980 . . . .

1996 . . . . .28.4[1]

Tertiary % of GNP per capita

1980 . . . .

1996 . . . . .43.0

Expenditure on teaching materials

Primary % of total for level (1996) . . . .

Secondary % of total for level (1996) 0.5

Primary pupil-teacher ratio per teacher (1996) 16

Duration of primary education years (1995) 4

Educational Attainment (10)

Age group (1989) . . . . .25+

Total population 2,282,191

Highest level attained (%)

No schooling 9.1

First level

Not completed 21.3

Completed . . . . .NA

Entered second level

S-1 . . . . .57.0

S-2 . . . . .NA

Postsecondary 12.6

Literacy Rates (11B)

Adult literacy rate

1980

Male . . . .-

Female . . . .-

1995

Male 100

Female 99

GOVERNMENT & LAW

Political Parties (12)

Parliament	No. of seats
Homeland Union/Conservative Party (TS) 69	
Christian Democratic Party (LKDP) 15	
Lithuanian Center Union (LCS) 15	
Democratic Labor Party of Lithuania (LDDP) 12	
Lithuanian Social Democratic Party (LSDP) 10	
Democratic Party (DP) 2	
Independents 12	
Others 6	

Government Budget (13A)

Year: 197

Total Expenditures: 10,515.0 Millions of Litai

Expenditures as a percentage of the total by function:

General public services and public order 13.58

Defense 2.85

Education 6.63

Health 13.53

Social Security and Welfare 32.07

Housing and community amenities . . . .-

Recreational, cultural, and religious affairs 2.29

Fuel and energy 1.58

Agriculture, forestry, fishing, and hunting 6.47

Mining, manufacturing, and construction 84

Transportation and communication 6.48

Other economic affairs and services 49

Military Affairs (14B)

	1992	1993	1994	1995
Military expenditures				
Current dollars (mil.)	NA	110	108	78
1995 constant dollars (mil.)	NA	115	111	78
Armed forces (000)	10	10	10	12
Gross national product (GNP)				
Current dollars (mil.)	21,420	14,990	15,160	15,300
1995 constant dollars (mil.)	23,040	15,720	15,540	15,300
Central government expenditures (CGE)				
1995 constant dollars (mil.)	7,741	3,506	3,932	3,733
People (mil.)	3.7	3.7	3.7	3.7
Military expenditure as % of GNP	NA	.7	.7	.5
Military expenditure as % of CGE	NA	3.3	2.8	2.1
Military expenditure per capita (1995 $)	NA	31	30	21
Armed forces per 1,000 people (soldiers)	2.6	2.7	2.7	3.3
GNP per capita (1995 $)	6,216	4,256	4,225	4,179
Arms imports[6]				
Current dollars (mil.)	0	10	5	5
1995 constant dollars (mil.)	0	10	5	5
Arms exports[6]				
Current dollars (mil.)	0	0	0	0
1995 constant dollars (mil.)	0	0	0	0
Total imports[7]				
Current dollars (mil.)	1,084	2,279	2,353	3,083
1995 constant dollars (mil.)	1,166	2,389	2,412	3,083
Total exports[7]				
Current dollars (mil.)	1,145	2,025	2,029	2,707
1995 constant dollars (mil.)	1,232	2,123	2,080	2,707
Arms as percent of total imports[8]	0.0	.4	0	.2
Arms as percent of total exports[8]	0.0	0	0	0

Crime (15)

Crime rate (for 1997)

Crimes reported 75,800

Total persons convicted 32,400

Crimes per 100,000 population 2,000

Persons responsible for offenses

Total number of suspects 25,500

Total number of female suspects 3,550

Total number of juvenile suspects 3,300

LABOR FORCE

Labor Force (16)

Total (million) 1.8

Industry and construction 42%

Agriculture and forestry .20%

Other 38%

Data for 1997.

Unemployment Rate (17)

6.7% (January 1998)

PRODUCTION SECTOR

Electric Energy (18)

Capacity . . . . .5.463 million kW (1995)

Production . . . . .14.33 billion kWh (1997 est.)

Consumption per capita . . . . .2,398 kWh (1995)

Transportation (19)

Highways:

total: 65,135 km

paved: 57,058 km (including 404 km of expressways)

unpaved: 8,077 km (1996 est.)

Waterways: 600 km perennially navigable

Pipelines: crude oil, 105 km; natural gas 760 km (1992)

Merchant marine:

total: 51 ships (1,000 GRT or over) totaling 307,947 GRT/341,733 DWT ships by type: cargo 25, combination bulk 11, oil tanker 2, railcar carrier 1, refrigerated cargo 8, roll-on/roll-off cargo 1, short-sea passenger 3 (1997 est.)

Airports: 96 (1994 est.)

Airports—with paved runways:

total: 25

over 3,047 m: 3

2,438 to 3,047 m: 2

1,524 to 2,437 m: 4

914 to 1,523 m: 2

under 914 m: 14 (1994 est.)

Airports—with unpaved runways:

total: 71

2,438 to 3,047 m: 1

1,524 to 2,437 m: 1

914 to 1,523 m: 6

under 914 m: 63 (1994 est.)

Top Agricultural Products (20)

Grain, potatoes, sugar beets, vegetables; meat, milk, eggs; fish; flax fiber.

MANUFACTURING SECTOR

GDP & Manufacturing Summary (21)

	1980	1985	1990	1992	1993	1994
Gross Domestic Product						
Millions of 1990 dollars	7,419	10,698	12,757	6,696	4,664	4,710
Growth rate in percent	NA	9.63	−6.74	−39.30	−30.35	0.99
Per capita (in 1990 dollars)	2,161.0	2,982.3	3,437.6	1,801.4	1,256.4	1,270.9
Manufacturing Value Added						
Millions of 1990 dollars	NA	NA	NA	NA	NA	NA
Growth rate in percent	NA	NA	NA	NA	NA	NA
Manufacturing share in percent of current prices	37.8	35.2	35.4	50.9	46.8	NA

FINANCE, ECONOMICS, & TRADE

Economic Indicators (22)

National product: GDP—purchasing power parity—$15.4 billion (1997 est.)

National product real growth rate: 6% (1997 est.)

National product per capita: $4,230 (1997 est.)

Inflation rate—consumer price index: 8.6% (1997 est.)

Balance of Payments (23)

	1993	1994	1995	1996
Exports of goods (f.o.b.)	2,026	2,029	2,706	3,413
Imports of goods (f.o.b.)	−2,180	−2,234	−3,404	−4,309
Trade balance	−155	−205	−698	−896
Services - debits	−257	−389	−562	−820
Services - credits	210	343	536	849
Private transfers (net)	95	118	61	73
Government transfers (net)	21	39	48	71
Overall balance	−86	−94	−614	−722

Exchange Rates (24)

Exchange rates:

Litai per US$1

Fixed rate since 1 May 1994	4.000
1994	3.978
1993	4.344
1992	1.773

Top Import Origins (25)

$4.4 billion (1996) Data are for 1996.

Origins	%
Russia	NA
Germany	NA
Poland	NA
Italy	NA
Denmark	NA

NA stands for not available.

Top Export Destinations (26)

$3.3 billion (1996) Data are for 1996.

Destinations	%
Russia	NA
Germany	NA
Belarus	NA
Latvia	NA
Ukraine	NA

NA stands for not available.

Economic Aid (27)

Recipient: ODA, $144 million (1993). Note: commitments from the West and international financial institutions, $765 million (1992-95).

Import Export Commodities (28)

Import Commodities	Export Commodities
Mineral production 20%	Agricultural products 16.9%
Machinery 16%	Mineral products 15.7%
Transport equipment 10%	Textiles 15.2%
Chemicals 10%	Machinery 11.4%
Textiles 8%	Live animals 7.7%
Foodstuff 6%	

LUXEMBOURG

CAPITAL: Luxembourg.

FLAG: The flag is a tricolor of red, white, and blue horizontal stripes.

ANTHEM: *Ons Hémecht (Our Homeland)*.

MONETARY UNIT: The Luxembourg franc (LFr) of 100 centimes is a paper currency equal in value to the Belgian franc. There are coins of 25 and 50 centimes and 1, 5, 10, and 20 francs, and notes of 50 and 100 francs. Belgian currency is legal tender in Luxembourg, and bills of 500, 1,000, and 5,000 Belgian francs are regularly circulated. LFr1 = $0.03204 (or $1 = LFr31.21).

WEIGHTS AND MEASURES: The metric system is the legal standard.

HOLIDAYS: New Year's Day, 1 January; Labor Day, 1 May; public celebration of the Grand Duke's Birthday, 23 June; Assumption, 15 August; All Saints' Day, 1 November; Christmas, 25–26 December. Movable religious holidays include Shrove Monday, Easter Monday, Ascension, and Pentecost Monday.

TIME: 1 PM = noon GMT.

LOCATION AND SIZE: A landlocked country in Western Europe, Luxembourg has an area of 2,586 square kilometers (998 square miles), slightly smaller than the state of Rhode Island. It has a total boundary length of 356 kilometers (221 miles). Luxembourg's capital city, also named Luxembourg, is located in the southcentral part of the country.

CLIMATE: Summers are generally cool, with a mean temperature of about 17°C (63°F); winters are seldom severe, average temperature being about 0°C (32°F). Precipitation throughout the country averages about 74 centimeters (29 inches) annually.

Grand Duchy of Luxembourg
French—*Grand-Duché de Luxembourg*
German—*Grossherzogtum Luxemburg*

INTRODUCTORY SURVEY

RECENT HISTORY

After World War II, the government agreed to form an economic union with Belgium and the Netherlands. The first phase, the Benelux Customs Union, took effect in 1948. In February 1958, a treaty of economic union was signed by representatives of the three countries. During the postwar decades, Luxembourg also became an active member of the North Atlantic Treaty Organization (NATO) and the European Community.

In April 1963, Luxembourg celebrated its 1,000th anniversary as an independent state. On 12 November 1964, Grand Duchess Charlotte abdicated in favor of her son, Jean, who became grand duke and who remained so as of 1994. His reign was marked by continued prosperity, as Luxembourg's economy shifted from dependence on steel to an emphasis on services, notably international banking.

In July 1992, Luxembourg approved the Maastricht Treaty that agreed upon closer European union.

GOVERNMENT

Luxembourg is a constitutional monarchy, with hereditary power passed down through the house of Nassau-Weilbourg. Legislative power is vested in the Chamber of Deputies, the 60 members of which are elected for five-year terms. In addition, the Council of State, composed of 21 members appointed for life by the sovereign, acts as a consulting body in legislative, administrative, and

LUXEMBOURG

courts, one in the city of Luxembourg and the other in Diekirch. The Superior Court of Justice acts as a court of appeal. The Court of Assizes, within the jurisdiction of the Superior Court, deals with criminal cases. Luxembourg is the site of the European Court of Justice.

Political Parties

Since 1947, the country has been governed by shifting coalitions among the three largest parties, The Christian Social Party (Parti Chrétien Social—PCS), which favors progressive labor legislation and protection for farmers and small business; the Socialist Party (Parti Ouvrier Socialiste Luxembourgeois—POSL), which supports expanding social welfare programs; and the Democratic Party (Parti Démocratique—PD), which favors minimal government activity in the economy.

DEFENSE

In 1967, Luxembourg abolished conscription and created a volunteer military force that is part of the North Atlantic Treaty Organization (NATO). In 1995 its army consisted of one infantry battalion of 800, and a police force of 560. Luxembourg has no air force or navy. Budgeted defense expenditures in 1995 were $141.3 million.

ECONOMIC AFFAIRS

In relation to its size and population, Luxembourg is one of the most highly industrialized countries in the world. Its standard of living rivals that of any country in Europe. Steel production, once the dominant industry, has declined since the 1970s. Plastics, rubber, chemicals, and other light industries have been developed. Banking and other service industries are a major part of the economy.

The gross domestic product increased by 3.9% in 1996. The unemployment rate was 3.7% in mid-1997. Although unemployment is low by international standards, it was at its highest since the end of World War II (1939–45).

Public Finance

The budget of the Luxembourg government is presented to the Chamber of Deputies late in each calendar year and becomes effective the following year. Government budgets showed steady surpluses from 1984 to 1990. The 1990 surplus, amounting to 3.4% of GDP, enabled the government to channel additional monies into investment funds and into a budget reserve exceeding LFr6 billion ($160 million). That a budget reserve exists

judicial matters and has the right of suspensive veto.

Executive power rests jointly in the sovereign, who may initiate legislation, and a prime minister (president of the government) who is appointed by the monarch, and who in turn selects a cabinet. Voting is compulsory, and eligibility begins at age 18.

Luxembourg is divided into 3 districts subdivided into 12 cantons, which in turn are divided into 118 communes.

Judiciary

Minor cases generally come before a justice of the peace. On a higher level are the two district

at all reflects the conservatively healthy management of Luxembourg's public finances.

Deficits in 1991 and 1992 were largely caused by the continued funding of the government's investment program. To fund the program, the government draws from accumulated surpluses and raises capital in financial markets.

The U.S. Central Intelligence Agency estimates that, in 1994, government revenues totaled approximately $4 billion and expenditures $4.05 billion. External debt totaled $800 million, approximately 99% of which was financed abroad.

The government's budget balance in 1996 amounted to 0.8% of GDP; government gross debt came to 5.9% of GDP that year.

Income

In 1997, Luxembourg's gross national product (GNP) was $13.48 billion, or $33,700 per person. For the period 1985–95 the average inflation rate was 4.7%, resulting in a real growth rate in GNP of 1% per person.

Industry

Massive reorganization of the steel industry and continuing diversification of industries characterized the 1980s. Chemicals, rubber, metal processing, glass, and aluminum gained growing importance. Production of steel in 1995 was 2.6 million tons; and rolled steel products, 3.7 million tons.

Banking and Finance

Banking has been gaining in importance since the 1970s; by 1980, the sector accounted for 18% of the GDP. The principal bank and the sole bank of issue is the International Bank of Luxembourg (Banque Internationale à Luxembourg), founded in 1856. The Belgium-Luxembourg monetary agreement, as renewed for 10 years in 1991, provided for the establishment of the Luxembourg Monetary Institute to represent the nation at international monetary conferences and institutions. The banking sector has benefitted from favorable laws governing holding companies. The European Investment Bank (an institution of the European Union) and the European Monetary Fund are headquartered in Luxembourg. As a financial center, Luxembourg has the advantages of strict banking secrecy, a trained multilingual workforce, and a government that is sympathetic to the sector's needs. These last two factors are proving attractive to the developing cross-border insurance business.

Faced with the impossibility of raising the capital through its steel industry alone, Luxembourg has always been open to the financial world. But its current success in the field owes more to legislation in neighboring countries and external economic factors than to any deliberate policy on the part of the government.

The Euro-markets have made Luxembourg the home of Cedel Bank, one of the two international clearing and settlement depositories, and has also had a positive effect on issues in Luxembourgish francs. In 1995 these represented 3.4% of world issues in terms of value and the total volume of Luxembourgish issues in circulation was LFr1.39 trillion at the end of 1996.

Luxembourg controls about 90% of Europe's offshore investment funds, making it the fourth largest world market.

The Luxembourg Bourse, founded in 1929 in the city of Luxembourg, primarily handles stocks and bonds issued by domestic companies, although it also lists Belgian securities. The exchange was closed down on 10 May 1940. Dealing resumed under the German occupation but was limited to domestic and German securities. The exchange was again closed down when the country was liberated, and did not reopen until 1 October 1945.

Economic Development

The keystone of the economic system is free enterprise, and the government has attempted to promote the well-being of private industry by every means short of direct interference. The full-employment policy pursued by every postwar government has produced a high ratio of economically active population to total population. The government encourages the diversification of industry by tax concessions and other means.

SOCIAL WELFARE

A broad system of social insurance covers practically all employees and their families. In the late 1980s, Luxembourg ranked second in the world after Sweden in spending on social security and housing as a percentage of the national budget. Sickness, maternity, old age, disability, and survivors' benefits are paid.

Although women are legally entitled to equal pay for equal work, their salaries on average are only 55% of men's earnings.

Healthcare

Luxembourg has an advanced national health service. In 1995, there were 870 physicians and 217 dentists. In 1994, there were 34 hospitals with 4,560 beds (11.3 per 1,000 inhabitants).

The average life expectancy is 77 years. Leading causes of death in 1992 were circulatory/heart diseases (1,686); cancer (996); road accidents (76); and suicides (59). There were 107 cases of AIDS in 1996.

Housing

The immediate post-World War II housing shortage has been relieved by large-scale construction of private homes and apartment buildings. In 1995, 2,676 new dwellings were built, down from 4,452 in 1991.

EDUCATION

There is practically no adult illiteracy. School attendance is compulsory between the ages of 6 and 15. Pupils attend primary schools for six years and then enter secondary schools for a period of up to seven years. In 1994, school enrollment included 27,595 elementary pupils. In 1995, there were 9,012 pupils in secondary schools. Luxembourg had 1,911 primary teachers and 2,115 secondary and university professors in 1994. The Central University of Luxembourg has about 500 students; most advanced students attend institutions of higher learning in Belgium and France.

1999 KEY EVENTS TIMELINE

January

- Luxembourg becomes one of eleven countries in the European Union to officially adopt the euro as a unit of currency.

March

- Luxembourg native Jacques Santer resigns as EU Commission president amid corruption allegations but announces intention of running for European Parliament.

April

- Eurozone countries, including Luxembourg, pledge economic reforms at Dresden meeting.

June

- EuroBusiness magazine reports that Luxembourg has world's second-wealthiest royal family.
- Socialist Party (POS) suffers major losses in general elections and loses place in ruling coalition.

October

- Luxembourg proposes flat-rate 10 percent withholding tax at meeting of EU finance ministers in Brussels.
- Kenyan president Daniel arap Moi visits Luxembourg on European tour that includes Germany and Belgium.

December

- Prime Minister Jean-Claude Juncker announces that Grand Duke Jean of Luxembourg, 78, will give up his throne in favor of his son, Prince Henri, 44.

ANALYSIS OF EVENTS: 1999

BUSINESS AND THE ECONOMY

In 1999 Luxembourg remained one of the world's top banking and financial centers, home to 225 foreign banks as well as headquarters of the European Investment Bank. Other important sectors of the economy were iron and steel production and light industry.

The beginning of the year marked an important economic milestone for Luxembourg, as it became one of eleven nations to officially adopt the new single European currency, the euro. (The euro would not actually go into circulation as legal tender until 2002, but all eleven nations began pegging their existing currencies to it.) The conversion rate for the Belgium and Luxembourg franc was 40.3399 francs to a single euro.

In spite of the unity represented by the new currency, the European Union (EU) member nations, including Luxembourg, remained divided on a number of economic policies in 1999. February found the group in a deadlock over budget reform issues including agricultural subsidies, with Luxembourg supporting a German co-financing plan calling for a financial contribution from individual member governments. In April, Luxembourg's prime minister, Jean-Claude Juncker, speaking at a meeting in Dresden, voiced concern over the budget effects of military and humanitarian expenditures stemming from the crisis in Kosovo. However, the EU economic controversy of most concern to Luxembourg was the plan to standardize rates of taxation in member nations, a move that would affect the country's financial sector by introducing taxation on interest and dividend income earned by non-residents. Luxembourg's representatives spoke in favor of exempting investment fund business from the proposed tax scheme. At an October meeting of finance ministers in Brussels, Luxembourg proposed a compromise agreement featuring a 10 percent flat-rate tax instead of the 20 percent that had originally been proposed.

Responding to a further EU policy initiative, Luxembourg abstained from voting on a measure to allow substitution of six types of fat for cocoa butter in chocolate manufactured in all EU countries, a move opposed by major chocolate producers including Luxembourg's neighbor, Belgium, which feared that the quality of the product would suffer.

GOVERNMENT AND POLITICS

In March Luxembourg's Jacques Santer resigned as president of the European Commission together with the rest of the commission members following a damaging report alleging fraud, corruption, and nepotism in this executive arm of the European Union. There was widespread concern in the EU over the discrediting of the commission during a crucial period in the organization's history, when it was undergoing significant expansion and implementing the introduction of the euro. Although Santer disclaimed direct involvement in any wrongdoing, critics termed his leadership of the commission since 1994 weak and ineffectual. Nevertheless, Luxembourg's ruling Christian Social Party almost immediately nominated Santer—a former prime minister of the country—as a candidate in June's European Parliament elections.

Luxembourg's Socialist Party (Parti Ouvrier Social-POS) suffered a significant loss in general elections in June. Its representation in the 60-member Chamber of Deputies fell from 17 seats to 13. The ruling Christian Social Party (Parti Chrétien Social-PCS) lost two seats, down from 21 to 19, and the Democratic Party (Parti Démocratique-PD)

increased its number of seats from 12 to 15. By coming in third in the vote, behind the two other major parties, the POS lost its place in the ruling coalition, and Grand Duke Jean formally asked Prime Minister Jean-Claude Juncker to form a new government.

Elections for seats in the European Parliament, the legislative organ of the European Union, were held at the same time as the national elections. Luxembourg's representation in the larger body remained almost unchanged, with the Christian Social Party and the Socialist Party retaining two seats apiece, while the Democratic Party won an extra seat, bringing its total up to two as well. Former president of the European Commission Jacques Sauter was one of the winning candidates.

CULTURE AND SOCIETY

Although their country is surrounded by the much larger neighbor states of France, Belgium, and Germany, Luxembourgers in 1999 had ample grounds for continuing to assert their individuality in the traditional motto ''Mir woelle bleiwe wat mir sin'' (We want to remain what we are). Their tiny principality, one of the world's top financial centers (and tax havens), was recognized as Europe's wealthiest country in terms of per capita economic output. Additional attention was drawn to Luxembourg's prosperity when an article in EuroBusiness magazine reported that the country's ''royals''—the family of the Grand Duke of Luxembourg—were the second wealthiest in Europe, surpassed only by the royal family of Liechtenstein. Great Britain's Windsors, who had been expected to top the list, came in third, with a fortune of 2.7 billion British pounds. Grand Duke Jean of Luxembourg was also named as the world's second-wealthiest reigning monarch, behind Queen Beatrix of the Netherlands and ahead of Prince Hans-Adam II of Liechtenstein.

DIRECTORY

CENTRAL GOVERNMENT

Head of State

Grand Duke
His Royal Highness Jean Benoit D'Aviano, Grand Ducal Palace, L-2013 Luxembourg

President of the Government, Prime Minister, Minister of Labour and Employment, Finance and the Treasury

Jean-Claude Juncker, Office of the Prime Minister and Ministry of State, Hotel de Bourgogne, 4 rue de la Congrégation, L-2910 Luxembourg

FAX: +352 461720

Ministers

Vice-President, Vice-Prime Minister, Minister of Foreign Affairs, Minister of Foreign Trade and Cooperation

Jacques Poos, Vice-President's Ministry, 5 rue Notre Dame, L-2940 Luxembourg

FAX: +352 223144

Minister of Agriculture, Viticulture and Rural Development, Middle Class, Housing and Tourism

Fernand Boden, Ministry of Agriculture, Viticulture and Rural Development, 4 rue de la Congrégation, L-2913 Luxembourg

FAX: +352 464027

Minister of Justice, Budget, European Union and Monetary Union, Relations with Parliament

Luc Frieden, Ministry of Justice, 16 boulevard Royal, L-2934 Luxembourg

FAX: +352 227661

Minister of the Family, Women's Affairs and the Handicapped

Marie-Josée Jacobs, Ministry of the Family, 12–14 avenue Emile Reuter, L-2919 Luxembourg

FAX: +352 4786570

Minister of Educational and Vocational Training, Minister of Culture and Religion

Erna Hennicot-Schoepges, Ministry of Cultural and Religious Affairs, 20 montée de la Petrusse, L-2912 Luxembourg

FAX: +352 402427

Minister of Interior, Civil Service and Administrative Reform

Michel Wolter, Ministry of the Interior, 15 rue Beaumont, L-2933 Luxembourg

Minister of Economy, Public Works and Energy

Robert Goebbels, Ministry of Economy and Trade, 6 boulevard Royal, L-2914 Luxembourg

FAX: +352 460448

Minister of Health, Physical Education and Sports

Georges Wolfhart, Ministry of Health, 57 boulevard de la Petrusse, L-2935 Luxembourg

FAX: +352 491337

Minister of Land Planning, Youth, Defense and Environment

Alex Bodry, Ministry of Defense, Plateau de St. Esprit, L-2915 Luxembourg

FAX: +352 462682

Minister of Social Security, Transportation and Communications

Mady Delvaux-Stehres, Ministry of Social Security, 26 rue Zithe, L-2936 Luxembourg

FAX: +352 4786328

State Secretary for Foreign Affairs, Foreign Trade and Cooperation

Lydie Err, Chambré des Députés, 9 rue du Saint-Esprit, L-1475 Luxembourg

PHONE: +352 466966

FAX: +352 220203

POLITICAL ORGANIZATIONS

Parti Chrétien Social-PCS (Christian Social People's Party)

4 rue de l'Eau, L-1449 Luxembourg

PHONE: +352 225731

FAX: +352 472716

E-MAIL: csv@chd.lu

TITLE: President

NAME: Erna Hennicot-Schoepges

Parti Ourvier Socialiste Luxembourgeois-POSL (Socialst Workers' Party of Luxembourg)

16 rue de Crécy, L-1364 Luxembourg

PHONE: +352 455991

FAX: +352 456575

E-MAIL: lasp@chd.lu

TITLE: President

NAME: Ben Fayot

Parti Democratique-PD (Democratic Party)

46 Grand rue, L-1669 Luxembourg

PHONE: +352 455991

FAX: +352 541620

E-MAIL: groupdp@chd.lu

TITLE: President

NAME: Lydie Würth-Polfer

Comité d'Action pour la Démocratie et la Justice-CADJ (Action Committee for Democracy and Justice)

9 rue de la Loge, L-1945 Luxembourg
PHONE: +352 463742
FAX: +352 463745
E-MAIL: adr@chd.lu
TITLE: President
NAME: Roby Mehlen

Déi Gréng (The Greens)

BP 454, L-2014 Luxembourg
PHONE: +352 463740
FAX: +352 463743
E-MAIL: greng@greng.lu
TITLE: Secretary
NAME: Abbes Jacoby

Parti Communiste Luxembourgeois (Communist Party)

16 rue Christophe Plantin, L-2339 Luxembourg-Gasperich
PHONE: +352 492095
FAX: +352 496920
TITLE: President
NAME: Aloyse Bisdorff

Déi Lénk (The Left)

BP 1228, L-1012 Luxembourg
PHONE: +352 426193
FAX: +352 426193
E-MAIL: info@dei-lenk.lu

DIPLOMATIC REPRESENTATION
Embassies in Luxembourg

Belgium
4 rue de Girondins, L-1626 Luxembourg
PHONE: +352 442746
FAX: +352 454182
TITLE: Ambasssador
NAME: Willy de Valck

Czech Republic
5 rue Notre Dame, L-2240 Luxembourg

France
8 blvd. Joseph 2, L-1840 Luxembourg
PHONE: +352 457271
FAX: +352 403016
TITLE: Ambasssador
NAME: Jane Debenest

Germany
20–22 avenue Emile Reuter, L-2420 Luxembourg
PHONE: +352 4534451
FAX: +352 455604
TITLE: Ambasssador
NAME: Horst Pakowski

Netherlands
5 rue C.M. Spoo, L-2546 Luxembourg
PHONE: +352 227570
FAX: +352 403016
TITLE: Ambasssador
NAME: J.S.L. Gualthérie van Weezel

Poland
5 rue Notre Dame, L-2240 Luxembourg

Slovakia
5 rue Notre Dame, L-2240 Luxembourg

United Kingdom
14 blvd Roosevelt, L-2450 Luxembourg
PHONE: +352 229864
FAX: +352 229867
TITLE: Ambasssador
NAME: John Nicholas Elam

United States
22 blvd E. Servais, L-2535 Luxembourg
PHONE: +352 460123
FAX: +352 461401
TITLE: Ambasssador
NAME: Clay Constatinou

JUDICIAL SYSTEM
High Court of Justice

Palais du Justice, 12 Côte D'Eich, L-1450 Luxembourg
PHONE: +352 475981

FURTHER READING
Articles

"Benelux: Elections in Belgium and Luxembourg." *The Economist* (June 19, 1999): 53.

Goddard, Sarah. "Duchy's Generous Tax-Free Reserves Under Scrutiny." *Business Insurance* (April 12, 1999): 41.

"In the Heart of the Euro Zone." *The New York Times*, 6 April 1999, p. 1.

McGee, Suzanne. "Tax Inquiry Turns Banking Grayer in Luxembourg." *The Wall Street Journal*, 20 July 1999, p. C1.

Books

Barteau, Harry C. *Historical Dictionary of Luxembourg*. Lanham, Md.: Scarecrow Press, 1996.

Newton, Gerald, ed. *Luxembourg and Letzebuergesch: Language and Communication at the Crossroads of Europe*. Oxford: Clarendon Press, 1996.

Toland, John. *Battle: The Story of the Bulge*. Lincoln: University of Nebraska Press, 1999.

LUXEMBOURG: STATISTICAL DATA

For sources and notes see "Sources of Statistics" in the front of each volume.

GEOGRAPHY

Geography (1)

Area:

Total: 2,586 sq km.

Land: 2,586 sq km.

Water: 0 sq km.

Area—comparative: slightly smaller than Rhode Island.

Land boundaries:

Total: 359 km.

Border countries: Belgium 148 km, France 73 km, Germany 138 km.

Coastline: 0 km (landlocked).

Climate: modified continental with mild winters, cool summers.

Terrain: mostly gently rolling uplands with broad, shallow valleys; uplands to slightly mountainous in the north; steep slope down to Moselle floodplain in the southeast.

Natural resources: iron ore (no longer exploited).

Land use:

Arable land: 24%

Permanent crops: 1%

Permanent pastures: 20%

Forests and woodland: 21%

Other: 34%

HUMAN FACTORS

Demographics (2A)

	1990	1995	1998	2000	2010	2020	2030	2040	2050
Population	382.0	408.9	425.0	432.6	453.6	454.5	435.2	400.8	360.3
Net migration rate (per 1,000 population)	NA	NA	NA	NA	NA	NA	NA	NA	NA
Births	NA	NA	NA	NA	NA	NA	NA	NA	NA
Deaths	2.3	NA	NA	NA	NA	NA	NA	NA	NA
Life expectancy - males	71.9	73.9	74.4	74.7	76.2	77.4	78.3	79.1	79.7
Life expectancy - females	79.7	80.2	80.7	81.0	82.4	83.5	84.4	85.2	85.7
Birth rate (per 1,000)	12.9	13.3	11.1	9.6	8.2	8.3	7.0	6.2	6.3
Death rate (per 1,000)	9.9	9.3	9.3	9.4	10.3	11.6	13.5	16.0	17.6
Women of reproductive age (15-49 yrs.)	97.2	101.8	103.8	104.2	103.1	93.0	84.9	75.7	62.8
of which are currently married	149.5	NA	NA	NA	NA	NA	NA	NA	NA
Fertility rate	1.6	1.8	1.6	1.5	1.4	1.4	1.3	1.3	1.3

Except as noted, values for vital statistics are in thousands; life expectancy is in years.

Infants and Malnutrition (5)

Under-5 mortality rate (1997) 7

% of infants with low birthweight (1990-97) . . . . . .NA

Births attended by skilled health staff % of total[a] . . .NA

% fully immunized (1995-97)

  TB 58

  DPT 94

  Polio 98

  Measles 91

Prevalence of child malnutrition under age 5
(1992-97)[b] . . . . .NA

Ethnic Division (6)

Celtic base (with French and German blend), Portuguese, Italian, and European (guest and worker residents).

Religions (7)

Roman Catholic 97%

Protestant and Jewish 3%

Languages (8)

Luxembourgian, German, French, English.

GOVERNMENT & LAW

Military Affairs (14B)

	1990	1991	1992	1993	1994	1995
Military expenditures						
Current dollars (mil.)	116	133	138	126	139	142
1995 constant dollars (mil.)	133	147	149	132	143	142
Armed forces (000)	1	1	1	1	1	1
Gross national product (GNP)						
Current dollars (mil.)	15,820	17,040	17,280	17,000	17,860	18,980[e]
1995 constant dollars (mil.)	18,180	18,830	18,580	17,830	18,310	18,980[e]
Central government expenditures (CGE)						
1995 constant dollars (mil.)	5,860	6,451	6,644	6,719	7,096	7,404[e]
People (mil.)	.4	.4	.4	.4	.4	.4
Military expenditure as % of GNP	.7	.8	.8	.7	.8	.7
Military expenditure as % of CGE	2.3	2.3	2.2	2.0	2.0	1.9
Military expenditure per capita (1995 $)	349	380	380	332	355	348
Armed forces per 1,000 people (soldiers)	2.6	2.6	2.6	2.5	2.5	2.4
GNP per capita (1995 $)	47,590	48,720	47,430	44,860	45,410	46,370
Arms imports[6]						
Current dollars (mil.)	20	20	10	5	0	0
1995 constant dollars (mil.)	23	22	12	5	0	0
Arms exports[6]						
Current dollars (mil.)	0	0	0	0	0	0
1995 constant dollars (mil.)	0	0	0	0	0	0
Total imports[7]						
Current dollars (mil.)	7,596	8,044	8,248	7,686	8,369	9,746
1995 constant dollars (mil.)	8,729	8,889	8,872	8,058	8,579	9,746
Total exports[7]						
Current dollars (mil.)	7,041	7,313	6,691	5,885	6,549	7,748
1995 constant dollars (mil.)	8,092	8,081	7,198	6,170	6,713	7,748
Arms as percent of total imports[8]	.3	.2	.1	.1	0	0
Arms as percent of total exports[8]	0	0	0	0	0	0

EDUCATION

Educational Attainment (10)

Age group (1991) . . . . .25+

Total population 262,628

Highest level attained (%)

No schooling . . . . .NA

First level

  Not completed 39.7

  Completed . . . . .NA

Entered second level

  S-1 . . . . .40.3

  S-2 . . . . .NA

Postsecondary 10.8

GOVERNMENT & LAW

Political Parties (12)

Chamber of Deputies	No. of seats
Christian Social People's Party (CSV)	21
Luxembourg Socialist Workers' Party (LSAP)	17
Democratic Party (DP)	12
Action Committee for Democracy and Pension Rights	5
Greens	5

Government Budget (13B)

Revenues . . . .$5.46 billion

Expenditures . . . .$5.44 billion

Capital expenditures . . . . .NA

Data for 1997 est. NA stands for not available.

Crime (15)

Crime rate (for 1997)

Crimes reported 24,400

Total persons convicted 9,600

Crimes per 100,000 population 5,800

Persons responsible for offenses

Total number of suspects 12,200

Total number of female suspects 1,650

Total number of juvenile suspects 1,050

LABOR FORCE

Labor Force (16)

Total 213,100

Trade, restaurants, hotels 20%

Mining, quarrying, manufacturing 16%

Other market services 18%

Community, social, personal services 14%

Construction 11%

Finance, insurance, real estate, business services . . .9%

Transport, storage, communications 8%

Agriculture, hunting, forestry, fishing 1%

Electricity, gas, water .1%

Data for 1995 est. One-third of labor force is foreign workers, mostly from Portugal, Italy, France, Belgium, and Germany.

Unemployment Rate (17)

3.5% (1997)

PRODUCTION SECTOR

Electric Energy (18)

Capacity .138,000 kW (1995)

Production . . . . .470 million kWh (1995)

Consumption per capita . . . . .13,518 kWh (1995)

Transportation (19)

Highways:

total: 5,160 km

paved: 5,160 km (including 115 km of expressways)

unpaved: 0 km (1996 est.)

Waterways: 37 km; Moselle

Pipelines: petroleum products 48 km

Merchant marine:

total: 32 ships (1,000 GRT or over) totaling 775,336 GRT/1,028,012 DWT ships by type: bulk 1, cargo 1, chemical tanker 1, container 3, liquefied gas tanker 11, oil tanker 5, passenger 2, roll-on/roll-off cargo 8 (1997 est.)

Airports: 2 (1997 est.)

Airports—with paved runways:

total: 1

over 3,047 m: 1 (1997 est.)

Airports—with unpaved runways:

total: 1

under 914 m: 1 (1997 est.)

Top Agricultural Products (20)

Barley, oats, potatoes, wheat, fruits, wine grapes; livestock products.

MANUFACTURING SECTOR

GDP & Manufacturing Summary (21)

Detailed value added figures are listed by both International Standard Industry Code (ISIC) and product title.

	1980	1985	1990	1994
GDP ($-1990 mil.)[1]	6,329	7,164	8,989	9,696
Per capita ($-1990)[1]	17,386	19,520	23,594	24,180
Manufacturing share (%) (current prices)[1]	27.6	26.2	25.1	NA

Manufacturing

	1980	1985	1990	1994
Value added ($-1990 mil.)[1]	1,670	1,946	2,316	2,354
Industrial production index	100	118	138	142
Value added ($ mil.)	1,168	944	2,130	2,035
Gross output ($ mil.)	3,269	2,916	6,056	6,428
Employment (000)	38	37	36	34

Profitability (% of gross output)

	1980	1985	1990	1994
Intermediate input (%)	70	73	73	73
Wages and salaries inc. supplements (%)	26	18	18	20
Gross operating surplus	3	9	9	8

Productivity ($)

	1980	1985	1990	1994
Gross output per worker	90,292	80,337	189,546	187,954
Value added per worker	28,479	24,028	54,403	53,895
Average wage (inc. supplements)	23,529	15,449	32,244	40,451

Value added ($ mil.)

	1980	1985	1990	1994
311/2 Food products	31	33	67	110
313 Beverages	32	24	59	65
314 Tobacco products	10	7	14	15
321 Textiles	24	15	88	133
322 Wearing apparel	5	3	8	13
323 Leather and fur products	—	—	—	NA
324 Footwear	—	—	—	NA
331 Wood and wood products	2	2	5	7
332 Furniture and fixtures	2	3	8	10
341 Paper and paper products	17	16	42	52
342 Printing and publishing	14	17	44	65
351 Industrial chemicals	31	31	100	137
352 Other chemical products	3	8	28	98
353 Petroleum refineries	—	—	—	—
354 Miscellaneous petroleum and coal products	1	1	2	2
355 Rubber products	127	110	199	125
356 Plastic products	13	14	53	73
361 Pottery, china and earthenware	10	6	18	14
362 Glass and glass products	13	14	55	57
369 Other non-metal mineral products	48	40	163	168
371 Iron and steel	592	405	623	341
372 Non-ferrous metals	32	26	62	70
381 Metal products	24	78	210	225
382 Non-electrical machinery	98	63	158	149
383 Electrical machinery	19	20	81	72
384 Transport equipment	7	4	19	12
385 Professional and scientific equipment	10	6	22	20
390 Other manufacturing industries	1	1	2	2

FINANCE, ECONOMICS, & TRADE

Economic Indicators (22)

National product: GDP—purchasing power parity—$13.48 billion (1997 est.)

National product real growth rate: 3.6% (1997 est.)

National product per capita: $33,700 (1997 est.)

Inflation rate—consumer price index: 2.3% (1995)

Exchange Rates (24)

Exchange rates:

Luxembourg francs (LuxF) per US$1

January 1998	37.459
1997	35.774
1996	30.962
1995	29.480
1994	33.456
1993	34.597

The Luxembourg franc is at par with the Belgian franc, which circulates freely in Luxembourg

Top Import Origins (25)

$9.4 billion (c.i.f., 1996)

Origins	%
Belgium	38
Germany	25
France	11
Netherlands	4

Top Export Destinations (26)

$7.1 billion (f.o.b., 1996).

Destinations	%
Germany	28
France	18
Belgium	15
United Kingdom	7
Netherlands	5

Economic Aid (27)

Donor: ODA, $50 million (1993).

Import Export Commodities (28)

Import Commodities	Export Commodities
Minerals	Finished steel products
Metals	Chemicals
Foodstuffs	Rubber products
Quality consumer goods	Glass
	Aluminum
	Other industrial products

Balance of Payments (23)

	1989	1990	1991	1992	1993
Exports of goods (f.o.b.)	89,988	107,654	106,019	113,638	103,873
Imports of goods (f.o.b.)	−89,020	−107,064	−106,085	−112,307	−99,905
Trade balance	968	590	−66	1,331	3,932
Services - debits	−67,902	−90,646	−101,703	−117,520	−109,283
Services - credits	71,850	96,971	108,251	125,144	120,527
Private transfers (net)	47	−597	−280	−503	−602
Government transfers (net)	−1,765	−1,369	−1,470	−1,984	−1,986
Long-term capital (net)	−2,437	−4	4,049	−7,710	9,503
Short-term capital (net)	−2,767	−1,650	−7,824	60	−23,234
Errors and omissions	−86	−2,844	−992	1,847	−938
Overall balance	−2,092	451	505	665	−2,081

MACAU

CAPITAL: Macau.

FLAG: The flag is light green with a white lotus flower above a stylized bridge and water and beneath an arc of five stars—one large and four smaller ones as on the flag of China.

ANTHEM: Chinese national anthem is used.

MONETARY UNIT: 1 yuan (¥) = 10 jiao.

WEIGHTS AND MEASURES: The metric system is used.

HOLIDAYS: New Year's Day, 1 January; Labor Day, 1 May; National Days, 1 and 2 October; Chinese New Year, three-day festival in January or February, depending on the year.

TIME: 8 PM = noon GMT.

LOCATION AND SIZE: Macau (Macao) is situated on the south coast of China, at the mouth of the Pearl (Zhu) River, almost directly opposite Hong Kong, which is about 65 km (40 mi.) away. Located at 22°6′ to 22°13′N and 113°33′ to 113°37′E, Macau consists of a peninsula, about 5 km (3 mi.) long and 1.6 km (1 mi.) wide, and two small islands, Taipa and Coloane. The total area is about 16 sq. km (6 sq. mi.), and the total coastline is 41 km (25 mi.).

CLIMATE: The climate is subtropical, with high humidity from April to October, when Macau receives most of its rainfall. Daily maximum temperatures average 29°C (84°F) during the summer; normal daily temperatures are less than 20°C (68°F) during the winter months.

INTRODUCTORY SURVEY

RECENT HISTORY

Macau is the oldest European settlement in the Far East. The first Portuguese attempts to establish relations with China were made in the early 16th century. In 1557, the Chinese authorities agreed to Portuguese settlement of Macau, with leaseholder rights. The Portuguese, however, treated Macau as their possession and established a municipal government in the form of a senate of the local inhabitants. Disputes concerning jurisdiction and administration developed. In 1833, Macau became an overseas province of Portugal under the control of the governor-general of Goa, and in 1849, Portugal succeeded in having Macau declared a free port. On 26 March 1887, China confirmed perpetual occupation and governance of Macau and its dependencies by Portugal, but the question of the delimitation of the boundaries was left unsettled.

As the only neutral port on the South China Sea during World War II, Macau enjoyed a modicum of prosperity. In 1949, the government of the PRC renounced the "unequal treaty" granting Portuguese suzerainty over Macau. Civil disturbances in late 1966 between Macau police and Chinese leftist groups resulted in concessions to the territory's pro-China elements. The 1974 military coup in Portugal led to a constitutional change in Macau's status from a Portuguese province to a "special territory." In January 1976, Portugal's remaining few hundred troops were withdrawn from Macau. China and Portugal established diplomatic ties in 1980. In March 1987, the PRC and Portugal reached an agreement for the return of Macau to the PRC in 1999. The PRC guaranteed not to interfere in Macau's capitalist economy and way of life for a period of 50 years.

GOVERNMENT

Before its return to China, Macau was ruled by a governor appointed by Portugal, although it was also empowered to make its own laws, appoint and control its own civil service, and contract directly

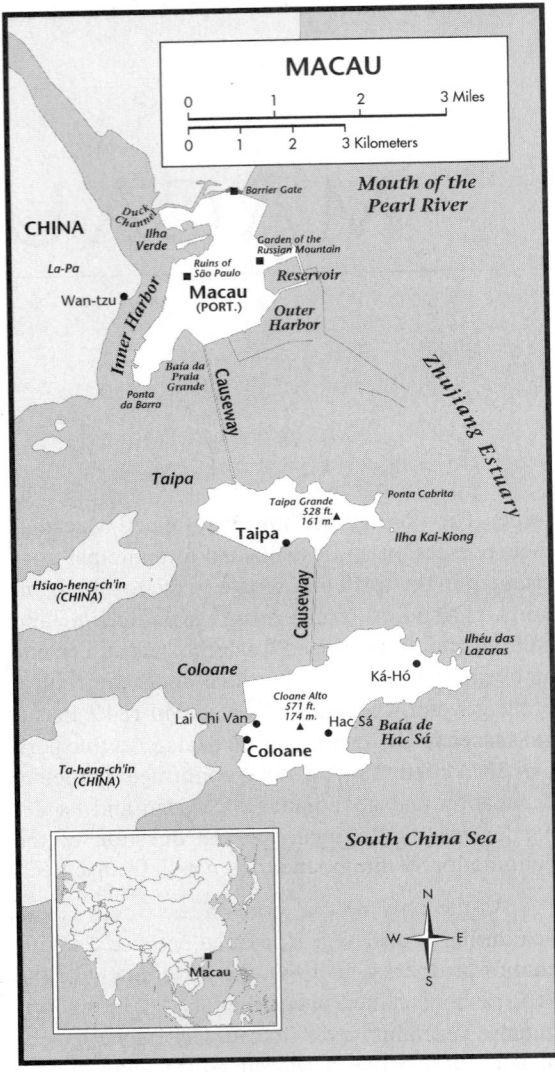

MACAU

cial system. Since ownership of Macau reverted to the People's Republic of China on December 20, 1999. its judicial system became subject to the Basic Law of the Macau Special Administrative Region of the People's Republic of China. The Basic Law was adopted earlier in the 1990s by the National People's Congress in China to serve as the area's constitutional law under the "one country, two systems" policy.

Political Parties

Since Macau's transition back to Chinese rule it has no formal political parties.

Public Finance

The unit of currency is the Macau pataca (P) of 100 avosqong Kong dollars also circulate freely. There are coins of 10, 20, ind 50 avos and 1 and 5 patacas, and notes of 5, 10, 50, 100, and 500 patacas. The pataca is linked to the Hong Kong dollar at the rate of HK$1 = P1.03. Corporate taxes and import duties are important sources of revenue; major expenditures are for finance, security, education, and health and welfare. The territory has its own currency-issuing bank, 12 commercial banks, and 10 foreign banks.

Industry

Macau's economy is consumer-oriented. There is little agriculture, and the territory is heavily dependent on imports from China for food, fresh water, and electricity. Important economic sectors are commerce, tourism, gambling, fishing, and light industry. There are small- or medium-scale enterprises concerned especially with the finishing of imported serni-manufactured goods, in particular the manufacture of clothing, ceramics, electronic equipment, toys, and fireworks, and the printing and dyeing of cloth and yarn.

Economic Development

Macau's historic role has been that of a gateway for southern China. It has close trade relations with neighboring Hong Kong, another free port, which serves as a point of transshipment for Macau's exports and imports. Gold trading, formerly a major facet in Macau's economy, virtually came to a halt in 1974–75 following Hong Kong's decision to lift its own restrictions on gold trading. Exports in 1995 were estimated at $1.9 billion, shipped mainly to the US, Hong Kong, Germany, China, and France. The principal exports are textiles, clothing, fireworks, artificial flowers, ceramics, optical equipment, electronic goods, leatherwork, toys, and fish. Textiles alone ac-

for foreign loans. A 17-member Legislative Assembly had 6 members elected directly, 6 members nominated by cultural, economic, and religious groups, and 5 appointed by the governor. Macau elected one delegate to Portugal's National Assembly.

After being returned to China, Macau came under the "one-country, two systems" formula implemented by China in 1997 when it regained control of Hong Kong. Macau continues to exercise local autonomy. Edmund Ho Hau-Wah, a member of a prominent Macanese family, was made the region's first chief executive in May 1999.

Judiciary

For most of 1999 Macau was ruled by the laws of Portugal as applied through the Portuguese judi-

counted for an estimated 76.9% of exports in 1994. The principal imports for domestic use are food, fuel, machinery, iron and steel, and automobiles. Total imports in 1994 were valued at just over $2 billion, of which Hong Kong provided 30%, China 19%, and Japan 13%. Transit trade still dominates the flow in and out of Macau.

With its picturesque seaport and varied gambling facilities, tourism provides about 25% of GDP, and the gambling industry accounts for about 40% of GDP. Before reassuring control of Macau in 1999 the Chinese government stated its intentions of reducing Macau's dependence on the gambling industry by diversifying its economy. Many hoped that this would also help reduce crime in the region. Other than diversification, China intends to leave Macau's economy alone.

In 1991 there were 1,695,453 visitors to Macau, over 80% from Hong Kong. Of those classed as tourists, 88,331 came from Japan, 7,209 from the UK, and 9,800 from the U.S. and Canada. Travelers must have a valid passport and a visa, which is generally purchased at the point of disembarkation.

Healthcare

The Medical and Health Department, although critically understaffed, operates a 400-bed hospital. The 800-bed Kiang Vu Hospital has a largely China-trained staff.

EDUCATION

Government schools are operated mainly for the children of civil servants and wealthier families, while poor Chinese students are educated in schools indirectly supported by China. Macau's University of East Asia opened in 1981.

1999 KEY EVENTS TIMELINE

January
- Ongoing conflicts between violent gangs lead to a major crime wave.

May
- Banker Edmund Ho elected to run Macau's post-transition government.

September
- China issues post-handover passports for Macau.

October
- China announces it will mobilize armed police during Macau handover.
- Governor Vieira urges China to honor human rights in Macau after it reassures control.
- The trial of triad boss Wan Kuik-koi begins.

December
- Macau returns to Chinese rule.

ANALYSIS OF EVENTS: 1999

BUSINESS AND THE ECONOMY

Macau, a former Portuguese territory, returned to Chinese rule on December 20. The effects on the business community were not immediately clear. As a Portuguese territory, Macau was developed into a tourist destination and gambling outpost. Officials estimate that in 1998 gambling brought $3 billion of total revenue into the territory. Macau's gambling, however, also has its dark side. As the territory neared its transfer to Chinese rule, organized crime gangs, called Triads, began violently fighting for control of gambling operations.

In 1999 the Asian financial crisis continued to have an impact on the Macau economy. Profits for both tourism and gambling were down, and unemployment was up, exceeding five percent. In preparation for the transfer to China, Governor General Vasco Rocha Vieira began an effort in 1991 to make Macau a principal gateway to China. Vieira launched projects that included building monuments, establishing an international airport, and starting construction on a bridge to China. The Asian recession, however, slowed Vieira's expansion projects, and it remains to be seen whether expansion and development will be a priority under Chinese rule.

GOVERNMENT AND POLITICS

On December 20, Macau's 427,000 inhabitants became Chinese citizens. Macau, a tiny peninsular territory at the mouth of the Zhu River, had been under Portuguese control for 442 years. Most of Macau's residents are ethnic Chinese, and like Hong Kong before them (in July 1997), Macau is reintegrating into China, becoming a Special Administrative Region. Unlike neighboring Hong

Kong, though, Macau's transition to Chinese rule was welcomed by most citizens who hope that the new government will be able to revive the economy and suppress crime.

Macau's transfer, though peaceful, has created regional tensions. Taiwan watched the transition closely. With Macau under Chinese rule, Taiwanese officials fear that China will more aggressively seek to bring Taiwan, regarded in China as a renegade province, back under Chinese rule. Adding to the tension was China's decision to mobilize 10,000 armed police and border guards during the handover to discourage any possible protests or uprisings.

Shortly after the transfer, a new government is to be formed. In its relations with China, the new government will operate under the one-country, two-systems policy, and the new government will follow Macau's Basic Law, which guarantees a high level of autonomy for fifty years after reverting to Chinese rule. However, the power of the Macau Basic Law remains to be seen. Hong Kong had similar protections in place that China did not honor.

In May Edmund Ho, a banker, was elected chief executive for the post-handover government. Ho was chosen by a Beijing-approved committee. Ho will head an inexperienced and untested government. Most of Macau's top officials and civil servants were Portuguese, and with the turnover, they were replaced by Macanese of Chinese ethnicity. Under post-handover law, in fact, all of Macau's top government positions must be filled by ethnic Chinese.

CULTURE AND SOCIETY

Shortly after New Year's celebrations stopped, gang violence erupted. These gangs, called Triads, used to keep their disputes underground, but with the Asian recession drying up profits, the gangs have become openly violent. In what was once considered a peaceful territory, there were twenty-three gang-related deaths in 1998, and in 1998 and 1999 gang violence included public shootings, street fighting, arson, and bombings.

China responded by pressuring Macanese officials to clamp down on Triad violence, and in May China chose Edmund Ho to lead the post-handover government. Ho, a former banker, admitted earlier in the year that he has had business dealings with Triads in the past. Instead of hurting Ho, this confession boosted his popularity. Ho is perceived as having the proper contacts and experience to clean up the Triads. If Ho fails, however, a Chinese security force could step in. China announced that it would send 1,500 armed police into Macau for handover ceremonies, and established a military garrison in the city after reassuming control. Many observers believe that these forces could be used against the Triads.

On October 12, the trial of an alleged Triad boss got underway. "Broken Tooth" Wan Kuok-koi was accused of leading the 14K gang, and faced a number of organized crime charges, though Wan denies any wrongdoing. Wan was convicted and sentenced to 15 years in prison shortly before Macau returned to Chinese control.

On October 3, outgoing Governor General Vasco Rocha Vieira urged China to honor Macanese basic rights. He asked China to protect the rights of ethnic Portuguese, whose status after the handover remains unclear. All Macanese citizens are afforded Portuguese citizenship. However, China plans to honor Portuguese passports only as travel documents to be used outside of China. On September 10, China unveiled new passports for the post-handover era. The passports will also serve as permanent-resident cards.

DIRECTORY

For most of 1999 Macau was administered under Portuguese authority. On December 19, 1999, it reverted to the People's Republic of China. Macau's administration since December 19 has changed to reflect this shift in sovereignty.

CENTRAL GOVERNMENT

Head of State

Chief Executive
Edmund Ho

Governor General
Vasco Joachim Rocha Viera, Office of the Governor, Government Palace, Ave. da Praia Grande, Macau
PHONE: +853 565555
FAX: +853 563377

Cabinet

Secretary for Administration and Justice
Florinda da Rosa Silva Chan

Secretary for Economy and Finance
Francis Tam Pak Un

Secretary for Security
Cheong Kuoc Va

Secretary for Social Affairs and Culture
Fernando Chui Sai On

Secretary for Transports and Public Works
Ao Man Long

POLITICAL ORGANIZATIONS
Macau has no formal political parties.

FURTHER READING
Articles
Baird, David. "Farewell to Asia's Last Colony: Portuguese for 442 Years, Macau Prepares for Chinese Rule." *Maclean's* (January 1, 1999): 32.

"Making Memories: What Will Happen Once Macau Reverts from Portuguese to Chinese Control." *The Economist* 352 (August 14,1999): 66.

Internet
Bezlova, Antoaneta. "Whither China: a Painless Handover, but Perhaps not for Long." *Asia Times Online*, 20 April 1999. Available Online @ atimes.com/ (December 8, 1999).

Chinoy, Mike. "Gang Shootings Give Bloody Start to New Year in Macau." *CNN Interactive*, 7 January 1999. Available Online @ www.cnn.com/ASIANOW/ (December 8, 1999).

"New Macau Leader to Focus on Crime, Chinese Handover." *CNN Interactive*, 15 May 1999. Available Online @ www.cnn.com/ASIANOW/ (December 8, 1999).

MACAU: STATISTICAL DATA

For sources and notes see "Sources of Statistics" in the front of each volume.

GEOGRAPHY

Geography (1)

Area:

Total: 21 sq km.

Land: 21 sq km.

Water: 0 sq km.

Area—comparative: about 0.1 times the size of Washington, DC.

Land boundaries:

Total: 0.34 km.

Border countries: China 0.34 km.

Coastline: 40 km.

Climate: subtropical; marine with cool winters, warm summers.

Terrain: generally flat.

Natural resources: NEGL.

Land use:

Arable land: 0%

Permanent crops: 0%

Permanent pastures: 0%

Forests and woodland: 0%

Other: 100% (1993 est.).

HUMAN FACTORS

Demographics (2A)

	1990	1995	1998	2000	2010	2020	2030	2040	2050
Population	NA	404.2	429.2	445.4	524.9	606.8	676.4	725.5	761.9
Net migration rate (per 1,000 population)	NA	NA	NA	NA	NA	NA	NA	NA	NA
Births	NA	NA	NA	NA	NA	NA	NA	NA	NA
Deaths	NA	NA	NA	NA	NA	NA	NA	NA	NA
Life expectancy - males	NA	77.8	78.7	78.9	80.3	80.8	80.9	81.0	81.0
Life expectancy - females	NA	85.7	84.7	85.6	86.5	86.8	86.9	87.0	87.0
Birth rate (per 1,000)	NA	14.5	12.8	12.2	11.5	11.1	9.3	9.0	8.9
Death rate (per 1,000)	NA	3.3	3.5	3.5	4.1	5.0	6.8	9.1	10.2
Women of reproductive age (15-49 yrs.)	NA	126.1	135.4	141.9	162.2	166.4	176.1	175.8	177.6
of which are currently married	NA	NA	NA	NA	NA	NA	NA	NA	NA
Fertility rate	NA	1.4	1.3	1.3	1.3	1.3	1.3	1.3	1.3

Except as noted, values for vital statistics are in thousands; life expectancy is in years.

Ethnic Division (6)

Chinese 95%

Portuguese 3%

Other 2%

Religions (7)

Buddhist 50%

Roman Catholic 15%

None and other 35%

Data for 1997 est.

Languages (8)

Portuguese, Chinese (Cantonese).

EDUCATION

Educational Attainment (10)

Age group (1991) . . . . .25+

Total population .1212,363

Highest level attained (%)

No schooling 13.1

First level

Not completed 16.0

Completed 19.9

Entered second level

S-1 . . . . .25.2

S-2 . . . . .19.9

Postsecondary 5.9

GOVERNMENT & LAW

Political Parties (12)

The legislative branch is a unicameral Legislative Assembly (23 seats; 8 elected by popular vote, 8 by indirect vote, and 7 appointed by the governor; members serve four-year terms).

Government Budget (13B)

Revenues . . . .$1.3 billion

Expenditures . . . .$1.07 billion

Capital expenditures .NA

Data for 1995 est. NA stands for not available.

Military Affairs (14A)

Availability of manpower

Males age 15-49 (1998 est.) 119,102

Fit for military service

Males (1998 est.) .65,530

Defense is the responsibility of Portugal.

Crime (15)

Crime rate (for 1997)

Crimes reported 8,150

Total persons convicted . . . . .NA

Crimes per 100,000 population 1,650

Persons responsible for offenses

Total number of suspects . . . . .NA

Total number of female suspects . . . . .NA

Total number of juvenile suspects . . . . .NA

LABOR FORCE

Labor Force (16)

Total 271,228

Industry 28%

Restaurants and hotels 28%

Other services 44%

Data for 1995.

Unemployment Rate (17)

3.6% (1995)

PRODUCTION SECTOR

Electric Energy (18)

Capacity . . . . .260,000 kW (1995)

Production . . . . .1.3 billion kWh (1995)

Consumption per capita . . . . . . .3,250 kWh (1996 est.)

Transportation (19)

Highways:

total: 50 km

paved: 50 km

unpaved: 0 km (1996 est.)

Merchant marine: none

Airports: 1 (1997 est.)

Airports—with paved runways:

total: 1

over 3,047 m: 1 (1997 est.)

Top Agricultural Products (20)

Rice, vegetables.

FINANCE, ECONOMICS, & TRADE

Economic Indicators (22)

National product: GDP—purchasing power parity—$7.8 billion (1997 est.)

National product real growth rate: -0.3% (1997 est.)

National product per capita: $15,600 (1997 est.)

Inflation rate—consumer price index: 3.9% (1997 est.)

Exchange Rates (24)

Exchange rates:

Patacas (P) per US$1

1997	.7.99
1996	.7.962
1993-95	.8.034
1992	.7.973

Linked to the Hong Kong dollar at the rate of 1.03 patacas per Hong Kong dollar.

Top Import Origins (25)

$1.99 billion (c.i.f., 1996 est.) Data are for 1996.

Origins	%
Hong Kong	.28.9
China	.21.8
European Union	.14.7
Japan	.10.5

Top Export Destinations (26)

$1.99 billion (f.o.b., 1996 est.) Data are for 1996.

Destinations	%
United States	.42
European Union	.31.7
Hong Kong	.10
China	.9.8

Economic Aid (27)

Recipient: ODA, $NA. NA stands for not available.

Import Export Commodities (28)

Import Commodities	Export Commodities
Raw materials	Textiles
Foodstuffs	Clothing
Capital goods	Toys
Fuels	Electronics
Lubricants	Cement

MACEDONIA

Former Yugoslav Republic of
Macedonia
Republika Makedonija

CAPITAL: Skopje.

FLAG: The flag consists of a gold sun with eight rays on a red field.

ANTHEM: *Denec Nad Makedonija (Today over Macedonia)*

MONETARY UNIT: The currency in use is the denar (Den). Denominations from smallest to largest are fifty deni, one denar, two denari, and five denari. In 1995, US$1 = Den38.8 (Den1 = US$0.0256), but exchange rates are likely to fluctuate.

WEIGHTS AND MEASURES: The metric system is in effect in Macedonia.

HOLIDAYS: Orthodox Christmas, 7 January; national holiday, 2 August; Day of Referendum, 8 September.

TIME: 1 PM = noon GMT.

LOCATION AND SIZE: Macedonia is a landlocked nation located in southeastern Europe. With a total area of 25,333 square kilometers (9,781 square miles), Macedonia is slightly larger than the state of Vermont. It has a total boundary length of 748 kilometers (465 miles). Macedonia's capital city, Skopje, is located in the northwestern part of the country.

CLIMATE: Macedonia's climate features hot summers and cold winters. The mean temperature is between 20 and 23°C (68 and 73°F) in July and between −20 and 0°C (−4 and 32°F) in January. Rainfall averages 48 centimeters (19 inches) a year. Snowfalls can be heavy in winter.

INTRODUCTORY SURVEY

RECENT HISTORY

During World War II (1939–45), Macedonia was occupied by Bulgaria and Albania. By the summer of 1943, Josip Tito, the leader of the Yugoslav Partisans, took over control of the Communist Party of Macedonia after winning its agreement to form a separate Macedonian republic as part of a Yugoslav federation.

After the war, Macedonia became one of the co-equal republics of the Federal Socialist Yugoslavia under the communist regime of Marshal Tito. The Macedonian language became its official language and was used as the language of instruction in schools.

A Macedonian University was established in Skopje, the capital city, and cultural, political, social, and economic institutions were developed within the framework of the Yugoslav Socialist system of self-management. All the republics of the former Federal Socialist Republic of Yugoslavia share a common history between 1945 and 1991, the year of Yugoslavia's break-up.

A conflict erupted between Tito and the Russian leader Joseph Stalin in 1948, and Tito was expelled from the Soviet Bloc. Yugoslavia then developed its own brand of Marxist economy based on workers' councils and self-management of enterprises and institutions, and became the leader of the nonaligned group of nations.

Being more open than the Soviet bloc to Western influences, the Yugoslav Communist regime relaxed its central controls somewhat. The 1974 constitution shifted much of the decision-making power from the federal level to the republics, further decentralizing the political process.

Following Tito's death in 1980, there was an economic crisis. Severe inflation and inability to pay the nation's foreign debts led to tensions between the different republics. There were demands for a reorganization of the Yugoslav federation into a confederation of sovereign states.

but only under the name of "Former Yugoslav Republic of Macedonia."

Greece proclaimed a trade embargo against Macedonia in 1994. In the fall of 1995, a preliminary agreement was reached between the two nations. Greece agreed to lift its blockade and assume diplomatic relations with Macedonia, while Macedonia agreed to restrict the use of certain national symbols in its flag and currency. However, the issue of the new nation's name was still unresolved.

In October 1995, Macedonian President Kiro Gligorov narrowly survived a car-bomb attack that killed his driver. Stojan Andov became interim president until early 1996, when Gligorov was able to resume his duties.

Ethnic violence erupted in July 1997 in Gostivar when police sent in forces to remove the illegal Albanian, Turkish, and Macedonian flags from the town hall. Thousands of protesters had gathered in a stalemate with police. During the confrontation, police killed three ethnic Albanians and several policemen were shot. Tensions between ethnic Albanians and Macedonians in the country are increasing.

The war in Kosovo and the movement of hundreds of thousands of Kosovar Albanian refugees into Macedonia brought more problems for this state in 1999. Although the Macedonian government claims that it cannot support more refugees, international pressure has forced the government to keep its borders open although the refugee flow slowed considerably. Observers believe that the Macedonian government fears that the large numbers of Kosovar Albanian refugees together with Macedonia's ethnic Albanian population may someday decide to separate from Macedonia, itself. Although foreign aid and relief for the refugees is coming in, it is too early to predict the long-term results of the Kosovo crisis on Macedonia.

GOVERNMENT

Macedonia became independent of the former Yugoslavia on 20 November 1991, having adopted its constitution on 17 November 1991. Macedonia has a single-chamber assembly of 120 seats, an executive branch consisting of a President (Kiro Gligorov) and a Council of Ministers (in 1994, the Prime Minister was Branko Crvenkovski).

Macedonia's 34 local governments are still based on the preexisting Yugoslav system.

Pressure towards individual autonomy for the regions and demand for a market economy grew stronger. These demands led to the formation of non-communist political parties. By 1990, the non-communists were able to win majorities in multiparty elections in Slovenia and Croatia. These defeats ended the era of Communist Party monopoly of power.

In the wake of developments in Slovenia and Croatia, Macedonia held its first multiparty elections in November/December 1990, with the participation of over 20 political parties. In January 1991, the Macedonian Assembly passed a declaration of sovereignty.

When the dissolution of Yugoslavia took place in 1990–91, Macedonia refused to join Serbia and Montenegro and instead opted for independence on 20 November 1991. Greece refused to recognize the newly independent Macedonia for fear of unrest among Slav Macedonians in Northern Greece. Greece also objected to the use of "Macedonia" for the name of the country. In April 1993, Macedonia gained membership in the United Nations,

Judiciary

The judicial system is comprised of three levels: municipal courts, district courts, and the Supreme Court. A Constitutional Court handles issues of constitutional interpretation, including protection of individual rights.

Political Parties

After the 1994 elections, party representation in the 120-seat Sobranje was as follows: the Social Democratic Alliance of Macedonia (former Communist Party), 58; Liberal Party, 29; Socialist Party of Macedonia, 8; Party for Democratic Prosperity, 10; National Democratic Party, 4; independents, 7; and others, 4.

DEFENSE

In January 1992, the Macedonian Assembly approved the formation of a standing army of 25,000–30,000 troops. However, the actual size of the military is estimated to be 10,400 regular soldiers. Reservists total 100,000.

ECONOMIC AFFAIRS

Although the poorest of the six former Yugoslav republics, Macedonia is capable of meeting its food and energy needs using its own agricultural and coal resources. Due to the shortage of fertile land in the Vardar River Valley and other valleys in the west, the employment of Macedonians in Serbia and Germany has become more common.

In August 1992, because it resented the use of ''Macedonia'' as the republic's name, Greece imposed a partial blockade on Macedonia. This blockade, combined with the United Nations sanctions on Serbia and Montenegro, cost the Macedonian economy some $2 billion by the end of 1994. Greece ended the embargo in 1995 after the European Union threatened to take legal action.

In 1995, mining and industry accounted for 44% of the domestic economy; agriculture and fishing, 24%; and services and trade, 32%.

Public Finance

Regional conflict, sanctions against Serbia and Montenegro, and a transition to a market economy severely disrupted the government's ability to account for public revenues and expenditures. The Macedonian government estimated in 1994 that it needed $200 million in immediate loans and another $500 million in soft loans to meet expenditures and commence the economic transition to recovery. External public debt was $737.1 million in 1994.

Income

In 1997, Macedonia's gross national product (GNP) was $2 billion, or about $960 per person. In 1996, about 47% of disposable income went to buy food. In 1995, the inflation rate was 14.8%, and the real growth rate in the domestic economy was 4%.

Industry

Steel and chemical production, along with textiles, furniture, and ceramics are important industries. Industry suffers from low levels of technology and overstaffing. The production of food, beverages, and textiles, accounted for 29% of the manufacturing sector's value in 1994.

Banking and Finance

In 1992, the National Bank of Macedonia was created to issue currency, conduct monetary polices, and regulate the banking sector of the country.

Commercial banks in Macedonia include the Komercijalna Banka and Scopanska Banka, both in Skopje. The currency unit is the Macedonia denar (Den) introduced on 10 May 1993, at a rate of 1:1,000 against the coupon. The central bank also introduced a floating rate for the denar against major currencies. Compared to the German mark (dm), the denar traded at around Den25: dm 1 in 1995, compared with Den24: dm 1 in 1993. There are no security exchanges in the country.

Under a five-year stabilization program agreed with the IMF, the government is focusing on reducing inflation, overhauling the financial system and launching structural reforms. Despite the Greek blockade, the program met its fiscal targets in 1994 with the state deficit declining to 2.5% of GDP in 1994. Reform of the state banking system made progress in 1996, although banks are still lending to inefficient state enterprises. Privatization has made some progress with the privatization agency raising $8 million in revenue in 1994 through the sale of four large companies and 14 medium-sized and small companies.

Economic Development

As of May 1994, the EBRD established a $10 million facility to guarantee Komercijalna Banka's designated correspondent banks against non-payment under confirmed letters of credit. By securing credit facilities, the bank's clients are able to stimulate production and increase exports. In 1995, net resource flows from international financial institutions consisted of $43 million from the World Bank, $37 million from the IMF, and $16 million from other institutions.

In 1995, the government began privatizing its largest state-owned industries. A total of 1,200 enterprises were to be privatized, 65% of them classified as small (fewer than 50 employees). The portion of a company's share capital which is community-owned is known as social capital, which forms the basis of the privatization process. In theory, social capital is owned by the company's employees. However, there are severe restrictions which make it non-transferable and hence valueless to the individual.

SOCIAL WELFARE

Macedonia, historically the poorest of the former Yugoslav republics, suffered further from the imposition of international sanctions against its trading partner Serbia, the rising tide of refugees, and increasing unemployment. Many of the state's social welfare programs for children have been inoperative due to the region's political and economic crises.

Although women have the same legal rights as men, the traditional cultures of both Christian and Muslim communities have limited their advancement in society.

Healthcare

Life expectancy in 1990–95 was 72 years. Physicians are adequately trained, but there is a shortage of medicines and medical equipment. Patients who are seriously ill must often go to another country for medical help.

Housing

During the years of the former Yugoslav SFR, there was a chronic shortage of housing. Since independence, the ability to find housing had improved. Bank loans are now available to finance building new housing.

EDUCATION

Education at the elementary level is free and compulsory for eight years. There are many secondary level schools. At the postsecondary level, there are two universities: Bitola University, founded in 1979, and the University of Skopje, founded in 1949.

1999 KEY EVENTS TIMELINE

February

- China threatens to veto the continued presence of a UN peacekeeping force in Macedonia.

March

- In response to Serb reprisals following the start of NATO's bombing campaign against Yugoslavia, Albanian refugees begin pouring into Macedonia.

- A pro-Serb mob attacks the U.S. embassy in Skopje.

- Isolated clashes occur between Albanians and Macedonians.

April

- Yugoslav soldiers mount a raid into Macedonia and capture three American soldiers on patrol along the Macedonia-Yugoslav border.

- The Macedonian government begins limiting the number of Kosovar Albanian refugees allowed to enter country.

May

- British Prime Minister Tony Blair and U.S. First Lady Hillary Rodham Clinton visit refugee camps in Macedonia.

- Hellenic Petroleum negotiates a deal to build an oil pipeline from Skopje to Thessaloniki, Greece.

June

- U.S. President Bill Clinton urges U.S. companies to continue production in Macedonia.

- The Kosovo war ends and some Albanian refugees begin to return home.

- NATO peacekeepers arrive transit Macedonia on their way to Kosovo.

July

- Mihail, Archbishop of the Macedonian Orthodox Church, dies at age eighty-eight.

November

- On November 22, Boris Trajkovski (VMRO-DPMNE) is reportedly the winner of the election runoff for president. Opposition candidates demand a repeat of the voting because of alleged voter fraud.

December

- Boris Trajkovski is declared the winner of the presidential election with almost 53 percent of the vote in the second round of voting. Opposition parties and independent election monitors again allege voter fraud. Trajkovski is inaugurated December 15.

ANALYSIS OF EVENTS: 1999

BUSINESS AND THE ECONOMY

During the early months of 1999 Macedonia's underdeveloped economy was subject to extraordinary strain resulting from the influx of ethnic Albanians refugees. The refugees were fleeing the fighting between the separatist Albanian Kosovo Liberation Army (KLA) and the Serbian troops in neighboring Kosovo province of Yugoslavia. Over the course of the year, with the help of foreign assistance and encouragement to foreign companies already operating in Macedonia, the economy remained strong enough to withstand this pressure.

Still, as a result of the chaos caused by the movement of refugees, some western European and U.S. companies operating in Macedonia became increasingly apprehensive regarding the security of their investments. Some firms, such as the American clothier Liz Claiborne, considered shutting down their operations in the country until U.S. President Bill Clinton publicly called on them to continue production as a show of confidence in Macedonia's future. Greece also increased its investment in Macedonia. In May, with the war still raging, Hellenic Petroleum signed an agreement estimated at $80 million with the Macedonian government calling for the construction of an oil pipeline from the Greek port of Thessaloniki to Skopje. Greece's Alpha Credit Bank also announced plans to acquire Macedonia's Credit Bank.

Macedonia stood to benefit from other pan-Balkan economic initiatives, such as President Clinton's proposed ''Balkan Marshall Plan,'' which promised to provide a bloc of American economic aid. Greece, meanwhile, proposed closer economic cooperation among the Balkan countries, including free trade and currency values tied to the euro.

GOVERNMENT AND POLITICS

The Kosovo war and its aftermath dominated all spheres of Macedonian politics and society in 1999. The massive influx of Kosovar Albanian refugees stretched the security and the economic resources of the country to the limit and threatened to destroy the fragile stability of the small, landlocked former Yugoslav republic. Yet as the year came to a close, Macedonia emerged from the conflict largely unscathed.

Macedonian politic life remained structured throughout the year by a fragile coalition composed of the main Macedonian nationalist party, the VMRO (the Internal Macedonian Revolutionary Organization), and the Albanian Social Democratic Alliance. The Alliance was home to a majority of the republic's twenty-five to thirty percent ethnic Albanians living in the northwestern corner of Macedonia along the border with Kosovo. These Albanian nationalists joined the coalition pledged to uphold the territorial integrity of the Republic of Macedonia.

Despite this pledge many ethnic Macedonians remained apprehensive as the Serb crackdown on Kosovar Albanians escalated throughout January and February. The Macedonians feared that the influx of Kosovar Albanian refugees (hundreds of thousands had fled Kosovo already since the spring of 1998) would be greeted by enthusiastic and armed support from their ethnic kin in Macedonia. This might provoke Serb aggression against Macedonia. The Macedonians feared that the deterioration of the situation in Kosovo and the spread of the conflict into Macedonia would threaten the very existence of the Macedonian republic itself. As a result, the vast majority of ethnic Macedonians vehemently opposed the NATO air war against Yugoslavia.

In early 1999 the war in Kosovo triggered this out-migration of Kosovar refugees. Within weeks over 300,000 had crossed the border into Macedonia. The exodus exceeded anything that NATO or international relief agencies, including the United Nations High Commissioner for Refugees (UNHCR) expected. Militarily unprepared and fearing a rise in tension both with the Serbs and with the ethnic Albanians in Macedonia (both Kosovar refugees and Macedonian nationals). The Macedonian government in Skopje followed a two-track policy of calling for increased humanitarian aid while simultaneously halting refugees at the border. These temporary border closings aroused sharp criticism from the international community and brought strong pressure to bear on Macedonia to accommodate more Albanians. Fortunately, the pledges of other NATO member-states to host more refugees helped to eased some of the pressure on Macedonia.

In spite of the obviously perilous security situation faced by Macedonia, the little republic emerged from the war intact. Ethnic tensions between Macedonians and Albanians remained in check and the ruling coalition held. Increased humanitarian aid—especially the construction of refugee shelters—came from international relief agencies such as Doctors Without Borders, Doctors of the World, the United Nations, and NATO member-states. Pro-Serb demonstrations, including an attack against the United States embassy in Skopje, did not degenerate into large-scale and widespread internal unrest. Macedonia also escaped being drawn into the conflict militarily. With the exception of the Serb capture of the three U.S. servicemen on patrol along the Kosovo-Macedonian border, no violation of Macedonian territory occurred. At the air campaign's conclusion, Macedonian allowed NATO peacekeepers to transit its territory on the way to Kosovo. The war's end also eased the refugee strain on Macedonia and many Kosovars returned to their abandoned homes as hastily as they had fled them. The return of the refugees was expected to continue into the year 2000.

The war in Kosovo also served to strengthen Macedonia's ties with some of its neighbors. Relations with Bulgaria were solidified by an agreement settling their language dispute (heretofore, Bulgaria had claimed that Macedonians spoke a western Bulgarian dialect and, therefore, were not a distinct nation). In addition, ties with Greece, Macedonia's neighbor to the south, warmed significantly as more Greek companies invested in Macedonia. Significantly, these ties continued despite the fact that Greece and Macedonia had not yet resolved their dispute over the latter republic's name. Greece objected to the name ''Macedonia,'' claiming that it implied a territorial claim on Greece's northern province). Internationally Macedonia was often recognized under the awkward name, ''Former Yugoslav Republic of Macedonia.''

CULTURE AND SOCIETY

As Macedonia entered 1999, hopes were high for better relations between the country's ethnic Macedonian majority and its Albanian minority. Although the Macedonian policy of periodic border closings against the refugees provoked the ire of the Albanian citizens of Macedonia, these confrontations did not reach the level of violence of previous years when Macedonian police clashed with ethnic Albanian students at the Albanian-language university in the republic's northwestern city of Tetovo. Indeed, some of the most serious unrest during the Kosovo war came as pro-Serb demonstrators attacked the U.S. embassy in Skopje. In other cultural news, Archbishop Mihail of the Macedonian Orthodox Church died at age eighty-eight in July. He played an important, though not a well-publicized role as a leading proponent of Macedonian nationalism.

DIRECTORY

CENTRAL GOVERNMENT
Head of State

President
Boris Trajkovski, Office of the President, 11 Oktomvrii b.b., 91000 Skopje, Macedonia
PHONE: +389 (91) 112255
FAX: +389 (91) 237947

Prime Minister
Ljubco Georgievski, Office of the Prime Minister, Ilindenska b.b., 91000 Skopje, Macedonia
PHONE: +389 (91) 115389
FAX: +389 (91) 119561

Vice President
Dosta Dimovska, Office of the Vice President

Vice President
Radmila Kiprijanova Radovanovic, Office of the Vice President

Vice President
Bedredin Ibrahimi, Office of the Vice President

Ministers

Minister of Defense
Nikola Kljusev, Ministry of Defense, Orce Nikolov Street b.b., 91000 Skopje, Macedonia
PHONE: +389 (91) 230928
E-MAIL: info@morm.gov.mk

Minister of Justice
Vlado Kambovski, Ministry of Justice, Veljko Vlahovich b.b., Skopje, Macedonia
PHONE: +389 (91) 230732; 226975

Minister of Finance
Boris Stojmenov, Ministry of Finance, Dane Gruev 14, Skopje, Macedonia
PHONE: +389 (91) 116012; 117280

Minister of Development
Milijana B. Danevska, Ministry of Development, Bote Bocevski 9, Skopje, Macedonia
PHONE: +389 (91) 112766; 112799

Minister of Labour and Social Welfare
Bedredin Ibrahimi, Ministry of Labour and Social Welfare, Dame Gruev 14, Skopje, Macedonia
PHONE: +389 (91) 117787; 220408

Minister of Traffic and Communications
Bobi Spirkovski, Ministry of Traffic and Communications, Ilendenska b.b., Skopje, Macedonia
PHONE: +389 (91) 123292

Minister of Science
Mirie Rusani, Ministry of Science, Ilendenska b.b., Skopje, Macedonia
PHONE: +389 (91) 238610; 235573

Minister of Culture
Dimitar Dimitrov, Ministry of Culture, Ilendenska b.b., Skopje, Macedonia
PHONE: +389 (91) 127136; 127112

Minister of Information
Redzep Zlatku, Ministry of Information, Guro Gakovik 64, 91000 Skopje, Macedonia
PHONE: +389 (91) 116476
FAX: +389 (91) 11486

Minister of Environment
Toni Popovski, Ministry of Environment, Drezdenska 52, 91000 Skopje, Macedonia
PHONE: +389 (91) 366930
FAX: +389 (91) 366931
E-MAIL: info@moe.gov.mk

Minister of Sports and Youth
Georgi Boev, Ministry of Sports and Youth, Drezdenska 52, 91000 Skopje, Macedonia
PHONE: +389 (91) 117268; 117631

Minister of Interior
Pavle Trajanov, Ministry of Interior, Dimche Mirchev b.b., 91000 Skopje, Macedonia
PHONE: +389 (91) 221972; 112468

Minister of Foreign Affairs
Aleksandar Dimitrov, Ministry of Foreign Affairs, Dame Gruev 6, 91000 Skopje, Macedonia
PHONE: +389 (91) 110333

FAX: +389 (91) 115790
E-MAIL: mailmnr@mnr.gov.mk

Minister of Economy
Mihajlo Tolevski, Ministry of Economy, Samoilova 10, Skopje, Macedonia
PHONE: +389 (91) 119628; 111541

Minister of Urban Planning, Construction and Environment
Dusko Kadievski, Ministry of Urban Planning, Construction and Environment, Dame Gruev 14, 91000 Skopje, Macedonia
PHONE: +389 (91) 117288
FAX: +389 (91) 117163
E-MAIL: gjorgeva@unet.com.mk

Minister of Agriculture, Forestry and Water Economy
Marjan Gjorcev, Ministry of Agriculture, Forestry and Water Economy, Vasil Gjorgov b.b., Skopje, Macedonia
PHONE: +389 (91) 113045; 211997

Minister of Education
Nenad Novkovski, Ministry of Education, Dimitrija Cuposki No 9, 91000 Skopje, Macedonia
PHONE: +389 (91) 117277
FAX: +389 (91) 117163
E-MAIL: mofk@mofk.gov.mk

Minister of Health
Dragan Danilovski, Ministry of Health, 50 Divizija b.b., Skopje, Macedonia
PHONE: +389 (91) 113429; 113014

Minister of Immigration
Martin Trenevski, Ministry of Immigration
PHONE: +389 (91) 117443

Minister of Trade
Nikola Gruevski, Ministry of Trade
PHONE: +389 (91) 127178

Minister of Local Self-Government
Dzevdat Nasufi, Ministry of Local Self-Government
PHONE: +389 (91) 128059

POLITICAL ORGANIZATIONS
Liberalno-Demokratska Partija-LDP (Liberal-Democratic Party)
NAME: Petar Gosev

Democratic Alternative
PHONE: +389 (91) 362713; 364130
FAX: +389 (91) 363089

Social Democratic League of Macedonia

Bihachska 8, Skopje, Macedonia
PHONE: +389 (91) 231371; 221071
TITLE: Leader
NAME: Branko Tsrvenkovski

Liberal Party

Ilindenska b.b., Skopje, Macedonia
PHONE: +389 (91) 288944; 228004
TITLE: Leader
NAME: Stojan Andov

Socialist Party of Macedonia

Oktomvri 17, Skopje 11, Macedonia
PHONE: +389 (91) 228015; 231255; 220075
TITLE: Leader
NAME: Ljubisav Ivanov

Social Democratic Party of Macedonia

ul. Kliment Ohridski 54, Skopje, Macedonia
PHONE: +389 (91) 222507; 224353
TITLE: Leader
NAME: Aleksandar Donev

Democratic Party

Partizanski odredi 89, Skopje, Macedonia
PHONE: +389 (91) 363099
TITLE: Leader
NAME: Petar Goshev

Democratic Party of Macedonia

Tetovo, Bazaar 3, Macedonia
PHONE: +389 (91) 20826; 20006; 20776
TITLE: Leader
NAME: Tomislav Stojanovski

Movement of Pan-Macedonian Action (MAAK)

Maksim Gorki 18/III, Skopje, Macedonia
PHONE: +389 (91) 116540
TITLE: Leader
NAME: Strasho Angelovski

Democratic Party for Macedonian National Unity

ul. "Makedonija" 17a, PF 903, 91000 Skopje, Macedonia
PHONE: +389 (91) 124244
FAX: +389 (91) 124366
E-MAIL: vmro_dpmne@vmro-dpmne.org.mk
TITLE: Leader
NAME: Ljupcho Georgievski

Fatherland Party

Marko Krale 34b, Skopje, Macedonia
PHONE: +389 (91) 23369
TITLE: Leader
NAME: Dimitar Tsrnomarov

Democratic Party

ul. Jane Sandanski 116/3–24, Skopje, Macedonia
PHONE: +389 (91) 419036
TITLE: Leader
NAME: Vladimir Golubovski

Macedonian National Democratic League

Sava Kovachevich 12, Skopje, Macedonia
PHONE: +389 (91) 781758
TITLE: Leader
NAME: Tomislav Stefkovski

United Party

Gemidzhiska 65, Skopje, Macedonia
TITLE: Leader
NAME: Atanas Aleksovski

Party for Democratic Prosperity of Macedonia

Karaorman 62, Tetovo, Macedonia
PHONE: +389 (91) 25709; 20435
TITLE: Leader
NAME: Abdurahman Haliti

National Democratic Party

Kiro Ristevski-Dane 23, Tetovo, Macedonia
PHONE: +389 (91) 31190
TITLE: Leader
NAME: Ilijaz Halimi

Demokratic Party of the Turks in Macedonia

ul. Krste Misirkov 67, Skopje, Macedonia
PHONE: +389 (91) 114696
TITLE: Leader
NAME: Erdogan Sarach

Party for Complete Emancipation of the Romanies in Macedonia

Shuto Orizari b.b., Skopje, Macedonia
PHONE: +389 (91) 612726
TITLE: Leader
NAME: Faik Abdi

Democratic Progressive Party of the Romanies in Macedonia

Demirhisarska 44, Skopje, Macedonia
PHONE: +389 (91) 266939
TITLE: Leader
NAME: Arif Bekir

Democratic Party of the Serbs in Macedonia

27 Mart 11, Skopje, Macedonia
PHONE: +389 (91) 254274; 722959; 222005
TITLE: Leader
NAME: Dragisha Miletich

Workers' Party

GTC Kula II, kat VIII, Skopje, Macedonia
PHONE: +389 (91) 236064; 232692
TITLE: Leader
NAME: Krste Jankovski

Communist League of Macedonia

ul. Marks i Engels 1/3–15, Skopje, Macedonia
TITLE: Leader
NAME: Milan Panchevski

Communist Party of Macedonia

Kozle 109, Skopje, Macedonia
TITLE: Leader
NAME: Todor Pelivanov

Macedonian National Front

Dimo Narednikot 53, Prilep, Macedonia
PHONE: +389 (91) 24911
TITLE: Leader
NAME: Ivan Spirkoski

Party for Democratic Action-Islamic Way

Ilindenska 191, Tetovo, Macedonia
PHONE: +389 (91) 32113
TITLE: Leader
NAME: Mazlam Kenan

Macedonian National Party

ul. 110 br. 8, Skopje, Macedonia
PHONE: +389 (91) 32113; 225246
TITLE: Leader
NAME: Vladimir Stefanovski

Civil Liberal Party

Venjamin Machukovski 5/2–11, Skopje, Macedonia
PHONE: +389 (91) 415490

TITLE: Leader
NAME: Boris Gegaj

Party for Democratic Movement of the Egyptians of Macedonia

Solunska 3, Struga, Macedonia
TITLE: Leader
NAME: Sinan Naser

Party for Democratic Action of Macedonia

Dzhon Kenedi 25–5–1, Skopje, Macedonia
PHONE: +389 (91) 415490
TITLE: Leader
NAME: Avdija Pepich

Albanian Democratic League-Liberal Party

Gale Hristov k. 3–6, Skopje, Macedonia
PHONE: +389 (91) 263523
TITLE: Leader
NAME: Dzhem Idrizi

Party for Democratic Prosperity-Party for National Union in Macedonia

Vtora makedonsko-albanska brigada 15–4, Skopje, Macedonia
PHONE: +389 (91) 31443
TITLE: Leader
NAME: Nevzat Halili

Party for Democratic Prosperity of the Albanians in Macedonia

Marshal Tito 2, Tetovo, Macedonia
PHONE: +389 (91) 31534
TITLE: Leader
NAME: Arben Dzhaferi

Party for Democratic Action-Civil League

Gjorgi Hristov 1/1–11, Skopje, Macedonia
PHONE: +389 (91) 266408; 238540
TITLE: Leader
NAME: Sadrija Hasanovich

Democratic Party for the Complete Emancipation of the Romanies in Macedonia

Ilindenska b.b., Kumanovo, Macedonia
PHONE: +389 (91) 112077
TITLE: Leader
NAME: Sevdzhan Sulejmanovski

Vnatrešno-Makedonska Revolucionerna Organizacija (Internal Macedonian Revolutionary Organization)

TITLE: President
NAME: Ljupco Georgievski

DIPLOMATIC REPRESENTATION
Embassies in Macedonia

Austria
Vasil Stefanovski 7, 91000 Skopje, Macedonia
PHONE: +389 (91) 109550
FAX: +389 (91) 130237
E-MAIL: austra@unet.com.mk
TITLE: Ambassador
NAME: Harald W. Kotschy

Canada
12-ta Udarna Brigada 2A, 91000 Skopje, Macedonia
PHONE: +389 (91) 125228; 122680
FAX: +389 (91) 122681
E-MAIL: dfaitmk@unet.com.mk
TITLE: Ambassador
NAME: Raphael Girard

China
Salvador Aljende 73, 91000 Skopje, Macedonia
PHONE: +389 (91) 176670; 176675
FAX: +389 (91) 133554
E-MAIL: embroc@unet.com.mk
TITLE: Charge d'Affaires
NAME: Cheng Po-chiu

France
Salvador Aljende 73, PO Box 557, 91000 Skopje, Macedonia
PHONE: +389 (91) 118749; 117574
FAX: +389 (91) 117760
E-MAIL: franamba@nic.mpt.com.mk
TITLE: Ambassador
NAME: Jacques Huntzinger

Germany
Dimitrija Chupovski 26, 91000 Skopje, Macedonia
PHONE: +389 (91) 110507
FAX: +389 (91) 117713
TITLE: Ambassador
NAME: Werner Burkart

Greece
Borka Talevski 6, 91000 Skopje, Macedonia
PHONE: +389 (91) 130198; 130208
FAX: +389 (91) 115718
TITLE: Ambassador
NAME: George Kaklikis

Italy
Osma Udarna brigada 22, 91000 Skopje, Macedonia
PHONE: +389 (91) 117430
FAX: +389 (91) 117087
E-MAIL: itl-emb@unet.com.mk
TITLE: Ambassador
NAME: Antonio Tarelli

Japan
Ul. Ilinden 9, 91000 Skopje, Macedonia
PHONE: +389 (91) 118731
FAX: +389 (91) 117087
TITLE: Ambassador
NAME: Yushu Takashima

Netherlands
Leninova 69–71, 91000 Skopje, Macedonia
PHONE: +389 (91) 129319; 109250
FAX: +389 (91) 129309
TITLE: Ambassador
NAME: Hendrik Heijnen

Russia
Pirinska 44, 91000 Skopje, Macedonia
PHONE: +389 (91) 117160
FAX: +389 (91) 117808
TITLE: Ambassador
NAME: Piotr Dobroserdov

Serbia
Pitu Guli 8, 91000 Skopje, Macedonia
PHONE: +389 (91) 129289; 131299; 128422
FAX: +389 (91) 129427
TITLE: Ambassador
NAME: Zoran Janackovic

Turkey
Slavej Planina bb, 91000 Skopje, Macedonia
PHONE: +389 (91) 113270; 112173
FAX: +389 (91) 117024
TITLE: Ambassador
NAME: Mustafa Fazli Kesmir

United Kingdom
Veljko Vlahovic 26, 91000 Skopje, Macedonia
PHONE: +389 (91) 117555; 117005
FAX: +389 (91) 117024
TITLE: Ambassador
NAME: Mark Dickinson

United States
Ul. Ilinden bb, 91000 Skopje, Macedonia
PHONE: +389 (91) 116180
FAX: +389 (91) 117103
TITLE: Ambassador

NAME: Michael Enik

JUDICIAL SYSTEM
Constitutional Court
Judicial Court of the Republic

FURTHER READING
Articles
Alter, Jonathan and Carla Power. ''The Next Balkan Domino?'' *Newsweek* (May 31 1999): 39.

''Macedonia and its Kosovars: In the Balance.'' *The Economist* (May 8, 1999): 51.

''Macedonia: The Next Domino?'' *National Interest* (Spring 1999): 42

Pope, Hugh. ''Macedonia Wants Firm Sign of Western Support; Request Is Condition for Troop Entry.'' *The Wall Street Journal,* 27 May 1999, p. A21.

''A Red Cross to Bear.'' *Civilization* (August/September 1999): 80.

''Still Nervous in Macedonia.'' *The Economist* (June 12, 1999).

Books
Abrahams, Fred. *A Threat to ''Stability:'' Human Rights Violations in Macedonia.* New York: Human Rights Watch, 1996.

Shea, John. *Macedonia and Greece: The Struggle to Define a New Balkan Nation.* Jefferson, N.C.: McFarland, 1997.

MACEDONIA
STATISTICAL DATA

For sources and notes see "Sources of Statistics" in the front of each volume.

GEOGRAPHY

Geography (1)

Area:

Total: 25,333 sq km.

Land: 24,856 sq km.

Water: 477 sq km.

Area—comparative: slightly larger than Vermont.

Land boundaries:

Total: 748 km.

Border countries: Albania 151 km, Bulgaria 148 km, Greece 228 km, Serbia and Montenegro 221 km (all with Serbia).

Coastline: 0 km (landlocked).

Climate: hot, dry summers and autumns and relatively cold winters with heavy snowfall.

Terrain: mountainous territory covered with deep basins and valleys; there are three large lakes, each divided by a frontier line; country bisected by the Vardar River.

Natural resources: chromium, lead, zinc, manganese, tungsten, nickel, low-grade iron ore, asbestos, sulfur, timber.

Land use:

Arable land: 24%

Permanent crops: 2%

Permanent pastures: 25%

Forests and woodland: 39%

Other: 10% (1993 est.).

HUMAN FACTORS

Demographics (2A)

	1990	1995	1998	2000	2010	2020	2030	2040	2050
Population	NA	1,967.0	2,009.4	2,035.0	2,125.9	2,167.4	2,161.1	2,094.5	1,977.2
Net migration rate (per 1,000 population)	NA	NA	NA	NA	NA	NA	NA	NA	NA
Births	NA	NA	NA	NA	NA	NA	NA	NA	NA
Deaths	NA	NA	NA	NA	NA	NA	NA	NA	NA
Life expectancy - males	NA	69.9	70.7	71.2	73.5	75.3	76.9	78.1	79.0
Life expectancy - females	NA	74.1	75.0	75.7	78.4	80.7	82.4	83.8	84.9
Birth rate (per 1,000)	NA	16.4	15.7	14.7	11.9	10.2	8.6	7.5	6.6
Death rate (per 1,000)	NA	8.3	8.1	8.0	8.4	9.2	10.3	12.0	13.6
Women of reproductive age (15-49 yrs.)	NA	507.0	520.1	524.2	527.8	518.6	486.3	436.9	379.4
of which are currently married	NA	NA	NA	NA	NA	NA	NA	NA	NA
Fertility rate	NA	2.1	2.0	1.9	1.6	1.5	1.4	1.4	1.3

Except as noted, values for vital statistics are in thousands; life expectancy is in years.

Ethnic Division (6)

Macedonian 65%

Albanian 22%

Turkish 4%

Serb 2%

Gypsies 3%

Other 4%

Religions (7)

Eastern Orthodox 67%

Muslim 30%

Other 3%

Languages (8)

Macedonian 70%, Albanian 21%, Turkish 3%, Serbo-Croatian 3%, other 3%.

EDUCATION

Educational Attainment (10)

Age group (1994) . . . . .15+

Total population 1,136,2492

Highest level attained (%)

   No schooling 28.0

   First level

      Not completed 28.2

      Completed . . . . .NA

   Entered second level

      S-1 . . . . .30.6

      S-2 . . . . .NA

   Postsecondary 6.7

GOVERNMENT & LAW

Political Parties (12)

Assembly	No. of seats
Social-Democratic Alliance of Macedonia (SDSM)	.58
Liberal Democratic Party (LDP)	.29
Socialist Party of Macedonia (SP)	.8
Party for Democratic Prosperity (PDP)	.10
Party for Albanians (DPA)	.4
Independents	.7
Other	.4

Government Budget (13B)

Revenues . . . .$1.06 billion

Expenditures . . . .$1 billion

   Capital expenditures . . . .$107 million

Data for 1996 est.

Military Affairs (14A)

Military age . . . . .19 years of age

Availability of manpower

   Males age 15-49 (1998 est.) 536,321

Fit for military service

   Males (1998 est.) 432,190

Reaching military age annually

   Males (1998 est.) 16,857

Total expenditures (1993 est.) . . . . .7 billion denars

Expenditures as % of GDP . . . . .NA%

Conversion of defense expenditures into US dollars using the current exchange rate could produce misleading results. NA stands for not available.

LABOR FORCE

Labor Force (16)

Total 591,773

Manufacturing and mining 40%

Data for 1992. Total for June 1994.

Unemployment Rate (17)

30% (1997 est.); many employed workers are, in fact, furloughees.

PRODUCTION SECTOR

Electric Energy (18)

Capacity . . . . .1.366 million kW (1995)

Production . . . . .5.4 billion kWh (1995)

Consumption per capita . . . . .2,584 kWh (1995)

Transportation (19)

Highways:

total: 10,591 km

paved: 5,500 km (including 133 km of expressways)

unpaved: 5,091 km (1997 est.)

Waterways: none, lake transport only

Pipelines: 0 km

Airports: 16 (1997 est.)

Airports—with paved runways:

total: 10

2,438 to 3,047 m: 2

under 914 m: 8 (1997 est.)

Airports—with unpaved runways:

total: 6

914 to 1,523 m: 2

under 914 m: 4 (1997 est.)

Top Agricultural Products (20)

Rice, tobacco, wheat, corn, millet, cotton, sesame, mulberry leaves, citrus, vegetables; beef, pork, poultry, mutton.

FINANCE, ECONOMICS, & TRADE

Economic Indicators (22)

National product: GDP—purchasing power parity—$2 billion (1997 est.)

National product real growth rate: 1.5% (1997 est.)

National product per capita: $960 (1997 est.)

Inflation rate—consumer price index: 3.5% (1997 est.)

Balance of Payments (23)

	1994	1996
Exports of goods (f.o.b.)	1,121	1,147
Imports of goods (f.o.b.)	−1,329	−1,464
Trade balance	−208	−317
Services - debits	−423	−384
Services - credits	200	200
Private transfers (net)	44	52
Government transfers (net)	180	161
Overall balance	−207	−288

Exchange Rates (24)

Exchange rates:

Denar per US$1

July 1997	.31
September 1996	.40.5
December 1995	.38.8
November 1994	.39
October 1992	.865

Top Import Origins (25)

$1.6 billion (c.i.f., 1996)

Origins	%
other former Yugoslav republics	NA
Germany	NA
Bulgaria	NA
Italy	NA
Austria	NA

NA stands for not available.

Top Export Destinations (26)

$1.2 billion (f.o.b., 1996).

Destinations	%
Bulgaria	NA
other former Yugoslav republics	NA
Germany	NA
Italy	NA

NA stands for not available.

Economic Aid (27)

Recipient: ODA, $NA. Note: US, $10 million (for humanitarian and technical assistance); in December 1995, the EU agreed to provide a credit line of ECU 21.7 million for investment projects. NA stands for not available.

Import Export Commodities (28)

Import Commodities	Export Commodities
Machinery and equipment 19%	Food
Chemicals 14%	Beverage
Fuels 12%	Tobacco 17.0%
	Machinery and transport equipment 13.3%
	Other manufactured goods 58%

MADAGASCAR

Democratic Republic of Madagascar
République Démocratique de Madagascar
Repoblika Demokratika n`i Madagaskar

INTRODUCTORY SURVEY

RECENT HISTORY

During World War II (1939–45), Madagascar was occupied by British troops to prevent its naval facilities from being used by the Japanese. In 1943, French administration was restored under General Charles de Gaulle's Free French government. Madagascar became a French overseas territory in 1946.

The Malagasy Republic became an independent nation on 26 June 1960 and on 20 September 1960 was elected to United Nations membership.

The constitution that was adopted in October 1958 and amended in June 1960 provided Madagascar with a strong presidential form of government. The president, Philibert Tsiranana, remained in power until 18 May 1972, when political protests throughout Madagascar led to the fall of his government. General Gabriel Ramanantsoa was immediately asked to form a nonpolitical ''government of national unity.'' Ramanantsoa raised the minimum wage, provided strike pay, prosecuted corrupt officials, and introduced price and currency controls. The new government also broke diplomatic ties with South Africa, established relations with the Communist countries, and arranged for the withdrawal of French military forces under new cooperation agreements with France.

In December 1975, the Second Malagasy Republic, to be called the Democratic Republic of Madagascar, was proclaimed, and Admiral Didier Ratsiraka was installed as president on 4 January

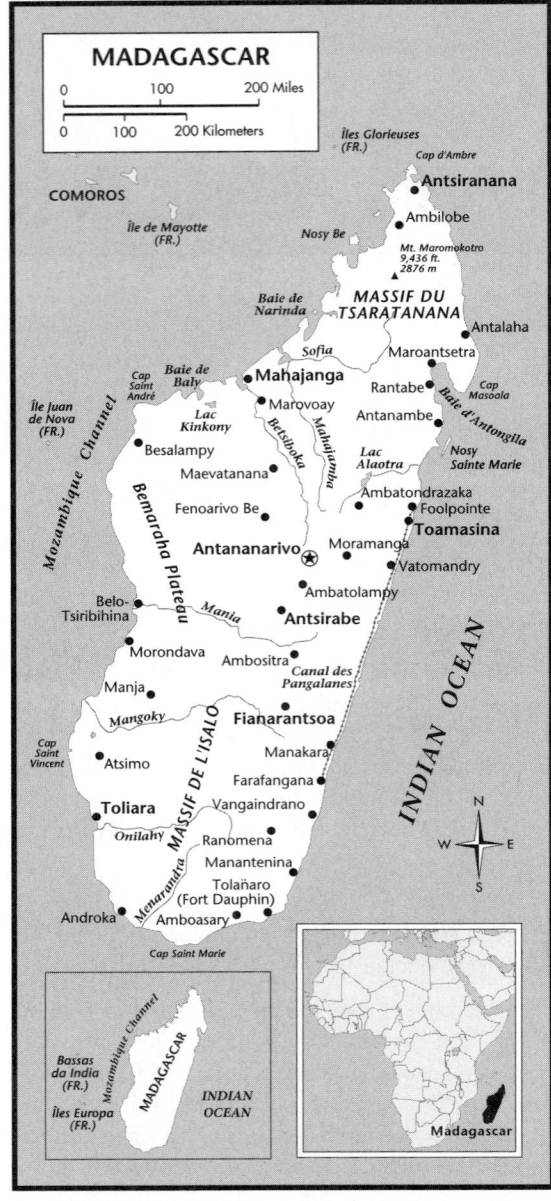

MADAGASCAR

0   100   200 Miles

0   100   200 Kilometers

COMOROS

Îles Glorieuses (FR.)

Cap d'Ambre

Antsiranana

Ambilobe

Île de Mayotte (FR.)

Nosy Be

Mt. Maromokotro 9,436 ft. 2876 m

Baie de Narinda

MASSIF DU TSARATANANA

Antalaha

Sofia

Maroantsetra

Mahajanga

Rantabe

Cap Masoala

Cap Saint André

Baie de Baly

Marovoay

Antanambe

Baie d'Antongila

Île Juan de Nova (FR.)

Lac Kinkony

Lac Alaotra

Nosy Sainte Marie

Besalampy

Maevatanana

Ambatondrazaka

Foolpointe

Mozambique Channel

Betsiboka

Mahajamba

Fenoarivo Be

Toamasina

Bemaraha Plateau

Antananarivo

Moramanga

Vatomandry

Ambatolampy

Belo-Tsiribihina

Mania

Antsirabe

Morondava

Ambositra

Canal des Pangalanes

Manja

Mangoky

Fianarantsoa

Manakara

Cap Saint Vincent

Atsimo

MASSIF DE L'ISALO

Farafangana

Vangaindrano

Toliara

Onilahy

Ranomena

Manantenina

Tolañaro (Fort Dauphin)

Androka

Mandrare

Amboasary

Cap Sainte Marie

INDIAN OCEAN

N   W   E   S

Bassas da India (FR.)

Mozambique Channel

MADAGASCAR

Îles Europa (FR.)

INDIAN OCEAN

Madagascar

Ratsiraka's Revolutionary Supreme Council stepped down from power.

On 19 August 1992, a new constitution was approved by national referendum. By the end of 1993, however, some of the provisions in the new constitution had not been met, such as the establishment of a senate and an independent judiciary. Territorial elections, the first step in the creation of the senate, were held in November 1995.

President Zafy was impeached in September 1995, and Ratsiraka defeated Zafy in a runoff election that December.

GOVERNMENT

The first government of the Third Republic was formed in late August 1993. Its August 1992 constitution provides for a two-chamber legislature—a 138-deputy National Assembly and a Senate. The National Assembly alone has the authority to choose the prime minister. Two-thirds of the senators are chosen indirectly by electors representing geographical areas and various economic and social sectors of the population, and one-third are appointed by the president.

Judiciary

At the top of the judicial system is the Supreme Court in Antananarivo. Other courts include the Court of Appeal, also in Antananarivo; courts for first trials of civil and criminal cases; ordinary and special criminal courts; and military courts. There are also a High Court of Justice to try high officials and a Constitutional Court. Military courts presided over by civilian magistrates hear cases involving national security.

The traditional courts *(dina)* continue to handle some civil disputes and recently have been used in criminal cases because of inconvenience and inadequacy of the formal court system.

Political Parties

After the democratic changes of 1992 and 1993, some 30 parties operate in Madagascar. Albert Zafy, the leader of the National Union for Democracy and Development (UNDD), heads a coalition of a dozen groups under the collective name of Comité des Forces Vives. Following his defeat in the presidential elections of 1993, Admiral Didier Ratsiraka created a new party, the Vanguard for Economic and Social Recovery (ARES—Avant Gardes pour le Redressement Économique et Social). It is a federalist party seek-

1976. The new regime accelerated growing state control of the economy, and Madagascar turned to the former Soviet Union and the Democratic People's Republic of Korea for military aid. By 1979, however, growing economic difficulties forced Ratsiraka to develop closer ties with the West. Ratsiraka was elected to a new term as president on 7 November 1982. By early 1987, the governing coalition appeared to be unraveling. On May Day, four of the parties called for the resignation of the government and early elections. By November, Ratsiraka agreed to share power with a transitional government headed by Albert Zafy, his main rival.

ing to deny central government control of the provinces. There are four other functioning parties.

DEFENSE

The armed forces of Madagascar were composed in 1995 of about 21,000 personnel, including an army of 20,000, a navy of 500 (100 marines), and an air force of 500. The navy had 2 ships and the air force 12 combat aircraft. Manpower is provided by conscription of all men from 20 to 50 for 18-month periods, but most servicemen are volunteers.

The paramilitary Gendarmerie National, which had a strength of 7,500 in 1995, is the main force for the maintenance of public order and internal security. Military spending was estimated at $49 million in 1995.

ECONOMIC AFFAIRS

Madagascar has an agriculture-based economy that supports 76% of the country's labor force. There are also substantial mineral deposits. Industry is centered on food processing and accounted for 15% of the gross domestic product (GDP) in 1995. Madagascar has made important investments in tourism.

Public Finance

Madagascar's budget has been consistently in deficit. Wages and salaries are the largest component of government expenditure. In 1991, the budget deficit amounted to 11.8% of GDP, due to a lack of revenues caused by striking civil servants who were paid wages and salaries nonetheless. Political instability in 1991 and 1992 promoted a rise in the budget deficit and slowed economic progress. Outstanding foreign debt represented 126% of GDP in 1992.

The U.S. Central Intelligence Agency estimates that, in 1993, government revenues totaled approximately $250 million and expenditures $265 million, including capital expenditures of $180 million. External debt totaled $4.3 billion.

Income

In 1997 Madagascar's gross national product (GNP) was $10.3 billion, or about $730 per person. For the period 1985–95 the average inflation rate was 17.9%, resulting in a decline in GNP of 2% per person.

Industry

Industrialization has been severely hampered by inadequate internal transportation and a re-

stricted local market. The majority of industrial enterprises process agricultural products: rice, sugar, flour, tobacco, tapioca, and sisal. In addition, there are some meat-packing plants. Urea- and ammonia-based fertilizers are produced in a plant that opened in 1985. Other industrial enterprises include two cement plants, a paper pulp factory, cotton spinning and weaving mills, and three automobile assembly plants. Industrial output grew by 2.5% annually during 1990–95.

Banking and Finance

Upon leaving the franc zone in June 1973, the government established the Central Bank of the Malagasy Republic (Banque Centrale de la République Magache). Also organized at that time were the Malagasy National Development Bank, an agricultural credit institution, and the National Investment Co., an industrial investment bank. In June 1975, the Ratsiraka government nationalized all private financial institutions. In December 1976, Bankin'ny Tantsaha Mpamokatra (BTM) was established as the national rural development bank, Bankin'ny Indostria (BNI) as the national industrial development bank, and Banky Drosoanafampan ny Varotra (BFV) as the national bank for commerce. BTM and BFV have outlets in many communities. BNI closed in the late 1980s. There is also a savings bank and a postal checking account system. Economic reforms in 1988 allowed private foreign investment in the banking sector for the first time since the banks were nationalized. In 1989, the Banque Nationale de Paris was the first French bank to open a private bank, the BMOI, since the nationalizations of 1975. Financial sector liberalization has been a key condition of adjustment support. In early 1993, the privatizaion of the three state banks was still incomplete, although from January it became possible for foreigners to buy shares in the BTM. A new bank, the Union Commercial Bank, incorporated in Mauritius, began operations in February 1993. Money supply, as measured by M1, was FMG1,848 billion at the end of 1995. There are no securities exchanges in Madagascar.

Economic Development

The 1982–84 development plan, more modest than the preceeding plans owing to limited resources, called for a shift from social investments (especially education and health) to agriculture, industry, and infrastructure. The following 1984–87 plan called for spending centered mainly on transport improvements and agricultural development.

The 1986–90 plan, which superseded the 1984–87 plan, had 30% of the budget coming from private sources and 40% from foreign sources. The plan called for investments of 47% in agriculture in the ongoing effort to achieve food self-sufficiency and crop diversification. Anti-government strikes, corruption, and a lack of commitment have limited progress on the reforms since the early 1990s.

Madagascar's main bilateral donors are France and Germany. Its main multilateral donors are the IDA and the EC. The United States, Japan, and the United Nations family of organizations are also aid contributors.

SOCIAL WELFARE

There is a National Social Security Fund that provides family allowances and workers' compensation for wage earners. Women in urban areas enjoy a highly visible and influential—although secondary—position in society. Women hold many posts in business and government. Rural women face greater hardships, engaging in subsistence labor while raising a family.

Healthcare

All medical services in Madagascar are free. Each province has a central hospital, and local clinics, dispensaries, and maternity-care centers are supplemented by mobile health units. Approximately 65% of the population has access to health care services. In 1993, there was one doctor for every 8,385 people. The most widespread diseases are malaria, leprosy, schistosomiasis, and tuberculosis. In 1994–95, 32% of the population had access to safe water, and only 17% had adequate sanitation. The average life expectancy was 58 years in 1995.

Housing

Malagasy houses, although constructed of varying materials in different parts of the island (brick and wood in the plateau, thatch and leaves in the west, and often on stilts in the east), are always rectangular, sited north–south, with the doorway opening to the west. The rapid growth of towns after the end of World War II in 1945 created grave housing and sanitation problems, especially in Antananarivo.

EDUCATION

Although education is free and compulsory between the ages of 6 and 12, there is still a considerable degree of illiteracy, estimated at 20%. In 1992, there were 1.6 million pupils attending 13,791 primary schools, secondary school enrollment was 340,191 pupils, and there were 35,824 students enrolled in higher education. The University of Madagascar in Antananarivo has several campuses. Also in Antananarivo are the Rural College of Ambatobe and the National Institute of Telecommunications and Posts.

1999 KEY EVENTS TIMELINE

January

- Frontier Resources International Inc. and Xpronet Inc. sign licensing agreements with Omnis, Madagascar's petroleum-granting authority, to conduct geological and geophysical studies in the Mozambique Channel.

February

- Madagascar's chief income source, vanilla, can now be genetically engineered in California.

- A report by UNESCO analyzes how the presence of NGOs changes social practices in Madagascar.

- An incomplete specimen of a newly named species, Rahona ostromi, is found in Madagascar; the bird fossil is a further link with dinosaur origins.

April

- Antananarivo, Madagascar is the site of a meeting to draw up a peace agreement between the island of Anjouan and the Comorian Federation.

June

- Statements by Osama bin Laden on Qatar television threatening to incite Muslim rebellion over U.S. "occupation" of Saudi Arabia results in the State Department closing U.S. embassies in Madagascar.

July

- The World Health Organization (WHO) recommends a high efficiency cholera vaccine to fight Madagascar's epidemic; over 200 people may have already died.

- The United States reopens its embassy in Madagascar.

August

- Manufacturers of vending machines for prepaid cell phones plan to make wireless communication available to Madagascar's 14 million people.

September

- Madagascar is among the heavily indebted countries eligible for U.S. debt relief.

- Madagascar fossils prove dinosaurs and early mammals existed at the same time.

October

- Paleontologists find earliest dinosaurs remains on the west side of Madagascar.

- South Africa's participation in the Slave Route Project acknowledges the former import of slaves from Madagascar to the Cape Colony.

ANALYSIS OF EVENTS: 1999

BUSINESS AND THE ECONOMY

Madagascar's economy is agricultural based, including fishing and forestry. Agriculture accounts for 32 percent of Gross Domestic Product (GDP) and contributes more than 70 percent to export earnings. Agricultural products are coffee, vanilla, sugarcane, cloves, cocoa, rice, tapioca (cassava), beans, bananas, peanuts, and livestock products. Declines in world coffee demand affect Madagascar's economy. Industrial production features textile production and the processing of agricultural products.

Soil degradation is a major problem for Madagascar. Erosion, overgrazing, deforestation, desertification, as well as surface water pollution are environmental issues. Several species of flora and fauna unique to Madagascar are endangered. The ancient fish, coelacanths that have existed for 400 million years, and once thought extinct, may now actually be going extinct.

Madagascar's biodiversity is attractive to both pharmaceutical companies and the tourism industry. In 1999 important fossil finds relating birds, mammals and dinosaurs and demonstrating the concurrence of mammals and dinosaurs has excited scientific communities and garnered popular press coverage.

GOVERNMENT AND POLITICS

The government of the Republic of Madagascar has a history of instability with political, ethnic, regional and industrial strife. Economic and governmental reforms are necessary for Madagascar's growth.

CULTURE AND SOCIETY

Madagascar's population was estimated as 14,873,387 in July 1999. Life expectancy at birth for the total population is only 53.24 years. Forty-five percent of the population falls in the age range of 0–14 years. In 1999 the infant mortality rate was as 89.1 deaths per 1,000 live births. In 1999 the total fertility rate was estimated as 5.7 children born per woman. The birth rate was 41.52 births per 1,000 population. Population growth outstrips economic growth.

Madagascar suffers from chronic malnutrition and underfunded health and education facilities. A cholera epidemic has spread rapidly around the capital, Antananarivo. Emergency supplies of cholera vaccine were shipped.

Ethnic groups are Malay-Indonesian, Cotiers (mixed African, Malayo-Indonesian, and Arab ancestry—Betsimisaraka, Tsimihety, Antaisaka, Sakalava), French, Indian, Creole, and Comoran. Indigenous beliefs predominate. Other belief systems are Christian and Muslim. Malagasy a language of Malayo-Polynesian origin is the official language. As a former French colony French is spoken among the educated. The literacy rate for the total population is 80 percent.

DIRECTORY

CENTRAL GOVERNMENT

Head of State

President
Didier Ratsiraka, Office of the President, Ambohitsirohitra 101, Antananarivo, Madagascar
PHONE: +261 (20) 33444

Prime Minister
Tantely Andrianarivo, Office of the Prime Minister, Palais de Mahazoarivo, Antananarivo, Madagascar

Ministers

Minister of Foreign Affairs
Ministry of Foreign Affairs, BP 836, Anosy,
Antananarivo 101, Madagascar
PHONE: +261 (20) 2234397; 2221198
FAX: +261 (20) 2234484

Minister of the Environment
Alphonse Randrianambinina, Ministry of the
Environment, B.P. 651 Anosy, Antananarivo
101, Madagascar
PHONE: +261 (20) 24710

Vice Prime Minister of Budget and Development of Autonomous Provinces
Pierrot Jocelyn Rajaonarivelo, Ministry of
Budget and Development of Autonomous
Provinces

Minister of Agriculture
Marcel Theophile Raveloarijaona, Ministry of
Agriculture

Minister of Armed Forces
Marcel Ranjeva, Ministry of the Armed Forces

Minister of the Civil Service, Labor, and Social Laws
Alice Razafinakanga, Ministry of the Civil
Service, Labor, and Social Laws

Minister of Commerce and Consumer Affairs
Alphonse Randrianambinina, Ministry Minister
of Commerce and Consumer Affairs

Minister of Economy and Finance
Tantely Andrianarivo, Ministry of Economy and
Finance

Minister of Energy and Mines
Charles Rasoza, Ministry of Energy and Mines

POLITICAL ORGANIZATIONS
Committee of Living Forces (CFV)
TITLE: President
NAME: Emmanuel Rakotovahiny

Support Committee for Democracy and Development in Madagascar (CSDDM)
TITLE: President
NAME: Francisque Ravony

Action and Reflection Group for the Development of Madagascar (GRAD)

Congress Party for Madagascar Independence and Renewal (AKFM-Fanavaozana)
TITLE: President
NAME: Richard Andriamanjato

Association of United Malagasys (Famima)
TITLE: Leader
NAME: Didier Ratsiraka

Confederation of Civil Societies for Development (CSCD)
NAME: Guy Willy Razanamasy

Militant Party for the Development of Madagascar (PMDM)
NAME: Manandafy Rakotonirina

Rally for Social Democracy (RPSD)
TITLE: President
NAME: Evariste Marson

DIPLOMATIC REPRESENTATION
Embassies in Madagascar

United States
14–16, rue Rainitovo, Antsahavola, BP 620,
Antananarivo, Madagascar
PHONE: +261 (22) 20089; 21257
FAX: +261 (22) 34539
TITLE: Charge d'Affaires
NAME: Howard T. Perlow

JUDICIAL SYSTEM
Supreme Court
High Constitutional Court

FURTHER READING
Articles

Fountain, Henry. ''Scientists Find what May Be
Oldest Known Dinosaur Bones.'' *The New
York Times,* 22 October 1999, p. A23.

Lemonick, Michael D. ''Bones from The Dawn
of Dinosaurs: Madagascar Fossils May Be the
Oldest Yet Found.'' *Time* (November 1,
1999): 83.

''Madagascar: U.S. Embassy Reopens .'' *The
New York Times,* 13 July 1999, p. A4.

Books

Allen, Philip M. *Madagascar: Conflicts of Authority in the Great Island.* Boulder: Westview Press, 1995.

Ellis, Royston and John R. Jones *Madagascar. Festivals of the World Series.* Milwaukee: G. Stevens Pub., 1999.

Middleton, Karen. *Ancestors, Power, and History in Madagascar.* Boston: Brill, 1999.

MADAGASCAR: STATISTICAL DATA

For sources and notes see "Sources of Statistics" in the front of each volume.

GEOGRAPHY

Geography (1)

Area:

Total: 587,040 sq km.

Land: 581,540 sq km.

Water: 5,500 sq km.

Area—comparative: slightly less than twice the size of Arizona.

Land boundaries: 0 km.

Coastline: 4,828 km.

Climate: tropical along coast, temperate inland, arid in south.

Terrain: narrow coastal plain, high plateau and mountains in center.

Natural resources: graphite, chromite, coal, bauxite, salt, quartz, tar sands, semiprecious stones, mica, fish.

Land use:

Arable land: 4%

Permanent crops: 1%

Permanent pastures: 41%

Forests and woodland: 40%

Other: 14% (1993 est.).

HUMAN FACTORS

Demographics (2A)

	1990	1995	1998	2000	2010	2020	2030	2040	2050
Population	11,524.8	13,288.9	14,462.5	15,294.5	20,095.6	25,987.5	32,827.6	40,358.6	48,327.1
Net migration rate (per 1,000 population)	NA	NA	NA	NA	NA	NA	NA	NA	NA
Births	NA	NA	NA	NA	NA	NA	NA	NA	NA
Deaths	NA	NA	NA	NA	NA	NA	NA	NA	NA
Life expectancy - males	49.3	50.8	51.7	52.3	55.3	58.3	61.1	63.8	66.3
Life expectancy - females	50.9	52.9	54.1	54.9	59.0	62.9	66.6	70.0	73.0
Birth rate (per 1,000)	44.5	43.0	41.9	41.2	37.5	33.7	29.8	26.4	23.4
Death rate (per 1,000)	16.0	14.7	13.8	13.3	10.9	9.1	7.8	7.1	6.7
Women of reproductive age (15-49 yrs.)	2,593.2	3,025.3	3,313.5	3,520.7	4,762.1	6,332.6	8,252.1	10,397.1	12,597.0
of which are currently married	NA	NA	NA	NA	NA	NA	NA	NA	NA
Fertility rate	6.2	5.9	5.8	5.6	5.0	4.3	3.7	3.3	2.9

Except as noted, values for vital statistics are in thousands; life expectancy is in years.

Health Personnel (3)

Total health expenditure as a percentage of GDP, 1990-1997[a]

Public sector 1.4

Private sector . . . . .NA

Total[b] . . . . .NA

Health expenditure per capita in U.S. dollars, 1990-1997[a]

Purchasing power parity . . . . .NA

Total . . . . .NA

Availability of health care facilities per 100,000 people

Hospital beds 1990-1997[a] 0.90

Doctors 1993[c] 24

Nurses 1993[c] 55

Health Indicators (4)

Life expectancy at birth

1980 51

1997 57

Daily per capita supply of calories (1996) 2,001

Total fertility rate births per woman (1997) 5.8

Maternal mortality ratio per 100,000 live births (1990-97) . . . . .500[d]

Safe water % of population with access (1995) 16

Sanitation % of population with access (1995) 34

Consumption of iodized salt % of households (1992-98)[a] 73

Smoking prevalence

Male % of adults (1985-95)[a] . . . .

Female % of adults (1985-95)[a] . . . .

Tuberculosis incidence per 100,000 people (1997) 205

Adult HIV prevalence % of population ages 15-49 (1997) 0.12

Infants and Malnutrition (5)

Under-5 mortality rate (1997) 158

% of infants with low birthweight (1990-97) 5

Births attended by skilled health staff % of total[a] . . .57

% fully immunized (1995-97)

TB 64

DPT 46

Polio 45

Measles 39

Prevalence of child malnutrition under age 5 (1992-97)[b] 34

Ethnic Division (6)

Malayo-Indonesian (Merina and related Betsileo), Cotiers (mixed African, Malayo-Indonesian, and Arab ancestry — Betsimisaraka, Tsimihety, Antaisaka, Sakalava), French, Indian, Creole, Comoran.

Religions (7)

Indigenous beliefs 52%

Christian 41%

Muslim 7%

Languages (8)

French (official), Malagasy (official).

EDUCATION

Public Education Expenditures (9)

Public expenditure on education (% of GNP)

1980 . . . . .4.4

1996 . . . . .1.9[1]

Expenditure per student

Primary % of GNP per capita

1980 . . . . .9.2

1996 . . . . .5.1[1]

Secondary % of GNP per capita

1980 . . . . .36.2

1996 . . . .

Tertiary % of GNP per capita

1980 . . . . .402.7

1996 . . . .

Expenditure on teaching materials

Primary % of total for level (1996) 1.1

Secondary % of total for level (1996) . . . .

Primary pupil-teacher ratio per teacher (1996) . . . . .37[1]

Duration of primary education years (1995) 5

Literacy Rates (11B)

Adult literacy rate

1980

Male 56%

Female 43%

1995

Male 60

Female 32

GOVERNMENT & LAW

Political Parties (12)

National Assembly	No. of seats
Committee of Living Forces (CFV) coalition	76
Militant Party for the Development of Madagascar (PMDM/MFM)	16
Confederation of Civil Societies for Development (CSCD)	11
Famima	10
Rally for Social Democracy (RPSD)	7
Various pro-Ratsiraka groups	10
Others	8

Government Budget (13A)

Year: 1996

Total Expenditures: 2,799.1 Billions of Francs

Expenditures as a percentage of the total by function:

General public services and public order	19.73
Defense	5.40
Education	9.13
Health	6.83
Social Security and Welfare	93
Housing and community amenities	....
Recreational, cultural, and religious affairs	24
Fuel and energy	....

Military Affairs (14B)

	1990	1991	1992	1993	1994	1995
Military expenditures						
Current dollars (mil.)	33	31	30	37	30	28
1995 constant dollars (mil.)	37	35	33	39	31	28
Armed forces (000)	21	21	21	21	21	21
Gross national product (GNP)						
Current dollars (mil.)	2,665	2,565	2,674	2,828	2,871	3,037
1995 constant dollars (mil.)	3,063	2,835	2,876	2,965	2,943	3,037
Central government expenditures (CGE)						
1995 constant dollars (mil.)	548	499	606	636	604	557
People (mil.)	11.5	11.9	12.2	12.6	12.9	13.3
Military expenditure as % of GNP	1.2	1.2	1.1	1.3	1.0	.9
Military expenditure as % of CGE	6.8	7.0	5.4	6.1	5.1	5.0
Military expenditure per capita (1995 $)	3	3	3	.3	2	2
Armed forces per 1,000 people (soldiers)	1.8	1.8	1.7	1.7	1.6	1.6
GNP per capita (1995 $)	266	239	236	236	228	229
Arms imports[6]						
Current dollars (mil.)	10	0	0	0	0	5
1995 constant dollars (mil.)	11	0	0	0	0	5
Arms exports[6]						
Current dollars (mil.)	0	0	0	0	0	0
1995 constant dollars (mil.)	0	0	0	0	0	0
Total imports[7]						
Current dollars (mil.)	571	450	448	468	428	499
1995 constant dollars (mil.)	656	497	482	491	439	499
Total exports[7]						
Current dollars (mil.)	319	305	277	261	406	364
1995 constant dollars (mil.)	367	337	298	274	416	364
Arms as percent of total imports[8]	1.8	0	0	0	0	1.0
Arms as percent of total exports[8]	0	0	0	0	0	0

Agriculture, forestry, fishing, and hunting 10.21

Mining, manufacturing, and construction . . . .

Transportation and communication 1.29

Other economic affairs and services 2.70

Crime (15)

Crime rate (for 1994)

Crimes reported 10,752

Total persons convicted .NA

Crimes per 100,000 population 75

Persons responsible for offenses

Total number of suspects 6,150

Total number of female suspects 781

Total number of juvenile suspects 30

LABOR FORCE

Unemployment Rate (17)

Rate not available.

PRODUCTION SECTOR

Electric Energy (18)

Capacity . . . . .220,000 kW (1995)

Production . . . . .595 million kWh (1995)

Consumption per capita . . . . .43 kWh (1995)

Transportation (19)

Highways:

total: 49,837 km

paved: 5,781 km

unpaved: 44,056 km (1996 est.)

Waterways: of local importance only; isolated streams and small portions of Canal des Pangalanes

Merchant marine:

total: 10 ships (1,000 GRT or over) totaling 20,624 GRT/28,621 DWT ships by type: cargo 4, chemical tanker 1, liquefied gas tanker 1, oil tanker 2, roll-on/roll-off cargo 2 (1997 est.)

Airports: 136 (1997 est.)

Airports—with paved runways:

total: 30

over 3,047 m: 1

2,438 to 3,047 m: 2

1,524 to 2,437 m: 3

914 to 1,523 m: 22

under 914 m: 2 (1997 est.)

Airports—with unpaved runways:

total: 106

1,524 to 2,437 m: 4

914 to 1,523 m: 60

under 914 m: 42 (1997 est.)

Top Agricultural Products (20)

Coffee, vanilla, sugarcane, cloves, cocoa, rice, cassava (tapioca), beans, bananas, peanuts; livestock products.

MANUFACTURING SECTOR

GDP & Manufacturing Summary (21)

Detailed value added figures are listed by both International Standard Industry Code (ISIC) and product title.

	1980	1985	1990	1994
GDP ($-1990 mil.)	2,194	2,076	2,376	2,292
Per capita ($-1990)	242	195	189	160
Manufacturing share (%) (current prices)	11.9	10.2	12.4	9.4
Manufacturing				
Value added ($-1990 mil.)	335	244	285	268
Industrial production index	100	75	92	66
Value added ($ mil.)	221	132	145	121
Gross output ($ mil.)	569	328	351	300
Employment (000)	41	47	47	49
Profitability (% of gross output)				
Intermediate input (%)	61	60	59	60
Wages and salaries inc. supplements (%)	15	16	13	13
Gross operating surplus	24	25	28	27
Productivity ($)				
Gross output per worker	14,005	6,872	7,089	5,721
Value added per worker	5,439	2,782	2,975	2,333
Average wage (inc. supplements)	2,083	1,099	972	804
Value added ($ mil.)				
311/2 Food products	23	45	19	18
313 Beverages	34	16	16	13
314 Tobacco products	3	3	2	1
321 Textiles	67	16	59	43

	1980	1985	1990	1994
322 Wearing apparel	19	6	4	4
323 Leather and fur products	3	1	1	1
324 Footwear	8	5	3	2
331 Wood and wood products	2	1	1	1
332 Furniture and fixtures	2	—	1	1
341 Paper and paper products	4	3	5	5
342 Printing and publishing	6	2	2	2
351 Industrial chemicals	1	1	1	—
352 Other chemical products	10	11	9	8
353 Petroleum refineries	11	7	9	9
354 Miscellaneous petroleum and coal products	—	—	—	—
355 Rubber products	1	1	1	1
356 Plastic products	3	2	2	2
361 Pottery, china and earthenware	—	—	—	—
362 Glass and glass products	2	—	1	1
369 Other non-metal mineral products	2	1	3	3
371 Iron and steel	—	—	—	—
372 Non-ferrous metals	—	—	—	—
381 Metal products	9	5	4	4
382 Non-electrical machinery	—	—	—	—
383 Electrical machinery	3	3	2	2
384 Transport equipment	7	2	2	2
385 Professional and scientific equipment	—	—	—	—
390 Other manufacturing industries	2	1	—	1

FINANCE, ECONOMICS, & TRADE

Economic Indicators (22)

National product: GDP—purchasing power parity—$10.3 billion (1997 est.)

National product real growth rate: 3% (1997 est.)

National product per capita: $730 (1997 est.)

Inflation rate—consumer price index: 19.8% (1996)

Exchange Rates (24)

Exchange rates:

Malagasy francs (FMG) per US$1

December 1997 . . . . .5,302.9

1997 . . . . .5,090.9

1996 . . . . .4,061.3

1995 . . . . .4,265.6

1994 . . . . .3,067.3

1993 . . . . .1,913.8

Balance of Payments (23)

	1992	1993	1994	1995	1996
Exports of goods (f.o.b.)	327	335	450	507	509
Imports of goods (f.o.b.)	−471	−514	−546	−628	−629
Trade balance	−144	−180	−96	−122	−120
Services - debits	−413	−456	−486	−533	−542
Services - credits	180	190	208	249	299
Private transfers (net)	79	81	56	61	137
Government transfers (net)	101	107	41	67	73
Overall balance	−197	−258	−277	−277	−153

Top Import Origins (25)

$612 million (f.o.b., 1996 est.) Data are for 1995.

Origins	%
France	.40
Japan	NA
Hong Kong	NA
Singapore	NA
United States	NA

NA stands for not available.

Top Export Destinations (26)

$493 million (f.o.b., 1996 est.) Data are for 1995.

Destinations	%
France	.41
United States	NA

Japan	NA
Italy	NA

NA stands for not available.

Economic Aid (27)

Recipient: ODA, $454 million (1992-96).

Import Export Commodities (28)

Import Commodities	Export Commodities
Intermediate manufactures 30%	Coffee 45%
Capital goods 28%	Vanilla 20%
Petroleum 15%	Cloves
Consumer goods 14%	Shellfish
Food 13%	Sugar
	Petroleum products

MALAWI

Republic of Malawi

INTRODUCTORY SURVEY

RECENT HISTORY

Between World Wars I (1914–18) and II (1939–45), Nyasaland seemed headed for eventual independence. In 1953, however, it was joined with the two Rhodesias—Northern Rhodesia (now Zambia) and Southern Rhodesia (now Zimbabwe)—in the Central African Federation.

When African citizens expressed angry opposition to the federation in 1959, a state of emergency was declared. In 1960, the Malawi Congress Party (MCP), headed by Dr. Hastings Kamuzu Banda, stepped up the campaign against federation rule. At a constitutional conference held in London in November 1962, it was agreed that Nyasaland should become fully self-governing early in 1963, and that Banda, who headed the MCP, should become prime minister.

On 6 July 1964, Nyasaland became a fully independent member of the British Commonwealth of Nations, and adopted the name Malawi. On 6 July 1966, Banda assumed the presidency. During the first decade of Banda's presidency, Malawi's relations with its neighbors, ruled by blacks, were sometimes stormy. In addition to claiming extensive territories outside the present boundaries of Malawi, Malawi became the first black African country to establish diplomatic relations with white-ruled South Africa; moreover, Banda became the first black African head of state to be officially received in South Africa, which supplied arms and development funds to Malawi.

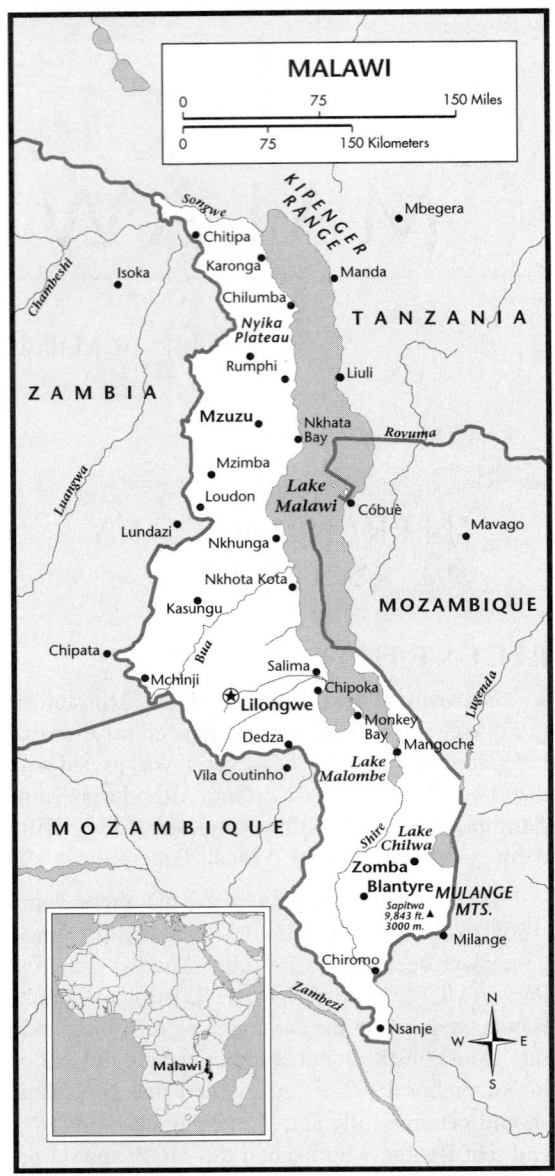

MALAWI

Banda continued to rule Malawi with an iron hand through the 1970s and into the late 1980s. During his rule his opponents were treated severely. Several thousand people were imprisoned for political offenses at one time or another, and leaders of opposition groups were persecuted.

Opposition to Banda's harsh rule strengthened and Banda's grip on the country began to weaken. Under mounting pressure, Banda agreed to hold a referendum early in 1993 on whether Malawi should remain a one-party state. On 14 June 1993, 63% of those voting favored adopting multiparty

democracy. Banda agreed to hold elections in 1994 and to draft a new constitution. Parliament adopted laws ending one-party rule and imprisonment without trial, and allowing dissidents to return home.

In the 17 May 1994 elections, Bakili Muluzi, a former cabinet minister, was elected president over Banda and two other candidates. Muluzi immediately ordered the release of political prisoners and the closing of the most notorious jails. The transition of power was fairly smooth, and an atmosphere of relative tolerance prevails.

GOVERNMENT

Malawi officially became a republic on 6 July 1966. The new constitution took effect on 18 May 1995. The president is the head of state and supreme executive authority. Legislative power is vested in the single-chamber National Assembly, and all adults may vote. Parliamentary elections are to occur every five years unless the president dissolves the National Assembly before then. In March 1995, the National Assembly voted to establish a second chamber of parliament (a senate of 80 seats) in 1999.

Judiciary

The constitution provides for an independent judiciary, and the government respects this provision. Defendants have the right to public trial, to have an attorney, to challenge evidence and witnesses, and to an appeal. There are numerous local courts throughout Malawi, with a chain of appeals from the local courts up to a Supreme Court of Appeal.

In 1993, the attorney general suspended the operation of regional and national level traditional courts. Traditional courts at the local level may survive the recent reforms and continue to hear cases involving small claims and customary law.

Political Parties

Malawi was officially a one-party state from October 1973 until July 1993. The Malawi Congress Party (MCP) was the national party and Hastings Kamuzu Banda was its president for life. In a referendum on 14 June 1993, voters rejected single-party rule by a margin of 63% to 35%, and opposition parties and coalitions blossomed. Elections were held on 17 May 1994, with seven parties participating. The United Democratic Front (UDF) won, trailed by the MCP and two other parties.

DEFENSE

In 1995, Malawi had an army of 9,800 men, organized into 3 infantry battalions and 1 support battalion. The air wing had 80 men and 6 transports. A 220-member naval force had 1 lake patrol craft. In 1995 Malawi spent $21 million on defense.

ECONOMIC AFFAIRS

Malawi's agricultural economy has been troubled in recent years by drought and financial instability. It is dependent for most of its income on the export sales of tobacco, tea, peanuts, coffee, and sugar. International aid donors, concerned about human rights abuses in Malawi, have tied future support to human rights reforms.

Public Finance

Government current revenues derive from import duties, income taxes on companies and individuals, income from government enterprises, excise duties, licenses, and sales tax. The fiscal year runs from 1 April to 31 March. The U.S. Central Intelligence Agency estimates that, in 1994, government revenues totaled approximately $530 million and expenditures $674 million, including capital expenditures of $129 million. External debt totaled $1.95 billion.

Income

In 1997, Malawi's gross national product (GNP) was $8.6 billion, or $900 per person. During 1985–95, the average annual decline of the GNP was 0.7% per person, and the inflation rate averaged 22%.

Industry

Malawi's manufacturing sector is diverse. The processing of tea, tobacco, sugar, coffee, and cotton accounts for most of its output. Factories manufacture soap, detergents, cigarettes, furniture, cookies, bread, blankets and rugs, clothing, and mineral waters. Other operations include a gin distillery, a cotton mill, and two textile plants.

Banking and Finance

The Reserve Bank of Malawi was established in Blantyre in 1964. It took over, by stages, the functions in Malawi of the former Bank of Rhodesia and Nyasaland until that bank wound up its affairs in June 1965. The main duties of the Reserve Bank are to maintain currency stability and to act as banker to the government and to the commercial banks. The Reserve Bank administers exchange control and acts as registrar for local registered stock. The Reserve Bank also handles the issue of treasury bills on behalf of the government. Money supply, as measured by M2, was K4,148 million at the end of 1995.

Malawi's financial services are unsophisticated and basic. Aside from the central bank, there are five licensed commercial banks, which are dominated by the two leading banks, the National Bank of Malawi and the Commercial Bank of Malawi, with branches or agencies throughout the country. In 1993, the former was 47% owned by Press Corp., 33% by ADMARC, and 20% by Standard Bank (UK); the latter was 40% owned by Press Corp., 30% by local interests, 20% by the Malawi Development Corp., and 10% by ADMARC. The Investment and Development Bank of Malawi (Indebank), formed in 1972 with foreign and local participation, provides medium- and long-term credit. The Finance Bank Malawi and the First Merchant Bank, which is privately owned by Malawian and Kenyan shareholders, were granted licenses in 1995. Although the country's financial market has been liberalized, the sole mortgage finance institution, the New Building Society, which came into operation at independence in March 1964, faces no competition. The New Building Society's assets stood at K3.7 billion ($244.5 million) in 1995.

A subsidiary of Indebank, the Investment and Development Fund (Indefund), finances small and medium-sized enterprises. The Malawi Development Corporation (MDC), which services the needs of large-scale industry, is state-owned. The Post Office Savings Bank (POSB) was restructured in 1994 and licensed as a commercial bank, the Malawi Savings Bank (MSB). Other major financial institutions include National Mercantile Credit, the Leasing and Financing Co. of Malawi, and the National Insurance Co. (NICO). In total, Malawi has two savings banks, four development finance institutions, four leasing and finance companies, and seven insurance companies.

The Malawi Stock Exchange (MSE) was established in December 1994 along with Stockbrokers Malawi to deal with listed company shares and to act as a broker in government and other securities approved by the Reserve Bank of Malawi (RBM). The stock exchange had no listings until November 1996, when shares in NICO were put up for sale. Since November 1994, the RBM has marketed Treasury bills of varying maturities (30, 61, 91, and 182 days) in an attempt to encourage greater participation by the private sector.

Foreign reserves in Malawi in 1996 improved to K2.66 billion ($175.6 million). The healthy growth of reserves helped the RBM to maintain the kwacha at a stable rate, although many independent economists argue that the currency is still slightly overvalued.

Economic Development

Malawi's public investment program is revised annually to take account of changing needs and the expected availability of resources. The development program continues to be financed largely from external sources, and priority in the use of local resources is given to counterpart contributions to these external loans, grants, and investments.

During the first decades of independence, agricultural development were emphasized. The government sought to implement this policy by providing the family farmer with basic agricultural support facilities, such as extension services, training, irrigation, and research, and by increasing the output of fertile areas through farm credit, marketing, and processing facilities. During this period, four major agricultural developments were sponsored: the Shire Valley Agricultural Development Project in the south; the Lilongwe Land Development Program and the Central Region Lakeshore Development Project, both in the Central Region; and the Karonga Rural Development Project in the north.

More recently, improvements in the transportation infrastructure, especially in roads, have been emphasized. In the manufacturing sector, the government has stressed diversification. With major constraints on its foreign exchange, Malawi aims to reduce the trade gap, encourage exports, and reduce government expenditures.

The United Kingdom is Malawi's principal aid donor. South Africa has been a significant source of aid as well, especially in financing construction in the capital at Lilongwe and the railway extension from Lilongwe to Mchinji. Other significant aid donors have included the European Community, France, Canada, Germany, Japan, the United States, Denmark, the African Development Bank, and the World Bank/IDA.

SOCIAL WELFARE

The Ministry of Community Services is responsible for social welfare generally. Government hospitals and clinics provide some medical services to residents without charge.

Beginning in 1992, a gradual improvement in Malawi's human rights record was evident. However, the use of excessive force and mistreatment of prisoners are still reported. Vigilante killings (executions conducted by a group of citizens that have taken the law into their own hands) are increasing.

Healthcare

Health services in Malawi rank among the poorest in Africa. The major health threats are malnutrition, malaria, and tuberculosis. In addition, there are thousands of acquired immune deficiency syndrome (AIDS) cases in Malawi. In 1994, an estimated 13.6% of all adults were infected with HIV, the virus that causes AIDS. There were 43,067 new cases of AIDS reported in 1996. Life expectancy averages 43 years. From 1988–93, there was one physician for approximately 50,360 people.

Housing

Government-built houses are either rented or sold. The Malawi Housing Corp. has also developed housing plots in order to relocate urban squatters.

EDUCATION

School attendance is compulsory for eight years at the primary level. In 1994, Malawi's 3,425 primary schools had 2.9 million pupils; secondary schools had 49,412 students. The University of Malawi has three campuses. In 1993 there were 309 teachers and 3,684 pupils at all higher level institutions.

1999 KEY EVENTS TIMELINE

January

- Conflicts in the Democratic Republic of the Congo, Sierra Leone and other parts of Africa push refugees to Malawi.

- A delegation from the Danish Ministry of Foreign Affairs visits Malawi and discusses with Malawi government officials on development cooperation.

- The German government, which is expected to finance a substantial part of Malawi's forthcoming elections, expresses concern over political violence in the run up to the elections.

February

- A prisoner dies due to the cash-strapped Malawi government's inability to buy food for its prison population.

- Cholera kills 500 people in Malawi.

- Libya donates some 20,000 metric tons of maize and six million U.S. dollars worth of fertilizer to boost Malawi's agriculture.

March

- The president of Malawi, Bakili Muluzi, and his wife separate.

- Cheaper chickens and eggs from Zimbabwe and South Africa smother Malawi's poultry industry with many local poultry producers closing down in the wake of the influx of the imported poultry products.

- Taiwan builds an $18-million hospital in the city of Mzuzu in northern Malawi.

- A senior World Bank official admits that Structural Adjustment Programs, introduced in developing countries such as Malawi to turn around stagnant economies, have failed to achieve the intended results because of the donors' administrative glitches.

April

- Malawi President Bakili Muluzi and visiting President Moi of Kenya officially open the first TV studios in Malawi.

- More than 2,000 people are reported to have been made homeless by floods in Karonga North in northern Malawi.

- Malawi's Tobacco Control Commission expresses optimism with the 1999 sales of tobacco at the local market with better prices than in 1998.

- Scores of supporters of Malawi's main opposition party, the Alliance for Democracy, are injured after a fight with supporters of President Bakili Muluzi's ruling party in the northern city of Mzuzu.

- Presidential candidates from various political parties present their nomination papers to the electoral commission for the forthcoming presidential election.

May

- Over-fishing and poaching cause depletion of fish populations, Malawi's main protein source, in Lakes Malawi, Malombe and Chilwa.

- Good rains produce a good maize crop this agricultural season ending, at least in the short term, the chronic food shortages in Malawi.

- Zanzibari president comes to Malawi on four-day official visit.

June

- With 51 percent of the votes, Bakili Muluzi, the incumbent president is declared winner in the multiparty elections held on June 15.

- Opposition leaders dispute election results and reject President Muluzi as winner.

- At least two persons die and ten mosques are razed to the ground as post-election violence erupts in the opposition alliance stronghold in Malawi's northern region.

- Bakili Muluzi is inaugurated for his second and final term as president of Malawi in a lavish and colorful ceremony amid opposition efforts to block ceremony.

- Muluzi names new cabinet in which some controversial members are dropped.

July

- A local NGO, the Coordination Unit for Rehabilitation of the Environment, embarks on a project aimed at extracting juice from wild fruits for sale.

- The price of bread and other essentials such as fuel go up by more than 8 percent.

- Tobacco sales in Malawi come to a close earning the national coffers some 16 million U.S. dollars.

- The government of Eritrea condemns the death of one Eritrean and the injuring of seven others while in police custody as illegal aliens in Malawi.

- Saudi Arabia and Malawi decide to establish diplomatic relations at the embassy level.

- Libyan and visiting Malawian officials hold talks in Libya on bilateral cooperation between the two countries.

September

- Exploration and research under the waters of Lake Malawi shows that the lake may have hydrocarbons in its rocks and could be drilled for oil.

- State House in Blantyre officially announces that the country is to have a new First Lady.

- The Botswana-based African Conference of NGOs Against War in Africa brings together feuding political parties in Malawi to a two-day peace conference in Blantyre.

- The Electoral Commission in Malawi suspends two of its commissioners allegedly for sympathizing with the opposition.

- The Malawi government arrests another eight illegal Eritrean immigrants from the Dzaleka refugee camp for deportation.

October

- Joseph, the son of Malawi parliament's Speaker Sam Mpasu, is arrested and jailed for two years for fraud in South Africa.

- Malawi's fish industry faces an additional setback to over-fishing, as hundreds of fish die in Lake Malawi due to unprecedented strong winds blowing on the lake causing up-welling and the rise of sulfur from the bottom. This poisons and suffocates the fish.

- Malawian police in the southern district of Machinga, about 120 km east of Blantyre, hold a 39-year-old man for trying to sell his own two-year-old daughter for 90,000 kwacha (about 2,000 U.S. dollars).

- President Bakili Muluzi remarries; he denies using public funds to fund his lavish marriage ceremony.

December

- Malawi qualifies for debt relief from Britain under that country's Heavily Indebted Poor Countries (HIPC) initiative. Malawi, a former British colony, owes about $2.3 billion.

- The health minister reports that cholera cases are on the rise, with 17 new urban cases and 52 from rural areas.

ANALYSIS OF EVENTS: 1999

BUSINESS AND THE ECONOMY

On the economic and business fronts, the year 1999 was a mixed one for Malawi. Part of the reason for the poor performance of the Malawian economy lies in the devastating effects of the World Bank-imposed Structural Adjustment Programs. However internal mismanagement and corruption also played a substantial role in the economic malaise. After over 15 years of structural adjustment, the Malawian economy is in far worse shape now than it was 15 years ago. Malawi, with more than 60 percent of its 11 million people living in abject poverty, has a budget deficit of 42 million U.S. dollars, an external debt of 2.4 billion dollars and inflation at 55 percent. Malawi, with an average annual per capita income of K8,800 (US$200), has been rated the eighth worst nation of the world in economic performance, according to the *World Development Report 1999/2000* compiled by the World Bank. Malawi's per capita income is about the same as that of Eritrea and only slightly better than Niger's U.S.$190, Burundi's U.S.$140, Sierra Leone's U.S.$160 and Ethiopia's U.S.$100.

Burdened by debt already owed to Western countries and by the World Bank's sets of conditions, the country this year sought aid from the Islamic nations of Kuwaiti, Saudi Arabia, Libya, and others. This was also in part due to the ascendancy to the presidency by Bakili Muluzi in 1994, himself a Muslim. For example, in 1999 Libya donated some 20,000 metric tons of maize and six million U.S. dollars worth of fertilizer to boost Malawi's agriculture. Other Islamic countries such as Saudi Arabia, Kuwaiti and the Gulf Emirates pledged financial support to the Muluzi government.

Good rains during the 1999 growing season meant bumper harvests of tobacco, the main cash crop, and maize, the main staple. Tobacco sales brought in 16 million U.S. dollars into government coffers. There were two other promising events: exploration and research under the waters of Lake Malawi revealed that the lake had potential for its rocks containing hydrocarbons which could be drilled for oil. Also, the World Bank was upbeat about Malawi's economy noting that despite

Malawi's current economic hardships, the economic reform measures the government has put in place were likely to bring inflation down to 23 percent from the current 55 percent. In spite of the good harvest, the economy faltered as prices of basic commodities such as bread, fuel and electricity rose due to the devaluation of the Kwacha and massive inflation.

The lowering of trade barriers brought the smothering of local industries by cheaper products from surrounding countries. One example was Malawi's poultry industry that has been out-competed by the influx of cheaper chickens and eggs from Zimbabwe and South Africa. The fish industry, a major source of protein for most Malawians, faced two setbacks: One was over-fishing. A second was the death of hundreds of fish in Lake Malawi due to strong winds blowing on the lake causing the rise of sulfur from the bottom, suffocating the fish.

GOVERNMENT AND POLITICS

The general parliamentary and presidential elections of June 15 took center stage in Malawi's political life. Beginning in January 1999 donors such as the governments of Germany and Denmark (both of which were to finance a substantial part of Malawi's elections) expressed concern over political violence in the run up to the elections. The ruling United Democratic Front under the incumbent president, Bakili Muluzi, and the main opposition party, the Alliance for Democracy clashed in pre-election violence. Bakili Muluzi also tried to legally rig the elections by re-drawing the boundaries of the constituencies, creating 70 new constituencies, 42 of which were to be allocated to the Southern Region—President Muluzi's ruling UDF stronghold.

To the dismay of the Alliance for Democracy, Muluzi emerged winner with 51 percent of the votes in the June 15 presidential elections. The elections were declared generally free and fair by international observers. However, after the election riots in the Northern Region broke out in protest again Muluzi's victory. At least two people died and 10 mosques were razed to the ground. The opposition refused to recognize Muluzi as the winner alleging that his party had rigged the elections. The opposition tried but failed to legally block the colorful and lavish inauguration ceremony to Bakili's second term that was held in Blantyre on June 21. Perhaps to placate his critics, Muluzi

named a new cabinet in which former key but controversial figures were dropped. Some of the other ministers were quick to criticize the government for corruption.

On other fronts, the Muluzi government continued to strengthen alliances with the Islamic countries of Saudi Arabia, Zanzibar, Libya, Kuwaiti, to mention a few, raising some eyebrows in Western donor community. Other leaders from southern and eastern Africa also paid official visits to Malawi to discuss issues concerning regional cooperation and development. Although Malawi stayed clear in the regional conflict brewing in the Democratic Republic of Congo (DRC), its effects were felt in the refugee entering Malawi from the DRC.

CULTURE AND SOCIETY

After separating from his first wife in March of 1999, President Muluzu publicly married his second wife in October. Muluzi has been publicly accused of insensitivity for spending hundreds of thousands of dollars, allegedly from government coffers on the private ceremony while most Malawians are poverty stricken. He denied everything on national television immediately after the wedding. Six heads of state, namely, Robert Mugabe of Zimbabwe, Fredrick Chiluba of Zambia, Joaquim Chissano of Mozambique, Pierre Buyoya of Burundi, King Mswati III of Swaziland and Pakaliti Mosisili of Lesotho were among the 5,000 invited guests at what has been dubbed ''Malawi's wedding of the millennium.''

Other important events that affected Malawian society included the appalling conditions in Malawian prisons where death, disease and misery have replaced the true mission of the prisons as institutions of rehabilitation. Health and health care continued to decline with diseases such as cholera, tuberculosis, and AIDS taking a toll of Malawian lives. The good rains meant flooding in the lowlands where many people drowned or were made homeless. On a positive note, the country saw the launching of its first television broadcasting studio, Television Malawi. Malawi police were also able to crack an inter-continental sex ring that lured young Malawian girls for commercial sex work in several European countries.

DIRECTORY

CENTRAL GOVERNMENT

Head of State

President and Minister of Defense
Bakili Muluzi, Office of the President

Vice President and Minister of Privatisation
Justin Malewezi, Office of the Vice President

Ministers

Minister of Agriculture and Irrigation Development
Aleke Banda, Ministry of Agriculture and Irrigation Development

Minister of Natural Resources and Environmental Affairs
Harry Thomson, Ministry of Natural Resources and Environmental Affairs

Minister of Foreign Affairs and International Cooperation
Brown Mpinganjira, Ministry of Foreign Affairs and International Cooperation

Minister of Justice and Attorney General
Peter Fatchi, Ministry of Justice and Attorney General

Minister of Finance
Cassim Chilumpha, Ministry of Finance, PO Box 30049, Capital City, Lilongwe 3, Malawi
PHONE: +265 782199
FAX: +265 781679

Minister of Home Affairs and Internal Security
Patrick Mbewe, Ministry of Home Affairs and Internal Security

Minister of State for Presidential Affairs
Rodwell Munyenyembe, Ministry of State for Presidential Affairs

Minister of Tourism, National Parks and Wildlife
George Mtafu, Ministry of Tourism, National Parks and Wildlife

Minister of Commerce and Industry
Kaliyoma Phumisa, Ministry of Commerce and Industry

Minister of Health
Lilian Patel, Ministry of Health

Minister of Transport and Public Works
Peter Chupa, Ministry of Transport and Public Works

Minister of Lands, Housing and Physical Planning
Thengo Maloya, Ministry of Lands, Housing and Physical Planning

Minister in the President's Office Responsible for District and Local Government Administration
Uladi Mussa, Ministry of District and Local Government Administration

Minister of Education, Sports and Culture
Ken Lipenga, Ministry of Education, Sports and Culture

Minister in the President's Office Responsible for Statutory Corporations
Bob Khamisa, Ministry of Statutory Corporations

Minister of Water Development
Yusufu Mwawa, Ministry of Water Development

Minister of Information
Clement Stambuli, Ministry of Information

Minister of Women, Children and Community Affairs
Mary Banda, Ministry of Women, Children and Community Affairs

Ministry of Labour and Vocational Training
Leonard Mangulama, Ministry of Labour and Vocational Training

POLITICAL ORGANIZATIONS

Democratic Front (UDF)

NAME: Bakili Muluzi

Congress Party (MCP)

TITLE: Secretary General
NAME: Gwanda Chakuamba

Alliance for Democracy (AFORD)

TITLE: Secretary General
NAME: Chakufwa Chihana

Socialist League of Malawi (LESOMA)

TITLE: Secretary General
NAME: Kapote Mwakusula

Malawi Democratic Union (MDU)

NAME: Harry Bwanausi

Congress for the Second Republic (CSR)

NAME: Kanyama Chiume

Malawi Socialist Labor Party (MSLP)

NAME: Stanford Sambanemanja

DIPLOMATIC REPRESENTATION

Embassies in Malawi

Canada
Accord Centre, PO Box 51902, Lilongwe 3, Malawi
PHONE: +265 645441
FAX: +265 645004

China
PO Box 30221, Lilongwe 3, Malawi
PHONE: +265 783611; 781527

Egypt
Area 10, Plot No. 247, Tsoka Road, PO Box 30451, Lilongwe 3, Malawi
PHONE: +265 730300

France
Area 40, Road No. 8, Capital City, PO Box 30054, Lilongwe 3, Malawi
PHONE: +265 783577; 783732; 783520
FAX: +265 780438

Italy
PO Box 40, Lilongwe 3, Malawi
PHONE: +265 720266; 720481
FAX: +265 723350

Netherlands
PO Box 5096, Lilongwe 3, Malawi
PHONE: +265 651171

South Africa
Mpico Building, City Centre, PO Box 30043, Lilongwe 3, Malawi
PHONE: +265 783722
FAX: +265 782571; 781042

United Kingdom
Capital City, PO Box 782, Lilongwe 3, Malawi
PHONE: +265 782400
FAX: +265 782657

United States
Area 40, Plot No. 24, PO Box 30016, Lilongwe 3, Malawi
PHONE: +265 783166; 783342
FAX: +265 780471
TITLE: Ambassador
NAME: Michael T. F. Pistor

JUDICIAL SYSTEM

Supreme Court of Appeal

High Court

Magistrate's Courts

FURTHER READING

Articles

"Bread Price Up 8 Percent in Malawi." PanAfrican News Agency, 23 July 1999.

"Conflicts Push Additional Refugees to Malawi." PanAfrican News Agency, 14 January 1999.

"Cholera Claims 500 Lives In Malawi." PanAfrican News Agency, 12 February 1999.

"Danish Officials Visit Malawi." PanAfrican News Agency, 19 January 1999.

"Eritrea Condemns Killing Of Its Citizen In Malawi." PanAfrican News Agency, 24 August 1999.

Gama, Hobbs. "Good Rains Produce Bumper Maize Crop." Africa Information Afrique, 13 May 1999.

"Germany Worried by Malawi's Pre-Election Violence." PanAfrican News Agency, 19 January 1999.

"Malawi." In Current History 98 (September 8, 1999): 302.

"Malawi: Over 2,000 Made Homeless by Floods in North, Appeal for Aid Made." MBC Radio, Blantyre, BBC Monitoring International Reports, 3 April 1999.

"Malawi: Parliament Passes Bill Postponing Elections to June." MBC Radio, Blantyre, BBC Monitoring International Reports, 21 May 1999.

Tenthani, Raphael. "Malawi Political Opponents Attend Peace Conference." PanAfrican News Agency, 10 September 1999.

———. "Muluzi Names New Cabinet, Drops Key Figures." PanAfrican News Agency, 28 June 1999.

———. "Opposition Supporters Clash With Ruling Party." PanAfrican News Agency, 28 April 1999.

———. "Post-Election Riots Claims 2 Lives And 10 Mosques." PanAfrican News Agency, 21 June 1999.

———. ''Prospects for Oil in Lake Malawi.''
PanAfrican News Agency, 14 September
1999.

———. ''World Bank Official on Why SAPs
Failed in Africa.'' PanAfrican News Agency,
30 March 1999.

Books

Briggs, Philip. *Malawi: The Bradt Travel Guide.*
Old Saybrook, Conn.: Globe Pequot Press,
1999.

Crul, R.C.M. *Management and Conservation of
the African Great Lakes: Lakes Victoria,
Tanganyika and Malawi: Comparative and
Comprehensive Study of Great Lakes.* Paris:
UNESCO Publishing, 1999.

Hope, Kempe R. *AIDS and Development in
Africa: A Social Science Perspective.* New
York: Haworth Press, 1999.

Puertas Donoso, Benjamin. *Across the Footsteps
of Africa: The Experiences of an Ecuadorian
Doctor in Malawi and Mozambique.* Trenton,
N.J.: Africa World Press, 1999.

Internet

Abwenzi African Studies. Available Online @
www.lettersfromafrica.org/index.html (October
28, 1999).

Malawi Home Page. Available Online @
www.math.unh.edu/~llk (October 18, 1999).

*Malawi, Ministry of Tourism, Parks and
Wildlife.* Available Online @ www.malawi-
tourism.com/ (October 18, 1999).

MALAWI: STATISTICAL DATA

For sources and notes see "Sources of Statistics" in the front of each volume.

GEOGRAPHY

Geography (1)

Area:

Total: 118,480 sq km.

Land: 94,080 sq km.

Water: 24,400 sq km.

Area—comparative: slightly smaller than Pennsylvania.

Land boundaries:

Total: 2,881 km.

Border countries: Mozambique 1,569 km, Tanzania 475 km, Zambia 837 km.

Coastline: 0 km (landlocked).

Climate: tropical; rainy season (November to May); dry season (May to November).

Terrain: narrow elongated plateau with rolling plains, rounded hills, some mountains.

Natural resources: limestone, unexploited deposits of uranium, coal, and bauxite.

Land use:

Arable land: 18%

Permanent crops: 0%

Permanent pastures: 20%

Forests and woodland: 39%

Other: 23% (1993 est.).

HUMAN FACTORS

Demographics (2A)

	1990	1995	1998	2000	2010	2020	2030	2040	2050
Population	9,139.4	9,374.3	9,840.5	10,154.3	11,329.6	12,052.1	13,090.4	14,903.1	16,884.0
Net migration rate (per 1,000 population)	NA	NA	NA	NA	NA	NA	NA	NA	NA
Births	NA	NA	NA	NA	NA	NA	NA	NA	NA
Deaths	NA	NA	NA	NA	NA	NA	NA	NA	NA
Life expectancy - males	39.4	37.1	36.6	36.3	34.8	39.0	52.0	64.9	69.2
Life expectancy - females	39.6	37.9	36.5	35.7	34.7	39.5	55.5	71.5	76.3
Birth rate (per 1,000)	48.1	42.4	40.2	38.8	32.6	27.5	23.5	19.7	16.7
Death rate (per 1,000)	23.3	23.5	23.7	24.0	25.3	21.7	12.2	6.1	5.6
Women of reproductive age (15-49 yrs.)	2,071.3	2,108.2	2,240.9	2,336.9	2,794.1	3,204.6	3,734.3	4,313.3	4,667.5
of which are currently married	NA	NA	NA	NA	NA	NA	NA	NA	NA
Fertility rate	6.9	6.1	5.6	5.3	3.9	3.0	2.4	2.2	2.1

Except as noted, values for vital statistics are in thousands; life expectancy is in years.

Health Personnel (3)

Total health expenditure as a percentage of GDP, 1990-1997[a]

Public sector 2.3

Private sector . . . . .NA

Total[b] . . . . .NA

Health expenditure per capita in U.S. dollars, 1990-1997[a]

Purchasing power parity . . . . .NA

Total . . . . .NA

Availability of health care facilities per 100,000 people

Hospital beds 1990-1997[a] 160

Doctors 1993[c] 2

Nurses 1993[c] 6

Health Indicators (4)

Life expectancy at birth

1980 44

1997 43

Daily per capita supply of calories (1996) 2,097

Total fertility rate births per woman (1997) 6.4

Maternal mortality ratio per 100,000 live births (1990-97) . . . . .620[d]

Safe water % of population with access (1995) 60

Sanitation % of population with access (1995) 64

Consumption of iodized salt % of households (1992-98)[a] 58

Smoking prevalence

Male % of adults (1985-95)[a] . . . .

Female % of adults (1985-95)[a] . . . .

Tuberculosis incidence per 100,000 people (1997) 404

Adult HIV prevalence % of population ages 15-49 (1997) 14.92

Infants and Malnutrition (5)

Under-5 mortality rate (1997) 215

% of infants with low birthweight (1990-97) 20

Births attended by skilled health staff % of total[a] . . .55

% fully immunized (1995-97)

TB 100

DPT 95

Polio 94

Measles 87

Prevalence of child malnutrition under age 5 (1992-97)[b] 30

Ethnic Division (6)

Chewa, Nyanja, Tumbuko, Yao, Lomwe, Sena, Tonga, Ngoni, Ngonde, Asian, European.

Religions (7)

Protestant 55%

Roman Catholic 20%

Muslim 20%

Traditional indigenous beliefs . . . .

Languages (8)

English (official), Chichewa (official), other languages important regionally.

EDUCATION

Public Education Expenditures (9)

Public expenditure on education (% of GNP)

1980 . . . . .3.4

1996 . . . . .5.5[1]

Expenditure per student

Primary % of GNP per capita

1980 . . . . .7.6

1996 . . . . .9.0[1]

Secondary % of GNP per capita

1980 . . . .

1996 . . . . .79.9

Tertiary % of GNP per capita

1980 . . . . .1,839.9

1996 . . . . .1,636.0[1]

Expenditure on teaching materials

Primary % of total for level (1996) . . . .

Secondary % of total for level (1996) . . . .

Primary pupil-teacher ratio per teacher (1996) . . . . .59[1]

Duration of primary education years (1995) 8

Educational Attainment (10)

Age group (1987) . . . . .25+

Total population 2,859,826

Highest level attained (%)

No schooling 55.0

First level

Not completed 31.8

Completed 8.0

Entered second level

S-1 . . . . .2.7

S-2 . . . . .2.1

Postsecondary 0.4

Literacy Rates (11A)

In thousands and percent[1]	1990	1995	2000	2010
Illiterate population (15+ yrs.)	2,366	2,587	2,587	2,732
Literacy rate - total adult pop. (%)	52.3	56.4	60.4	68.1
Literacy rate - males (%)	69.2	71.9	74.6	79.5
Literacy rate - females (%)	36.9	41.8	46.8	57.0

GOVERNMENT & LAW

Political Parties (12)

National Assembly	No. of seats
United Democratic Front (UDF) 84	
Alliance for Democracy (AFORD) 33	
Malawi Congress Party (MCP) 55	
Others 5	

Military Affairs (14B)

	1990	1991	1992	1993	1994	1995
Military expenditures						
Current dollars (mil.)	13[e]	13[e]	11[e]	15[e]	19	21
1995 constant dollars (mil.)	15[e]	14[e]	12[e]	16[e]	19	21
Armed forces (000)	7	8	10	10	10	10
Gross national product (GNP)						
Current dollars (mil.)	1,046	1,158	1,072	1,268	1,115	1,310
1995 constant dollars (mil.)	1,202	1,279	1,153	1,330	1,143	1,310
Central government expenditures (CGE)						
1995 constant dollars (mil.)	317	331[e]	315[e]	450[e]	NA	NA
People (mil.)	9.1	9.4	9.7	9.7	9.6	9.4
Military expenditure as % of GNP	1.3	1.1	1.1	1.2	1.7	1.6
Military expenditure as % of CGE	4.8	4.4	3.9	3.5	NA	NA
Military expenditure per capita (1995 $)	2	2	1	2	2	2
Armed forces per 1,000 people (soldiers)	.8	.8	1.0	1.0	1.0	1.0
GNP per capita (1995 $)	132	136	119	136	119	139
Arms imports[6]						
Current dollars (mil.)	0	0	0	20	0	0
1995 constant dollars (mil.)	0	0	0	21	0	0
Arms exports[6]						
Current dollars (mil.)	0	0	0	0	0	0
1995 constant dollars (mil.)	0	0	0	0	0	0
Total imports[7]						
Current dollars (mil.)	581	703	718	546	491	NA
1995 constant dollars (mil.)	668	777	772	572	503	NA
Total exports[7]						
Current dollars (mil.)	417	472	383	320	325	NA
1995 constant dollars (mil.)	479	522	412	335	333	NA
Arms as percent of total imports[8]	0	0	0	3.7	0	NA
Arms as percent of total exports[8]	0	0	0	0	0	NA

Government Budget (13B)

Revenues . . . .$530 million

Expenditures . . . .$674 million

Capital expenditures . . . .$129 million

Data for 1993.

LABOR FORCE

Labor Force (16)

Total (million) 3.5

Agriculture 86%

Wage earners 14%

Data for 1990 est.

Unemployment Rate (17)

Rate not available.

PRODUCTION SECTOR

Electric Energy (18)

Capacity . . . . .185,000 kW (1995)

Production . . . . .800 million kWh (1995)

Consumption per capita . . . . .82 kWh (1995)

Transportation (19)

Highways:

total: 28,400 km

paved: 5,254 km

unpaved: 23,146 km (1996 est.)

Waterways: Lake Nyasa (Lake Malawi); Shire River, 144 km

Airports: 45 (1997 est.)

Airports—with paved runways:

total: 6

over 3,047 m: 1

1,524 to 2,437 m: 1

914 to 1,523 m: 4 (1997 est.)

Airports—with unpaved runways:

total: 39

1,524 to 2,437 m: 1

914 to 1,523 m: 14

under 914 m: 24 (1997 est.)

Top Agricultural Products (20)

Tobacco, sugarcane, cotton, tea, corn, potatoes, cassava (tapioca), sorghum, pulses; cattle, goats.

MANUFACTURING SECTOR

GDP & Manufacturing Summary (21)

Detailed value added figures are listed by both International Standard Industry Code (ISIC) and product title.

	1980	1985	1990	1994
GDP ($-1990 mil.)[1]	1,638	1,855	2,145	1,934
Per capita ($-1990)[1]	265	256	229	178
Manufacturing share (%) (current prices)[1]	17.6	17.5	16.6	20.4
Manufacturing				
Value added ($-1990 mil.)[1]	220	236	315	267
Industrial production index	100	116	155	166
Value added ($ mil.)	123	90	133	92
Gross output ($ mil.)	340	330	586	377
Employment (000)	39	31	46	50
Profitability (% of gross output)				
Intermediate input (%)	64	73	77	76
Wages and salaries inc. supplements (%)	12	10	10	11
Gross operating surplus	24	18	13	13
Productivity ($)				
Gross output per worker	8,783	10,745	12,793	7,594
Value added per worker	3,174	2,923	3,030	1,950
Average wage (inc. supplements)	1,046	1,035	1,282	874
Value added ($ mil.)				
311/2 Food products	54	14	26	19
313 Beverages	8	7	12	7
314 Tobacco products	9	5	8	5
321 Textiles	12	14	18	12
322 Wearing apparel	2	1	1	1
323 Leather and fur products	—	—	—	—
324 Footwear	1	3	4	2
331 Wood and wood products	2	2	2	1
332 Furniture and fixtures	1	1	1	1
341 Paper and paper products	2	2	1	—
342 Printing and publishing	8	6	9	6

	1980	1985	1990	1994
351 Industrial chemicals	2	8	7	5
352 Other chemical products	5	14	21	16
353 Petroleum refineries	—	—	—	—
354 Miscellaneous petroleum and coal products	—	—	—	—
355 Rubber products	1	1	—	—
356 Plastic products	2	2	5	4
361 Pottery, china and earthenware	—	—	—	—
362 Glass and glass products	—	—	—	—
369 Other non-metal mineral products	3	1	8	6
371 Iron and steel	—	—	—	—
372 Non-ferrous metals	—	—	—	—
381 Metal products	6	6	5	3
382 Non-electrical machinery	—	1	3	2
383 Electrical machinery	5	1	1	—
384 Transport equipment	1	1	1	1
385 Professional and scientific equipment	—	—	—	—
390 Other manufacturing industries	—	—	—	—

FINANCE, ECONOMICS, & TRADE

Economic Indicators (22)

National product: GDP—purchasing power parity—$8.6 billion (1997 est.)

National product real growth rate: 6% (1997 est.)

National product per capita: $900 (1997 est.)

Inflation rate—consumer price index: 83.4% (1995)

Exchange Rates (24)

Exchange rates:

Malawian kwacha (MK) per US$1

October 1997	17.5300
1996	15.3085
1995	15.2837
1994	8.7364
1993	4.4028

Top Import Origins (25)

$475 million (f.o.b., 1995).

Origins	%
South Africa	NA
Zimbabwe	NA
Japan	NA
United States	NA
United Kingdom	NA
Germany	NA

NA stands for not available.

Balance of Payments (23)

	1990	1991	1992	1993	1994
Exports of goods (f.o.b.)	406	475	400	317	363
Imports of goods (f.o.b.)	−280	−416	−415	−340	−639
Trade balance	126	60	−15	−23	−276
Services - debits	−357	−449	−422	−331	−321
Services - credits	46	46	35	32	24
Private transfers (net)	79	66	57	90	106
Government transfers (net)	21	50	61	66	18
Overall balance	−86	−228	−285	−166	−449

Top Export Destinations (26)

$405 million (f.o.b., 1995).

Destinations	%
United States	NA
South Africa	NA
Germany	NA
Japan	NA

NA stands for not available.

Economic Aid (27)

Recipient: donor pledges, $332 million (1996).

Import Export Commodities (28)

Import Commodities	Export Commodities
Food	Tobacco
Petroleum products	Tea
Semimanufactures	Sugar
Consumer goods	Coffee
Transportation equipment	Peanuts
	Wood products

MALAYSIA

CAPITAL: Kuala Lumpur.

FLAG: The national flag consists of 14 alternating horizontal stripes, of which 7 are red and 7 white; a gold 14-pointed star and crescent appear on a blue field in the upper left corner.

ANTHEM: *Negara Ku (My Country)*.

MONETARY UNIT: The Malaysian ringgit (M$), or dollar, is divided into 100 sen, or cents. There are coins of 1, 5, 10, 20, and 50 sens and 1 ringgit, and notes of 1, 5, 10, 20, 100, 500, and 1,000 ringgits. M$1 = US$0.3741 (or US$1 = M$2.6730).

WEIGHTS AND MEASURES: The metric system became the legal standard in 1982, but some British weights and measures and local units are also in use.

HOLIDAYS: National Day, 31 August; Christmas, 25 December. Movable holidays include Vesak Day, Birthday of His Majesty the Yang di-Pertuan Agong, Hari Raya Puasa, Hari Raya Haji, the 1st of Muharram (Muslim New Year), Milad an-Nabi, Dewali, Thaipusam, and the Chinese New Year. Individual states celebrate the birthdays of their rulers and other holidays observed by native ethnic groups.

TIME: 7 PM = noon GMT.

LOCATION AND SIZE: Situated in Southeast Asia, Malaysia, with an area of 329,750 square kilometers (127,581 square miles), consists of two separate, nonadjoining areas: Peninsular Malaysia on the Asian mainland, and the states of Sarawak and Sabah, known together as East Malaysia, on the island of Borneo. Comparatively, the area occupied by Malaysia is slightly larger than the state of New Mexico.

CLIMATE: The climate of Peninsular Malaysia is characterized by fairly high but uniform temperatures (ranging from 23° to 31°C/73° to 88°F throughout the year), high humidity, and heavy rainfall, averaging about 250 centimeters (100 inches) annually. There are seasonal variations in rainfall, with the heaviest rains from October to December or January. The nights are usually cool because of the nearby seas. The climate of East Malaysia is relatively cool for an area so near the equator.

INTRODUCTORY SURVEY

RECENT HISTORY

Japanese forces invaded Malaya and the Borneo territories in December 1941 and occupied them throughout World War II (1939–45). Within a year after the Japanese surrender in September 1945, the British formed the Malayan Union, succeeded by the Federation of Malaya on 1 February 1948. Over the next decade, Malaya progressed toward self-government. On 31 August 1957, the Federation of Malaya became an independent member of the Commonwealth of Nations.

On 16 September 1963, the Federation of Malaya, the State of Singapore, and the newly independent British colonies of Sarawak and Sabah merged to form the Federation of Malaysia, but by 1965, Singapore seceded from the Federation and established an independent republic. Internal disorders stemming from hostilities between Chinese and Malay communities in Kuala Lumpur disrupted the 1969 national elections and prompted the declaration of a state of emergency lasting from mid-1969 to February 1971. Successive governments managed to sustain political stability until 1987, when racial tensions between Chinese and Malay increased over a government plan to assign non-Mandarin-speaking administrators to Chinese-language schools.

The rise of Dayak nationalism in Sarawak was also considered a threat to political stability after the 1987 state elections, but it had been diffused by the 1991 elections, when The Sarawak Native People's Party (PBDS, Parti Bansa Dayak Sarawak)

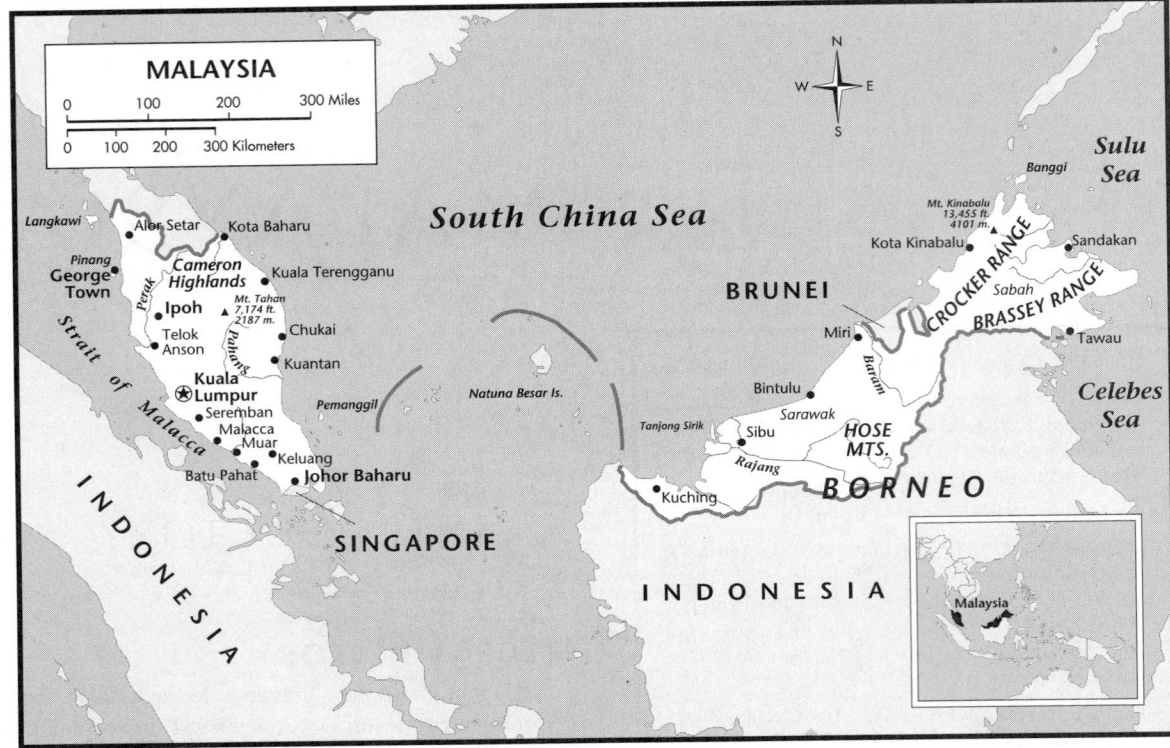

retained only 7 of the 15 seats it had won in 1987. In 1991, Malaysia's ruling party, the United Malays National Organization (UMNO) raised the issue of the alleged abuse of privilege by Malaysia's nine hereditary rulers, and in January 1993 proposed Constitutional amendments which passed, limiting their powers and removing their immunity from legal prosecution. In 1994, the government moved to ban the Islamic sect, Al-Arqam.

GOVERNMENT

Malaysia is a constitutional monarchy consisting of 13 states. The constitution of 1957, subsequently amended, provides for the election of a royal head of state, the yang di-pertuan agong (or "paramount ruler"), for a single term of five years. He is elected by the Conference of Rulers, nine hereditary sultans whose consent must be obtained for any law that alters state boundaries; affects the rulers' privileges or honors; or extends any religious observances or ceremonies to the country as a whole.

The yang di-pertuan agong, who must be one of the hereditary sultans, is commander-in-chief of the armed forces and has the power to designate judges for the Federal Court and the High Courts

on the advice of the prime minister, whom he appoints.

Executive power rests with the cabinet, chosen by the prime minister, who is the leader of the majority party or coalition of the House of Representatives (Dewan Rakyat), the lower house of Parliament. The 192 members of the House of Representatives must be at least 21 years old; they are elected by universal adult vote. Their term is five years unless the House is dissolved earlier.

The 70-member Senate (Dewan Negara) consists of 26 elected members (2 from each state); 4 members appointed by the paramount ruler to represent the Federal Territories of Kuala Lumpur and the island of Labaun; and 40 members appointed by the paramount ruler on the basis of distinguished public service or their eligibility to represent an ethnic minority. Senators, who serve six-year terms, must be at least 30 years old.

Of the thirteen Malaysian states, nine are headed by sultans; the other four are headed by federally appointed governors.

Judiciary

Most cases come before magistrates and sessions courts. Religious courts decide questions of Islamic law and custom. The Federal Court, the highest court in Malaysia, reviews decisions referred from the High Court of Peninsular Malaysia, the High Court of Sabah and Sarawak, and subordinate courts. The Federal Court, of which the *yang di-pertuan agong* (paramount ruler) is lord president, has original jurisdiction in disputes among states, or between a state and the federal government.

Political Parties

As of 1992 there were more than 30 registered parties, 13 of which are represented in the federal parliament. Some of the main parties are: the Barisan Nasional (National Front), a broad coalition comprising the United Malays National Organization (UMNO) and 12 other parties, most ethnically based; DAP (the Chinese-based Democratic Action Party); Parti Se-Islam Malaysia (PAS); Parti Bersatu Sabah (PBS); the Malaysian Chinese Association (MCA); and Semangat 46. In the election held on 25 April 1995, of the 192 seats the results were: National Front (162 seats), DAP (9), PBS (8), PAS (7), Semangat 46 (6).

DEFENSE

In 1995, the all-volunteer armed forces numbered 114,500. The total strength of the army was 90,000, including 36 infantry and armored battalions, 5 artillery regiments, and supporting air defense, signal, engineer, special forces, and administrative units. Contingents of the Malaysian army patrol the Malaysia-Thailand border against communist guerrillas and provide four United Nations observer teams.

The navy had 12,000 personnel, 4 frigates, 8 missile-equipped fast-attack craft, and 29 large patrol craft. The air force had 12,500 personnel and 79 combat aircraft. Paramilitary forces numbered 20,100, and the People's Volunteer Corps had 240,000. There are 35,800 reserves. Malaysian arms and equipment are a mixture of domestic, United Kingdom, and United States material.

ECONOMIC AFFAIRS

Malaysia is one of the most prosperous nations in Southeast Asia. Until the 1970s, Malaysia's economy was based chiefly on its plantation and mining activities, with rubber and tin the principal exports. Since then, however, Malaysia has added palm oil, tropical hardwoods, petroleum, natural gas, and manufactured items to its export list. Malaysia is the world's third largest producer of semiconductors (after the United States and Japan).

In 1985–86 Malaysia's long period of high growth abruptly halted as oil and palm oil prices were halved. Recovery began in late 1986–87; growth was spurred by foreign demand for exports. Growth rates continued on the average in the 8–9% range from 1987–92. As of 1997, the economy had annually grown by an average of nearly 9% for eight years.

Sarawak's basic economy is based on agriculture, supplemented by petroleum production and refining, the collection of forest produce, fishing, and the cultivation of cash crops, primarily rubber, timber and pepper. Sabah's economy rests on logging, petroleum production, rubber, pepper, and timber.

Public Finance

In spite of increased capital expenditures and fiscal concessions, the overall budget deficit for 1994 was M$605 million, due to efforts to restrict current expenditure growth to 3%. In 1992 Malaysia's total public debt stood at M$96,830 million, of which M$20,922 million was financed abroad.

The U.S. Central Intelligence Agency estimates that, in 1995, government revenues totaled approximately $20.2 billion and expenditures $19.9 billion, including capital expenditures of $4.8 billion. External debt totaled $27.4 billion.

Income

In 1997, Malaysia's gross national product (GNP) was US$227 billion at current prices, or about US$11,100 per person. For the period 1985–95 the average inflation rate was 3.3%, resulting in a real growth rate in GNP of 5.7% per person.

Industry

The leading manufacturing industries include rubber processing, the manufacture of tires and other rubber products, palm oil processing, and tin smelting. Other manufactured goods include electrical/electronic machinery and appliances; textiles, clothing and footwear; chemicals and petroleum products; other machinery and transport equipment; and iron and steel products. Malaysia is also a leading exporter of semiconductor devices.

Malaysia is developing what it calls the ''multimedia super corridor'' (MSC), an area it hopes will become a world-class research and development site for industry. The MSC is composed of several projects: the completion of the Petronas Twin Towers in Kuala Lumpur (the tallest building in the world); the building of an $8 billion city and technology center; a $3.6 billion international airport; and a massive fiber-optic telecommunications system linking them all.

Banking and Finance

In 1958, the Bank Negara Tanah Melayu (renamed the Bank Negara Malaysia in 1963) was created as the central banking institution. During 1975–85, the bank's foreign assets grew from M$3,943 million to M$9,111 million. Malaysian currency in circulation amounted to M$ 12,070 million at the end of 1991, as compared with M$ 6,773 million at the close of 1985.

Bank Negara requires banks to maintain a minimum risk-weighted capital ration (RWCR) of 8%; the average for commercial banks at the end of 1995 was 11.5%. Money supply was M$198,873 million at the end of 1995. Foreign reserves, excluding gold, totaled $23,774 million at the end of 1995.

At the end of 1996, Malaysia had 37 licensed commercial banks, through 1,433 offices. A total of 29 foreign banks have offices in Malaysia, but their banking privileges are restricted. Other financial institutions include 12 merchant banks and a national savings bank. Specialized credit institutions include the Federal Land Development Authority (FELDA), the Agricultural Bank of Malaysia (Bank Pertanian Malaysia), and Bank Rakyat, serving rural credit cooperative societies. International trade is financed mainly by the commercial banks.

As an alternative system, Malaysia offers Islamic banking, which is based on the concept of profit sharing as opposed to the use of interest in the conventional banking system. The sole Islamic bank is Bank Islam Malaysia Berhad.

The central bank has embarked on a plan to develop Malaysia as a regional Islamic financial center. Toward this end, the central bank formed a consultative committee on Islamic banking in January 1996 to serve as a think-tank group to develop strategies and proposals to map out the future direction of Islamic banking. Although Islamic operations are still only a small proportion of total business (in 1995, deposits amounted to M$4.9 billion out of total commercial bank deposits of M$187 billion), Malaysia has achieved more than most other Islamic countries in this respect, and its developments are regarded as models by them.

The principal market for securities is the Kuala Lumpur Stock Exchange (KLSE), which separated from the joint Stock Exchange of Malaysia and Singapore in 1973. A second, smaller exchange has operated since 1970 to serve indigenous Malay interests. In October 1991 the Kuala Lumpur Stock Exchange completely severed its links with the Singapore Stock Exchange. As of 31 December 1995, the KLSE was capitalized at approximately M$565.6 billion. Foreign investors are permitted to buy and sell on the stock market, subject only to compliance with regulatory requirements. In June 1995, a wide range of measures liberalizing the Malaysian capital market were introduced. These included the lowering of commission rates on the KLSE, the easing of controls on loans secured against shares and less stringent conditions for overseas fund managers. Overseas funds can now set up 100% subsidiaries for conducting non-Malaysian business, and rules on work permits for expatriate staff have been relaxed.

Economic Development

The government remains generally committed to a policy of free enterprise, although it owns and operates the railway and communications systems and has become increasingly involved in certain key industries. In 1970, a government holding company, Perbadanan Nasional (PERNAS), was created to encourage Malay-controlled businesses; in 1975, the government attempted, through PERNAS, to strengthen Malaysian interests in the tin-mining sector. Also in 1975, the government established the National Oil Co. (PETRONAS), with the overall aim of acquiring majority control of the country's petroleum operations. The Industrial Coordination Act of 1975 attempted to accelerate indigenous Malay participation in the economy by setting limits on foreign participation in the processing, domestic distribution, and export of local raw materials. In 1971, the New Economic Policy (NEP) was adopted, with the aim of channeling a greater share of future economic growth into Malay hands. It specifically called for raising the level of corporate ownership by ethnic Malays to 30% by 1990, reducing corporate ownership by other Malaysians (i.e., Chinese and Indians) to 40%, and restricting foreigners to ownership of no more than 30%. Short-term investment strategies are set forth in a series of economic plans. The Fourth Malaysia Plan (1981–85) proposed a level of development spending of M$42.8 billion and called for acceleration of the NEP goals for Bumiputra economic participation. Major industrial and infrastructural development projects included a M$900-million bridge between Pulau Pinang and the mainland and a M$600-million automobile-manufacturing plant, both of which opened in 1985. Recent economic planning has stressed a ''look East'' policy, with Malaysia attempting to emulate the economic successes of Japan and the Republic of Korea by importing technology from those countries. In response to deteriorating prices for oil and other exports, the Fifth Malaysia Plan (1986–90) has moved away from the goals of the NEP, aiming instead at promoting foreign investment, particularly in export industries.

The year 1990 marked the culmination of several economic development plans: the Fifth Malaysia Plan (FMP) 1986–90); the conclusion of the First Outline Perspective Plan (OPP1) 1971–90; and the completion of the New Economic Policy (NEP) 1971–90. A post-1990 NEP defined Malaysian economic strategy for full development by 2020. Three ten-year Outline Perspective Plans which include a New Development Plan and six five-year plans make up the NEP. A Second Outline Perspective Plan (OPP2) 1991–2000 aims to sustain growth momentum and to achieve a more balanced development of the economy. The Sixth Malaysia Plan calls for an average annual growth rate of 7.5%, and expenditures on infrastructure are included to ensure prospects for further development. Development trends are toward privatization, encouraging the spread of industry throughout the country, increasing manufacturing in the free trade zones, and providing financing for industry through the establishment of specialized financing institutions.

The five-year development plan beginning on 6 May 1996 forecasted average growth of 8% a year for 1996 to 2000. But it also tackled issues that bother skeptics of the Malaysian economy: Low rises in productivity, a skills shortage, and a gaping current-account deficit.

From 1953 through 1986, Malaysia received more than U.S.$3,295 million in multilateral development assistance, chiefly from the IBRD ($2,079 million) and ADB ($1,137 million). Economic aid also included U.S. Export-Import (FY 1970–84) $170 million; and Western (non-US) countries, ODA and OOF bilateral commitments (1970–89), $4.7 million, and OPEC bilateral aid (1979–89), $42 million. ODA aid in 1993 totaled $45 million.

SOCIAL WELFARE

Public financial assistance is provided within the framework of Malaysian society's highly developed sense of family and clan responsibility. The government has generally encouraged volunteer social welfare activities and has subsidized programs of private groups. The government's program of public assistance takes the form of cash, commodities, and institutional care.

Children's services, begun in 1952, provide case-work services and administer children's homes. A probation service provides care and assistance for juvenile delinquents and dependents, and a handicapped persons' service aids the deaf, mute, and blind. In addition, care is provided for the aged and chronically ill.

Women make up more than 40% of the nation's total labor force, but except in teaching and nursing, are underrepresented in professional occupations. In family and religious matters, Muslim women are subject to Islamic law, which allows polygyny (multiple wives) and favors men in matters of inheritance.

Healthcare

Malaysia enjoys a comparatively high standard of health, due to the government's long-established health and medical services. The country has improved its health care and social conditions, and is considering a national health insurance plan. As of 1990, the government paid for three-fourths of health care expenses. About 80% of the population had access to health care facilities in 1993.

In 1994–95, 90% of the population had access to safe water and 94% had adequate sanitation. In 1989–95, 23% of children under five years of age were considered malnourished. Life expectancy was 72 years in 1995.

Housing

The need for urban housing is acute: an estimated 24% of Kuala Lumpur's population consists of recently arrived squatters living in overcrowded shantytowns with few urban amenities. The total number of housing units is about 3.4 million units: 92% of all housing units are detached houses, 7% are apartments, and 1% are single rooms.

EDUCATION

Six years of free primary education is followed by three years of comprehensive general and prevocational education. A two-year pre-university course prepares students for admission to the universities. Malay is the language of instruction in primary and secondary schools, with English a compulsory second language.

School enrollment in Malaysia in 1993 was 2.8 million pupils instructed by 140,342 teachers in 6,965 primary schools. In all secondary schools, there were 84,744 teachers and 1.6 million pupils. In 1993, 170,145 students were enrolled in institutions of higher education, which include the University Kebangsaan Malaysia (the National University of Malaysia), the University of Malaya, and the Technological University of Malaysia, all in or near Kuala Lumpur, and the University of Science Malaysia.

1999 KEY EVENTS TIMELINE

January

- Prime Minister Mahathir Mohammad shuffles his cabinet.

February

- Restrictions on foreign investors are eased.

March

- Over one million pigs are destroyed to ward off a deadly virus.

April

- Anwar Ibrahim is sentenced to six years in prison; Ibrahim supporters protest and riot.

June

- A new government capital complex opens.

July

- Cyberjaya, Malaysia's Silicon Valley, opens.

August

- Malaysia's economy recovers from a recession.

September

- Canadian reporter Murray Hiebert is imprisoned.

October

- Canadian Murray Hiebert is released from prison after serving only four weeks.

November

- Liberal reformers in Malaysia are seriously disappointed when Dr. Mahathir Mohamad, Malaysia's authoritarian political leader for the past 18 years, is returned to power for the fifth time in the general election held November 29.

- At an informal meeting in Manila, Philippines, six members of the Association of Southeast Asian Nations (ASEAN)—Brunei, Indonesia, Malaysia, Philippines, Singapore, and Thailand—agree to establish a free-trade zone by eliminating duties on most goods traded in the region by 2010. The remaining four newer and less-developed nation members—Cambodia, Laos, Myanmar (Burma), and Vietnam—will eliminate duties by 2015. Rice will be excluded from trade agreements, however.

ANALYSIS OF EVENTS: 1999

BUSINESS AND THE ECONOMY

Malaysia entered 1999 in the midst of a major recession. In September 1998, during the height of the Asian recession, Malaysian Prime Minister Mahathir Mohammad had announced strict controls on foreign investors, including a ban that prohibited investors from taking their money out of Malaysia. Mahathir blamed Malaysia's recession on foreign speculators. In February 1999, Mahathir started easing currency controls. The prohibition against withdrawing funds from the country was changed to a graduated exit tax, with tax penalties starting at thirty percent but eventually falling to zero.

Malaysia's version of Silicon Valley officially opened in July. Called Cyberjaya, this high-tech mini-city is part of Mahathir's plan to transform Malaysia into a developed country by attracting high-technology businesses. Cyberjaya is part of the Super Corridor construction project, which includes the Petronas Towers, the world's tallest building, the futuristic Kuala Lumpur International Airport, and the new capital complex. Though already officially open, construction in Cyberjaya will not be fully completed until 2011.

In August the shaky Malaysian stock market received a boost of confidence when Morgan Stanley Capital International (MSCI) decided to once again include Malaysia on its international stock market index. The MSCI financial index is used by global fund managers to invest billions of dollars, and inclusion in the MSCI index would help lure foreign investors back into the country. Furthermore, investors planning to leave the Malaysian market would now be more inclined to stay.

On August 25, 1999 the government announced that the country's Gross Domestic Product (GDP) grew by 4.1 percent during the second quarter. Prime Minister Mahathir further predicted continued growth in 2000 of five percent or better. With the release of these numbers, the government announced that the Malaysian recession was officially over.

GOVERNMENT AND POLITICS

The year started with Prime Minister Mahathir Mohammad rearranging his cabinet and naming Abdullah Ahmad Badawi the new Deputy Prime Minister. The deputy post had been empty since Anwar Ibrahim, who was once considered Mahathir's heir-apparent, was fired in September 1998 and later arrested on corruption and morality charges.

Throughout the year, the Mahathir-Anwar battle continued to hold center stage in Malaysian politics. On January 5, the Attorney General admitted that Anwar had been beaten while in custody, officially confirming what was already widely known, and, on January 7, Inspector General of Police Abdul Rahim Noor resigned, claming responsibility for Anwar's beating.

On April 14 Anwar was sentenced to six years in prison for sodomy and abuse of power. With the verdict, Mahathir tightened his reign on power and almost assured himself of reelection. Anwar's imprisonment was not popular among Malays, most of whom consider Anwar the victim of political conspiracy. Irregularities in the trail fueled dissent. After the verdict was handed down, large protests and riots broke out in the streets of Kuala Lumpur.

According to Malaysian law, elections must be held by June of 2000, though with the economy improving, Mahathir may stage elections early. With Mahathir firmly controlling the media, the opposition party is at a distinct disadvantage. Anwar's wife, Dr. Wan Azizah Ismail, started her own political party to challenge Mahathir, but summer polls showed the Prime Minister far ahead of any opponents. However, in September the opposition gained a boost when allegations arose that Anwar had been poisoned while in jail. Though medical investigations failed to find evidence of poisoning, doctors did note that Anwar's health was frail. Again, angry Anwar supporters took to the streets, engaging in violent protests.

In September Malaysia began sending peacekeeping troops to war-torn East Timor. In October, the United Nations asked Malaysia to send more troops, which Mahathir said he would agree to only if the UN financed the operation.

CULTURE AND SOCIETY

Freedom of expression was a hot topic in Malaysia this year. Following on the heels of Anwar Ibrahim's imprisonment, came the imprisonment of Canadian journalist Murray Hiebert. Hiebert lost an appeal to overturn a 1997 contempt of court conviction over an article he wrote that criticized Malaysian courts. On September 11, Hiebert was sentenced to six weeks in prison. Malaysia was widely criticized for this move. U.S. President Clinton expressed his concern, as did international free speech and human rights organizations. After serving four weeks of his term, Hiebert was released on October 11.

Other events further damaged the cause of free speech. In March, the son of Prime Minister Mahathir Mohammad sued the *Wall Street Journal* over an article questioning the younger Mahathir's business acumen, and a string of defamation suits were filed against other journalists. In February the Malaysian government forbid any of its agencies from subscribing to publications critical of Malaysia, including the *International Herald Tribune* and *Asiaweek.*

A mysterious virus killed over 100 people in Malaysia in 1999. The virus was eventually identified as the Hendra virus, a form of encephalitis, which initially infects pigs, but then can transmitted from pigs to humans through any direct contact. In a move to stem the spread of the virus, 1.3 million infected pigs were destroyed in March.

On June 21, Prime Minister Mahathir Mohammad's $5.3-billion-dollar Putrajaya capital complex opened. More of a small metropolis than a simple government building, the capital is part of a massive construction project called the super corridor. Along with the capital, Malaysia's super corridor includes the Kuala Lumpur International Airport, a high-tech business complex, and the eighty-eight-story Petronas Twin Towers, the world's largest building. While Mahathir has pronounced this construction to be the cornerstone of future Malaysian progress, critics have dismissed the project, claiming that Prime Minister Mahathir is busily constructing monuments to himself.

DIRECTORY

CENTRAL GOVERNMENT

Head of State

Paramount Ruler
Tuanku Ja'afar ibni al-Marhum Tuanku Abdul
Rahman, Istana Negara, Jalan Istana, 50500
Kuala Lumpur, Malaysia
PHONE: +60 (3) 2388311

Deputy Paramount Ruler
Tunku Salahuddin Abdul Aziz Shah ibni al-
Marhum Sultan Hisammuddin Alam Shah, Office
of the Deputy Paramount Ruler

Ministers

Prime Minister
Mahathir bin Mohamad, Prime Minster's
Department, Jalan Dato'Onn, 50502 Kuala
Lumpur, Malaysia
PHONE: +60 (3) 2321957
FAX: +60 (3) 2329227

Deputy Prime Minister
Abdullah bin Ahmad Badawi, Prime Minsters
Department, Jalan Dato'Onn, 50502 Kuala
Lumpur, Malaysia
PHONE: +60 (3) 2321957
FAX: +60 (3) 2329227

**Minister of Special Functions in the
Department of the Prime Minister**
Daim Zainuddin, Ministry of Special Functions
in the Department of the Prime Minister

Minister of Agriculture
Sulaiman bin Daud, Ministry of Agriculture,
Wisma Tani, Jalan Sultan Salahuddin, 50624
Kuala Lumpur, Malaysia
E-MAIL: menteri@smtp.moa.my

Minister of Culture, Arts, and Tourism
Sabaruddin bin Chik, Ministry of Culture, Arts,
and Tourism

Minister of Defense
Abang Abu Bakar bin Mustapha, Ministry of
Defense, Kementerian Pertahanan, Jalan Padang
Tembak, 50634 Kuala Lumpur, Malaysia
PHONE: +60 (3) 2314891
FAX: +60 (3) 2914163
E-MAIL: cpa@mod.gov.my

**Minister of Domestic Trade and Consumer
Affairs**
Megat Junid bin Megat Ayob, Ministry of
Domestic Trade and Consumer Affairs, Tingkat
33, Menara Dayabumi, Jalan Sultan
Hishamuddin, 50623 Kuala Lumpur
PHONE: +60 (3) 2743983
FAX: +60 (3) 2744520
E-MAIL: mjunid@kpdnhq.gov.my

Minister of Education
Mohamed Najib bin Abdul Razak, Ministry of
Education
E-MAIL: najib@moe.gov.my

**Minister of Energy, Communications, and
Multimedia**
Leo Moggie Anak Irok, Ministry of Energy,
Communications and Multimedia, 1st Floor,
Wisma Damansara, Jalan Semantan, 50668
Kuala Lumpur, Malaysia
PHONE: +60 (3) 2575000
FAX: +60 (3) 2533485
E-MAIL: Webmaster@ktkm.gov.my

Minister of Entrepreneur Development
Mustapa Mohamed, Ministry of Entrepreneur
Development, Tingkat 14–16 and 22–26, Medan
Mara, Jalan Raja Laut, 50652 Kuala Lumpur,
Malaysia
PHONE: +60 (3) 2985022
FAX: +60 (3) 2917623

Minister of Finance
Tun Dato' Daim bin Zainuddin, Ministry of
Finance, Perbendaharaan Malaysia, Block 9,
Kompleks Kerajaan Jalan Duta, 50592 Kuala
Lumpur, Malaysia
PHONE: +60 (3) 2582000
FAX: +60 (3) 2556264
E-MAIL: webmaster@treasury.gov.my

Minister of Foreign Affairs
Syed Hamid bin Syed Jaafar Albar, Ministry of
Foreign Affairs, Wisma Putra, 50602 Kuala
Lumpur, Malaysia
PHONE: +60 (3) 2488088
FAX: +60 (3) 2424551
E-MAIL: webmaster@kln.gov.my

Minister of Health
Chua Jui Meng, Ministry of Health, Block E,
Jalan Dungun, Buit Damansara, 54200 Kuala
Lumpur, Malaysia
PHONE: +60 (3) 2540088
FAX: +60 (3) 2561566
E-MAIL: zainal@dph.gov.my

Minister of Home Affairs
Abdullah bin Ahmad Badawi, Ministry of Home
Affairs, Jalan Dato' Onn, 50546 Kuala Lumpur,
Malaysia

PHONE: +60 (3) 2309344
FAX: +60 (3) 2936122
E-MAIL: irg@kdn.gov.my

Minister of Housing and Local Government
Ting Chew Peh, Ministry of Housing and Local
Government

Minister of Human Resources
Lim Ah Lek, Ministry of Human Resources,
Level 2–4, Block B North, Jalan Damanlela,
Pusat Bandar, Damansara, 50530 Kuala Lumpur,
Malaysia
PHONE: +60 (3) 2557200
FAX: +60 (3) 2554700
E-MAIL: mhr@po.jaring.my

Minister of Information
Mohamed bin Rahmat, Ministry of Information

Minister of International Trade and Industry
Rafidah binti Abdul Aziz, Ministry of
International Trade and Industry

**Minister of Land and Cooperative
Development**
Kasitah bin Gaddam, Ministry of Land and
Cooperative Development

**Minister of National Unity and Social
Development**
Zaleha binti Ismail, Ministry of National Unity
and Social Development, Tingkat 20/21, Wisma
Bumi Raya, Jalan Raja Laut, 50562 Kuala
Lumpur, Malaysia
PHONE: +60 (3) 2925022
FAX: +60 (3) 2937353
E-MAIL: zaleha@kempadu.gov.my

Minister of Primary Industries
Lim Keng Yaik, Ministry of Primary Industries,
Tingkat 6–8, Menara Dayabumi, Jalan Sultan
Hishamuddin, 50654 Kuala Lumpur, Malaysia
PHONE: +60 (3) 22747511
FAX: +60 (3) 22745014
E-MAIL: samilhah@kpu.gov.my

Minister of Rural Development
Annuar bin Musa, Ministry of Rural
Development

**Minister of Science, Technology, and
Environment**
Law Hieng Ding, Ministry of Science,
Technology, and Environment, Tingkat 14,
Wisma Sime Darby, Jalan Raja Laut, 50662
Kuala Lumpur, Malaysia
PHONE: +60 (3) 2938955
FAX: +60 (3) 2936006

E-MAIL: lhd@mastic.gov.my

Minister of Transport
Ling Liong Sik, Ministry of Transportation,
Level 3, Wisma Perdana, Jalan Dungun,
Damansara Height, 50616 Kuala Lumpur,
Malaysia
PHONE: +60 (3) 2548122
FAX: +60 (3) 2557041
E-MAIL: info@jpj.gov.my

Minister of Works
S. Samy Vellu, Ministry of Works

Minister of Youth and Sports
Muhyiddin bin Mohamed Yassin, Ministry of
Youth and Sports, Level 6, Block K, Pusat
Bandar Damansara, 50570 Kuala Lumpur,
Malaysia
PHONE: +60 (3) 2552255
FAX: +60 (3) 2537877

POLITICAL ORGANIZATIONS
Democratic Action Party (DAP)
24 Jalan 20/9, Petaling Jaya, 46300 Selangor,
Malaysia
PHONE: +60 (3) 7578022
FAX: +60 (3) 757571
E-MAIL: dap.malaysia@pobox.com
TITLE: National Chairman
NAME: Chen Man Hin

Malaysian Chinese Association
8th Floor, Wisma MCA, 163, Jalan Ampang,
50450 Kuala Lumpur, Malaysia
PHONE: +60 (3) 2618044
FAX: +60 (3) 2619772
E-MAIL: info@mca.org.my
TITLE: President
NAME: Datuk Seri Dr Ling Liong Sik

Menara Manickavasagam Congress (Malaysian Indian Congress)
Tingkat 6, 1 Jalan Rahmat, Kuala Lumpur,
Malaysia
E-MAIL: mic.malaysia.org
TITLE: President
NAME: Dato' Seri S. Samy Vellu

Parti Gerakan Rakyat Malaysia (Malaysian People's Movement Party)
Level 5, Menara PGRM, 8 Jalan Pudu Ulu,
Cheras, 56100 Kuala Lumpur, Malaysia
PHONE: +60 (3) 9876868

FAX: +60 (3) 9878866
E-MAIL: pgrmhq@pgrmhq.po.my
TITLE: President
NAME: Datuk Seri Dr Lim Keng Yaik

Parti Islam Se Malaysia (Pan Malaysian Islamic Party)

Lrg Hj Hassan, Tmn Melewar, Batu Caves,
68100 Selangor, Malaysia
PHONE: +60 (3) 6895612
FAX: +60 (3) 6889520
E-MAIL: webmaster@parti-pas.org

Parti Progresif Penduduk Malaysia (People's Progressive Party Of Malaysia)

Jalan Maharajarela, 29A, 50150 Kuala Lumpur,
Malaysia
PHONE: +60 (3) 2441922
FAX: +60 (3) 2442041
TITLE: President
NAME: Datuk M. Kayveas

Sabah Progressive Party

2nd Floor, Lot 23, Bornion Centre, Luyang,
88300 Kota Kinabalu, Sabah, Malaysia
PHONE: +60 (88) 242107
FAX: +60 (88) 249188
E-MAIL: sapp@po.jaring.my

United Malay National Organisation

DIPLOMATIC REPRESENTATION
Embassies in Malaysia

Australia
No 6, Jalan Yap Kwan Seng, 50450 Kuala
Lumpur, Malaysia
PHONE: +60 (3) 2465555
FAX: +60 (3) 2415773
E-MAIL: pa@austhc.po.my
TITLE: High Commissioner
NAME: Bob Cotton

Canada
7th floor, Plaza MBF, 172 Jalan Ampang, 50540
Kuala Lumpur, Malaysia
PHONE: +60 2612000
FAX: +60 2613428

Chile
8th Floor, West Block, Wisma Selangor
Dredging, 142-C, Jalan Ampang, 50450 Kuala
Lumpur, Malaysia
PHONE: +60 (3) 2616203

FAX: +60 (3) 2622219
E-MAIL: prochile@ppp.nasionet.net

Denmark
Wisma Denmark, 22nd Floor, 86 Jalan Ampang,
50450 Kuala Lumpur, Malaysia
PHONE: +60 (3) 2022001
FAX: +60 (3) 2022012
E-MAIL: denmark@rdembsy.po.my
TITLE: Ambassador
NAME: Lasse Reimann

Japan
No. 11, Pesiaran Stonor, off Jalan Tun Razak,
50450 Kuala Lumpur, Malaysia
PHONE: +60 (3) 2427044
FAX: +60 (3) 2672314
TITLE: Ambassador
NAME: Hideki Harashima

Singapore
209 Jalan Tun Razak, 50400 Kuala Lumpur,
Malaysia
PHONE: +60 (3) 2616277
FAX: +60 (3) 2616343
E-MAIL: shckl@pd.jaring.my
TITLE: High Commissioner
NAME: Krishnasamy Kesavapany

United Kingdom
185, Jalan Semantan Ampang, 50450 Kuala
Lumpur, Malaysia
TITLE: D. J. Moss

United States
376 Jalan Tun Razak, PO Box 10035, 50700
Kuala Lumpur, Malaysia
PHONE: +60 (3) 2685000
FAX: +60 (3) 2422207
TITLE: Ambassador
NAME: B. Lynn Pascoe

JUDICIAL SYSTEM
Federal Court of Malaysia

Bangunan Sultan Abdul Samad, Jalan Raja,
50506 Kuala Lumpur, Malaysia
PHONE: +60 (3) 293901

Court of Appeal

Bangunan Sultan Abdul Samad, Jalan Raja,
50506 Kuala Lumpur, Malaysia
PHONE: +60 (3) 2929011

FURTHER READING
Articles

Gecker, Jocelyn. ''High-tech 'Cyberjaya' Rises in Malaysian Jungle.'' *The Seattle Times*, 9 July 1999.

''Mahathir's Great Guessing Game.'' *The Economist* (August 7, 1999): 30–31.

''Mahathir's Riddle.'' *The Economist* (May 8, 1999): 32–33.

''Malaysia Expected to Confirm End of Recession.'' Reuters News Services, 24 August 1999.

''Malaysia's Stockmarket: Ready, Steady.'' *The Economist* (August 21, 1999): 64–66.

Mays, Patricia J. ''U.S. Scientists Seek to Unravel Malaysian Virus.'' *The Seattle Times*, 4 May 1999.

''The Verdict on Malaysia.'' *The Economist* (April 17, 1999): 43–44.

Internet

Naji, Kari. ''Malaysia Releases Jailed Canadian Journalist.'' *CNN Interactive*, 11 October 1999. Available Online @ www.cnn.com/ ASIANOW/ (December 8, 1999).

MALAYSIA: STATISTICAL DATA

For sources and notes see "Sources of Statistics" in the front of each volume.

GEOGRAPHY

Geography (1)

Area:

Total: 329,750 sq km.

Land: 328,550 sq km.

Water: 1,200 sq km.

Area—comparative: slightly larger than New Mexico.

Land boundaries:

Total: 2,669 km.

Border countries: Brunei 381 km, Indonesia 1,782 km, Thailand 506 km.

Coastline: 4,675 km (Peninsular Malaysia 2,068 km, East Malaysia 2,607 km).

Climate: tropical; annual southwest (April to October) and northeast (October to February) monsoons.

Terrain: coastal plains rising to hills and mountains.

Natural resources: tin, petroleum, timber, copper, iron ore, natural gas, bauxite.

Land use:

Arable land: 3%

Permanent crops: 12%

Permanent pastures: 0%

Forests and woodland: 68%

Other: 17% (1993 est.).

HUMAN FACTORS

Demographics (2A)

	1990	1995	1998	2000	2010	2020	2030	2040	2050
Population	17,507.3	19,614.8	20,932.9	21,820.1	26,465.5	31,582.6	36,909.8	42,146.6	47,288.7
Net migration rate (per 1,000 population)	NA	NA	NA	NA	NA	NA	NA	NA	NA
Births	NA	NA	NA	NA	NA	NA	NA	NA	NA
Deaths	83.2	NA	NA	NA	NA	NA	NA	NA	NA
Life expectancy - males	65.1	66.5	67.4	67.9	70.3	72.4	74.1	75.6	76.7
Life expectancy - females	70.7	72.6	73.6	74.3	77.2	79.5	81.4	82.8	83.9
Birth rate (per 1,000)	29.0	27.8	26.5	25.6	23.5	22.0	20.0	18.6	17.6
Death rate (per 1,000)	6.1	5.6	5.4	5.2	5.0	5.2	5.7	6.3	6.8
Women of reproductive age (15-49 yrs.)	4,518.0	5,039.3	5,386.8	5,629.8	6,759.5	7,811.0	9,022.1	10,125.6	11,129.8
of which are currently married	NA	NA	NA	NA	NA	NA	NA	NA	NA
Fertility rate	3.5	3.5	3.4	3.3	3.1	2.9	2.8	2.6	2.5

Except as noted, values for vital statistics are in thousands; life expectancy is in years.

Health Personnel (3)

Total health expenditure as a percentage of GDP, 1990-1997[a]

Public sector 1.4

Private sector 1.5

Total[b] 2.9

Health expenditure per capita in U.S. dollars, 1990-1997[a]

Purchasing power parity 317

Total 140

Availability of health care facilities per 100,000 people

Hospital beds 1990-1997[a] 200

Doctors 1993[c] 43

Nurses 1993[c] 160

Health Indicators (4)

Life expectancy at birth

1980 67

1997 72

Daily per capita supply of calories (1996) 2,899

Total fertility rate births per woman (1997) 3.2

Maternal mortality ratio per 100,000 live births (1990-97) . . . . .34[b]

Safe water % of population with access (1995) 89

Sanitation % of population with access (1995) 94

Consumption of iodized salt % of households (1992-98)[a] . . . .

Smoking prevalence

Male % of adults (1985-95)[a] 41

Female % of adults (1985-95)[a] 4

Tuberculosis incidence per 100,000 people (1997) 112

Adult HIV prevalence % of population ages 15-49 (1997) 0.62

Infants and Malnutrition (5)

Under-5 mortality rate (1997) 11

% of infants with low birthweight (1990-97) 8

Births attended by skilled health staff % of total[a] . . .98

% fully immunized (1995-97)

TB 100

DPT 91

Polio 90

Measles 89

Prevalence of child malnutrition under age 5 (1992-97)[b] 20

Ethnic Division (6)

Malay and other indigenous 58%

Chinese 26%

Indian 7%

Others 9%

Religions (7)

Peninsular Malaysia—Muslim (Malays), Buddhist (Chinese), Hindu (Indians); Sabah—Muslim 38%; Christian 17%; other 45%; Sarawak—tribal religion 35%; Buddhist and Confucianist 24%; Muslim 20%; Christian 16%; other 5%.

Languages (8)

Peninsular Malaysia—Malay (official), English, Chinese dialects, Tamil; Sabah—English, Malay, numerous tribal dialects, Chinese (Mandarin and Hakka dialects predominate); Sarawak—English, Malay, Mandarin, numerous tribal languages.

EDUCATION

Public Education Expenditures (9)

Public expenditure on education (% of GNP)

1980 . . . . .6.0

1996 . . . . .5.2

Expenditure per student

Primary % of GNP per capita

1980 . . . . .12.0

1996 . . . . .11.4[1]

Secondary % of GNP per capita

1980 . . . .

1996 . . . .

Tertiary % of GNP per capita

1980 . . . . .148.9

1996 . . . . .78.8[1]

Expenditure on teaching materials

Primary % of total for level (1996) 6.0

Secondary % of total for level (1996) . . . . .14.7[1]

Primary pupil-teacher ratio per teacher (1996) . . . . .20[1]

Duration of primary education years (1995) 6

Educational Attainment (10)

Age group (1996) . . . . .25+

Total population 9,654,600

Highest level attained (%)

No schooling 16.7

First level

Not completed 13.0

Completed 20.7

Entered second level

S-1 . . . . .19.4

S-2 . . . . .23.6

Postsecondary 6.9

Literacy Rates (11A)

In thousands and percent[1]	1990	1995	2000	2010
Illiterate population (15+ yrs.)	2,190	2,057	1,891	1,490
Literacy rate - total adult pop. (%)	80.2	83.5	86.9	92.0
Literacy rate - males (%)	86.9	89.1	91.2	94.2
Literacy rate - females (%)	73.6	78.1	82.6	89.8

GOVERNMENT & LAW

Political Parties (12)

House of Representatives	No. of seats
National Front	.162
Democratic Action Party (DAP)	.9
Sabah United Party (PBS)	.8
Parti Islam SeMalaysia (PAS)	.7
Spirit of '46	.6

Military Affairs (14B)

	1990	1991	1992	1993	1994	1995
Military expenditures						
Current dollars (mil.)	1,271	1,829	1,856	2,061	2,247	2,444
1995 constant dollars (mil.)	1,461	2,021	1,996	2,161	2,303	2,444
Armed forces (000)	130	128	128	115	115	122
Gross national product (GNP)						
Current dollars (mil.)	46,200	51,860	57,210	63,910	71,210	80,810
1995 constant dollars (mil.)	53,100	57,310	61,530	67,000	73,000	80,810
Central government expenditures (CGE)						
1995 constant dollars (mil.)	15,810	17,310	19,170	19,050	19,120	19,730
People (mil.)	17.5	17.9	18.3	18.7	19.1	19.5
Military expenditure as % of GNP	2.8	3.5	3.2	3.2	3.2	3.0
Military expenditure as % of CGE	9.2	11.7	10.4	11.3	12.0	12.4
Military expenditure per capita (1995 $)	83	113	109	115	120	125
Armed forces per 1,000 people (soldiers)	7.4	7.1	7.0	6.1	6.0	6.2
GNP per capita (1995 $)	3,033	3,200	3,359	3,578	3,814	4,134
Arms imports[6]						
Current dollars (mil.)	30	110	130	270	850	750
1995 constant dollars (mil.)	34	122	140	283	871	750
Arms exports[6]						
Current dollars (mil.)	0	0	0	0	10	40
1995 constant dollars (mil.)	0	0	0	0	10	40
Total imports[7]						
Current dollars (mil.)	29,260	36,650	39,930	45,660	58,580	77,750
1995 constant dollars (mil.)	33,620	40,500	42,950	47,870	61,070	77,750
Total exports[7]						
Current dollars (mil.)	29,420	34,350	40,710	47,120	58,760	74,040
1995 constant dollars (mil.)	33,810	37,960	43,790	49,400	60,230	74,040
Arms as percent of total imports[8]	.1	.3	.3	.6	1.4	1.0
Arms as percent of total exports[8]	0	0	0	0	0	.1

Government Budget (13A)

Year: 1997

Total Expenditures: 55,481 Millions of Ringgit

Expenditures as a percentage of the total by function:

General public services and public order . . . . . .16.30[f]

Defense . . . . .11.14[f]

Education . . . . .22.80[f]

Health . . . . .6.26[f]

Social Security and Welfare . . . . .7.20[f]

Housing and community amenities . . . . .7.31[f]

Recreational, cultural, and religious affairs . . . .-[f]

Fuel and energy . . . .-[f]

Agriculture, forestry, fishing, and hunting . . . . .4.65[f]

Mining, manufacturing, and construction . . . .-[f]

Transportation and communication . . . . .9.89[f]

Other economic affairs and services . . . . .7.07[f]

Crime (15)

Crime rate (for 1997)

Crimes reported 126,600

Total persons convicted 28,000

Crimes per 100,000 population 575

Persons responsible for offenses

Total number of suspects 47,900

Total number of female suspects 86

Total number of juvenile suspects 2,700

LABOR FORCE

Labor Force (16)

Total (million) 8.398

Manufacturing 25%

Agriculture, forestry, and fisheries 21%

Local trade and tourism 17%

Services 12%

Government 11%

Construction 8%

Data for 1996 est. Percent distribution for 1996.

Unemployment Rate (17)

2.6% (1996 est.)

PRODUCTION SECTOR

Electric Energy (18)

Capacity . . . . .7.83 million kW (1995)

Production . . . . .42 billion kWh (1995)

Consumption per capita . . . . .2,132 kWh (1995)

Transportation (19)

Highways:

total: 94,500 km

paved: 70,970 km (including 580 km of expressways)

unpaved: 23,530 km (1996 est.)

Waterways: 7,296 km (Peninsular Malaysia 3,209 km, Sabah 1,569 km, Sarawak 2,518 km)

Pipelines: crude oil 1,307 km; natural gas 379 km

Merchant marine:

total: 359 ships (1,000 GRT or over) totaling 4,586,576 GRT/6,747,771 DWT ships by type: bulk 57, cargo 132, chemical tanker 23, container 48, liquefied gas tanker 17, livestock carrier 1, oil tanker 63, refrigerated cargo 2, roll-on/roll-off cargo 5, short-sea passenger 1, specialized tanker 2, vehicle carrier 8 (1997 est.)

Airports: 114 (1997 est.)

Airports—with paved runways:

total: 33

over 3,047 m: 5

2,438 to 3,047 m: 4

1,524 to 2,437 m: 11

914 to 1,523 m: 6

under 914 m: 7 (1997 est.)

Airports—with unpaved runways:

total: 81

1,524 to 2,437 m: 1

914 to 1,523 m: 8

under 914 m: 72 (1997 est.)

Top Agricultural Products (20)

Peninsular Malaysia—natural rubber, palm oil, rice; Sabah— subsistence crops, rubber, timber, coconut, rice; Sarawak— rubber, pepper; timber.

MANUFACTURING SECTOR

GDP & Manufacturing Summary (21)

Detailed value added figures are listed by both International Standard Industry Code (ISIC) and product title.

	1980	1985	1990	1994
GDP ($-1990 mil.)[1]	23,997	30,794	42,822	59,071
Per capita ($-1990)[1]	1,744	1,964	2,393	2,999
Manufacturing share (%) (current prices)[1]	21.2	19.9	26.5	NA

	1980	1985	1990	1994
Manufacturing				
Value added ($-1990 mil.)[1]	4,708	6,066	11,493	18,733
Industrial production index	100	120	239	414
Value added ($ mil.)	3,623	4,879	9,068	18,560
Gross output ($ mil.)	13,181	18,359	35,422	68,789
Employment (000)	456	473	831	1,210
Profitability (% of gross output)				
Intermediate input (%)	73	73	74	73
Wages and salaries inc. supplements (%)	8	9	8	8
Gross operating surplus	20	18	18	19
Productivity ($)				
Gross output per worker	28,526	38,561	42,503	56,486
Value added per worker	8,060	10,249	10,881	15,317
Average wage (inc. supplements)	2,253	3,375	3,240	4,555
Value added ($ mil.)				
311/2 Food products	668	703	865	1,480
313 Beverages	106	122	201	170
314 Tobacco products	94	205	127	172
321 Textiles	185	133	297	577
322 Wearing apparel	67	100	280	432
323 Leather and fur products	3	2	6	20
324 Footwear	11	5	4	16
331 Wood and wood products	388	263	584	1,378
332 Furniture and fixtures	34	40	70	231
341 Paper and paper products	34	55	155	289
342 Printing and publishing	144	197	266	494
351 Industrial chemicals	79	616	748	1,468
352 Other chemical products	115	153	232	417
353 Petroleum refineries	115	136	199	213
354 Miscellaneous petroleum and coal products	2	21	32	65
355 Rubber products	295	250	528	836
356 Plastic products	69	92	261	646
361 Pottery, china and earthenware	10	13	36	61
362 Glass and glass products	24	23	73	104
369 Other non-metal mineral products	169	297	411	717
371 Iron and steel	78	153	287	540
372 Non-ferrous metals	39	35	63	135
381 Metal products	140	147	316	798
382 Non-electrical machinery	116	99	348	920
383 Electrical machinery	435	738	1,945	5,088
384 Transport equipment	153	211	494	873
385 Professional and scientific equipment	25	30	97	214
390 Other manufacturing industries	23	39	111	204

FINANCE, ECONOMICS, & TRADE

Balance of Payments (23)

	1991	1992	1993	1994	1995
Exports of goods (f.o.b.)	33,712	39,823	46,238	56,897	72,053
Imports of goods (f.o.b.)	−33,321	−36,673	−43,201	−55,320	−72,153
Trade balance	391	3,150	3,037	1,577	−100
Services - debits	−10,462	−12,088	−14,734	−17,955	−21,283
Services - credits	5,799	6,598	8,419	11,628	13,874
Private transfers (net)	8	67	57	51	38
Government transfers (net)	80	105	230	178	110
Overall balance	−4,183	−2,168	−2,991	−4,521	−7,362

FINANCE, ECONOMICS, & TRADE

Economic Indicators (22)

National product: GDP—purchasing power parity—$227 billion (1997 est.)

National product real growth rate: 7.4% (1997 est.)

National product per capita: $11,100 (1997 est.)

Inflation rate—consumer price index: 36% (1996)

Exchange Rates (24)

Exchange rates:

Ringgits (M$) per US$1

January 1998	4.3985
1997	2.8133
1996	2.5159
1995	2.5044
1994	2.6243
1993	2.5741

Top Import Origins (25)

$78.4 billion (1996) Data are for 1995.

Origins	%
Japan	27
United States	16
Singapore	12
Taiwan	5
Germany	4
South Korea	4

Top Export Destinations (26)

$78.2 billion (1996) Data are for 1995.

Destinations	%
United States	21
Singapore	20
Japan	12
Hong Kong	5
United Kingdom	4
Thailand	4
Germany	3

Economic Aid (27)

Recipient: ODA, $45 million (1993).

Import Export Commodities (28)

Import Commodities	Export Commodities
Machinery and equipment	Electronic equipment
Chemicals	Petroleum and petroleum products
Food 4%	Palm oil
	Wood and wood products
	Rubber
	Textiles

MALDIVES

CAPITAL: Malé.

FLAG: The national flag consists of a white crescent at the center of a green field which, in turn, is at the center of a red field.

MONETARY UNIT: The Maldivian rupee, or rufiyaa (MR), is a paper currency of 100 laris. There are notes of 1/2, 1, 2, 5, 10, 50, and 100 rufiyaa. The dollar circulates freely and is the only currency accepted at some resorts. MR1 = $0.08496 (or $1 = MR11.770).

WEIGHTS AND MEASURES: The metric system has been adopted, but some local units remain in use.

HOLIDAYS: National Day, 7 January; Independence Day, 26 July; Republic Day, 11 November; Fishermen's Day, 10 December. 'Id al-Fitr, 'Id al-'Adha', and Milad an-Nabi are some of the Muslim religious holidays observed.

TIME: 5 PM = noon GMT.

LOCATION AND SIZE: The smallest country in Asia, the Republic of Maldives consists of an archipelago (a large group of islands) of nearly 1,200 coral islands and sand banks in the Indian Ocean, about 200 of which are inhabited. The area occupied by Maldives is slightly more than 1.5 times the size of Washington, D.C.

Maldives' capital, Malé, is situated on the largest island in the entire chain, in the Malé Atoll.

CLIMATE: The Maldives' equatorial climate is generally hot and humid, with a mean temperature of about 27°C (81°F). Annual rainfall in the south averages about 380 centimeters (150 inches); in the north, 250 centimeters (100 inches).

INTRODUCTORY SURVEY

RECENT HISTORY

Although it gained independence from the United Kingdom in 1948, the Maldives remained under the protection of Great Britain. In 1959,

government forces crushed rebellions in two of the southernmost atolls. The Sultanate of the Maldive Islands achieved complete independence on 26 July 1965. A new republican constitution came into force on 11 November 1968, establishing the Republic of Maldives. Britain left the Gan air base on 31 December 1975, and the United Kingdom-Maldivian protection accord was formally terminated the following year.

In November 1988, President Maumoon Abdul Gayoom successfully resisted an attempt to overthrow him by hired soldiers from Sri Lanka. He was helped by an Indian military contingent flown to the Maldives at his request. Gayoom was reelected for a fifth term as president in 1998/99.

GOVERNMENT

Under the 1968 constitution, the president is elected to a five-year term by the Citizens' Majlis (parliament) but must be confirmed in office by popular referendum. The president heads the executive branch and appoints the cabinet. The Majlis has 48 members, 40 directly elected and 8 appointed by the president.

The Maldives is divided into 19 districts, each headed by a government-appointed *verin,* or chief.

Judiciary

Justice is carried out according to traditional Islamic law *(Shari`a)* by the High Court and lower courts appointed for that purpose by the president. Civil law is also applied but remains subordinate to Shari'a.

On the capital island, Malé, there is a High Court and eight lower courts. On the other islands, there is one all-purpose lower court, and complex

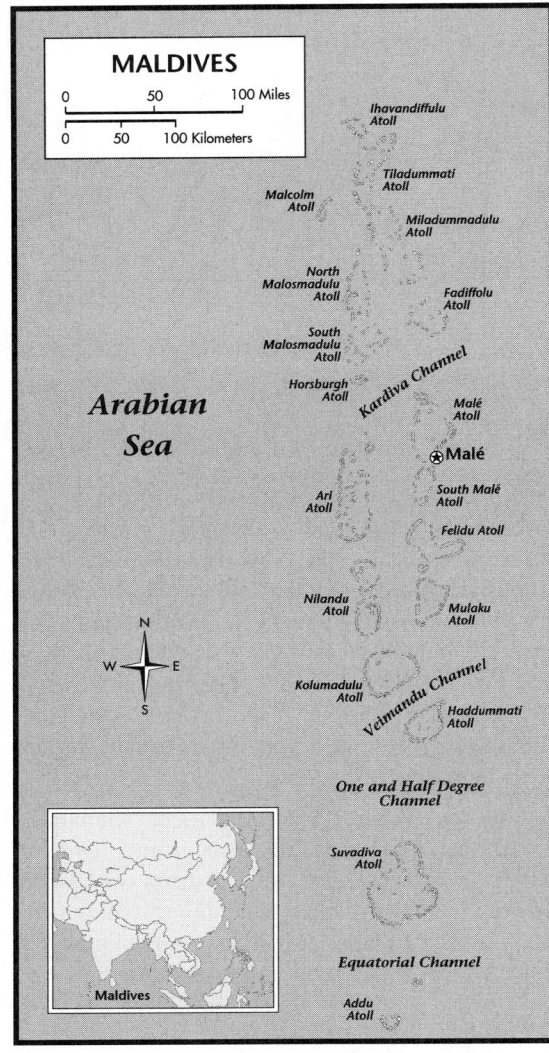

cases are referred to the appropriate specialized court in Malé.

Political Parties

There are no organized political parties. Candidates run for election as independents and campaign based on their personal and family reputations.

DEFENSE

The armed forces of the Maldives consist of a paramilitary National Security Service and Militia of only a few hundred. Defense spending may reach $1.8 million a year.

ECONOMIC AFFAIRS

The Maldives is among the least developed countries in the world. Fishing, tourism, and ship-

ping are the mainstays of the economy. The government is seeking to diversify the economy through further promotion of tourism, processing industries, and garment production.

Public Finance

Public enterprises, including the State Trading Organization, the state shipping line, and public utilities, account for nearly half of government revenues; customs and tourist receipts make up most of the rest.

The U.S. Central Intelligence Agency estimates that, in 1995, government revenues totaled approximately $88 million and expenditures $141 million. External debt totaled $137.5 million, approximately 47% of which was financed abroad.

Income

In 1997, Maldives's gross national product (GNP) was $500 million at current prices, or about $1,800 per person. For the period 1985–95 the average inflation rate was 9.2%, resulting in a real growth rate in GNP of 6.7% per person.

Industry

After the fishing industry, important traditional industries in the Maldives include the manufacture of coir (a rope made from dried coconut fibers) and lacemaking.

Banking and Finance

The Maldives Monetary Authority, established 1 July 1981, issues currency, advises the government on banking and monetary matters, supervises commercial banks, and manages exchange rates and exchange assets. Other banking services are provided by the Bank of Maldives (created in 1982) and branches of the Bank of India, Habib Bank Ltd. of Pakistan, and the Bank of Ceylon. There is no securities exchange.

Economic Development

The government has implemented a series of development programs to improve and expand fishing and related industries, textile manufacturing, food processing, tourism, communications, and health and education services. Part of the economic thrust has been to lessen the reliance on fishing and to diversify the economy. In 1986, Malé's new commercial harbor was opened, considerably speeding up cargo handling from 200–300 tons to 1,500 tons a day.

Malé's international airport was upgraded in the late 1980s, comprising a critical factor in the growth of the country's tourism sector. Given the growing wealth in the country in recent years, the government is considering bolstering government development revenues by instituting a personal income tax, though concerns remain that enforcement may prove difficult. Continued expansion of tourism has been particularly targeted in government development plans for the immediate future, along with facilitating a spread of economic activity to outlying island groups.

SOCIAL WELFARE

There is no organized social welfare system. Assistance is traditionally provided through the extended family. In spite of traditional Islamic restrictions on women, they have increased their participation in public life.

Healthcare

In 1993, the Maldives had 15 physicians and 6 midwives. There is an 86-bed hospital in Malé, backed by a 12-bed regional hospital and medical rescue services in the outlying atolls. Life expectancy was 64 years.

Housing

Most houses have coral or coconut-wood walls; the roofs are tiled or made of corrugated galvanized iron. The poorer houses are walled from the street with mats, called *cadjan*, or palm leaves.

EDUCATION

An estimated 7% of the adult population was illiterate in 1995. In 1993 there were 48,321 students in primary schools, and secondary schools had 18,678 students.

1999 KEY EVENTS TIMELINE

January

- Maldives officials take part in a meeting in Kathmandu, Nepal, to fight crime against women and children.

- The movie ''The Prince of Egypt'' is banned from Maldives theaters because the portrayal of Moses is offensive to the Islamic religion.

February

- The South Asian Association for Regional Cooperation (SAARC), of which Maldives is a member, plans to create a South Asian free trade area.

March

- Deputy Prime Minister John Prescott of Britain visits the Maldives, announcing a £300,000 grant for coral conservation in South Asia.

April

- Scientists find a dense cloud of pollution hanging over the Indian Ocean.

June

- Amnesty International reports that dozens of prisoners of conscience were held in the Maldives, some of them ill-treated.

July

- Representatives from SAARC meet to address concerns about controlling tuberculosis among women.

August

- Maldives signs a treaty to abolish landmines.

September

- Maldives athletes compete in the South Asian Federation Games.

October

- A military coup d'état takes place in Pakistan, and SAARC members argue over the new government's legitimacy.

November

- Elections are held on November 19 for 40 seats in the 48-seat parliament (eight seats are filled by appointment). Since political parties are banned in Maldives, all 125 candidates running for parliament campaign as independents.

ANALYSIS OF EVENTS: 1999

BUSINESS AND THE ECONOMY

The Republic of Maldives consists of 1,190 islands, composing 90,000 square kilometers of land, which are currently under threat of sinking into the Indian Ocean. It is estimated that one third of the beaches surrounding inhabited islands are being swept away by rising sea levels, a product of global warming. This does not bode well for the islands' 256,000 inhabitants or its economy. Land for housing has become scarce, and the tourism industry, a primary force in the islands' economy, will suffer from the environmental damage caused by pollution and the affects of global warming.

Maldives' idyllic sandy white beaches, tropical fish, and extensive coral reefs drive its tourism industry. Over the years the waters surrounding the islands have risen in temperature by two or three degrees, a deceptively small change with major environmental repercussions. In some parts of Maldives over 90% of the coral has lost its color and died, and many reefs are now devoid of fish. Scientists working on the Indian Ocean Experiment (INDODEX) have also found a dark band of pollution stretching from the Indian Ocean for up to three kilometers high, reducing the amount of sunlight that reaches ocean-dwelling creatures.

Tourism Minister Hassan Sobir hopes the coral will grow and help hold back the encroaching ocean, but the environmental damage affecting the coral is not a trend that can be easily reversed. As tourism falters, the economy is giving new consideration to the fishing industry. While new investment may arrive with the emerging South Asian free trade region, the fishing industry, currently carried out with lines and nets from man-powered boats, will probably not be able to maintain the current average annual per capita GDP of $1,080.

GOVERNMENT AND POLITICS

On November 11, 1998, President Mamour Abdul Gayoom was reelected for a fifth consecutive term. He had no rival candidates and gained almost 90% of the vote. The Maldives gained its independence from the British Empire in 1947. Since then, the islands' democratic processes have been rife with government corruption and bribe taking. Economic disparity between the upper and lower classes is profound. President Gayoom has pledged to resolve the housing and land crises by creating a new island, but he has not stated how this will be done. Meanwhile, his country continues to be threatened by the rising water of the ocean. During a visit to the Maldives in March, British Deputy Prime Minister John Prescott granted one half million dollars for coral preservation in South Asia, but the problem is truly global and can not be easily resolved locally.

In 1985 Maldives, Nepal, India, Pakistan, Bangladesh, Sri Lanka and Bhutan gathered for the first SAARC meeting. Within this organization, the member countries can exert more clout than they would individually. Formed as an economic alliance, SAARC has expanded into a regional organization that encompasses both economic and political issues.

CULTURE AND SOCIETY

Islam has contributed to the Maldives' culture and religion since 1153 AD, and it was only about thirty years ago, with right restrictions, that the islands were open to tourists and the western world. To protect its Muslim citizens, laws are in place to keep western culture and tourists separate from the natives. For instance, Steven Spielberg's animated film "The Prince of Egypt" was banned from theaters in Maldives because its portrayal of Moses was considered offensive to Islam. The Ministry for Tourism keeps most tourist islands separate from residential islands, allowing development only on uninhabited islands so that the native culture can be maintained. Exotic and remote, with a constant temperature between eighty and ninety degrees, the islands create the perfect refuge for tourists seeking a unique vacation spot.

DIRECTORY

CENTRAL GOVERNMENT
Head of State

President
Maumoon Abdul Gayooom, Office of the President
PHONE: +960 323701
FAX: +960 325500

Ministers

Minister of Atolls Administration
Abdulla Hameed, Ministry of Atolls Administration, Faashanaa Building, Boduthakurufaanu Magu, Male, 20 05, Republic of Maldives
PHONE: +960 323070
FAX: +960 327750

Minister of Construction and Public Works
Umar Zahir, Ministry of Construction and Public Works, Izzuddeen Magu, Male, 20 01, Republic of Maldives
PHONE: +960 323234
FAX: +960 326637
E-MAIL: mcpw@dhivehinet.net.mv

Minister of Defense and National Security

Maumoon Abdul Gayoom, Ministry of Defense
and National Security, Bandaara Koshi, Ameer
Ahmed Magu, Male, 20 05, Republic of
Maldives
PHONE: +960 322607
FAX: +960 325525

Minister of Education

Mohammed Latheef, Ministry of Education,
Ghaazee Building, Ameer Ahmed Magu, Male,
20 05, Republic of Maldives
PHONE: +960 323262
FAX: +960 321201
E-MAIL: educator@dhivehinet.net.mv

Minister of Finance and Treasury

Maumoon Abdul Gayoom, Ministry of Finance
and Treasury, Ameenee Magu, Male, 20 04,
Republic of Maldives
PHONE: +960 322269
FAX: +960 324432
E-MAIL: educator@dhivehinet.net.mv

Minister of Fisheries, Agriculture and Marine Resources

Abdul Rasheed Hussain, Ministry of Fisheries,
Agriculture and Marine Resources, Ghaazee
Building, Ameer Ahmed Magu, Male, 20 05,
Republic of Maldives
PHONE: +960 322625
FAX: +960 326558
E-MAIL: fishagri@dhivehinet.net.mv

Minister of Foreign Affairs

Fathulla Jameel, Ministry of Foreign Affairs,
Boduthakurufaanu Magu, Male, 20 05, Republic
of Maldives
PHONE: +960 323400
FAX: +960 323841
E-MAIL: admin@foreign.gov.mv

Minister of Health

Ahmed Abdulla, Ministry of Health, Ghaazee
Building, Ameer Ahmed Magu, Male, 20 05,
Republic of Maldives
PHONE: +960 328887
FAX: +960 328889
E-MAIL: moh@dhivehinet.net.mv

Minister of Home Affairs, Housing and Environment

Ismail Shafeeu, Ministry of Home Affairs,
Housing and Environment, Huravee Building,
Ameer Ahmed Magu, Male, 20 05, Republic of
Maldives
PHONE: +960 323820

FAX: +960 324739

Minister of Human Resources, Employment and Labour

Abdulla Kamaludheen, Ministry of Human
Resources, Employment and Labour

Minister of Information, Arts and Culture

Ibrahim Manik, Ministry of Information, Arts
and Culture, Buruzu Magu, Male, 20 04,
Republic of Maldives
PHONE: +960 323838
FAX: +960 326211
E-MAIL: informat@dhivehinet.net.mv

Minister of Justice

Ahmed Zahir, Ministry of Justice, Justice
Building, Orchid Magu, Male, 20 02, Republic
of Maldives
PHONE: +960 322303
FAX: +960 324103
E-MAIL: informat@dhivehinet.net.mv

Minister of Planning and National Development

Ibrahim Hussain Zaki, Ministry of Planning and
National Development, Ghaazee Building, Ameer
Ahmed Magu, Male, 20 05, Republic of
Maldives
PHONE: +960 323919
FAX: +960 327351
E-MAIL: mpre@dhivehinet.net.mv

Minister of Tourism

Hassan Sabir, Ministry of Tourism,
Boduthakurufaanu Magu, Male, 20 05, Republic
of Maldives
PHONE: +960 323224
FAX: +960 322512
E-MAIL: tourism@dhivehinet.net.mv

Minister of Trade and Industries

Abdulla Yameen, Ministry of Trade and
Industries, Ghaazee Building, Ameer Ahmed
Magu, Male, 20 05, Republic of Maldives
PHONE: +960 323668
FAX: +960 323840

Minister of Transport and Civil Aviation

Ilyas Ibrahim, Ministry of Transport and Civil
Aviation, Ghaazee Building, Ameer Ahmed
Magu, Male, 20 05, Republic of Maldives
PHONE: +960 323991/323344
FAX: +960 323994

Minister of Women's Affairs and Social Security

Rashida Yoosuf, Ministry of Women's Affairs and Social Security, Umar Shopping Arcade, 2nd Floor, Chaandhanee Magu, Male, 20 05, Republic of Maldives
PHONE: +960 317165
FAX: +960 316237
E-MAIL: kamana@dhivehinet.net.mv

Minister of Youth and Sports

Mohammed Zahir Hussain, Ministry of Youth and Sports, Ghaazee Building, Ameer Ahmed Magu, Male, 20 05, Republic of Maldives
PHONE: +960 326986
FAX: +960 327162
E-MAIL: mys@dhivehinet.net.mv

DIPLOMATIC REPRESENTATION
Embassies in Maldives

Denmark

25 Boduthakurufaanu Magu, Male 20–05, Maldives
PHONE: +960 322451
FAX: +960 323523

JUDICIAL SYSTEM
High Court of Maldives

Moonlight Hingun, Male, 20 06, Republic of Maldives
PHONE: +960 323082
FAX: +960 316371

Civil Court

Justice Building, Orchid Magu, Male, 20 02, Republic of Maldives
PHONE: +960 323682
FAX: +960 323986

Criminal Court

Justice Building, Orchid Magu, Male, 20 02, Republic of Maldives

PHONE: +960 323268
FAX: +960 322304

FURTHER READING
Articles

Casimiro, Steve. "Dive In: When You've Graduated from the Frattish, Corona-Soaked Fiesta of the Yucatan, Head for the Maldives—the Peaceable Paradise." *Fortune* (May 24, 1999): 335–36.

Kirby, Alex. "Coral's Worsening Crisis." BBC, 15 March 1999.

———. "Global Warming Threatens Tourism." BBC, 29 August 1999.

———. "Indian Ocean Haze Startles Scientists." BBC, 1 April 1999.

Leopold, Evelyn. "Report: Corruption Ruining Economies of South Asia." Reuters, 1 November 1999.

"Mamoun Abdul Gayoom has been Sworn-in as President of Maldives for Fifth Consecutive Term." BBC, 11 November 1999.

"Pakistan Wants Summit to Go Ahead, Slams India." Reuters, 4 November 1999.

Peschardt, Michael. "Climate Change Killing Coral Reefs." Reuters, 17 August 1999.

"Sinking in Maldives." *The Economist* (January 9, 1999): 39–40.

Books

Haq, Khadija. *Crisis of Government in South Asia.* New York: Mahbub ul Haq Foundation, 1999.

Internet

Haveeru Daily. Available Online @ www/ haveeruonline.com/english/ (November 18, 1999).

Permanent Mission of the Republic of Maldives to the United Nations. Available Online @ www.undp.org/missions/maldives/ (November 18, 1999).

MALDIVES: STATISTICAL DATA

For sources and notes see "Sources of Statistics" in the front of each volume.

GEOGRAPHY

Geography (1)

Area:

Total: 300 sq km.

Land: 300 sq km.

Water: 0 sq km.

Area—comparative: about 1.7 times the size of Washington, DC.

Land boundaries: 0 km.

Coastline: 644 km.

Climate: tropical; hot, humid; dry, northeast monsoon (November to March); rainy, southwest monsoon (June to August).

Terrain: flat, with white sandy beaches.

Natural resources: fish.

Land use:

Arable land: 10%

Permanent crops: 0%

Permanent pastures: 3%

Forests and woodland: 3%

Other: 84% (1993 est.).

HUMAN FACTORS

Infants and Malnutrition (5)

Under-5 mortality rate (1997) 74

% of infants with low birthweight (1990-97) 13

Births attended by skilled health staff % of total[a] . . .NA

Demographics (2A)

	1990	1995	1998	2000	2010	2020	2030	2040	2050
Population	217.7	261.3	290.2	310.4	422.9	554.2	691.6	824.8	949.5
Net migration rate (per 1,000 population)	NA	NA	NA	NA	NA	NA	NA	NA	NA
Births	NA	NA	NA	NA	NA	NA	NA	NA	NA
Deaths	NA	NA	NA	NA	NA	NA	NA	NA	NA
Life expectancy - males	60.4	64.0	65.9	67.2	72.3	75.8	77.9	79.2	80.0
Life expectancy - females	62.7	67.1	69.3	71.0	77.1	81.2	83.7	85.2	86.0
Birth rate (per 1,000)	46.2	42.8	40.1	38.5	32.6	27.6	22.4	19.1	16.7
Death rate (per 1,000)	9.3	7.0	6.0	5.3	3.5	2.9	2.8	3.4	4.3
Women of reproductive age (15-49 yrs.)	47.2	55.1	61.8	67.2	99.8	136.9	179.5	217.5	242.7
of which are currently married	69.3	NA	NA	NA	NA	NA	NA	NA	NA
Fertility rate	6.6	6.2	5.8	5.6	4.4	3.4	2.7	2.3	2.2

Except as noted, values for vital statistics are in thousands; life expectancy is in years.

Infants and Malnutrition (5)

% fully immunized (1995-97)

TB 99

DPT 97

Polio 97

Measles 96

Prevalence of child malnutrition under age 5
(1992-97)[b] . . . . .NA

Ethnic Division (6)

Sinhalese, Dravidian, Arab, African.

Religions (7)

Sunni Muslim.

Languages (8)

Maldivian Divehi (dialect of Sinhala, script derived
from Arabic), English spoken by most government
officials.

EDUCATION

Educational Attainment (10)

Age group (1990) . . . . .25+

Total population 66,977

Highest level attained (%)

No schooling 0.9

First level

Not completed 61.6

Completed 10.8

Entered second level

S-1 . . . . .6.3

S-2 . . . . .17.1

Postsecondary 1.7

Literacy Rates (11A)

In thousands and percent[1]	1990	1995	2000	2010
Illiterate population (15+ yrs.)	9	9	10	10
Literacy rate - total adult pop. (%)	92.2	93.2	94.0	95.5
Literacy rate - males (%)	92.5	93.3	94.0	95.3
Literacy rate - females (%)	91.9	93.0	94.1	95.7

GOVERNMENT & LAW

Political Parties (12)

The legislative branch is a unicameral Citizens' Council
(48 seats; 40 elected by popular vote, 8 appointed by
the president; members serve five-year terms). Although
political parties are not banned, none exist.

Government Budget (13A)

Year: 1997

Total Expenditures: 1,935.9 Millions of Rufiyaa

Expenditures as a percentage of the total by function:

General public services and public order . . . . .23.16[P]

Defense . . . . .18.33[P]

Education . . . . .16.50[P]

Health . . . . .11.49[P]

Social Security and Welfare . . . . .2.56[P]

Housing and community amenities . . . . .7.97[P]

Recreational, cultural, and religious affairs . . . .-[P]

Fuel and energy . . . . .1.10[P]

Agriculture, forestry, fishing, and hunting . . . . .1.48[P]

Mining, manufacturing, and construction . . . .-[P]

Transportation and communication . . . . .11.36[P]

Other economic affairs and services . . . . .1.58[P]

Military Affairs (14A)

Availability of manpower

Males age 15-49 (1998 est.) 63,879

Fit for military service

Males (1998 est.) 35,610

Total expenditures . . . .$NA

Expenditures as % of GDP . . . . .NA%

NA stands for not available.

Crime (15)

Crime rate (for 1997)

Crimes reported 6,950

Total persons convicted 4,100

Crimes per 100,000 population 2,800

Persons responsible for offenses

Total number of suspects 3,250

Total number of female suspects 175

Total number of juvenile suspects 400

LABOR FORCE

Labor Force (16)

Total 56,435
Fishing industry and agriculture 25%
Services 21%
Manufacturing and construction 21%
Trade, restaurants, and hotels 16%
Transport and communication 10%
Other 7%

Data for 1990 est.

Unemployment Rate (17)

Negligible.

PRODUCTION SECTOR

Electric Energy (18)

Capacity . . . . .14,000 kW (1995)
Production . . . . .50 million kWh (1995)
Consumption per capita . . . . .191 kWh (1995)

Transportation (19)

Highways:

total: NA km

paved: NA km

unpaved: NA km; note—Male has 9.6 km of coral highways within the city (1988 est.)

Merchant marine:

total: 20 ships (1,000 GRT or over) totaling 70,703 GRT/108,485 DWT ships by type: cargo 17, container 1, oil tanker 1, short-sea passenger 1 (1997 est.)

Airports: 2 (1997 est.)

Airports—with paved runways:

total: 2

over 3,047 m: 1

2,438 to 3,047 m: 1 (1997 est.)

Top Agricultural Products (20)

Coconuts, corn, sweet potatoes; fishing.

FINANCE, ECONOMICS, & TRADE

Economic Indicators (22)

National product: GDP—purchasing power parity—$500 million (1997 est.)

National product real growth rate: 6.2% (1997 est.)

National product per capita: $1,800 (1997 est.)

Inflation rate—consumer price index: 6.3% (1996)

Exchange Rates (24)

Exchange rates:

Rufiyaa (Rf) per US$1
  1995-January 1998 .11.770
  1994 . . . . .11.586
  1993 . . . . .10.957

Top Import Origins (25)

$302 million (f.o.b., 1996)

Origins	%
Singapore	NA
India	NA
Sri Lanka	NA
Hong Kong	NA
Japan	NA
Thailand	NA

NA stands for not available.

Balance of Payments (23)

	1992	1993	1994	1995	1996
Exports of goods (f.o.b.)	51	39	75	85	92
Imports of goods (f.o.b.)	−168	−178	−195	−236	−266
Trade balance	−117	−139	−120	−151	−174
Services - debits	−69	−78	−87	−100	−106
Services - credits	171	181	201	238	295
Private transfers (net)	14	8	16	23	26
Government transfers (net)	−19	−20	−22	−27	−33
Overall balance	−20	−48	−11	−17	9

Top Export Destinations (26)

$59 million (f.o.b., 1996).

Destinations	%
Sri Lanka	NA
United States	NA
Germany	NA
Singapore	NA
United Kingdom	NA

NA stands for not available.

Economic Aid (27)

Recipient: ODA, $NA. NA stands for not available.

Import Export Commodities (28)

Import Commodities	Export Commodities
Consumer goods	Fish
Intermediate and capital goods	Clothing
Petroleum products	

MALI

Republic of Mali
République du Mali

INTRODUCTORY SURVEY

RECENT HISTORY

Around 1880, the French began their advance into what was to become the Republic of Mali. Under French administration, the area became known as French Sudan (Soudan Français) and was a part of French West Africa. In 1946, the Sudanese became French citizens, with representation in the French parliament. In 1958, under the constitution of the Fifth French Republic, French Sudan became an autonomous republic, called the Sudanese Republic, within the French Community. Achievements under French rule included the building of a railway, and development of the Niger River delta.

In June 1960, the new Mali Federation, consisting of the Sudanese Republic and Senegal, became a sovereign state. However, disagreements soon arose. On 22 September 1960, the Sudan declared itself independent as the Republic of Mali, and all ties between Senegal and Mali were soon severed as well.

The one-party dictatorship led by President Modibo Keita evolved into a socialist regime modeled on that of the People's Republic of China. However, by 1968, economic problems and discontent became severe. On 19 November, Keita was overthrown in a bloodless coup led by Lieutenant (later General) Moussa Traoré. The 1960 constitution was abolished, and a 14-member Military Committee for National Liberation took command. Lieutenant Traoré became president in 1969. The military regime's efforts to improve the economic situation in Mali were frustrated by the prolonged

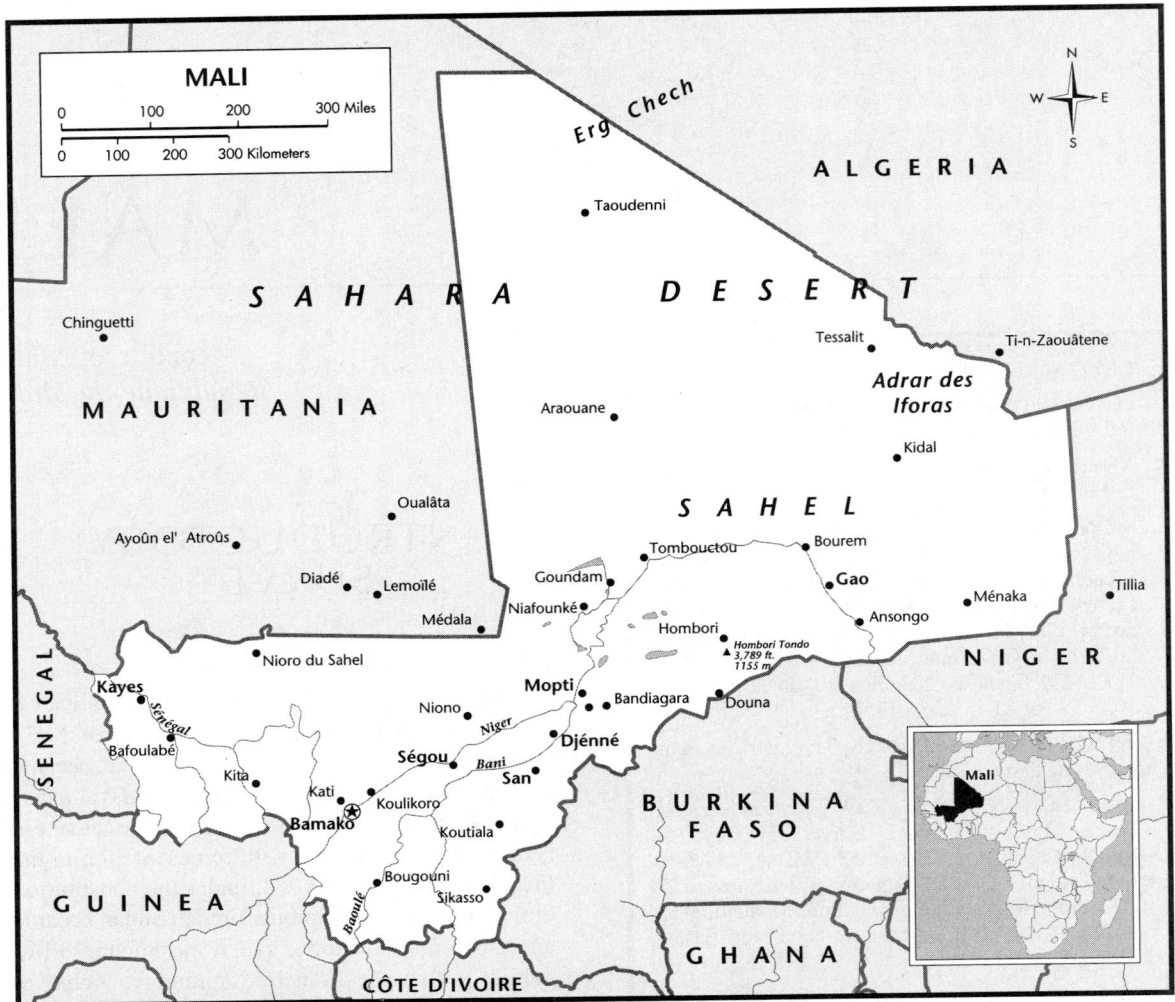

period of drought that began in 1968 and peaked in 1973.

Traoré was elected president in 1979 under a new constitution, which also confirmed Mali as a one-party state. He was reelected in 1985. However, on 26 March 1991, Lieutenant Colonel Amadou Toumani Touré engineered a coup that toppled the Traoré government.

After the coup, a National Conference drafted new electoral rules, party statutes and a new constitution. The new constitution was adopted by referendum in January 1992. It established an agenda for the transition to a multi-party state. New elections were held and in April 1992 Dr. Alpha Oumar Konaré, the leader of the Alliance for Democracy in Mali (ADEMA), became Mali's first democratically elected president with 69% of the vote, and The Third Republic was launched.

One of the last acts of the Touré transitional government was to negotiate (with Algerian mediation) a peace treaty in April 1992 with rebel members of the ethnic Tuaregs in the north. The government acknowledged the northerners' special status, and the Tuaregs renounced their claims to independence. Student unrest continued and in April 1993, the government was forced to resign. Abdoulaye Sekou Sow replaced Younoussi Touré as prime minister, but his government fell from power in February 1994, as violence continued among students and the unemployed. In January 1996, the government cracked down, arresting several leaders of student groups that had been protesting mostly for economic reasons.

GOVERNMENT

The 1979 constitution was replaced by a new constitution adopted by referendum in January

1992. The National Assembly now has 116 deputies with 10 parties represented. The president, elected by popular vote, chooses the prime minister who selects a cabinet (currently 22 ministers, including five from opposition parties).

Judiciary

A Supreme Court was established in Bamako in 1969. It is made up of 19 members, nominated for five years. The judicial section has three civil chambers and one criminal chamber. The administrative section deals with appeals and fundamental rulings. The Court of Appeal is also in Bamako. There are two magistrate courts, courts for labor disputes, and a special court of state security. The 1992 Constitution established a separate constitutional court and a High Court of Justice charged with responsibility for trying senior government officials accused of treason.

Political Parties

The Democratic Union of Malian People (Union Démocratique de Peuple Malien—UDPM) was created as the sole legal political party in 1979. Shortly after the military coup in March 1991, some 48 parties were functioning, of which 23 contested the 1992 elections and ten elected deputies to the National Assembly. The Alliance for Democracy in Mali (ADEMA) is the majority party, but the prime minister and government formed on 12 April 1993, brought opposition parties into the cabinet. The UDPM, the former ruling party, relaunched itself in mid-1993.

DEFENSE

Armed forces' strength was 7,350 in 1995: 6,900 were in the ground forces, 50 in the marine forces, and 400 in the air forces, (all considered part of the army). Overall, the army consisted of 13 mixed battalions and an air defense missile battery. The air force was equipped with 16 aircraft, and the navy possessed 3 river patrol boats. In 1995 Mali spent $56 million on defense, or 2.5% of the gross domestic product (GDP).

ECONOMIC AFFAIRS

Economic activity in Mali centers on domestic agricultural and livestock production. Vast stretches of Sahara desert limit Mali's agricultural potential and subject the country to severe, prolonged, recurrent drought (1968–74, 1982–85). In periods of adequate rainfall, Mali approaches food self-sufficiency.

In January 1994 France devalued the CFA franc, cutting its value in half overnight. Mali did not benefit very much from the devaluation because it has few exports. Inflation reached 35% after the devaluation but dropped off to 8% in 1995.

Public Finance

The U.S. Central Intelligence Agency estimated that, in 1995, government revenues totaled approximately $376 million and expenditures $697 million. External debt totaled $2.8 billion. Foreign assistance accounts for about 20% of Mali's national budget.

Income

In 1997 Mali's gross national product (GNP) was $6 billion, or about $600 per person. For the period 1985–95 the average inflation rate was 151.9%, resulting in a real growth rate in GNP of 0.6% per person.

Industry

Mali has a very small industrial sector, mostly government-owned plants producing textiles and consumer goods. Textiles account for about 50% of the industrial output's value. Ground nut (peanut) oil, rice polishing, fruit preserving, sugar distilling, tea, and cottonseed oil and cottonseed cake plants are in operation, as are three slaughterhouses. Other industrial facilities include a vinegar factory, a cigarette factory, a soft-drink plant, a flour mill, a shoe factory, a tannery, and two textile plants. There are a few construction related facilities, including a cement works, a brick factory, and a ceramics factory.

Banking and Finance

In 1959, the Central Bank of the West African States (Banque Centrale des États de l'Afrique de l'Ouest—BCEAO) succeeded the Currency Board of French West Africa and Togo as the bank of issue for the former French West African territories, known now as the franc zone: Benin, Burkina Faso, Côte d'Ivoire, Mali, Niger, Senegal, and Togo. Foreign exchange receipts of the member states went into the franc zone's exchange pool, which in turn covered their foreign exchange requirements. In July 1962, however, Mali withdrew from the BCEAO and West African Monetary Union and established a bank of its own, the Bank of the Republic of Mali, which issued a new currency, the Malian franc.

In 1967, Mali returned to the franc zone, with its franc set at half the value of the CFA franc. In March 1968, the banking system was reorganized, and the Central Bank of Mali was established as the central issuing bank. In December 1982, Mali's application to rejoin the West African Monetary Union was rejected, as Upper Volta (now Burkina Faso), which had a border dispute with Mali, continued to oppose Mali's re-admission until 1983. In 1984 it rejoined the BCEAO and the monetary union. Foreign assets came to $323 million in 1995, while the money supply, as measured by M2, was CFA Fr256.55 billion at the end of 1995.

In addition to the Central Bank, commercial banks in 1997 included: the Bank of Africa, Banque Commerciale de Sahel, Banque Malienne de Crédit et du Depots, and the Financial Bank Mali. Development banks in Mali include the Banque de Développpment du Mali, and the Banque Nationale de Développpment Agricole. The banks routinely blame the BCEAO's tight liquidity regulations, but in reality remain tentative about many lending propositions. Domestic savings have increased since 1994. Along with other members of the Union économique at minétaire ouest-africaine (UEMOA), Mali now faces the problem of diversifying credit instruments in favor of small and medium-sized enterprises, which have historically relied upon informal sources of investment.

Economic Development

Fiscal management reform and continued dependence on foreign aid into the foreseeable future are the hallmarks of the economic development effort in the coming years. The 1994 devaluation of the CFA franc resulted in increased exports of cotton, livestock, gold, and other products. Strong prices for cotton worldwide, combined with record production in Mali in 1995, were both positive factors for the Mali economy. However, the agricultural sector is still highly vulnerable to drought and, in spite of its natural potential, unlikely to produce at self-sufficiency levels.

SOCIAL WELFARE

Social welfare is basically an extension of the labor code, which includes provisions for medical care, workers' compensation, and retirement benefits. A system of family allowances for wage earners provides small maternity and children's allowances, along with classes in prenatal and infant care. Traditionally, the individual's basic welfare needs were cared for by the tribal organization.

This system, however, is breaking down as the country develops.

Healthcare

Most health care is provided by the public medical services. The number of private doctors and well-equipped medical institutions is small. In 1993, the population per physician was about 18,376. In 1985–95, only 30% of the population had access to health care services.

The principal diseases are malaria, leprosy, tuberculosis, enteritis and other intestinal diseases, cholera, pneumonia, and infectious and parasite-related diseases, such as schistosomiasis, onchocerciasis, and trypanosomiasis. Anemia, malnutrition, and tetanus are also widespread. In 1990–95, only 37% of the population had access to safe water and 31% had adequate sanitation. The average life expectancy was 50 years.

Housing

Housing structures in Bamako are mainly like those of a European city. Elsewhere, housing ranges from typical urban structures to the tents of Tuareg nomads, the circular mud huts with thatched roofs characteristic of native African villages, and traditional Sudanese architecture whose buildings resemble those in North Africa and the Middle East.

Since World War II (1939–45), the growth of Bamako and other towns has been rapid, with government activity largely concentrated on improvement of urban housing and sanitation. The Real Estate Trust, a public corporation established in 1949, provides housing loans to persons wishing to build on their own land.

EDUCATION

In 1995, 69% of the adult population of Mali was illiterate (60.6% of males and 76.9% of females). In 1994, there were 1,732 primary schools with 8,274 teachers and 542,891 pupils. In the general secondary schools, there were 99,379 pupils. In addition, vocational schools had 11,876 pupils.

Located in Koulikoro is the Rural Polytechnic Institute of Katibougou. There are schools of business, administration, engineering, medicine and dentistry, and education in Bamako.

1999 KEY EVENTS TIMELINE

January

- President Alpha Oumar Konaré commutes the death sentences imposed on Moussa Traoré, former president and dictator, and his wife, to life in prison.

- Customs duties are lowered as part of the move towards a free-trade area in the Union Economique et Monétaire Ouest-Africaine (UEMOA).

February

- A Paris, France court sentences a Mali woman to eight years in jail for having circumcised some 50 girls.

March

- Experts from ECOWAS member states gather at the *Palais des Congrès* at a meeting jointly organized by ECOWAS and the United Nations to develop an implementation plan for the Program for Coordination and Assistance for Security and Development.

- The Mali government's three-year enhanced structural adjustment facility (ESAF) with the IMF expires.

- Alassane Dramane Ouattara, International Monetary Fund (IMF) deputy managing director, and opposition figure in CÔte d'Ivoire, visits Bamako.

- Mali government signs an agreement with a foreign consortium that includes a Japanese company, Omiken, and a Brazilian company, Zillo Lorenzetti, to establish a cotton factory in the central town of Fana in the heart of Mali's cotton-growing area.

April

- Studies reveal serious vitamin deficiencies in Mali diet.

May

- A joint IMF-World Bank mission visits Mali to begin discussions on a new ESAF for the period 1999–2002.

- First stage of the municipal elections takes place.

June

- The Malian cabinet adopts a draft law privatizing forest management in southern Mali.

- Second stage of municipal elections takes place.

- Mali receives a delegation from Niger, led by Colonel Moumouni Boureima, Minister of the Interior.

July

- Malian gendarmes arrest three counterfeit currency dealers trying to introduce fake money at a local market 130 kilometers from Bamako.

- Ethnic clashes break out between Peuls and Soninkés, leaving 11 dead at Nioro, and between Arabs at Gao and Kidal, leaving 38 dead.

- The umbrella union, UNTM, calls for a general strike, paralyzing public administration, transportation, and health services.

August

- Mali launches "Operation Green Mali," a vast tree-planting campaign to cover all eight regions of the country.

- The Sadiola Hill gold mine, a joint venture of the government and International Finance Corporation, ends its first year of full production. About 380,000 ounces of gold was produced by the mine, expecting to operate for another seven years.

September

- Strong September rains follow on a much better than average rainfall in the months from June-August making this one of the wettest seasons in the past three decades.

- Mali public health workers go on a general strike in violation of national laws preventing the shut down of public health facilities.

October

- Secretary of State Madeleine Albright visits Mali on her Africa tour.

- Former President Carter visits Mali in connection with the Carter Center's Guinea worm eradication program.

- Continuing steady rains lead famine early warning experts to predict the best harvests of millet and sorghum in the last 30 years.

- Some thirty people are killed in fighting that breaks out between pastoralists and farmers in the north of Mali.

November

- Plans for privatization of the electric utility, Energie du Mali (EDM), are announced.

December

- Plans to privatize the airport management company, Aéroports du Mali (ADM), are announced.

- President Alpha Oumar Konare restructures the Ministry of Defense and armed forces, appointing Colonel Pangassy Sangare chief of staff of the army, and naming the former army chief to the post of special envoy to the president, to assist in military and security affairs.

ANALYSIS OF EVENTS: 1999

BUSINESS AND THE ECONOMY

The year 1999 proved better than average economically for Mali. A landlocked, geographically diverse and predominantly rural place, Mali has few natural resources. Yet the government pleased the economically conservative observers in the West by proceeding with privatization of government-founded enterprises. Also, very favorable weather conditions led to better than expected crop production. Rice production exceeded the country's domestic consumption requirements. Gross Domestic Product (GDP) in 1999 is likely to meet or exceed the government's target of 6% real GDP growth. However, not everyone shared in the economic prosperity. Reports by international organizations note that while GDP is growing, the poverty rate is also on the rise, increasing by 2% from 1994 to 1996.

A recovery in the world prices for cotton coupled with higher production and a shift toward local processing will increase agricultural revenues in Mali. An agreement between the government and Japanese and Brazilian companies will establish a new factory that is expected to produce 6,000 tons of cotton lint per year. This is the third factory coming on line in Mali. Currently, 98% of Mali's cotton is exported in raw form. The development of new gold mining sites will also attract more foreign direct investment. Inflation is expected to fall from 4% in 1998 to 3% in 1999–2000.

The communications system in Mali is also improving. New roads and bridges were being planned in three isolated regions: north-Kayes, Mopti, and Timbuktu. There are plans to build a bridge across the Niger at Gao, which currently has only a ferry service. The bridge may revive interest in the Saharan highway project. The European Union (EU) agreed to provide $82.2 million for these roads while the West African Development Bank will make a loan to upgrade urban roads.

One problem area for the economy is that the proposed free trade zone between the EU and West Africa will likely lead to higher imports from Europe, while Mali will be unable to increase its exports to the EU in the period 2005–17. For that reason, a study suggests that Mali maintain its present arrangements, which gives it preferential access to the EU's common market as an African, Caribbean and Pacific (ACP) country. Mali continues to be a leader in international politics, hosting several regional meetings of African states as they consider the path to economic development in light of the policies of the developed world.

GOVERNMENT AND POLITICS

In 1991, Mali ousted dictator Moussa Traoré. In 1999, it took a step toward national healing when President Alpha Oumar Konaré commuted the death sentences imposed on Traoré and his wife after they were convicted of embezzlement. Also in 1999 the successful municipal elections strengthened Mali's quest for decentralized democracy. The only significant flaw—low voter turnout based on the boycott of the radical left—was minimized when opposition groups won nearly 40% of the nearly 10,000 council seats even though they were markedly under-funded. The president's ADEMA party won the remainder. Voter turnout was 38.5% in the primary elections, and 43.5% in the general elections. None of the opposition parties was able to gain more than 10% of the seats, indicative of ADEMA's domination.

Observers feel that the radical left, grouped under the *Collectif des Partis Politiques de l'Opposition* (COPPO), marginalized by its boycott, will probably want to contest future elections. Mali's 682 local government units form the foundation of its plan to make a more representative, participatory political system. Its more than 50 FM radio stations are part of this process to increase information flows as Malians, in the transition to civil society, are expected to be more aware and involved in public affairs.

Under Konaré, the government has found ways to innovate African democracy. The *Espace d'Interpellation Démocratique* (EID) or Forum for Democratic Consultation, is a means of modernizing the ancient tradition of palaver at which ordinary citizens bring grievances directly to the attention of their chief. In the modern version, the day is well-publicized, and the session takes place on the banks of the Niger in Bamako. Grievances must be sent in the form of a letter. The lucky ones are selected for government response.

CULTURE AND SOCIETY

Malians were buzzing with their plans to host the Africa Soccer Cup Championship in 2002. The event has assumed larger than life proportions symbolized by a large soccer balloon figure fixed high above a downtown street. The sports fever provides some respite from the uncertainties of social development. Unfortunately, kidnappings, assassinations, ethnic clashes, and general lawlessness rose in 1999. In response to these challenges, a national coalition of civic associations for peace and disarmament was founded. A moratorium on small arms was being promoted by a private citizens' group.

Although the peace coalition is led by a woman physician, Dr. Myriam Maiga, women and girls have few rights in male-dominated Malian society. Divorce, inheritance, circumcision are among the issues that Malian society will have to address. Female circumcision, or female genital mutilation, is a practice defended as a marker for a rite of passage, but international pressure to end it is growing as evidenced by the sentencing this year of a Malian woman in Paris to eight years in prison for circumcising some 50 girls. During her visit U.S. Secretary of State Albright announced a grant of $2 million for women's and girls' education in Mali underscoring the challenge girls face in overcoming unequal relationships in Malian society.

DIRECTORY

CENTRAL GOVERNMENT
Head of State

President
Alpha Oumar Konaré, Office of the President, Koulouba, Bamako, Mali

Prime Minister
Ibrahima Boubacar Keita, Office of the Prime Minister, Primature, Quartier du Fleuve BPE 790, Bamako, Mali
PHONE: +223 225534
FAX: +223 228583

Ministers

Minister of Foreign Affairs and Malians Abroad
Modibo Sidibe, Ministry of Foreign Affairs and Malians Abroad, Koulouba, Bamako, Mali
PHONE: +223 225226
FAX: +223 225634

Minister of Public Works and Transport
Ibréhima Siby, Ministry of Public Works and Transport, Route de Koulouba BP 78, Bamako, Mali
PHONE: +223 222901
FAX: +223 220874

Minister of Health, Solidarity, and the Elderly
Diakate Fatoumata N'diaye, Ministry of Health, Solidarity, and the Elderly, Koulouba BP 232, Bamako, Mali
PHONE: +223 225302
FAX: +223 230203

Minister of Industry, Handicrafts, and Tourism
Ministry of Industry, Handicrafts, and Tourism, Quartier du Fleuve BP 1759, Bamako, Mali
PHONE: +223 228058
FAX: +223 230267

Minister of Youth and Sports
Ministry of Youth and Sports, Route de Koulouba BP 91, Bamako, Mali
PHONE: +223 223153
FAX: +223 231087

Minister of Armed Forces and War Veterans
Mohamed Salia Sokona, Ministry of Armed Forces and War Veterans, Route de Koulouba BP 2083, Bamako, Mali
PHONE: +223 225021
FAX: +223 232318

Minister of Employment, Civil Service, and Labor
Ousmane Oumaru Sidibe, Ministry of Employment, Civil Service, and Labor, Route de Koulouba BP 80, Bamako, Mali
PHONE: +223 223431
FAX: +223 223431

Minister of Rural Development and the Environment

Modibo Traore, Ministry of Rural Development and the Environment, Quartier du Fleuve, Bamako, Mali
PHONE: +223 222979
FAX: +223 220295

Minister of Secondary and Higher Education and Scientific Research

Younous Hamaye Dicko, Ministry of Secondary and Higher Education and Scientific Research, Bagadadji BP 2468, Bamako, Mali
PHONE: +223 225530
FAX: +223 228297

Minister of Territorial Administration and Security

Sada Samake, Ministry of Territorial Administration and Security, Face Direction de la RCFM, Bamako, Mali
PHONE: +223 224212

Minister of Justice and Keeper of Seals

Hamidou Diabate, Ministry of Justice and Keeper of Seals, Quartier du Fleuve BP 97, Bamako, Mali
PHONE: +223 222651
FAX: +223 230063

Minister of Culture and Communication

Ministry of Culture and Communication, Quartier du Fleuve BP 116, Bamako, Mali
PHONE: +223 222647
FAX: +223 228319

Minister of Finance and Commerce

Ministry of Finance and Commerce, Quartier du Fleuve, Bamako, Mali
PHONE: +223 225687
FAX: +223 228853

Minister of Elementary Education

Adama Samassekou, Ministry of Elementary Education, Bamako Coura BP 71, Bamako, Mali
PHONE: +223 222450
FAX: +223 222126

Minister of Mining Industry and Hydraulics

Ministry of Mining Industry and Hydraulics, Quartier duFleuve BP 1909, Bamako, Mali
PHONE: +223 224184
FAX: +223 222160

POLITICAL ORGANIZATIONS

Alliance pour la Démocratie en Mali-ADEMA (Alliance for Democracy in Mali)

NAME: Ibrahim N'diaye

Democratic and Social Convention-CDS

NAME: Mamadou Bakary Sangare

Congres Nationale pour la Initiative Démocratie-CNIS (National Congress for Democratic Initiative)

NAME: Mountaga Tall

Parti pour la Démocratie et le Progrès-PDP (Party for Democracy and Progress)

NAME: Idrissa Traore

Party for National Renewal (PARENA)

Mouvement Populaire pour la Développement et la République Unie de l'Afrique de l'Ouest-MPD (Popular Movement for the Development of the Republic of West Africa)

Union Soudanaise-US (Sudanese Union)

NAME: Mamadou Bamou Toure

Union pour Démocratie et Développement-UDD (Union for Democracy and Development)

NAME: Moussa Balla Coulibaly

DIPLOMATIC REPRESENTATION

Embassies in Mali

Algeria
Daoudabougou, route aéroport, Bamako, Mali
PHONE: +223 225176
FAX: +223 229374

Burkina Faso
Hippodrome, rue 224 BP 9022, Bamako, Mali
PHONE: +223 223171
FAX: +223 229266

Canada
Hippodrome, route de Koulikoro BP 198, Bamako, Mali
PHONE: +223 222236
FAX: +223 224362

China
Hippodrome, route de Koulikoro BP 112, Bamako, Mali

PHONE: +223 223597
FAX: +223 223597

Cuba
PHONE: +223 222844

Egypt
Badala est avenue de l'OUA BP 44, Bamako, Mali
PHONE: +223 223565
FAX: +223 220891

France
Square Patrice Lumumba BP 17, Bamako, Mali
PHONE: +223 222951
FAX: +223 226697

Germany
Badala est, rue de l'OUA BP 100, Bamako, Mali
PHONE: +223 223299
FAX: +223 229650

Guinea
Immeuble Saybou Maïga, Quartier du fleuve BP 118, Bamako, Mali
PHONE: +223 222975; 230897

Iran
Hippodrome BP 2136, Bamako, Mali
PHONE: +223 223593
FAX: +223 220731

Iraq
Badala est BP 2512, Bamako, Mali
PHONE: +223 223860
FAX: +223 222416

Korea
Sogoniko, face autocars sise Sotelma BP 76, Bamako, Mali
PHONE: +223 225183
FAX: +223 225183

Libya
Ngolonina Immeuble Nimaga BP 1670, Bamako, Mali
PHONE: +223 222518
FAX: +223 226697

Malaysia
PHONE: +223 222783

Mauritania
Hippodrome route de Koulikoro BP 135, Bamako, Mali
PHONE: +223 224815
FAX: +223 224908

Morocco
Badala est avenue de l'OUA B.P.2013, Bamako, Mali

PHONE: +223 222123; 222423
FAX: +223 227787

Nigeria
Badala est BP 57, Bamako, Mali
PHONE: +223 225771
FAX: +223 225284

Netherlands
Hippodrome angle de la rue 437 route de Koulikoro BP 2220, Bamako, Mali
PHONE: +223 229582; 229572

Saudi Arabia
Sogoniko, route de l'aéroport, Bamako, Mali
PHONE: +223 222528; 223910
FAX: +223 225074

Senegal
Quartier du fleuve BP 42, Bamako, Mali
PHONE: +223 228274

United States
Avenue Mohamed V, rue de Rochester BP 34, Bamako, Mali
PHONE: +223 225470, 225663
FAX: +223 223712
TITLE: Ambassador
NAME: David Rawson

JUDICIAL SYSTEM
Supreme Court
Court of Appeal
High Court of Justice

FURTHER READING
Articles

Boukhari, Sophie. "Mali: Growth Without Development." *UNESCO Courier* (March 1999): 25.

Lerner, Dietlind. "Mali's Direct Democracy. (Espace d'Interpellation Democratique)." *UNESCO Courier* (May 1999): 40+.

Ross, Priscilla. "Mali's Golden Star Rises." *African Business* (July-August 1999): 20.

Books

Africa on File. New York: Facts on File, 1997.

Ajayi, J.F.A., and Michael Crowder, eds. *History of West Africa*, vol. 1. New York: Columbia University Press, 1976.

Economist Intelligence Unit, Ltd. *Mali.* London: EIU Country Reports, 1999.

Foltz, William J. *From French West Africa to the Mali Federation*. New Haven: Yale University Press, 1965.

Internet

Africa News Online. Available Online @ www.africanews.org/west/stories/ 1999_feat1.html (October 28, 1999).

Africaonline. Available Online @ www.africaonline.com (October 28, 1999).

Integrated Regional Information Network (IRIN). Available Online @ www.reliefweb.int/IRIN (October 28, 1999).

MALI: STATISTICAL DATA

For sources and notes see "Sources of Statistics" in the front of each volume.

GEOGRAPHY

Geography (1)

Area:

Total: 1.24 million sq km.

Land: 1.22 million sq km.

Water: 20,000 sq km.

Area—comparative: slightly less than twice the size of Texas.

Land boundaries:

Total: 7,243 km.

Border countries: Algeria 1,376 km, Burkina Faso 1,000 km, Guinea 858 km, Cote d'Ivoire 532 km, Mauritania 2,237 km, Niger 821 km, Senegal 419 km.

Coastline: 0 km (landlocked).

Climate: subtropical to arid; hot and dry February to June; rainy, humid, and mild June to November; cool and dry November to February.

Terrain: mostly flat to rolling northern plains covered by sand; savanna in south, rugged hills in northeast.

Natural resources: gold, phosphates, kaolin, salt, limestone, uranium, bauxite, iron ore, manganese, tin, and copper deposits are known but not exploited.

Land use:

Arable land: 2%

Permanent crops: 0%

Permanent pastures: 25%

Forests and woodland: 6%

Other: 67% (1993 est.).

HUMAN FACTORS

Demographics (2A)

	1990	1995	1998	2000	2010	2020	2030	2040	2050
Population	8,231.0	9,182.1	10,108.6	10,750.7	14,611.0	19,676.9	25,869.5	32,916.8	40,433.2
Net migration rate (per 1,000 population)	NA	NA	NA	NA	NA	NA	NA	NA	NA
Births	NA	NA	NA	NA	NA	NA	NA	NA	NA
Deaths	NA	NA	NA	NA	NA	NA	NA	NA	NA
Life expectancy - males	42.4	44.4	45.7	46.5	50.9	55.4	59.7	63.8	67.4
Life expectancy - females	44.4	46.9	48.4	49.5	55.0	60.5	65.8	70.5	74.5
Birth rate (per 1,000)	51.3	51.0	49.9	49.1	44.5	39.2	33.6	28.5	24.3
Death rate (per 1,000)	22.8	20.5	19.0	18.1	13.7	10.2	7.7	6.1	5.3
Women of reproductive age (15-49 yrs.)	1,843.8	2,056.7	2,265.4	2,406.1	3,314.4	4,666.0	6,423.4	8,538.5	10,783.3
of which are currently married	NA	NA	NA	NA	NA	NA	NA	NA	NA
Fertility rate	7.3	7.2	7.0	6.9	6.1	5.1	4.2	3.4	2.9

Except as noted, values for vital statistics are in thousands; life expectancy is in years.

Health Personnel (3)

Total health expenditure as a percentage of GDP,
1990-1997[a]

Public sector 2.0

Private sector 1.5

Total[b] 2.7

Health expenditure per capita in U.S. dollars,
1990-1997[a]

Purchasing power parity .17

Total 8

Availability of health care facilities per 100,000 people

Hospital beds 1990-1997[a] . . . . .NA

Doctors 1993[c] 4

Nurses 1993[c] 9

Health Indicators (4)

Life expectancy at birth

1980 42

1997 50

Daily per capita supply of calories (1996) 2,027

Total fertility rate births per woman (1997) 6.6

Maternal mortality ratio per 100,000 live births
(1990-97) . . . . .580[d]

Safe water % of population with access (1995) 48

Sanitation % of population with access (1995) 37

Consumption of iodized salt % of households
(1992-98)[a] 9

Smoking prevalence

Male % of adults (1985-95)[a] . . . .

Female % of adults (1985-95)[a] . . . .

Tuberculosis incidence per 100,000 people
(1997) 292

Adult HIV prevalence % of population ages
15-49 (1997) 1.67

Infants and Malnutrition (5)

Under-5 mortality rate (1997) 239

% of infants with low birthweight (1990-97) 16

Births attended by skilled health staff % of total[a] . . .24

% fully immunized (1995-97)

TB 76

DPT 74

Polio 52

Measles 56

Prevalence of child malnutrition under age 5
(1992-97)[b] 40

Ethnic Division (6)

Mande 50% (Bambara Malinke, Sarakole), Peul 17%,
Voltaic 12%, Songhai 6%, Tuareg and Moor 10%, other
5%.

Religions (7)

Muslim 90%

Indigenous beliefs 9%

Christian 1%

Languages (8)

French (official), Bambara 80%, numerous African
languages.

EDUCATION

Public Education Expenditures (9)

Public expenditure on education (% of GNP)

1980 . . . . .3.7

1996 . . . . .2.2[1]

Expenditure per student

Primary % of GNP per capita

1980 . . . . .31.7

1996 . . . . .15.4[1]

Secondary % of GNP per capita

1980 . . . .

1996 . . . .

Tertiary % of GNP per capita

1980 . . . . .924.4[1]

1996 . . . .

Expenditure on teaching materials

Primary % of total for level (1996) . . . . .2.2[1]

Secondary % of total for level (1996) . . . .

Primary pupil-teacher ratio per teacher (1996) . . . . .70[1]

Duration of primary education years (1995) 6

Literacy Rates (11A)

In thousands and percent[1]	1990	1995	2000	2010
Illiterate population (15+ yrs.)	3,686	3,917	4,111	4,355
Literacy rate - total adult pop. (%)	24.6	31.0	38.0	52.9
Literacy rate - males (%)	32.5	39.4	46.5	60.8
Literacy rate - females (%)	17.3	23.1	29.8	45.4

GOVERNMENT & LAW

Political Parties (12)

National Assembly	No. of seats
Alliance for Democracy (ADEMA) 130	
Party for National Renewal (PARENA) 8	
Democratic and Social Convention (CDS) 4	
Union for Democracy and Development (UDD) 3	
Party for Democracy and Progress (PDP) 2	

Government Budget (13B)

Revenues . . . .$730 million
Expenditures . . . .$770 million
 Capital expenditures . . . .$320 million

Data for 1997 est.

LABOR FORCE

Labor Force (16)

Total . . . . .NA
Agriculture 80%
Services 19%
Industry and commerce .1%

Data for 1981. NA stands for not available.

Unemployment Rate (17)

Rate not available.

GOVERNMENT & LAW

Military Affairs (14B)

	1990	1991	1992	1993	1994	1995
Military expenditures						
Current dollars (mil.)	NA	NA	50[e]	47[e]	42	43[e]
1995 constant dollars (mil.)	NA	NA	54[e]	49[e]	43	43[e]
Armed forces (000)	13	13	12	12	8	8
Gross national product (GNP)						
Current dollars (mil.)	1,856	1,920	2,137	2,155	2,210	2,428
1995 constant dollars (mil.)	2,133	2,121	2,299	2,260	2,265	2,428
Central government expenditures (CGE)						
1995 constant dollars (mil.)	NA	NA	569[e]	NA	NA	NA
People (mil.)	8.2	8.4	8.6	8.9	9.1	9.4
Military expenditure as % of GNP	NA	NA	2.3	2.2	1.9	1.8
Military expenditure as % of CGE	NA	NA	9.4	NA	NA	NA
Military expenditure per capita (1995 $)	NA	NA	6	6	5	5
Armed forces per 1,000 people (soldiers)	1.6	1.5	1.4	1.4	.9	.9
GNP per capita (1995 $)	259	252	266	255	249	259
Arms imports[6]						
Current dollars (mil.)	10	10	0	0	0	0
1995 constant dollars (mil.)	11	11	0	0	0	0
Arms exports[6]						
Current dollars (mil.)	0	0	0	0	0	0
1995 constant dollars (mil.)	0	0	0	0	0	0
Total imports[7]						
Current dollars (mil.)	602	460	608	842	NA	NA
1995 constant dollars (mil.)	692	508	654	883	NA	NA
Total exports[7]						
Current dollars (mil.)	359	312	343	415	NA	NA
1995 constant dollars (mil.)	413	345	369	435	NA	NA
Arms as percent of total imports[8]	1.7	2.2	0	0	NA	NA

PRODUCTION SECTOR

Electric Energy (18)

Capacity . . . . .87,000 kW (1995)

Production . . . . .290 million kWh (1995)

Consumption per capita . . . . .31 kWh (1995)

Transportation (19)

Highways:

total: 15,100 km

paved: 1,827 km

unpaved: 13,273 km (1996 est.)

Waterways: 1,815 km navigable

Airports: 28 (1997 est.)

Airports—with paved runways:

total: 6

2,438 to 3,047 m: 4

914 to 1,523 m: 2 (1997 est.)

Airports—with unpaved runways:

total: 22

2,438 to 3,047 m: 1

1,524 to 2,437 m: 3

914 to 1,523 m: 8

under 914 m: 10 (1997 est.)

Top Agricultural Products (20)

Cotton, millet, rice, corn, vegetables, peanuts; cattle, sheep, goats.

FINANCE, ECONOMICS, & TRADE

Economic Indicators (22)

National product: GDP—purchasing power parity—$6 billion (1997 est.)

National product real growth rate: 6% (1997 est.)

National product per capita: $600 (1997 est.)

Inflation rate—consumer price index: 3% (1997 est.)

Balance of Payments (23)

	1990	1991	1992	1993	1994
Exports of goods (f.o.b.)	338	356	336	341	320
Imports of goods (f.o.b.)	−432	−447	−484	−446	−422
Trade balance	−95	−91	−149	−105	−102
Services - debits	−456	−412	−450	−427	−365
Services - credits	100	82	88	101	72
Private transfers (net)	121	157	163	113	146
Government transfers (net)	80	89	94	105	85
Overall balance	−250	−176	−253	−213	−164

MANUFACTURING SECTOR

GDP & Manufacturing Summary (21)

	1980	1985	1990	1992	1993	1994
Gross Domestic Product						
Millions of 1990 dollars	1,748	2,006	2,510	2,583	2,781	2,848
Growth rate in percent	4.01	8.50	2.41	3.11	7.67	2.40
Per capita (in 1990 dollars)	254.6	253.4	272.4	263.1	274.4	272.2
Manufacturing Value Added						
Millions of 1990 dollars	86	160	196	206	218	227
Growth rate in percent	1.58	4.37	−2.35	3.22	5.37	4.38
Manufacturing share in percent of current prices	4.3	7.5	8.2	7.0	9.2	8.8

FINANCE, ECONOMICS, & TRADE

Exchange Rates (24)

Exchange rates:

CFA francs (CFAF) per US$1

January 1998	.608.36
1997	.583.67
1996	.511.55
1995	.499.15
1994	.555.20
1993	.283.16

Beginning 12 January 1994, the CFA franc was devalued to CFAF 100 per French franc from CFAF 50 at which it had been fixed since 1948.

Top Import Origins (25)

$797 million (f.o.b., 1996 est.)

Origins	%
mostly franc zone and Western Europe	NA

NA stands for not available.

Top Export Destinations (26)

$473 million (f.o.b., 1996 est.).

Destinations	%
mostly franc zone and Western Europe	NA

NA stands for not available.

Economic Aid (27)

Recipient: ODA, $NA. NA stands for not available.

Import Export Commodities (28)

Import Commodities	Export Commodities
Machinery and equipment	Cotton
Foodstuffs	Livestock
Construction materials	Gold
Petroleum	
Textiles	

MALTA

The Republic of Malta
Repubblika Ta' Malta

INTRODUCTORY SURVEY

RECENT HISTORY

During almost the entire nineteenth century, a British military governor ruled the colony. The Maltese remained loyal to Britain in World War I (1914–18) and World War II (1939–45). For gallantry under heavy fire during the German-Italian siege (1940–43), the entire population was awarded the George Cross.

Although the Maltese enjoyed a great degree of self-government, they wanted complete independence, except in matters of defense and foreign affairs. Malta became a sovereign and independent nation within the British Commonwealth of Nations on 21 September 1964. At the same time, mutual defense and financial agreements were signed with the United Kingdom.

On 13 December 1974, Malta formally adopted a republican form of government, and the former governor-general, Sir Anthony Mamo, became the first president. Dom Mintoff, leader of the Malta Labour Party and prime minister from 1971 through 1984, adopted socialist measures domestically and initiated a nonaligned policy in foreign affairs. The Nationalists, under Eddie Fenech Adami, have been in power since 1987.

Maltese politics has revolved around foreign policy issues, in particular, Malta's relationship with Europe. The Nationalist Party government has been a strong advocate of European Union membership. Malta has applied for full membership in the European Union. However, since the Labor

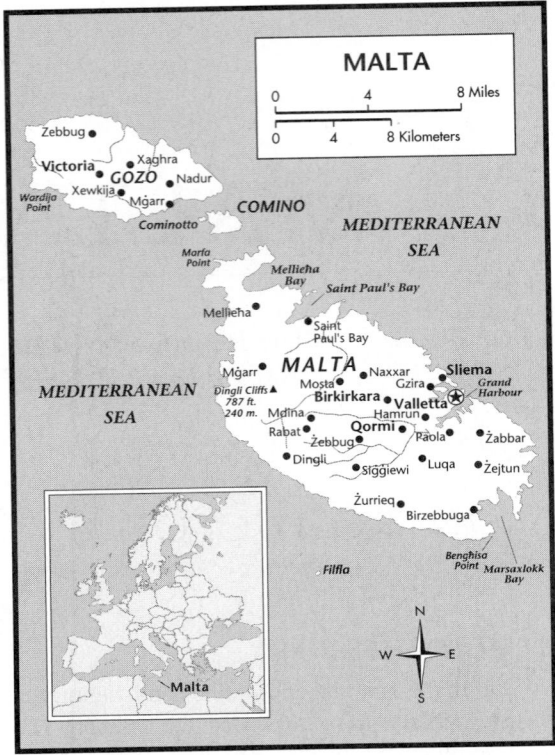

MALTA

0   4   8 Miles

0   4   8 Kilometers

Party won the 1996 elections, the government's stance has shifted towards maintaining neutrality. The government has begun to renegotiate Malta's relationship with the European Union but has not withdrawn its application.

GOVERNMENT

The single-chamber parliament, the House of Representatives, consists of 65 members (1994) elected for a five-year term by universal adult suffrage. The House elects the head of state, called the president of the republic, who in turn appoints the prime minister.

Judiciary

The superior courts consist of the Constitutional Court, the court of appeal, the court of criminal appeal, two civil courts, the criminal court, and the commercial court.

Political Parties

There are two major political parties, the Nationalist Party (PN) and the Malta Labour Party (MLP), which have alternated in political power. The MLP regained a majority in 1996 after nine years of PN control.

DEFENSE

The volunteer army of 1,950 has one infantry battalion and a mixed air and naval battalion. Malta spends $31 million on defense (1995).

ECONOMIC AFFAIRS

Until 1964, the dominant factor in the economy was the presence of British military forces. Malta's economy now relies on light industry, tourism, and other service industries.

Public Finance

The principal sources of recurrent revenues are income taxes, and customs and excise taxes.

The U.S. Central Intelligence Agency estimates that, in 1995, government revenues totaled approximately $1.4 billion and expenditures $1.4 billion, including capital expenditures of $215 million. External debt totaled $603 million, approximately 17% of which was financed abroad.

Income

In 1997, Malta's gross national product (GNP) was 4.9 billion or about $12,900 per person. For the period 1985–95 the average inflation rate was 2.9%, resulting in a real growth rate in GNP of 5.1% per person.

Industry

Malta's principal industries are shipbuilding (including maintenance and repairs), food processing, electronics, and textiles and clothing. Industry (including ship building and repair) accounts for 34% of the gross domestic product (GDP).

Banking and Finance

In June 1968, activities of the Currency Board were transferred to the new Central Bank of Malta. The Central Bank is responsible for the regulation of the banking system, the money supply, the issue of currency, and the administration of exchange control. The Central Bank manages the official external reserves and advises the Minister of Finance regarding the exchange rate of the Maltese lira. The Maltese lira is calculated on the basis of a currency basket, which currently consists of the ECU, pound sterling, and U.S. dollar. Foreign reserves, excluding gold, totaled $1,605 million at the end of 1995. There are four commercial banks—the Bank of Valletta, Mid-Med Bank, Lombard Bank Malta, and APS Bank—as well as the National Savings Bank.

In November 1995, Midland Bank (UK) became the first foreign bank to be granted a license to operate in the domestic market. Six international banking institutions are established in Malta: Turkiye Garanti Bankas, First Austrian Bank Malta, First International Merchant Bank, Izola Bank, Bank of Valletta International, and Mid-Med Bank Overseas. Total assets/liabilities of the deposit-money banks stood at LM1.88 billion in 1995, while the assets/liabilities of domestic and international banking institutions amounted to LM155 million and LM407.7 million, respectively.

Money supply, as measured by M2, was LM1,753.4 million in 1995. A stock exchange was founded in 1992. Turnover at the Malta Stock Exchange dropped sharply to LM25.2 million ($70 million) in 1996, a fall of LM21 million compared with levels in 1995. Most of the drop was due to a decline in the trading of government stocks, although trading inequities also fell slightly.

In 1994 the Malta International Business Authority became the Malta Financial Services Center (MFSC), responsible for the regulation and registration of financial services provided in and from Malta.

Economic Development

The government's primary aim is to increase Malta's productive capacity. Under the LM123-million development plan for 1973–80, manufacturing, shipbuilding, and tourism expanded rapidly. The new Marsa shipyard and a 300,000-ton dock were completed by 1980; the Marsaxlokk harbor complex was to be developed into a free port.

Legislation adopted in 1988 provides for the establishment of offshore businesses and trusts. The Malta Development Corp. is a public agency that encourages new investment in industry. As of 1996, leading incentives for investment in industrial projects included: a ten-year tax holiday to new industries that export 95% of their products; an investment allowance of up to 30% on capital equipment and 15% on industrial buildings; accelerated depreciation rates; duty-free imports of plant machinery; and subsidized rent for factory space.

SOCIAL WELFARE

The National Insurance Act of 1956 provides benefits for sickness, unemployment, old age, widowhood, orphanhood, disability, and industrial injuries. A constitutional amendment in 1993 requires government protection of all groups against economic, social, and political discrimination.

Healthcare

British, Belgian, and other foreign nationals work in Malta's eight hospitals. Average life expectancy is 77 years.

Housing

At the end of 1983, there were approximately 111,700 dwellings on Malta. New housing units completed during 1983 totaled roughly 2,400.

EDUCATION

Primary education is compulsory between the ages of 6 and 16. Maltese law requires that the teachings of the Roman Catholic Church be included in the public school curriculum. In 1993, there were 35,366 students in primary schools, 34,955 in secondary schools, 5,873 in vocational schools, and 5,177 enrolled in higher level institutions.

1999 KEY EVENTS TIMELINE

February

- The European Commission begins screening Maltese legal code in preparation for the European Union application process; in response to the October 1998 request by Malta to reactivate its application for EU membership, the Commission initiated the process of analyzing Maltese legislation for compatibility with EU standards.

April

- Guido de Marco, former Deputy Prime Minister and Minister of Foreign Affairs, begins a five-year term as Maltese President after being unanimously approved by the government.

- Air Malta resumes air service to Libya after a seven-year hiatus due to United Nations sanctions imposed in 1992 which forced Libya to extradite of two of its citizens suspected of responsibility in the 1988 bombing of a U.S. airliner.

May

- Jaak Joeruut, the first ambassador from recently independent Estonia, arrives to lead his nation's diplomatic mission to Malta. In their meeting, Joeruut and President Guido de Marco discussed items of bilateral trade (especially tourism) and accession to the EU.

June

- "The Beheading of St. John the Baptist," Caravaggio's masterpiece completed in 1608 while he was living in Malta, is returned to a 16th-century Maltese Cathedral after a three-year stint in Florence, Italy. Officials hired experts to restore the work in exchange for its exhibition during a series of European summit meetings.

- Midland Bank, part of Hong Kong and Shanghai Banking Corporation (HSBC), buys a controlling stake in Malta's Mid-Med Bank; the acquisition is regarded as an important signal of growing international interest in Malta. Pressure from the Maltese political opposition Labour Party ensured that the state-owned bank's sale was widened so that small shareholders would have the opportunity to sell their shares to Midland at a fixed price.

July

- Arvid Pardo, Malta's first representative to the United Nations, renowned for establishing sponsorship of the U.N. Conference on the Law of the Sea, dies at age 85.

September

- In European Championship qualifying, the Maltese national soccer team loses to Ireland, 3–2; the Maltese team had never scored a goal against Ireland in any of their previous 16 meetings.

October

- As Chair of the European Commission, Roberto Prodi announced that EU leaders will meet in December to make a firm commitment to a strategy on accession. The European Union suggests Malta should begin negotiations for the application process.

- In the first high-level visit to Estonia by a Maltese government official, Foreign Minister Joseph Borg of Malta meets with Estonian Prime Minister Mart Laar, Foreign Minister Toomas Hendrik Ilves, and others to discuss continuing trade growth and the mutual abolition of visas.

December

- A oil tanker registered in Malta sinks off the coast of France, creating an oil slick in the ocean ten miles long and four miles wide.

ANALYSIS OF EVENTS: 1999

BUSINESS AND THE ECONOMY

Island businesses prepared the nation's economy for accession to the European Union. In the spirit of reform, state-owned businesses were in the process of being transformed into privately-owned companies. The national privatization committee, established in 1999, determined that Malta's container hub port (Malta Freeport Corp.) and Air Malta (the national airline) are prime candidates for sale. The committee will continue to identify candidates for sale and decide how to sell them. The options currently are the public sale of shares, sale to a strategic partner, or a combination. The sale of the Mid-Med Bank this year serves as a prime example of the combination of public sale of shares and the sale to a partner, in this case Midland Bank of the United Kingdom. Privatization will boost Malta's candidacy for EU by cutting public spending and ensuring a more competitive economy. Malta is likely to be accepted by the European Union in the next round of admissions, and will enter into negotiations in the end of 1999.

GOVERNMENT AND POLITICS

In 1999, the Maltese government was also focused on administrative and legislative reforms intended to prepare the island nation for accession to the European Union. In a move designed to increase government efficiency, Finance Minister John Dalli announced plans to raise national insurance contributions by one percentage point in order to bring the deficit down.

Malta affirmed its stance on nuclear weapons, by issuing a declaration to the EU supporting the early entry into force of the Comprehensive Test Ban Treaty. Walter Bazan was appointed the new Permanent Representative of Malta to the United Nations. In October, Greece and Malta signed a bilateral agreement for cooperation in the communications sector. Latvia and Malta signed a tourism cooperation agreement, establishing a joint Latvian-Maltese tourism committee. However, the major event of domestic politics was the election of the new president, Guido de Marco. De Marco is an experienced politician from the Nationalist Party, which in 1999 continued to hold an absolute majority in the unicameral House of Representatives.

CULTURE AND SOCIETY

Tourism continued to account for more than 30 percent of Malta's GDP in 1999. A projected 1.3 million visitors were attracted by Malta's charm and climate. Two five-star hotels opened in 1999, boosting Malta's image as a destination for higher-spending travelers. Besides tourists, financial services companies are increasingly finding Malta an attractive destination.

Independent financial adviser Blackstone Franks moved its 200 million pounds trust business from Guernsey Island to Malta. The Chief Executive Officer, David Franks, cited the prevalence of English speakers and the presence of English-derived laws, in combination with a European time zone and lower labor costs for the move. Industry observers expect that Malta will continue to attract the back-offices of expanding financial firms. In a somewhat different vein, overseas lending specialist Conti Financial Services expanded its international coverage to Malta. It specializes in packaging loans secured on overseas properties for U.K. nationals. The move suggests that Malta will become a more attractive destination for foreign purchases of accommodations.

DIRECTORY

CENTRAL GOVERNMENT
Head of State

President
Guido de Marco, Office of the President, The Palace, Valletta CMR 02, Malta
PHONE: +356 221221; 238156
FAX: +356 241241

Ministers

Prime Minister
Eddie Fenech Adami, Office of the Prime Minister, Auberge de Castille, Valletta CMR 02, Malta
PHONE: +356 242560
FAX: +356 249888

Minister of Social Policy
Lawrence Gonzi, Ministry of Social Policy, Palazzo Ferreria, Republic Street, Valletta CMR 02, Malta
PHONE: +356 225709
FAX: +356 243017

Minister of Education
Louis Galea, Ministry of Education, Great Siege Road, Floriana CMR 02, Malta
PHONE: +356 221401
FAX: +356 221634

Minister of Finance
John Dalli, Ministry of Finance, 158, Old Mint Street, Valletta CMR 02, Malta
PHONE: +356 249640
FAX: +356 224667

Minister of Environment, Drainage, Public Cleansing and Waste, Capital Construction Projects, Works
Francis Zammit Dimech, Ministry of Environment, Drainage, Public Cleansing and Waste, Capital Construction Projects, Works, Block B, Floriana CMR 02, Malta
PHONE: +356 222378; 224501
FAX: +356 243306

Minister of Tourism
Michael A. Refalo, Ministry of Tourism, Palazzo Spinola, St. Julians CMR 02, Malta
PHONE: +356 383847
FAX: +356 383834

Minister of Transport and Communications
Censu Galea, Ministry of Transport and Communications, House of Four Winds, Hastings Gardens, Valletta CMR 02, Malta
PHONE: +356 225200; 220604
FAX: +356 248937; 233970

Minister of Economic Services
Josef Bonnici, Ministry of Economic Services, Auberge d'Aragon, Independence Square, Valletta CMR 02, Malta
PHONE: +356 226263
FAX: +356 226261

Minister of Home Affairs
Tonio Borg, Ministry of Home Affairs, Casa Leoni, St. Joseph High Road, Santa Venera CMR 02, Malta
PHONE: +356 485100
FAX: +356 485800

Minister of Agriculture and Fisheries
Ninu Zammit, Ministry of Agriculture and Fisheries, Barriera Wharf, Valletta CMR 02, Malta
PHONE: +356 225236
FAX: +356 231294

Minister of Gozo
Giovanna Debono, Ministry of Gozo, St. Francis Square, Victoria Gozo, Malta
PHONE: +356 563202; 559482
FAX: +356 561755

Minister of Health
Louis Deguara, Ministry of Health, Palazzo Castellania, Merchants Stree, Valletta CMR 02, Malta
PHONE: +356 224071
FAX: +356 252574

Minister of Foreign Affairs
Joe Borg, Ministry of Foreign Affairs, Palazzo Parisio, Merchants Street, Malta
PHONE: +356 242853
FAX: +356 237822

Minister of Justice and Local Government
Austin Gat, Ministry of Justice and Local Government, Auberge de Castille, Valletta CMR 02, Malta
PHONE: +356 226808
FAX: +356 250700

POLITICAL ORGANIZATIONS

Malta Labour Party (MLP)
National Labour Centre, Mile End Street, Hamrun, HMR 02, Malta
PHONE: +356 252001
TITLE: Leader
NAME: Alfred Sant

DIPLOMATIC REPRESENTATION

Embassies in Malta

Costa Rica
PHONE: +356 2201602
FAX: +356 2203738
TITLE: Consul Honorario
NAME: David Reuben

Delegation of the European Commission
Villa "The Vines," 51 Ta'Xbiex Sea Front, Ta'Xbiex, MSD 11, Malta
PHONE: +356 344891
FAX: +356 344897

United States
Development House, 3rd Floor, Anne Street, Floriana, Malta
PHONE: +356 235960
FAX: +356 243229
TITLE: Consul
NAME: James M. Perez

JUDICIAL SYSTEM
Constitutional Court
Court of Appeal

FURTHER READING
Articles
"Malta Changes its Mind, Again." *The Economist* 348 (September 12, 1998): 58(1).

Pflum, Mary E. "Maltese Falcon? Better Rent a Video; Malta's Wish to Join EU Clashes with Tradition of Hunting Now-endangered Birds." *The Christian Science Monitor,* 16 July 1999 p. 7.

Books
Background Notes. Washington, D.C.: U.S. Government Printing Office, 1995, s.v. "Malta."

Berg, Warren G. *Historical Dictionary of Malta.* Lanham, Md.: Scarecrow Press, 1995.

Malta in Your Pocket. Clermont-Ferrand, France: Pneumatiques Michelin, 1999.

Internet
In-Nazzjon. Available Online @ www.vol.net.mt/ nazzjon/ (November 30, 1999).

"Malta Arrests Asian Illegal Immigrants." BBC Online News, 11 October 1999. Available Online @ news2.thls.bbc.co.uk/hi/english/ world/europe/newsid%5F471000/471648.stm (December 13, 1999).

Malta Labour Party. Available Online @ www.mlp.org.mt/ (November 30, 1999).

Maltamag. Available Online @ www.maltamag.com/ (November 30, 1999).

"Six New Candidates for EU." BBC Online News, 13 October 1999. Available Online @ news2.thls.bbc.co.uk/hi/english/world/europe/ newsid%5F473000/473254.stm (December 13, 1999).

MALTA: STATISTICAL DATA

For sources and notes see "Sources of Statistics" in the front of each volume.

GEOGRAPHY

Geography (1)

Area:

Total: 320 sq km.

Land: 320 sq km.

Water: 0 sq km.

Area—comparative: slightly less than twice the size of Washington, DC.

Land boundaries: 0 km.

Coastline: 140 km.

Climate: Mediterranean with mild, rainy winters and hot, dry summers.

Terrain: mostly low, rocky, flat to dissected plains; many coastal cliffs.

Natural resources: limestone, salt.

Land use:

Arable land: 38%

Permanent crops: 3%

Permanent pastures: NA%

Forests and woodland: NA%

Other: 59% (1993 est.).

HUMAN FACTORS

Demographics (2A)

	1990	1995	1998	2000	2010	2020	2030	2040	2050
Population	354.0	371.4	379.6	383.3	394.3	395.6	382.0	355.9	324.8
Net migration rate (per 1,000 population)	NA	NA	NA	NA	NA	NA	NA	NA	NA
Births	NA	NA	NA	NA	NA	NA	NA	NA	NA
Deaths	NA	NA	NA	NA	NA	NA	NA	NA	NA
Life expectancy - males	73.7	74.9	75.3	75.6	76.8	77.7	78.6	79.2	79.8
Life expectancy - females	78.1	79.5	80.1	80.4	82.0	83.3	84.3	85.1	85.7
Birth rate (per 1,000)	15.2	13.5	11.7	10.3	9.4	8.3	6.8	6.2	5.9
Death rate (per 1,000)	7.8	7.3	7.3	7.4	8.5	10.1	12.4	14.5	15.9
Women of reproductive age (15-49 yrs.)	90.5	95.1	94.8	94.6	93.3	89.1	79.5	67.4	55.7
of which are currently married	NA	NA	NA	NA	NA	NA	NA	NA	NA
Fertility rate	2.0	2.0	1.7	1.5	1.3	1.3	1.3	1.3	1.3

Except as noted, values for vital statistics are in thousands; life expectancy is in years.

Infants and Malnutrition (5)

Under-5 mortality rate (1997) 10

% of infants with low birthweight (1990-97) . . . . . .NA

Births attended by skilled health staff % of total[a] . . .NA

% fully immunized (1995-97)

  TB 96

  DPT 84

  Polio 92

  Measles 51

Prevalence of child malnutrition under age 5
(1992-97)[b] . . . . .NA

Ethnic Division (6)

Maltese (descendants of ancient Carthaginians and Phoenicians, with strong elements of Italian and other Mediterranean stock).

Religions (7)

Roman Catholic 98%.

Languages (8)

Maltese (official), English (official).

EDUCATION

Literacy Rates (11B)

Adult literacy rate

  1980

    Male . . . . —

    Female . . . . —

  1995

    Male 91

    Female 92

GOVERNMENT & LAW

Political Parties (12)

House of Representatives	% of seats
Malta Labor Party (MLP)	.50.7
Nationalist Party (NP)	.46.5

Government Budget (13A)

Year: 1996

Total Expenditures: 500.00 Millions of Liri

Expenditures as a percentage of the total by function:

General public services and public order 14.37

Defense 2.22

Education 11.49

Health 8.89

Social Security and Welfare 34.61

Housing and community amenities 9.90

Recreational, cultural, and religious affairs 1.48

Fuel and energy 05

Agriculture, forestry, fishing, and hunting 1.31

Mining, manufacturing, and construction 2.33

Transportation and communication 5.24

Other economic affairs and services 3.19

Crime (15)

Crime rate (for 1997)

  Crimes reported 13,300

  Total persons convicted . . . . .NA

  Crimes per 100,000 population 3,500

Persons responsible for offenses

  Total number of suspects . . . . .NA

  Total number of female suspects . . . . .NA

  Total number of juvenile suspects . . . . .NA

LABOR FORCE

Labor Force (16)

Total . . . . .148,085 (September 1996)

Public services 34%

Other services 32%

Manufacturing and construction 22%

Agriculture 2%

Data for 1996.

Unemployment Rate (17)

3.7% (September 1996)

PRODUCTION SECTOR

Electric Energy (18)

Capacity .250,000 kW (1994)

Production . . . . .1.45 billion kWh (1995)

Consumption per capita . . . . .3,923 kWh (1995)

Transportation (19)

Highways:

total: 1,582 km

paved: 1,471 km

unpaved: 111 km (1993 est.)

Merchant marine:

total: 1,287 ships (1,000 GRT or over) totaling 22,396,164 GRT/37,390,720 DWT

Airports: 1 (1997 est.)

Airports—with paved runways:

total: 1

over 3,047 m: 1 (1997 est.)

Top Agricultural Products (20)

Potatoes, c*auliflower, grapes, wheat, barley, tomatoes, citrus, cut flowers, green peppers; pork, milk, poultry, eggs.*

GOVERNMENT & LAW

Military Affairs (14B)

	1990	1991	1992	1993	1994	1995
Military expenditures						
Current dollars (mil.)	16	17[e]	21	21	NA	32
1995 constant dollars (mil.)	18	19[e]	23	22	NA	32
Armed forces (000)	2	2	2	2	1	1
Gross national product (GNP)						
Current dollars (mil.)	1,922	2,097	2,224	2,358	NA	2,832[e]
1995 constant dollars (mil.)	2,208	2,318	2,392	2,472	NA	2,832[e]
Central government expenditures (CGE)						
1995 constant dollars (mil.)	912	974	880	919	NA	NA
People (mil.)	.4	.4	.4	.4	.4	.4
Military expenditure as % of GNP	.8	.8	.9	.9	NA	1.1
Military expenditure as % of CGE	2.0	2.0	2.6	2.4	NA	NA
Military expenditure per capita (1995 $)	51	53	63	60	NA	87
Armed forces per 1,000 people (soldiers)	5.6	5.6	5.5	5.5	2.7	2.7
GNP per capita (1995 $)	6,238	6,484	6,633	6,779	NA	7,619
Arms imports[6]						
Current dollars (mil.)	0	0	0	0	0	0
1995 constant dollars (mil.)	0	0	0	0	0	0
Arms exports[6]						
Current dollars (mil.)	0	0	0	0	0	0
1995 constant dollars (mil.)	0	0	0	0	0	0
Total imports[7]						
Current dollars (mil.)	1,964	2,130	2,331	2,174[e]	2,448	2,890
1995 constant dollars (mil.)	2,257	2,354	2,507	2,279[e]	2,509	2,890
Total exports[7]						
Current dollars (mil.)	1,133	1,234	1,540	1,355[e]	1,518	1,861
1995 constant dollars (mil.)	1,302	1,364	1,656	1,421[e]	1,556	1,861
Arms as percent of total imports[8]	0	0	0	0	0	0
Arms as percent of total exports[8]	0	0	0	0	0	0

MANUFACTURING SECTOR

GDP & Manufacturing Summary (21)

Detailed value added figures are listed by both International Standard Industry Code (ISIC) and product title.

	1980	1985	1990	1994
GDP ($-1990 mil.)[1]	1,578	1,716	2,318	2,805
Per capita ($-1990)[1]	4,871	4,989	6,547	7,706
Manufacturing share (%) (current prices)[1]	33.1	29.5	27.0	NA
Manufacturing				
Value added ($-1990 mil.)[1]	464	458	554	686
Industrial production index	100	111	184	254
Value added ($ mil.)	302	265	511	550
Gross output ($ mil.)	706	650	1,637	2,121
Employment (000)	29	26	27	27
Profitability (% of gross output)				
Intermediate input (%)	57	59	69	74
Wages and salaries inc. supplements (%)	23	22	17	14
Gross operating surplus	20	19	15	12
Productivity ($)				
Gross output per worker	23,265	24,271	58,341	75,489
Value added per worker	9,945	9,914	18,230	19,583
Average wage (inc. supplements)	5,653	5,561	10,150	11,095

Value added ($ mil.)

311/2 Food products	20	25	56	56
313 Beverages	20	22	42	51
314 Tobacco products	8	8	9	6
321 Textiles	17	8	17	14
322 Wearing apparel	88	65	80	76
323 Leather and fur products	4	1	2	4
324 Footwear	8	9	12	14
331 Wood and wood products	2	1	2	3
332 Furniture and fixtures	14	9	28	29
341 Paper a*nd paper products	2	3	7	8
342 Printing and publishing	22	17	34	51
351 Industrial chemicals	1	2	2	3
352 Other chemical products	5	6	14	20
353 Petroleum refineries	—	—	—	—
354 Miscellaneous petroleum and coal products	—	—	—	—
355 Rubber products	10	7	17	18
356 Plastic products	6	4	11	14
361 Pottery, china and earthenware	1	—	1	1
362 Glass and glass products	2	1	2	2

Continued on next page.

FINANCE, ECONOMICS,& TRADE

Balance of Payments (23)

	1992	1993	1994	1995	1996
Exports of goods (f.o.b.)	1,610	1,408	1,618	1,948	1,840
Imports of goods (f.o.b.)	−2,123	−1,976	−2,221	−2,671	−2,595
Trade balance	−513	−568	−602	−723	−755
Services - debits	−705	−731	−837	−1,055	−1,091
Services - credits	1,155	1,154	1,214	1,369	1,393
Private transfers (net)	51	21	32	10	56
Government transfers (net)	43	40	62	41	40
Overall balance	30	−84	−131	−358	−358

MANUFACTURING SECTOR

GDP & Manufacturing Summary (21) cont.

	1980	1985	1990	1994
369 Other non-metal mineral products	6	7	15	18
371 Iron and steel	—	—	—	—
372 Non-ferrous metals	—	—	—	—
381 Metal products	14	10	26	22
382 Non-electrical machinery	5	8	8	11
383 Electrical machinery	22	31	61	74
384 Transport equipment	6	3	27	8
385 Professional and scientific equipment	12	12	19	20
390 Other manufacturing industries	8	5	21	28

FINANCE, ECONOMICS, & TRADE

Economic Indicators (22)

National product: GDP—purchasing power parity—$4.9 billion (1997 est.)

National product real growth rate: 2.8% (1997 est.)

National product per capita: $12,900 (1997 est.)

Inflation rate—consumer price index: 2.3% (1996)

Exchange Rates (24)

Exchange rates:

Maltese liri (LM) per US$1

January 1998 . . . . .0.3960

1997	0.3857
1996	0.3604
1995	0.3529
1994	0.3776
1993	0.3821

Top Import Origins (25)

$2.8 billion (c.i.f., 1996).

Origins	%
Italy	27
Germany	14
United Kingdom	13
United States	9

Top Export Destinations (26)

$1.7 billion (f.o.b., 1996).

Destinations	%
Japan	22
Italy	16
France	14

Economic Aid (27)

Recipient: ODA, $NA. NA stands for not available.

Import Export Commodities (28)

Import Commodities	Export Commodities
Food	Machinery and transport equipment
Petroleum	Clothing and footware
Machinery and semimanufactured goods	Printed matter

ISLE OF MAN

INTRODUCTORY SURVEY

RECENT HISTORY

The Isle of Man has been inhabited since the early prehistoric Mesolithic Period. The Isle took its name from later inhabitants, the Celts, whose language, Manx, persisted until the nineteenth century. The distinctive domestic Manx cat is also believed to have originated on the island.

Following Viking invasions around 800, the Isle remained a dependency of Norway until 1266. During this period, a Scandinavian system of government developed and remains the basis of present-day government.

In 1266 the Isle of Man was ceded to Scotland and in 1341 came under the control of England. A succession of feudal lords ruled the Isle until Sir John Stanley was granted possession of Man in 1406 by the English Crown. The Stanley family ruled for over 300 years until 1736 when the Atholl family acquired lordship. When increasing island contraband trade decreased England's customs revenues parliament purchased sovereignty over Man in 1765. By 1828 England acquired all of the Atholl's interests in Man. The Isle became a British Crown possession and remained a dependency of the Crown. The Isle is locally self-ruling with its own legislative assemblies, system of law, and taxation systems. Although not part of the United Kingdom (including England, Wales, Scotland, and Northern Ireland), the Isle of Man maintains an association with it.

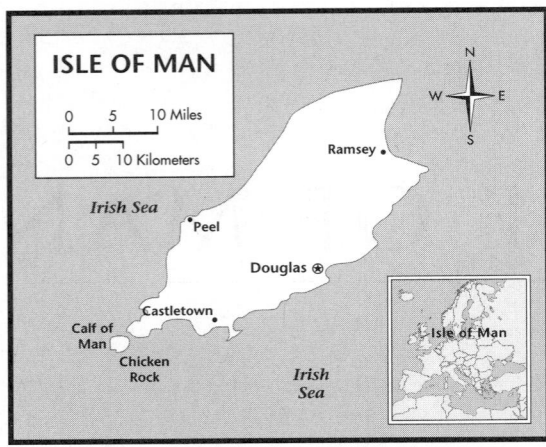

GOVERNMENT

The Isle of Man is an autonomous sovereign country under the British Crown with its own legislature and judiciary. The head of state, referred to as the Lord of Mann, is the British monarch. The British monarch's personal representative on the island is the lieutenant-governor, appointed by the Crown for a five year term.

The island is administered by the head of government known as the President of Tynwald and a bicameral legislature, known as Tynwald, consisting of the Legislative Council and the House of Keys. The Legislative Council is composed of the President of Tynwald, the Lord Bishop of Sodor and Man, a non-voting attorney general, and eight members selected by the House of Keys. The House of Keys, one of the most ancient legislative assemblies in the world, has twenty-four members elected by adult suffrage, twenty-four years of age and older, for five year terms. These two branches of Tynwald sit as one body but vote separately on questions except on certain occasions. Chosen by the Legislative Council and House of Keys, the President of Tynwald presides over both assemblies.

Until 1990 the lieutenant-governor presided over Tynwald. In that year a Council of Ministers was established to replace an Executive Council which had previously acted as an advisory body to the lieutenant-governor. The Council of Ministers consists of the Chief Minister and ministers of major departments, including Treasury; Agriculture; Fisheries and Forestry; Education; Health and Social Security, Home Affairs, Local Government and the Environment; Tourism and Leisure, Trade and Industry, and Transport.

Twenty-four local authorities are elected in the Isle. The Isle of Man is represented in neither the United Kingdom nor European parliaments.

Judiciary

The Isle of Man administers its own common and statute law which essentially parallels the law and principles of equity in English courts, but modified to meet local needs. Although based on the English system, the Isle's judiciary operates independently and includes the High Court of Justice and the Manx Court of Appeal.

Justices are appointed by the Lord Chancellor of England generally upon nomination of the lieutenant-governor. Deemsters, the High Bailiff, Mayor of Douglas, and chairmen of the town and village commissioners are EX-OFFICIO justices of the peace.

The final court of appeal for court decisions in the Isle of Man is the Judicial Committee of the Privy Council in England.

Political Parties

No political party system operates on the Isle of Man. Members of the legislature sit as independents.

DEFENSE

The defense of the Isle of Man is the responsibility of the United Kingdom. The Isle makes financial contributions to defray costs of this service.

ECONOMIC AFFAIRS

Offshore financial services, high technology manufacturing, and tourism are key sectors of the Isle of Man's economy. With the ability to set low taxation rates, the government successfully attracted high technology companies and financial institutions. Banking and other services contribute approximately 80% of the Isle's gross domestic product (GDP) while tourism accounts for 6%. Income from construction, transport and communication, and retail distribution is also significant.

Fishing and agriculture, once important mainstays of the economy, now account for only 2% of GDP. Scallops are the principle fish of the Manx fleet. The agricultural sector produces cereals and potatoes in addition to raising sheep, cattle, poultry, and pigs.

Although the Isle of Man is neither a member nor contributes funds to or receives money from the European Union (EU) trade organization, a special relationship limited to trade rights does exist between the two. The Isle enjoys free access to EU markets for trade and adopts EU's external trade policies and tariff with non-EU countries. The Isle of Man's rate of inflation was 3% at the end of 1998.

Public Finance

Major revenue areas are customs duties and income tax. The standard personal income tax rate is primarily 15% although a 20% rate also exists. Business tax rate is 20% of taxable income. Revenue is also raised through taxes on expenditures, health and social security contributions, and fees and charges for services. Major expenditure items are social security, health services, and education.

The Isle of Man is required by law to budget for a surplus of estimated revenue over expenditure. In 1998–99 the Isle budgeted 458 million for expenditures and 461 million for revenues.

Income

The 1996–97 GDP purchasing power parity was 645 million. The service sector accounts for 82% of the GDP with the single largest contributor being financial services. Agriculture contributes less than 2% of the GDP. Approximately 67% of national income is personal income with the remainder being company income.

Industry

In 1999 banking and financial services coupled with professional and scientific services accounted for 36% of employment. The manufacturing, construction, transport and communication, and retail distribution industries each employed approximately 10% of the labor force.

Banking and Finance

The Isle of Man Government Financial Supervision Commission regulates licensing authorization and supervision of banks, building societies, and investment businesses. Likewise, the commission is responsible for financial intermediaries who give financial advice and those who receive clients' money for investment and management. In 1991 the Commission established a compensation fund to protect investors.

In 1998 approximately 67 banks, 81 investment businesses and three building societies were licensed in the Isle. The Insurance and Pensions Authority regulates the insurance industry with 200 companies licensed. The Isle of Man issues its own notes and coin. United Kingdom coins and notes are also legal tender.

SOCIAL WELFARE

Major government expenditures include social security, health services, and education. Approximately 60% of social security system government expenditures went to the elderly in 1997–98. Benefits to residents include retirement pensions, unemployment benefit, sick and disablement benefit, child benefit, and supplementary benefit.

Healthcare

Since 1948 the Isle of Man's National Health Service has provided medical, dental, and ophthalmic services. The Isle has two hospitals and a third was under construction in 1999. Life expectancy for the total population by 1999 estimates is 77.8 years, male 74.3 years, and female 81.5 years.

EDUCATION

Between the ages of five and sixteen education is compulsory. In 1998 approximately 6,300 students attended thirty-three primary schools and 4700 attended secondary schools operated by the Department of Education. The Department also operates one college. Education is a primary government expenditure.

1999 KEY EVENTS TIMELINE

July

- Tynwald, the Isle of Man's parliament, passes the Limited Liability Companies and Financial Services (Amendment) Bill of 1999 to amend the Limited Liability Companies Act 1996. The amendment enables Lloyd's of London to take advantage of the island's tax-free environment.

August

- The three largest bookmaking (betting) companies in the UK-Coral, William Hill, and Ladbroke-object to the nine percent tax levied by the UK and investigate plans to relocate. Coral has already moved its operations, and the other two are considering moves to the Isle of Man or Gibraltar.

- Filming of the adaptation of the *Thomas, the Tank Engine* children's stories by the Reverend W. Awdry begins under criticism that the story and characters are being Americanized. The film stars Peter Fonda and Alec Baldwin, with the voice of Thomas being provided by John Bellis, a Manx fireman and part-time cabby who is given an audition by the director, Britt Alcott, when Bellis picks her up in his cab.

- A sighting is reported of the corncrake, a bird formerly common but believed to be endangered. This is the first time a corncrake has been spotted on the Isle of Man since 1988.

September

- Stamps honoring the singing group the Bee Gees are issued. Members of the Bee Gees, brothers Barry Gibb, and twins Robin and Maurice, were born in the capital, Douglas. Their family moved to Australia, and the three brothers now live in the United States, in Miami, Florida.

December

- A new British Irish Council is formed to provide a forum for regional debate. The Council includes representatives from the U.K., Ireland, Northern Ireland, Jersey, Guernsey, and the Isle of Man.

ANALYSIS OF EVENTS: 1999

BUSINESS AND THE ECONOMY

The economy grew at an annual rate of about seven percent during the 1990s, and unemployment is near zero. Forty-two thousand companies are registered on the Isle of Man, over half of which are there for tax exempt purposes. Per capita gross domestic product is also growing. As with other offshore tax havens, such as Gibraltar and the Channel Islands, international forces are exerting pressure for a change in the island's tax structure. The European Union is seeking to introduce tax parity across Europe, and the United Nations is urging a crackdown on international money laundering, a practice often associated with tax havens.

Six sets of stamps honoring the rock group the Bee Gees were issued October 12. The stamps recognized the accomplishments of the three Gibb brothers, Barry, Robin, and Maurice, who were born in Douglas, the capital. (Robin and Maurice, twins, will celebrate their fiftieth birthday December 22.) The Bee Gees' songs depicted on the

stamps were popular in the 1960s and 1970s. A charity CD including the songs "Massachusetts," "Words," and "I've Gotta Get A Message To You," "Night Fever," "Stayin' Alive," and "Ellan Vannin," a traditional Manx song, is being issued along with the stamps.

GOVERNMENT AND POLITICS

Debates on how to address the threat to the Isle of Man's tax status dominate the activities in the Tynwald, the Isle of Man's parliament. Members of the Tynwald, determined to ward off threats to the island's economy, continued to take action to maintain the island's attractiveness to business. In July the Limited Liability Companies and Financial Services (Amendment) Bill of 1999 passed to amend the Limited Liability Companies Act 1996, clearing the way for further expansion of insurance ventures within the island's tax-free environment.

CULTURE AND SOCIETY

Manx famous citizens, Barry, Robin, and Maurice Gibb, were honored with an issue of stamps commemorating the success of their rock music group, the Bee Gees, popular in the 1960s and 1970s. The island's citizens grudgingly welcomed Hollywood filmmakers producing an adaptation of the beloved children's stories, *Thomas the Tank Engine*; local objections were voiced about the Americanization of the sets (addition of U.S.-style fire hydrants, cars, and telephone booths) and characters.

DIRECTORY

CENTRAL GOVERNMENT
Head of State

Monarch
Elizabeth II, Queen of England

Lieutenant-Governor
Timothy Daunt

Chief Minister
D. J. Gelling, Office of the Chief Minister
PHONE: +44 (0) 1624685711

Ministers

Minister of Agriculture, Fisheries and Forestry
T. A. Warren, Ministry of Agriculture, Fisheries and Forestry, Murray House, Mount Havelock, Douglas, Isle of Man

PHONE: +44 (0) 1624685835

Minister of Education

R. B. Cowin, Ministry of Education, Murray House, Mount Havelock, Douglas, IM1 2SG, Isle of Man
PHONE: +44 (0) 1624685820
FAX: +44 (0) 1624685834

Minister of Health and Social Security

Ministry of Health and Social Security, Markwell House, Market Street, Douglas, IM1 2RZ, Isle of Man
PHONE: +44 (0)1624 685028

Minister of Home Affairs

M. Williams, Ministry of Home Affairs, Homefield, 88 Woodbourne Road, Douglas, IM2 3AP, Isle of Man
PHONE: +44 (0) 1624623355
FAX: +44 (0) 1624621298

Minister of Local Government and the Environment

R. A. Hamilton, Ministry of Local Government and the Environment, Murray House, Mount Havelock, Douglas, IM1 2SF, Isle of Man
PHONE: +44 (0) 1624685954

Minister of Tourism and Leisure

T. P. Toohey, Ministry of Tourism and Leisure, Sea Terminal Building, Douglas, IM1 2RG, Isle of Man
PHONE: +44 (0) 1624686801

Minister of Trade and Industry

K. B. Bawden, Ministry of Trade and Industry, Illiam Dhone House, 2 Circular Road, Douglas, IM1 1PJ, Isle of Man
PHONE: +44 (0) 1624685675
FAX: +44 (0) 1624685683

Minister of Transport

N. R. Cooil, Ministry of Transport, Sea Terminal Building, Douglas, Isle of Man
PHONE: +44 (0) 1624686600

Minister of the Treasury

J. A. Cashen, Ministry of the Treasury, Government Office, Buck's Road, Douglas, Isle of Man
PHONE: +44 (0) 1624685586

POLITICAL ORGANIZATIONS

Mec Vannin

E-MAIL: mkermode@mcb.net

JUDICIAL SYSTEM

High Court

PHONE: +44 (0) 1624685242

FURTHER READING

Articles

Cowell, Alan and Edmund L. Andrews. ''Undercurrents at a Safe Harbor.'' *The New York Times,* 24 September 1999, p. C1.

''Isle of Man'' *Financial Times Survey,* 14 July 1999, p. i-iv.

Unsworth, Edwin. ''Isle of Man Changes LLC Law.'' *Business Insurance,* 5 July 1999, p. 52.

Books

Robinson, Vaughan and Danny McCarroll, eds. *The Isle of Man: Celebrating a Sense of Place.* Liverpool: Liverpool University Press, 1990.

ISLE OF MAN: STATISTICAL DATA

For sources and notes see "Sources of Statistics" in the front of each volume.

GEOGRAPHY

Geography (1)
Area:

Total: 588 sq km.

Land: 588 sq km.

Water: 0 sq km.

Area—comparative: slightly more than three times the size of Washington, DC.

Land boundaries: 0 km.

Coastline: 113 km.

Climate: cool summers and mild winters; humid; overcast about half the time.

Terrain: hills in north and south bisected by central valley.

Natural resources: lead, iron ore.

Land use:

Arable land: NA%

Permanent crops: NA%

Permanent pastures: NA%

Forests and woodland: NA%

Other: NA% (extensive arable land and forests).

HUMAN FACTORS

Ethnic Division (6)
Manx (Norse-Celtic descent), Briton.

Religions (7)
Anglican, Roman Catholic, Methodist, Baptist, Presbyterian, Society of Friends.

Demographics (2A)

	1990	1995	1998	2000	2010	2020	2030	2040	2050
Population	68.8	73.1	75.1	76.2	80.8	83.6	83.1	80.4	76.2
Net migration rate (per 1,000 population)	NA	NA	NA	NA	NA	NA	NA	NA	NA
Births	NA	NA	NA	NA	NA	NA	NA	NA	NA
Deaths	NA	NA	NA	NA	NA	NA	NA	NA	NA
Life expectancy - males	72.5	73.3	74.0	74.5	76.5	77.9	78.8	79.5	80.0
Life expectancy - females	78.1	80.7	81.3	81.7	83.1	84.2	85.0	85.6	86.0
Birth rate (per 1,000)	12.9	12.3	12.5	12.3	10.6	10.0	9.1	8.2	7.8
Death rate (per 1,000)	13.8	12.3	11.7	11.4	10.2	10.1	11.2	12.6	14.3
Women of reproductive age (15-49 yrs.)	16.5	17.7	18.1	18.2	19.2	19.1	17.3	16.0	14.4
of which are currently married	NA	NA	NA	NA	NA	NA	NA	NA	NA
Fertility rate	1.8	1.7	1.7	1.7	1.6	1.6	1.6	1.5	1.5

Except as noted, values for vital statistics are in thousands; life expectancy is in years.

Languages (8)

English, Manx Gaelic.

GOVERNMENT & LAW

Political Parties (12)

The legislative branch is a bicameral body consisting of the Legislative Council (a 10-member body composed of the Lord Bishop of Sodor and Man, a nonvoting attorney general, and 8 others named by the House of Keys) and the House of Keys (24 seats members are elected by popular vote to serve five- year terms). There is no party system.

Government Budget (13B)

Revenues . . . .$333.7 million

Expenditures . . . .$333.5 million

  Capital expenditures . . . . .NA

Data for FY94/95 est. NA stands for not available.

Military Affairs (14A)

Defense is the responsibility of the UK.

LABOR FORCE

Labor Force (16)

Total 33,577

Manufacturing 11%

Construction 10%

Transport and communication 8%

Retail distribution 9%

Professional and scientific services 18%

Public administration 6%

Banking and finance 18%

Data for 1996.

Unemployment Rate (17)

2% (1996 est.)

PRODUCTION SECTOR

Electric Energy (18)

No data available.

Transportation (19)

Highways:

total: 640 km

paved: 320 km

unpaved: 320 km

Merchant marine:

total: 140 ships (1,000 GRT or over) totaling 4,481,925 GRT/7,663,593 DWT ships by type: bulk 28, cargo 8, chemical tanker 8, combination bulk 3, container 14, liquefied gas tanker 9, oil tanker 46, passenger 2, railroad carrier 1, refrigerated cargo 3, roll-on/roll-off cargo 15, short-sea passenger 1, vehicle carrier 2.
note: a flag of convenience registry; UK owns 11 ships, Switzerland 2, South Africa 1, Denmark 1, Sweden 1, Belgium 1, and Netherlands 1 (1997 est.)

Airports: 1 (1997 est.)

Airports—with paved runways:

total: 1

1,524 to 2,437 m: 1 (1997 est.)

Top Agricultural Products (20)

Cereals, vegetables; cattle, sheep, pigs, poultry.

FINANCE, ECONOMICS, & TRADE

Economic Indicators (22)

National product: GDP—purchasing power parity—$780 million (1994 est.)

National product real growth rate: NA%

National product per capita: $10,800 (1994 est.)

Inflation rate—consumer price index: 2% (1996 est.)

Exchange Rates (24)

Exchange rates:

Manx pounds (£M) per US$1

  January 1998 . . . . .0.6115

  1997 . . . . .0.6106

  1996 . . . . .0.6403

  1995 . . . . .0.6335

  1994 . . . . .0.6529

  1993 . . . . .0.6658

The Manx pound is at par with the British pound

Economic Aid (27)

Recipient: ODA, $NA. NA stands for not available.

Import Export Commodities (28)

Import Commodities	Export Commodities
Timber	Tweeds
Fertilizers	Herring
Fish	Processed shellfish
	Beef
	Lamb

MARSHALL ISLANDS

Republic of the Marshall Islands

CAPITAL: Majuro, Majuro Atoll.

FLAG: The flag, adopted in 1979, is blue, with two diagonal strips of orange over white; in the canton is a white star with 4 large rays and 20 shorter ones.

ANTHEM: *Ij iokwe lok aelon eo ao ijo iaar lotak ie* (I Love My Island, Where I Was Born).

MONETARY UNIT: The U.S. dollar is the official medium of exchange.

WEIGHTS AND MEASURES: British units are used, as modified by U.S. usage.

HOLIDAYS: The government has not legislated official holidays.

TIME: 11 PM = noon GMT.

LOCATION AND SIZE: The Marshall Islands is located in the central Pacific Ocean, just north of the equator. The country consists of 29 atolls (ring-shaped coral islands) and 5 islands extending over a sea area exceeding 1.9 million square kilometers (750,000 square miles), but a land area of only about 181 square kilometers (70 square miles), slightly larger than Washington, D.C.

The capital city of the Marshall Islands, Majuro, is located on the island of Majuro.

CLIMATE: The climate is hot and humid, with little seasonal temperature change. Daily variations generally range between 21° and 34°C (70° and 93°F). Rainfall averages about 30–38 centimeters (12–15 inches) per month.

INTRODUCTORY SURVEY

RECENT HISTORY

During World War II (1939–45), after bitter fighting between United States and Japanese forces, the islands came under U.S. control. In 1947, the Marshalls became part of a United Nations trusteeship administered by the United States. The United States used Bikini and Enewetak atolls as nuclear testing sites from 1946 to 1958, exploding 66 atomic and nuclear tests during this period and displacing the native people.

In 1979, the Republic of the Marshall Islands became a self-governing territory, and Amata Kabua was elected its first president. A Compact of Free Association with the United States, providing for full self-government except for defense, was ratified by the United States in 1986 and went into effect the same year.

In February 1990, the United States agreed to pay $45 million to the victims of the nuclear testing program. The Republic became an independent state and joined the United Nations in September 1991.

In the late 1990s, global warming and the possibility of rising sea levels have raised concern over the long-term prospects for the low-lying islands in the middle of the Pacific Ocean.

GOVERNMENT

The Marshall Islands is an independent republic. The constitution provides for three main branches of government: the legislature, the executive, and the judiciary. Legislative power is vested in the 33-member Parliament, or Nitijela. Executive power is vested in the cabinet, headed by the president, who is also head of state.

There are 24 local governments for the inhabited islands and atolls.

Judiciary

The judiciary consists of the Supreme Court, the High Court, the District Court, and 22 community courts. The Supreme Court has final appellate

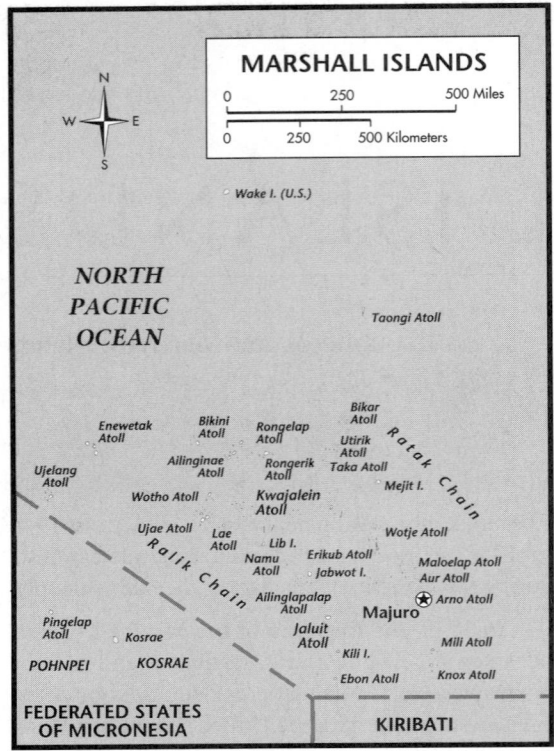

Public Finance

Government revenues are derived from domestic sources and U.S. grants. Domestic revenues are from taxes and nontax sources (fishing rights, philatelic sales, and user charges). The leading areas of expenditure include health services, education, public works, and transportation and communication. The U.S. Central Intelligence Agency estimates that, in 1995, government revenues totaled approximately $67.2 million and expenditures $79.6 million. External debt totaled $170 million.

Income

In 1996, the Marshall Islands' gross domestic product (GNP) was 98 million or $1.680 per person. During 1985–95, the average annual inflation rate was 5.4%.

Industry

The economy's small manufacturing sector is centered largely in Majuro. The largest industrial operation is a copra-processing mill. Other manufacturing consists of small-scale operations, such as coir making, furniture making, handicrafts, and boat making.

Banking and Finance

Financial services are provided by three commercial banks, the Bank of Guam, and the Bank of Marshalls, located in Majuro, and the Bank of Hawaii, located in Ebeye. The Marshall Islands Development Loan Office in Majuro was established as an independent government corporation in 1982. There were four credit unions, operated by over 2,000 members. The Marshall Islands has no stock issues or securities trading.

Economic Development

The first five-year national development plan (1985–89), which was rephased to 1986/87–1990/91 to meet the requirements of the Compact of Free Association with the U.S., constituted the first phase of a 15-year development program. The plan focused on economic development, with emphasis on private-sector expansion, personnel development and employment creation, regional development, population planning and social development, and cultural and environmental preservation. Total funding requirements for implementation of the plan were $201 million, compared with identified funding sources of $155 million.

In 1991, the Marshall Islands received $154,000 in socioeconomic development aid through the United Nations. Financial aid from the

jurisdiction. Community courts in local government areas rule on civil and criminal cases.

Political Parties

The Our Island's Party has been in power since 1979. The Ralik Ratak Democratic Party, founded in June 1991, acts as the opposition to the majority.

DEFENSE

There are no armed forces. Under the Compact of Free Association, the United States provides defense for a minimum 15-year period and operation of the missile range on Kwajalein Atoll for 30 years.

ECONOMIC AFFAIRS

The commercial economy, concentrated in Majuro and Ebeye, is sustained largely by the government and Kwajalein Missile Range employees. Copra (dried coconut meat) production provides a source of income for outer-atoll families engaged in agriculture.

In 1994, the United States government provided grants of $50 million. The grants accounted for 55% of the Marshallese gross domestic product and 74% of the budget.

United States totals over U.S.$65 million per year. Current development projects include a new capitol building, docks, and causeways.

SOCIAL WELFARE

The Ministry of Social Services is involved in five major areas: housing, women's and youth development, feeding programs, aging, and other community development welfare programs. A social security system provides old age, disability, and survivor benefits.

The Marshallese society has a matrilineal structure. Each person belongs to the *bwij*, or clan, of his or her mother, through whom traditional rank and property are inherited.

Healthcare

The leading causes of death after infancy are respiratory diseases, diarrhea and other intestinal diseases, diabetes, and heart disease. Alcoholism and drug abuse are common, and there is a relatively high incidence of sexually transmitted diseases. There are two hospitals: the Armer Ishoda Hospital in Majuro and a recently renovated hospital in Ebeye. In 1991, there were 20 doctors, 130 nurses, and 4 midwives. Health care on the outer atolls is provided through 69 dispensaries.

Housing

Houses in the urban centers are simple wooden or cement-block structures, with corrugated iron roofs; because of the limited land availability, houses are heavily crowded. In 1988, there were 4,943 dwellings on the Marshall Islands.

EDUCATION

About 93% of the Marshallese are literate. The public elementary education provides eight years of basic education to those aged 7–14.

The Majuro campus of the College of Micronesia opened its School of Nursing and Science Center in 1986. In 1991, Marshall Islands became a member of the University of the South Pacific.

1999 KEY EVENTS TIMELINE

February

- Government officials say the Marshall Islands ship registry has become the world's tenth largest, with 236 ships registered in Majuro in 1999.

March

- A new multi-million dollar fresh water distribution system in Majuro is revealed to be inoperative.

May

- Alan Stayman, the new U.S. negotiator for the Compacts of Free Association, announces that the migration policy will be a major issue when the United States and the Marshall Islands negotiate terms of a new compact starting at the end of 1999.

August

- A 140-member Taiwanese delegation, headed by Vice Foreign Affairs Minister David Lee, makes an official visit to the Marshall Islands.

September

- The U.S. government agrees to a one-time payment of about $3.8 million to former residents of the Pacific Ocean atoll of Bikini, which was used as an atomic bomb testing site after World War II.

October

- Taiwan helps the Marshall Islands with a $28 million deal to purchase two German-made airplanes.

- A former senator's businesses continue to be torched by an arsonist; the latest hit is a six-unit resort.

- Three traditional Marshall Islands sailing canoes are shipped to New Zealand in preparation for a dawn sea ceremony to greet the first sunrise of the new millennium.

November

- Elections are held for the 33-seat legislature on November 22. Eighteen of the members elected to four-year terms are members of the United Democratic Party.

ANALYSIS OF EVENTS: 1999

BUSINESS AND THE ECONOMY

The government wants to focus on boosting income and encouraging job creation at its more isolated atolls. In May it took steps toward this goal when Japan promised to deliver a $3 million grant to help establish a community-based commercial fishing operation on Jaluit, a remote atoll. Islanders on Jaluit want to build a fish handling facility. Initial plans call for cold storage, fish processing, and marketing facilities.

A large delegation from Taiwan visited the Marshall Islands in August, bringing aid and promises of more help. Vice Foreign Affairs Minister David Lee, who headed the 140-member delegation, formally dedicated a new Taiwan-aid farming project during the group's four-day stay. The Marshall Islands established diplomatic relations with Taiwan in November 1998, and severed its ties to the People's Republic of China. Taiwanese business delegates met with high ranking members of the Marshall Islands government and considered means to support fishing and tourism activities in the future.

GOVERNMENT AND POLITICS

Allen Stayman, the new U.S. negotiator for the Compacts of Free Association with the Marshall Islands and the Federated States of Micronesia, said in May that the United States wanted to discuss migration issues during renewal negotiations. The compacts are due to expire in 2001 and negotiations for a new pact were expected to get under way in October 1999.

Under the compacts, Marshall Islanders and citizens of the Federated States of Micronesia have nearly unrestricted access to the United States and its territories for employment and education. The islands also receive U.S. financial assistance. The agreement has raised concerns from nearby Guam, the Commonwealth of the Northern Mariana Islands, and Hawai'i. Often, these two territories and the state of Hawai'i end up absorbing the costs of educating and providing other assistance to new migrants. U.S. negotiator Stayman said the U.S. government would consider continuing assistance to migrants.

The Marshall Islands are also seeking further assistance to offset past failed economic plans and in settlement of claims over nuclear testing.

In July, officials from over forty small island nations gathered in the Marshall Islands to bring attention to rising sea levels. The Marshall Islands, where the highest point above sea level is about seven feet, seemed to be an appropriate place to discuss the effects of greenhouse gases on the environment. Many Marshall Islands residents are con-

cerned about the rising waters. The meeting was staged to pressure industrialized nations to reduce gases and help island nations cope with weather changes.

CULTURE AND SOCIETY

A government survey in August showed that more than 50 percent of students attending primary school in Majuro were malnourished. Officials said students relied on a heavy diet of foods low in nutritional value. Island officials said the survey was done to raise awareness and to teach parents to feed their children better food. The survey also found that many students don't eat breakfast and attend school on an empty stomach.

The art of canoe making was once considered a vanishing art in the Marshall Islands, but more islanders have been making and sailing canoes in recent years. In October three traditional Marshall Islands sailing canoes were shipped to New Zealand in preparation for participation in a ceremony to greet the first sunrise of the new millennium. Maori groups and local authorities in New Zealand planned the cultural event, which was expected to feature canoes from many Pacific islands.

DIRECTORY

CENTRAL GOVERNMENT
Head of State

President
Imata J. Kabua, Office of the President, PO Box 1, 96960 Marshall Islands
PHONE: +692 6254022; 6252233; 6253213
FAX: +692 6254021; 6253649

Ministers

Minister of Transportation and Communication
Kunio D. Lemari, Ministry of Transportation and Communication, PO Box 2, 96960 Marshall Islands
PHONE: +692 6252233; 6253213; 6253445
FAX: +692 6254021; 6253649

Minister of Education
Justin deBrum, Ministry of Education, PO Box 2, 96960 Marshall Islands
PHONE: +692 6254673; 6255262; 6256646
FAX: +692 6257735

Minister of Foreign Affairs
Phillip Muller, Ministry of Foreign Affairs, PO Box 2, 96960 Marshall Islands
PHONE: +692 6253181; 6253012
FAX: +692 6253685; 6254979

Minister of Finance
Tony deBrum, Ministry of Finance, PO Box 2, 96960
PHONE: +692 6258320; 6258311
FAX: +692 6253607

Minister in Assistance to the President
Johnsay Riklon, Ministry in Assistance to the President, PO Box 2, 96960 Marshall Islands
PHONE: +692 6254022; 6252233; 6253213
FAX: +692 6254021; 6253649

Minister of Resources and Development
Johnsay Riklon, Ministry of Resources and Development, PO Box 2, 96960 Marshall Islands
PHONE: +692 6252233; 6253213; 6253445
FAX: +692 6254021; 6253649

Minister of Internal Affairs
Hiroshi Yamamura, Ministry of Internal Affairs, PO Box 2, 96960 Marshall Islands
PHONE: +692 6253845; 6258240; 6258225
FAX: +692 6255353

Minister of Health and Environment
Tom D. Kijiner, Ministry of Health and Environment, PO Box 2, 96960 Marshall Islands
PHONE: +692 6254680; 6253480; 6255660
FAX: +692 6253432

Minister of Justice
Hemos A. Jack, Ministry of Justice, PO Box 2, 96960 Marshall Islands
PHONE: +692 6252233; 6253213; 6253445
FAX: +692 6254021; 6253649

POLITCAL ORGANIZATIONS
Our Islands Party
Ralik/Ratak Democratic Party (RRDP)
NAME: Ramsey Reimers

DIPLOMATIC REPRESENTATION
Embassies in Marshall Islands
United States
Oceanside Mejen Weto, Long Island, Majuro, Marshall Islands, 20521-4380
PHONE: +692 2474011
FAX: +692 2474012
TITLE: Ambassador
NAME: Joan M. Plaisted

JUDICIAL SYSTEM
Supreme Court
High Court
PHONE: +692 6253201; 6253279
FAX: +692 6253323

District Court

FURTHER READING
Articles
"House Approves Payment to Former Bikini Residents." The Associated Press, 13 September 1999.

"Majuro's New Eater System is Not Working." Pacific Islands Development Program/East-West Center, Center for Pacific Islands Studies/University of Hawai'i at Manoa, 19 March 1999.

"Marshall Islands Concerned about Rising Sea Levels." Pacific Islands Development Program/East-West Center, Center for Pacific Islands Studies/University of Hawai'i at Manoa, 5 July 1999.

"Marshall Islands Moving into Black Pearl Production." Pacific Islands Development Program/East-West Center, Center for Pacific Islands Studies/University of Hawai'i at Manoa, 16 August 1999.

"Marshall Islands' Traditional Sailing Canoes to New Zealand for Millenium." Pacific Islands Development Program/East-West Center, Center for Pacific Islands Studies/University of Hawai'i at Manoa, 28 October 1999.

"Marshallese head to Washington for Better Nuclear Deal." Pacific Islands Development Program/East-West Center, Center for Pacific Islands Studies/University of Hawai'i at Manoa, 2 May 1999.

"Pardoned Embezzler Holds Marshall Islands Finance Post." Pacific Islands Development Program/East-West Center, Center for Pacific Islands Studies/University of Hawai'i at Manoa, 2 September 1999.

"Survey Shows Malnutrition Rampant in Marshall Islands Children." Pacific Islands Development Program/East-West Center, Center for Pacific Islands Studies/University of Hawai'i at Manoa, 16 August 1999.

''Talks on New U.S.-FSM-Marshall Islands Compacts to Consider Migration Concerns.'' Pacific Islands Development Program/East-West Center, Center for Pacific Islands Studies/University of Hawai'i at Manoa, 20 May 1999.

Internet

Kingdom of EneKio Atoll. Available Online @ www.enenkio.wakeisland.org/ (November 16, 1999).

RMI Online. Available Online @ www.rmiembassyus.org/ (November 16, 1999).

MARSHALL ISLANDS: STATISTICAL DATA

For sources and notes see "Sources of Statistics" in the front of each volume.

GEOGRAPHY

Geography (1)

Area:

Total: 181.3 sq km.

Land: 181.3 sq km.

Water: 0 sq km.

Note: includes the atolls of Bikini, Enewetak, and Kwajalein.

Area—comparative: about the size of Washington, DC.

Land boundaries: 0 km.

Coastline: 370.4 km.

Climate: wet season from May to November; hot and humid; islands border typhoon belt.

Terrain: low coral limestone and sand islands.

Natural resources: phosphate deposits, marine products, deep seabed minerals.

Land use:

Arable land: NA%

Permanent crops: 60%

Permanent pastures: NA%

Forests and woodland: NA%

Other: 40%

HUMAN FACTORS

Demographics (2A)

	1990	1995	1998	2000	2010	2020	2030	2040	2050
Population	46.2	56.2	63.0	68.1	100.3	144.3	200.6	269.3	348.1
Net migration rate (per 1,000 population)	NA	NA	NA	NA	NA	NA	NA	NA	NA
Births	NA	NA	NA	NA	NA	NA	NA	NA	NA
Deaths	NA	NA	NA	NA	NA	NA	NA	NA	NA
Life expectancy - males	60.3	61.9	62.9	63.5	66.5	69.1	71.3	73.2	74.8
Life expectancy - females	63.3	65.1	66.1	66.8	70.1	73.0	75.5	77.7	79.5
Birth rate (per 1,000)	48.0	46.0	45.4	45.3	43.1	38.8	35.0	31.0	27.1
Death rate (per 1,000)	8.6	7.5	6.9	6.6	5.1	4.1	3.7	3.4	3.4
Women of reproductive age (15-49 yrs.)	9.4	11.6	13.3	14.6	21.8	32.3	47.1	65.1	86.7
of which are currently married	NA	NA	NA	NA	NA	NA	NA	NA	NA
Fertility rate	7.1	6.9	6.7	6.6	6.0	5.3	4.6	4.0	3.4

Except as noted, values for vital statistics are in thousands; life expectancy is in years.

Infants and Malnutrition (5)

Under-5 mortality rate (1997) 92

% of infants with low birthweight (1990-97) 14

Births attended by skilled health staff % of total[a] . . .NA

% fully immunized (1995-97)

TB 94

DPT 78

Polio 71

Measles 52

Prevalence of child malnutrition under age 5
(1992-97)[b] . . . . .NA

Ethnic Division (6)

Micronesian.

Religions (7)

Christian (mostly Protestant)

Languages (8)

English (universally spoken and is the official
language), two major Marshallese dialects from the
Malayo-Polynesian family, Japanese.

EDUCATION

Literacy Rates (11B)

Adult literacy rate

1980

Male . . . .—

Female . . . .—

1995

Male . . . .—

Female 90%

GOVERNMENT & LAW

Political Parties (12)

The legislative branch is a unicameral Parliament (33
seats; members elected by popular vote to serve four-
year terms). No data on election results are available.

Government Budget (13B)

Revenues . . . .$80.1 million

Expenditures . . . .$77.4 million

Capital expenditures . . . .$19.5 million

Data for FY95/96 est.

Military Affairs (14A)

Defense is the responsibility of the US.

Crime (15)

Crime rate (for 1994)

Crimes reported 1,761

Total persons convicted . . . . .NA

Crimes per 100,000 population 3,261

Persons responsible for offenses

Total number of suspects 1,761

Total number of female suspects 81

Total number of juvenile suspects . . . . .NA

LABOR FORCE

Labor Force (16)

Total 4,800. Data for 1986.

Unemployment Rate (17)

16% (1991 est.)

PRODUCTION SECTOR

Electric Energy (18)

Capacity . . . . .16,000 kW (1994)

Production . . . . .57 million kWh (1994)

Consumption per capita .NA

Transportation (19)

Highways:

total: NA

paved: NA

unpaved: NA. Note: paved roads on major islands
(Majuro, Kwajalein), otherwise stone-, coral-, or
laterite-surfaced roads and tracks

Merchant marine:

total: 128 ships (1,000 GRT or over) totaling 6,274,057
GRT/10,641,686 DWT

Airports: 16 (1997 est.)

Airports—with paved runways:

total: 4

1,524 to 2,437 m: 3

914 to 1,523 m: 1 (1997 est.)

Airports—with unpaved runways:

total: 12

914 to 1,523 m: 7

under 914 m: 5 (1997 est.)

Top Agricultural Products (20)

Coconuts, cacao, taro, breadfruit, fruits; pigs, chickens.

FINANCE, ECONOMICS, & TRADE

Economic Indicators (22)

National product: GDP—purchasing power parity— $98 million (1996 est.)

National product real growth rate: 2% (1996 est.)

National product per capita: $1,680 (1996 est.)

Inflation rate—consumer price index: 4% (FY95/96)

Exchange Rates (24)

Exchange rates: US currency is used

Top Import Origins (25)

$71.8 million (c.i.f., 1996 est.)

Origins	%
United States	NA
Japan	NA
Australia	NA
NZ	NA

NA stands for not available.

Top Export Destinations (26)

$17.5 million (f.o.b., 1996 est.).

Destinations	%
United States	NA
Japan	NA
Australia	NA

NA stands for not available.

Economic Aid (27)

Recipient: under the terms of the Compact of Free Association, the US is to provide approximately $68 million in aid annually.

Import Export Commodities (28)

Import Commodities	Export Commodities
Foodstuffs	Fish
Machinery and equipment	Coconut oil
	Trochus shells
Fuels	
Beverages and tobacco	

MARTINIQUE

Department of Martinique
Departement de la Martinique

INTRODUCTORY SURVEY

RECENT HISTORY

First inhabited by Carib Indians, Martinique was discovered by Columbus in 1502, and colonized by the French in 1635. Except for the periods 1762–63, 1793–1802, and 1809–15, the island has remained in French hands ever since.

GOVERNMENT

It is represented in the French parliament by four deputies and two senators.

ECONOMIC AFFAIRS

Martinique's economy is agricultural. Sugarcane and bananas are the leading crops; pineapples, citrus fruit, mangoes, avocados, coffee, and cacao are also grown.

Industry

Sugar refining, rum distilling, and fruit processing are the chief industries. Bananas, petroleum products, and rum are the principal exports; foodstuffs and oil are the main imports. Martinique produced about 4.8 million barrels of refined petroleum products in 1994 from imported crude oil. Timber production was 12,000 cu m in 1995, and the fish catch in 1994 was 5,905 tons. In 1994, exports totaled U.S.$218.6 million; imports totaled U.S.$1,642.3 million. Trade is mainly with France, which heavily subsidizes the budget. Tourism has become more important than agriculture as a source of foreign exchange.

SOCIAL WELFARE

Healthcare

Martinique has 16 hospitals. The infant mortality rate in 1996 was estimated at 7.1 per 1,000 births, down from 14 in 1985. Life expectancy was 78.8 years in 1996.

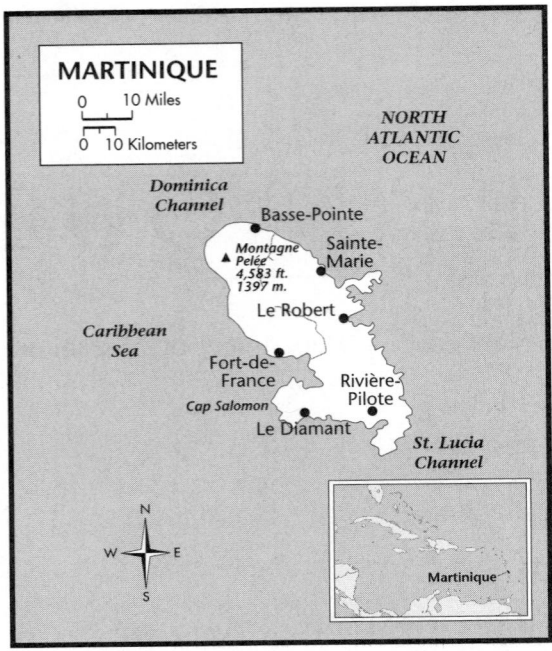

EDUCATION

Education is compulsory through primary and secondary levels. There is a branch of the Centre Universitaire Antilles-Guyana.

1999 KEY EVENTS TIMELINE

May

• Le Mai de St.-Pierre, month-long arts and cultural program.

June

• June regattas are held.

July

• Population of Martinique is estimated at 411,539.

• Tour de la Martinique, weeklong bicycle race, is held.

August

• 15th Tour des Yoles Rondes takes place.

October

• Cultural center CMAC observes 25th birthday.

November

• Fort de France Half-Marathon is run.

December

• An international jazz festival is held in Martinique.

ANALYSIS OF EVENTS: 1999

BUSINESS AND THE ECONOMY

In 1999 agriculture and tourism were the most important sectors of Martinique's economy. Bananas and pineapples were the major export crops, having replaced sugar, which was now used primarily in manufacturing the island's unique rum-called *rhum agricole*—a product that differed from most other rum in being made directly from sugarcane rather than from molasses. Only one sugar refinery remained on the island. Other agricultural exports included citrus fruits, spices, and exotic flowers. While accounting for most of the island's exports, agriculture employed only about 10 percent of its work force.

The island's steadily growing tourist industry—which had grown 25 percent in the course of the decade—was a major source of foreign exchange. Martinique's golden and black sand beaches, rain forests, historic sights from the colonial past, including ruins from the 1902 destruction of St. Pierre in a volcanic eruption, and famed Creole cuisine drew roughly a million visitors a year. About half were overnight visitors, while the others were cruise ship passengers. About 80 percent came from France, with 10 percent from the United States and Canada. Beneficiaries of tourism revenue included hotels, restaurants, car rental companies, diving clubs, tour operators, and local craft artisans.

Although the economy touted healthy profits, especially in tourism and agriculture, as well as other sectors including boat construction and both wholesale and retail commerce, Martinique continued to depend on France for more than half its gross income. Many of its residents maintained a relatively high standard of living, but the island had a chronic trade deficit, and unemployment was 25 percent or higher.

GOVERNMENT AND POLITICS

A French *département* since 1946, Martinique is governed locally by a General Council and a

Regional Assembly, as well as a *préfect* appointed by France. Neither elections for council seats nor contests for Martinique's six seats in the French parliament were held in 1999. The next upcoming electoral contest was the General Council election scheduled for 2000.

The most compelling political issue on Martinique remained the ideological controversy over the desirability of independence from France, favored by younger intellectual figures like Edouard Glissant and Raphael Confiant, who urged cutting all official ties with the former colonial power and criticized venerable statesman and poet Aimé Césaire for his failure to support their position. Candidates of the pro-independence MIM (Mouvement Indépendantiste Martiniquais) had done extremely well in the 1998 Regional Assembly elections, garnering nearly twice as many votes as their nearest competitor, the PPM (Parti Progressiste Martiniquais), but the drive for independence had yet to gain overwhelming popular support. A contributing factor may have been the increased autonomy enjoyed by all French departments as a result of government decentralization in the 1980s.

CULTURE AND SOCIETY

Martinique's cosmopolitan population—officially estimated at 411,539 as of July—blended French and Creole influences in virtually all areas of its culture, including its language, music, and cuisine. The island was known for its active cultural scene, which featured a variety of festivals and frequent performances by theater and dance groups, including the famed Grands Ballets de la Martinique, one of the premier dance troupes of the Caribbean. In October the *Centre Municipal d'Actions Culturelles* celebrated its 25th birthday.

Traditional festivals observed in 1999 included carnival celebrations, which began early in January and lasted through King Carnival's final procession on Ash Wednesday in mid-February. On March 11 Lenten fasting was suspended for Mi-Carême, and balls were held in most towns. Easter Sunday and Monday were observed in April, and parades and races were held on May 1 in honor of Labor Day. The island's colonial heritage was recalled in diverse ways on Slavery Abolition Day (May 22) and Bastille Day (July 14). Candles were lit in all cemeteries on All Saints Day (November 1), and traditional festivities for Christmas included midnight mass and the feast known as *réveillon*.

Major cultural events included le Mai de St.-Pierre, a month-long celebration of this city's historic heritage with music, dance, and theater performances and art exhibitions; the 28th Festival of Fort-de-France, held in July; the Festival du Marin in August; and Martinique's renowned biennial International Jazz Festival, held in December. Other traditional events in December included the Rum Festival and the Fête du Conte, an island-wide celebration of storytelling.

Martinique was also the scene of several high-profile sporting events in 1999. These included Nautical Week in February; the June Regattas, a weeklong yachting event; the Tour de la Martinique, a mini-version of the Tour de France, in July; and, in August, the 15th *Tour des Yoles Rondes*, a unique and picturesque race featuring special yawls with round keels, which sail around the island making seven stopovers. Scheduled for late November was the Half-Marathon, a 21.1 km race around Fort-de-France that draws thousands of competitors annually.

DIRECTORY

CENTRAL GOVERNMENT
Head of State

Prefect
Dominique Bellion

President
Jacques Chirac, Office of the President, Palais de l'Elysée, 55, rue du faubourg Saint-Honoré, 75008 Paris, France
PHONE: +33 (1) 42928100
FAX: +33 (1) 47422465

President of the General Council
Claude Lise, Office of the President of the General Council

POLITICAL ORGANIZATIONS
Rally for the Republic (RPR)

NAME: Andre Lesueur

Martinique Forces

NAME: Maurice Laouchez

Martinique Socialist Party (PPM)

NAME: Ernest Wan-Ajouhu

Movement for a Liberated Martinique

NAME: Philippe Petit

Combat Worker

NAME: Gerard Beaujour

DIPLOMATIC REPRESENTATION
Embassies in Martinique

Belgium
Pointe des Sables, 97200, Fort de France, Martinique
PHONE: +596 595051

Germany
Acajou, 97232 Le Lamentin, Martinique
PHONE: +596 503839

Italy
28, Boulevard Allegre, 97200, Fort de France, Martinique
PHONE: +596 705475

Mexico
31 Rue Moreau de Jonnes, 97200, Fort de France, Martinique
PHONE: +596 605024

Netherlands
44/46 Avenue Maurice Bishop, 97200, Fort de France, Martinique
PHONE: +596 733161

Spain
PHONE: +596 542779

Sweden
Immeuble Kerlys, 97200, Fort de France, Martinique
PHONE: +596 605454

Switzerland
Lotissement La Trompeuse, 97232, Le Lamentin, Martinique
PHONE: +596 501243

United Kingdom
Route du Phare, 97200, Fort de France, Martinique
PHONE: +596 615630

Venezuela
Rue du Prof R. Garcin, 97200, Fort de France, Martinique
PHONE: +596 633416

JUDICIAL SYSTEM
Court of Appeal

FURTHER READING
Articles

Delp, Laurel. ''Martinique: Sweetest Island of All.'' *Travel Holiday* (March 1999): 110.

Marcus, Frances Frank. ''Doing What the Islands Do Best.'' *The New York Times,* 24 October 1999, p. TR10.

Vienne, Veronique. ''Martinique Chic.'' *Town & Country Monthly,* (March 1999): 65.

Books

Crane, Janet. *Martinique.* Oxford: Clio, 1995.

Dessalles, Pierre. *Sugar and Slavery, Family and Race: The Letters and Diary of Pierre Dessalles, Planter in Martinique,1808–1856.* Ed. and trans. Elborg Forster and Robert Forster. Baltimore: Johns Hopkins University Press, 1996.

Luntta, Karl. ''Martinique.'' *Caribbean Vacations.* Chico Calif.: Moon Publications, 1999.

Tomich, Dale W. *Slavery in the Circuit of Sugar: Martinique and the World Economy, 1830–1848.* Baltimore: Johns Hopkins University Press, 1990.

Internet

Caribbean Week. Available Online @ www.cweek.com (November 3, 1999).

InfoMartinique Website. Available Online @ www.infomartinique.i12.com/english.html (November 3, 1999).

MARTINIQUE: STATISTICAL DATA

For sources and notes see "Sources of Statistics" in the front of each volume.

GEOGRAPHY

Geography (1)

Area:

Total: 1,100 sq km.

Land: 1,060 sq km.

Water: 40 sq km.

Area—comparative: slightly more than six times the size of Washington, DC.

Land boundaries: 0 km.

Coastline: 350 km.

Climate: tropical; moderated by trade winds; rainy season (June to October); vulnerable to devastating cyclones (hurricanes) every eight years on average; average temperature 17.3 degrees C; humid.

Terrain: mountainous with indented coastline; dormant volcano.

Natural resources: coastal scenery and beaches, cultivable land.

Land use:

Arable land: 8%

Permanent crops: 8%

Permanent pastures: 17%

Forests and woodland: 44%

Other: 23% (1993 est.).

HUMAN FACTORS

Ethnic Division (6)

African and African-white-Indian mixture 90%

White 5%

East Indian, Lebanese, Chinese . . . . <5%

Demographics (2A)

	1990	1995	1998	2000	2010	2020	2030	2040	2050
Population	373.6	394.3	407.3	415.7	450.3	473.2	490.0	493.8	480.7
Net migration rate (per 1,000 population)	NA	NA	NA	NA	NA	NA	NA	NA	NA
Births	NA	NA	NA	NA	NA	NA	NA	NA	NA
Deaths	NA	NA	NA	NA	NA	NA	NA	NA	NA
Life expectancy - males	74.4	75.9	76.3	76.6	77.7	78.5	79.2	79.7	80.0
Life expectancy - females	80.0	81.5	82.0	82.3	83.5	84.4	85.1	85.6	86.0
Birth rate (per 1,000)	17.2	16.8	16.5	16.0	12.5	11.5	11.0	9.8	9.4
Death rate (per 1,000)	6.0	5.8	5.9	6.0	6.4	7.2	8.5	10.8	13.5
Women of reproductive age (15-49 yrs.)	103.7	110.1	112.4	113.6	119.0	111.6	104.3	102.0	96.2
of which are currently married	75.2	NA	NA	NA	NA	NA	NA	NA	NA
Fertility rate	2.0	1.8	1.8	1.8	1.8	1.8	1.7	1.7	1.7

Except as noted, values for vital statistics are in thousands; life expectancy is in years.

Religions (7)

Roman Catholic 95%

Hindu and pagan African .5%

Languages (8)

French, Creole patois.

EDUCATION

Educational Attainment (10)

Age group (1982) . . . . .25+

Total population 157,574

Highest level attained (%)

No schooling 8.1

First level

Not completed 55.5

Completed . . . . .NA

Entered second level

S-1 . . . . .30.9

S-2 . . . . .NA

Postsecondary 5.6

GOVERNMENT & LAW

Political Parties (12)

The legislative branch is a unicameral General Council (45 seats; members are elected by popular vote to serve six-year terms) and a unicameral Regional Assembly (Conseil Regional; 41 seats; members are elected by popular vote to serve six- year terms).

Government Budget (13B)

Revenues . . . .$658 million

Expenditures . . . .$2.2 billion

Capital expenditures . . . .$164 million

Data for 1994.

Military Affairs (14A)

Defense is the responsibility of France.

LABOR FORCE

Labor Force (16)

Total 160,000

Agriculture 10%

Industry 17%

Services 73%

Data for 1992.

Unemployment Rate (17)

23.5% (1994)

PRODUCTION SECTOR

Electric Energy (18)

Capacity .115,000 kW (1995)

Production . . . . .900 million kWh (1995)

Consumption per capita . . . . .2,280 kWh (1995)

Transportation (19)

Highways:

total: 2,724 km

paved: NA km

unpaved: NA km (1994)

Merchant marine: none

Airports: 2 (1997 est.)

Airports—with paved runways:

total: 1

over 3,047 m: 1 (1997 est.)

Airports—with unpaved runways:

total: 1

914 to 1,523 m: 1 (1997 est.)

Top Agricultural Products (20)

Pineapples, avocados, bananas, flowers, vegetables, sugarcane for rum.

FINANCE, ECONOMICS, & TRADE

Economic Indicators (22)

National product: GDP—purchasing power parity—$3.95 billion (1995 est.)

National product real growth rate: NA%

National product per capita: $10,000 (1995 est.)

Inflation rate—consumer price index: 3.9% (1990)

Exchange Rates (24)

Exchange rates:

French francs (F) per US$1

January 1998 . . . . .6.0836

1997 . . . . .5.8367

1996 . . . . .5.1155

1995 . . . . .4.9915

1994 . . . . .5.5520

1993 . . . . .5.6632

MANUFACTURING SECTOR

GDP & Manufacturing Summary (21)

	1980	1985	1990	1992	1993	1994
Gross Domestic Product						
Millions of 1990 dollars	1,734	2,159	2,800	2,842	2,995	3,195
Growth rate in percent	2.80	4.50	2.94	5.68	5.38	6.68
Per capita (in 1990 dollars)	5,320.2	6,330.6	7,777.8	7,722.2	8,071.7	8,519.0
Manufacturing Value Added						
Millions of 1990 dollars	72	101	162	92	97	106
Growth rate in percent	−9.91	26.89	2.95	2.22	5.43	8.98
Manufacturing share in percent of current prices	5.1	NA	NA	NA	NA	NA

FINANCE, ECONOMICS, & TRADE

Top Import Origins (25)

$1.6 billion (c.i.f., 1994) Data are for 1991.

Origins	%
France	.62
United Kingdom	NA
Italy	NA
Germany	NA
Japan	NA
United States	NA

NA stands for not available.

Top Export Destinations (26)

$220 million (f.o.b., 1994) Data are for 1991.

Destinations	%
France	.57
Guadeloupe	.31
French Guiana	NA

NA stands for not available.

Economic Aid (27)

Recipient: ODA, $NA. Note: substantial annual French aid. NA stands for not available.

Import Export Commodities (28)

Import Commodities	Export Commodities
Petroleum products	Refined petroleum products
Crude oil	
Foodstuffs	Bananas
Construction materials	Rum
Vehicles	Pineapples
Clothing and other consumer goods	

MAURITANIA

Mauritanian Islamic Republic
Arabic—*Al-Jumhuriyah al-Islamiyah al-Muritaniyah*

CAPITAL: Nouakchott.

FLAG: The flag consists of a gold star and crescent on a light green field.

ANTHEM: *Mauritania* (no words).

MONETARY UNIT: The ouguiya (UM), a paper currency of 5 khoums, issued by the Central Bank of Mauritania, replaced the Communauté Financière Africaine franc on 29 June 1973. There are coins of 1 khoum and 1, 5, 10, and 20 ouguiyas, and notes of 100, 200, 500, and 1,000 ouguiyas. UM1 = $0.00715 (or $1 = UM139.86).

WEIGHTS AND MEASURES: The metric system is the legal standard.

HOLIDAYS: New Year's Day, 1 January; Labor Day, 1 May; African Liberation Day, 25 May; Anniversary of the Proclamation of the Republic, 28 November. Movable religious holidays include Laylat al-Miraj, 'Id al-Fitr, 'Id al-'Adha', 1st of Muharram (Muslim New Year), and Milad an-Nabi.

TIME: GMT.

LOCATION AND SIZE: Situated in West Africa, Mauritania has an area of over 1 million square kilometers (almost 398,000 square miles), slightly larger than three times the size of the state of New Mexico. Its total estimated boundary length is 5,828 kilometers (3,622 miles). The capital city, Nouakchott, is located on the Atlantic Coast.

CLIMATE: Although conditions are generally desert like, three climatic regions can be distinguished. Southern Mauritania has one rainy season from July to October. Annual rainfall averages 66 centimeters (26 inches) in the far south; at Nouakchott the annual average is 14 centimeters (5.5 inches). The coastal region is arid, with an average maximum temperature for October of 32°C (90°F) and an average minimum of 13°C (55°F) for January. Most of Mauritania north of Atar has a desert climate with daytime temperatures exceeding 38°C (100°F) in most areas for over six months of the year.

INTRODUCTORY SURVEY

RECENT HISTORY

In 1946, a Mauritanian Territorial Assembly was established, with some control over internal affairs. Complete independence was attained on 28 November 1960. Since independence, the government of Mauritania has enjoyed considerable stability. Two problems that have dominated internal politics are conflicts between regions and trade union pressures for pro-labor policies and higher wages. Mauritania joined the Arab League in 1973, but ties with Europe, especially France and the United States, remain strong. The disastrous drought that struck Mauritania and the rest of the region during 1968–74 elicited substantial aid from the European Community (EC), the United States, Spain, France, and the Arab countries.

In 1976, forces supported by Algeria launched a war in neighboring Western Sahara following the end of Spanish control over the region. Guerrilla raids on the Mauritanian railway, iron mines, and coastal settlements forced Mauritania to call French and Moroccan troops to its defense. The effects of the war weakened the government both economically and politically, and in July 1978 Moktar Ould Daddah, Mauritania's president since 1961, was overthrown by a military coup. Lieutenant–Colonel Khouna Ould Haydalla became chief of state in January 1980. A military coup on 12 December 1984 brought Colonel Moaouia Ould Sidi Mohamed Taya to power.

Many problems, including an unsuccessful coup attempt in 1987, are linked to ethnic conflict.

It is estimated that Moors account for between 60–80% of the population. The remainder are blacks, concentrated along the Senegal River border. Mass deportations of blacks have fueled charges that Mauritania is trying to eliminate its non-Moorish population. On 26 January 1992, Taya was elected in Mauritania's first multiparty presidential election, with 63% of the vote. A new cabinet was formed in January 1993.

GOVERNMENT

The July 1991 constitution delegates most powers to the executive branch. The president is to be elected by universal suffrage (vote) for a six-year term. The prime minister is appointed. Parliament, composed of a directly elected National Assembly and an indirectly elected Senate, is controlled by the president's party. Competing political parties were legalized in July 1991.

Judiciary

The 1991 Constitution completely revised the judicial system. The revised judicial system includes lower, middle, and upper level courts, each with specialized jurisdiction. Department-level tribunals now bridge the traditional and modern court systems. These courts are staffed by *qadis,* traditional magistrates trained in Koranic law. General civil cases are handled by 10 regional courts. Three regional courts of appeal hear challenges to decisions at the department level. A supreme court reviews appeals taken from decisions of the regional courts of appeal.

Political Parties

The Front for the Liberation of Africans in Mauritania (FLAM) played a major role in stirring the 1989 unrest that led to multiparty elections in 1993. Coup leader Colonel Moaouia Ould Sidi Mohamed Taya formed the Democratic and Social Republican Party (Parti Republicain et Democratique Social—PRDS). Chief among 14 opposition parties has been the Union of Democratic Forces (UFD).

DEFENSE

The army had 15,000 men in 1993; the navy, 500 men and 11 patrol boats; and the air force, 150 men and 7 combat aircraft.

ECONOMIC AFFAIRS

While Mauritania is an agricultural country dependent on livestock production, its significant iron ore deposits have been the backbone of the export economy in recent years. The droughts of the 1970s and 1980s transformed much of Mauritania, as the herds died off and the population shifted to urban areas. Droughts have led to a build up of foreign debt, leaving the country dependent on financial aid flows from international donors.

Public Finance

Mauritania's budget is habitually in deficit. Mismanagement of public enterprises and an abundance of public sector employees led to large deficits in the early 1980s. In 1985, the government began an IMF-sponsored adjustment program to stabilize the economy and diminish the role of the public sector. The overall fiscal cash deficit (excluding debt forgiveness) fell from 12% GDP in 1985 to 5.4% in 1989. From 1989 to 1992, however, due to the Persian Gulf Crisis and turmoil with Senegal, the adjustment effort was set back.

In 1994, the government instituted fiscal reform designed to broaden the tax base and reduce exemptions. The U.S. Central Intelligence Agency estimates that, in 1994, government revenues totaled approximately $254 million and expenditures $280 million, including capital expenditures of $94 million. External debt totaled $1.9 billion. A VAT introduced in 1995 helped increase revenues by 6.5% and reduce the deficit to 0.4% of GDP in 1995.

Income

In 1996, Mauritania's gross national product (GNP) was $4.1 billion, or about $1,750 per person. During 1985–95, the average annual growth of the GNP per person was 0.5%. During the same period, the average annual inflation rate was 6.9%.

Industry

Fish processing, the principal industrial activity, is carried out in Nouadhibou. A rolling mill at Nouadhibou produces small quantities of iron rods and steel. A petroleum refinery with an annual capacity of 1 million tons resumed operation in 1987 with help from Algeria. It produced 2 million barrels of refined petroleum products in 1995.

Banking and Finance

At independence, Mauritania became a member of the West African Monetary Union (Union Monétaire Ouest Africaine–UMOA), but withdrew in 1973 to demonstrate its independent economic identity. When it withdrew, the government also relinquished membership in the African Financial Community (Communauté Financière Africaine–CFA), whose currency—the CFA franc—was freely convertible to French francs. Mauritania then created its own currency, the ouguiya, and a national bank, the Central Bank of Mauritania (Banque Centrale de Mauritanie), which was established in 1973.

Banks in Mauritania in 1991 included Banque Arbe Libyene-Mauritanienne pour le Commerce Extérieur et le Développement (BNM). BALM, founded in 1990, is 51% owned by Libyans and 49% owned by the state. Other banks included Banque Al-Baraka Mauritanie Islamique (BAMIS), Banque Mauritanie pour le Commerce Internationale (BMCL), and Banque Nationale de

Mauritania (BNM). BAMIS, established in 1990, is 50% Saudi owned and 10% BCM owned. BMCL, founded in 1990, is 10% BCM owned, and 90% of the bank is held by private interests. BNM, established in 1988, is 50% state owned.

A significant drawback for the Mauritanian economy, partly due to the small number and low income of the population, is a dearth of domestic capital. The poor reputation of the domestic banking system, notwithstanding its recent overhaul, has further discouraged local savings. Despite considerable improvement in regulation and restructuring under an ongoing World Bank-assisted program, the banking system remains fragile, and further donor support will be required to consolidate good practice.

Money supply, as measured by M2, totaled UM26,019 million at the end of 1995. Foreign reserves, excluding gold, totaled $85.5 million at the end of 1995.

Economic Development

Until the export earning capacity of Mauritania improves, its economy will remain fragile. External deficit management dominates the public investment horizon.

SOCIAL WELFARE

Slavery has been abolished several times in Mauritania, most recently in 1980. However, there are an estimated 90,000 slaves held in Mauritania, but it is illegal to suggest that a slave trade exists in the country. Slavery is based on race, with lighter-skinned Moors from the north enslaving darker-skinned farmers from the south. Some black groups however, such as the Soninké and Fulani, practice a more concealed form of slavery.

Healthcare

Mauritania's public health system consists of administrative units and health facilities organized in pyramid style. The only major hospital is in Nouakchott. Although medical services is available free to those unable to pay, only about 63% of the population has access to health care services. The main health problems include malaria, tuberculosis, measles, dysentery, and influenza.

Housing

The phenomenal growth of Nouakchott and the effects of rural migration, impelled by drought, have strained housing resources. As of 1990, 67% of urban and 65% of rural dwellers had access to a public water supply.

EDUCATION

Education is compulsory, but only a minority of school-age children attend school. In 1994, there were 268,216 students in primary schools. In 1993, 45,810 students were enrolled in secondary schools. All higher level institutions had a total of 266 teachers and 7,501 pupils in 1992; these include the National Institute of Higher Islamic Studies and the University of Nouakchott.

1999 KEY EVENTS TIMELINE

January

- The government orders a local council vote to be retaken in districts surrounding the capital.
- Opposition leader Ahmed Ould Daddah is re-arrested less than two weeks after being released from prison.

March

- Ahmed Ould Daddah faces trial for threatening public order; he is acquitted.
- A suspected associate of Saudi terrorist Osama bin Laden is arrested.

April

- Clashes erupt near the border with Mali.
- A new West African peacekeeping force is established.

May

- Mauritania is among the North African nations reviving the Maghreb Union.

July

- Jordan's new ruler King Abdullah visits Mauritania on regional tour.
- A Mauritanian army captain is arrested in France on torture charges.

October

- Mauritania establishes diplomatic ties with Israel, earning it antagonism from the Arab world.

November

- Diplomatic ties with Iraq are broken over recognition of Israel.
- An Arabic newspaper apologizes for its claim that the Mauritanian prime minister allowed the burial of Israeli nuclear waste in the country.

December

- UK Chancellor Gordon Brown reports that the UK is implementing a program to cancel millions of pounds of debt for some of the world's most indebted nations. The first four countries on the list, Uganda, Mozambique, Bolivia, and Mauritania, are expected to qualify for the debt forgiveness program by the end of January 2000.

ANALYSIS OF EVENTS: 1999

BUSINESS AND THE ECONOMY

Agriculture continued to dominate the economy in spite of the fact that in recent decades many nomads and subsistence farmers had moved to the cities to escape the Sahelian drought. Other important sectors were mining (the country's principal industry), government services, and fishing (although the fishing industry was threatened by stock depletion from environmental damage and over fishing). Drought and economic mismanagement led Mauritania to amass a large foreign debt, and the government began to implement the second phase of an economic reform package worked out with international agencies and donor nations. Vulnerability to climate conditions and swift population growth, however, as well as the cost of servicing the country's substantial debt, continued to create economic uncertainty.

In January the Arab Fund for Economic and Social Development (AFESD) signed a $11.6 million loan agreement for the development of small dams, and in June the World Bank approved a $15 million loan to encourage foreign investment in the country's mining sector.

GOVERNMENT AND POLITICS

In January Ahmed Ould Daddah, leader of the opposition party Union of Democratic Forces, was freed from detention by the government, but he was re-arrested less than two weeks later after leading a demonstration in the capital. Daddah's party boycotted local council elections held in last week of the month. Following the elections the government ordered a new round of voting in the nine communes (districts) of the capital city of Nouakchott due to allegations of fraud. In March Daddah was tried for threatening public order and acquitted.

Between April and June ethnic clashes erupted along the Mali/Mauritania border, and both nations increased security in the area.

Mauritania also took part in two regional initiatives to further multilateral diplomacy. The first was an April agreement, signed in Senegal, to establish a new West African peacekeeping force. The second was an attempt to revive the Arab Maghreb Union, a ten-year-old organization of North African states that had become inactive following a dispute between Algeria and Morocco.

Relations between Mauritania and France were strained when a Mauritanian army captain, taking part in a training program, was arrested in France in July and charged with torturing members of Mauritania's black minority. The charges were brought by two Mauritanians now living in France, who claimed that the officer, Captain Ely Ould Dha, had tortured them in a Mauritanian prison in the early 1990s. When France refused to release the officer, Mauritania retaliated by expelling French military advisors, requiring all French visitors to have visas, and recalling all Mauritanian military officers undergoing training in France.

In October Mauritania became the third Arab state (after Egypt and Jordan) to establish full diplomatic relations with Israel. The action drew condemnation from the Arab League, Libya, and Iraq, and ministers from Algeria, Morocco, and Tunisia met to discuss the decision. Libyan leader Muammar Gaddafi denounced the move as tantamount to a coup against Mauritania's North African neighbors. Following strong criticism by Iraqi president Saddam Hussein, Mauritania recalled its ambassador to Iraq and banned the pro-Iraqi radical political party Attalia, which it accused of conspiring to destabilize its government with the aid of Iraq.

CULTURE AND SOCIETY

Traditional Islam rather than contemporary radicalism continued to hold sway in this overwhelmingly Muslim country. Throughout the 1990s drought had driven large numbers of people from the countryside to the cities, and roughly half the population consisted of city dwellers, as compared with one-quarter a decade earlier.

In January, fifty competitors in the Dakar Rally, which passes through Mauritania on the way from Paris to Dakar, Senegal, were waylaid by robbers in the 12th stretch of the race, between Nema and Tichit. The armed attackers stole several vehicles and siphoned gas from many more. They also robbed the competitors of money and documents, but no racers were harmed.

In March Mauritania was at the center of a history-making event as the Breitling Orbiter 3 completed its circumnavigation of the globe—the first ever made in a balloon—when it crossed a finish line over the northern part of the country. The two pilots—one British and one Swiss—had been aloft for 20 days and traveled 26,600 miles (42,197 kilometers).

Fatimata Mbaye, Mauritania's first female lawyer, was awarded the Nuremberg International Human Rights Award in September for her work toward the goal of ending slavery and other human rights abuses in Mauritania. Upon receiving the award, Mbaye, who had been jailed and tortured because of her activities, condemned ongoing abuses including the barter of women and children.

DIRECTORY

CENTRAL GOVERNMENT
Head of State

President
Maaouya Ould Sid Ahmed Taya, Office of the President

Prime Minister
Cheikel Afia Ould Mohamed Khouna, Office of the Prime Minister

Ministers
Minister of Civil Service, Labor, Youth, and Sports
Baba Ould Sidi, Ministry of Civil Service, Labor, Youth, and Sports

Minister of Communications and Relations with Parliament
Rachid Ould Saleh, Ministry of Communications and Relations with Parliament

Minister of Culture and Islamic Orientation
Moustaph Ould sid 'El Isselmou, Ministry of Culture and Islamic Orientation

Minister of Education
Sghair Ould M'Bareck, Ministry of Education

Minister of Equipment and Transportation
N'Galde Lamine Kayo, Ministry of Equipment and Transportation

Minister of Finance
Camara Aly Gueladio, Ministry of Finance

Minister of Fisheries and Maritime Economy
Mohamed el Moctar Ould Zamel, Ministry of Fisheries and Maritime Economy

Minister of Foreign Affairs and Cooperation
Ahmed Ould Sidi Ahmed, Ministry of Foreign Affairs and Cooperation

Minister of Health and Social Affairs
Diye Ba, Ministry of Health and Social Affairs

Minister of Hydraulics and Energy
Mohamed Salem Ould Merzoug, Ministry of Hydraulics and Energy

Minister of Interior, Post, and Telecommunications
Dahould Abdel Jelil, Ministry of Interior, Post, and Telecommunications

Minister of Justice
Mohamed Ould Ahmed Lemine, Ministry of Justice

Minister of Mines and Industry
Ishagh Ould Rajel, Ministry of Mines and Industry

Minister of National Defense
Kaba Ould Elewa, Ministry of National Defense

Minister of Planning
Mohamedou Ould Michel, Ministry of Planning

Minister of Rural Development and Environment
Mohamed Ould Sid' Ahmed Lekhal, Ministry of Rural Development and Environment

Minister of Trade, Handicrafts, and Tourism
Ehemdi Ould Hamadi, Ministry of Trade, Handicrafts, and Tourism

Minister of Women's Affairs
Mintata Mint Hiddeid, Ministry of Women's Affairs

POLITICAL ORGANIZATIONS
Democratic and Social Republican Party
TITLE: President
NAME: Maaouya Ould Sid'Ahmed Taya

Union of Democratic Forces-New Era
NAME: Ahmed Ould Daddah

Assembly for Democracy and Unity
NAME: Ahmed Ould Sidi Baba

Popular Social and Democratic Union

NAME: Mohamed Mahmoud Ould Mah

Mauritanian Party for Renewal

NAME: Hameida Bouchraya

National Avant-Garde Party

NAME: Khattry Ould Jiddou

Mauritanian Party of the Democratic Center

NAME: Bamba Ould Sidi Badi

Action for Change

NAME: Messoud Ould Boulkheir

DIPLOMATIC REPRESENTATION

Embassies in Mauritania

United Kingdom
B9, 2069 Nouakchott, Mauritania
TITLE: Honorary Consul

United States
Rue Abdallahi Oul Oubeid, B.P. 222,
Nouakchott, Mauritania
PHONE: +222 (2) 52660; 52663
FAX: +222 (2) 51592
TITLE: Ambassador
NAME: Timberlake Foster

JUDICIAL SYSTEM
High Supreme Court

FURTHER READING
Articles
''Mauritania.'' *Middle East Economic Digest* (January 15, 1999): 20.

''Mauritania.'' *Middle East Economic Digest* (June 18, 1999): 22.

Books
Calderini, Simonetta, Delia Cortese, and James L.A. Webb, Jr. *Mauritania.* Santa Barbara, Calif.: Clio Press, 1992.

Handloff, Robert E., ed. *Mauritania, a Country Study.* Federal Research Division, Library of Congress. 2nd ed. Washington, D.C.: U.S. Government Printing Office, 1990.

Pazzanita, Anthony G. *Historical Dictionary of Mauritania.* 2nd ed. Lanham, Md.: Scarecrow Press, 1996.

Internet
Africa News Online. Available Online @ www.africanews.org/west/mauritania/ (November 12, 1999).

Africaonline. Available Online @ www.africaonline.com (October 28, 1999).

CIA World Factbook, 1998. Available Online @ www.odci.gov/cia/publications/factbook/mr.html (November 12, 1999).

Integrated Regional Information Network (IRIN). Available Online @ www.reliefweb.int/IRIN (October 28, 1999).

MAURITANIA: STATISTICAL DATA

For sources and notes see "Sources of Statistics" in the front of each volume.

GEOGRAPHY

Geography (1)

Area:

Total: 1,030,700 sq km.

Land: 1,030,400 sq km.

Water: 300 sq km.

Area—comparative: slightly larger than three times the size of New Mexico.

Land boundaries:

Total: 5,074 km.

Border countries: Algeria 463 km, Mali 2,237 km, Senegal 813 km, Western Sahara 1,561 km.

Coastline: 754 km.

Climate: desert; constantly hot, dry, dusty.

Terrain: mostly barren, flat plains of the Sahara; some central hills.

Natural resources: iron ore, gypsum, fish, copper, phosphate.

Land use:

Arable land: 0%

Permanent crops: 0%

Permanent pastures: 38%

Forests and woodland: 4%

Other: 58% (1993 est.).

HUMAN FACTORS

Demographics (2A)

	1990	1995	1998	2000	2010	2020	2030	2040	2050
Population	1,978.7	2,334.2	2,511.5	2,660.2	3,581.9	4,765.1	6,172.8	7,720.3	9,328.7
Net migration rate (per 1,000 population)	NA	NA	NA	NA	NA	NA	NA	NA	NA
Births	NA	NA	NA	NA	NA	NA	NA	NA	NA
Deaths	NA	NA	NA	NA	NA	NA	NA	NA	NA
Life expectancy - males	43.6	45.7	46.9	47.8	52.4	56.9	61.3	65.3	68.7
Life expectancy - females	49.0	51.5	53.1	54.2	59.6	64.7	69.4	73.4	76.7
Birth rate (per 1,000)	45.6	45.6	44.5	43.8	39.8	35.4	30.4	25.9	22.2
Death rate (per 1,000)	17.8	15.8	14.6	13.8	10.4	7.9	6.3	5.3	4.9
Women of reproductive age (15-49 yrs.)	452.9	533.4	574.6	609.8	844.3	1,171.0	1,586.0	2,059.5	2,524.8
of which are currently married	NA	NA	NA	NA	NA	NA	NA	NA	NA
Fertility rate	6.6	6.6	6.4	6.3	5.5	4.6	3.8	3.1	2.6

Except as noted, values for vital statistics are in thousands; life expectancy is in years.

Health Personnel (3)

Total health expenditure as a percentage of GDP, 1990-1997[a]

Public sector 1.8

Private sector 4.1

Total[b] 5.2

Health expenditure per capita in U.S. dollars, 1990-1997[a]

Purchasing power parity 81

Total 28

Availability of health care facilities per 100,000 people

Hospital beds 1990-1997[a] 70

Doctors 1993[c] 11

Nurses 1993[c] 27

Health Indicators (4)

Life expectancy at birth

1980 47

1997 53

Daily per capita supply of calories (1996) 2,653

Total fertility rate births per woman (1997) 5.5

Maternal mortality ratio per 100,000 live births (1990-97) ....800[c]

Safe water % of population with access (1995) 64

Sanitation % of population with access (1995) 32

Consumption of iodized salt % of households (1992-98)[a] 3

Smoking prevalence

Male % of adults (1985-95)[a] ....

Female % of adults (1985-95)[a] ....

Tuberculosis incidence per 100,000 people (1997) 226

Adult HIV prevalence % of population ages 15-49 (1997) 0.52

Infants and Malnutrition (5)

Under-5 mortality rate (1997) 183

% of infants with low birthweight (1990-97) 11

Births attended by skilled health staff % of total[a] ...40

% fully immunized (1995-97)

TB 69

DPT 28

Polio 28

Measles 20

Prevalence of child malnutrition under age 5 (1992-97)[b] 23

Ethnic Division (6)

Mixed Maur/black 40%

Maur 30%

Black 30%

Religions (7)

Muslim 100%

Languages (8)

Hasaniya Arabic (official), Pular, Soninke, Wolof (official), French.

EDUCATION

Public Education Expenditures (9)

Public expenditure on education (% of GNP)

1980 ....

1996 ....5.1[1]

Expenditure per student

Primary % of GNP per capita

1980 ....30.5

1996 ....11.2

Secondary % of GNP per capita

1980 ....

1996 ....70.3[1]

Tertiary % of GNP per capita

1980 ....

1996 ....205.6[1]

Expenditure on teaching materials

Primary % of total for level (1996) ....

Secondary % of total for level (1996) 1.4

Primary pupil-teacher ratio per teacher (1996) 50

Duration of primary education years (1995) 6

Educational Attainment (10)

Age group (1988) ....25+

Total population 679,667

Highest level attained (%)

No schooling 60.8

First level

Not completed 34.1

Completed ....NA

Entered second level

S-1 ....3.8

S-2 ....NA

Postsecondary 1.3

Literacy Rates (11A)

In thousands and percent[1]	1990	1995	2000	2010
Illiterate population (15+ yrs.)	723	806	904	1,099
Literacy rate - total adult pop. (%)	35.2	37.7	40.1	44.6
Literacy rate - males (%)	47.1	49.6	52.0	56.1
Literacy rate - females (%)	23.9	26.3	28.7	33.4

GOVERNMENT & LAW

Political Parties (12)

National Assembly	No. of seats
Democratic and Social Republican Party (PRDS) . . .71	
Action for Change (AC) 1	
Independents and other 7	

Government Budget (13B)

Revenues . . . .$329 million
Expenditures . . . .$265 million
  Capital expenditures . . . .$75 million

Data for 1996 est.

Military Affairs (14B)

	1990	1991	1992	1993	1994	1995
Military expenditures						
Current dollars (mil.)	31[e]	30[e]	37[e]	36[e]	36[e]	33
1995 constant dollars (mil.)	36[e]	33[e]	39[e]	38[e]	37[e]	33
Armed forces (000)	17	17	16	16	10	10
Gross national product (GNP)						
Current dollars (mil.)	744	799	834	890	971	1,044
1995 constant dollars (mil.)	855	883	897	933	995	1,044
Central government expenditures (CGE)						
1995 constant dollars (mil.)	NA	NA	NA	NA	399[e]	NA
People (mil.)	1.9	2.0	2.1	2.1	2.2	2.3
Military expenditure as % of GNP	4.2	3.7	4.4	4.1	3.7	3.2
Military expenditure as % of CGE	NA	NA	NA	NA	9.3	NA
Military expenditure per capita (1995 $)	18	16	19	18	17	15
Armed forces per 1,000 people (soldiers)	8.8	8.5	7.8	7.5	4.6	4.4
GNP per capita (1995 $)	442	442	436	439	454	461
Arms imports[6]						
Current dollars (mil.)	0	0	0	0	0	5
1995 constant dollars (mil.)	0	0	0	0	0	5
Arms exports[6]						
Current dollars (mil.)	0	0	0	0	0	0
1995 constant dollars (mil.)	0	0	0	0	0	0
Total imports[7]						
Current dollars (mil.)	639	502[e]	NA	378[e]	355[e]	NA
1995 constant dollars (mil.)	734	555[e]	NA	396[e]	364[e]	NA
Total exports[7]						
Current dollars (mil.)	469	518[e]	444[e]	425[e]	390[e]	NA
1995 constant dollars (mil.)	539	572[e]	478[e]	446[e]	400[e]	NA
Arms as percent of total imports[8]	0	0	NA	0	0	NA

Crime (15)

Crime rate (for 1997)

Crimes reported 4,750

Total persons convicted 3,550

Crimes per 100,000 population 225

Persons responsible for offenses

Total number of suspects 4,750

Total number of female suspects . . . . .NA

Total number of juvenile suspects . . . . .NA

LABOR FORCE

Labor Force (16)

Total 465,000

Agriculture 47%

Services 29%

Industry and commerce 14%

Government 10%

Data for 1981 est. 45,000 of total are wage earners (1980).

Unemployment Rate (17)

23% (1995 est.)

PRODUCTION SECTOR

Electric Energy (18)

Capacity . . . . .105,000 kW (1995)

Production . . . . .143 million kWh (1995)

Consumption per capita . . . . .63 kWh (1995)

Transportation (19)

Highways:

total: 7,660 km

paved: 866 km

unpaved: 6,794 km (1996 est.)

Waterways: mostly ferry traffic on the Senegal River

Merchant marine: none

Airports: 26 (1997 est.)

Airports—with paved runways:

total: 8

2,438 to 3,047 m: 3

1,524 to 2,437 m: 4

914 to 1,523 m: 1 (1997 est.)

Airports—with unpaved runways:

total: 18

2,438 to 3,047 m: 2

1,524 to 2,437 m: 5

914 to 1,523 m: 9

under 914 m: 2 (1997 est.)

Top Agricultural Products (20)

Dates, millet, sorghum, root crops; cattle, sheep; fish products.

FINANCE, ECONOMICS, & TRADE

Economic Indicators (22)

National product: GDP—purchasing power parity—$4.1 billion (1996 est.)

National product real growth rate: 6% (1996 est.)

National product per capita: $1,750 (1996 est.)

Inflation rate—consumer price index: 4.7% (1996)

MANUFACTURING SECTOR

GDP & Manufacturing Summary (21)

	1980	1985	1990	1992	1993	1994
Gross Domestic Product						
Millions of 1990 dollars	856	852	1,052	1,111	1,167	1,220
Growth rate in percent	0.70	3.35	6.26	1.81	4.96	4.60
Per capita (in 1990 dollars)	551.7	482.4	525.1	527.5	539.8	550.4
Manufacturing Value Added						
Millions of 1990 dollars	62	100	119	142	149	160
Growth rate in percent	−1.43	22.44	22.15	11.07	5.50	6.95
Manufacturing share in percent of current prices	5.6	12.8	12.9	9.7	11.1	NA

FINANCE, ECONOMICS,& TRADE

Balance of Payments (23)

	1991	1992	1993	1994	1995
Exports of goods (f.o.b.)	436	407	403	400	476
Imports of goods (f.o.b.)	−399	−461	−400	−352	−293
Trade balance	37	−55	3	47	184
Services - debits	−186	−209	−282	−229	−267
Services - credits	33	21	22	27	29
Private transfers (net)	99	96	100	100	79
Government transfers (net)	−13	28	−16	−15	−4
Overall balance	−30	−118	−174	−70	22

Exchange Rates (24)

Exchange rates:

Ouguiyas (UM) per US$1

January 1998	169.880
1997	148.916
1996	137.222
1995	129.768
1994	123.575
1993	120.806

Top Import Origins (25)

$457 million (c.i.f., 1996)

Origins	%
France	30
Algeria	10
Spain	7
China	6
United States	3

Top Export Destinations (26)

$494 million (f.o.b., 1996).

Destinations	%
Japan	22
Italy	16
France	14

Economic Aid (27)

Recipient: ODA, $NA. NA stands for not available.

Import Export Commodities (28)

Import Commodities	Export Commodities
Foodstuffs	Fish and fish products
Consumer goods	Iron ore
Petroleum products	Gold
Capital goods	

MAURITIUS

Republic of Mauritius

INTRODUCTORY SURVEY

RECENT HISTORY

When slavery was abolished in the British Empire in the 1830s, many former slaves left Mauritius for Africa, causing a labor shortage. From 1837 to 1907, indentured workers were imported to Mauritius from India. About 450,000 Indians went to Mauritius under this system. Since 1948, politicians of Indian descent have dominated the government.

Mauritius became independent on 12 March 1968. Sir Seewoosagur Ramgoolam, chief minister in the colonial government, became the first prime minister after independence. Ramgoolam's Mauritius Labor Party (MLP) held power alone, or in coalition with others, until June 1982, when a coalition known as the Militant Socialist Movement (MSM) formed a government. Its leader, Aneerood Jugnauth, became prime minister.

Elections in August 1983 produced a clear mandate for a new coalition forged by Jugnauth, which won clear-cut electoral victories in August 1987 and September 1991. The new alliance amended the constitution making Mauritius a republic within the British Commonwealth. Since March 12, 1992, Queen Elizabeth II has been replaced by a Mauritian chief of state.

GOVERNMENT

The Mauritian government is parliamentary, with executive power vested under the constitution in a president and a prime minister, who is leader of the majority party in parliament.

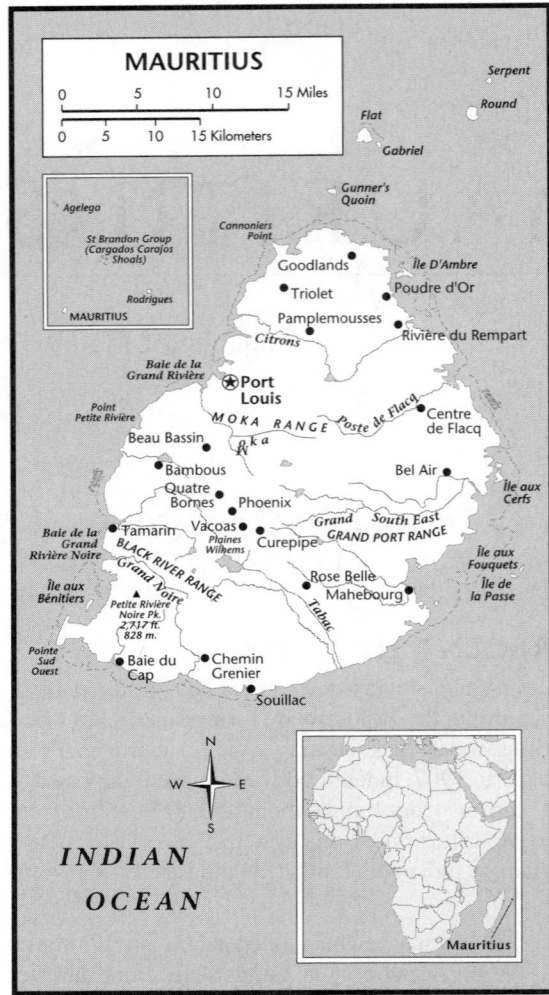

Judiciary

The Supreme Court has a chief justice and six other judges who also serve on the Court of Criminal Appeal, the Court of Civil Appeal, the Intermediate Court, the Industrial Court, and ten district courts.

Political Parties

The Mauritius Labor Party (MLP) received popular support during 1947–82. In the 1982 elections, the MMM (Mauritian Militant Movement) captured 42 seats in parliament and joined the Mauritian Socialist Party (Parti Socialiste Mauricien—PSM) in a ruling coalition under Aneerood Jugnauth. Jugnauth's government fell apart in the early months of 1983, and he then formed the Mauritian Socialist Movement (Mouvement Socialiste Mauricien—MSM).

A MMM/MLP coalition won 60 of 66 seats in the December 1995 elections.

DEFENSE

The National Police Force, which includes a military Special Mobile Force, is responsible for defense. In 1995, it had some 1,800 members.

ECONOMIC AFFAIRS

The Mauritius economy is based on export-oriented manufacturing (mainly clothing), sugar, and tourism. Economic growth declined in 1990 as the economy started to experience labor shortages, rising inflation, and capacity constraints. In the early 1990s, the economy showed modest recovery. In 1995, economic growth was estimated at 5%.

Public Finance

From the mid-1970s to 1981, the ratio of fiscal deficit to GDP increased from under 10% to 14%, due to deficit public spending. During the 1980s, an export-oriented economy caused the fiscal deficit to decline to 3% of GDP by 1989, and to 2% by 1991. In 1992 Mauritius' total public debt stood at R16,035.5 million, of which R5,475.6 million was financed abroad.

The U.S. Central Intelligence Agency estimates that, in 1993, government revenues totaled approximately $653 million and expenditures $567 million, including capital expenditures of $143 million. External debt totaled $996.8 million.

Income

In 1996 Mauritius's gross national product (GNP) was $11.7 billion, or about $10,300 per person. For the period 1985–95 the average inflation rate was 8.8%, and the average annual real growth rate of the GNP per person was 5.7%.

Industry

Manufacturing centers on the processing of agricultural products, especially sugar cane and its by-products, including molasses and rum. Local tobacco is made into cigarettes, and four factories are maintained to process tea. Other small industries produce goods for local consumption, such as beer and soft drinks, shoes, metal products, and paints.

The Export Processing Zone (EPZ) is an important part of Mauritius's industrial development. Imported goods are processed for export in the EPZ, which gives investors special tax breaks and duty exemption. Textiles generate 80% of exports from the EPZ. EPZ industries also produce sunglasses, toys, nails, razor blades, tires, and audio cassettes.

Banking and Finance

The Bank of Mauritius is the central bank. The Development Bank of Mauritius was established in March 1964 to provide loans for agricultural and industrial enterprises. The 13 commercial banks operating in the country had foreign assets of R14,194 million in 1993.

The government made it clear early in the first quarter of 1997 that the Bank of Mauritius would intervene in the foreign exchange market in order to stabilize the value of the rupee. Interventions in the last three months by the central bank helped the rupee to rebound after its decline against most foreign currencies, during the first nine months of 1996.

The country has a security exchange, the Stock Exchange of Mauritius. The number of domestic listed shares on 31 August 1993 was 31.

A market for securities or shares is not new to Mauritius. Shares of companies have been traded in Mauritius in a market environment since the nineteenth century. The main difference between the market organized by Chambre de Courtiers de l'île Maurice and the market in its present form is the legal framework within which dealings in shares must now take place and the regular meetings for share dealing.

Economic Development

France has backed training for labor, a stock exchange (which opened under the Stock Exchange Act of 1988), and irrigation projects. The EU is supporting efforts at diversifying agriculture. The Mauritius plan to become an international financial center advanced as liberalized currency rules were put into effect in 1986. In 1995, Mauritius became the twelfth member of the Southern African Development Community (SADC).

SOCIAL WELFARE

Mauritius has a universal system of pensions that supplements an earnings related pension system. Women do not face significant legal discrimination, but most remain limited to traditional roles in the household and workplace.

Healthcare

Mauritius has seven general hospitals, and two private hospitals. There are also 74 maternity, child health, and family planning centers. There is 1 physician per 1,165 people. The average life expectancy is 71 years.

Housing

There are three basic types of houses: wattle and daub (woven poles or sticks with plaster) construction with thatched roofs; galvanized sheet-iron structures; and houses constructed of wood.

EDUCATION

Education is free up to college level and is compulsory between the ages of 5 and 12. The estimated adult illiteracy rate in 1995 was 17%. In 1993, an estimated 281 primary schools had 125,543 pupils and 5,931 teachers, and general secondary schools had 87,661 pupils.

Postsecondary institutions include the University of Mauritius, the Mauritius College of the Air, and the Mahatma Gandhi Institute. In 1993, universities had 2,161 students.

1999 KEY EVENTS TIMELINE

February

- At least four people die in clashes with police in Port Louis, in what is called the worst violence in 30 years. Riots break out after reggae star Kaya dies while under police custody. Kaya was arrested after allegedly smoking marijuana at a rally to promote legalization of the drug.

April

- Mozambique and Mauritius sign agreement allowing their citizens to visit each other's countries for up to thirty days without requiring visas.

May

- Police say seven people burned to death when rioters threw firebombs into a Port Louis casino. The violence followed a soccer match between Scouts Club and Fire Brigade. At least two of the dead were children.

July

- The government of Mauritius announces its opposition to the transfer of nuclear wastes and fuels from France to Japan via the Indian Ocean.
- Responding to critical water shortages, the government plans to set up a plant to process waste

water from hotels and restaurants for use in irrigation.

August

- The daily newspaper, *L'Express*, begins publishing the registration numbers of smoke-emitting vehicles and the names of their owners. The paper hopes to shame owners into complying with pollution laws.

October

- Hundreds of cypress trees die throughout Mauritius during 1999, apparently affected by massive attacks from millions of tiny insects called *Cinara cupressi*.

- Facing its worst drought in 95 years, the government limits water usage in the capital city of Port Louis to no more than six hours each day.

- Police officials say some 10,000 cases of theft have taken place since the start of 1999, with simple larceny topping the list with over 6,800 cases.

November

- Residents of *Quatre Bornes*, a small town near Port Louis, block streets to protest against poor water distribution.

- The government announces tough new measures to deal with noise pollution. Noisy motorcycles will not be tolerated and discotheques will be forced to reduce music levels.

ANALYSIS OF EVENTS: 1999

BUSINESS AND THE ECONOMY

The extended drought, which began at the end of 1998 and continued past November 1999, was expected to have serious consequences for Mauritius, which depends on sugar exports for a large portion of its foreign earnings.

In August, agriculture officials said the drought would prevent Mauritius from honoring its export quotas to European and American markets. The 1999 harvest was expected to yield between 360,000 and 380,000 metric tons of sugar, with losses of about $160 million from last year.

GOVERNMENT AND POLITICS

Mauritius takes pride in its racial diversity and harmony among different ethnic groups, but the death of a popular reggae star in February brought underlying racial tensions to the surface. At least four people died and dozens were injured in widespread riots after singer Joseph Reginald Topize, more commonly known as Kaya, died in police custody on February 21. He was arrested for smoking marijuana at a rally to promote legalization of the drug. Kaya's supporters believe police beat the popular singer to death.

Most of the resulting riots were confined to poor areas that are home to the country's African Creole minority. Shops, businesses, and schools were closed by the violence, considered the worst in 30 years. A Mauritian official told a Reuters reporter that in some areas young Creole men and members of the island's Hindu majority, which has dominated government since the island's independence in 1968, were fighting one another.

The government decided in May to stop pumping wastewater into the Indian Ocean, opting instead to clean and recycle it for irrigation in sugar cane fields. They expected to have two treatment facilities operating by 2002, capable of treating up to 600,000 cubic meters of water per year. In July the government approved tough new measures to decrease water usage. Under the new regulations residents would not be allowed to wash cars, sidewalks, or use water for lawns. Violators faced an $80 fine and up to two years in prison. Tougher penalties against polluters of water sources were also announced.

By November Mauritius was facing the worst drought in about 95 years, forcing the government to take drastic measures to cut water consumption. In the capital, water usage was limited to six hours a day, while some outlying areas only could use water for one hour per day. The drastic measures were unpopular and met with resistance. Residents of a small town near Port Louis burned tires and blockaded streets to protest poor water distribution. Some residents said they had not had any drinking water for weeks. Government officials assured residents they would have water until December, when summer rains were expected to return and fill up the reservoirs.

CULTURE AND SOCIETY

Mauritius's 1.2 million people faced a severe drought throughout most of 1999, while the government sought to alleviate some of the country's environmental problems by initiating new programs and regulations to cut down on water, air, and noise pollution.

In October a group of students launched a new program to teach primary school children about the environment. Using sketches, puppets, and songs, students were taught about marine environments and how to protect them.

Officials said the government would deal more harshly with heavily polluting vehicles by the year 2000. While there are laws to prevent pollution, penalties were not common, and regulations were too loose. The government also said it planned to reduce lead in gasoline, as well as carbon monoxide and hydrocarbons in the air. One of the island's daily newspapers, *L'Express*, began to publish the plates of smoke-emitting vehicles, and the names of their owners. The editor of the newspaper said laws had failed to curb the pollution problem. ''The objective is to get the owners to take stock of their ghastly impact on the air we breathe, to force them to change their way and be more responsible,'' the editor told the media.

In November Environment Minister Siddick Chady said the government was getting tough on noise pollution, prohibiting the use of noisy motorcycles, and telling discotheques to moderate the volume of their music.

DIRECTORY

CENTRAL GOVERNMENT

Head of State

President
Cassam Uteem, Office of the President, Government House, Port Louis, Mauritius
PHONE: +230 4543021
FAX: +230 4645370
E-MAIL: statepas@intnet.mu

Ministers

Prime Minister
Navinchandra Ramgoolam, Office of the Prime Minister, New Government Centre, 6th Floor, Port Louis, Mauritius
PHONE: +230 2011018
FAX: +230 2129393

Minister of Defense and Home Affairs
Navinchandra Ramgoolam, Ministry of Defense and Home Affairs, 4th Floor Government Centre, Port Louis, Mauritius
PHONE: +230 2029020; 2029024
FAX: +230 2117907

Minister of External Communications and Outer Islands
Navinchandra Ramgoolam, Ministry of External Communications and Outer Islands, 5th Floor, Air Mauritius Building, Port Louis, Mauritius
PHONE: +230 2101122
FAX: +230 2117708

Minister of Foreign Affairs and International Trade
Rajkeswur Purryag, Ministry of Foreign Affairs and International Trade, Level Five, New Government Centre, Port Louis, Mauritius
PHONE: +230 2011416
FAX: +230 2126764

Minister of Industry, Commerce, Corporate Affairs and Financial Services
Charles Gaetan Xavier-Luc Duval, Ministry of Industry, Commerce, Corporate Affairs and Financial Services, 7th Floor, Air Mauritius Centre, John Kennedy Street, Port Louis, Mauritius
PHONE: +230 2107100
FAX: +230 2128201
E-MAIL: minic@intnet.mu

Minister of Justice, Human Rights and Reform Institutions
Abdool Razack Mohamed Ameen Peeroo, Ministry of Justice, Human Rights and Reform Institutions

Minister of Land Transport, Shipping, and Port Development
Clarel Désiré Malherbe, Ministry of Land Transport, Shipping, and Port Development

Minister of Public Utilities
Ahmed Rashid Beebeejaun, Ministry of Public Utilities, 10th Floor, Medcor Building, John Kennedy Street, Port Louis, Mauritius
PHONE: +230 2103994
FAX: +230 2086497
E-MAIL: minpuuti@intnet.mu

Minister of Finance
Vasant Kumar Bunwaree, Ministry of Finance, Ground Floor, Government House, Port Louis, Mauritius
PHONE: +230 2011777

FAX: +230 2087854
E-MAIL: mof@bow.intnet.mu

Minister of Education and Scientific Research
Ramsamy Chedumbarum Pillay, Ministry of
Education and Scientific Research, IVTB House,
Pont Fer, Phoenix, Mauritius
PHONE: +230 6980464; 6977862; 6977730
FAX: +230 6982550
E-MAIL: meduhrd@bow.intnet.mu

**Minister of Local Government, Outer Islands
Development and Small and Medium
Enterprises and Handicraft**
James Burty David, Ministry of Local
Government, Outer Islands Development and
Small and Medium Enterprises and Handicraft,
Level 3, Emmanuel Anquetil Building, c/r S.S.R.
and J. Koenig Streets, Port Louis, Mauritius
PHONE: +230 2011216
FAX: +230 2011216
E-MAIL: Minlogov@intnet.mu

**Minister of Agriculture, Food Technology and
Natural Resources**
Arvin Boolell, Ministry of Agriculture, Food
Technology and Natural Resources, 9th Floor,
Renganaden Seeneevassen Building, Port Louis,
Mauritius
PHONE: +230 2120814
FAX: +230 2124427

**Minister of Labor and Industrial Relations,
Employment and Human Resource
Development**
Satya Veyash Faugoo, Ministry of Labor and
Industrial Relations, Employment and Human
Resource Development

**Minister of Civil Service Affairs and
Administrative Reform**
Sachindev Mahess Kumar Soonarane, Ministry
of Civil Service Affairs and Administrative
Reform, 6th Floor, New Government Centre,
Port Louis, Mauritius
FAX: +230 2129528
E-MAIL: civser@bow.intnet.mu

**Minister of Economic Development,
Productivity and Regional Development**
Rundheersing Bheenick, Ministry of Economic
Development, Productivity and Regional
Development, 9th Floor, Emmanuel Anquetil
Building, Cnr SSR and Jules Koenig Streets,
Port Louis, Mauritius
PHONE: +230 2012533; 2011585
FAX: +230 2124124

E-MAIL: medrc@intnet.mu

Minister of Arts and Culture
Tsang Fan Hin Tsang Mang Kin, Ministry of
Arts and Culture, 7th Floor,Renganaden
Seeneevassen Building, c/r Pope Hennessy and
Maillard Streets, Port Louis, Mauritius
PHONE: +230 2129993
FAX: +230 2129366; 2113196
E-MAIL: culture@intnet.mu

Minister of Environment
Mohummud Siddick Chady, Ministry of
Environment

Minister of Urban and Rural Development
Mohummud Siddick Chady, Ministry of Urban
and Rural Development, 7th, 12th and 13th
Floor, Sterling House, Lislet Geoffrey Street,
Port Louis, Mauritius
PHONE: +230 2103215; 2100129; 2102776

Minister of Public Infrastructure
Devanand Virahsawmy, Ministry of Public
Infrastructure, Treasury Building, Intendence
Street, Port Louis, Mauritius
PHONE: +230 2083063; 2126071; 2121876
FAX: +230 2087149

**Minister of Women, Family Welfare and
Child Development**
Indira Savitree Thacoor-Sidaya, Ministry of
Women, Family Welfare and Child
Development, CSK Building, Corner Remy
Ollier/Emmanuel Anquetil Streets, Port Louis,
Mauritius
PHONE: +230 2401377
FAX: +230 2407717
E-MAIL: mwfwcd@bow.intnet.mu

Minister of Tourism and Leisure
Marie Joseph Jacques Chasteau De Baylon,
Ministry of Tourism and Leisure, Level 12, Air
Mauritius Centre, John Kennedy Street, Port
Louis, Mauritius
PHONE: +230 2101329
FAX: +230 2086776
E-MAIL: mot@intnet.mu

Minister of Health and Quality of Life
Nankeswarsingh Deerpalsingh, Ministry of
Health and Quality of Life
PHONE: +230 2011910; 2116204
E-MAIL: Keswar@intnet.mu

Minister of Housing and Lands
Sathiamoorthy Sunassee, Ministry of Housing
and Lands, 4th, 5th, 6th Floors, Sugar Industry

Labor Welfare Fund Building, Edith Cavell St., Port Louis, Mauritius
PHONE: +230 2082831
FAX: +230 2129369

Minister of Telecommunications and Information Technology

Sarat Dutt Lallah, Ministry of Telecommunications and Information Technology, Level 9, Air Mauritius Centre, President John Kennedy Street, Port Louis, Mauritius
PHONE: +230 2100201
FAX: +230 2121673
E-MAIL: mintelit@intnet.mu

Minister of Rodrigues

Joseph Benoit Jolicoeur, Ministry of Rodrigues, 5th Floor, Fon Sing Building, Edith Cavell Street, Port Louis, Mauritius
PHONE: +230 2088472
FAX: +230 2126329
E-MAIL: minrodr@bow.intnet.mu

Minister of Social Security, National Solidarity and Senior Citizens Welfare

Ved Prakash Bundhun, Ministry of Social Security, National Solidarity and Senior Citizens Welfare, R. Seeneevassen Building, Jules Koenig St., Port Louis, Mauritius
PHONE: +230 2129813; 2123001
FAX: +230 2128190
E-MAIL: mssns@intnet.mu

Minister of Fisheries and Co-operatives

Dhaneshwar Beeharry, Ministry of Fisheries and Co-operatives, 3rd and 4th Level, LICI Building, John Kennedy Street, Port Louis, Mauritius
PHONE: +230 2088319

Minister of Youth and Sports

Marie Claude Arouff-Parfait, Ministry of Youth and Sports, Headquarters, 3rd Level, Emmanuel Anquetil Bldg, Port Louis, Mauritius

POLITICAL ORGANIZATIONS

Parti Travailliste (Mauritius Labor Party)

7, Guy Rozemont Square, Port Louis, Mauritius
PHONE: +230 2126691
E-MAIL: Labor@intnet.mu
TITLE: Leader
NAME: Navinchandra Ramgoolam

Mouvement Militant Mauricien (Mauritian Militant Movement)

NAME: Paul Berenger

Organisation du Peuple Rodriguais (Organization of the People of Rodrigues)

NAME: Louis Serge Clair

Mouvement Rodriguais (Rodrigues Movement)

NAME: Nicolas Vonmally

Parti Gaetan Duval (Gaetan Duval Party)

NAME: Gaetan Duval

Hizbullah (Party of God)

NAME: Imam Mustapha Beeharry

DIPLOMATIC REPRESENTATION

Embassies in Mauritius

Australia
2nd Floor, Rogers House, Port Louis, Mauritius
PHONE: +230 2081700

Austria
PHONE: +230 2086801

Belgium
Dr Ferriere Street, Port Louis, Mauritius
PHONE: +230 2081241

Canada
King Georges Avenue, Floreal, Mauritius
PHONE: +230 6865796

China
Royal Road, Belle Rose, Mauritius
PHONE: +230 4643073

Denmark
4 Edith Cavell Street, Port Louis, Mauritius
PHONE: +230 2085051

Egypt
King George Avenue, Floreal, Mauritius
PHONE: +230 6962605

Finland
5 Pres. John Kennedy Street, Port Louis, Mauririus
PHONE: +230 2086801

France
5 bis, Rue Champ de Lort-BP 12, Port Louis, Mauritius
PHONE: +230 2087981; 2087984
FAX: +230 2088432
E-MAIL: port_louis@dree.org

Germany
60 SS Ramgoolam Street, Port Louis, Mauritius
PHONE: +230 2080666

Great Britain
Les Cascades Building, Edith Cavell Street, Port Louis, Mauritius
PHONE: +230 2111361
FAX: +230 2111369

India
Sir William Newton Street, Port Louis, Mauritius
PHONE: +230 2080666

Netherlands
Docteur Ferriere Street, Port Louis, Mauritius
PHONE: +230 2082811

Korea
Rainbow House, Port Louis, Mauritius
PHONE: +230 2083308

Malaysia
Queen Mary Avenue, Floreal, Mauritius
PHONE: +230 6865015

Norway
5 Pres. John Kennedy St., Port Louis, Mauritius
PHONE: +230 2086801

Pakistan
7th Floor, Anglo Mauritius House, Port Louis, Mauritius
PHONE: +230 2126547

Russia
Queen Mary Avenue, Floreal, Mauritius
PHONE: +230 6961545

South Africa
Pope Hennessy St, Port Louis, Mauritius
PHONE: +230 2126926

JUDICIAL SYSTEM
Supreme Court

FURTHER READING
Articles

"Assessing a Higher Education Project: A Mauritius Feasibility Study." *Applied Economics* (January 1999): 27.

"Mauritius Limits Water Use." The Associated Press, 30 October 1999.

"Mauritius, Rethinking the Miracle." *Current History* (May 1999): 228.

"Parrots Faced with Threat of Extinction." *The Guardian of London*, 6 August 1999.

"Rioting in Mauritius Set Off by Jail Death of Singer." *The Guardian of London*, 25 February 1999.

"Search is on for Sugars with More Complex Tastes." *The Seattle Times*, 26 May 1999.

Books

Bowman, Larry W. *Mauritius: Democracy and Development in the Indian Ocean.* Boulder, Colo.: Westview Press, 1991.

Spectrum Guide to Mauritius. Brooklyn, N.Y.: Interlink, 1997.

Internet

Africa News Online. Available Online @ www.africanews.org/west/mauritania/ (November 12, 1999).

Africaonline. Available Online @ www.africaonline.com (October 28, 1999).

"Birdman Saves Species: Mauritius Kestrel." BBC Online Network, 7 August 1999. Available Online @ news2.thls.bbc.co.uk/hi/ english/special%5Freport/regions/wales/ newsid%5F414000/414093.stm (December 13, 1999).

CIA World Factbook, 1998. Available Online @ www.odci.gov/cia/publications/factbook/ mr.html (November 12, 1999).

"Four Dead in Reggae Riot." BBC Online Network, 24 February 1999. Available Online @ news2.thls.bbc.co.uk/hi/english/world/ africa/newsid%5F285000/285797.stm (December 13, 1999).

MAURITIUS: STATISTICAL DATA

For sources and notes see "Sources of Statistics" in the front of each volume.

GEOGRAPHY

Geography (1)

Area:

Total: 1,860 sq km.

Land: 1,850 sq km.

Water: 10 sq km.

Note: includes Agalega Islands, Cargados Carajos Shoals (Saint Brandon), and Rodrigues.

Area—comparative: almost 11 times the size of Washington, DC.

Land boundaries: 0 km.

Coastline: 177 km.

Climate: tropical, modified by southeast trade winds; warm, dry winter (May to November); hot, wet, humid summer (November to May).

Terrain: small coastal plain rising to discontinuous mountains encircling central plateau.

Natural resources: arable land, fish.

Land use:

Arable land: 49%

Permanent crops: 3%

Permanent pastures: 3%

Forests and woodland: 22%

Other: 23% (1993 est.).

HUMAN FACTORS

Demographics (2A)

	1990	1995	1998	2000	2010	2020	2030	2040	2050
Population	1,073.5	1,128.2	1,168.3	1,196.2	1,327.7	1,440.0	1,529.0	1,583.7	1,614.0
Net migration rate (per 1,000 population)	NA	NA	NA	NA	NA	NA	NA	NA	NA
Births	NA	NA	NA	NA	NA	NA	NA	NA	NA
Deaths	NA	NA	NA	NA	NA	NA	NA	NA	NA
Life expectancy - males	65.5	66.5	67.1	67.4	69.0	70.5	71.9	73.1	74.1
Life expectancy - females	73.4	74.1	74.7	75.2	76.9	78.4	79.8	80.9	81.9
Birth rate (per 1,000)	21.0	19.2	18.6	18.4	16.1	14.9	14.0	13.2	12.7
Death rate (per 1,000)	6.6	6.6	6.7	6.7	7.0	7.8	9.3	10.6	11.2
Women of reproductive age (15-49 yrs.)	295.9	319.0	333.2	337.2	350.4	357.2	363.8	370.3	369.7
of which are currently married	NA	NA	NA	NA	NA	NA	NA	NA	NA
Fertility rate	2.3	2.2	2.2	2.2	2.1	2.1	2.0	2.0	1.9

Except as noted, values for vital statistics are in thousands; life expectancy is in years.

Health Personnel (3)

Total health expenditure as a percentage of GDP, 1990-1997[a]

Public sector 2.2

Private sector 1.7

Total[b] 4.0

Health expenditure per capita in U.S. dollars, 1990-1997[a]

Purchasing power parity 304

Total 116

Availability of health care facilities per 100,000 people

Hospital beds 1990-1997[a] 310

Doctors 1993[c] 85

Nurses 1993[c] 241

Health Indicators (4)

Life expectancy at birth

1980 66

1997 71

Daily per capita supply of calories (1996) 2,952

Total fertility rate births per woman (1997) 1.9

Maternal mortality ratio per 100,000 live births (1990-97) . . . . .110[b]

Safe water % of population with access (1995) 100

Sanitation % of population with access (1995) 100

Consumption of iodized salt % of households (1992-98)[a] 0

Smoking prevalence

Male % of adults (1985-95)[a] 47

Female % of adults (1985-95)[a] 4

Tuberculosis incidence per 100,000 people (1997) 66

Adult HIV prevalence % of population ages 15-49 (1997) 0.08

Infants and Malnutrition (5)

Under-5 mortality rate (1997) 23

% of infants with low birthweight (1990-97) 13

Births attended by skilled health staff % of total[a] . . .97

% fully immunized (1995-97)

TB 84

DPT 87

Polio 87

Measles 84

Prevalence of child malnutrition under age 5 (1992-97)[b] . . . . .NA

Ethnic Division (6)

Indo-Mauritian 68%

Creole 27%

Sino-Mauritian 3%

Franco-Mauritian 2%

Religions (7)

Hindu 52%

Christian 28.3%

Roman Catholic 26%

Protestant 2.3%

Muslim 16.6%

Other 3.1%

Languages (8)

English (official), Creole, French, Hindi, Urdu, Hakka, Bojpoori.

EDUCATION

Public Education Expenditures (9)

Public expenditure on education (% of GNP)

1980 . . . . .5.3

1996 . . . . .4.3[1]

Expenditure per student

Primary % of GNP per capita

1980 . . . . .15.8

1996 . . . . .9.8

Secondary % of GNP per capita

1980 . . . .

1996 . . . .

Tertiary % of GNP per capita

1980 . . . . .343.6

1996 . . . . .67.5

Expenditure on teaching materials

Primary % of total for level (1996) 0.0

Secondary % of total for level (1996) . . . .

Primary pupil-teacher ratio per teacher (1996) 24

Duration of primary education years (1995) 6

Educational Attainment (10)

Age group (1990) . . . . .25+

Total population 540,244

Highest level attained (%)

No schooling 18.3

First level

Not completed 42.6

Completed 6.1

Entered second level

S-1 . . . . .7.2

S-2 . . . . .23.9

Postsecondary 1.9

GOVERNMENT & LAW

Political Parties (12)

National Assembly	No. of seats
Mauritian Labor Party (MLP)	.35
Mauritian Militant Movement (MMM)	.25
Allies of MLP and MMM on Rodrigues Island	.2

Government Budget (13A)

Year: 1997

Total Expenditures: 20,260 Millions of Rupees

Expenditures as a percentage of the total by function:

General public services and public order . . . . .18.65[P]

Defense . . . . .1.10[P]

Education . . . . .17.77[P]

Health . . . . .7.87[P]

Social Security and Welfare . . . . .19.43[P]

Housing and community amenities . . . . .6.15[P]

Recreational, cultural, and religious affairs . . . . .1.84[P]

Fuel and energy . . . . .04[P]

Agriculture, forestry, fishing, and hunting . . . . .4.74[P]

Continued on next page.

Military Affairs (14B)

	1990	1991	1992	1993	1994	1995
Military expenditures						
Current dollars (mil.)	9	11	12	11	12	14
1995 constant dollars (mil.)	10	12	13	12	12	14
Armed forces (000)	1	1	1	1	1	1
Gross national product (GNP)						
Current dollars (mil.)	2,694	2,949	3,221	3,480	3,697	3,920
1995 constant dollars (mil.)	3,096	3,258	3,465	3,649	3,790	3,920
Central government expenditures (CGE)						
1995 constant dollars (mil.)	752	772	847	825	891	891
People (mil.)	1.1	1.1	1.1	1.1	1.1	1.1
Military expenditure as % of GNP	.3	.4	.4	.3	.3	.4
Military expenditure as % of CGE	1.3	1.5	1.5	1.4	1.4	1.6
Military expenditure per capita (1995 $)	9	11	12	11	11	12
Armed forces per 1,000 people (soldiers)	.9	.9	.9	.9	.9	1.2
GNP per capita (1995 $)	2,884	3,004	3,161	3,295	3,390	3,474
Arms imports[6]						
Current dollars (mil.)	5	0	5	5	0	0
1995 constant dollars (mil.)	6	0	5	5	0	0
Arms exports[6]						
Current dollars (mil.)	0	0	0	0	0	0
1995 constant dollars (mil.)	0	0	0	0	0	0
Total imports[7]						
Current dollars (mil.)	1,618	1,576	1,630	1,715	1,930	1,959
1995 constant dollars (mil.)	1,859	1,742	1,753	1,798	1,978	1,959
Total exports[7]						
Current dollars (mil.)	1,194	1,195	1,297	1,299	1,347	1,537
1995 constant dollars (mil.)	1,372	1,320	1,395	1,362	1,381	1,537
Arms as percent of total imports[8]	.3	0	.3	.3	0	0
Arms as percent of total exports[8]	0	0	0	0	0	0

Government Budget (13A) cont.

Mining, manufacturing, and construction 79ᴾ

Transportation and communication 3.01ᴾ

Other economic affairs and services 3.79ᴾ

Crime (15)

Crime rate (for 1997)

Crimes reported 37,800

Total persons convicted 19,600

Crimes per 100,000 population 3,400

Persons responsible for offenses

Total number of suspects 29,400

Total number of female suspects 3,900

Total number of juvenile suspects 3,650

LABOR FORCE

Labor Force (16)

Total 514,000

Construction and industry 36%

Services 24%

Agriculture and fishing 14%

Trade, restaurants, hotels 16%

Transportation and communication 7%

Finance 3%

Data for 1995. Percent distribution for 1995.

Unemployment Rate (17)

1.8% (1995)

PRODUCTION SECTOR

Electric Energy (18)

Capacity .361,000 kW (1995)

Production . . . . .960 million kWh (1995)

Consumption per capita . . . . .852 kWh (1995)

Transportation (19)

Highways:

total: 1,860 km

paved: 1,732 km (including 30 km of expressways)

unpaved: 128 km (1996 est.)

Merchant marine:

total: 20 ships (1,000 GRT or over) totaling 241,799 GRT/336,316 DWT ships by type: cargo 7, combination bulk 2, container 6, liquefied gas tanker 1, oil tanker 1, refrigerated cargo 3. Note: a flag of convenience registry; India owns 1 ship (1997 est.)

Airports: 5 (1997 est.)

Airports—with paved runways:

total: 2

2,438 to 3,047 m: 1

914 to 1,523 m: 1 (1997 est.)

Airports—with unpaved runways:

total: 3

914 to 1,523 m: 1

under 914 m: 2 (1997 est.)

Top Agricultural Products (20)

Sugarcane, tea, corn, potatoes, bananas, pulses; cattle, goats; fish.

FINANCE, ECONOMICS, & TRADE

Economic Indicators (22)

National product: GDP—purchasing power parity—$11.7 billion (1996 est.)

National product real growth rate: 5.4% (1996 est.)

National product per capita: $10,300 (1996 est.)

Inflation rate—consumer price index: 6.5% (1996)

MANUFACTURING SECTOR

GDP & Manufacturing Summary (21)

	1980	1985	1990	1992	1993	1994
Gross Domestic Product						
Millions of 1990 dollars	1,409	1,769	2,559	2,839	2,992	3,142
Growth rate in percent	−10.06	6.88	7.15	6.21	5.38	5.00
Per capita (in 1990 dollars)	1,458.8	1,741.6	2,421.0	2,631.5	2,742.6	2,845.8
Manufacturing Value Added						
Millions of 1990 dollars	200	299	502	565	621	667
Growth rate in percent	−7.03	15.27	7.72	6.40	10.00	7.36
Manufacturing share in percent of current prices	15.0	20.3	23.1	19.7	20.8	20.8

FINANCE, ECONOMICS,& TRADE

Balance of Payments (23)

	1992	1993	1994	1995	1996
Exports of goods (f.o.b.)	1,335	1,334	1,377	1,572	1,793
Imports of goods (f.o.b.)	−1,494	−1,576	−1,774	−1,812	−2,087
Trade balance	−159	−242	−397	−241	−295
Services - debits	−603	−588	−603	−713	−751
Services - credits	668	636	664	830	940
Private transfers (net)	5	8	9	6	12
Government transfers (net)	88	93	95	95	111
Overall balance	−0	−92	−232	−22	17

Exchange Rates (24)

Exchange rates:

Mauritian rupees (MauRs) per US$1

January 1998	22.220
1997	20.561
1996	17.948
1995	17.386
1994	17.960
1993	17.648

Top Import Origins (25)

$2.2 billion (c.i.f., 1996 est.) Data are for 1995.

Origins	%
France	20
India	8
Hong Kong	7
United Kingdom	6
Germany	5

Top Export Destinations (26)

$1.6 billion (f.o.b., 1996 est.) Data are for 1995.

Destinations	%
United Kingdom	34
France	21
United States	15
Germany	6
Italy	4

Economic Aid (27)

Recipient: ODA, $NA. NA stands for not available.

Import Export Commodities (28)

Import Commodities	Export Commodities
Manufactured goods 37%	Clothing and textiles 55%
Capital equipment 19%	Sugar 24%
Foodstuffs 13%	
Petroleum products 8%	
Chemicals 7%	

COLOR FLAGS, SEALS AND REGIONAL MAPS

Color seals for Guadeloupe, Martinique and Serbia are not available at this time.

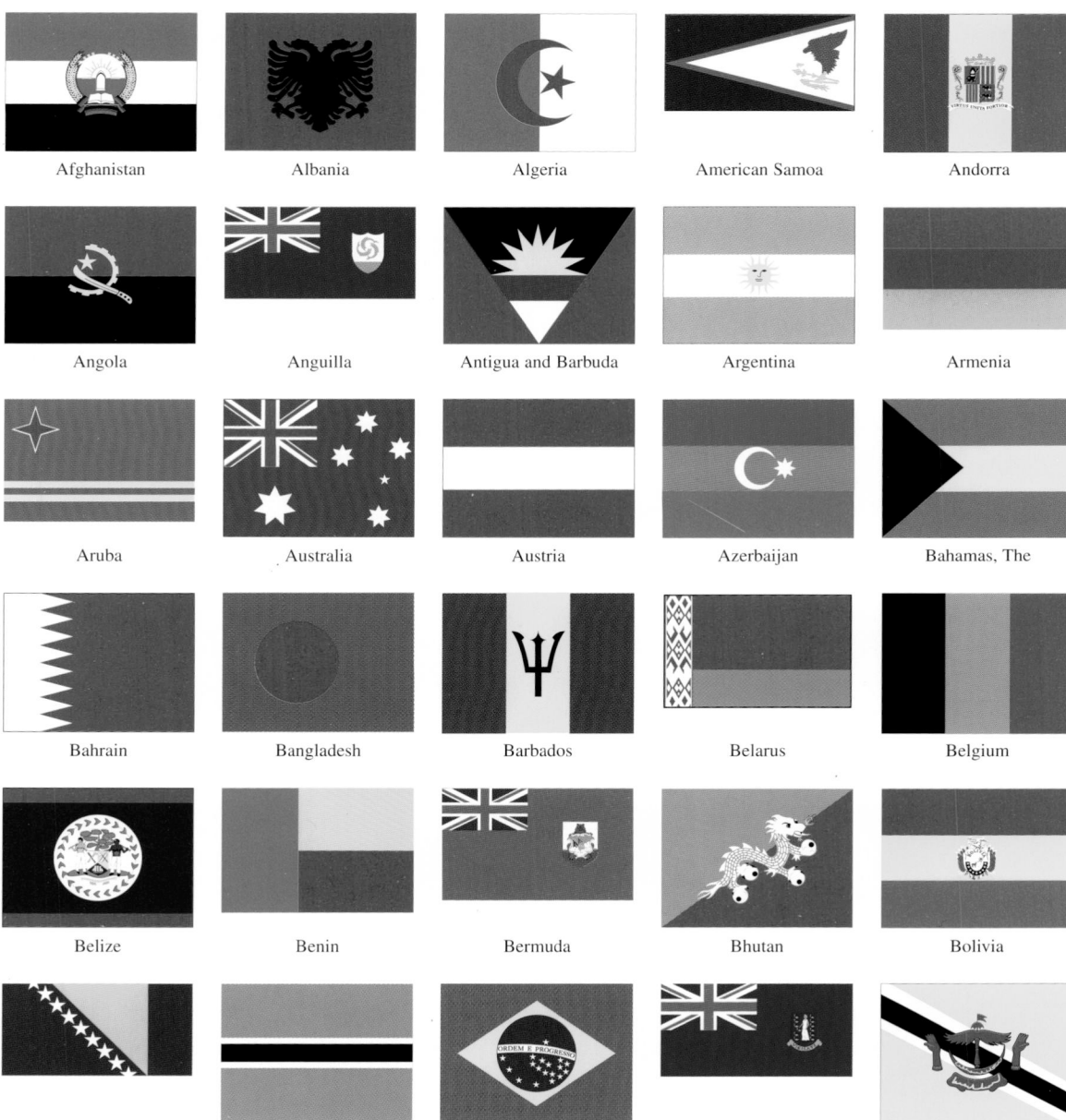

Afghanistan	Albania	Algeria	American Samoa	Andorra
Angola	Anguilla	Antigua and Barbuda	Argentina	Armenia
Aruba	Australia	Austria	Azerbaijan	Bahamas, The
Bahrain	Bangladesh	Barbados	Belarus	Belgium
Belize	Benin	Bermuda	Bhutan	Bolivia
Bosnia and Herzegovina	Botswana	Brazil	British Virgin Islands	Brunei

Bulgaria

Burkina Faso

Burundi

Cambodia

Cameroon

Canada

Cape Verde

Cayman Islands

Central African Republic

Chad

Chile

China

Christmas Island

Colombia

Comoros

Congo, Democratic
Republic of the

Congo, Republic of the

Cook Islands

Costa Rica

Cote d'Ivoire

Croatia

Cuba

Cyprus

Czech Republic

Denmark

Djibouti

Dominica

Dominican Republic

Ecuador

Egypt

El Salvador

Equatorial Guinea

Eritrea

Estonia

Ethiopia

Falkland Islands

Faroe Islands

Fiji

Finland

France

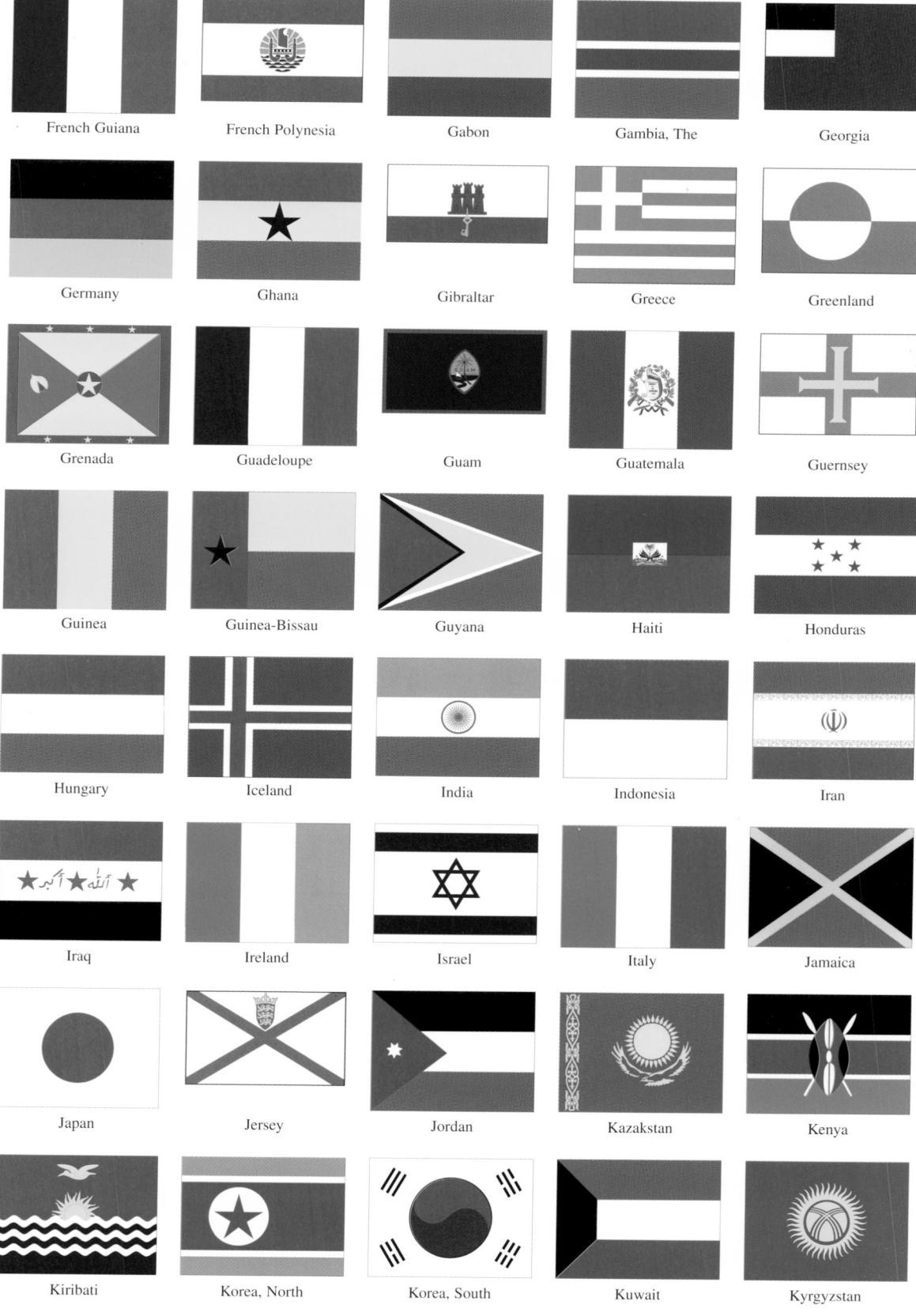

French Guiana

French Polynesia

Gabon

Gambia, The

Georgia

Germany

Ghana

Gibraltar

Greece

Greenland

Grenada

Guadeloupe

Guam

Guatemala

Guernsey

Guinea

Guinea-Bissau

Guyana

Haiti

Honduras

Hungary

Iceland

India

Indonesia

Iran

Iraq

Ireland

Israel

Italy

Jamaica

Japan

Jersey

Jordan

Kazakstan

Kenya

Kiribati

Korea, North

Korea, South

Kuwait

Kyrgyzstan

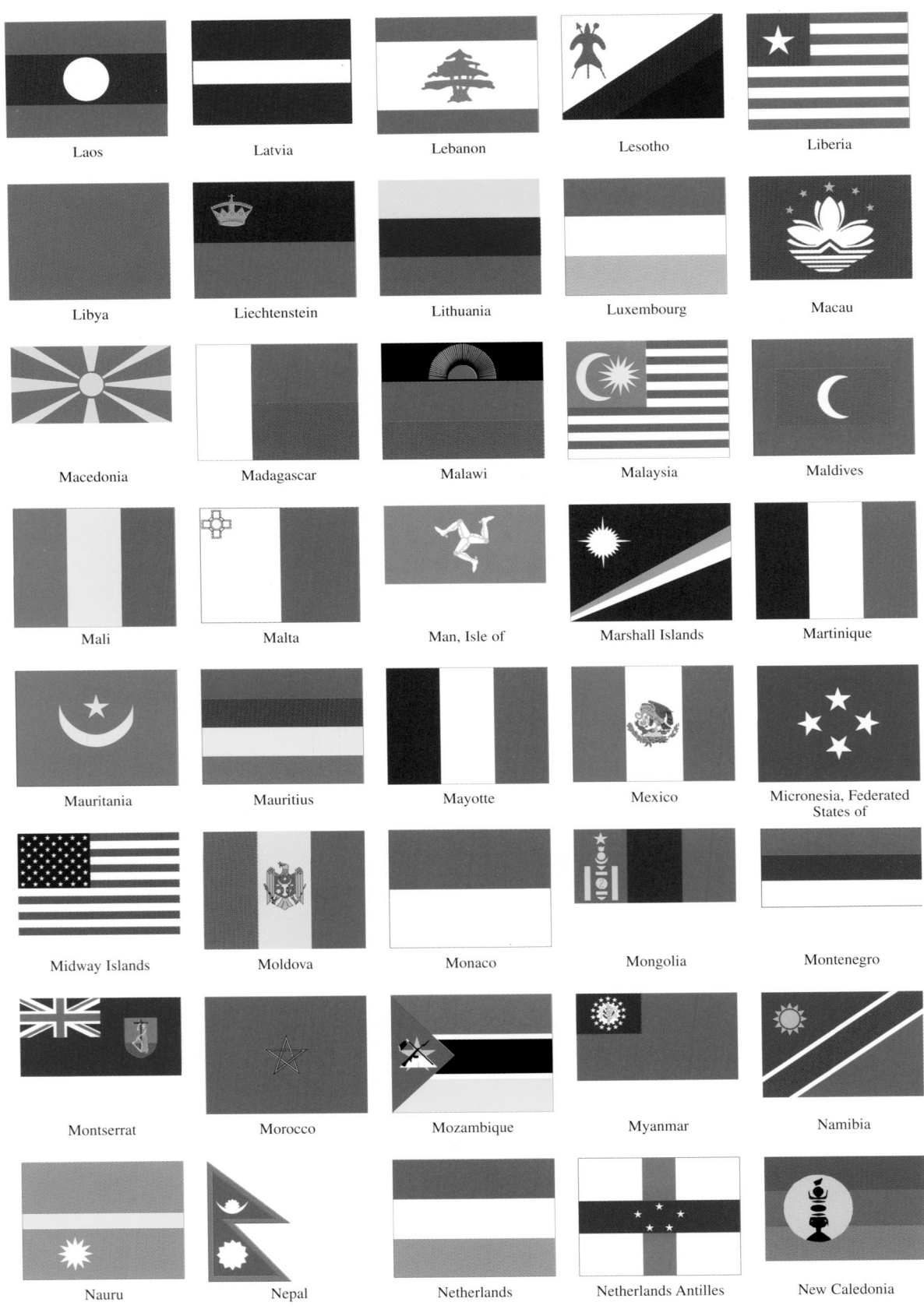

Laos

Latvia

Lebanon

Lesotho

Liberia

Libya

Liechtenstein

Lithuania

Luxembourg

Macau

Macedonia

Madagascar

Malawi

Malaysia

Maldives

Mali

Malta

Man, Isle of

Marshall Islands

Martinique

Mauritania

Mauritius

Mayotte

Mexico

Micronesia, Federated States of

Midway Islands

Moldova

Monaco

Mongolia

Montenegro

Montserrat

Morocco

Mozambique

Myanmar

Namibia

Nauru

Nepal

Netherlands

Netherlands Antilles

New Caledonia

New Zealand

Nicaragua

Niger

Nigeria

Niue

Norfolk Island

Northern Mariana Islands

Norway

Oman

Pakistan

Palau

Panama

Papua New Guinea

Paraguay

Peru

Philippines

Poland

Portugal

Puerto Rico

Qatar

Reunion

Romania

Russia

Rwanda

Saint Helena

Saint Kitts and Nevis

Saint Lucia

Saint Pierre and Miquelon

Saint Vincent and the Grenadines

Samoa

San Marino

Sao Tome and Principe

Saudi Arabia

Senegal

Serbia

Seychelles

Sierra Leone

Singapore

Slovakia

Slovenia

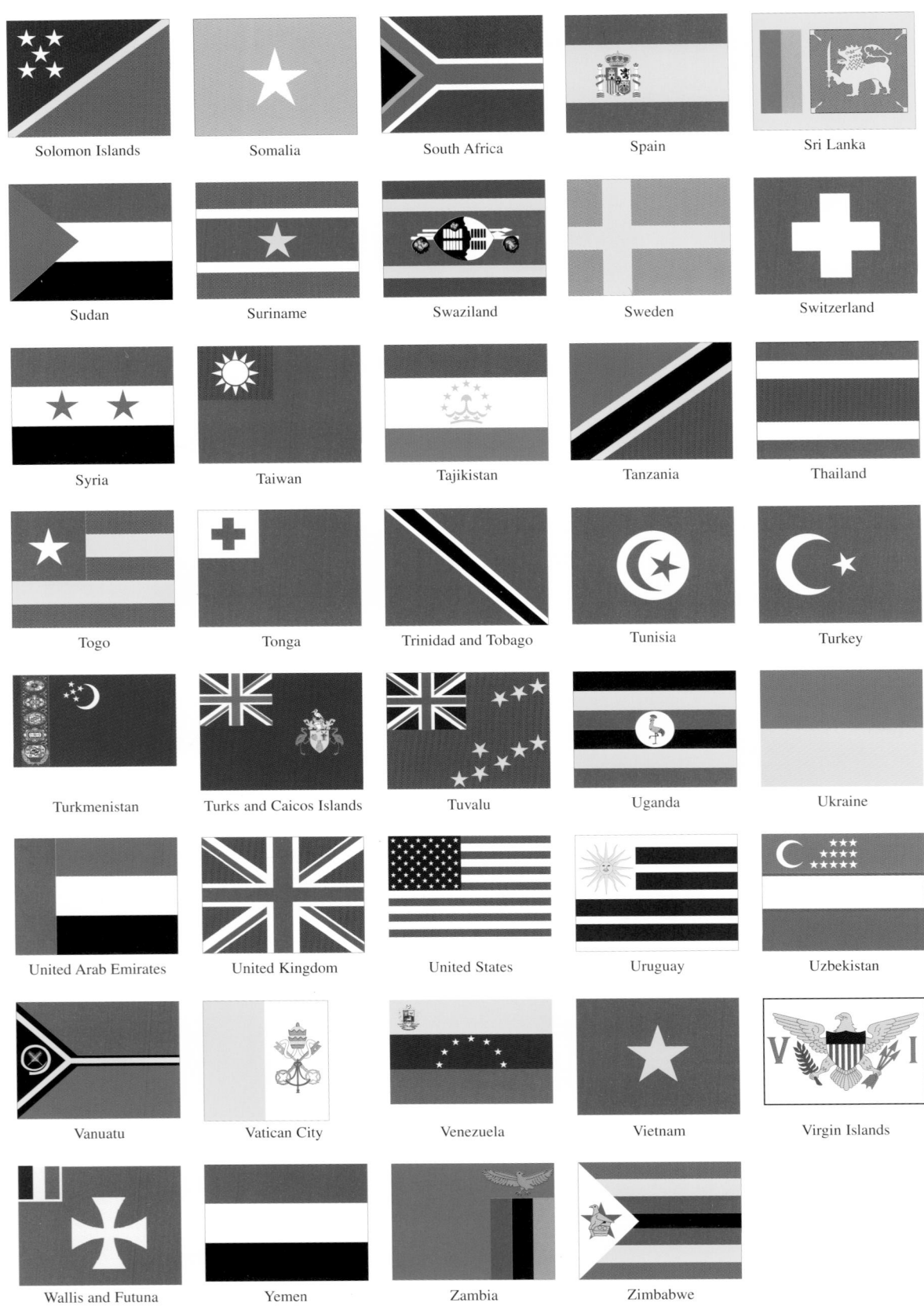

Solomon Islands	Somalia	South Africa	Spain	Sri Lanka
Sudan	Suriname	Swaziland	Sweden	Switzerland
Syria	Taiwan	Tajikistan	Tanzania	Thailand
Togo	Tonga	Trinidad and Tobago	Tunisia	Turkey
Turkmenistan	Turks and Caicos Islands	Tuvalu	Uganda	Ukraine
United Arab Emirates	United Kingdom	United States	Uruguay	Uzbekistan
Vanuatu	Vatican City	Venezuela	Vietnam	Virgin Islands
Wallis and Futuna	Yemen	Zambia	Zimbabwe	

Afghanistan	Albania	Algeria	American Samoa	Andorra
Angola	Anguilla	Antigua and Barbuda	Argentina	Armenia
Aruba	Australia	Austria	Azerbaijan	Bahamas, The
Bahrain	Bangladesh	Barbados	Belarus	Belgium
Belize	Benin	Bermuda	Bhutan	Bolivia
Bosnia and Herzegovina	Botswana	Brazil	British Virgin Islands	Brunei
Bulgaria	Burkina Faso	Burundi	Cambodia	Cameroon
Canada	Cape Verde	Cayman Islands	Central African Republic	Chad

Chile	China	Christmas Island	Columbia	Comoros
Congo, Democratic Republic of the	Congo, Republic of the	Cook Islands	Costa Rica	Cote d'Ivoire
Croatia	Cuba	Cyprus	Czech Republic	Denmark
Djibouti	Dominica	Dominican Republic	Ecuador	Egypt
El Salvador	Equatorial Guinea	Eritrea	Estonia	Ethiopia
Falkland Islands	Faroe Islands	Fiji	Finland	France
French Guiana	French Polynesia	Gabon	Gambia, The	Georgia
Germany	Ghana	Gibraltar	Greece	Greenland

Grenada

Guam

Guatemala

Guernsey

Guinea

Guinea-Bissau

Guyana

Haiti

Honduras

Hungary

Iceland

India

Indonesia

Iran

Iraq

Ireland

Israel

Italy

Jamaica

Japan

Jersey

Jordan

Kazakstan

Kenya

Kiribati

Korea, North

Korea, South

Kuwait

Kyrgyzstan

Laos

Latvia

Lebanon

Lesotho

Liberia

Libya

Liechtenstein

Lithuania

Luxembourg

Macau

Macedonia

Madagascar

Malawi

Malaysia

Maldives

Mali

Malta

Man, Isle of

Marshall Islands

Mauritania

Mauritius

Mayotte

Mexico

Micronesia, Federated States of

Midway Islands

Moldova

Monaco

Mongolia

Montenegro

Montserrat

Morocco

Mozambique

Myanmar

Namibia

Nauru

Nepal

Netherlands

Netherlands Antilles

New Caledonia

New Zealand

Nicaragua

Niger

Nigeria

Niue

Norfolk Island

Northern Mariana Islands

Norway

Oman

Pakistan

Palau

Panama

Papua New Guinea

Paraguay

Peru

Philippines

Poland

Portugal

Puerto Rico

Qatar

Reunion

Romania

Russia

Rwanda

Saint Helena

Saint Kitts and Nevis

Saint Lucia

Saint Pierre and Miquelon

Saint Vincent and the Grenadines

Samoa

San Marino

Sao Tome and Principe

Saudi Arabia

Senegal

Seychelles

Sierra Leone

Singapore

Slovakia

Slovenia

Solomon Islands

Somalia

South Africa

Spain

Sri Lanka

Sudan

Suriname

Swaziland

Sweden

Switzerland

Syria

Taiwan

Tajikistan

Tanzania

Thailand

Togo

Tonga

Trinidad and Tobago

Tunisia

Turkey

Turkmenistan

Turks and Caicos Islands

Tuvalu

Uganda

Ukraine

United Arab Emirates

United Kingdom

United States

Uruguay

Uzbekistan

Vanuatu

Vatican City

Venezuela

Vietnam

Virgin Islands

Wallis and Futuna

Yemen

Zambia

Zimbabwe

EUROPE

0   200   400 Miles

0   200   400 Kilometers

RUSSIA

0   250   500 Miles

0   250   500 Kilometers

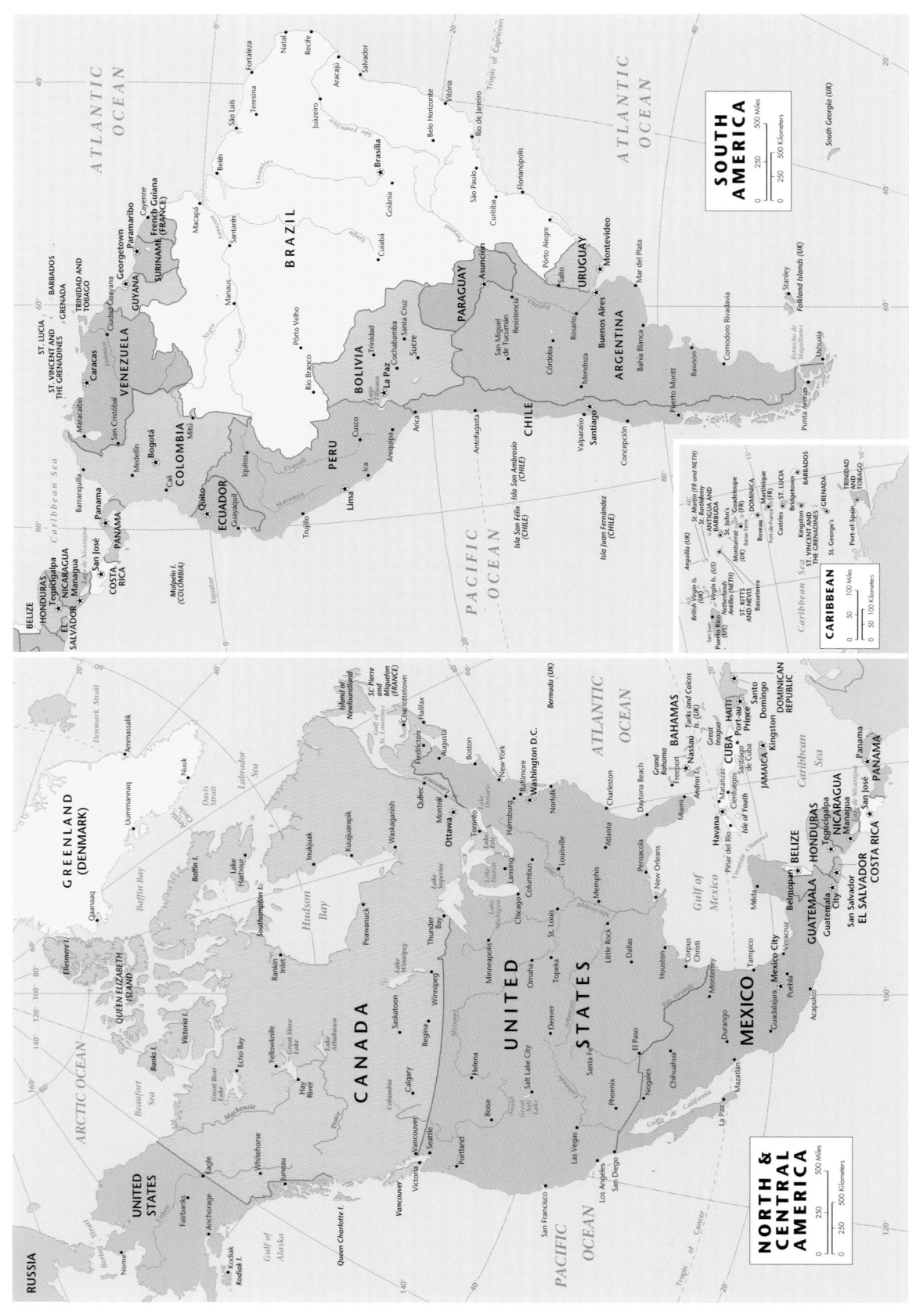

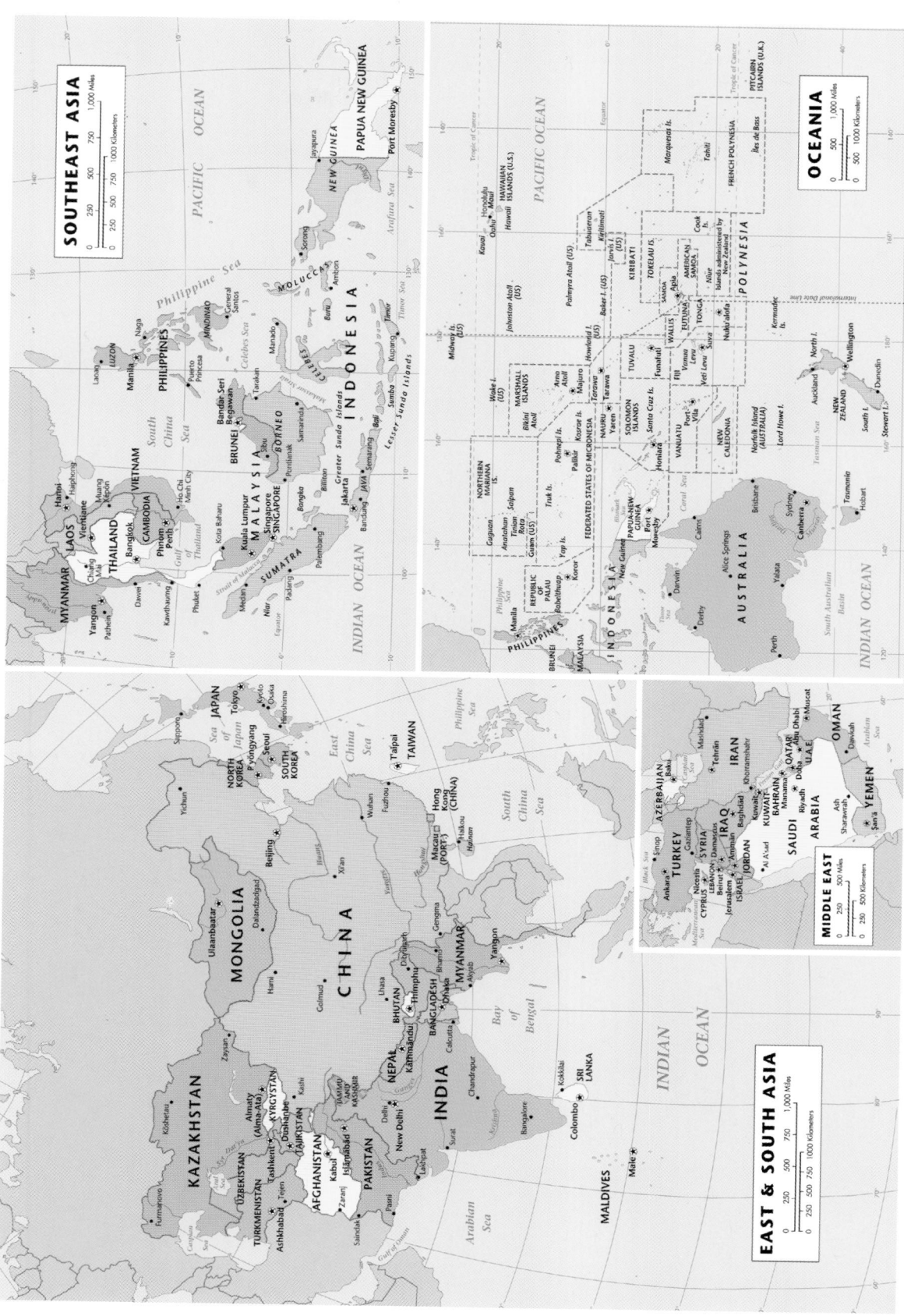

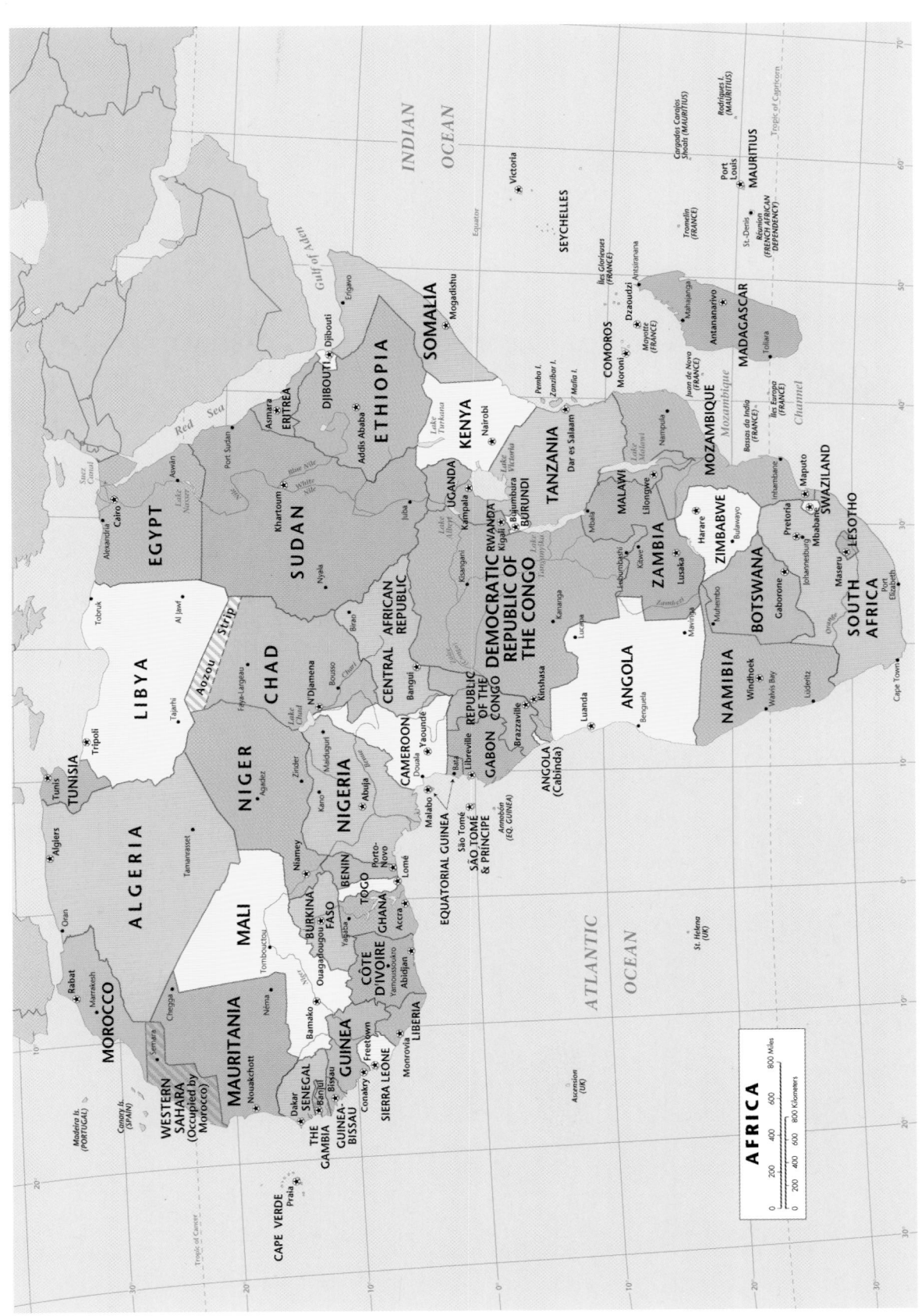

MAYOTTE

INTRODUCTORY SURVEY

RECENT HISTORY

The island of Mayotte experienced several waves of invasion and resettlement in its early history. In the fifteenth century Arab peoples invaded Mayotte converting its inhabitants to Islam.

Over three hundred years later near the end of the eighteenth century a Malagasy tribe from Madagascar invaded and settled on the island. Although visiting Mayotte as early as the sixteenth century, the French did not take colonial control over the island until 1843. The Comoro island group, including Mayotte, other Comoro islands, and Madagascar, became a single French Overseas Territory early in the twentieth century. Reflecting their diverse history, most people of Mayotte are of Malagasy origin and Muslim faith and are strongly influenced by French culture.

In 1975 three of the northernmost islands of the Comoro group voted for independence as the Comoro state. Choosing to remain a French dependency, Mayotte voted against independence. Since the Comoros declared independence, France has administered Mayotte separately as a distinct political entity granting the island a special status of COLLECTIVITE TERRITORIALE (territorial collectivity). Territorial collectivity is thought of as being a status midway between an overseas territory and a French department, the higher status. Mayotte continued to reject proposals from the Comoros for reunification.

In 1979 the French National Assembly extended Mayotte's special status even though the United Nations, at the same time, passed a resolution supporting Comoros' sovereignty over Mayotte. Political pressure from Mayotte for full French departmental status has not been approved by France, and Mayotte, remains a territorial collectivity at the close of the twentieth century.

Under French control Mayotte's relative stability contrasted with severe political and economic upheaval in the Comoros' state. During the 1990s

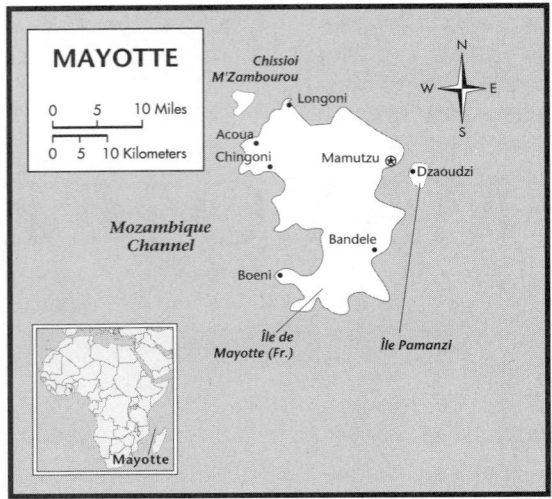

illegal immigration from the Comoros to Mayotte led to persistent racial tension and attacks against Comoran immigrants residing in Mayotte.

Although solidly aligned with France, Mayotte's specific status remains under constant examination by commissions charged with developing a more appropriate status for the twenty-first century. The most severe problem facing Mayotte is a high birth rate resulting in 50% of its population being under the age of fifteen. The population increased by an annual average of 5.7% between 1991 and 1997. Unemployment was 41.2% in 1997 with half of those unemployed under twenty-five years of age.

GOVERNMENT

The chief of state is the President of France. Representing the French government is an appointed prefect. The legislative branch is the unicameral General Council of nineteen members elected by universal adult suffrage including those eighteen years and older. The President of the General Council is elected by its members. Mayotte elects one member to the French Senate, one member to the French National Assembly, and is represented in the European Parliament.

Judiciary

Mayotte's justice system is based on French law and systems. The *Tribunal de Première Instance* and the appeal court, the *Tribunal Supérieur d'Appel*, form the court system.

Political Parties

Political parties include the Mahoran Popular Movement (MPM), Mahoran Rally for the Repub-

lic (RPR), Democratic Front (FD), Association for French Mayotte, Socialist Party (PS), and Union for French Democracy (UDF).

DEFENSE

Defense of Mayotte is the responsibility of France. A small contingent of French troops are stationed on the island. Mayotte has been used as a strategic military base on occasion. A build up French troops occurred in 1989 for possible intervention in the Comoros after the assassination of the Comoran President. Likewise, in late 1990 a French build up began in response to the possibility of French participation in the Persian Gulf War in 1991.

ECONOMIC AFFAIRS

Economic activity is based predominately on the agricultural sector. Principle crops are ylang-ylang, vanilla, coconuts, cinnamon, coffee, and copra. Fishing, livestock raising, and the cultivation of rice, cassava, and corn contribute to domestic needs.

Due to Mayotte's remote location, tourism has failed to develop.

Mayotte must import a large portion of its foodstuffs which accounted for 22% of the total value of imports in 1988. Additional imports include building materials, machinery, and transportation equipment, metals, chemicals, and clothing. France along with Africa and Southeast Asia are Mayotte's suppliers. Exports include vanilla, ylang-ylang, and copra. France is the chief recipient of exports. The Comoros and Réunion also receive Mayotte's exports.

A high trade deficit exists with the value of imports in 1996 reaching $131.5 million and exports $3.64 million. Due to increased international competition and falling prices, exports of ylang-ylang and vanilla significantly decreased in 1997–98. The island is heavily dependent on French financial assistance.

Public Finance

Mayotte depends on extensive French financial assistance. French aid amounted to U.S. $107.7 million in 1995.

In the late 1980s the French government granted financial aid for construction projects in an unsuccessful attempt to develop tourism. Implementation of an Economic Development Plan to improve infrastructure continued from 1986 to

1993. For the period of 1995–99 Mayotte signed an economic and social development plan with France for financial aid to further develop infrastructure.

Income

The gross domestic product (GDP) estimate for 1998 was U.S. $85 million with French supplemental assistance. The GDP per capita by 1998 estimate was U.S. $600. High unemployment, particularly among youth, persists. In 1997 the minimum monthly wage was thirty-nine francs an hour.

Industry

Construction of public buildings and works is the chief industry. A lobster and shrimp industry was created in the late 1990s with production at 1,500 tons in 1997.

Banking and Finance

Currency is the French franc. The Institut d'Émission d'Outre-mer maintains a branch bank in Mamudzou as does the Banque Française Commerciale in Dzaoudzi.

SOCIAL WELFARE

Free medical services are available to the Mayotte population.

Healthcare

Mayotte has two hospitals with a total of one hundred beds. One is located at Dzaoudzi and the other at Mamoudzou. Mayotte is divided into six medical sectors, each with a doctor and medical workers. Malaria, parasitic infections, and tuberculosis are major illnesses.

EDUCATION

Education is compulsory for children from six to sixteen years of age. The education system includes traditional Islamic schools and French primary and secondary schools. Students receive five years of primary and five years of secondary education. In 1997 25,805 pre-primary and primary students were enrolled. Eight secondary schools served 6,190 students. The explosive birth rate of forty-six births per 1,000 population estimated in 1999 kept pressure on the education system to build more schools and hire more teachers. Vocational training is provided on Mayotte and further technical training is available on Réunion.

1999 KEY EVENTS TIMELINE

April

- The Organization for African Unity holds talks in Madagascar aimed at resolving the conflict between neighboring Comoros and its breakaway island, Anjouan. It results in agreement to grant both Anjouan and Moheli, two of the three Comoros Islands, greater autonomy. The agreement sparks confrontations on Grande Comore, targeting people of Anjouan descent.

September

- At least thirteen die when their boat strikes a coral reef and capsizes. The boat is carrying people from Anjouan who are fleeing fighting on Anjouan and seek asylum on Mayotte.

- Mayotte expels thirty people seeking asylum from neighboring Anjouan.

ANALYSIS OF EVENTS: 1999

GOVERNMENT AND POLITICS

Mayotte, an overseas territory of France, is neighbor to the Comoros islands, a former French territory that gained its independence in 1975. Mayotte has attempted to avoid involvement in the burgeoning conflict between the government of Comoros and its rebellious island, Anjouan. (Anjouan declared independence from Comoros in 1997 and wants to return to French rule.) In September two rival factions on Anjouan fought for the right to lead the island's independence movement. Fouad Mohamed Ahmed (known as Kitogno) and his entourage were forced to leave Anjouan. Kitogno and his group of about thirty traveled by boat to neighboring Mayotte, where they sought asylum. Mayotte refused to grant asylum and expelled the group from its borders.

DIRECTORY

CENTRAL GOVERNMENT
Head of State
Conseil General
Office of the Conseil General

PHONE: +269 611233
FAX: +269 611018

Prefect

Philip Boisadam, Office of the Prefecture, BP
20, 97610 Dzaoudzi, Mayotte
PHONE: +269 601054
FAX: +269 601850

Ministers

Minister of Employment

Ministry of Employment, 4, place du Mariage,
97600 Mamoudzou, Mayotte
PHONE: +269 611657
FAX: +269 610337

Minister of Education

Ministry of Education, Rue du College, 97600
Mamoudzou, Mayotte
PHONE: +269 611024
FAX: +269 610987

Minister of Agriculture and Forestry

Ministry of Agriculture and Forestry, 15, rue
Mariaze, 97600 Mamoudzou, Mayotte
PHONE: +269 611213
FAX: +269 611031

Minister of Youth and Sports

Ministry of Youth and Sports, 15, Rue Mariaze,
97600 Mamoudzou, Mayotte
PHONE: +269 611087
FAX: +269 610126

Minister of Sanitary and Social Affairs

Ministry of Sanitary and Social Affairs, 15, rue
Mariaze, 97600 Mamoudzou, Mayotte
PHONE: +269 611225
FAX: +269 601956

POLITICAL ORGANIZATIONS

Association pour Mayotte Francaise (Association for French Mayotte)

NAME: Didier Beoutis

Democratic Front (FD)

NAME: Youssouf Moussa

Mahoran Popular Movement (MPM)

NAME: Younoussa Bamana

Mahoran Rally for the Republic (RPR)

NAME: Mansour Kamardine

Union for French Democracy (UDF)

NAME: Henri Jean-Baptiste

DIPLOMATIC REPRESENTATION

Embassies in Mayotte

None. Territorial collectivity of France.

JUDICIAL SYSTEM

Tribunal Administrator

Les Hauts des Jardeis du College, 97600
Mamoudzou, Mayotte
PHONE: +269 611095
FAX: +269 611856

FURTHER READING

Articles

''Freedom's Follies: Comoros Islands.'' *The Economist* 344 (September 13, 1997): 47.

Internet

''Coral Causes Comoran Boat to Capsize.'' BBC Online, 1 September 1999. Available Online @ http://news2.thls.bbc.co.uk/hi/english/world/africa/newsid%5F435000/435736.stm (December 13, 1999).

''Faction Leader Forced Off Anjouan.'' BBC Online, 7 September 1999. Available Online @ news2.thls.bbc.co.uk/hi/english/world/africa/newsid%5F441000/441071.stm (December 13, 1999).

Hawley, Caroline. ''The Comoros-History of Instability.'' BBC Online, 30 April 1999. Available Online @ news2.thls.bbc.co.uk/hi/english/world/africa/newsid%5F332000/332469.stm (December 13, 1999).

''Thirty Reported Arrested in Anjouan.'' BBC Online, 21 September 1999. Available Online @ news2.thls.bbc.co.uk/hi/english/world/africa/newsid%5F445000/445040.stm (December 13, 1999).

MAYOTTE: STATISTICAL DATA

For sources and notes see "Sources of Statistics" in the front of each volume.

GEOGRAPHY

Geography (1)

Area:

Total: 375 sq km.

Land: 375 sq km.

Water: 0 sq km.

Area—comparative: slightly more than twice the size of Washington, DC.

Land boundaries: 0 km.

Coastline: 185.2 km.

Climate: tropical; marine; hot, humid, rainy season during northeastern monsoon (November to May); dry season is cooler (May to November).

Terrain: generally undulating, with deep ravines and ancient volcanic peaks.

Natural resources: Negl.

Land use:

Arable land: NA%

Permanent crops: NA%

Permanent pastures: NA%

Forests and woodland: NA%

Other: NA%

HUMAN FACTORS

Religions (7)

Muslim 99%; Christian (mostly Roman Catholic).

Languages (8)

Mahorian (a Swahili dialect), French.

Demographics (2A)

	1990	1995	1998	2000	2010	2020	2030	2040	2050
Population	89.7	120.7	141.9	156.9	234.7	321.3	422.5	530.3	640.0
Net migration rate (per 1,000 population)	NA	NA	NA	NA	NA	NA	NA	NA	NA
Births	NA	NA	NA	NA	NA	NA	NA	NA	NA
Deaths	NA	NA	NA	NA	NA	NA	NA	NA	NA
Life expectancy - males	54.0	56.0	57.2	58.0	61.8	65.3	68.3	70.9	73.1
Life expectancy - females	58.1	60.6	62.0	63.0	67.6	71.7	75.1	78.0	80.2
Birth rate (per 1,000)	51.8	49.4	47.0	45.3	39.1	34.6	29.3	24.7	21.3
Death rate (per 1,000)	12.3	10.3	9.2	8.6	6.4	5.3	4.7	4.5	4.5
Women of reproductive age (15-49 yrs.)	19.1	25.8	30.2	33.3	51.8	74.9	105.0	141.3	174.3
of which are currently married	NA	NA	NA	NA	NA	NA	NA	NA	NA
Fertility rate	7.0	6.7	6.5	6.3	5.4	4.4	3.5	2.9	2.5

Except as noted, values for vital statistics are in thousands; life expectancy is in years.

GOVERNMENT & LAW

Political Parties (12)

General Council	No. of seats
Mahoran Popular Movement (MPM) 8	
Mahoran Rally for the Republic (RPR) 5	
Independent candidates 5	
Socialist Party (PS) 1	

Government Budget (13B)

Revenues . . . . .NA

Expenditures . . . .$73 million

   Capital expenditures . . . . .NA

Data for 1991 est. NA stands for not available.

Military Affairs (14A)

Defense is the responsibility of France; small contingent of French forces stationed on the island.

LABOR FORCE

Unemployment Rate (17)

38% (1991 est.)

PRODUCTION SECTOR

Electric Energy (18)

No data available.

Transportation (19)

Highways:

total: 93 km

paved: 72 km

unpaved: 21 km

Merchant marine: none

Airports: 1 (1997 est.)

Airports—with paved runways:

total: 1

914 to 1,523 m: 1 (1997 est.)

Top Agricultural Products (20)

Vanilla, ylang-ylang (perfume essence), coffee, copra.

FINANCE, ECONOMICS, & TRADE

Economic Indicators (22)

National product: GDP—purchasing power parity—$63 million (1997 est.)

National product real growth rate: NA%

National product per capita: $600 (1997 est.)

Inflation rate—consumer price index: NA%

Exchange Rates (24)

Exchange rates:

French francs (F) per US$1

January 1998 . . . . .6.0836	
1997 . . . . .5.8367	
1996 . . . . .5.1155	
1995 . . . . .4.9915	
1994 . . . . .5.5520	
1993 . . . . .5.6632	

Top Import Origins (25)

$131.5 million (f.o.b., 1996)

Origins	%
France 66	
Africa 14	
Southeast Asia 20	

Top Export Destinations (26)

$3.64 million (f.o.b., 1996).

Destinations	%
France 80	
Comoros 15	
Reunion . . . . .NA	

NA stands for not available.

Economic Aid (27)

Recipient: ODA, $NA. Note: extensive French financial assistance. NA stands for not available.

Import Export Commodities (28)

Import Commodities	Export Commodities
Building materials	Ylang-ylang (perfume essence)
Machinery and transportation equipment	Vanilla
Metals	Copra
Chemicals	
Rice	
Clothing	
Flour	

MEXICO

United Mexican States

Estados Unidos Mexicanos

CAPITAL: Mexico City (México).

FLAG: The national flag is a tricolor of green, white, and red vertical stripes; at the center of the white stripe, in brown and green, is an eagle with a snake in its beak, perched on a cactus.

ANTHEM: *Mexicanos, al grito de guerra* (Mexicans, to the Cry of War).

MONETARY UNIT: The peso (P) is a paper currency of 100 centavos. There are coins of 1, 5, 10, 20, 50, 100, 500, 1,000 and 5,000 pesos and notes of 2,000, 5,000, 10,000, 20,000, 50,000 and 100,000 pesos. As of 1 January 1993, a new unit of currency (the new peso) was issued, worth 1,000 of the pesos that were used until 31 December 1992. P1 = $0.12425 (or $1 = P8.048).

WEIGHTS AND MEASURES: The metric system is the legal standard, but some old Spanish units are still in use.

HOLIDAYS: New Year's Day, 1 January; Constitution Day, 5 February; Birthday of Benito Juárez, 21 March; Labor Day, 1 May; Anniversary of the Battle of Puebla (1862), 5 May; Opening of Congress and Presidential Address to the Nation, 1 September; Independence Day, 16 September; Columbus Day, 12 October; Revolution Day (1910), 20 November; Christmas, 25 December. Movable religious holidays include Holy Thursday, Good Friday, and Holy Saturday. All Souls' Day, 2 November, and Our Lady of Guadalupe Day, 12 December, are not statutory holidays but are widely celebrated.

TIME: 6 AM = noon GMT.

LOCATION AND SIZE: Situated south of the United States on the North American continent, Mexico has an area of nearly 2 million square kilometers (762,000 square miles), slightly less than three times the size of the state of Texas. It has a total boundary length of 13,857 kilometers (8,610 miles), including the narrow peninsula of Baja California.

Mexico's capital city, Mexico City, is located in the south-central part of the country.

CLIMATE: The climate varies according to altitude and rainfall from 25–27°C (77–81°F) to 17°C (63°C).

INTRODUCTORY SURVEY

RECENT HISTORY

The years since World War II (1939–45) have been marked by political stability, economic expansion, and the rise of the middle class, but also by general neglect of the poorest segments of the population. An economic boom during the late 1970s, brought about by huge oil export earnings, benefitted only a small percentage of the people. Declining world oil prices in 1981 led to a severe financial crisis in 1982.

Mexico City was devastated by a major earthquake in September 1985. The official death toll was 7,000, although unofficial estimates were as high as 20,000. In addition, 300,000 were left homeless. There was widespread protest over the fact that many of the buildings destroyed had been built in violation of construction regulations, and there were claims that foreign emergency aid had been mishandled by the government.

In August 1992, formal negotiations regarding the North American Free Trade Agreement (NAFTA) were concluded, whereby Mexico would join the United States and Canada in the elimination of trade barriers, the promotion of fair competition, and increased investment opportunities. NAFTA went into effect on 1 January 1994.

In January 1994, a primarily Amerindian group calling itself the Zapatista Army of National Liberation resorted to an armed uprising, initially taking control of four municipalities in the state of Chiapas on the Isthmus of Tehuantepec, to protest

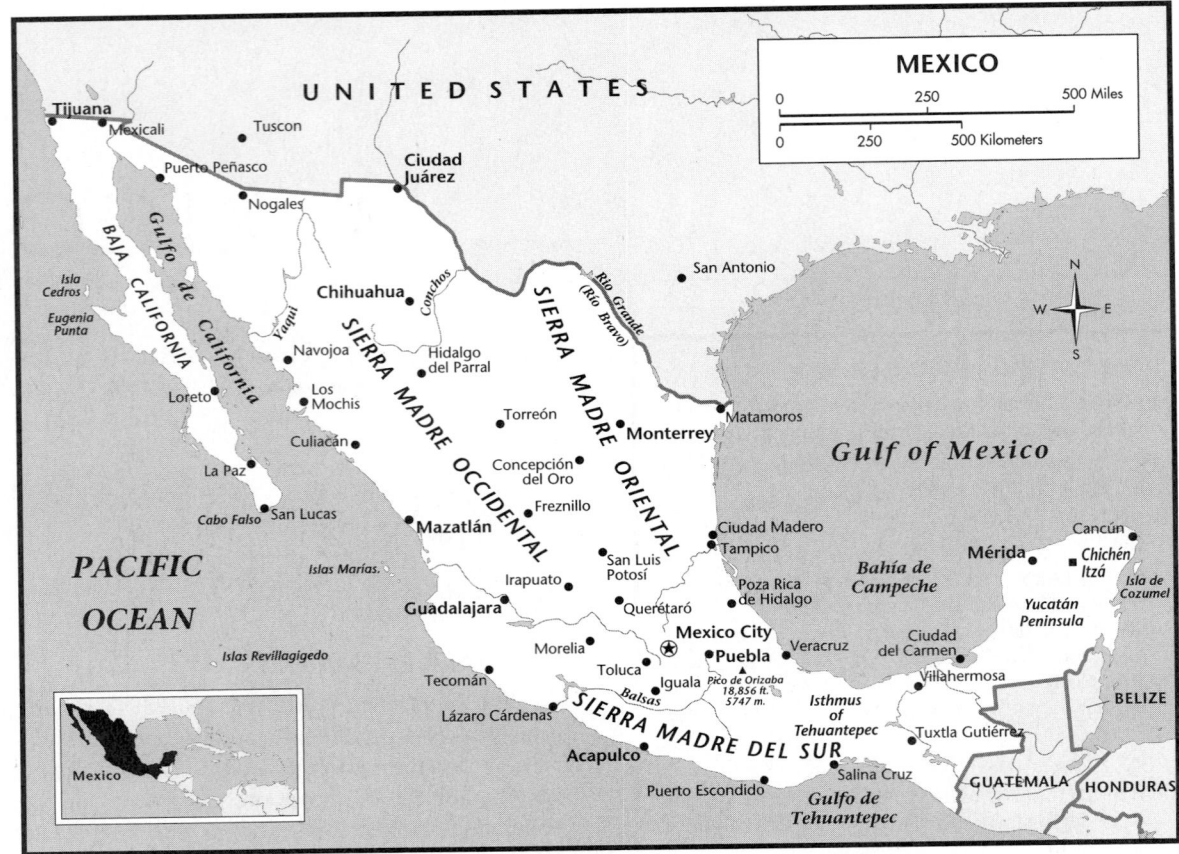

what it regarded as government failure to deal effectively with regional social and economic problems. Two months later, Mexico had its first high-level assassination in over 60 years when PRI presidential candidate Luis Donaldo Colosio was murdered in Tijuana. His replacement, Ernesto Zedillo, was elected at the end of the year in a closely monitored campaign.

In December 1994, the Mexican peso was devalued. The economy went into its worst recession in over 50 years. During the first five months of 1995, over 1 million Mexicans lost their jobs. The United States offered a multimillion-dollar bailout to keep the economy from getting worse.

The public discontent with the economic crisis, poverty, crime, and corruption led to a rejection of the PRI. Until then, the PRI had ruled in Mexico for about 70 years as a virtual one-party system. In June 1997, the PRI lost its majority in the lower house of the National Congress to the combined power of the Party of the Democratic Revolution (PRD) and the National Action Party (PAN).

In January 1998, tens of thousands of Mexicans supporting the Zapatista movement demonstrated in Mexico City against the December 1997 massacre of 45 Indians by pro-government gunmen in Chiapas.

GOVERNMENT

Mexico is a federal republic consisting of 31 states and the Federal District. The president, elected for a six-year term (by universal adult vote beginning at age 18) and not eligible for reelection, appoints the attorney-general and a cabinet, which may vary in number. There is no vice-president. If the president dies or is removed from office, Congress is constitutionally empowered to elect a provisional president.

The two-chamber Congress, also elected by direct universal suffrage, is composed of a Senate (Cámara de Senadores), made up of 128 members (4 from each state and 4 from the Federal District), and a Chamber of Deputies (Cámara de Diputados) made up of 500 members. Senators are elected for six years (half the Senate is elected every three years) and deputies for three years, and both groups are ineligible for immediate reelection.

In an effort to unite various interest groups within the government party, a National Consultative Committee, composed of living ex-presidents of Mexico, was formed in 1961 by President Adolfo López Mateos (1958–64).

Mexico has 2,359 municipalities, which are the principal units of state government.

Judiciary

Federal courts include the Supreme Court, with 21 magistrates; 32 circuit tribunals, and 98 district courts, with 1 judge each.

The jury system is not commonly used in Mexico, but judicial protection is provided by the Writ of Amparo, which allows a person convicted in the court of a local judge to appeal to a federal judge. Low pay and high caseloads increase the possibility of corruption in the judicial system. In 1995, a judicial reform law provided for a competitive examination for selecting most lower court judges.

Political Parties

From 1929 to 1997, the majority party and the only political group to gain national importance was the Institutional Revolutionary Party (Partido Revolucionario Institucional—PRI). The PRI includes only civilians and embraces all shades of political opinion. Three large pressure groups operate within the PRI: labor, the peasantry, and the ''popular'' sector (such as bureaucrats, teachers, and small business people).

In the July 1997 elections, the PRI failed to keep a majority of seats in the 500-member lower house for the first time in nearly 70 years. The Party of Democratic Revolution (PRD) won 125 seats and formed a coalition with the National Action Party (Partido de Acción Nacional—PAN), which won 122 seats. The PRI held 239 seats.

DEFENSE

Total full-time strength of the armed forces was 175,000 in 1995. The army had 130,000 personnel. Regular army units included the presidential guard, 3 infantry brigades, 1 armored brigade, an airborne brigade, and support units. The navy, including naval air force and marines, had 37,000 personnel. The air force had 8,000 personnel and 97 combat aircraft. Paramilitary forces included 14,000 rural defense militia; military reserves numbered 300,000. Defense expenditures in 1995 amounted to $2.7 billion.

Under the required military training program, all 18 year-old males must complete one year of part-time basic army training. In 1995, 60,000 draftees were on active duty, drawn by lottery.

ECONOMIC AFFAIRS

Although Mexico's economy once was mostly agricultural, commerce and industry have long been the nation's chief income earners. A great mining nation, Mexico is the world's leading producer of silver and is well endowed with sulfur, copper, manganese, iron ore, lead, and zinc.

Since 1960 there has been a gradual improvement in social and economic equality, but because of the rapid rate of population increase, many Mexicans still remain in poverty. While peasant wages remained static during the 1960s, industrial wages increased more than 80%, leading to large-scale migration from countryside to city. Mexico City's enormous population growth has been accompanied by mass poverty.

In December 1987, the Pact for Stability and Economic Growth (PECE), a series of price and wage agreements between government, labor, and business, went into effect. The PECE helped curb inflation to 51.6% in 1988 without causing a recession. Gradual recovery has seen the inflation rate fall to 20% in 1991, 11.9% in 1992, and to around 10% in 1993.

The North American Free Trade Agreement (NAFTA), in effect as of 1 January 1994, opened the domestic market to foreign trade by eliminating trade barriers between Mexico, the United States, and Canada over the next 15 years.

Mexico's domestic economy declined by 6.9% in 1995. The problem began with a massive devaluation of the peso in December 1994, which brought on a financial crisis and exposed certain weak spots in the economy. Inflation and interest rates soared, which discouraged foreign investment. The United States provided $20 billion of a $50 billion assistance package, but the Mexican government only used half of that amount for its recovery in 1996.

Public Finance

Major sources of revenue are income taxes, a value-added tax, and public enterprise revenues. Among regular government departments, education receives the largest budget allocation, but outlays for debt service, subsidies to federal enterprises, and capital expenditures for highways, irrigation, and hydroelectric projects have exceeded regular departmental expenditures in recent years. The public-sector deficit usually increases sharply in the last year of a presidential term as the outgoing administration strives to complete its public works program.

During the 1960s, government revenues rose at a faster rate than GDP, with revenues from income taxes (including surcharges) increasing by 170% in the 1960–69 period. Budgets in the 1970s and early and mid-1980s continued to show current-account "surpluses," or minimal apparent deficits; the fact that borrowings and transfers are built into the budget structure masked the true magnitude of annual deficits. In the late 1970s and the early 1980s, real budget deficits increased substantially, reaching nearly 18% of the GDP by 1982. By slashing public spending, the government was able to bring the deficit down to 8.9% of the GDP in 1983 and 7.1% in 1984, but the collapse of the world oil price sent it up to 16.3% in 1986. By the early 1990s, however, public finances were strengthening, and a surplus (on a cash basis) of P35,054 million was recorded in 1992, equivalent to 3.4% of GDP in 1991. Non-recurrent revenues amounted to P30,123 million, mainly derived from the sale of shares of the state-owned telephone company and bank privatization. Excluding privatization revenues, the surplus in 1992 was equivalent to 1.5% of GDP in 1992, as opposed to a deficit of 1.5% in 1991. Public revenues policy in 1992 sought to widen the tax base and simplify and enforce tax administration. At the same time, public expenditures have been reoriented to provide basic infrastructure and services.

The U.S. Central Intelligence Agency estimates that, in 1995, government revenues totaled approximately $56 billion and expenditures $54 billion. External debt totaled $155 billion.

Income

In 1997, Mexico's gross national product (GNP) was $694.3 billion, or about $7,700 per person. For the period 1985–95, the average inflation rate was 36.7%, and the real growth rate in per person GNP was 0.1%.

Industry

Mexico is one of the leading manufacturing nations in Latin America. The principal manufacturing industries include automobile and related parts production, steel, textiles, cement and related construction materials, chemicals and petrochemicals, paper and paper products, food processing, breweries, and glass. In 1995, Mexico produced 935,017 vehicles; the leading manufacturers were Ford, Chrysler, General Motors, and Volkswagen.

Maquiladoras, which are facilities engaged in what is known as re-export processing, play an important role in Mexican manufacturing. Usually located near the United States border and owned by a foreign corporation, maquiladoras assemble or process imported goods brought in from the U.S. and then re-export them duty free. In 1992, there were some 2,042 maquiladora factories employing 494,721 workers.

Banking and Finance

The Bank of Mexico (established 1925), in which the government owns 51% of the capital stock, is also the central bank and bank of issue. Together with the National Banking and Insurance Commission and the National Securities Commission, it supervises commercial, savings, trust, mortgage, capitalization, and investment institutions. National institutions for economic development extend agricultural and long-term industrial credit and finance and develop public works, international trade, cooperatives, and the motion picture industry; they also operate savings accounts. The National Financing Agency (founded in 1934) acts as a financing and investing corporation; it also regulates the Mexican stock market and long-term credits. As of 1995, the money supply was P562,121 million, as measured by M2. Foreign reserves, excluding gold, totaled $16,847 million at the end of 1995.

In September 1982, in order to stop the flight of capital, the government nationalized all 57 private banks; their combined assets were estimated at $48.7 billion. After the inauguration of President de la Madrid in December 1982, it was announced that 34% of the shares of the nationalized banks would be sold to bank workers and users and to federal, state, and municipal agencies. No single shareholder would be allowed to purchase more than 1% of the stock, and the federal government would retain a 66% controlling interest. The government had consolidated the commercial banking system into 19 financial institutions by the end of 1986. In November 1986 the government introduced a plan that would privatize 18 of Mexico's 19 state owned commercial banks. The sale of the banks began in 1987. In 1990 the government began allowing foreigners to buy up to 30% of the state's banks. By July 1992 the banking system was completely private. The only foreign bank permitted to operate within Mexico as of 1993 was Citibank; another 100 foreign banks had representatives in Mexico, however.

The past few years have brought fundamental change to the financial sector. Apart from liberalization of interest rates and credit terms and the elimination of obligatory lending to the public sector, there has been the creation of new financial instruments and institutions. At the end of 1994, there were around 50 commercial banks in operation compared with just 19 two years earlier. The newly privatized commercial banks have had problems almost from the outset. The principal cause has been poor asset quality which has manifested itself in an increasingly serious burden of non-performing loans.

Faced with the prospect of a wholesale banking collapse, the government has come up with a succession of different measures to deal with the problem of bad debts. There has been a scheme to enable bank loans to be rescheduled using index-linked *Unidades de Inversión* (UDIs) and a program of support for bank debtors (*Apoyo a Deudores*, ADE) designed to help as many as eight million people reschedule debts of up to P200,000 (U.S. $26,000). In May 1996, the government announced a further scheme to help mortgage debtors under which it was to assume 30% of monthly payments due during the year, the proportion falling progressively to 5% over 10 years.

Apart from providing relief for debtors, the government has also set up a program to enable banks to meet capital and loan loss provisions (*Programa Temporal de Capitalización Temporal*), as well as a fund (*Fondo Bancario de Protección de Ahorro-Fobaproa*) to take over banks' bad debts in exchange for new capital injections by shareholders. Nevertheless, it has had to step in and take control of a number of institutions.

While needing to shore up the banking sector in order to get the economy going again, the government has also been aware that the financial institutions must apply U.S. General Accounting Principles from the beginning of 1997.

The reserve package is costing the government a considerable sum, equivalent to about $24 billion. However, it has been able to limit the damage by selling off banks in its control, mainly to foreign investors. Foreign investors have also been helping to capitalize banks which have remained in private hands.

There are a number of state development banks, including Nacional Financiera (Nafin, mainly for small and medium-sized businesses), Banco Nacional de Comercio Exterior (Bancomext, foreign trade), Banco Nacional de Obras y Servicios Públicos (Banobras, public works and services), Financiera Azucarera (sugar industry), Banco Nacional de Comercio Interior, and Banco Nacional de Crédito Rural. Nafin and Bancomext are by far the most important.

In mid-March 1997, after two years of preparation, the government introduced measures to curb money laundering. It has been established that anywhere between $4 billion and $30 billion of drug money is laundered in Mexico every year. Starting in 1998, banks, brokerages, and large foreign exchange houses will have to report all cash transactions involving $10,000 or more to the central bank.

The National Securities Commission (founded in 1946) supervises stock transactions. The Stock Exchange of Mexico (Bolsa Mexicana de Valores), the largest stock exchange in Latin America, was organized in its present form in 1933. It lists the stocks of the most important industrial companies, as well as a few mining stocks. Two smaller exchanges at Monterrey and Guadalajara were absorbed in 1976 by the Mexico City exchange. Trading on the exchange increased tenfold between 1976 and 1981, but dropped thereafter with the prolonged recession. It recovered to its 1979 level by 1986 and rose 124% in 1987 despite a spectacular crash in October and November of that year tied to the Wall Street's crash. The greatest part of the trading is in fixed-interest, high-yield bonds and bank deposit paper. Under new rules, which came into force in November 1989, foreigners are allowed to purchase almost any stock through a "neutral" trust, although as of 1997 they still did not have voting rights. In 1992, the market behaved erratically, largely because of sensitivity to the political and economic situation in the U.S. and uncertainty about NAFTA.

In 1996, the recovery in the stock market strengthened as the economy began to pull out of recession, inflation and interest rates fell, and the currency held steady. As confidence grew, so foreign investment flowed back into the market. By mid-year, the total value of foreign investment in the stock exchange was $33.8 billion compared with $27.8 billion at the end of 1995, $34.4 billion at the end of 1994, and \$54.6 billion at the end of 1993.

Economic Development

Modern Mexican economic policy derives in principle from the constitution of 1917, which, in Article 27, proclaims national ownership of subsoil rights, provides for expropriation of property needed for national purposes, and provides for the breaking up of large estates and the establishment of village communal land holdings (ejidos). The property of foreign oil companies was expropriated in 1938, and production, refining, and distribution were placed under the government-controlled PEMEX. The government has also nationalized the railway and banking systems, owns most electric power plants, and partly owns some industrial establishments. Majority Mexican ownership was required in virtually all sectors until early 1984, when restrictions on foreign investment were relaxed somewhat.

The government encourages local industry by giving financial support, customs protection, and tax exemption to approved or new enterprises. The National Financing Agency has supported new industries by purchasing their stock and then re-selling it to the public when the firm is established. The executive branch of government may set ceiling prices on foodstuffs, drugs, and other basic necessities, such as workers' rents.

Major development projects in the 1970s included an attempt to increase agricultural productivity, modernization of the nation's railroads, expansion of the fishing fleet, and resettlement of some 50,000 families from the northern states to the southern states Campeche, Yucatán, and Quintana Roo.

When the exploitation of huge oil deposits began in the mid-1970s, the Mexican government embarked on an expansionist economic policy, which included an ambitious public-spending program financed to a great degree by foreign borrowing. A 17-point development program announced in 1978 created about 3 million new jobs by 1981, but it was not fully implemented because of the drop in world oil prices and the subsequent financial crisis. The crisis reached its climax in August 1982, when the government suspended all payments of foreign debt principal and had to resort to emergency credits to avoid default.

New credits from the IMF were conditional upon Mexico's acceptance of an austerity program that entailed reduction of the budget deficit from 17.9% of the GDP in 1982 to 8.5% in 1983. Other austerity measures included tax increases, increases in the prices of controlled commodities, such as bread and salt, and steps to decrease tax evasion and reduce inflation. The de la Madrid administration simultaneously pursued policies to reduce the inflated value of the peso and to generate massive trade surpluses; indicative of their effectiveness were the 1983 and 1984 surpluses, over \$13 billion in each year. The government, moreover, pursued rescheduling of its foreign debt, winning agreements in 1983 (\$14 billion) and 1986 (\$43.7 billion). In 1985 and 1986, however, the earthquake and the fall in world oil prices undermined the recovery; export revenues plunged, and inflation soared. The 1986 rescheduling was conditional upon Mexico's agreement to increase development of the export sector and encourage efficient import-substitution policies, as well as foreign investment.

Since Mexico joined GATT in 1986, trade barriers have been eliminated and tariffs reduced. Privatizations since 1989 include: the telephone company, Telmex; Mexico's 18 commercial banks; the airlines, Aeromexico and Mexicana; two large copper mines, Cananea and Mexicana de Cobre; and two large steel companies, Sicartsa and AHMSA. Privatizations have produced large one-time revenues for the government, while simultaneously reducing the government's role in the economy thus garnering savings by reducing its transfers to inefficient enterprises. Furthermore, these new profit-making private sector companies have widened the tax base.

The North American Free Trade Agreement (NAFTA), ratified in 1992 and implemented in 1994, culminated several years of trade liberalization efforts begun in 1986. NAFTA's goal is the creation of a market of 360 million consumers with \$6 trillion in annual output. Tariffs on most industrial and agricultural goods will be eliminated or phased out within 15 years. NAFTA trading benefits are only given to goods produced wholly or principally in NAFTA countries. NAFTA also eliminates trade barriers and investment restrictions on participating countries autos, trucks, buses and auto parts within 10 years. NAFTA also proposes to safeguard domestic agricultural production of the dairy, egg, poultry, and sugar sectors. NAFTA also opens up foreign investment possibilities in the Mexican energy sector. NAFTA also has provisions for the textiles and services sectors, banking, investment, and intellectual property rights. Labor and environmental impacts are also addressed.

Mexico has also recently established free trade agreements with Venezuela and Colombia as a member of the Group of Three, and with several other Central American nations. Mexico also signed a free trade agreement with Chile in 1991.

SOCIAL WELFARE

Mexico's social security system includes old age pensions, disability, medical, and work injury benefits. Insured workers receive medical aid in addition to wage benefits, and the insured worker's family receives first-aid treatment. During pregnancy and childbirth and for a period thereafter, insured women receive obstetrical care, nursing aid, a cash subsidy, and a layette. A worker who has been 60% disabled for at least 12 months is eligible for an invalid's pension, and all residents are eligible for old age pensions at age 60.

Government employees are covered by the Security and Social Services Institute for Civil Workers. Programs for children, including a primary-school breakfast program, are overseen by the National Institute for Child Protection. The Mexican Institution for Child Welfare provides care for neglected, abandoned, or sick children.

Women have held top political and union leadership roles, have the right to file for separation or divorce, and the right to own property in their own name. Domestic violence, however, remains a problem.

Indigenous peoples have full protection under the law, but in practice they face discrimination.

Healthcare

Mexico has made slow but measurable progress in public health. Average life expectancy rose from 32.4 years in 1930 to 57.6 in 1965; by 1995, it was estimated at 72 years. Cholera, yellow fever, plague, and smallpox have been virtually eliminated, and typhus has been controlled. Permanent campaigns are waged against malaria, poliomyelitis, skin diseases, tuberculosis, leprosy, onchocercosis, and serious childhood diseases. In 1990–95, 83% of the population had access to safe water, and 50% had adequate sanitation.

In 1993, there was one doctor for every 615 people, and one hospital bed per 1,704 people. That

year, 91% of the population had access to health care services.

Housing

Mexico's housing shortage was worsened by high population growth in the 1980s. The government allocated $1.93 billion in 1989 to build 250,000 low-cost housing units, and expected to receive an additional $700 million from the World Bank to build more. The 1990 National Housing Plan predicted a shortage of 6.1 million homes, to be felt most severely in the outskirts of urban areas, including Mexico City, Guadalajara, Monterey, and cities in the northern states. In 1992, Mexico had 15.1 million dwellings, of which 49.9% had piped water, 51% had flush toilets, and 87.5% had electric lighting.

EDUCATION

A government literacy program helped reduce Mexico's adult illiteracy rate from 37.8% in 1960 to an average of about 10% in 1995 (males: 8.2% and females: 12.6%).

Primary schooling is compulsory and free. In 1995, Mexico had 507,669 teachers and 14.6 million students at the primary level. At the secondary level, there were 448,407 teachers and 7.3 million students.

Major universities include the National Autonomous University (founded in 1551), the National Polytechnic Institute, and Iberoamericana University (private), all in Mexico City. There were 145,789 teachers and 1.4 million students in all higher level institutions in 1993.

The government provides adult education through cultural and motorized missions, community development brigades, reading rooms, and special centers for workers' training, art education, social work, and primary education.

1999 KEY EVENTS TIMELINE

January

- The after effects of the 1998 global economic crisis: Mexico's Central Bank predicts stability in 1999.

- Pope John Paul II delivers outdoor Mass to more than 1 million Mexicans. It is his fourth visit since 1979.

- Human Rights abuses: The New York-based group Human Rights Watch charges that Mexico's police and military kidnap, torture and kill people. Prosecutors and judges routinely use illegally obtained evidence, the group claims.

- Raúl Salinas de Gortari, the multimillionaire brother of former President Carlos Salinas de Gortari, is convicted of planning assassination. Sentenced to 50 years in prison, he planned to appeal.

February

- President Bill Clinton says Mexico should not be penalized for its performance against illegal drugs.

- Film director Hector Alejandro Galindo, known for his movies about the underworld, dies. He was 92

- Mexican President Ernesto Zedillo warns the growing nation soon will overwhelm the state-run power plants. He urges privatization.

- Mexican authorities announce they will spend up to $500 million in a total war against drug trafficking in the next three years.

March

- National Autonomous University of Mexico (UNAM), the nation's largest university, raises registration fees for the first time since 1948: from 2 cents to 68 dollars per semester.

- Mexican authorities say Mexico has reached 98.1 million people, and will surpass the 100 million mark before the end of 1999.

- Celebrated poet Jaime Sabines dies of Cancer. He was 72.

- The PRI celebrates 70 years in power.

April

- Political reforms: the governing Institutional Revolutionary Party (PRI) approves the first national presidential primary. In the past, PRI candidates were selected by their successors.

June

- Top Mexico and U.S. officials meet in Mexico to discuss bilateral problems. Attorney General Janet Reno attends.

- Thousands march in the streets of Mexico City to protest against a student strike and takeover of the UNAM campus. The university has been closed for 65 days.

- Mexico's most vilified former President returns from self-exile. Carlos Salinas de Gortari left the country in 1995.

July

- The Institutional Revolutionary Party (PRI) captures the governor's post in the state of Mexico, the nation's most populated state. The PRI loses the governorship in Nayarit.

- A Mexican biologist says the country's national symbol, the golden eagle, is endangered. The eagle adorns the national flag.

- Mexican television curtails violent shows. The gritty tabloid-type show "Tough and Direct" ceases broadcasting after an appeal from President Ernesto Zedillo.

- The International Monetary Fund approves $4.12 billion loan for Mexico.

- Archeologists announce the discovery of the tomb of an ancient Mayan ruler.

- Inscriptions are expected to provide new information about Maya society in southeastern Mexico.

August

- Nation's second largest television station, Azteca, announces it will begin airing "The Candidate," a soap opera that focuses on a presidential campaign laced with infidelity, crime, and betrayal. Real Presidential elections will take place in 2000.

- Presidential election campaign kickoff: the government offers federal police officers as bodyguards to all presidential candidates. They refuse.

- $30 million settlement: insurers for American clothing company agree to compensate the families of Mexican workers killed and injured in bus accident.

- Alberto Gironella, leading Mexican surrealist painter, dies after a long illness. He was 70

September

- The government announces the arrest of eight federal police officers on charges of kidnapping and extortion.

- Cuauhtemoc Cardenas, first elected mayor of Mexico City, resigns to seek the presidency in 2000.

- Oil revenues rise, but Mexico does not plan to go on a spending spree.

- A 7.5-magnitude earthquake rattles southern Mexico. More than 20 people are reported dead, and thousands of buildings are damaged in the state of Oaxaca. Mexico City shakes, but damages are minimal.

- Dengue fever crosses Mexican border into Texas. Authorities confirm 11 cases since June. Several hundred cases are confirmed in Mexico.

- Huge explosion in Celaya kills 56 people. Fireworks are blamed.

- Rosario Robles Berlanga becomes the first woman mayor of Mexico City.

October

- Torrential rains displace more than 300,000 people. At least 600 may have died as a dozen states declare a state of emergency to deal with the catastrophe.

November

- Former interior minister Francisco Labastida sweeps the primary elections to become the presidential candidate of Mexico's governing party with a margin of victory that puts him in a position to win elections next year.

- Mexico's Congress releases a long-awaited list of names of prominent bankers who allegedly conducted illegal transactions during a costly banking crisis.

- Trade officials from Mexico and the European Union sign a preliminary free trade agreement, the first between Europe and a Latin American country.

December

- A new plan requires motorists driving vehicles with foreign registrations to post deposits of up to $800 when entereing Mexico. A U.S. boycott of Mexican products such as tequila and Corona beer is organized by Mexican groups, contributing to the government's decision to suspend the deposit requirement after only two days.

ANALYSIS OF EVENTS: 1999

BUSINESS AND THE ECONOMY

On January 1, the price of corn tortillas—a basic staple—rose to 3.50 pesos per kilo, compared with 1.90 pesos a year ago. Mexico's poor have seen subsidies for staples disappear one by one, even as minimum salaries continued to go down, to about 35 pesos ($3.55) per day. While the government attempted to curb poverty with other programs, tightening belts seemed to be the order of the day in 1999. University students didn't fare any better. The nation's largest university, UNAM, raised its fees from the equivalent of 2 cents U.S. to U.S. $68 per semester. Striking students took over the campus and shut it down.

The best news for Mexico came from the Central Bank, which predicted stability would follow the 1998 global economic crisis. Despite the forecast, Mexico asked the International Monetary Fund for a $4.2 billion standby credit. By mid-year, Mexico was eligible to borrow up to $24 billion over the next 18 months. And they may have to borrow at least some of it. A 7.5-magnitude earthquake in Oaxaca in late September, and severe floods in southern Mexico states in early October killed many people, and destroyed thousands of buildings.

In the past five years, the Mexican government has aggressively dismantled its trade barriers with the Latin American market, bolstering its own economy while hindering Clinton administration efforts to create a hemisphere-wide trading bloc, The Los Angeles Times reported in October. Mexico has used its NAFTA influence to sign similar free trade agreements with Chile, Venezuela, Colombia, Bolivia, Costa Rica and Nicaragua.

Mexico, the report goes on to say, was ready to strike agreements with eight more Latin American countries, and was negotiating a free-trade agreement with the 15-nation European Community. The Mexicans were also negotiating with Japan, South Korea, China and Israel.

The agreement has placed Mexico in a favorable position, but it could hurt United States' efforts to create a 34-nation Free Trade Area of the Americas, the article said. Mexico has quickly become a hub for domestic and international companies that want to export their products in the Americas. Even some U.S. automakers, and telecommunications companies have expanded their operations in Mexico to take advantage of its tariff-free access to other Latin American countries. With the loss of its "fast-track" negotiating authority, The United States may fall farther behind.

"Mexico has been one of—if not the most—successful countries in the world at eliminating impediments to their exports," a senior U.S. trade official told *The Los Angeles Times*. "Meanwhile, it is the only country in Latin America with duty-free access to the biggest market, the United States, and it has little motive to see that advantage whittled away by a regional trade pact. They are improving their commercial prospects in Latin America, potentially at our expense."

CULTURE AND SOCIETY

In March, Mexico announced its population had grown to 98.1 million, and that the country was expected to have more than 100 million citizens by the end of 1999. Mexicans took the official announcement with aplomb. After all, it appeared to be a victory for population control. If birth rates had not decreased over past years, Mexico would have been facing a population of well over 140 million before the end of the century.

So it wasn't more mouths to feed that worried the nation. News in August that presidential candidates refused to accept bodyguards from the government only confirmed what most Mexicans already knew. When it comes to cops and robbers, it is a lot easier to distrust the cops.

Mexico entered 1999 facing an unprecedented crime wave. In Mexico City alone, crime had grown by nearly 60 percent between 1994 and 1997. By 1999, despite enormous efforts to stop criminals, including rogue police officers who made money on the side with kidnappings and extortion, the city had barely made a dent in the crime statistics.

By mid-1999, though, the numbers had taken a slight dip, almost enough for Cuauhtemoc Cardenas, the city's first elected mayor, to declare a partial victory. Reception of the news was lukewarm at best.

As Mexico City goes, so goes the nation. And convincing Mexicans that something is being done about crime is not getting any easier. In polls, crime remains the top priority, and an embarrassing and

economically damaging fact for Mexico, which is the seventh most visited country in the world. Nineteen million foreign tourists were expected to visit in 1999. Mexicans are so tired of crime that powerful television stations came under fire for some of their most graphic and violent tabloid-type shows. One of the worst offenders agreed to end programming after an appeal by President Ernesto Zedillo. Some news broadcasts have switched to black and white images to blunt the power of horrendous crime scenes.

Mexico's image was badly bruised in January, when the New York-based Human Rights Watch group accused Mexican police officers and soldiers of kidnappings, torture, and murder. The judiciary didn't fare any better. The group claimed judges routinely used illegal evidence against defendants. The international repercussions didn't end there. To keep the United States from getting too nervous, Mexican officials promised to spend up to $500 million in the next three years to combat illicit drugs. That, and a few key arrests of suspected drug traffickers, was enough for U.S. president Bill Clinton to say Mexico should not be penalized for its performance. At least for 1999, Mexico would not be subjected to the much-hated "decertifying" process, which carries stiff economic penalties for countries that are deemed as not doing enough to fight illegal drugs.

Mexico's importance reaches beyond the border, which is why Pope John Paul II came calling in January for the fourth time since 1979. While Mexico is overwhelmingly Catholic, the government and the Vatican have a troubled history. Diplomatic relations were only established in 1992, and the Pope has not been shy about criticizing the government for its reluctance to dedicate more resources to help indigenous people, among the poorest in the nation. Mexico has been accused of insensitivity to its native people before, even though the nation has been quick to point to its rich cultural diversity to boost the tourism industry. But landing on postcards, brochures and tourism posters is not enough. With Chiapas leading the way, Mexico's indigenous peoples continued to press the government for more rights in 1999. Attention also came from other quarters. Archaeologists announced the discovery of a tomb of a Maya ruler and well-preserved inscriptions that were expected to provide new information about Indian societies of southeastern Mexico. And a major Maya art exhibit in Venice, with important artifacts from Mexico,

Belize, Guatemala and Honduras, was expected to welcome more than 1 million visitors.

Torrential rains in southeastern Mexico in October inundated 175 towns and cities in 12 states, displaced more than 300,000 people and may have killed as many as 600. It was one of the worst natural disasters to hit Mexico in several decades. Dozens of bridges and roads were closed and the government was blamed for contributing to the magnitude of the disaster. Critics said corruption, poor planning, and neglect made things worse to people affected by the disaster. The mountain town of Teziutlan became so frustrated at the lack of help that it created its own web page on the Internet to appeal for help. In another location, Mexican police roughed up and arrested several homeless survivors after their protests became violent. President Zedillo, who visited several of the affected areas, was forced to shout to defend himself against irate citizens. In the meantime, the opposition took the opportunity to criticize the government as well.

GOVERNMENT AND POLITICS

Mexicans showed little enthusiasm when Cuauhtemoc Cardenas quit his job as mayor of Mexico City in late September and announced his candidacy for the presidency in 2000. In a city where air pollution sends hundreds of thousands of people to hospitals each year, the city's first elected mayor had managed to clear up the air a bit, but not his political future.

His 1997 triumph, and victories by his left-of-center Party of the Democratic Revolution (PRD) and the right-wing National Action Party (PAN) dealt a historic blow to the ruling Institutional Revolutionary Party (PRI). The mighty PRI not only lost Mexico City that year, but saw its majority in the lower house of Congress vanish for the first time in more than six decades.

But Mexico City proved resistant to change, and Cardenas couldn't deliver on his campaign promises. A mangled bureaucracy and a defiant PRI stood in his way, and after 21 months in office, the luster was gone. So were many of his supporters. By the time of his announcement, most polls placed Cardenas in third place in the presidential race, behind the PRI and the PAN.

During Cardenas' tenure in Mexico City, the PRI was busy reinventing itself nationwide. Party leaders wanted to prove wrong all those who had predicted their demise by doing what many critics

said they could not do: create a more democratic institution.

In March, President Zedillo marked the 70th anniversary of the PRI by breaking with tradition. Within the authoritarian regime of the PRI, Mexican presidents personally picked their successors. But Zedillo said there would be no "dedazo" (roughly pointing a presidential finger at the new candidate) this time around. The dedazo would be replaced by a presidential primary election.

In a preview of things to come, the PRI on July 4th won the governor's seat in the state of Mexico, the country's largest with approximately 13 million people. The state, which surrounds Mexico City on three sides, is often seen as a political testing ground. Their victory, with 41 percent of the vote, gave the PRI hope for the presidential election. PAN remained close with 35 percent, and a weakened PRD followed with 21 percent. Some analysts believe those numbers will be the same in 2000.

The PRI is taking no chances. It lost the governor's race in the state of Nayarit despite capturing 43 percent of the vote after the PRD and the PAN banded together behind a single candidate, a former PRI member. Despite the rhetoric, the PRI remained vulnerable and far from being the institutional evolutionary party, as The Economist called it in a March 13th article. Political conflicts have forced many party loyalists to defect to the two other parties, with at least four recent elections won by defectors.

Many observers believe the PAN and the PRD will have to rally behind a single candidate to break up the PRI's monopoly on the presidency. While they have toyed with the idea, both sides have dismissed a united front. For one, the Panistas are conservative and favor a free-market economy. And they firmly believe in their candidate, the charismatic Vicente Fox.

This is Cardenas' third try at the presidency. Electoral fraud may have killed his bid in 1988, and a weak campaign certainly killed his chances in 1994. Now, with a less than stellar performance as mayor of the country's biggest city, he faces strong opponents. Yet, Cardenas, 65, and son of one of Mexico's most enduring former presidents, remains undeterred.

Campaign intrigue was not the only topic in 1999, a year when the nation's second largest television station, Azteca, began airing "The Candidate," a soap opera about a presidential campaign plagued by crime and betrayal, among other juicy plot lines. Television executives claimed there was absolutely no connection with reality. Yet, fresh in Mexico's memory are the 1994 assassinations of presidential candidate Luis Donaldo Colosio, who was shot in the border town of Tijuana, and Jose Francisco Ruiz Massieu, the PRI's secretary general, who was gunned down in Mexico City. The murders spun the nation into a deep political crisis.

In January, Raul Salinas de Gortari, the multimillionaire brother of former President Carlos Salinas de Gortari, was sentenced to 50 years for planning the murder of Ruiz Massieu, his brother-in-law. The verdict shocked Mexicans unaccustomed to seeing any member of the elite accountable for anything. In September, Mario Ruiz Massieu, Jose Francisco's brother and former top drug prosecutor, died from an apparent suicide in New Jersey. Mario Ruiz Massieu had been accused of money laundering and protecting drug traffickers by Mexican authorities and was being held in the United States. In a suicide note, Ruiz blamed President Zedillo and his administration for driving him to his death, charges that were rejected by the presidency.

"This struggle for power, this level of corruption has the makings of a Shakespearean tragedy," historian and political commentator Lorenzo Meyer told the media after Mario Ruiz Massieu's death. "No one knows exactly who killed the first Ruiz Massieu (Jose Francisco), nor Colosio. No one will be able to untangle this series of killings."

When President Zedillo visited Chiapas in March to inaugurate a hospital, it marked his 12th visit to the state in one year. The number of visits underscored the importance of Chiapas to the government, which has been mired in conflict with the Zapatista rebels since January 1994. The conflict has not been good for Mexico or its relations with other countries sympathetic to the Zapatista cause. In January, Canada urged Mexico to restart the peace process in Chiapas, but the government has been slow to respond. Finally in September, government officials said they were willing to meet with rebel leader Subcommander Marcos in a bid to renew the peace talks that broke off in 1996.

In an open letter sent to the Zapatista National Liberation Army (EZLN), Interior Minister Diodoro Carrasco proposed freeing jailed rebels and creating a new body to mediate peace talks. Critics said calls for talks were politically motivated. The government, they said, was trying to cool tensions before presidential elections. In August, the government cancelled plans to build a road through the Zapatista-controlled highlands of Chiapas following two weeks of confrontations between rebel sympathizers and troops. The government also released three rebel supporters arrested after a scuffle with an army patrol. In other developments, resentment against foreigners, and even Mexican nationals from outside Chiapas, has grown. In past years, the Zapatistas welcomed foreigners as a shield against the government. But dozens have been deported, and many Chiapans now resent their presence. They were hurting tourism, and negotiations with the government. Several towns in Chiapas during 1999 held marches to tell their helpers to get out.

DIRECTORY

CENTRAL GOVERNMENT
Head of State

President
Ernesto Zedillo Ponce de León, Office of the President, Puerta Centrale Premiere Piso, Col. San Miguel, Chapultepec, 11850 Mexico City, DF, Mexico
PHONE: +52 (5) 5157994
FAX: +52 (5) 5165762

Cabinet

Secretary of Agrarian Reform
Arturo Warman Gryj, Department of Agrarian Reform, Rio Sena No. 49, Col. Cuauhtemoc, 06500 México City, DF, Mexico
PHONE: +52 (5) 5257580

Secretary of Agriculture, Livestock, and Rural Development
Romarico Arroyo Marroquin, Department of Agriculture, Livestock, and Rural Development

Secretary of Commerce and Industrial Development
Herminio Blanco Mendoza, Department of Commerce and Industrial Development

Secretary of Communications and Transport
Carlos Ruiz Sacristan, Department of Communications and Transport, Xola Y Avenida Universidad, Cuerpo C, Piso 1 Col., Navarte, Del. Benito Juarez, 03028 Mexico City, DF, Mexico

PHONE: +52 (5) 5309203
FAX: +52 (5) 5190692

Secretary of Comptroller General and Administrative Development
Arsenio Farell Cubillas, Department of the Comptroller General and Administrative Development, Insurgentes sur 1735, Col. Guadalupe Inn, 01020 México City, DF, Mexico
PHONE: +52 (5) 6633636

Secretary of Education
Miguel Limon Rojas, Department of Education

Secretary of Energy
Luis Tellez Kuenzler, Department of Energy, Insurgentes Sur 890, Col. Del Valle, 03100 México City, DF, México
PHONE: +52 (5) 4486000
E-MAIL: energia1@energia.gob.mx

Secretary of Environment, Natural Resources, and Fisheries
Julia Carabias Lillo, Department of the Environment, Natural Resources, and Fisheries, Periférico Sur 4209, Fraccionamiento Jardines en la Montaña, Delegación Tlalpan, 14210 México City, DF, Mexico
PHONE: +52 (5) 6280600

Secretary of Finance and Public Credit
Jose Angel Gurria Trevino, Department of Finance and Public Credit

Secretary of Foreign Relations
Rosario Green, Department of Foreign Relations

Secretary of Government
Francisco Labastida Ochoa, Department of Government

Secretary of Health
Juan Ramon De La Fuente Ramirez, Department of Health, Lieja, 7-1er Piso, Col. Juárez, 06696 Mexico City, DF, Mexico
PHONE: +52 (5) 5536967
FAX: +52 (5) 5537917
E-MAIL: ssa@ssa.gob.mx

Secretary of Labor and Social Welfare
Jose Antonio Gonzalez Fernandez, Department of Labor and Social Welfare

Secretary of National Defense
Enrique Cervantes Aguirre, Department of National Defense

Secretary of the Navy
Jose Ramon Lorenzo Franco, Office of the Navy

Secretary of Social Development
Carlos M. Jarque, Department of Social Development, Av. Constituyentes 947, Edif. B, P.A., Col. Belén de las Flores, Del. Alvaro Obregón, 01110 México City, DF, Mexico
PHONE: +52 (5) 2718481
FAX: +52 (5) 2718862

Secretary of Tourism
Oscar Espinosa Villarreal, Department of Tourism

POLITICAL ORGANIZATIONS
Zapatista Front of National Liberation
Calle Zapotecos 7 bis, Colonia Obrera, Del. Cuauhtmoc, 06800 Mexico City, DF, Mexico
PHONE: +52 (5) 7614236
FAX: +52 (5) 7614236
E-MAIL: floresu@spin.com.mx

Partido Accion Nacional (National Action Party)
Angel Urraza 812, Del Valle, 03109 Mexico City, DF, Mexico
PHONE: +52 (5) 5596300
FAX: +52 (5) 5590975
E-MAIL: relaciones@cen.pan.org.mx
TITLE: Presidente Nacional
NAME: Luis Felipe Bravo Mena

Partido de la Revolucion Democratica (Democratic Revolutionary Party)
Monterrey 50, PB, Col. Roma, 06700 Mexico City, DF, Mexico
PHONE: +52 (5) 5256059
FAX: +52 (5) 2087863
TITLE: Presidente Nacional
NAME: Pablo Gomez Alvarez

Partido de la Revolucionario Institucional (Institutional Revolutionary Party)
NAME: Santiago Onate Laborde

Partido de Trabajo-PT (Worker's Party)
Av. Cuauhtemoc 47, Col. Roma, 06700 Mexico City, DF, Mexico
PHONE: +52 (5) 2074441
FAX: +52 (5) 5252727
E-MAIL: pt@pt.org.mx
TITLE: Dirigente Nacional
NAME: Alberto Anaya Gutirrez

Partido Verde Ecologista de Mexico (Green Ecological Party of Mexico)

Medicina 74 Col., Copilco Universidad, 04360 Mexico City, DF, Mexico
PHONE: +52 (5) 6598272
E-MAIL: pvem@pvem.org.mx
TITLE: Presidente Nacional
NAME: Jorge Gonz lez Torres

DIPLOMATIC REPRESENTATION
Embassies in Mexico

Angola
Schiller 503 Col. Polanco, 11560 México City, DF, Mexico
PHONE: +52 (5) 5455883
FAX: +52 (5) 5452733
E-MAIL: info@palanca-negra.org

Canada
Calle Schiller 529, Colonia Rincon Del Bosque, Polanco, 11560 Mexico City, DF, Mexico
PHONE: +52 (5) 7247900
FAX: +52 (5) 7247982
TITLE: Ambassador
NAME: Stanley Gooch

France
Campos Elíseos 339, Col. Polanco, 11560 Mexico City, DF, Mexico
PHONE: +52 (5) 2829700
FAX: +52 (5) 2829703
TITLE: Ambassador
NAME: Bruno Delaye

Italy
Paseo de las Palmas 1994, Col. Lomas de Chapultepec, 11000 México City, DF, Mexico
PHONE: +52 (5) 5963655
FAX: +52 (5) 5967710
E-MAIL: embitaly@data.net.mx

Japan
Domicillio Del Centro Cultural, Paseo de law Reforma 295, Piso 3, Col Cuauhtemoc, 06500 Mexico City, DF, Mexico
PHONE: +52 (5) 5144507

United Kingdom
Col. Cuauhtémoc, 06500 México City, DF, Mexico
PHONE: +52 (5) 2072089
FAX: +52 (5) 2077672
TITLE: Ambassador

NAME: Adrian Charles Thorpe

United States
Paseo de la Reforma 305, Col. Cuauhtémoc, 06500 Mexico City, DF, Mexico
PHONE: +52 (5) 2099100
FAX: +52 (5) 5119980
E-MAIL: ccs@usembassy.net.mx

JUDICIAL SYSTEM
Supreme Court

Pino Suárez No. 2, Col. Centro, 06065 México City, DF, México

FURTHER READING
Articles

"Bank Bailout will Cost More Than $100 Billion." The Associated Press, 31 August 1999.

"Dengue Fever Crosses Mexican Border into Texas." *The Dallas Morning News*, 29 September 1999.

"A Discredited President Returns to Mexico." *The New York Times*, 13 June 1999.

"A Greener, or Browner, Mexico?" *The Economist* (August 7, 1999): 26.

"Key Player in Mexico's Power Politics Dies in U.S." *The Seattle Times*, 16 September 1999.

"IMF Approves Loan Package." The Associated Press, 7 July 1999.

"The Institutional Evolutionary Party." *The Economist* (March 13, 1999): 45.

"Let Them Eat Hamburgers." *The Economist* (January 9, 1999): 32.

"Lusty New Papers Take On the Powerful in Mexico." *The New York Times*, 3 January 1999.

"Mexican Candidates Balk at Bodyguards." *The Washington Post*, 10 August 1999.

"Mexican TV Curbs Graphic Crime Programs." *Los Angeles Times*, 12 July 1999.

"Mexico: The History Man." *The Economist* (September 25, 1999): 38.

"Mexico: Voting Lesson." *The Economist* (July 10, 1999): 33.

"Mexico's Central Bank Is Optimistic on Economy." *The New York Times*, 27 January 1999.

"The New Rules of Latin America's Political Game." *The Economist* (May 22, 1999): 35.

''A Primary Experience for Mexico's PRI.'' *The Economist* (August 21, 1999): 27.

''Uncle Sam's War on Drugs.'' *The Economist* (February 20, 1999): 33.

''Under the Hood: Guerrilla Movements in Mexico.'' *The Economist* (March 27, 1999): 37.

MEXICO: STATISTICAL DATA

For sources and notes see "Sources of Statistics" in the front of each volume.

GEOGRAPHY

Geography (1)

Area:

Total: 1,972,550 sq km.

Land: 1,923,040 sq km.

Water: 49,510 sq km.

Area—comparative: slightly less than three times the size of Texas.

Land boundaries:

Total: 4,538 km.

Border countries: Belize 250 km, Guatemala 962 km, US 3,326 km.

Coastline: 9,330 km.

Climate: varies from tropical to desert.

Terrain: high, rugged mountains, low coastal plains, high plateaus, and desert.

Natural resources: petroleum, silver, copper, gold, lead, zinc, natural gas, timber.

Land use:

Arable land: 12%

Permanent crops: 1%

Permanent pastures: 39%

Forests and woodland: 26%

Other: 22% (1993 est.).

HUMAN FACTORS

Demographics (2A)

	1990	1995	1998	2000	2010	2020	2030	2040	2050
Population	84,748.2	93,324.5	98,552.8	102,026.7	118,828.5	134,387.3	148,261.4	159,472.4	167,479.5
Net migration rate (per 1,000 population)	NA	NA	NA	NA	NA	NA	NA	NA	NA
Births	NA	NA	NA	NA	NA	NA	NA	NA	NA
Deaths	422.8	NA	NA	NA	NA	NA	NA	NA	NA
Life expectancy - males	65.6	67.6	68.6	69.3	72.4	74.7	76.5	77.8	78.8
Life expectancy - females	71.5	73.7	74.8	75.6	78.7	81.1	82.9	84.1	85.0
Birth rate (per 1,000)	29.1	26.8	25.5	24.5	20.3	17.6	15.6	14.0	13.1
Death rate (per 1,000)	5.9	5.2	4.9	4.8	4.5	4.8	5.6	6.7	8.3
Women of reproductive age (15-49 yrs.)	21,545.7	24,539.9	26,275.9	27,378.3	32,486.4	35,928.1	37,426.6	38,076.5	37,757.2
of which are currently married	10,410.3	NA	NA	NA	NA	NA	NA	NA	NA
Fertility rate	3.5	3.1	2.9	2.8	2.4	2.2	2.1	2.0	2.0

Except as noted, values for vital statistics are in thousands; life expectancy is in years.

Health Personnel (3)

Total health expenditure as a percentage of GDP,
1990-1997[a]

Public sector 2.8

Private sector 1.9

Total[b] 4.7

Health expenditure per capita in U.S. dollars,
1990-1997[a]

Purchasing power parity 361

Total 200

Availability of health care facilities per 100,000 people

Hospital beds 1990-1997[a] 120

Doctors 1993[c] 107

Nurses 1993[c] 40

Health Indicators (4)

Life expectancy at birth

1980 67

1997 72

Daily per capita supply of calories (1996) 3,137

Total fertility rate births per woman (1997) 2.8

Maternal mortality ratio per 100,000 live births
(1990-97) . . . . .110[c]

Safe water % of population with access (1995) 95

Sanitation % of population with access (1995) 76

Consumption of iodized salt % of households
(1992-98)[a] 99

Smoking prevalence

Male % of adults (1985-95)[a] 38

Female % of adults (1985-95)[a] 14

Tuberculosis incidence per 100,000 people
(1997) 41

Adult HIV prevalence % of population ages
15-49 (1997) 0.35

Infants and Malnutrition (5)

Under-5 mortality rate (1997) 35

% of infants with low birthweight (1990-97) 7

Births attended by skilled health staff % of total[a] . . .75

% fully immunized (1995-97)

TB 99

DPT 95

Polio 95

Measles 91

Prevalence of child malnutrition under age 5
(1992-97)[b] 14

Ethnic Division (6)

Mestizo (Amerindian-Spanish) 60%

Amerindian or predominantly Amerindian 30%

White 9%

Other 1%

Religions (7)

Nominally Roman Catholic 89%

Protestant 6%

Languages (8)

Spanish, various Mayan, Nahuatl, and other regional
indigenous languages.

EDUCATION

Public Education Expenditures (9)

Public expenditure on education (% of GNP)

1980 . . . . .4.7

1996 . . . . .4.9[1]

Expenditure per student

Primary % of GNP per capita

1980 . . . . .4.4

1996 . . . . .11.9[1]

Secondary % of GNP per capita

1980 . . . .

1996 . . . . .17.9[1]

Tertiary % of GNP per capita

1980 . . . . .26.4

1996 . . . . .46.9[1]

Expenditure on teaching materials

Primary % of total for level (1996) . . . .

Secondary % of total for level (1996) . . . .

Primary pupil-teacher ratio per teacher (1996) . . . . .28[1]

Duration of primary education years (1995) 6

Educational Attainment (10)

Age group (1990) . . . . .25+

Total population 31,188,180

Highest level attained (%)

No schooling 18.8

First level

Not completed 28.6

Completed 19.9

Entered second level

S-1 . . . . .12.7

S-2 . . . . .10.7

Postsecondary 9.2

Literacy Rates (11A)

In thousands and percent[1]	1990	1995	2000	2010
Illiterate population (15+ yrs.)	6,162	6,246	6,015	5,086
Literacy rate - total adult pop. (%)	88.0	89.6	91.2	94.0
Literacy rate - males (%)	90.9	91.8	93.0	95.4
Literacy rate - females (%)	85.0	87.4	89.3	92.7

GOVERNMENT & LAW

Political Parties (12)

Chamber of Deputies	% of seats
Institutional Revolutionary Party (PRI) 39	
National Action Party (PAN) 27	
Party of the Democratic Revolution (PRD) 26	

Government Budget (13A)

Year: 1996

Total Expenditures: 387,810 Millions of New Pesos

Continued on next page.

Military Affairs (14B)

	1990	1991	1992	1993	1994	1995
Military expenditures						
Current dollars (mil.)	1,058	1,058	1,400	1,566	1,992	2,321
1995 constant dollars (mil.)	1,215	1,215	1,505	1,642	2,042	2,321
Armed forces (000)	175	175	175	175	175	175
Gross national product (GNP)						
Current dollars (mil.)	204,200	221,500	234,000	241,000	254,300	237,000
1995 constant dollars (mil.)	234,600	244,800	251,700	252,700	260,700	237,000
Central government expenditures (CGE)						
1995 constant dollars (mil.)	47,980	42,940	41,160	43,410	47,780	45,760
People (mil.)	85.1	86.9	88.6	90.4	92.2	94.0
Military expenditure as % of GNP	.5	.6	.6	.6	.8	1.0
Military expenditure as % of CGE	2.5	3.1	3.7	3.8	4.3	5.1
Military expenditure per capita (1995 $)	14	16	17	18	22	25
Armed forces per 1,000 people (soldiers)	2.1	2.0	2.0	1.9	1.9	1.9
GNP per capita (1995 $)	2,756	2,818	2,840	2,795	2,827	2,521
Arms imports[6]						
Current dollars (mil.)	110	70	100	20	110	20
1995 constant dollars (mil.)	126	77	108	21	113	20
Arms exports[6]						
Current dollars (mil.)	20	20	20	20	20	20
1995 constant dollars (mil.)	23	22	22	21	21	20
Total imports[7]						
Current dollars (mil.)	29,970	38,120	48,160	50,150	60,980	46,890
1995 constant dollars (mil.)	34,440	42,130	51,800	52,570	62,510	46,890
Total exports[7]						
Current dollars (mil.)	27,130	27,320	27,700	30,240	34,530	48,430
1995 constant dollars (mil.)	31,180	30,190	29,800	31,700	35,400	48,430
Arms as percent of total imports[8]	.4	.2	.2	0	.2	0
Arms as percent of total exports[8]	.1	.1	.1	.1	.1	0

Government Budget (13A) cont.

Expenditures as a percentage of the total by function:

General public services and public order 6.23

Defense 3.66

Education 24.50

Health 3.32

Social Security and Welfare 19.28

Housing and community amenities 3.38

Recreational, cultural, and religious affairs 55

Fuel and energy 1.73

Agriculture, forestry, fishing, and hunting 4.22

Mining, manufacturing, and construction 13

Transportation and communication 4.25

Other economic affairs and services 4.40

Crime (15)

Crime rate (for 1994)

Crimes reported . . . . .NA

Total persons convicted 116,489

Crimes per 100,000 population . . . . .NA

Persons responsible for offenses

Total number of suspects . . . . .NA

Total number of female suspects . . . . .NA

Total number of juvenile suspects . . . . .NA

LABOR FORCE

Labor Force (16)

Total (million) 36.6

Services 28.8%

Agriculture, forestry, hunting and fishing 21.8%

Commerce 17.1%

Manufacturing 16.1%

Construction 5.2%

Public administration, national defense 4.4%

Transport and communications 4.1%

Data for 1996.

Unemployment Rate (17)

3.7% (1997 est.) urban; plus considerable
underemployment.

PRODUCTION SECTOR

Electric Energy (18)

Capacity . . . . .35.466 million kW (1995)

Production . . . . .145.199 billion kWh (1995)

Consumption per capita . . . . .1,533 kWh (1995)

Transportation (19)

Highways:

total: 252,000 km

paved: 94,248 km (including 6,740 km of expressways)

unpaved: 157,752 km (1996 est.)

Waterways: 2,900 km navigable rivers and coastal
canals

Pipelines: crude oil 28,200 km; petroleum products
10,150 km; natural gas 13,254 km; petrochemical 1,400
km

Merchant marine:

total: 53 ships (1,000 GRT or over) totaling 899,224
GRT/1,312,505 DWT ships by type: bulk 2, cargo 1,
chemical tanker 4, combination bulk 1, container 4,
liquefied gas tanker 7, oil tanker 29, roll-on/roll-off
cargo 2, short-sea passenger 3 (1997 est.)

Airports: 1,810 (1997 est.)

Airports—with paved runways:

total: 231

over 3,047 m: 9

2,438 to 3,047 m: 25

1,524 to 2,437 m: 94

914 to 1,523 m: 78

under 914 m: 25 (1997 est.)

Airports—with unpaved runways:

total: 1,579

over 3,047 m: 1

2,438 to 3,047 m: 1

1,524 to 2,437 m: 65

914 to 1,523 m: 472

under 914 m: 1,040 (1997 est.)

Top Agricultural Products (20)

Corn, wheat, soybeans, rice, beans, cotton, coffee, fruit,
tomatoes; beef, poultry, dairy products; wood products.

MANUFACTURING SECTOR

GDP & Manufacturing Summary (21)

Detailed value added figures are listed by both International
Standard Industry Code (ISIC) and product title.

	1980	1985	1990	1994
GDP ($-1990 mil.)[1]	149,092	164,099	175,839	195,137
Per capita ($-1990)[1]	2,223	2,173	2,081	2,124
Manufacturing share (%) (current prices)[1]	21.9	23.1	22.5	19.9

	1980	1985	1990	1994
Manufacturing				
Value added ($-1990 mil.)[1]	32,931	35,007	40,055	43,956
Industrial production index	100	106	122	133
Value added ($ mil.)	43,048	46,373	41,416	49,208
Gross output ($ mil.)	102,047	106,972	95,678	114,648
Employment (000)	2,417	2,314	2,145	1,993
Profitability (% of gross output)				
Intermediate input (%)	58	57	57	57
Wages and salaries inc. supplements (%)	14	9	9	8
Gross operating surplus	28	34	35	35
Productivity ($)				
Gross output per worker	42,221	46,227	44,602	57,296
Value added per worker	17,811	20,040	19,307	27,697
Average wage (inc. supplements)	5,846	4,192	3,872	4,514
Value added ($ mil.)				
311/2 Food products	6,989	7,015	6,240	7,282
313 Beverages	2,723	2,589	2,377	3,181
314 Tobacco products	623	740	571	838
321 Textiles	3,133	3,099	2,216	2,266
322 Wearing apparel	1,277	1,094	863	943
323 Leather and fur products	366	397	250	297
324 Footwear	845	658	414	440
331 Wood and wood products	919	786	609	597
332 Furniture and fixtures	784	498	407	426
341 Paper and paper products	1,189	1,180	1,196	1,343
342 Printing and publishing	1,050	1,250	1,192	1,414
351 Industrial chemicals	2,235	2,982	2,738	3,167
352 Other chemical products	2,235	2,562	2,972	3,567
353 Petroleum refineries	1,917	4,341	3,987	4,750
354 Miscellaneous petroleum and coal products	222	529	489	576
355 Rubber products	767	1,164	865	981
356 Plastic products	754	767	774	891
361 Pottery, china and earthenware	383	420	287	332
362 Glass and glass products	566	529	511	623
369 Other non-metal mineral products	1,464	1,113	752	872
371 Iron and steel	2,070	2,227	1,955	2,067
372 Non-ferrous metals	562	506	430	391
381 Metal products	1,961	1,849	1,718	1,995
382 Non-electrical machinery	2,074	1,643	1,463	1,621
383 Electrical machinery	1,900	1,635	1,374	1,570
384 Transport equipment	2,980	3,621	3,542	4,976
385 Professional and scientific equipment	305	381	485	849
390 Other manufacturing industries	754	798	738	952

FINANCE, ECONOMICS, & TRADE

Economic Indicators (22)

National product: GDP—purchasing power parity—$694.3 billion (1997 est.)

National product real growth rate: 7.3% (1997 est.)

National product per capita: $7,700 (1997 est.)

Inflation rate—consumer price index: 15.7% (1997 est.)

Balance of Payments (23)

	1992	1993	1994	1995	1996
Exports of goods (f.o.b.)	46,196	51,885	60,882	79,542	96,000
Imports of goods (f.o.b.)	−62,130	−65,366	−79,346	−72,453	−89,469
Trade balance	−15,934	−13,481	−18,464	7,089	6,531
Services - debits	−23,957	−25,770	−28,648	−26,117	−27,918
Services - credits	12,064	12,211	13,668	13,493	14,933
Private transfers (net)	113	96	62	64	57
Government transfers (net)	3,272	3,544	3,720	3,896	4,474
Overall balance	−24,442	−23,400	−29,662	−1,576	−1,923

Exchange Rates (24)

Exchange rates:

Market rate of Mexican pesos (Mex$) per US$1

January 1998	.8.1798
1997	.7.9141
1996	.7.5994
1995	.6.4194
1994	.3.3751
1993	.3.1156

Top Import Origins (25)

$109.8 billion (f.o.b., 1997 est.), includes in-bond industries
Data are for 1997 est.

Origins	%
United States	.74.8
Japan	.4.1
Germany	.3.5
Canada	.1.8
South Korea	.1.4
Italy	.1.2
France	.1.1

Top Export Destinations (26)

$110.4 billion (f.o.b., 1997 est.), includes in-bond industries
Data are for 1997 est.

Destinations	%
United States	.85
Canada	.2.1
Japan	.1
Spain	.1
Chile	.1
Brazil	.1

Economic Aid (27)

Recipient: ODA, $85 million (1993).

Import Export Commodities (28)

Import Commodities	Export Commodities
Metal-working machines	Crude oil
Steel mill products	Oil products
Agricultural machinery	Coffee
Electrical equipment	Silver
Car parts for assembly	Engines
Repair parts for motor vehicles	Motor vehicles
	Cotton
Aircraft and aircraft parts	Consumer electronics

MICRONESIA

Federated States of Micronesia

INTRODUCTORY SURVEY

RECENT HISTORY

The string of islands known as the Carolinian archipelago was sighted by European navigators in the sixteenth century. Until the end of the nineteenth century, the islands were under Spanish colonial administration.

In 1899, following the Spanish-American War, Spain sold the islands to Germany. The Japanese took control at the end of World War I (1914–18). Following the defeat of Germany and Japan by the Allies in World War II (1939–45), the four states of the Federated States of Micronesia (FSM) came under United States administration as part of the United Nations Trust Territory of the Pacific Islands.

On 10 May 1979, a constitution drafted by a popularly elected constitutional convention went into effect. The United Nations Security Council voted in December 1990 to terminate the FSM's status as a United Nations Trust Territory. A capital, Palikir, was built in the Palikir Valley; it has served the FSM since 1990. The FSM became an independent state and joined the United Nations in September 1991. Its congress last met in March 1995.

GOVERNMENT

The national executive branch includes the president and vice-president, who serve four-year terms. The judiciary consists of a Supreme Court which applies criminal and civil laws and procedures that are similar to those of the United States.

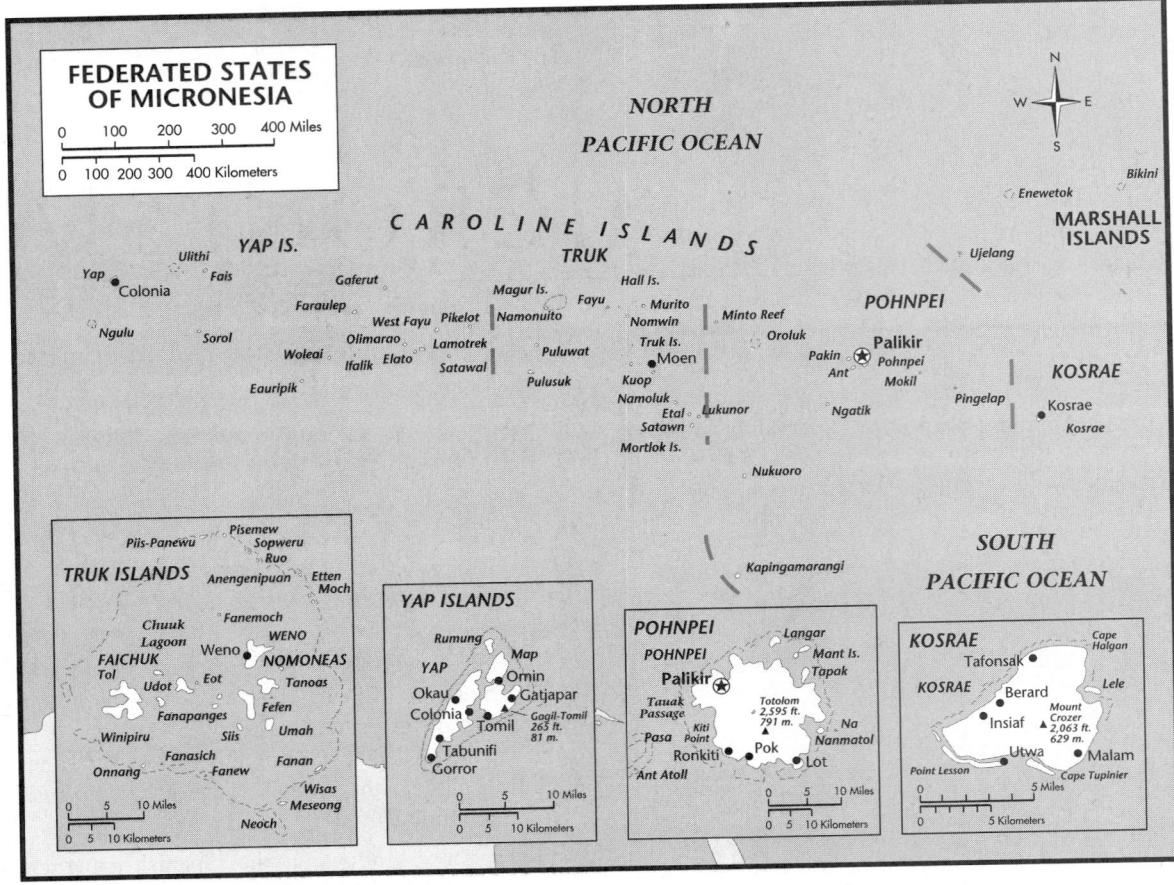

The legislature consists of a single-chamber Congress of 14 senators.

Each of Micronesia's four states has a legislature, governor, and lieutenant-governor.

Judiciary

The national judiciary consists of a Supreme Court, headed by a chief justice, and subordinate courts established by statute. The Supreme Court has both trial and appellate divisions and reviews cases that require interpretation of the Constitution, national law, or treaties.

Political Parties

There are no formal political parties.

DEFENSE

The Federated States of Micronesia (FSM) maintains no armed forces. External security is the responsibility of the United States.

ECONOMIC AFFAIRS

The gross domestic product (GDP) in 1996 was $220 million—$100 million of it was grant aid from the United States. The economy faces serious disadvantages, including shortages of technical and managerial skills, and large trade deficits. Grants from the United States are scheduled to end in 2002. The Asian Development Bank helped put together an economic development plan for Micronesia in 1995. Privatization, reduction of government employment, and the development of tourism and fisheries were recommended.

Income

In 1995, Micronesia's gross national product (GNP) was estimated to be between $766 and $3,035 per person. During 1985–95, the average annual inflation rate was 4.5%.

Industry

Handicrafts and small-scale processing are carried out in all states. A clothing plant in Yap is the country's largest private-sector industrial enterprise. Truk has a garment factory, a coconut-processing plant, a boat-building plant, and a breadfruit flour plant. Industry in other states includes a coconut-processing and soap and oil plant, a feedmill, an ice production plant, a brick-manufacturing plant, and a wood-processing plant.

SOCIAL WELFARE

Rapid changes in society have resulted in increasing juvenile delinquency, drug and alcohol abuse, and crime, which are being addressed by national and state social programs. A social insurance system includes old age, disability, and survivor benefits. Both sex discrimination and violence against women are serious problems.

Healthcare

A community health center was established in Pohnpei in 1986. In the outer islands, medical services are provided through dispensaries. Life expectancy was 68 years in 1998. The entire population has access to safe water and sanitation.

Housing

In 1980, the total housing consisted of 11,562 units. There has been a movement away from traditional construction materials toward imported lumber, plywood, and corrugated metal roofing.

EDUCATION

The state governments are responsible for the provision of education. Secondary education is provided through five public and five private high schools. The Community College of Micronesia is located in Pohnpei.

1999 KEY EVENTS TIMELINE

February

- The United States gives a slight increase in aid to the Federated States of Micronesia for the year 2000, from $110.2 million to $112.2 million.

- Former President Bailey Olter dies from a stroke after an extended illness at the age of 66.

April

- Micronesia raises the cost of passports from $15 to $50 for a 10-year passport, an increase of 230%.

May

- Leo A. Falcam, of Pohnpei, becomes the fifth president of the Federated States of Micronesia. Redley Killion, of Chuuk, is elected vice president at the first regular session of the 11th Congress. Falcam, who previously served as the vice president, succeeded Jacob Nena.

July

- The United States gives Micronesia a $900,000 grant to help it resolve Y2K computer problems.

September

- China's eastern province of Zhejiang establishes sister city relations with the State of Pohnpei.

- Madison Nena, the conservation officer for Kosrae's Utwe-Walung Conservation Area Marine, is named the 1999 Indigenous Conservationist of the Year by the Seacology Foundation.

October

- The Federated States of Micronesia signs the UNESCO constitution in London, England.

ANALYSIS OF EVENTS: 1999

BUSINESS AND THE ECONOMY

In July, prior to Compact of Free Association negotiations, the U.S. Congress asked the Federated States of Micronesia and the Marshall Islands for a full account of about $3 billion in U.S. funding before any other assistance was considered.

The U.S. General Accounting Office was asked to prepare a summary of U.S. funding provided to the FSM over the past thirteen years. Some U.S. officials believe funding has had little impact on breaking the dependency of the islands on the United States.

GOVERNMENT AND POLITICS

Officials from the United States and Micronesia met in Hawaii in November to begin discussions on renewing their Compact of Free Association, which is due to expire in 2001. The compact between the FSM and the United States ended United Nations trusteeship in 1986. With U.S. assistance, the four major island states in Micronesia—Pohnpei, Yap, Chuuk, and Kosrae—began self-rule as a constitutional democracy.

FSM chief negotiator Peter Christian said the compact had allowed the islands to develop politically and economically, but he acknowledged that much more needed to be done before they were self-reliant. A major portion of the compact deals with security. For the islands this means social, economic, and political stability. Christian said the goal for the FSM is self-reliance and an end to dependence on direct U.S. grants.

Chief U.S. negotiator Allen Stayman said the FSM had done well in its political transition, developing into successful self-government, but the islands had not met economic expectations. The United States, with a new compact, was prepared to continue helping the FSM by promoting growth, reforms, and good government. Stayman did warn that U.S. legislators and federal officials would ask tough questions before approving a new compact. First, several members of Congress wanted the FSM to account for all the money invested by the United States in the islands during the life of the compact, as well as a strategy for advancing economic self-sufficiency before more funding was approved.

CULTURE AND SOCIETY

A study by the Pacific Resources for Education and Learning showed that teachers in the FSM were absent from their classrooms about eleven days per year, a rate higher than the national U.S. average.

Stress and burnout do not account for the high rate, according to the study. Most teachers miss time to attend funerals, a Pacific Island tradition that carries great significance. In some islands, teachers receive up to five days of funeral leave. The Pacific Resources for Education and Learning is considering incentives to keep teachers in the classroom.

DIRECTORY

CENTRAL GOVERNMENT
Head of State

President
Leo A. Falcam, Office of the President, POB PS-53, Palikir, Pohnpei, Federated States of Micronesia 96941

PHONE: +691 3202228
FAX: +691 3202785

Vice President
Redley Killion, Office of the Vice President, POB PS-53, Palikir, Pohnpei, Federated States of Micronesia 96941
PHONE: +691 3202228
FAX: +691 3202785

Cabinet

Secretary of Foreign Affairs
Epel K. Ilon, Department of Foreign Affairs, POB PS-123, Palikir, Pohnpei, Federated States of Micronesia 96941
PHONE: +691 3202641
FAX: +691 3202933
E-MAIL: foreignaffairs@mail.fm

Secretary of Economic Affairs
Sebastian L. Anefal, Department of Economic Affairs, POB PS-12, Palikir, Pohnpei, Federated States of Micronesia 96941
PHONE: +691 3202646
FAX: +691 3205854
E-MAIL: fsmrd@mail.fm

Secretary of Transportation, Communication, and Infrastructure
Lukner Weilbacher, Department of Transportation, Communication, and Infrastructure, POB PS-2, Palikir, Pohnpei, Federated States of Micronesia 96941
PHONE: +691 3202865
FAX: +691 3205853
E-MAIL: fsmrd@mail.fm

Secretary of Finance and Administration
John Ehsa, Department of Finance and Administration, POB PS-158, Palikir, Pohnpei, Federated States of Micronesia 96941
PHONE: +691 3202640
FAX: +691 3202380

Secretary of Health, Education, and Social Services
Eliuel K. Pretrick, Department of Health, Education, and Social Services, POB PS-70, Palikir, Pohnpei, Federated States of Micronesia 96941
PHONE: +691 3202872
FAX: +691 3205263

Secretary of Justice
Emilio Musrasrik, Department of Justice, POB PS-105, Palikir, Pohnpei, Federated States of Micronesia 96941

PHONE: +691 3202644
FAX: +691 3202234

DIPLOMATIC REPRESENTATION
Embassies in Micronesia

Australia
H and E Enterprises Bldg., P.O. Box S, Kolonia, Pohnpei, Federated States of Micronesia 96941
PHONE: +691 3205448; 3205463
FAX: +691 3205449

United States
P.O. Box 1286, Kolonia, Pohnpei, Federated States of Micronesia 96941
PHONE: +691 3202187
FAX: +691 3202186

JUDICIAL SYSTEM
Supreme Court

PS-J, Palikir Station, Pohnpei, Federated States of Micronesia 96941
PHONE: +691 3202357
FAX: +691 3202756

FURTHER READING
Articles

"China's Zhejiang Establishes Friendly Ties with Pohnpei, FSM." Pacific Islands Development Program/East-West Center, Center for Pacific Islands Studies/University of Hawai'i at Manoa, 25 September 19999.

"FSM Signs UNESCO Constitution." Pacific Islands Development Program/East-West Center, Center for Pacific Islands Studies/ University of Hawai'i at Manoa, 19 October 1999.

"Federated States of Micronesia President, Vice President and Members of Congress Inaugurated." Federated States of Micronesia

Pacific Islands Development Program/East-West Center, Center for Pacific Islands Studies/University of Hawai'i at Manoa, 24 July 1999.

"FSM Establishes Trust Fund." Pacific Islands Development Program/East-West Center, Center for Pacific Islands Studies/University of Hawai'i at Manoa, 7 May 1999.

"FSM Founding Father Retires: Mangefel Expresses Personal Views on Nation." Pacific Islands Development Program/East-West Center, Center for Pacific Islands Studies/ University of Hawai'i at Manoa, 14 January 1999.

"Teacher Absenteeism in Micronesia Exceeds U.S. Average." Pacific Islands Development Program/East-West Center, Center for Pacific Islands Studies/University of Hawai'i at Manoa, 29 July 1999.

"U.S. tells Marshall Islands and Federated States of Micronesia to Account for $3 Billion in Funding." Pacific Islands Development Program/East-West Center, Center for Pacific Islands Studies/University of Hawai'i at Manoa, 20 July 1999.

Books

Hanlon, David L. *Remaking Micronesia: Discourses over Development in a Pacific territory, 1944–1982.* Honolulu: University of Hawai'i Press, 1998.

Meredith, Joseph C. *A Handful of Emeralds: On Patrol with the Hanna in the Postwar Pacific.* Annapolis, Md.: Naval Institute Press, 1997.

Internet

Embassy of the Federated States of Micronesia. Available Online @ www.fsmembassy.org/ (November 15, 1999).

National Government of the Federated States of Micronesia (FSM). Available Online @ www.fsmgov.org/ (November 15, 1999).

MICRONESIA, FEDERATED STATES OF: STATISTICAL DATA

For sources and notes see "Sources of Statistics" in the front of each volume.

GEOGRAPHY

Geography (1)

Area:

Total: 702 sq km.

Land: 702 sq km.

Water: 0 sq km.

Note: includes Pohnpei (Ponape), Truk (Chuuk) Islands, Yap Islands, and Kosrae.

Area—comparative: four times the size of Washington, DC.

Land boundaries: 0 km.

Coastline: 6,112 km.

Climate: tropical; heavy year-round rainfall, especially in the eastern islands; located on southern edge of the typhoon belt with occasionally severe damage.

Terrain: islands vary geologically from high mountainous islands to low, coral atolls; volcanic outcroppings on Pohnpei, Kosrae, and Truk.

Natural resources: forests, marine products, deep-seabed minerals.

Land use:

Arable land: NA%

Permanent crops: NA%

Permanent pastures: NA%

Forests and woodland: NA%

Other: NA%

HUMAN FACTORS

Demographics (2B)

Population (July 1998 est.) 129,658

Age structure:

0-14 years . . . . .NA

15-64 years . . . . .NA

65 years and over . . . . .NA

Population growth rate (1998 est.) 3.31%

Birth rate, 1998 est. (births/1,000 population) 27.55

Death rate, 1998 est. (deaths/1,000 population) . . .6.07

Net migration rate, 1998 est.
(migrant(s)/1,000 population) 11.65

Infant mortality rate, 1998 est.
(deaths/1,000 live births) 34.51

Life expectancy at birth (years):

Total population 68.34

Male 66.38

Female (1998 est.) 70.34

Total fertility rate, 1998 est.
(children born/woman) .3.9

Ethnic Division (6)

Nine ethnic Micronesian and Polynesian groups.

Religions (7)

Roman Catholic 50%

Protestant 47%

Other and none 3%

Languages (8)

English (official and common language), Trukese, Pohnpeian, Yapese, Kosrean.

EDUCATION

Literacy Rates (11B)

Adult literacy rate

1980

Male . . . .-

Female . . . .-

1995

Male . . . .-

Female 79%

GOVERNMENT & LAW

Political Parties (12)

The legislative branch is a unicameral Congress (14 seats members elected by popular vote four—one elected from each of state—to serve four-year terms and 10—elected from single-member districts delineated by population—to serve two-year terms). There are no formal parties.

Government Budget (13B)

Expenditures . . . .$52 million

  Capital expenditures . . . .$4.7 million

Data for FY95/96 est.

Military Affairs (14A)

Defense is the responsibility of the US.

LABOR FORCE

Labor Force (16)

Two-thirds are government employees.

Unemployment Rate (17)

27% (1989)

PRODUCTION SECTOR

Electric Energy (18)

Capacity . . . . .38,500 kW (1995)

Production . . . . .NA kWh

Consumption per capita . . . . .NA kWh

NA stands for not available.

Transportation (19)

Highways:

total: 240 km

paved: 42 km

unpaved: 198 km (1996 est.)

Merchant marine: none

Airports: 6 (1997 est.)

Airports—with paved runways:

total: 5

1,524 to 2,437 m: 4

914 to 1,523 m: 1 (1997 est.)

Airports—with unpaved runways:

total: 1

914 to 1,523 m: 1 (1997 est.)

Top Agricultural Products (20)

Black pepper, tropical fruits and vegetables, coconuts, cassava (tapioca), sweet potatoes; pigs, chickens.

FINANCE, ECONOMICS, & TRADE

Economic Indicators (22)

National product: GDP—purchasing power parity—$220 million (1996 est.) note: GDP is supplemented by grant aid, averaging perhaps $100 million annually

National product real growth rate: 1% (1996 est.)

National product per capita: $1,760 (1996 est.)

Inflation rate—consumer price index: 4% (1996 est.)

Exchange Rates (24)

Exchange rates: US currency is used

Top Import Origins (25)

$168 million (c.i.f., 1996 est.)

Origins	%
United States	NA
Japan	NA
Australia	NA

NA stands for not available.

Top Export Destinations (26)

$73 million (f.o.b., 1996 est.).

Destinations	%
Japan	NA
United States	NA
Guam	NA

NA stands for not available.

Economic Aid (27)

Recipient: under terms of the Compact of Free Association, the US will provide $1.3 billion in grant aid during the period 1986-2001.

Import Export Commodities (28)

Import Commodities	Export Commodities
Food	Fish
Manufactured goods	Garments
Machinery and equipment	Bananas
Beverages	Black pepper

MIDWAY ISLANDS

CAPITAL: None; administered by Washington, D.C.

FLAG: The flag of the United States is used.

MONETARY UNIT: The U.S. dollar is the official medium of exchange.

TIME: Midnight = noon GMT.

LOCATION AND SIZE: The Midway Islands are an atoll in Oceania, part of the North Pacific Ocean, about one-third of the way (1,304 miles, or 2,098 kilometers) from Honolulu, Hawaii to Tokyo, Japan. The two main islands, with a total area of two square miles (five square kilometers), are Eastern Island and Sand Island. This represents a comparative area about nine times the size of the Mall in Washington, D.C.

CLIMATE: Although Midway is not a South Sea island, the climate is semitropical due partly to the moderating effects of the prevailing easterly winds. The weather is generally uniform throughout the year with two distinguishable seasons, summer and winter. Midway summers are warm and slightly humid, prevailing from July to October, with an average high of 78°. The highest temperature ever recorded was 92°. During the winter months of January through March, temperatures average 66°, with the lowest temperature ever recorded at 51°. In the winter the relative humidity is high as well, and winds have been known to blow quite severely at times—hard enough to blow down shallow–rooted ironwood trees and uproot shrubbery. At times it is cold enough to require space heaters. Annual rainfall is 42 inches.

INTRODUCTORY SURVEY

RECENT HISTORY

Discovered and claimed by the United States in 1859 and formally annexed in 1867, Midway became a submarine cable station early in the twentieth century and an airlines station in 1935. Made a U.S. naval base in 1941, Midway was attacked by the Japanese in December 1941 and January 1942. In one of the great battles of World War II, a Japanese naval attack on June 3–6 1942 was repelled by U.S. warplanes.

In the years following World War II, Midway went from a critical war outpost to Navy caretaker status. In its heyday the island held two thousand residents but by the late seventies and early eighties the population dwindled to a few hundred. In 1992 the Navy announced the closing of Midway as its outpost.

GOVERNMENT

Midway is a U.S. unincorporated territory. In 1993 administrative control of Midway was transferred from the U.S. Department of the Navy to the U.S. Department of the Interior's Fish and Wildlife Service as part of the National Wildlife Refuge system.

DEFENSE

Military defense is the responsibility of the United States.

ECONOMIC AFFAIRS

Industry

The local economy is based on providing support services for the national wildlife refuge activities, but all food and manufactured goods have to be imported. The naval station is inactive since its closing in 1992.

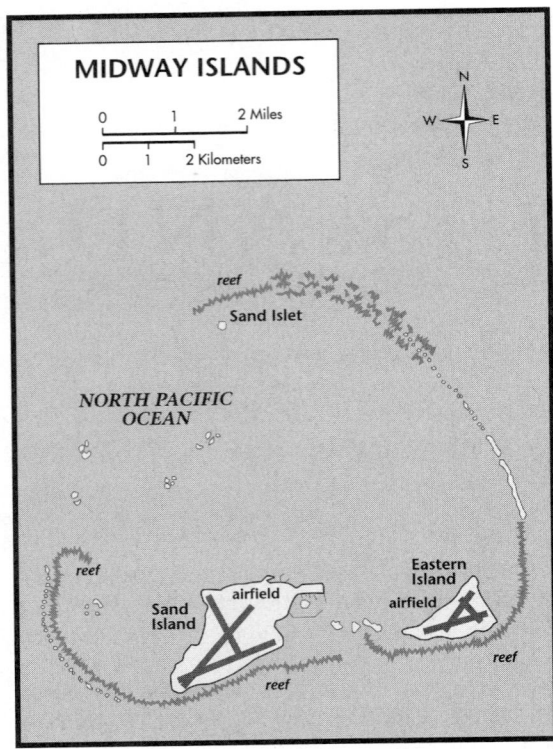

MIDWAY ISLANDS

0   1   2 Miles

0   1   2 Kilometers

reef

Sand Islet

NORTH PACIFIC OCEAN

reef

Eastern Island

airfield

Sand Island   airfield

reef

reef

1999 KEY EVENTS TIMELINE

March

- Pairs of nesting albatrosses and their fledgling chicks cover open areas as the migration season begins. The birds need a long open area for their characteristic running take-off into flight.

- Fishing season opens.

April

- Diving season begins.

August

- The albatross migration is complete, and all nesting pairs and their offspring have left the Midway Islands.

- A record setting 100-pound sailfish is caught, tagged, and released.

- Filming is completed for an episode of "Inside Big Game Fishing with Norm Isaacs," to be broadcast on a date to be announced by the cable sports network ESPN.

November

- Albatross return to Midway in November to begin their nesting season, which lasts through July.

- Tropical storms occur frequently, bringing an end to the fishing and diving seasons until around March.

ANALYSIS OF EVENTS: 1999

BUSINESS AND THE ECONOMY

Since 1997 the National Wildlife Refuge of the Midway Islands has been accessible to one hundred visitors per week. From November to August thousands of albatross pairs nest on the islands, posing a threat to air traffic. (The danger exists that a bird will be sucked into an aircraft's engines, or that an aircraft will collide with nesting birds.) To minimize the chances of an accident involving a collision between aircrafts and albatrosses, flights from Kauai, Hawaii, are scheduled at night. Visitors are met, and must dodge, huge numbers of birds on the ground and flying through the air.

GOVERNMENT AND POLITICS

The Battle of Midway was a turning point during World War II when U.S. forces defeated the Japanese navy. This event made the world's public aware of the tiny islands. Until the 1990s about three thousand U.S. military personnel were stationed at Midway; during the Vietnam war, hundreds of ships and thousands of aircraft landed there as they traveled between the mainland United States and Vietnam. Before leaving the islands, the U.S. government invested $82 million to remove military debris, such as leaky fuel tanks, underground metals, and toxic paint, from the environment. On June 30, 1997, the last personnel of the U.S. Navy vacated the islands.

U.S. President Bill Clinton signed an executive order on October 31, 1996, creating Midway Atoll National Wildlife Refuge and transferring control of Midway Atoll to the U.S. Fish and Wildlife Service, part of the U.S. Department of the Interior.

To operate the National Wildlife Refuge, the U.S Fish and Wildlife Service entered into an agreement with a private corporation, the Midway Phoenix Corporation. Under the terms of the agreement there is a limit of one hundred visitors per week to the atoll. Midway Phoenix operates the airfield and visitor accommodations at no cost to the federal government. Through a subcontractor Midway Phoenix manages excursions such as scuba diving, catch-and-release fishing, and snorkeling and diving trips for visitors.

CULTURE AND SOCIETY

Midway Atoll is comprised of three low-lying coral islands and a reef surrounding a lagoon measuring about twenty-four square miles. About 150 people live on Sand Island, the largest of the three islands, measuring about 1.2 miles wide by 1.8 miles long. Midway is home to a number of bird species. The world's largest colony (over 500,000 nesting pairs) of laysan albatross, known as "gooney birds" during World War II, and the world's second-largest colony of black-footed albatross nest on Midway.

There are an estimated two million birds in the Midway Islands, representing fifteen seabird species. The black-footed albatross, wedge-tailed shearwaters, bonin petrels, great frigatebirds, red-footed oobies, bristle-thighed curlews, wandering tattlers, Pacific golden plovers, ruddy turnstones, red-tailed tropicbird, black noddies, and white tern are among the birds inhabiting the islands. Because the bird species all seem to exhibit little fear of humans it is possible to observe them at close range. Every visitor to Midway must attend a mandatory orientation at the headquarters of the wildlife refuge. Monk seals, an endangered species, and green sea turtles, a threatened species, along with over 250 species of marine animals are also visible in the harbor and surrounding ocean areas. In 1998 marine scientist Robert Ballard of Connecticut's Mystic Aquarium discovered the sunken U.S.S. Yorktown, a World War II aircraft carrier, about 200 miles off Midway in 16,650 feet of water (about a mile deeper than the Titanic).

DIRECTORY

CENTRAL GOVERNMENT

The Midway Islands are managed by the Fish and Wildlife service of the U.S. Department of the Interior as part of the National Wildlife Refuge system. The islands are an unincorporated territory of the United States and are open to the public for wildlife-related recreation.

The islands were previously administered by the U.S. Navy, which held military operations on the island until 1993. In 1996 an executive order transferred management to the U.S. Department of the Interior.

FURTHER READING
Articles

Gorman, Stephen. "Midway to Paradise: Every Year, Albatrosses Fly from around the Pacific to Midway Atoll. Now a Few Lucky Humans Are Flying Here Too." *Audubon* (September-October 1998): 74+.

McCarthy, Lloyd and Mary McCarthy. "The Nature of Midway Atoll." *PSA Journal* (February 1999): 12.

Books

Kinkopf, Jack. *Pacific Journal, Fall 1996.* Ohio: 1997.

United States Senate. *Committee on Energy and Natural Resources. Battle of Midway National Memorial Act: Report.* Washington, D.C.: U.S. Government Printing Office, 1997.

Internet

Midway Atoll. Available Online @ www.midway-atoll.com (November 19, 1999).

Midway Island. Available Online @ www.midwayisland.com/Home.html (November 19, 1999).

MIDWAY ISLANDS: STATISTICAL DATA

For sources and notes see "Sources of Statistics" in the front of each volume.

GEOGRAPHY

Geography (1)

Area:

Total: 6.2 sq km.

Land: 6.2 sq km.

Water: 0 sq km.

Note: includes Eastern Island and Sand Island.

Area—comparative: about nine times the size of The Mall in Washington, DC.

Land boundaries: 0 km.

Coastline: 15 km.

Climate: tropical, but moderated by prevailing easterly winds.

Terrain: low, nearly level.

Natural resources: fish, wildlife.

Land use:

Arable land: 0%

Permanent crops: 0%

Permanent pastures: 0%

Forests and woodland: 0%

Other: 100%

HUMAN FACTORS

Demographics (2B)

Population: no indigenous inhabitants Population growth rate: 0% (1998 est.)

Languages (8)

GOVERNMENT & LAW

Political Parties (12)

Unincorporated territory of the US; formerly administered from Washington, DC, by the US Navy, under Naval Facilities Engineering Command, Pacific Division; this facility has been operationally closed since 10 September 1993; on 31 October 1996, through a Presidential executive order, the jurisdiction and control of the atoll was transferred to the Fish and Wildlife Service of the US Department of the Interior as part of the National Wildlife Refuge system.

Military Affairs (14A)

Defense is the responsibility of the US.

PRODUCTION SECTOR

Electric Energy (18)

No data available.

Transportation (19)

Highways:

total: 32 km

paved: NA km

unpaved: NA km

Pipelines: 7.8 km

Airports: 3 (1997 est.)

Airports—with paved runways:

total: 2

1,524 to 2,437 m: 2 (1997 est.)

Airports—with unpaved runways:

total: 1

914 to 1,523 m: 1 (1997 est.)

Top Agricultural Products (20)

No agricultural products.

FINANCE, ECONOMICS, & TRADE

Economic Aid (27)

No data available.

MOLDOVA

Republic of Moldova
Republica Moldoveneasca

INTRODUCTORY SURVEY

RECENT HISTORY

When World War II (1939–45) broke out in Europe, the 1939 Nazi-Soviet pact assigned Moldova to the Soviet area of control, and Soviet forces seized it in June 1940. After the Nazi invasion of the Soviet Union, Germany helped Romania to regain Moldova, which it held from 1941 until Soviet forces reconquered the area in 1944.

Moldova declared its independence from the Soviet Union on 27 August 1991. Russian forces, however, have remained on Moldovan territory east of the Dnister River and have supported the Russian minority (who form 30% of the population in this small region) in proclaiming an independent "Transdnister Republic." This move prompted fighting until a truce was called by Russia, Moldova, Ukraine, and Romania.

Moldova adopted a new constitution on 28 July 1994, replacing the old Soviet constitution of 1979.

GOVERNMENT

Elections to Moldova's first post-independence parliament were held on 27 February 1994. The new parliament consists of a single chamber of 104 seats. The president is elected separately in a popular election. Local administration is divided into 38 districts *(rayons)* and 10 cities.

Judiciary

There are lower-level courts at the city and district *(rayon)* levels with a Supreme Court acting as an appeals court. The Supreme Court is divided into civil and criminal sections. Reforms approved in 1995 include the creation of a court to deal with constitutional issues and a system of appeals courts.

Political Parties

Although 26 parties or coalitions of parties participated in the February 1994 elections, only four received more than the 4% of the national vote required to gain seats.

The Agrarian Party is the largest political group in the parliament, with 46 of 104 seats in 1995. The Socialist/Unity Bloc held 26 seats.

MOLDOVA

and trade disruptions following the dissolution of the former Soviet Union combined to cause steep declines in the economy during the early 1990s. The Moldovan government has adopted an ambitious economic reform agenda, including a stable convertible currency, price reform, privatization, and the removal of controls over exports and interest rates.

Public Finance

Moldova traditionally enjoyed a budget surplus, and the fiscal position was essentially in equilibrium in 1991 as rising expenditures were covered partially by revenue measures. In 1992, however, a significant and sudden drop in revenue, together with unexpected expenditures related to the Trans-Dnister conflict, increased public service wage expenses, and copious lending to public enterprises caused the fiscal deficit to swell to 21% of the GDP. As of 1992, Moldova had not yet signed an agreement with Russia concerning its liability for former Soviet debt. During the first year of its independence, Moldova contracted debts of about $90 million with nations outside the former USSR. Those debts grew to a total of $550 million through 1995 and some $250 million was owed to Russia.

Moldova projected a budget of $523.2 million in 1996, with a budget deficit of approximately 3.4%. The government financed the debt with the sale of securities, national bank profits and borrowing, but planned a budget policy and tax review to stem a long-term deficit.

Income

In 1997, Moldova's gross national product (GNP) was $10.8 billion, or about $2,400 per person. For the period 1985–95, the average decline of the GNP per person was 8.2%.

Industry

Moldova's industry has been concentrated mostly in light manufacturing, including processed food and beverages and cigarettes, but other activities include consumer durables, garments, high-technology electrical motors, precision tools, and farm machinery.

Banking and Finance

Moldova's banking sector will play a key role in the country's transition from a managed economy to a market economy. The banking system was reformed in 1991. The National Bank of Moldova (NBM) is charged with implementing monetary policy and issuing currency. State banks include the State Savings Bank, with 1,000

DEFENSE

The military is organized into the Ground Forces, Air and Air Defense Force, and the Security Forces (internal and border troops). There were about 11,900 personnel in Moldova's armed forces in 1995, including 10,600 army personnel and 900 air force personnel. Defense expenditures in 1995 were $45 million, or 2.5% of the gross domestic product (GDP).

ECONOMIC AFFAIRS

Agriculture is the most important area of Moldova's economy. Manufacturing is concentrated mainly in food processing and other light industry. The country's wide range of crops provides export revenue and employment. Droughts

branches, and the Bank for Foreign Economic Exchange. Holdovers from the old Soviet system include three regional banks, which have been changed to joint-stock companies whose shares are owned by state enterprises. There is one private bank in the country. The currency unit is the leu, introduced in late November 1993.

November 1993 was a turning point for Moldova's financial stability. The NBM became a fully independent central bank with its own administrative council, and was no longer required to finance industrial and agricultural funding shortfalls. As the leu was introduced, the NBM started phasing out credit emissions. As of January 1994, the NBM became fully responsible for monetary policy.

The bank has two policy instruments, reserve requirements which were raised progressively throughout 1994, and interest rates. The discount rate reached a peak of 377% in February 1994, and was kept high despite the subsequent dramatic fall in inflation. As of mid-1996, the key discount rate was 21%.

The banking system comprises four former Soviet banks, Agroindbank, Molindconbank, Moldotsbank, and the Savings Bank, as well as 23 commercial banks at the end of 1996. As in many other republics of the former Soviet Union, licensing procedures in the early 1990s were quite lax, with the result that the country is now overbanked, with too many small institutions, and a relatively high level of non-performing loans (11% of total commercial bank balance sheets as of mid-1996).

Moldova's 15 voucher funds have played an important role in the privatization program. Most citizens have opted to invest their vouchers in the funds rather than directly acquire shares in newly privatized companies.

The Chisinau-based Moldovan Stock Exchange opened for business in June 1995. Trading is electronic and is based on an order-driven system. As of mid-1996, it listed 11 shares. The most actively traded shares are Cupicini Canning Factory and Banea de Economii. A commodity exchange is planned.

Foreign currency reserves at the NBM rose by one-third in 1996, from $226.7 million at the end of 1995 to $304.1 million. This is to be explained by the substantial inflows of funds from multilateral institutions, notably, the World Bank and the European Bank for Reconstruction and Development. In December 1996, Moldova made its debut in the international bond market with a $30 million floating rate note issued as a private placement through Merrill Lynch. The bond has a call option effective in two years time.

Economic Development

In March 1993, the Moldovan government inaugurated the Program of Activity of the Government 1992–95 to make the transition to a market-oriented economy. The first stage focuses on stabilization, including price liberalization, and the second stage concentrates on economic recovery and growth, including privatization, agrarian reform, infrastructure development, social protection, and trade reform. However, the government has been slow to institute privatization in the agricultural sector. Although the government has backed privatization, freed prices and interest rates, and removed export controls, economic growth has been difficult. Moldova experienced a 3% contraction of the economy in 1995, the third straight year of negative growth. The government introduced a new convertible currency—the leu—in 1993.

SOCIAL WELFARE

Moldova has broad legislation for the protection of children, including programs for paid maternity leave and family allowances. There are extensive vaccination and other health care programs for children.

Although women are accorded equal rights under the law, they are under-represented in government and other leadership positions. There is also higher unemployment among women than men.

Healthcare

Moldova has been working on developing its own standards for health care, among other major programs. Average life expectancy is 67 years. Only half the population had access to sanitation in 1993. In that year, there was one doctor for every 250 people and one hospital bed per 80 people.

Housing

In 1989, 18.2% of all privately owned housing had running water, 16% had sewer lines, and 91.3% had gas. In 1990, Moldova had 17.9 square meters (193 square feet) of housing space per person. A program begun in March 1993 has privatized 80% of all housing units.

EDUCATION

While Moldova was a part of the Soviet Union, its education system was based on the Soviet pattern, and Russian was the language of instruction. However, after its separation, large-scale changes were introduced. Expenditures on education amounted to about 5.5% of the country's total gross national product in 1994. The Moldovan State University was founded in 1945 and uses both Moldovan and Russian as languages of instruction.

1999 KEY EVENTS TIMELINE

February

- President Petru Lucinschi appoints Serafim Urecheanu as the new prime minister, whose attempt to form a new government failed.

March

- Ion Sturza is appointed prime minister and charged with forming new government.

- A parliamentary vote of confidence in the new government is challenged as unconstitutional.

May

- A referendum to adopt a presidential system fails due to a low voter turnout.

June

- The electoral commission validates the results of the referendum proposing to adopt a presidential system.

July

- A summit on the future of the breakaway Transdniestria region fails to produce a breakthrough.

- Cevat Soysal, second-ranking leader of a Kurdish rebel group, is reportedly captured in Moldova.

August

- The International Monetary Fund (IMF) releases a $34 million payment to Moldova.

September

- Moldova participates in talks with former Soviet republics on fighting terrorism.

November

- New government crisis erupts on November 9 as parliament defeats prime minister Ion Sturza's privatization package and calls a no-confidence vote. In response, the International Monetary Fund (IMF) suspends loans to the country.

December

- Parliament approves the appointment of Dumitru Barghis, age 42, as prime minister. Barghis is the third candidate put forth by President Lucinschi, but the first to finally be approved by parliament.

ANALYSIS OF EVENTS: 1999

BUSINESS AND THE ECONOMY

In 1999 Moldova remained one of the poorest countries in Europe, with no energy resources of its own and an economy that had shrunk by two-thirds since the break-up of the Soviet Union in 1991. Its external debt was expected to top $1.1 billion; the cost of servicing it alone equaled two-thirds of the government's revenues. The nation was—and for the foreseeable future would remain—dependent on foreign aid, and its economy was highly vulnerable to economic conditions in neighboring countries that imported its goods. Financial reverses in Russia over the previous year had decimated Moldova's wine and brandy export market. Nevertheless, its economy was expected to grow by 2% in 2000.

World Bank and IMF aid was dependent on government cooperation with the economic policies favored by these international agencies, including privatization of government-owned and operated enterprises. Moldova's projected privatization plans included land reforms that would give former workers on state-owned collective farms about a hectare of land apiece. In August the IMF paid out $34 million of a $195 million loan, and promised another payment of roughly the same amount later in the year. In November, however, Moldova's parliament rejected government plans to sell off five state-owned firms, and the IMF halted further loan payments, claiming the vote constituted a change in the country's economic policy. Aid programs run by other international agencies were suspended as well, as the country's political crisis expanded into the economic arena.

GOVERNMENT AND POLITICS

By November Moldova had been hit with two political crises. The first came in February and March, as two successive prime ministers attempted to form a new government. The first attempt, by Serafim Urecheanu in February, failed, and he was replaced by former deputy prime minister Ion Sturza, whose new government won parliamentary approval in March in a highly controversial vote, with the deciding vote cast from prison by a deputy charged with war crimes in the disputed Transdnietria district.

The second major crisis occurred in November, when the nation's 101-member parliament defeated the government privatization proposal, which would have sold off five state-owned wine and tobacco businesses. Following the vote the International Monetary Fund suspended loans to the country, and parliament called for a new confidence vote on the beleaguered government.

Further controversy was aroused by President Petru Lucinschi's attempt to expand his largely ceremonial powers in a June referendum declared void by parliament but upheld by the central electoral commission.

In July Lucinschi met with leaders from Ukraine, Russia, and the breakaway Transdniestria region between the Dniester river and Moldova's northern border with Ukraine in an effort to resolve the dispute over the area, but no real breakthrough resulted from the summit. A long impasse since the civil war of 1992 had encouraged the growth of autonomy in the region, but its ultimate status remained unresolved. All parties at the summit agreed to keep working gradually toward a resolution that would include an acceptable demarcation of the area's boundaries and an agreement as to its status.

CULTURE AND SOCIETY

Eight years after the demise of communism in the former Soviet Union, the lot of many Moldovans was a precarious one. Government employees received an average monthly wage equivalent to about U.S.$35, and sometimes even this was unpaid. Political instability threatened direly needed aid from the IMF and other international agencies.

The country's economic crisis was accompanied by social problems that included the spread of HIV infection and AIDS, which had become a serious problems in the nations of the former Soviet bloc, primarily because of intravenous drug use. Other factors blamed for the spread of the disease were the collapse of traditional social structures and increased population mobility. Non-governmental agencies began to fund programs in the region, which one official described as the northern hemisphere's major crisis center for the spread of the disease.

Moldova was cited in connection with another type of ''epidemic'' in the Transparency International 1999 report on corruption, released in October. The report, which rates countries throughout the world for bribe-taking and corruption by public officials, revealed the level of corruption to be generally high among the former Soviet republics, with the worst rating going to Azerbaijan—1.7 on a scale of 0 (worst) to 10 (best). Moldova and neighboring Ukraine both received ratings of 2.6.

DIRECTORY

CENTRAL GOVERNMENT
Head of State

President
Petru Lucinschi, Office of the President

Prime Minister
Dumitru Barghis, Office of the Prime Minister

Ministers

Deputy Prime Minister
Nicolae Andronic, Office of the Deputy Prime Minister

Deputy Prime Minister
Valentin Dolganiuc, Office of the Deputy Prime Minister

Deputy Prime Minister
Oleg Stratulat, Office of the Deputy Prime Minister

Minister of Agriculture, Food Industry, and Forestry
Valeriu Bulgari, Ministry of Agriculture, Food Industry, and Forestry, bd Stefan cel Mare 162, MD-2002 Chisinau, Moldova
PHONE: +373 (2) 233427

Minister of Culture
Gennadie Ciobanu, Ministry of Culture

Minister of Defense
Valeriu Pasat, Ministry of Defense

Minister of Economy and Reform
Ion Sturza, Ministry of Economy and Reform

Minister of Education and Sciences
Anatol Grimalschi, Ministry of Education and Sciences

Minister of Environment Protection
Arcadie Capcelea, Ministry of Environment Protection

Minister of Finance
Anatol Arapu, Ministry of Finance

Minister of Foreign Affairs
Nicolae Tabacaru, Ministry of Foreign Affairs

Minister of Industry and Trade
Ion Tanase, Ministry of Industry and Trade

Minister of Interior
Victor Catan, Ministry of Interior

Minister of Justice
Ion Paduraru, Ministry of Justice

Minister of Labor, Social Protection, and Family
Vladimir Guritenco, Ministry of Labor, Social Protection, and Family

Minister of National Security
Tudor Botnaru, Ministry of National Security

Minister of Public Health
Eugen Gladun, Ministry of Public Health

Minister of State
Nicolae Cernomaz, Ministry of State

Minister of Territory Development, Construction and Communal Services
Mihai Severovan, Ministry of Territory Development, Construction and Communal Services

Minister of Transportation and Communications
Boris Gherasim, Ministry of Transportation and Communications

POLITICAL ORGANIZATIONS

Furnica-Speranta (Social Democratic Union)

Partidul Democrat Agrar din Moldova-PDAM (Agrarian Democratic Party)

TITLE: Chairman
NAME: Dumitru Motpan

PPSM (Party for Social Progress)

TITLE: Chairman

NAME: Eugen Sobor

Partidul Renasterii ci Concilierii din Moldova-PRCM (Party of Revival and Conciliation of Moldova)

TITLE: Chairman
NAME: Mircea Snegur

Frontul Popular Crestin si Democrat-FPCD (Christian Democratic Popular Front)

TITLE: Chairman
NAME: Iurie Rosca

Partidul Comunistilor din Moldova-PCM (Communist Party of Moldova)

TITLE: First Chairman
NAME: Vladimir Voronin

Conventia Democrata din Moldova-CDM (Democratic Convention of Moldova)

Pentru o Moldova Democrata si Prospera-PMDP (Movement for a Democratic and Prosperous Moldova)

NAME: Dumitru Diacov

Partidul Socialist-PSM (Socialist Party of Moldova)

TITLE: Co-Chairmen
NAME: Valeriu Senic; Victor Morev

Miscarea Yedinstvo (Unity Movement)

TITLE: Chairman
NAME: Vladimir Solonari

Alianta Taranilor Liberi-ATL (Alliance of Free Farmers)

Congresul Intelectualitatji-CI (Congress of Intellectuals)

CI-ATL (Peasants and Intellectuals Block)

TITLE: Chairwoman
NAME: Lidia Istrati

Partidul National Liberal-PNL (National Liberal Party)

DIPLOMATIC REPRESENTATION
Embassies in Moldova

Russia
ul. Stefan del Mare 151, 277019 Chisinau, Moldova
PHONE: +373 (2) 232600
FAX: +373 (2) 232600

JUDICIAL SYSTEM
Supreme Court

FURTHER READING
Articles
''Gazprom Russian Joint Stock Co. Cuts Off Moldova's Gas Supply.'' *Platt's Oilgram News*, 19 April 1999, p. 6.

''Nowhereland.'' *The Economist* (June 26, 1999): 61.

''Stalemate Across the Dniester.'' *The Economist* (June 26, 1999): 61.

Books
Bruchis, Michael. *The Republic of Moldavia: From the Collapse of the Soviet Empire to the Restoration of the Russian Empire*. Trans. Laura Treptow. East European Monographs. New York: Columbia University Press, 1996.

Dawisha, Karen, and Bruce Parrot, ed. *Democratic Changes and Authoritarian Reactions in Russia, Ukraine, Belarus, and Moldova*. New York: Cambridge University Press, 1997.

Fedor, Helen, ed. *Belarus and Moldova: Country Studies*. Federal Research Division, Library of Congress. 1st ed. Washington, D.C.: U.S. Government Printing Office, 1995.

Moldova: Moving to a Market Economy. A World Bank country study. Washington, D.C.: World Bank, 1994.

Internet
Moldova on the Net. Available Online @ www.moldova.org/ (November 15, 1999).

MOLDOVA: STATISTICAL DATA

For sources and notes see "Sources of Statistics" in the front of each volume.

GEOGRAPHY

Geography (1)

Area:

Total: 33,700 sq km.

Land: 33,700 sq km.

Water: 0 sq km.

Area—comparative: slightly more than twice the size of Hawaii.

Land boundaries:

Total: 1,389 km.

Border countries: Romania 450 km, Ukraine 939 km.

Coastline: 0 km (landlocked).

Climate: moderate winters, warm summers.

Terrain: rolling steppe, gradual slope south to Black Sea.

Natural resources: lignite, phosphorites, gypsum.

Land use:

Arable land: 53%

Permanent crops: 14%

Permanent pastures: 13%

Forests and woodland: 13%

Other: 7% (1993 est.).

HUMAN FACTORS

Health Personnel (3)

Total health expenditure as a percentage of GDP, 1990-1997[a]

Public sector 6.2

Private sector . . . . .NA

Total[b] . . . . .NA

Continued on next page.

Demographics (2A)

	1990	1995	1998	2000	2010	2020	2030	2040	2050
Population	4,397.8	4,461.5	4,457.7	4,466.8	4,619.3	4,783.0	4,872.7	4,902.4	4,810.6
Net migration rate (per 1,000 population)	NA	NA	NA	NA	NA	NA	NA	NA	NA
Births	NA	NA	NA	NA	NA	NA	NA	NA	NA
Deaths	NA	NA	NA	NA	NA	NA	NA	NA	NA
Life expectancy - males	63.9	60.4	59.6	59.9	63.7	68.2	71.9	74.8	76.9
Life expectancy - females	71.0	69.4	69.3	69.2	71.7	75.7	78.9	81.4	83.3
Birth rate (per 1,000)	18.3	14.4	14.4	14.5	16.8	12.3	11.5	9.9	8.4
Death rate (per 1,000)	10.1	11.9	12.4	12.6	11.7	10.0	9.8	10.6	11.2
Women of reproductive age (15-49 yrs.)	1,107.5	1,159.6	1,199.9	1,210.1	1,211.9	1,205.5	1,212.9	1,099.8	1,057.5
of which are currently married	NA	NA	NA	NA	NA	NA	NA	NA	NA
Fertility rate	2.4	1.9	1.9	1.8	2.0	1.8	1.7	1.5	1.5

Except as noted, values for vital statistics are in thousands; life expectancy is in years.

Health Personnel (3) cont.

Health expenditure per capita in U.S. dollars,
1990-1997[a]

Purchasing power parity . . . . .NA

Total . . . . .NA

Availability of health care facilities per 100,000 people

Hospital beds 1990-1997[a] 12.10

Doctors 1993[c] 356

Nurses 1993[c] 1,020

Health Indicators (4)

Life expectancy at birth

1980 66

1997 67

Daily per capita supply of calories (1996) 2,562

Total fertility rate births per woman (1997) 1.6

Maternal mortality ratio per 100,000 live births
(1990-97) . . . . .23[b]

Safe water % of population with access (1995) 56

Sanitation % of population with access (1995) 50

Consumption of iodized salt % of households
(1992-98)[a] . . . .

Smoking prevalence

Male % of adults (1985-95)[a] . . . .

Female % of adults (1985-95)[a] . . . .

Tuberculosis incidence per 100,000 people
(1997) 73

Adult HIV prevalence % of population ages
15-49 (1997) 0.11

Ethnic Division (6)

Moldavian/Romanian .64.5%

Ukrainian 13.8%

Russian 13%

Gagauz 3.5%

Jewish 1.5%

Bulgarian 2%

Other 1.7%

Note: internal disputes with ethnic Russians and Ukrainians in
the Nistru region and Gagauz Turks in the south. 1989 figures.

Religions (7)

Eastern Orthodox 98.5%

Jewish 1.5%

Baptist 1,000

The large majority of churchgoers are ethnic Moldavian. Data
for 1991.

Languages (8)

Moldovan (official, virtually the same as the Romanian
language), Russian, Gagauz (a Turkish dialect).

EDUCATION

Public Education Expenditures (9)

Public expenditure on education (% of GNP)

1980 . . . .

1996 . . . . .9.7

Expenditure per student

Primary % of GNP per capita

1980 . . . .

1996 . . . .

Secondary % of GNP per capita

1980 . . . .

1996 . . . .

Tertiary % of GNP per capita

1980 . . . .

1996 . . . . .57.9

Expenditure on teaching materials

Primary % of total for level (1996) . . . .

Secondary % of total for level (1996) . . . .

Primary pupil-teacher ratio per teacher (1996) 23

Duration of primary education years (1995) 4

Educational Attainment (10)

Age group (1989) . . . . .25+

Total population 2,499,613

Highest level attained (%)

No schooling 12.7

First level

Not completed 17.1

Completed . . . . .NA

Entered second level

S-1 . . . . .58.9

S-2 . . . . .NA

Postsecondary 11.3

Literacy Rates (11B)

Adult literacy rate

1980

Male . . . .—

Female . . . .—

1995

Male 98

Female 99

GOVERNMENT & LAW

Political Parties (12)

Parliament	No. of seats
Agrarian Democratic Party of Moldova (PDAM) . . .56	
Socialist/Yedinstvo Bloc 28	
Peasants and Intellectuals Bloc 11	
Christian Democratic Popular Front (FPCDM) 9	

Government Budget (13B)

Revenues . . . .$570 million

Expenditures . . . .$641 million

  Capital expenditures . . . .$28 million

Data for 1997 est.

Military Affairs (14B)

	1992	1993	1994	1995
Military expenditures				
Current dollars (mil.)	NA	NA	205	222
1995 constant dollars (mil.)	NA	NA	210	222
Armed forces (000)	9	13	11	12
Gross national product (GNP)				
Current dollars (mil.)	11,500	10,530	10,710	10,400
1995 constant dollars (mil.)	12,370	11,040	10,980	10,400
Central government expenditures (CGE)				
1995 constant dollars (mil.)	8,115	NA	NA	NA
People (mil.)	4.4	4.5	4.5	4.5
Military expenditure as % of GNP	NA	NA	1.9	2.1
Military expenditure as % of CGE	NA	NA	NA	NA
Military expenditure per capita (1995 $)	NA	NA	47	50
Armed forces per ,000 people (soldiers)	2.1	2.9	2.5	2.7
GNP per capita (1995 $)	2,781	2,477	2,464	2,332
Arms imports[6]				
Current dollars (mil.)	5	0	0	0
1995 constant dollars (mil.)	5	0	0	0
Arms exports[6]				
Current dollars (mil.)	0	0	80	40
1995 constant dollars (mil.)	0	0	82	40
Total imports[7]				
Current dollars (mil.)	576	912	1,251	822[e]
1995 constant dollars (mil.)	620	956	1,282	822[e]
Total exports[7]				
Current dollars (mil.)	366	332	398	720[e]
1995 constant dollars (mil.)	393	348	408	720[e]
Arms as percent of total imports[8]	0.9	0	0	0
Arms as percent of total exports[8]	0.0	0	20.1	5.6

Crime (15)

Crime rate (for 1997)

  Crimes reported 39,900

  Total persons convicted 23,900

  Crimes per 100,000 population 1,050

Persons responsible for offenses

  Total number of suspects 16,400

  Total number of female suspects 1,700

  Total number of juvenile suspects 1,850

LABOR FORCE

Labor Force (16)

Total (million) 2.42

Agriculture 46.1%

Industry 13.9%

Other 40.0%

Data for 1995. Percent distribution for 1996.

Unemployment Rate (17)

1.4% (includes only officially registered unemployed; large numbers of underemployed workers) (March 1997).

PRODUCTION SECTOR

Electric Energy (18)

Capacity . . . . .2.906 million kW (1997)

Production . . . . .1.5 billion kWh (1997)

Consumption per capita . . . . .324 kWh (1996 est.)

Transportation (19)

Highways:

total: 12,300 km

paved: 10,738 km

unpaved: 1,562 km (1996 est.)

Waterways: 424 km (1994)

Pipelines: natural gas 310 km (1992)

Airports: 26 (1994 est.)

Airports—with paved runways:

total: 8

over 3,047 m: 1

2,438 to 3,047 m: 2

1,524 to 2,437 m: 2

under 914 m: 3 (1994 est.)

Airports—with unpaved runways:

total: 18

2,438 to 3,047 m: 3

1,524 to 2,437 m: 2

914 to 1,523 m: 5

under 914 m: 8 (1994 est.)

Top Agricultural Products (20)

Vegetables, fruits, wine, grain, sugar beets, sunflower seed, tobacco; meat, milk.

FINANCE, ECONOMICS, & TRADE

Economic Indicators (22)

National product: GDP—purchasing power parity—$10.8 billion (1997 est.)

National product real growth rate: -2% (1997 est.)

National product per capita: $2,400 (1997 est.)

Inflation rate—consumer price index: 11.2% (1997 est.)

Balance of Payments (23)

	1994	1995	1996
Exports of goods (f.o.b.)	618	739	828
Imports of goods (f.o.b.)	−672	−809	−1,113
Trade balance	−54	−70	−285
Services - debits	−105	−242	−237
Services - credits	44	122	235
Private transfers (net)	—	—	46
Government transfers (net)	—	56	27
Overall balance	−115	−134	−214

Exchange Rates (24)

Exchange rates:

Lei (MLD) per US$1 (end of period)

January 1997	4.6870
1997	4.6628
1996	4.6743
1995	4.4990
1994	4.2700
1993	3.6400
1992	0.4145

Period average

January 1998	4.6758
1997	81.6637
1996	4.6045
1995	4.4958

MANUFACTURING SECTOR

GDP & Manufacturing Summary (21)

	1980	1985	1990	1992	1993	1994
Gross Domestic Product						
Millions of 1990 dollars	4,769	5,630	7,926	5,196	4,468	3,481
Growth rate in percent	1.48	−9.76	8.17	−25.00	−14.00	−22.10
Per capita (in 1990 dollars)	1,189.0	1,336.0	1,817.0	1,182.2	1,013.7	787.5
Manufacturing Value Added						
Millions of 1990 dollars	NA	NA	2,159	1,399	1,404	984
Growth rate in percent	NA	NA	NA	−27.09	0.31	-29.92
Manufacturing share in percent of current prices	NA	NA	27.2	30.3	31.4	31.9

FINANCE, ECONOMICS, & TRADE

Top Import Origins (25)

$1.16 billion (1997)

Origins	%
Russia	NA
Ukraine	NA
Uzbekistan	NA
Romania	NA
Germany	NA

NA stands for not available.

Top Export Destinations (26)

$816 million (1997).

Destinations	%
Russia	NA
Kazakhstan	NA
Ukraine	NA
Romania	NA
Germany	NA

NA stands for not available.

Economic Aid (27)

Recipient: IMF and World Bank, $512 million (1992-97).

Import Export Commodities (28)

Import Commodities	Export Commodities
Oil	Foodstuffs
Gas	Wine
Coal	Tobacco
Steel	Textiles and footwear
Machinery	Machinery
Foodstuffs	
Automobiles	
Other consumer durables	

MONACO

Principality of Monaco
Principauté de Monaco

CAPITAL: The seat of government is at Monaco-Ville.

FLAG: The national flag consists of a red horizontal stripe above a white horizontal stripe.

ANTHEM: *Hymne Monégasque,* beginning ''Principauté Monaco, ma patrie'' (''Principality of Monaco, my fatherland'').

MONETARY UNIT: Monaco uses the French franc (Fr), and all monetary restrictions in effect in France apply also in Monaco. Monégasque coins, on a par with French coinage, also circulate; denominations are 10, 20, and 50 centimes, and, 1, 2, 5, 10, and 50 francs. Fr1 = $0.19585 (or $1 = Fr5.106).

WEIGHTS AND MEASURES: The metric system is the legal standard.

HOLIDAYS: New Year's Day, 1 January; St. Dévôte, 27 January; Labor Day, 1 May; Assumption, 15 August; All Saints' Day, 1 November; National Day, 19 November; Immaculate Conception, 8 December; Christmas, 25 December. Movable religious holidays include Easter Monday, Ascension, Pentecost Monday, and Fête-Dieu.

TIME: 1 PM = noon GMT.

LOCATION AND SIZE: The second-smallest country in both Europe and the world after the Vatican, Monaco is situated in the southeastern part of the French administrative district of Alpes-Maritimes. Its area is 1.9 square kilometers (0.73 square miles), about three times the size of the mall in Washington, D.C. Monaco has a total boundary length of 12.7 kilometers (7.9 miles).

CLIMATE: Winters are mild, with temperatures rarely below freezing and a January average of about 8°C (46°F). Summer heat is tempered by sea breezes; the average maximum in July and August is 26°C (79°F). Rainfall averages about 77 centimeters (30 inches) a year.

INTRODUCTORY SURVEY

RECENT HISTORY

The economic development of Monaco proceeded rapidly with the opening of the railroad in 1868 and of the gambling casino. Since that time, the principality has become world famous as a tourist and recreation center.

Monaco has been a constitutional monarchy since the early twentieth century. In 1956 Prince Rainier III married the popular American actress, Grace Kelly, with whom he had three children: Princess Caroline, Prince Albert (the heir to the throne), and Princess Stephanie. Princess Grace was killed in a 1982 car accident.

Monaco joined the United Nations on 28 May 1993. That year, Prince Rainier ordered an investigation of Monaco's principal state-owned company. There had been complaints about threats used to recover loans from gamblers at the casinos.

GOVERNMENT

Monaco is a constitutional monarchy ruled by the hereditary princes of the Grimaldi line. A constitution adopted on 17 December 1962 provides for a single-chamber National Council of 18 members elected by direct popular vote every five years; it shares legislative functions with the prince.

Judiciary

A justice of the peace tries petty cases. Other courts are the Court of First Instance, the Court of Appeal, the Court of Revision, and the Criminal

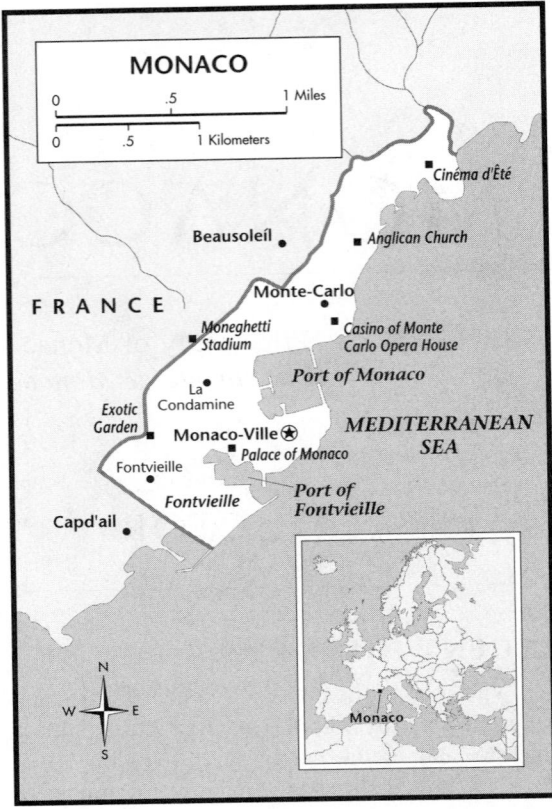

de Mer—SBM), in which the government owns 69%. The SBM operates the gambling casino at Monte Carlo as well as several luxury hotels and motion-picture theaters.

Public Finance

Revenues are derived mostly from commercial and transactional taxes, income resulting from the customs agreement with France, the sale of postage stamps, and the sale of tobacco and matches. The U.S. Central Intelligence Agency estimates that, in 1994, government revenues totaled approximately $660 million and expenditures $586 million.

Income

In 1996 the gross domestic product (GDP) was $800 million, or about $25,000 per person, in current United States dollars.

Industry

The tourist industry dominates Monaco's economic life, but small-scale industries produce a variety of items for domestic use and for export, contributing 27% of business turnover in 1990. About 700 small businesses make pottery and glass objects, paper and cards, jewelry, perfumes, dolls, precision instruments, plastics, chemicals and pharmaceuticals, machine tools, watches, leather items, and radio parts.

Banking and Finance

Foreign currency circulates within Monaco under the supervision of the French government. The most important local bank is Crédit Foncier de Monaco, founded in 1922. As of 1994, there were 45 banks operating in Monaco. There is no securities exchange.

Economic Development

The government strenuously promotes Monaco as a tourist and convention attraction. A government-financed International Convention Center offers large conference rooms, projection equipment, television and radio recording studios, telex communications, and simultaneous translation into five languages.

Two major development and reclamation projects have been undertaken under Prince Rainier. These are the major landfill and reclamation project at Fontvieille, and the Monte Carlo Bord de Mer. At Fontvieille, the government financed the reclamation of 220,000 sq m (2,368,000 sq ft) of inundated shore, creating a ''platform'' for residential construction and new port facilities.

Court. The highest judicial authority is vested in the Supreme Tribunal.

Political Parties

Monaco does not formally have political parties, but candidates compete on the basis of various lists. The major political groups have been the National and Democratic Union (Union Nationale et Democratique–UNI); Communist Action (Action Communale–AC); Èvolution Communale (EC); and the Movement of Democratic Union (MUD).

DEFENSE

France assumed responsibility for the defense of Monaco as part of the Versailles Treaty in 1919. There is no army in the principality. A private guard protects the royal family, and a police force of 390 ensures public safety.

ECONOMIC AFFAIRS

For its livelihood, Monaco depends chiefly on tourism, real estate, financial services, and light industry. A substantial part of the principality's revenue from tourist sources comes from the operations of Sea-Bathing Company (Société des Bains

The Monte Carlo seashore scheme, also government-financed, involved the relocation of railroad tracks underground in order to create a man-made beach, with a boardwalk and other tourist attractions. The beach lies between two other land reclamation projects: the Larvotto, a sports complex financed by SBM, and the Portier, an entertainment complex developed by the government.

Near the Larvotto the government has reserved a zone for the construction of residential and tourist accommodations. In the 1980s, Monaco concentrated on the development of business tourism, with the construction of the Monte Carlo Convention Center and the International Conference Center.

SOCIAL WELFARE

Social security benefits are financed by both employers and employees. There is a home for the aged attached to the Princess Grace Polyclinic. There is equal legal treatment of men and women who are born in Monaco.

Healthcare

In 1995, Monaco had approximately 42 physicians. There were 432 hospital beds and 16 pharmacies.

Housing

In 1991, there were 12,000 principal residences in Monaco. In recent years, the government has stressed the construction of luxury housing.

EDUCATION

Education is compulsory from age 6 to 16. Attendance is 90%, and nearly all adults are literate. In 1994, Monaco's seven public primary schools had a total of 1,838 students. The public secondary schools had 2,861 students.

1999 KEY EVENTS TIMELINE

January

- Princess Caroline marries Germany's Prince Ernst August of Hanover.

May

- Prince Albert hosts the World Music Awards at Monte Carlo.

June

- Prince Albert travels to El Salvador to attend the swearing-in ceremony of its new president.

July

- Prince Albert visits China to promote commercial ties.

October

- Monaco hosts European Technology Roundtable Exhibition (ETRE).

December

- Billionaire banker Edmond J. Safra and one of his nurses die of smoke inhalation, barracaded in a bathroom and refusing to leave when his penthouse apartment in Monte Carlo is destroyed by fire. Safra believed that armed intruders were waiting to attack him, and remained inside the bathroom. An American man working as a nurse for Safra, who had Parkinson's disease, admits to setting the fire.

ANALYSIS OF EVENTS: 1999

BUSINESS AND THE ECONOMY

With its resorts, its status as a tax haven for the rich, and its culture of celebrity, Monaco maintains its fairy-tale status among the countries of the world. Its industries are non-polluting, its unemployment rate (3.1 percent) is miniscule, and its life expectancy at birth (82 years for women and 75 years for men) is almost thirty years longer than that of some African nations. Still, the task of governing the principality keeps the royal family busy. Prince Albert, heir to the throne, visited China in July to promote trade between China and Monaco. The prince's visit, during which he met with high-ranking political and business leaders in Beijing and Shanghai, reflects China's growing interest in expanding its commercial ties around the globe. Prince Albert also visited an archeological site in China's Sha'anxi province.

Monaco practices a kind of exceptional regulatory identity among the nations of the world. Not only does its lack of income tax and its low business tax attract the rich, but it has also deliberately established less stringent regulations in other fields. One small example (which it shares with other

European countries) is Monaco's rules on retirement for commercial aircraft pilots. Monaco is one of 11 nations that are not members of the European Union but nevertheless subscribe to the regulations of the EU's Joint Aviation Authorities, the European counterpart of the Federal Aviation Administration (FAA) in the U.S. In July, all but one of the 26 member countries of the Joint Aviation Authorities raised the mandatory retirement age to 65. European nations are thus attracting pilots from the United States, where the FAA stipulates retirement at sixty years of age.

Monaco was the site of the European Technology Roundtable Exhibition (ETRE) conference in October. A highlight of the conference was a presentation by Bill Gates, chairman and CEO of Microsoft. Gates justified Microsoft's investment in interactive TV, saying that his company's commitment to applications like WebTV would pay off in the long run in financial and human resource terms.

GOVERNMENT AND POLITICS

As compared with the poorer nations of the world, much of the everyday business of governing Monaco is ceremonial and the crown-prince Albert dutifully discharges these tasks. In June, he was among the dignitaries from around the world who traveled to San Salvador to attend the swearing-in ceremony of the new president of El Salvador.

A less ceremonial and more pragmatic aspect of Monaco's attraction for the rich and famous is apparent in newspaper headlines. In April reports of an investigation by Italy's Finance Ministry indicated that at least some of Monaco's glitterati may be using their Monte Carlo addresses to avoid paying taxes in their home countries. Italian authorities insist that opera singer Luciano Pavarotti owes $2.5 million in taxes to the Italian government. Pavarotti appealed the assessment on the basis that his primary residence was his two-bedroom apartment in Monaco. The appeal was rejected, with authorities maintaining that the apartment was too small for Pavarotti's family, who live in Modena, Italy on a property worth $3 million. Italian tax officials suggested they would undertake investigations into the tax histories of other prominent individuals in entertainment, sports, and business who maintain Monte Carlo addresses.

Life in Monaco is so agreeable for its absentee population of foreign nationals that sometimes they are loath to leave the favored vacation spot, even

when circumstances would seem to call for their return. In one recent case a British businessman was named in a warrant issued by Great Britain's Serious Fraud Office (SFO). The man was charged with the theft of £2.4 million in connection with a food service company that he ran in Britain. He refused to return to Britain to face the charges.

Another, more reputable case of trying to manage an absentee career while living in Monaco came to light in June, when a Finnish national living in Monaco announced his candidacy for the position of Finland's representative to the European Union. The candidate would benefit from his fame as a champion race car driver, but his residency in Monaco could prove a liability. The election in question is an important one, since it is Finland's turn to head the EU and the winner of the upcoming election will be EU president for six months.

Monaco is rich enough to be responsive to the demands of Europe's most robust variety of opposition politics. Greenpeace activists demonstrated outside an October meeting in Malta at which twenty Mediterranean nations discussed the implementation of the protocols of a 1975 Barcelona convention on protecting the Mediterranean Sea. Monaco is the only state to have ratified all the protocols, although they have been signed by nearly every Mediterranean country.

CULTURE AND SOCIETY

In a private civil ceremony in the Room of Mirrors in the Royal Palace in Monte Carlo, Princess Caroline of Monaco married Prince Ernst August of Hanover, the head of one of the oldest aristocratic families in Germany. The wedding took place in January and coincided with the princess' forty-second birthday. The ceremony was not held in church because the marriage is the third for the princess, who is Catholic, and a religious ceremony would require a special dispensation from the Vatican, though a church wedding may be a possibility in the future. Because of the blood relationship between the Hanovers and the Windsors of England, which makes Prince Ernst August a close cousin of Queen Elizabeth II, the marriage links the Grimaldis of Monaco with the British royal family.

In February, Princess Caroline, along with Queen Beatrix of the Netherlands, were evacuated by helicopter from a ski resort in Lech, Austria, to escape hazardous conditions and the threat of avalanche. Over 60 people died in European avalanches during the year, the highest death toll in two decades.

In May, Prince Albert again hosted the World Music Awards at Monte Carlo. Pamela Anderson was among the presenters, with the Corrs (from Ireland), Des'ree, Janet Jackson, Cher, and Ricky Martin among those receiving honors.

DIRECTORY

CENTRAL GOVERNMENT
Head of State

Prince

Rainier III, Monarch, Palais de Monaco, Boit Postal 518, 98015 Monte Carlo

Ministers

Minister of State

Michel Lévèque, Ministry of State, Place de la Visitation, Monaco-Ville 98015, Monaco
PHONE: +37 (7) 93158000

POLITICAL ORGANIZATIONS
Union Nationale et Démocratique-UND (National and Democratic Union)

NAME: Jean-Louis Campora

Liste Campora-LC (Campora List)

NAME: Anne-Marie Campora

Liste Médecin (Medecin List)

NAME: Jean-Louis Médecin

DIPLOMATIC REPRESENTATION
Embassies in Monaco

Austria
PHONE: +37 (7) 93302300
TITLE: Consul General
NAME: Jacques de Beer de Laer

Belgium
PHONE: +37 (7) 93505989
TITLE: Consul General
NAME: André Ortmans

Brazil
PHONE: +37 (7) 93307615
TITLE: Consul General
NAME: François Ragazzoni

Cameroon
PHONE: +37 (7) 93502113
TITLE: Consul General
NAME: Jacqueline Aubery

Canada
E-MAIL: consul-canada@monte-carlo.mc

Costa Rica
PHONE: +37 (7) 92052232
TITLE: Consul General
NAME: Lucille Pellegrini

Côte d'Ivoire
PHONE: +37 (7) 93309700
TITLE: Consul General
NAME: Jean-François Cullieyrier

Cyprus
PHONE: +37 (7) 93159055
E-MAIL: consul-chypre@monte-carlo.mc
TITLE: Consul General
NAME: Lucas Haji Ioannou

Denmark
PHONE: +37 (7) 93500203
TITLE: Consul General
NAME: Kund Stefen Gam

Dominican Republic
PHONE: +37 (7) 93302914
TITLE: Consul General
NAME: Elisabeth-Anne Croesi-Notari

El Salvador
PHONE: +37 (7) 93251454
TITLE: Consul General
NAME: Laura Chatelin

Finland
PHONE: +37 (7) 93509021
TITLE: Consul General
NAME: Rainier Boisson

France
PHONE: +37 (7) 92165460
TITLE: Consul General
NAME: Jean-Bernard De Vaivre

Germany
PHONE: +37 (7) 93301949
TITLE: Consul General
NAME: Christine Esswein

Greece
PHONE: +37 (7) 93257655
TITLE: Consul General
NAME: Maria Economou

Guatemala
PHONE: +37 (7) 93506747

TITLE: Consul General
NAME: Odette Fissore

Honduras
PHONE: +37 (7) 93307059
TITLE: Consul General
NAME: Louisette Van Antwerpen

Hungary
PHONE: +37 (7) 93502018
TITLE: Consul General
NAME: Etienne Elek

Ireland
PHONE: +37 (7) 93157000
TITLE: Consul General
NAME: Michaël W.J. Smurfit

Italy
PHONE: +37 (7) 93502271
E-MAIL: ital-consul@monte-carlo.mc
TITLE: Consul General
NAME: Giovanni Andriani

Japan
PHONE: +37 (7) 92165151
TITLE: Consul General
NAME: Edmond Pastor

Jordan
PHONE: +37 (7) 93506393
TITLE: Consul General
NAME: Mohamed Tarif Al-Ayoubi

Liberia
PHONE: +37 (7) 93304030
TITLE: Consul General
NAME: Roger Richelmi

Luxembourg
PHONE: +37 (7) 93253037
TITLE: Consul General
NAME: Edmond Lecourt

Madagascar
PHONE: +37 (7) 93506237
TITLE: Consul General
NAME: Jacques Ferreyrolles

Mexico
PHONE: +37 (7) 93506647
TITLE: Consul General
NAME: Louis Orecchia

Morocco
PHONE: +37 (7) 93254026
TITLE: Consul General
NAME: Victor Pastor

Netherlands
PHONE: +37 (7) 92051502

TITLE: Consul General
NAME: Robert Smulders

Norway
PHONE: +37 (7) 93509101
FAX: +37 (7) 92161646
TITLE: Consul General
NAME: Claire Notari

Panama
PHONE: +37 (7) 93503206
TITLE: Consul General
NAME: Hubert Schurr

Peru
PHONE: +37 (7) 92165888
TITLE: Consul General
NAME: Michel Pastor

Philippines
PHONE: +37 (7) 93301010
TITLE: Consul General
NAME: Stefen Zuellig

Poland
PHONE: +37 (7) 93254312
TITLE: Consul General
NAME: Wojcieck Fibak

Portugal
PHONE: +37 (7) 93506394
TITLE: Consul General
NAME: Louis-Paul Colozier

Rwanda
PHONE: +37 (7) 92165454
TITLE: Consul General
NAME: Jean-Antoine Pastor

Senegal
PHONE: +37 (7) 93300481
TITLE: Consul General
NAME: Jacques Brillant de Boisbrillant

Seychelles
PHONE: +37 (7) 93302796
TITLE: Consul General
NAME: Michel Chiappori

Slovakia
PHONE: +37 (7) 93255006
TITLE: Consul General
NAME: Cristina Noghes-Menio

South Africa
PHONE: +37 (7) 93252426
E-MAIL: consul-afrisud@monte-carlo.mc
TITLE: Consul General
NAME: Jacques Orecchia

Spain

PHONE: +37 (7) 93302498
TITLE: Consul General
NAME: Michel Boeri

Sweden

PHONE: +37 (7) 93507560
TITLE: Consul General
NAME: François de Montseignat

Thailand

PHONE: +37 (7) 93309494
TITLE: Consul General
NAME: Jean-Claude Mourou

Turkey

PHONE: +37 (7) 93309240
TITLE: Consul General
NAME: Tuna Koprülü

United Kingdom

PHONE: +37 (7) 93509966
TITLE: Consul General
NAME: Eric Gordon Franck Blair

Uruguay

PHONE: +37 (7) 93506341
TITLE: Consul General
NAME: Ercole Canali

Venezuela

PHONE: +37 (7) 92160202
TITLE: Consul General
NAME: Mario Aletti Fabro

JUDICIAL SYSTEM

Supreme Tribunal

FURTHER READING

Background Notes on Countries of the World. Washington, D.C.: U.S. Government Printing Office, 1999, s.v. ''Principality of Monaco.''

Davis, Alisha. ''Newsmakers.'' *Newsweek* (May 17, 1999): 92.

''Grand Prix de Monaco.'' *On Track* (July 1, 1999): 19.

Kehoe, John. ''Grace Kelly.'' *Biography* (August 1999): 116.

Rich, Alan. ''Too Much is Never Enough.'' *Gentleman's Quarterly (GQ)* (May 1999): 172+.

Seligmann, Jean. ''A Little Grace.'' *Newsweek* (January 25, 1999): 45.

''Uneasy Crowns.'' *Time Canada* (June 14, 1999): 110.

''Weddings of the Year.'' *People* (July 5, 1999): 76.

Books

Schlegelmich, Rainer W., Hartmut Lehbrink, et al. *Grand Prix de Monaco: Portrait of a Legend.* Konemann, 1998.

MONACO:
STATISTICAL DATA

For sources and notes see "Sources of Statistics" in the front of each volume.

GEOGRAPHY

Geography (1)

Area:

Total: 1.95 sq km.

Land: 1.95 sq km.

Water: 0 sq km.

Area—comparative: about three times the size of The Mall in Washington, DC.

Land boundaries:

Total: 4.4 km.

Border countries: France 4.4 km.

Coastline: 4.1 km.

Climate: Mediterranean with mild, wet winters and hot, dry summers.

Terrain: hilly, rugged, rocky.

Natural resources: none.

Land use:

Arable land: 0%

Permanent crops: 0%

Permanent pastures: 0%

Forests and woodland: 0%

Other: 100% (urban area).

HUMAN FACTORS

Demographics (2A)

	1990	1995	1998	2000	2010	2020	2030	2040	2050
Population	30.0	31.5	32.0	32.2	33.0	33.6	33.9	33.9	33.9
Net migration rate (per 1,000 population)	NA	NA	NA	NA	NA	NA	NA	NA	NA
Births	NA	NA	NA	NA	NA	NA	NA	NA	NA
Deaths	NA	NA	NA	NA	NA	NA	NA	NA	NA
Life expectancy - males	73.0	74.2	74.8	75.2	76.9	78.1	78.9	79.6	80.0
Life expectancy - females	81.0	81.8	82.2	82.5	83.6	84.5	85.2	85.6	86.0
Birth rate (per 1,000)	10.9	10.7	10.7	10.6	10.8	10.0	9.8	9.8	9.5
Death rate (per 1,000)	12.6	12.1	11.9	11.7	11.5	11.5	12.4	12.9	12.9
Women of reproductive age (15-49 yrs.)	6.9	7.4	7.4	7.4	7.2	7.1	7.0	6.9	6.8
of which are currently married	NA	NA	NA	NA	NA	NA	NA	NA	NA
Fertility rate	1.7	1.7	1.7	1.7	1.7	1.7	1.7	1.7	1.7

Except as noted, values for vital statistics are in thousands; life expectancy is in years.

Infants and Malnutrition (5)

Under-5 mortality rate (1997) 5

% of infants with low birthweight (1990-97) . . . . . .NA

Births attended by skilled health staff % of total[a] . . .NA

% fully immunized (1995-97)

TB 90

DPT 99

Polio 99

Measles 98%

Prevalence of child malnutrition under age 5
(1992-97)[b] . . . . .NA

Ethnic Division (6)

French 47%

Monegasque 16%

Italian 16%

Other 21%

Religions (7)

Roman Catholic 95%

Languages (8)

French (official), English, Italian, Monegasque.

GOVERNMENT & LAW

Political Parties (12)

National Council	No. of seats
National and Democratic Union	15
Other	3

Government Budget (13B)

Revenues . . . .$623.3 million

Expenditures . . . .$638.7 million

Capital expenditures . . . . .NA

Data for 1995 est. NA stands for not available.

Military Affairs (14A)

Defense is the responsibility of France.

Crime (15)

Crime rate (for 1997)

Crimes reported 1,100

Total persons convicted 575

Crimes per 100,000 population 3,600

Persons responsible for offenses

Total number of suspects 800

Total number of female suspects 175

Total number of juvenile suspects 85

LABOR FORCE

Labor Force (16)

Total 30,540 (1 January 1994).

Unemployment Rate (17)

3.1% (1994)

PRODUCTION SECTOR

Electric Energy (18)

Capacity: 10,000 kW standby. Electricity imported from France.

Transportation (19)

Highways:

total: 50 km

paved: 50 km

unpaved: 0 km (1996 est.)

Merchant marine: none

Airports: linked to airport in Nice, France, by helicopter service.

Top Agricultural Products (20)

None.

FINANCE, ECONOMICS, & TRADE

Economic Indicators (22)

National product: GDP—purchasing power parity—$800 million (1996 est.)

National product real growth rate: NA%

National product per capita: $25,000 (1996 est.)

Inflation rate—consumer price index: NA%

Exchange Rates (24)

Exchange rates:

French francs (F) per US$1

January 1998 . . . . .6.0836

1997 . . . . .5.8367

1996 . . . . .5.1155

1995 . . . . .4.9915

1994 . . . . .5.5520

1993 . . . . .5.6632

Economic Aid (27)

$NA. NA stands for not available.

MONGOLIA

Mongol Uls

INTRODUCTORY SURVEY

RECENT HISTORY

The Mongolian People's Republic (MPR), the second communist country in world history, was proclaimed on 26 November 1924. With the support of the former Soviet Union (which formed in 1922 and broke apart in 1991), communist rule was gradually consolidated. Lands of the feudal lords were confiscated, starting in 1929, and those of monasteries in 1938.

On 14 February 1950, the People's Republic of China and the Soviet Union signed a treaty that guaranteed the MPR's independence. In October 1961, the MPR became a member of the United Nations. In June 1987, the MPR and the United States established diplomatic relations.

Following in the footsteps of the former Soviet Union, the MPR initiated its own policy of "openness" *(il tod)* in the late 1980s and began the transition from a centrally planned, collective economy toward a market economy. The ruling Mongolian People's Revolutionary Party (MPRP) opted for political as well as economic reforms. The MPRP's leadership resigned in March 1990 and in May the constitution was amended to allow for new, multiparty elections, which took place in July.

During 1991, the new government issued vouchers to all citizens for the purchase of state property, but economic reform was made more difficult by the economic collapse of the former Soviet Union. Elections in June 1992 created a new legislature, the State Great Hural (SGH), and in June 1993 President Punsalmaagiyn Ochirbat was elected in the first direct presidential elections. By September 1992, some 67,000 former Soviet troops (in the MPR since 1966) completed a process of withdrawal which began in 1990.

In the 1996 parliamentary elections, discontent among younger voters led to the defeat of the MPRP. The winners from the Democratic Union

coalition were mostly political novices who promised to intensify market reforms. The election results marked the first smooth transfer of power in Mongolia's modern history.

GOVERNMENT

The 1992 constitution went into effect on 12 February, replacing the 1960 constitution and completing Mongolia's transition from a single-party state to a multiparty, parliamentary form of government. At that time, the country's official name was changed from ''Mongolian People's Republic'' to ''Mongolia.'' The legislature, the State Great Hural (SGH), has 76 members, who are elected by district to four-year terms.

The president, the head of state, is selected by direct, popular vote for a four-year term. The prime minister, the head of government, is nominated by the president and confirmed by the SGH. The prime minister selects a cabinet which must be confirmed by the SGH.

Mongolia consists of 18 provinces *(aymag),* divided into 299 counties *(somon),* and three autonomous cities *(hot).*

Judiciary

There is a Supreme Court elected by the People's Great Hural; province and city courts, elected by the corresponding assemblies of people's deputies; and lower courts. Under the 1992 Constitution, the Supreme Court remains the highest judicial body. There is a Constitutional Court that has sole authority for constitutional review.

Political Parties

The Mongolian People's Revolutionary Party (MPRP), the single ruling party between 1924 and 1996, legalized opposition parties in 1990. Other major parties include the Social Democratic Party (SDP), the National Democratic Party (NDP), and the United Party of Mongolia.

In the elections of June 1996, the Democratic Union (which included the NDP, SDP, and two smaller parties) won 50 of 76 seats.

DEFENSE

In 1995, the armed forces totaled 21,000. The army had 15,500 personnel (11,000 draftees) in four divisions, and a reserve strength of 200,000. Mongolia spent an estimated $19 million for defense in 1995.

ECONOMIC AFFAIRS

After 70 years as a centrally planned economy, Mongolia has undergone a difficult transition towards a free market system since 1990. A number of factors, including the sudden halt to economic aid from the former Soviet Union and allied countries, the disruption of trade with traditional trading partners, as well as a severe winter in 1990–91, caused a steep decline in the country's economic activity. Despite these difficulties, the government has continued Development of oil and mineral resources is a high priority.

Public Finance

The annual budget is submitted to the People's Great Hural for approval. In 1996, the budget of Mongolia called for total revenues in the amount of T159.2 billion (including foreign aid) and total expenditures of T174.2 billion, leaving a deficit of T15 billion. Current revenues and expenditures totaled T152.8 billion and T128.2 billion, respectively. Capital revenues amounted to T2 billion in 1996; capital expenditures, T26 billion. Budget expenditures on goods and services in 1996 totaled T92.4 billion, including T32.8 billion for salaries, T4.9 billion for social insurance, and T1 billion for health insurance. Subsidies consumed T33.6 billion. Accounting for inflation, the 1996 budget revenues declined by 31.4% from 1995.

The U.S. Central Intelligence Agency estimates that in 1994 government revenues totaled approximately $1.5 billion and expenditures $1.3 billion. External debt totaled $473.7 million.

Income

In 1997 the gross national product (GNP) was $5.6 billion, or about $2,200 per person.

Industry

Small-scale processing of livestock and agricultural products has historically been the mainstay of Mongolia's industrial sector. Metal processing first became important in the 1970s. In 1996, the leading industries included metals, accounting for 32.6% of industrial output; energy production, 19.1%; and processed foods, 15.8%.

Banking and Finance

Before 1924, Mongolia lacked its own banks and currency. Mongolians bartered, using such commodities as livestock, tea, and salt for exchange, or such foreign currencies as the U.S. dollar, the Russian ruble, and the British pound in commerce. Chinese and Russian banks offered credit, as did monasteries and private moneylenders. The government began to transform this chaotic monetary situation with a series of reforms, starting with the establishment of Mongolbank, or the Mongolian Trade-Industrial Bank, in June 1924. Mongolbank was founded as a Mongolian-Soviet joint-stock company. In February 1925, the tugrik was made the official national currency, and it was slowly introduced into circulation over the next three years. In April 1928, all other currencies were withdrawn from circulation. In 1929, the government drove private moneylenders out of business by establishing a monopoly on foreign trade and outlawing private lending.

In April 1954, the Soviet Union handed over its shares in Mongolbank, which was renamed the State Bank of the Mongolian People's Republic.

The State Bank of Mongolia remains the official bank of Mongolia but recent economic reforms have allowed the formation of a commercial banking sector. The economic reforms were brought about by the collapse of the Soviet Union.

Now Mongolia has a two-tier banking system where control of the money supply is invested in the central bank. The Bank of Mongolia has established lending rules the commercial banks must follow. Also, reserve requirements are set by the national bank. In 1991, commercial functions were separated from the Mongol Bank, and two commercial banks were created. In 1996, there were 13. Total reserves, excluding gold, reached $117 million in 1995. Mongolia's currency, the tugrik, is not yet convertible. Money supply, as measured by M2, totaled T113,984 million at the end of 1995.

The Mongolian Securities Exchange opened in August 1995. About 60,000 individuals have opened accounts on the stock market. By 1996, more than 7.8 million shares from 400 companies had been traded and 28,000 contracts concluded; average daily trade volume is 60,000–80,000 shares.

Economic Development

In the past, Mongolia operated on the basis of a planned economy, with five-year plans implemented from 1947 until 1990, with assistance from the former USSR and China. In 1990, with the establishment of a new consensus government, there followed a three-year plan that aimed for achieving greater efficiency in the allocation of resources and a diversified economic base by undertaking a sustained transition to a free market economy. The change was a fundamental shift, as the government relinquished its role as the primary factor in the economy and began limiting itself to policies supporting a market-oriented economy. Main components of the government's program have included privatization of state enterprises, price liberalization, changes in national law, as well as drafting an action plan for environmental protection. Current plans specify development of the country's energy and mining sectors, and further action in environmental protection as well as continued reforms in a number of areas including fiscal management, land tenure, and social benefit entitlements.

In 1996, the initial phase of privatization of state property was completed. According to the government, 100% of small- and medium-sized enterprises have been privatized as well as 97% of the country's livestock. In 1994, the private sector accounted for 60% of GDP, and over 10,000 private businesses have been created since 1991. At the end of 1995, however, the government still held shares in more than 200 companies. The next phase of privatization will utilize securities market activities to replace the transitional voucher program.

SOCIAL WELFARE

The social insurance program provides for free medical services, benefits for temporary disability, and pensions for permanent disability and old age. Although women receive equal pay for equal work, they fill almost no positions at the highest levels of government or the professions.

Healthcare

In 1990, there were 5,625 physicians and, in 1991, 10,340 nurses. There were about 371 people per physician in 1993. In 1990–95, 95% of the population had access to health care services. Average life expectancy was an estimated 65 years in 1995. Pulmonary and bronchial infections, including tuberculosis and brucellosis, are widespread but are being brought under control.

Housing

The standard housing of the nomadic herders, as well as of many city dwellers, is the yurt—a light, movable, dome-shaped tent consisting of a skin or felt covering stretched over a lattice frame. Large apartment-house complexes with stores, services, and cultural facilities are being built in Ulaanbaatar, as well as in various other cities and towns.

EDUCATION

Ten years of schooling is compulsory, starting at age six. In 1995, the United Nations Educational, Scientific and Cultural Organization (UNESCO) estimated the illiteracy rate of 10.9% for males and 21.9% for females. In 1994, there were 6,704 teachers and 158,990 pupils in primary schools. General secondary schools had 12,938 teachers and 229,769 pupils. The Mongolian State University, in Ulaanbaatar, was founded in 1942.

1999 KEY EVENTS TIMELINE

March

- Wife of slain political leader Sanjaasurengiin Zorig is arrested as suspect in his 1998 murder.

July

- Prime Minister Janlaviin Narantsatsaralt and his government resign following parliamentary no confidence vote.

- Parliament votes to appoint Renchinnyamiin Amarjargal as new prime minister.

August

- Corruption trial of four high-level political figures begins in Ulaanbaatar.

- New prime minister vows to speed pace of economic reforms.

September

- Asian Development Bank approves $25 million loan to fund second phase of road development plan.

October

- Turkey's State Minister, Abdullah Mehmet Chai, visits Mongolia, agrees on closer cooperation between the two countries in the 21st century.

December

- President Natsangiyn Bagabandi arrives in Moscow for talks on economic and trade issues with Russian president Boris Yeltsin.

ANALYSIS OF EVENTS: 1999

BUSINESS AND THE ECONOMY

As the decade ended, Mongolia continued its painful transition from Communism to a free-market economy. Prime Minister Renchinnyamiin Amarjargal—an economist by training who took office at the end of July—pledged to speed up the pace of privatization and encourage foreign investment, which was expected to grow from the previous year's total of $39.1 million to $60 million for 1999. He cited as special priorities the privatization of large state-owned enterprises-beginning with oil trader Neft Import Concern, the Trade and Development Bank, and insurer Mongol Daatgal-and the restructuring of the country's energy sector, which was heavily subsidized by the government. Although his privatization measures were expected to face opposition from the rival Mongolian People's Revolutionary Party, Amarjargal stressed that all groups favored privatization, but only disagreed over its pace.

In addition to its progress in bringing inflation down from 268 percent to under 10 percent over the past five years, the government had also taken the more recent step of bringing three state-owned banks under strict central bank control. Weakened by bad loans, the banks had posted losses collectively totaling around 4 percent of the nation's GDP. The central bank planned to either close the banks or sell them to the private sector.

Mongolia's cashmere industry, one of the most important segments of its economy, remained in crisis as larger volumes of lower-quality cashmere from cross-breeding fetched lower prices on the world market and created a glut exacerbated by the large volume of Chinese production.

Mongolia continued to attract high levels of foreign aid, thanks to its adherence to the development model favored by the International Monetary Fund, including its control of inflation and privatization policies, and its democratic government.

GOVERNMENT AND POLITICS

Nine years after the end of Communist rule in Mongolia, democracy was still going strong, although undergoing a period of instability that had started the previous year when the divisive issue of banking reform had brought down the government. By mid-1999 the country had had four different prime ministers in less than 18 months and suffered the murder of its most popular political figure, Sanjaasurengiin Zorig, in October 1998. (Zorig's wife was arrested as a suspect in the crime in March 1999).

In the wake of debate over the privatization of the country's major copper mine, Janlaviin Narantsatsaralt resigned as prime minister in July, after seven months in office, following a parliamentary vote of no confidence and was replaced by Renchinnyamiin Amarjargal. He headed a caretaker government, with parliament expected to approve a new cabinet in October. The new leader vowed to fight government corruption, which was seen as a major obstacle to effective free-market reform. In a related development, Mongolia's first major corruption trial began the following month, when three politicians from the ruling party and one from the opposition party were charged in connection with the award of a casino license to a joint Mongolian-Macau venture called MonMacau, which proceeded to invest over $13 million in a casino located in Ulaanbaatar's largest hotel. All three politicians had denied the charges against them.

In October Mongolia's foreign minister met with his Turkish counterpart in Ulaanbaatar. The two statesmen discussed Turkish investment in Mongolia and pledged to establish close cooperation and regular high-level diplomat contacts between their countries.

CULTURE AND SOCIETY

In spite of positive economic indicators and plentiful foreign aid, the bulk of the Mongolian population-an estimated two-fifths-continued to live in poverty, with monthly incomes roughly equivalent to US$16.30. The educational system was in disarray, and social problems such as alcoholism, domestic violence, and child abandonment were on the rise, as critics complained that too much money was being spent on large construction projects and not enough on social welfare.

The government that took over at mid-year promised that social reforms would go hand in hand with economic reforms, recognizing that further economic progress depended strongly on development of the country's human resources. Among the measures proposed were increases in public sector salaries; restructuring of health care resources for greater cost efficiency so that doctors' salaries could be increased; and the creation of enough new jobs to bring unemployment down from its current level of nearly 6 percent to 5 percent within one year.

A government spokesman noted that Mongolia could not observe the UN's "20/20 Initiative"—the goal of directing 20 percent of development aid to the social sector—because much of the foreign aid it received was earmarked specifically for other purposes, such as infrastructure. However, a new program to address poverty, based on studies to be conducted by the World Bank and the UN in September, was to be launched late in the year or early in 2000.

DIRECTORY

CENTRAL GOVERNMENT

Head of State

President
Natsagiyn Bagabandi, Office of the President

Ministers

Prime Minister
Janlavyn Narantsatsralt, Office of the Prime Minister

Minister of External Relations of Mongolia
Rinchinnyamyn Amarjargal, Ministry of External Relations of Mongolia

Minister of Health and Social Welfare
Ministry of Health and Social Welfare
PHONE: +976 (1) 321485
FAX: +976 (1) 321485
E-MAIL: mhsw@magicnet.mn

Minister of Infrastructure Development
Gavaa Batkhuu, Ministry of Infrastructure Development, Street of Unite Nation 5/2, Government Building 2, Mongolia
E-MAIL: batkhuu@mid.pmis.gov.mn

POLITICAL ORGANIZATIONS

Mongolian People's Revolutionary Party (MPRP)

TITLE: General Secretary
NAME: N. Enkhbayar

Democratic Union Coalition (DUC)

TITLE: General secretary
NAME: Mendsaihan Enhsaihan

Mongolian Social Democratic Party (MSDP)

TITLE: Chairman
NAME: Radnaasumbereliyn Gonchigdorj

Green Party (NYAM)

Mongolian Democratic Party of Believers (MDPB)

Jargalsaihan-MCP (Mongolian Conservative Party)

Democratic Power Coalition

TITLE: Chairman
NAME: D. Byambasuren

Mongolian National Solidarity Party (MNSP)

Bourgeois Party

TITLE: Chairman
NAME: Vargalsaihan

United Heritage Party (UHP)

TITLE: Chairman
NAME: B. Jamtsai

Independence Party

Traditional United Conservative Party

Mongolian United Private Property Owners Party

Workers' Party

DIPLOMATIC REPRESENTATION

Embassies in Mongolia

Canada
P.O. Box 243-210644, Ulaanbaatar, Mongolia
PHONE: +976 (1) 328281
FAX: +976 (1) 328289

Russia
Friendship Street 6, Ulaanbaatar, Mongolia

PHONE: +976 72851; 26836; 27506

JUDICIAL SYSTEM

Supreme Court

FURTHER READING

Articles

''The Cashmere Crash.'' *The Economist* (August 14, 1999): 55.

''An Improbable Textbook Case.'' *The Economist* (July 3, 1999): 34.

Books

Atal, Yogesh. *Poverty in Transition and Transition in Poverty: Studies of Poverty in Countries-in-Transition: Hungary, Bulgaria, Romania, Georgia, Russia, Mongolia.* United Nations Educational, Scientific and Cultural Organization. New York: Berghahn Books, 1998.

Bruun, Ole, and Ole Odgaard, ed. *Mongolia in Transition.* Surrey, UK: Curzon, 1996.

Worden, Robert L., and Andrea Matles Savada. *Mongolia, a Country Study.* Federal Research Division, Library of Congress. Washington, D.C.: U.S. Government Printing Office, 1991.

MONGOLIA: STATISTICAL DATA

For sources and notes see "Sources of Statistics" in the front of each volume.

GEOGRAPHY

Geography (1)

Area:

Total: 1.565 million sq km.

Land: 1.565 million sq km.

Water: 0 sq km.

Area—comparative: slightly smaller than Alaska.

Land boundaries:

Total: 8,114 km.

Border countries: China 4,673 km, Russia 3,441 km.

Coastline: 0 km (landlocked).

Climate: desert; continental (large daily and seasonal temperature ranges).

Terrain: vast semidesert and desert plains; mountains in west and southwest; Gobi Desert in southeast.

Natural resources: oil, coal, copper, molybdenum, tungsten, phosphates, tin, nickel, zinc, wolfram, fluorspar, gold.

Land use:

Arable land: 1%

Permanent crops: 0%

Permanent pastures: 80%

Forests and woodland: 9%

Other: 10% (1993 est.).

HUMAN FACTORS

Demographics (2A)

	1990	1995	1998	2000	2010	2020	2030	2040	2050
Population	2,216.1	2,453.9	2,578.5	2,654.6	3,018.2	3,392.8	3,693.9	3,912.2	4,057.4
Net migration rate (per 1,000 population)	NA	NA	NA	NA	NA	NA	NA	NA	NA
Births	NA	NA	NA	NA	NA	NA	NA	NA	NA
Deaths	NA	NA	NA	NA	NA	NA	NA	NA	NA
Life expectancy - males	58.5	58.5	59.4	60.0	62.9	65.6	68.0	70.2	72.0
Life expectancy - females	62.4	62.4	63.6	64.4	68.3	71.7	74.7	77.2	79.3
Birth rate (per 1,000)	35.4	26.5	23.6	21.5	19.4	17.2	14.4	13.7	13.0
Death rate (per 1,000)	9.8	8.9	8.2	7.8	6.9	6.9	7.5	9.0	10.4
Women of reproductive age (15-49 yrs.)	524.0	617.6	678.4	722.3	907.1	960.7	975.8	936.4	909.0
of which are currently married	NA	NA	NA	NA	NA	NA	NA	NA	NA
Fertility rate	4.5	3.2	2.7	2.5	2.0	2.0	2.0	2.0	2.0

Except as noted, values for vital statistics are in thousands; life expectancy is in years.

Health Personnel (3)

Total health expenditure as a percentage of GDP,
1990-1997[a]

Public sector 4.3

Private sector 0.4

Total[b] 4.7

Health expenditure per capita in U.S. dollars,
1990-1997[a]

Purchasing power parity 82

Total 26

Availability of health care facilities per 100,000 people

Hospital beds 1990-1997[a] 1,150

Doctors 1993[c] 268

Nurses 1993[c] 452

Health Indicators (4)

Life expectancy at birth

1980 58

1997 66

Daily per capita supply of calories (1996) 2,098

Total fertility rate births per woman (1997) 2.6

Maternal mortality ratio per 100,000 live births
(1990-97) . . . . .65[c]

Safe water % of population with access (1995) 54

Sanitation % of population with access (1995) . . . .

Consumption of iodized salt % of households
(1992-98)[a] 62

Smoking prevalence

Male % of adults (1985-95)[a] 40

Female % of adults (1985-95)[a] 7

Tuberculosis incidence per 100,000 people
(1997) 205

Adult HIV prevalence % of population ages
15-49 (1997) 0.01

Infants and Malnutrition (5)

Under-5 mortality rate (1997) 150

% of infants with low birthweight (1990-97) 7

Births attended by skilled health staff % of total[a] . . .99

% fully immunized (1995-97)

TB 96

DPT 92

Polio 92

Measles 91

Prevalence of child malnutrition under age 5
(1992-97)[b] 12

Ethnic Division (6)

Mongol 90%

Kazakh 4%

Chinese 2%

Russian 2%

Other 2%

Religions (7)

Predominantly Tibetan Buddhist, Muslim 4%. Previously limited religious activity because of communist regime.

Languages (8)

Khalkha Mongol 90%, Turkic, Russian, Chinese.

EDUCATION

Public Education Expenditures (9)

Public expenditure on education (% of GNP)

1980 . . . .

1996 . . . . .6.4

Expenditure per student

Primary % of GNP per capita

1980 . . . .

1996 . . . .

Secondary % of GNP per capita

1980 . . . .

1996 . . . . .46.2

Tertiary % of GNP per capita

1980 . . . .

1996 . . . . .52.1

Expenditure on teaching materials

Primary % of total for level (1996) . . . .

Secondary % of total for level (1996) . . . .

Primary pupil-teacher ratio per teacher (1996) 31

Duration of primary education years (1995) 3

Educational Attainment (10)

Age group (1989) . . . . .25+

Total population .770,641

Highest level attained (%)

No schooling 13.4

First level

Not completed 22.8

Completed . . . . .NA

Entered second level

S-1 . . . . .13.9

S-2 . . . . .26.5

Postsecondary 23.4

Literacy Rates (11A)

In thousands and percent[1]	1990	1995	2000	2010
Illiterate population (15+ yrs.)	259	256	250	232
Literacy rate - total adult pop. (%)	79.9	82.9	85.6	89.5
Literacy rate - males (%)	86.6	88.6	90.3	92.8
Literacy rate - females (%)	73.2	77.2	80.8	86.2

GOVERNMENT & LAW

Political Parties (12)

State Great Hural	% of seats
Democratic Union Coalition (DUC) 66	
Mongolian People's Revolutionary Party (MPRP) . . .33	
Mongolian Conservative Party (MCP) 1	

Government Budget (13B)

Revenues . . . . .NA

Expenditures . . . . .NA

NA stands for not available.

Military Affairs (14B)

	1990	1991	1992	1993	1994	1995
Military expenditures						
Current dollars (mil.)	68[e]	36[e]	19	22	20	20
1995 constant dollars (mil.)	79[e]	40[e]	21	23	20	20
Armed forces (000)	32	31	21	18	21	21
Gross national product (GNP)						
Current dollars (mil.)	877	843	741	741	777	844
1995 constant dollars (mil.)	1,008	931	797	776	797	844
Central government expenditures (CGE)						
1995 constant dollars (mil.)	669	444	223	251	209	286
People (mil.)	2.2	2.3	2.3	2.4	2.4	2.5
Military expenditure as % of GNP	7.8	4.3	2.6	3.0	2.5	2.4
Military expenditure as % of CGE	11.7	9.0	9.3	9.2	9.7	7.0
Military expenditure per capita (1995 $)	35	18	9	10	8	8
Armed forces per 1,000 people (soldiers)	14.4	13.7	9.2	7.6	8.7	8.6
GNP per capita (1995 $)	455	410	344	328	331	344
Arms imports[6]						
Current dollars (mil.)	0	0	0	0	0	0
1995 constant dollars (mil.)	0	0	0	0	0	0
Arms exports[6]						
Current dollars (mil.)	0	0	0	0	0	0
1995 constant dollars (mil.)	0	0	0	0	0	0
Total imports[7]						
Current dollars (mil.)	924	361	418	362	223	NA
1995 constant dollars (mil.)	1,062	399	450	380	229	NA
Total exports[7]						
Current dollars (mil.)	661	348	389	381	324	400[e]
1995 constant dollars (mil.)	760	385	418	399	332	400[e]
Arms as percent of total imports[8]	0	0	0	0	0	NA
Arms as percent of total exports[8]	0	0	0	0	0	0

Crime (15)

Crime rate (for 1997)

Crimes reported 24,700

Total persons convicted 21,000

Crimes per 100,000 population 1,050

Persons responsible for offenses

Total number of suspects 21,600

Total number of female suspects 1,550

Total number of juvenile suspects 1,500

LABOR FORCE

Labor Force (16)

Total 1.115 million (mid-1993 est.). Primarily herding/agricultural.

Unemployment Rate (17)

15% (1997 est.)

PRODUCTION SECTOR

Electric Energy (18)

Capacity . . . . .901,000 kW (1995)

Production . . . . .3.15 billion kWh (1995)

Consumption per capita . . . . .1,303 kWh (1995)

Transportation (19)

Highways:

total: 46,470 km

paved: 3,730 km

unpaved: 42,740 km (1997 est.) note: much of the unpaved rural road system consists of rough cross-country tracks

Waterways: 397 km of principal routes (1988)

Airports: 34 (1994 est.)

Airports—with paved runways:

total: 8

2,438 to 3,047 m: 7

under 914 m: 1 (1994 est.)

Airports—with unpaved runways:

total: 26

over 3,047 m: 3

2,438 to 3,047 m: 5

1,524 to 2,437 m: 10

914 to 1,523 m: 3

under 914 m: 5 (1994 est.)

Top Agricultural Products (20)

Wheat, barley, potatoes, forage crops; sheep, goats, cattle, camels, horses.

FINANCE, ECONOMICS, & TRADE

Economic Indicators (22)

National product: GDP—purchasing power parity—$5.6 billion (1997 est.)

National product real growth rate: 3.3% (1997 est.)

National product per capita: $2,200 (1997 est.)

Inflation rate—consumer price index: 17.5% (1997 est.)

MANUFACTURING SECTOR

GDP & Manufacturing Summary (21)

	1980	1985	1990	1992	1993	1994
Gross Domestic Product						
Millions of 1990 dollars	1,139	1,587	1,869	1,387	1,369	1,414
Growth rate in percent	3.43	6.19	−2.07	−11.64	−1.30	3.30
Per capita (in 1990 dollars)	684.7	831.3	858.4	610.2	590.6	598.5
Manufacturing Value Added						
Millions of 1990 dollars	288	428	521	387	369	379
Growth rate in percent	8.03	3.07	2.43	−14.93	−4.61	2.81
Manufacturing share in percent of current prices	24.2	26.6	27.9	NA	NA	NA

FINANCE, ECONOMICS,& TRADE

Balance of Payments (23)

	1991	1992	1993	1994	1995
Exports of goods (f.o.b.)	346	356	366	367	451
Imports of goods (f.o.b.)	−448	−385	−344	−333	−426
Trade balance	−101	−29	21	34	25
Services - debits	−71	−97	−88	−114	−124
Services - credits	27	35	27	49	60
Private transfers (net)	42	38	71	78	77
Government transfers (net)	—	−3	−0	—	—
Overall balance	−104	−56	31	46	39

Exchange Rates (24)

Exchange rates:

Tughriks (Tug) per US$1

December 1997	.812.09
1997	.789.99
1996	.548.40
1995	.448.61
1994	.412.72

Top Import Origins (25)

$443.4 million (f.o.b., 1997 est.) Data are for 1996.

Origins	%
Russia	.34
China	.15

Top Export Destinations (26)

$418 million (f.o.b., 1997 est.) Data are for 1996.

Destinations	%
Russia	.21
China	.18

Economic Aid (27)

Recipient: ODA $250 million (1998 est.).

Import Export Commodities (28)

Import Commodities	Export Commodities
Machinery and equipment	Copper
Fuels	Livestock
Food products	Animal products
Industrial consumer goods	Cashmere
Chemicals	Wool
Building materials	Hides
Sugar	Fluorspar
Tea	Other nonferrous metals

MONTENEGRO

CAPITAL: Podgorica.

FLAG: The flag is comprised of three horizontal bands of red (top), blue, and white (bottom).

MONETARY UNIT: 1 Yugoslav New Dinar (YD) = 100 paras.

HOLIDAYS: St. Vitus Day, 28 June.

TIME: 1 PM = noon GMT.

LOCATION AND SIZE: Montenegro lies in the southeastern region of Europe, bordered by the Adriatic Sea, between Albania and Bosnia-Herzegovina (44°N, 21°E). It comprises a total mass of 13,938 sq. km, including 13,724 sq. km of land and 214 sq. km of water. It shares its borders with Albania (173 km), Bosnia-Herzegovina (215 km), and Croatia (25 km). The internal boundary between Montenegro and Serbia is 211 km.

CLIMATE: Montenegro is often exposed to extremes as it is subjected to destructive earthquakes and the Adriatic climate along its coast. Its summers are hot and dry, with autumns and relatively cold winters experiencing heavy snowfall inland. There is year-round precipitation, but it is heaviest from October through December.

INTRODUCTORY SURVEY

RECENT HISTORY

Montenegro is part of the Balkan States, a group of nations located in the largely mountainous region of inland far southeastern Europe. As part of the Roman Empire, the region of modern-day Montenegro formed part of the Illyria province. With Slavic settlement in the seventh century came independence as the province of Zeta until the late twelfth century when it became part of the Serbian empire. Following defeat of the Serbs by Turkey in 1389, Montenegro emerged once again as an independent state having been protected by its mountainous terrain. Often at war with Albanians and Turks, an alliance with Russia began in 1711. Unsettled boundaries, particularly to the south due to the conflicts with Albania, persisted through the nineteenth century. Montenegro's independence became internationally recognized and its geographic size doubled in 1878 by the Congress of Berlin settlement at the conclusion of the Russo-Turkish War. Following the Balkan Wars of 1912–13 in which Montenegro joined with Serbia against Turkey, Montenegro grew further in size to its north and east. With the conclusion of World War I, Montenegro joined with Serbia to form the Kingdom of Serbia, Croats, and Slovenes which later became Yugoslavia in 1929.

Germany invaded the region in April of 1941 leading to later partial occupation by Italian troops. Montenegro experienced continuous fighting through World War II until 1944 when communist factions gained control. Under a 1946 Yugoslavian federal constitution, Montenegro gained recognition as one of six autonomous federated units. The socialist government ruled for over forty years under President Josip Tito who poured considerable economic investments into Montenegrin industry, leading to economic stability. However, as the government began to weaken in the late 1980s inter-ethnic tensions mounted. Disintegration of the Yugoslav nation came in 1991 with only Montenegro choosing to remain with Serbia in a newly constituted federation.

Disputes over political dominance and boundaries raged through the 1990s between Bosnia, Herzegovina, Serbia, Montenegro, Croatia, Macedonia, and Kosovo. Charges of extensive human rights violations by the Serbian military fighting ethnic Albanians in Kosovo in the late 1990s fur-

ther spurred interests in Montenegro for independence from Serbia. By the late 1990s Montenegro more assertively challenged the validity of the federation's government, actually boycotting the federation's parliament, halting the transfer of tax revenue to the federation, and increasingly behaving as an independent nation. By the end of 1999 tensions were mounting that Montenegro could become the next Kosovo in a struggle for independence from the Yugoslav federation. Montenegrin leaders were striving for a public referendum on independence, possibly by early 2000.

GOVERNMENT

Since disintegration of communist Yugoslavia in 1991, Montenegro is a constituent republic and Serbia's junior partner in the Federal Republic of Yugoslavia. The United States has denied recognition of the Republic as a continuation of the former Socialist Federal Republic of Yugoslavia.

Through much of the 1990s Montenegro operated under two governments. The new Yugoslav federation operates under a constitution adopted in 1992. Chief of state is the federation president, which has been President Slobodan Milosevic since 1997. The Federal Executive Council serves as cabinet. A prime minister, selected by the president and approved by parliament, manages the federation's government. The two chambers of parliament are The Chamber of the Republics composed of forty members, twenty each from Serbia and Montenegro, and the Chamber of Citizens consisting of 138 members elected by popular vote.

Though a partner with Serbia in the Yugoslav federation, Montenegro and Serbia each maintain their own republican governments. The chief of state is the President of Montenegro, which has been Milo Djukanovic since January of 1998. Heading Montenegrin government is a prime minister and deputy prime minister. The legislative body of Montenegro is the unicameral National Assembly composed of 85 members elected by popular vote. Suffrage is universal for residents over eighteen years of age and those employed over sixteen years of age.

The Federation and Montenegro enjoy little international recognition, being excluded from the UN General Assembly, the International Monetary Fund, and the World Bank. As the Federation was coming under increasing authoritarian rule with Milosevic in the late 1990s, efforts by Montenegro to became a more open democratic polity were growing.

Judiciary

Based on a civil law system, in 1997 Montenegro had two District Courts, fifteen Communal Courts, and two Economic Courts of Law. The Yugoslav Federation also has two Supreme Courts. Supreme Court judges and other Federal Court judges are elected by the Republic's Federal Assembly to nine-year terms.

Political Parties

During the 1996 Chamber of Citizens public elections, political parties winning most of the 138 seats included the Coalition of the Left, Zajedno (Together), Democratic Party of Socialists of Montenegro, and the Radical Serb Party. Given the political instability of the region, numerous political parties are active in Montenegro and the Republic. The political organizations include the Serbian Socialist Party (SPS), Serbian Radical Party, Serbian Renewal Movement, Yugoslav United Left, Party of Democratic Action, and the Liberal Alliance of Montenegro among others. In the 1998 Montenegrin elections, the Coalition for a Better Life outgained the Socialist People's Party of Montenegro.

DEFENSE

Since 1997 Montenegro has assembled a fairly well-armed police force of approximately 12,000 men, roughly equivalent in size to the Yugoslavian Federation troops stationed in Montenegro by Federation President Milosevic. NATO bombing in early 1999 primarily of Serbian targets also hit hard at Yugoslav army and navy facilities in Montenegro. Montenegro in general was spared much of the substantial destruction inflicted on Serbia. Traditionally, males over 19 years of age were required to serve military duty in Montenegro for twelve to fifteen months.

ECONOMIC AFFAIRS

Highly destructive warfare since the 1991 collapse of the Yugoslav socialist federation greatly disrupted economies in the region. Output in Montenegro dropped significantly in 1992 and 1993. With many physical assets destroyed, reliance increased on other nations in the area for imports. A new currency was introduced in 1993 following a brief period of rampant inflation. Relative price stability resulted from 1995 to 1997 but ended in 1998. The Serbian emphasis on political dominance came at a cost of economic stability for the Republic and Montenegro.

Historically Montenegro relied economically on cereal-grain farming and sheep and goat raising until the mid-20th century. In 1998 potatoes and sheep dominated agricultural activity. Following World War II, Yugoslavia invested large sums into electrical power production in Montenegro to fuel steel and iron and non-ferrous-metal industries in addition to processing of agricultural products.

Exports largely to neighboring countries and Italy from Serbia and Montenegro was estimated in 1998 at U.S. $2.3 billion. Exports were primarily manufactured goods, processed foods, and raw materials. Imports constituting an estimated U.S. $3.9 million primarily came from Germany, Italy, and Russia in 1998. Famous for its Adriatic coastal resorts, a significant national debt was accumulating, as war had significantly reduced Montenegro's tourist trade by late 1999.

Public Finance

Being the junior partner with Serbia in the Federation, by late 1999 Montenegro's economy amounted to only 5% of Serbia's shattered economy, owing to international sanctions and war. By the end of the 1990s smuggling had become a key contributor to the Montenegrin economy. By 1999 the smuggling of cigarettes into Italy was estimated to be placing approximately U.S. $40 million dollars into Montenegro's economy annually and helping to address budget deficits. As part of Yugoslavia, Montenegro remains under certain economic sanctions including denial of access to funding institutions such as the World Bank and International Monetary Fund, which could greatly aid economic recovery and development. By late 1999 Montenegro established a second currency, tied to the German mark, in addition to the Yugoslav dinar.

Income

The gross domestic product (GDP) purchasing power parity for Serbia and Montenegro estimated in 1998 was U.S. $25.4 billion at an annual growth rate of 3.5%. Per capita GDP purchasing power parity was estimated at U.S. $2,300. Heavy industry was a large contributor at 50% with agriculture and services each contributing 25% of the GDP.

Industry

Industrial production in 1997 included lignite and bauxite minerals, carded cotton yarn, and heavy manufactured items. In 1999 a single large aluminum factory represented approximately half of Montenegro's gross national product. Increased privatization of industry is a goal as Montenegro seeks to become more Westernized and less tied to Serbia.

Banking and Finance

The National Bank is the Federation's bank of issue. In 1989 banks were transformed into shareholding companies. In 1998 the National Bank's reserves amounted to less than U.S. $200 million.

SOCIAL WELFARE

Given the region's pervasive political turmoil, the unemployment rate was estimated in 1997 at 33%. In 1997 the Federation provided cash benefits for disabled, old-age, and survivors of pensioners. Unemployment compensation and family allowances are also provided.

Healthcare

Montenegro suffers from poor nutrition and significant health problems. Infant mortality in Montenegro has consistently been high. The communist government introduced a national health insurance program following World War II and successfully fought many serious diseases which had been earlier rampant. Pregnant women, infants, and children below age sixteen receive complete health care. Life expectancy estimated in 1999 was 76.3 years for the total population with 72.9 years for males and 80.1 for females.

Housing

Yugoslavia in general suffers from crowded housing and poor sanitation services. Montenegro's more rural character alleviates some of the problems. Most villagers build their own homes.

EDUCATION

In 1997 Montenegro had 485 primary schools, forty-three secondary schools, and one high school. Twelve schools of higher learning were also available. Education in the Yugoslav republics is compulsory for eight years. The adult literacy rate in 1995 was 98%.

1999 KEY EVENTS TIMELINE

May

- Yugoslav soldiers block Montenegro's border with Croatia, confiscating Italian humanitarian aid and turning back trucks.

June

- Montenegro wants to redefine its relations with Serbia. The smaller republic is looking at new tax and customs laws, among many other changes.

- Montenegro's president offers to assist NATO peacekeeping troops in Kosovo.

- The U.S. State Department cautions Montenegro not to seek independence from Belgrade.

July

- Western nations pledge to defend Montenegro, which is making moves to break away from Yugoslavia. Montenegro proposes to transform centralized Serb-led Yugoslavia into a loose two-state confederation.

- Montenegro's president snubs the Yugoslav army during a wreath-laying ceremony at the tomb of the unknown soldier. His actions worsen ties between Montenegro and the Yugoslav military.

August

- Yugoslav President Slobodan Milosevic's party offers to hold early elections. The offer is seen as a last-minute concession aimed at defusing Yugoslavia's political crisis. The opposition says it is prepared to accept the offer only if Milosevic steps down and allows a transitional government before elections.

- Montenegrin officials say they want to abolish the Yugoslav federation in favor of a loose partnership with Serbia that would allow the two republics to go their own ways, but officials indicate they are in no rush to proclaim full independence.

- About 2,000 Montenegrin residents gather to protest against government efforts to break away from Yugoslavia. They chant in favor of Milosevic.

October

- Some Serbian officials say they will allow pro-Western Montenegro to leave the Yugoslav federation without bloodshed if the republic decides to do so. It is considered a major policy shift.

December

- The airport in Podgorica is seized by Yugoslav troops.

ANALYSIS OF EVENTS: 1999

BUSINESS AND THE ECONOMY

On November 2, Montenegro introduced the German mark as the official currency of the Republic. The move prompted the pro-Milosevic Yugoslav National Bank to impose a ban on financial transactions between Montenegrin companies and those in Serbia.

Serbian leaders criticized Montenegro's move, calling it unconstitutional and dangerous to the economic well-being of Yugoslavia. The currency change was seen as the latest effort to seek independence.

GOVERNMENT AND POLITICS

In March U.S. President Bill Clinton declared that Yugoslav President Slobodan Milosevic had rejected diplomatic efforts to make peace in Kosovo and indicated his support for air strikes in the region. NATO bombs began to punish Yugoslavia, marking NATO's first strike against a sovereign country in its 50-year history.

Serbia, under Milosevic's control, endured most of the bombing. Montenegro, the smaller of the two Yugoslav republics, was not spared, but NATO kept bombings to a minimum. The United

States considered Montenegro democratic and pledged to support the smaller Yugoslav republic. Montenegrin president Milo Djukanovic, who took office in 1998, had been openly critical of Milosevic's policies on Kosovo, and his government refused to support the war. Djukanovic's position, however, was weakened by NATO air strikes. Many Montenegrins remained loyal to Milosevic, while others worried about the thousands of ethnic Albanian refugees pouring into the republic and their effects on the economy.

Djukanovic had other concerns. During NATO bombings the Yugoslav army tightened its control over Montenegro, and there were frequent rumors of an impending coup. Djukanovic's meetings with some key European leaders and his continued threats to break away from Yugoslavia had angered Milosevic.

In June Montenegrin officials announced that they wanted to redefine their republic's relations with Serbia. The U.S. State Department cautioned Djukanovic not to seek independence from Belgrade. Western nations felt Montenegro could influence democratic changes in Serbia. Yet, after Milosevic capitulated to Western demands over Kosovo, Montenegro continued on a path to independence.

Djukanovic understood that Milosevic could trigger another war in the Balkans to stop Montenegro from leaving the Yugoslav republic. Yet, in November, he said Montenegro would seek independence if Milosevic's dictatorship prevailed.

"I respect the interests of the international community," Djukanovic told the media. "But I have to watch the interests of Montenegro, which are its democratization, economic prosperity and integration" to the rest of Europe. "Considering Mr. Milosevic's natural tendency, the fifth Balkan war cannot be ruled out. But it must be clear to the international community that there cannot be stability in the Balkans with the preservation of the dictatorship in the heart of the Balkans."

CULTURE AND SOCIETY

Montenegro has a population of about 630,000. About 62% are Montenegrins, 9% are Serbs, 7% are Albanians, and 1% are Croatian. Most Montenegrins are Orthodox Christian. About 15% are Muslim, and some are Roman Catholic.

DIRECTORY

CENTRAL GOVERNMENT

Montenegro and Serbia assert that together they compose a joint independent state, the Federal Republic of Yugoslavia. The United States does not formally recognize this entity as a state. Both Montenegro and Serbia have a significant amount of autonomy. Members of the governments of the Federal Republic of Yugoslavia and the Republic of Montenegro are noted here.

FEDERAL REPUBLIC OF YUGOSLAVIA

Head of State

President of the Federal Republic of Yugoslavia
Slobodan Milosevic, Office of the Federal President, Savezna Skupstina, 11000 Belgrade, Serbia, Yugoslavia

Prime Minister
Momir Bulatovic, Office of the Federal Prime Minister, Palace of Federation, Belgrade, Serbia, Yugoslavia
PHONE: +381 (11) 3117087

Ministers

Deputy Prime Minister
Vladan Kutlesic, Office of the Deputy Prime Minister

Deputy Prime Minister
Zoran Lilic, Office of the Deputy Prime Minister

Deputy Prime Minister
Nikola Sainovic, Office of the Deputy Prime Minister

Deputy Prime Minister
Danilo Vuksanovic, Office of the Deputy Prime Minister

Deputy Prime Minister
Jovan Zebic, Office of the Deputy Prime Minister

Minister of Agriculture
Nedeljko Sipovac, Ministry of Agriculture

Minister for Coordination of Relations with International Organizations
Nebojsa Maljkovic, Ministry for Coordination of Relations with International Organizations

Minister of Defense
Pavle Bulatovic, Ministry of Defense

Minister of Domestic Trade
Slobodan Nenadovic, Ministry of Domestic Trade

Minister for Economy and Industry
Rade Filipovic, Ministry for Economy and Industry

Minister of Finance
Bozidar Gazivoda, Ministry of Finance

Minister of Foreign Affairs
Zivadin Jovanovic, Ministry of Foreign Affairs

Minister of Foreign Trade
Borisa Vukovic, Ministry of Foreign Trade

Minister of Internal Affairs
Zoran Sokolovic, Ministry of Internal Affairs

Minister of Justice
Zoran Knezevic, Ministry of Justice

Minister of Labor, Health, and Social Policy
Miroslav Ivanisevic, Ministry of Labor, Health, and Social Policy

Minister of Science, Development, and Ecology
Jagos Zelenovic, Ministry of Science, Development, and Ecology

Minister of Sport
Velizar Djeric, Ministry of Sport

Minister of Telecommunication
Dojcilo Radojevic, Ministry of Telecommunication

Minister of Trade and Tourism
Djordje Siradovic, Ministry of Trade and Tourism

Minister of Transportation
Dejan Drobnjakovic, Ministry of Transportation

GOVERNMENT OF THE REPUBLIC OF MONTENEGRO

Head of State

President
Milo Djukanovic, Office of the President
E-MAIL: predsjednik@cg.yu

Ministers

Prime Minister
Filip Vujanovic, Office of the Prime Minister, Podgorica, Republic of Montenegro, Yugoslavia
E-MAIL: vlada@cg.yu

Minister of Justice
Dragan Soc, Ministry of Justice

Minister of Interior
Vukasin Maras, Ministry of Interior

Minister of Foreign Affairs
Branko Perovic, Ministry of Foreign Affairs
E-MAIL: smipdsik@eunet.yu

Minister of Finance
Bozidar Gazivoda, Ministry of Finance

Minister of Education and Science
Dragan Kujovic, Ministry of Education and Science

Minister of Culture
Budimir Dubak, Ministry of Culture

Minister of Energy, Industry and Mining
Vojin Djukanovic, Ministry of Energy, Industry and Mining

Minister of Transportation
Jusuf Kalamperovic, Ministry of Transportation

Minister of Agriculture, Forestry and Water Management
Milutin Simovic, Ministry of Agriculture, Forestry and Water Management

Minister of Tourism
Vlado Mitrovic, Ministry of Tourism

Minister of Trade
Ramo Bralic, Ministry of Trade

Minister of Urban Development
Radovan Bakic, Ministry of Urban Development

Minister of Environment Protection
Miladin Vukotic, Ministry of Environment Protection

Minister of Health
Miomir Mugosa, Ministry of Health

Minister of Labor and Social Care
Predrag Drecun, Ministry of Labor and Social Care

Minister of Religion
Slobodan Tomovic, Ministry of Religion

Minister for the Protection of National and Ethical Minorities
Ljuidj Juncaj, Ministry for the Protection of National and Ethical Minorities

Minister of Sports
Slavoljub Stijepovic, Ministry of Sports

POLITICAL ORGANIZATIONS
Democratic Party of Socialists

TITLE: President

NAME: Milo Dujkanovic

Liberal Alliance of Montenegro

TITLE: President
NAME: Slavko Perovic

Social Democratic Party

TITLE: President
NAME: Zarko Rakcevic

Albanian Democratic League

TITLE: President
NAME: Mehmed Bardhi

Albanian Democratic Union

TITLE: President
NAME: Fermat Dinaso

JUDICIAL SYSTEM

Supreme Court

Federal Court

District Court

Economic Court

FURTHER READING
Articles

"Analysts Say Lust for Power Makes Milosevic Tick." *The Seattle Times*, 11 April 1999.

"Milosevic Tells Serbs: We Won." *The Seattle Times*, 11 June 1999.

"Montenegro and Serbia Discuss Ties." Reuters, 24 October 1999.

"Montenegro Files Charges Against Yugoslav Premier." The Associated Press, 20 September 1999.

"Montenegro Prepares Platform for More Independence and a Separate Currency." The Associated Press, 27 June 1999.

"Montenegro Proposes Abolishing 'Dead End' Yugoslavia." The Associated Press, 5 August 1999.

"Montenegro Speeds Up Drive to Break from Serbia." The Associated Press, 10 July 1999.

"Peace Agreement Leaves Winners and Losers." *The Seattle Times*, 10 June 1999.

"Serbia and Montenegro: Montenegro's Push for Autonomy may Hurt Republic." *The Economist* (July 17, 1999): 44.

"Serbia Would Let Montenegro Go Without Bloodshed, Officials Indicate." The Associated Press, 22 October 1999.

"Serbia's Opposition." *The Economist* (October 9, 1999): 61.

"The Serbian Kickback: With the Bombing Over, Strong Anti-Milosevic Sentiment is Producing a Political Groundswell." *Time International* (July 19, 1999): 20.

"State Department Cautions Montenegro Against Seeking Independence." The Associated Press, 25 June 1999.

Books

United States President. *Continuation of the National Emergency with Respect to the Federal Republic of Yugoslavia (Serbia and Montenegro) and the Bosnian Serbs: Message from the President of the United States Transmitting Notification that the Federal Republic of Yugoslavia (Serbia and Montenegro) and the Bosnian Serbs Emergency is to Continue Beyond May 30, 1997, pursuant to 50 U.S.C. 1622(d).* Washington, D.C.: U.S. Government Printing Office, 1997.

Internet

Development Fund of the Republic of Montenegro. Available Online @ www.fzrcg.cg.yu/ (November 15, 1999).

MONTENEGRO: STATISTICAL DATA

For sources and notes see "Sources of Statistics" in the front of each volume.
The following information is for Montenegro and Serbia combined unless otherwise noted.

GEOGRAPHY

Geography (1) (Montenegro)

Area:

Total: 13,938 sq km.

Land: 13,724 sq km.

Water: 214 sq km.

Area—comparative: slightly smaller than Connecticut.

Land boundaries:

Total: 624 km.

Border countries: Albania 173, Bosnia and Herzegovina 215 km Croatia (south) 25 km, Serbia 211 km.

Coastline: 199 km.

Climate: in the north, continental climate (cold winter and hot, humid summers with well distributed rainfall); central portion, continental and Mediterranean climate; to the south, Adriatic climate along the coast, hot, dry summers and autumns and relatively cold winters with heavy snowfall inland.

Terrain: extremely varied; to the north, rich fertile plains; to the east, limestone ranges and basins; to the southeast, ancient mountains and hills; to the southwest, extremely high shoreline with no islands off the coast.

Natural resources: oil, gas, coal, antimony, copper, lead, zinc, nickel, gold, pyrite, chrome.

Land use:

Arable land: NA%

Permanent crops: NA%

Permanent pastures: NA%

Forests and woodland: NA%

Other: NA%

HUMAN FACTORS

Demographics (2A) (Montenegro)

	1990	1995	1998	2000	2010	2020	2030	2040	2050
Population	NA	670.8	679.9	680.7	693.7	696.1	682.8	651.3	603.4
Net migration rate (per 1,000 population)	NA	NA	NA	NA	NA	NA	NA	NA	NA
Births	NA	NA	NA	NA	NA	NA	NA	NA	NA
Deaths	NA	NA	NA	NA	NA	NA	NA	NA	NA
Life expectancy - males	NA	72.1	72.7	73.1	74.8	76.2	77.4	78.4	79.1
Life expectancy - females	NA	79.4	79.9	80.2	81.6	82.8	83.8	84.6	85.2
Birth rate (per 1,000)	NA	14.6	13.5	12.8	10.9	9.2	7.8	7.0	6.3
Death rate (per 1,000)	NA	7.2	7.4	7.5	8.4	9.7	11.0	13.2	15.2
Women of reproductive age (15-49 yrs.)	NA	173.5	177.3	176.6	171.6	159.7	145.4	127.8	109.7
of which are currently married	NA	NA	NA	NA	NA	NA	NA	NA	NA
Fertility rate	NA	1.9	1.8	1.7	1.5	1.4	1.4	1.3	1.3

Except as noted, values for vital statistics are in thousands; life expectancy is in years.

Ethnic Division (6)

Serbs 63%

Albanians 14%

Montenegrins 6%

Hungarians 4%

Other 13%

Religions (7)

Orthodox 65%

Muslim 19%

Roman Catholic 4%

Protestant 1%

Other 11%

Languages (8)

Serbo-Croatian 95%, Albanian 5%.

GOVERNMENT & LAW

Political Parties (12)

Chamber of Citizens	No. of seats
Serbian Socialist Party (SPS), Yugoslav United Left (JUL), New Democracy (ND) 64	
Zajedno 22	
Democratic Party of Socialists of Montenegro (DPSCG) 20	
Serbian Radical Party (SRS) 16	
People's Party of Montenegro (NS) 8	
Alliance of Vojvodina Hungarians (SVM) 3	
Other 5	

Government Budget (13B)

Revenues . . . . .NA

Expenditures . . . . .NA

Capital expenditures . . . . .NA

NA stands for not available.

Military Affairs (14B)

	1992	1993	1994	1995
Military expenditures				
Current dollars (mil.)	NA	NA	2,900[P,E]	NA
1995 constant dollars (mil.)	NA	NA	2,943[P,E]	NA
Armed forces (000)	137[e]	100	130	130
Gross national product (GNP)				
Current dollars (mil.)	13,500	NA	NA	20,600
1995 constant dollars (mil.)	14,520	NA	NA	20,600
Central government expenditures (CGE)				
1995 constant dollars (mil.)	NA	NA	NA	NA
People (mil.)	10.5	10.5	10.5	10.6
Military expenditure as % of GNP	NA	NA	NA	NA
Military expenditure as % of CGE	NA	NA	NA	NA
Military expenditure per capita (1995 $)	NA	NA	282	NA
Armed forces per 1,000 people (soldiers)	13.1	9.5	12.3	12.3
GNP per capita (1995 $)	1,389	NA	NA	1,948
Arms imports[6]				
Current dollars (mil.)	0	0	0	0
1995 constant dollars (mil.)	0	0	0	0
Arms exports[6]				
Current dollars (mil.)	0	0	0	0
1995 constant dollars (mil.)	0	0	0	0
Total imports[7]				
Current dollars (mil.)	NA	NA	NA	NA
1995 constant dollars (mil.)	NA	NA	NA	NA
Total exports[7]				
Current dollars (mil.)	NA	NA	NA	NA
1995 constant dollars (mil.)	NA	NA	NA	NA
Arms as percent of total imports[8]	NA	NA	NA	NA
Arms as percent of total exports[8]	NA	NA	NA	NA

LABOR FORCE

Labor Force (16)

Total (million) 2.178

Industry 41%

Services 35%

Trade and tourism 12%

Transportation and communication 7%

Agriculture 5%

Data for 1994.

Unemployment Rate (17)

More than 35% (1995 est.)

PRODUCTION SECTOR

Electric Energy (18)

Capacity . . . . .11.779 million kW (1995)

Production . . . . .33.4 billion kWh (1995)

Consumption per capita . . . . .3,009 kWh (1995)

Transportation (19)

Highways:

total: 49,525 km

paved: 28,873 km

unpaved: 20,652 km (1996 est.)

Waterways: NA km

Pipelines: crude oil 415 km; petroleum products 130 km; natural gas 2,110 km

Merchant marine:

total: 20 ships (1,000 GRT or over) totaling 322,391 GRT/533,935 DWT (owned by Montenegro) ships by type: bulk 6, cargo 11, container 3 note: Montenegrin ships operate under the flag of Malta (1997 est.)

Airports: 48 (Serbia 43, Montenegro 5) (1997 est.)

Airports—with paved runways:

total: 18

over 3,047 m: 2 (Serbia 2, Montenegro 0)

2,438 to 3,047 m: 5 (Serbia 3, Montenegro 2)

1,524 to 2,437 m: 5 (Serbia 4, Montenegro 1)

914 to 1,523 m: 2 (Serbia 2, Montenegro 0)

under 914 m: 4 (Serbia 4, Montenegro 0) (1997 est.)

Airports—with unpaved runways:

total: 30

1,524 to 2,437 m: 2 (Serbia 2, Montenegro 0)

914 to 1,523 m: 14 (Serbia 13, Montenegro 1)

under 914 m: 14 (Serbia 13, Montenego 1) (1997 est.)

Top Agricultural Products (20)

Cereals, fruits, vegetables, tobacco, olives; cattle, sheep, goats.

FINANCE, ECONOMICS, & TRADE

Economic Indicators (22)

National product: GDP—purchasing power parity—$24.3 billion (1997 est.)

National product real growth rate: 7% (1997 est.)

National product per capita: $2,280 (1997 est.)

Inflation rate—consumer price index: 7% (1997)

Exchange Rates (24)

Exchange rates:

Yugoslav New Dinars (YD) per US $1

Official rate:

December 1997 . . . . .5.85

September 1996 . . . . .5.02

early 1995 . . . . .1.5

Black market rate:

December 1997 . . . . .8.9

early 1995 . . . . .2 to 3

Top Import Origins (25)

$6.2 billion (1996 est.)

Origins	%
Germany	NA
Italy	NA
Russia	NA

NA stands for not available.

Top Export Destinations (26)

$2.8 billion (1996 est.).

Destinations	%
Russia	NA
Italy	NA
Germany	NA

NA stands for not available.

Economic Aid (27)

Recipient: ODA, $NA. NA stands for not available.

Import Export Commodities (28)

Import Commodities	Export Commodities
Machinery and transport equipment	Manufactured goods
Fuels and lubricants	Food and live animals
Manufactured goods	Raw materials
Chemicals	
Food and live animals	
Raw materials	

MONTSERRAT

INTRODUCTORY SURVEY

RECENT HISTORY

Christopher Columbus, who discovered Montserrat in November 1493, gave it the name Montserrat because its rugged terrain reminded him of the site of the Abbey of Montserrat in the Spanish highlands near Barcelona. English and Irish colonists from St. Kitts settled on the island in 1632, and the first African slaves arrived 32 years later. Throughout the 18th century, the British and French warred for possession of Montserrat, which was finally confirmed as a British possession by the Treaty of Versailles (1783). By the early 19th century, Montserrat had a plantation economy, but the abolition of slavery in 1834, the elimination of the apprentice system, the declining market for sugar, and a series of natural disasters brought the downfall of the sugar estates. In the mid-19th century, Joseph Sturge of Birmingham, England, organized a company that bought up the abandoned estates, planted them with limes (a product for which Montserrat is still famous), and sold plots of land to small farmers. From 1871 to 1956, Montserrat formed part of the Federation of the Leeward Islands, and after two years as a separate colony it became part of the Federation of the West Indies (1958–62).

GOVERNMENT

Since the breakup of the Federation, Montserrat has been separately administered, under a constitution effective 1 January 1960. The crown is represented by an appointed governor, who pres-

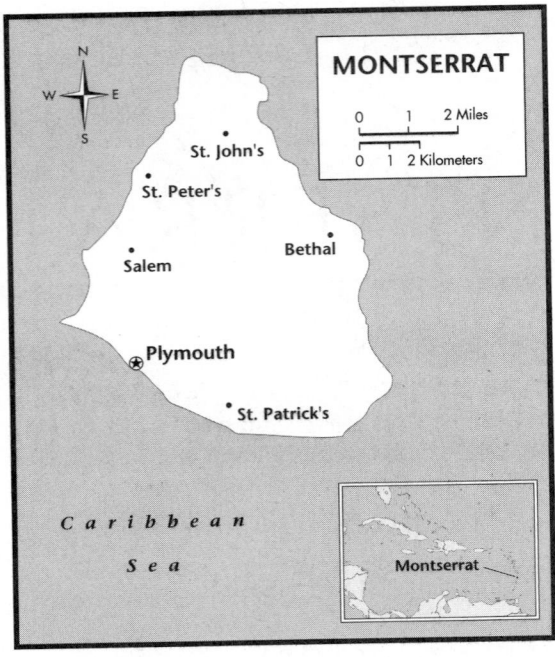

Income

In 1994, GDP per capita was $4,500. Exports that year were $2.3 million; imports, chiefly of industrial goods, foodstuffs, and mineral fuels, totaled some $80.6 million. Governmental revenues in 1994 were $15.7 million; expenditures, $15.6 million. Effective corporate income tax rates are 20–40%; the maximum personal income tax rate is 30%. A property tax is also levied.

Industry

Tourism accounts for about one-fourth of the annual GDP; the islands had some 17,000 visitors in 1992. Important crops include hot peppers (mostly for export), limes and other orchard fruits, tomatoes, and vegetables. Exports of live cattle and leather are significant, as are such light industrial exports as plastic bags, cotton garments, and electronic parts.

Banking and Finance

Montserrat uses the East Caribbean dollar.

SOCIAL WELFARE
Healthcare

The principal health facility is a 67-bed general hospital maintained by the government; provisions for social welfare include a family planning association and an old people's welfare association. Free dental care is provided by the government for all schoolchildren, elderly persons, and expectant or nursing mothers.

EDUCATION

Education is free and compulsory up to age 14. The government maintains 15 schools; one infant school (ages 5–7), nine primary schools (ages 5–12), two all-age schools (ages 5–15), and three secondary schools (ages 10–19).

1999 KEY EVENTS TIMELINE

January

- A coroner's inquest finds Britain partly responsible for the deaths of nine people in the 1997 eruption of the Soufriere Hills volcano.

May

- Britain's Department for International Development (DFID) announces inauguration of its Evacuee Return Air Fare Scheme (ERAFS),

ides over an Executive Council structured like that of Anguilla. There is also a Legislative Council which, like Anguilla's, includes two appointed and two ex officio members. The seven elected members of the legislature are chosen from single-member constituencies by universal adult suffrage at age 19. The legislators serve terms of up to five years.

Judiciary

Montserrat's judicial system consists of a magistrate's court and a Court of Summary jurisdiction; appeals are to the Eastern Caribbean Supreme Court on St. Lucia.

Political Parties

In elections held in November 1978, the People's Liberation Movement, headed by John Osborne, swept all seven elective seats; the party was returned to power in the February 1983 general election, though with a reduced majority of five seats, two having been captured by the Progressive Democratic Party.

ECONOMIC AFFAIRS

Governmental revenues in 1994 were $15.7 million; expenditures, $15.6 million. Exports that year were $2.3 million; imports, chiefly of industrial goods, foodstuffs, and mineral fuels, totaled some $80.6 million.

which provides the cost of the return of evacuees to Montserrat.

June

- Britain eases its travel advisory for Montserrat and declares more of the island safe for tourists.

July

- The EU-funded Caribbean Export Development Agency (CEDA) pledges assistance to Montserrat.

- The Montserrat government announces that utility workers will be let go without severance pay.

October

- Small eruptions occur at Soufriere Hills, causing no damage or casualties.

ANALYSIS OF EVENTS: 1999

BUSINESS AND THE ECONOMY

Several academic research teams and agencies from abroad began to consider ways to reclaim areas devastated by the Soufriere Hills volcano in 1997. Plans include re-vegetation efforts and possible ways of commercially utilizing volcanic debris. Pumice and ash might be incorporated into building materials, and the volcanic ash might be used for fertilizer. Replanting would offset erosion and prevent the ash from becoming airborne. Presently, the area affected by the volcano is uninhabited and totally unproductive economically, and the island's economy as a whole has been devastated, with 85% of its income derived from the British government. Researchers hope to obtain a grant of £250,000 for Montserrat from Britain's Department for International Development (DFID).

The regional Multi-Disciplinary Group (MDG), which is aimed at helping the island in the area of human resources, is putting its efforts behind development of the private sector to ensure employment and economic stability in the long term. Since the volcanic eruption of 1995, Montserrat has experienced a boom in the construction industry as houses and businesses have been rebuilt in the northern half of the island. The Caribbean Export Development Agency (CEDA), funded mostly by the European Union (EU),

pledged to assist in developing Montserrat's export capability.

The Montserrat Volcano Observatory (MVO) submitted a request to the DFID for the return of a small helicopter that it had provided for observing the Soufriere Hills volcano at a cost of $19,000 per month. A larger helicopter, brought from Antigua to the MVO for 90 minutes per week at a rate of $5,760 for a three-hour visit per week, had been substituted for the smaller to cut costs. The larger helicopter was inadequate for the type of monitoring the MVO needed to do on the volcano.

Montserrat's Ministry of Communications and Works announced in July that workers in the government-run electric and water utility companies may have to be laid off without severance pay when the utilities are merged in the near future. Due to the total depopulation of just under half of the island nation's 40 square miles, the utilities have recorded a loss of around $300,000, leaving them unable to afford severance pay. The ministry may apply to the DFID for funds to provide for the workers.

The updating of Britain's travel advisory for Montserrat, where more areas have now been declared safe for tourism, is expected to increase travel to the island. Tourism has always been a mainstay of Montserrat's economy, with most tourists hailing from the U.S., Canada, and Britain; but over the last four years visitors have amounted to less than 15% of the total in 1994, before the eruption of the Soufriere Hills volcano.

GOVERNMENT AND POLITICS

A January inquest by Montserrat's coroner into the deaths of 19 people in the 1997 eruption found British authorities liable in the deaths of nine. The inquest concluded that both local and UK officials were negligent in finding safe land to relocate the farmers who were killed, but the UK Foreign Office and the DFID maintain that it was impossible to find farming land in the safe areas of the island and that the farmers refused to leave, despite having full knowledge of the risks of remaining in the danger zone.

In March, the UK announced its decision to extend citizenship to the 150,000 inhabitants of its thirteen dependent territories, which will have to bring their legal system into conformity with Britain's as a condition for citizenship status. Britain will continue aid programs for Montserrat and St. Helena, its least developed territories. Inhabitants of Montserrat had already been granted full British citizenship after the 1997 eruption of the island's volcano.

Britain announced in April that it would fulfill its promise to provide the cost of travel to people who had been forced by volcanic activity in Montserrat to relocate to the United Kingdom or to other Caribbean countries. Britain's DFID is funding the Evacuee Return Air Fare Scheme (ERAFS), which will initially be in effect for two years beginning the first of May. It has been determined that the Soufriere Hills volcano is now quiet enough to allow a return to Montserrat.

In July, the government of Montserrat asked Britain that the proposed Caribbean Court of Justice (CCJ), which is expected to become a reality in 2000, be Montserrat's final court of appeal in cases dealing with the Caribbean Community (CARICOM) Single Market and Economy. Britain has already barred Montserrat, a dependent British territory, from recourse to the CCJ in criminal and civil matters, in which Britain's Privy Council remains the final court of appeal for Montserrat, as it does for most Caribbean states.

CULTURE AND SOCIETY

In October, heavy rains triggered relatively small explosions in the Soufriere Hills volcano, which erupted seriously in 1995 and again in 1997, when 19 people were killed. The latest explosions hurled ash and debris 15,000 feet into the air just after dawn and sprinkled mud onto houses in the surrounding area but caused no real damage. Scientists said the incident was an indication that the volcano is cooling down and returning to dormancy.

The head of the Montserrat Volcano Observatory announced in October that islanders may soon be able to move back into the southern areas of the island, where the Soufriere Hills volcano is located, and resettle villages that were abandoned when the volcano erupted in 1997. Authorities are still wary of health risks due to deposits of volcanic ash, which can cause lung disease when airborne. Several thousand people were evacuated to the north of Montserrat and abroad because of the eruption.

Animals left behind by evacuees in the eruption of Montserrat's volcano in 1995 reverted to the wild. Abandoned cattle and sheep were quickly adopted by farmers, but cats, dogs, and donkeys were left to multiply, causing problems for the island's inhabitants. The London-based World So-

ciety for the Protection of Animals captured hundreds of cats and dogs and sent them to shelters in the U.S., but donkeys have been left to roam. The Montserrat government placed a number of donkeys into corrals, where it is keeping them at a cost of almost $2,000 a month, until such time as they might be adopted. Meanwhile, donkeys still running loose cause damage to farms and interfere with road traffic. Montserrat's minister of agriculture was also looking into exporting some of the donkeys to the nearby islands of Grenada, Guadeloupe, Haiti, and Jamaica, though it was estimated that shipping the estimated 700 animals out of Montserrat would cost around $7,500, a sum difficult for the government to find.

DIRECTORY

CENTRAL GOVERNMENT
Head of State

Monarch
Elizabeth II, Queen of England

Governor
Anthony John Abbot, Governor's Office

Ministers

Prime Minister
David Brandt, Office of the Prime Minister, Old Towne, Brades, Montserrat
PHONE: +(664) 4912702
FAX: +(664) 4912711

Minister of Finance and Economic Development
David Brandt, Ministry of Finance and Economic Development
PHONE: +(664) 4913463

Minister of Education, Health, and Community Services
Adelina Tuitt, Ministry of Education, Health, and Community Services
PHONE: +(664) 4912541

Minister of Agriculture, Trade and the Environment
P. Austin Bramble, Ministry of Agriculture, Trade and the Environment
PHONE: +(664) 491 2546

Minister of Communications and Work
Rupert Weekes, Ministry of Communications and Work
PHONE: +(664) 4912521

POLITICAL ORGANIZATIONS

National Progressive Party (NPP)

NAME: Reuben T. Meade

Movement for National Reconstruction (MNR)

NAME: Percival Austin Bramble

People's Progressive Alliance (PPA)

NAME: Bertrand Osborne

National Develoment Party (NDP)

People's Liberation Movement (PLM)

NAME: Noel Tuitt

JUDICIAL SYSTEM

Magistrate's Court

Court of Summary

Eastern Caribbean Supreme Court

FURTHER READING
Articles

Hawley, Chris. "Volcano Leaves Donkey Debacle in Montserrat." *The Seattle Times*, 26 October 1999.

Howe, Darcus. "It's Time to Stop the Supply of Golden Elephants." *New Statesman*, 31 May 1999, p. 14.

Meyers, Gay Nagle. "Tourism Director Spearheads Montserrat's Slow Comeback." *Travel Weekly,* 16 September 1999, p. 1.

"The Montserrat Story." *Superscience* (October 1999): 4.

"Other World News: World News in Brief." *Facts on File*, 29 April 1999, p. 316.

Palmer, Stanley H. "Review of Books: Caribbean and Latin America." *American Historical Review* (April 1999): 612.

Voight, B. and R.S.J. Sparks. "Magma Flow Instability and Cyclic Activity at Soufriere Hills Volcano, Montserrat, British West Indies." *Science* (February 19, 1999): 1142.

MONTSERRAT: STATISTICAL DATA

For sources and notes see "Sources of Statistics" in the front of each volume.

GEOGRAPHY

Geography (1)

Area:

Total: 100 sq km.

Land: 100 sq km.

Water: 0 sq km.

Area—comparative: about 0.6 times the size of Washington, DC.

Land boundaries: 0 km.

Coastline: 40 km.

Climate: tropical; little daily or seasonal temperature variation.

Terrain: volcanic islands, mostly mountainous, with small coastal lowland.

Natural resources: NEGL.

Land use:

Arable land: 20%

Permanent crops: 0%

Permanent pastures: 10%

Forests and woodland: 40%

Other: 30% (1993 est.).

HUMAN FACTORS

Demographics (2B)

Population (July 1998 est.) 12,828

Age structure:

  0-14 years . . . . .NA

  15-64 years . . . . .NA

  65 years and over . . . . .NA

Population growth rate (1998 est.) 0.23%

Birth rate, 1998 est. (births/1,000 population) 14.27

Death rate, 1998 est. (deaths/1,000 population) . . .9.86

Net migration rate, 1998 est.
(migrant(s)/1,000 population) . . . .−2.12

Infant mortality rate, 1998 est.
(deaths/1,000 live births) 11.91

Life expectancy at birth (years):

  Total population 75.6

  Male 73.83

  Female (1998 est.) 77.4

Total fertility rate, 1998 est.
(children born/woman) 1.83

Demographic figures include an estimated 8,000 refugees who left the island following the resumption of volcanic activity in July 1995.

Ethnic Division (6)

Black, white.

Religions (7)

Anglican, Methodist, Roman Catholic, Pentecostal, Seventh-Day Adventist, other Christian denominations.

Languages (8)

English.

EDUCATION

Educational Attainment (10)

Age group (1980) . . . . .25+

Total population 5,544

Highest level attained (%)

  No schooling 1.7

  First level

    Not completed 84.6

    Completed . . . . .NA

  Entered second level

    S-1 . . . . .7.9

    S-2 . . . . .NA

  Postsecondary 5.8

GOVERNMENT & LAW

Political Parties (12)

Legislative Council	No. of seats
People's Progressive Alliance (PPA) 2	
Reconstruction (MNR) 2	
National Progressive Party (NPP) 1	
Independent 2	

Government Budget (13B)

Revenues . . . . .NA
Expenditures . . . . .NA

NA stands for not available.

Military Affairs (14A)

Defense is the responsibility of the UK.

LABOR FORCE

Labor Force (16)

Total 4,521
. . . . .40.5%
Construction 13.5%
Trade, restaurants, and hotels 12.3%
Manufacturing 10.5%
Agriculture, forestry, and fishing 8.8%
Other 14.4%

Data for 1992 Percent distribution for 1983 est. Total later substantially lowered by flight of people from volcanic activity.

Unemployment Rate (17)

6% (1995)

PRODUCTION SECTOR

Electric Energy (18)

Capacity . . . . .4,000 kW (1995)
Production . . . . .15 million kWh (1995)
Consumption per capita . . . . .1,178 kWh (1995)

Transportation (19)

Highways:
total: 269 km
paved: 203 km
unpaved: 66 km (1995)
Merchant marine: none
Airports: 1 (1997 est.)
Airports—with paved runways:
total: 1
914 to 1,523 m: 1 (1997 est.)

Top Agricultural Products (20)

Cabbages, carrots, cucumbers, tomatoes, onions, peppers; livestock products.

FINANCE, ECONOMICS, & TRADE

Economic Indicators (22)

National product: GDP—purchasing power parity—$43 million (1996 est.)
National product real growth rate: -20.2% (1996 est.)
National product per capita: $5,000 (1996 est.)
Inflation rate—consumer price index: 6.2% (1996 est.)

MANUFACTURING SECTOR

GDP & Manufacturing Summary (21)

	1980	1985	1990	1992	1993	1994
Gross Domestic Product						
Millions of 1990 dollars	48	54	71	69	69	74
Growth rate in percent	10.22	4.73	−10.83	1.30	−0.30	6.62
Per capita (in 1990 dollars)	4,029.6	4,880.7	6,464.6	6,288.8	6,269.9	6,685.3
Manufacturing Value Added						
Millions of 1990 dollars	3	3	4	4	4	4
Growth rate in percent	10.71	0.00	−10.42	2.79	1.37	7.51
Manufacturing share in percent of current prices	5.7	5.5	4.6	NA	NA	NA

FINANCE, ECONOMICS,& TRADE

Balance of Payments (23)

	1990	1991	1992	1993	1994
Exports of goods (f.o.b.)	1	1	2	2	3
Imports of goods (f.o.b.)	−42	−34	−30	−24	−30
Trade balance	−41	−33	−28	−22	−27
Services - debits	−15	−14	−14	−15	−20
Services - credits	19	19	21	24	28
Private transfers (net)	−0	−0	1	—	1
Government transfers (net)	14	6	7	3	−1
Overall balance	−23	−21	−13	−10	−19

Exchange Rates (24)

Exchange rates: East Caribbean dollars (EC$) per US$1—2.7000 (fixed rate since 1976)

Top Import Origins (25)

$29.9 million (f.o.b., 1994 est.)

Origins	%
NA	NA

NA stands for not available.

Top Export Destinations (26)

$12.1 million (f.o.b., 1995 est.).

Destinations	%
United States	NA
Ireland	NA

NA stands for not available.

Economic Aid (27)

$NA. NA stands for not available.

Import Export Commodities (28)

Import Commodities	Export Commodities
Machinery and transportation equipment	Electronic components
Foodstuffs	Plastic bags
Manufactured goods	Apparel
Fuels	Hot peppers
Lubricants and related materials	Live plants
	Cattle

MOROCCO

Kingdom of Morocco
Al-Mamlakah al-Maghribiyah

CAPITAL: Rabat.

FLAG: The national flag consists of a green five-pointed star at the center of a red field.

ANTHEM: The *Hymne Chérifien* is a twentieth-century composition without words.

MONETARY UNIT: The dirham (DH) is a paper currency of 100 Moroccan centimes. There are coins of 1, 5, 10, and 20 Moroccan centimes and 1, and 5 dirhams, and notes of 5, 10, 50, 100, and 200 dirhams. DH1 = $0.11515 (or $1 = DH8.684).

WEIGHTS AND MEASURES: The metric system is the legal standard.

HOLIDAYS: New Year's Day, 1 January; Anniversary of the King's Accession, 3 March; Labor Day, 1 May; National Day, 14 August; Anniversary of the Green March, 6 November; Independence Day, 18 November. Movable religious holidays include 'Id al-Fitr, 'Id al-'Adha', 1st of Muharram (Muslim New Year), and Milad an-Nabi.

TIME: GMT.

LOCATION AND SIZE: Situated at the northwestern corner of Africa, Morocco claims a total area of 446,550 square kilometers (172,414 square miles), of which the Western Sahara comprises 252,120 square kilometers (97,344 square miles). The Western Sahara is claimed and administered by Morocco but, as of 1997, its ownership has been under dispute.

Comparatively, the area occupied by Morocco is slightly larger than the state of California. Morocco's total boundary length is 3,837 kilometers (2,389 miles). All data include Western Sahara unless otherwise noted. The capital city, Rabat, is located on the Atlantic coast.

CLIMATE: The rugged mountain ranges and the Atlantic Ocean moderate the tropical heat of Morocco. Temperatures in Casablanca range from an average minimum of 7°C (45°F) to a maximum of 17°C (63°F) in January and from a minimum of 18°C (64°F) to a maximum of 26°C (79°F) in July. Maximum annual rainfall of 75–100 centimeters (30–40 inches) occurs in the northwest, while other parts of the country receive much less.

INTRODUCTORY SURVEY

RECENT HISTORY

On 30 March 1912, the French made Morocco a protectorate under Marshal Louis Lyautey. The Moroccans sought independence, first in the Rif War (1921–26), in which they were defeated by the combined French and Spanish forces, and later by forming the National Action Bloc in 1934. The Franco-Moroccan agreement of 2 March 1956 granted independence, and Muhammad V became king of Morocco. Incorporated into the new nation was Tangier, formerly a British territory.

After the death of Muhammad V on 26 February 1961, his son was crowned King Hassan II and became head of government. A third constitution, approved on 1 March 1972, transferred many of the king's executive and legislative powers to a parliament which was to have two-thirds of its members directly elected.

In 1975, Spain announced its intention of withdrawing from phosphate-rich Spanish Sahara (now the Western Sahara), and ceded the northern two-thirds of the region to Morocco and the southern third to Mauritania. However, the guerrilla group Polisario, backed by Algeria, challenged the annexation and proclaimed Western Sahara as the Saharan Arab Democratic Republic (SADR). By the early 1980s, Morocco had moved up to 100,000 soldiers into Western Sahara in a costly effort to put down the Polisario revolt.

In 1988, United Nations (UN) Secretary General Perez de Cuellar persuaded Moroccan and

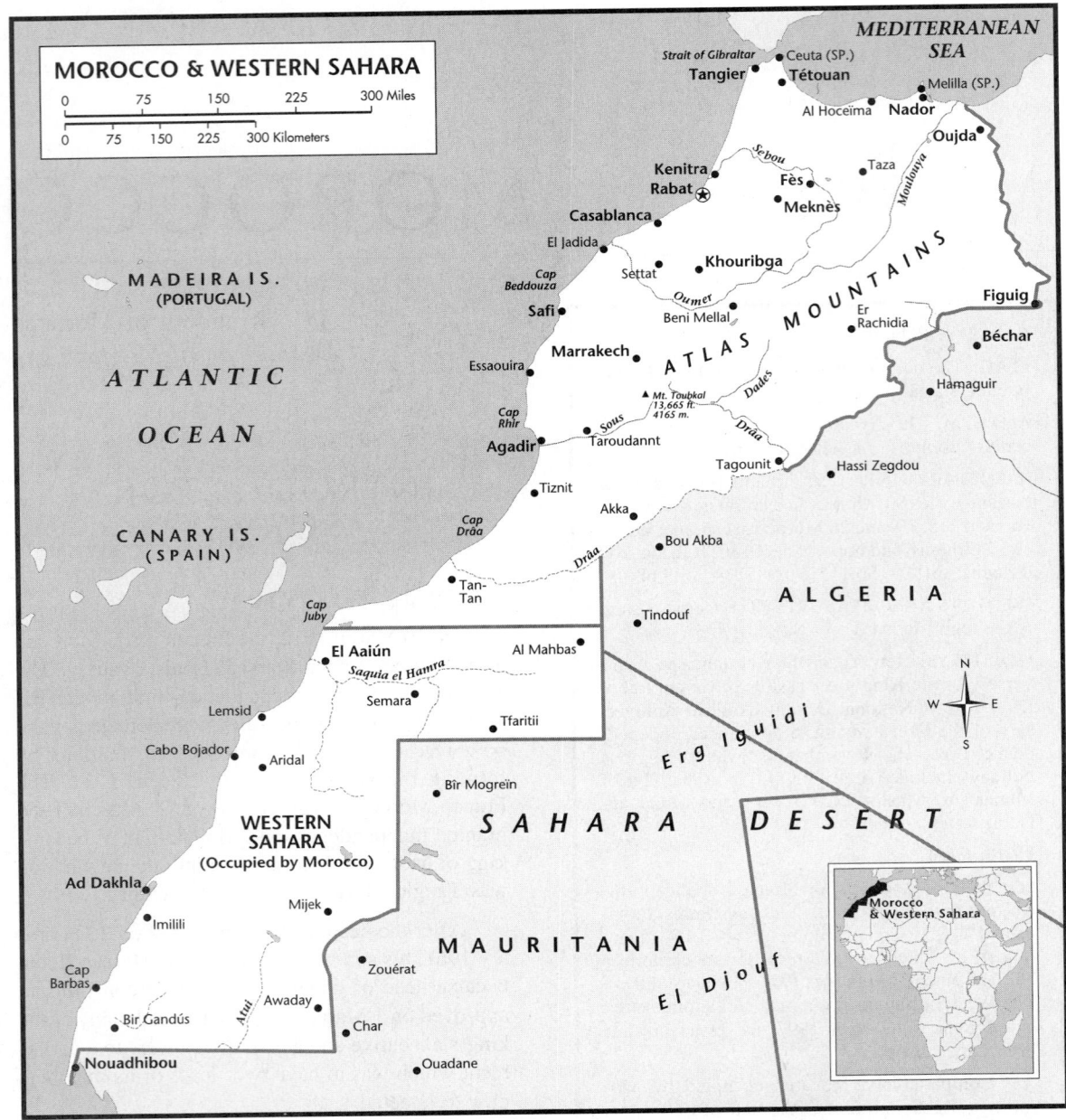

MOROCCO & WESTERN SAHARA

0   75   150   225   300 Miles

0   75   150   225   300 Kilometers

Polisario representatives to accept a peace plan which included a cease-fire (effective in September 1991), and a referendum for the territory on independence or integration with Morocco.

Israeli Prime Minister Yitzhak Rabin made a public visit in 1993 as King Hassan continued to play a moderate role in the search for an Arab-Israel settlement. King Hassan's government maintains close relations with Saudi Arabia and the other Gulf states and was the first Arab nation to condemn the Iraqi invasion of Kuwait.

In 1996, King Hassan proposed to make the entire parliament directly elected. Previously, one-third of the deputies were appointed, giving the king power to undermine any opposition majority.

GOVERNMENT

The Moroccan crown is hereditary, and the king claims descent from the Prophet Muhammad. He can dismiss the parliament (if in session) and bypass elected institutions by submitting a referendum to the people on any major issue, or whenever parliament rejects a bill he favors. He presides over the cabinet and under certain circumstances may declare a state of emergency. The constitution of 1992, approved by referendum, provides for a constitutional monarchy with increased authority for the prime minister. In 1997, King Hassan proposed revising the constitution to make the entire parliament directly elected and to create a new chamber of appointed ministers. The proposal was accepted in time for the 1997 elections.

Judiciary

Morocco has a dual legal system consisting of secular courts based on French legal tradition, and Islamic courts which rule on family and inheritance cases for Moroccan Muslims. The secular system includes district courts, appellate courts, and a Supreme Court. A special court may try officials on charges raised by a two-thirds majority of the full Majlis (legislature). The Islamic court system does not provide for appeals. Cases are decided on the basis of the Koran and derivative Shari'a.

Political Parties

Morocco has a well-developed multiparty system with 16 officially recognized parties. The National Union of Popular Forces (Union Nationale des Forces Populaires–UNFP), formed in September 1959, formally split into two parties in 1974. The more radical trade union wing called itself the UNFP and the political wing formed the Socialist Union of Popular Forces (Union Socialiste des Forces Populaires–USFP). The program of the Moroccan Communist Party has been similar to that of the UNFP. From 1969 to 1974 it was banned, but since then it has appeared under various names, including the Party for Progress and Socialism (Parti du Progrès et du Socialisme–PPS). The Istiqlal (Independence) Party follows a reformist program and backs the king only on specific issues.

DEFENSE

Total Moroccan armed strength in 1995 was 194,000. The army had 175,000 men, the navy 6,000, and the air force 13,000. Military hardware included 826 main battle tanks and 100 light tanks; 1 frigate and 27 patrol and coastal combatant ships and boats; and 112 combat aircraft, including 3 jet squadrons. Some 60 Moroccan troops were stationed in Equatorial Guinea and 2,000 in the United Arab Emirates. Polisario, the Western Saharan insurgent force, had 10,000 men. The United Nations has 370 observers in Morocco. The 1996 budget called for defense expenditures of $1.3 billion, or 4.2% of the gross domestic product (GDP).

ECONOMIC AFFAIRS

The major resources of the Moroccan economy are agriculture, phosphates, and tourism. Morocco is the world's third-largest producer of phosphates, and varying prices for phosphates on the international market greatly influence Morocco's economy. Tourism and money sent home by Moroccans working abroad have played a critical role since independence.

The high cost of imports, especially of petroleum imports, is a major problem. Another chronic problem is unreliable rainfall, which produces drought or sudden floods. Morocco suffers from unemployment, inflation, a large debt, and a shortage of trained managers and administrators.

Public Finance

The U.S. Central Intelligence Agency estimates that, in 1994, government revenues totaled approximately $8.1 billion and expenditures $8.9 billion. External debt totaled $20.5 billion, approximately 67% of which was financed abroad.

Prior to 1996, the budget year coincided with the calendar year. Because of agriculture's large impact on the economy, Moroccans voted to amend the constitution so that the budget would be issued in July instead of January. This shift of six months gives the government time to take agricultural output into account before releasing the budget.

The 1996–97 budget called for a 3.4% decline in the deficit. The reduction would be achieved by cuts in subsidies and government investments and by increases in revenues because of new initiatives aimed at reducing tax evasion and fraud.

Income

In 1997 Morocco's gross national product (GNP) was $107 billion, or about $3,500 per person. For the period 1985–95 the average inflation rate was 4.8%, resulting in a real growth rate in GNP of 0.8% per person.

Industry

The manufacturing sector produces light consumer goods, especially foodstuffs, beverages, textiles, matches, and metal and leather products. Heavy industry is largely limited to petroleum refining, chemical fertilizers, automobile and tractor assembly, foundry work (making objects by pouring metal into a mold), asphalt, and cement. Many of the processed agricultural products and consumer goods are primarily used for local consumption, but Morocco exports canned fish and fruit, wine, leather goods, and textiles, as well as such traditional Moroccan handicrafts as carpets and brass, copper, silver, and wood implements.

There are three oil refineries, several petrochemical plants, a polyvinyl chloride factory, and four phosphate-processing plants. There are four plants assembling cars and small utility vehicles: Renault Moroc, Sopriam, Somaca, and Smeia. Nine cement factories reached a total of 6.35 million tons in 1995. Output of phosphoric acid is typically 1.1 million tons per year.

Banking and Finance

The Bank of Morocco (Bank al-Maghrib), the central bank, has the sole privilege of note issue. It is required to maintain a gold or convertible currency reserve equal to one-ninth of its note issue. The Ministry of Finance is responsible for the organization of banking and the money market. The money supply, as measured by M2, amounted to DH186.66 billion as of December 1995. In February 1996 the central bank gave clearance for banks and finance houses to issue corporate bonds. Consumer credit companies are expected to be the first to take advantage of the new ruling. Other reforms scheduled for 1996 included a secondary market in public debt, an interbank foreign exchange market, and the launch of privatization bonds and global depository receipts (GDRs). By 1997, only the interbank foreign exchange market had been implemented. From May 2, commercial banks were permitted to buy and sell foreign currency at market-determined rates, where previously foreign exchange rates were fixed on a daily basis by the central bank.

Exchange control regulations are set and administered by an agency of the Ministry of Finance. Most exports are not licensed. An exporter must repatriate any exchange received, and according to 1971 regulations, foreign exchange brought into Morocco must be declared and exchanged for dirhams at authorized banks. There is no foreign exchange market in Morocco.

Commercial banks must have 51% majority ownership; some foreign banks were Moroccanized in 1975. There were 14 commercial banks in 1996, most of which are partly owned by European banks. The largest private commercial bank is the Banque Commerciale du Maroc (BCM), which is 32% owned by foreign banks, including Banco Central Hispano, Credito Italiano, and Crédit Commercial de France. Public sector financial organizations specializing in development finance include the National Bank for Economic Development, Moroccan Bank for Foreign Trade, National Agricultural Credit Bank, and Deposit and Investment Fund. Also instrumental in development finance is the Bureau of Mineral Exploration and Participation, which has participatory interests in the production of all coal, petroleum, lead, and manganese. The National Bank for Economic Development, established in 1959, has been particularly active in financing manufacturing. The Agricultural Credit Bank makes loans to credit organizations, public institutions, and cooperatives. Private individuals borrow from local agricultural credit banks or from the agricultural credit and provident societies. The stock exchange (Bourse des Valeurs) at Casablanca handles mostly European and a few North African issues.

The Casablanca stock market is undergoing a program of reform designed to attract increased interest from overseas and local investors. In 1993 the government approved legislation to turn the bourse into a private company with stock held by brokers, to create new stock trading bodies and to channel the funds of small savers into share issues and unit trusts. In 1995, France agreed to finance further improvements, modeling the exchange on the Paris bourse and introducing computerization.

Economic Development

Government policy stresses expansion and development of the economy, essentially through private enterprise. Morocco decided to abide by the IMF's Article VIII, thus beginning the privatization of 112 public entities—mainly manufacturing enterprises, hotels, and financial institutions—slated for divestiture under the 1989 privatization law.

Morocco has instituted a series of development plans to modernize the economy and increase production. Net investment under the five-year plan for 1960–64 was DH6.6 billion (about $1.3 billion). The plan called for a growth rate of 6.2%, but by 1964 the growth rate had reached only 3%. A new three-year plan (1965–67) was inaugurated in 1965, with a revised annual growth target of 3.7%. The main emphasis of the plan was on the development and modernization of the agricultural sector. The five-year development plan for 1968–72 called for expenditures of DH998 million, of which DH460 million was for agriculture and irrigation. The development of the tourist industry also figured prominently in the plan. The objective was to attain an annual 5% growth rate in GDP; the real growth rate actually exceeded 6% a year.

The five-year plan for 1973–77 envisaged an investment of DH26.3 billion and a real economic growth of 7.5% annually. Industries singled out for development included chemicals (especially phosphoric acid), phosphate production, paper products, and metal fabrication. Tourist development was also stressed. In 1975, King Hassan II announced a 50% increase in investment targets to allow for the effects of inflation.

The 1978–80 plan was one of stabilization and retrenchment, designed to improve Morocco's balance of payments position, but the 4% annual growth rate achieved was disappointing. The ambitious five-year plan for 1981–85, estimated to cost more than $18 billion, aimed at achieving a growth rate of 6.5% annually. The plan's principal priority was to create some 900,000 new jobs and to train managers and workers in modern agricultural and industrial techniques. Other major goals were to increase production in agriculture and fisheries to make the country self-sufficient in food, and to develop energy (by building more hydroelectric installations and by finding more petroleum and other fossil fuels), industry, and tourism to enable Morocco to lessen its dependence on foreign loans. The plan called for significant expansion of irrigated land, for increased public works projects such as hospitals and schools, and for economic decentralization and regional development through the construction of 25 new industrial parks outside the crowded Casablanca-Kénitra coastal area. Proposed infrastructural improvements included the $2 billion rail line from Marrakech to El Aaiún; a new fishing port at Ad-Dakhla, near Argoub in the Western Sahara; and a bridge-tunnel complex across the Strait of Gibraltar to link Morocco directly with Spain. New large industrial projects include phosphoric acid plants, sugar refineries, mines to exploit cobalt, coal, silver, lead, and copper deposits, and oil-shale development. The drought and Morocco's growing debt problem held back some of these projects, however.

By 1991, U.S. bilateral aid amounted to $137.8 million. Outstanding foreign debt commitments and their serving remain a significant obstacle to economic development. The 1992 financing requirements were mostly covered, largely because of grants and bilateral credit. Despite the cancellation by Saudi Arabia of $2.8 billion of debt, the total still exceeded $23 billion. Despite reschedulings through both the Paris Club of official creditors and the London Club of commercial creditors, servicing the debt accounted for 30% of exports of goods and services.

SOCIAL WELFARE

The social security system covers employees and apprentices in industrial and commercial fields and the professions, as well as in agriculture and forestry. There is also voluntary coverage for persons leaving covered employment, and voluntary complementary insurance is available. Benefits include maternity allowances, disability pensions, old age pensions, death allowances, and allowances for illness.

Women comprise about 35% of the work force and are employed mostly in the industrial, service, and teaching sectors. They have the right to vote and run for office (in 1993 two women were elected to parliament). However, women do not have equal status under Islamic family and estate laws. In 1995, women obtained the right to get a passport without the husband's permission.

Healthcare

Health conditions are relatively poor, but programs of mass education in child and parent hygiene, as well as government supervised health services in schools and colleges, have helped to raise standards. Campaigns have been conducted against malaria, tuberculosis, venereal diseases, and cancer. However, gastrointestinal infections, malaria, typhoid, trachoma, and tuberculosis remain widespread. The World Health Organization (WHO) and the United Nations Children's Fund (UNICEF) have cooperated in the government's campaigns against eye disorders and venereal diseases.

In 1989–95, 70% of the population had access to health care services. There was one physician per 4,665 people in 1993. The average estimated life expectancy was 66 in 1995.

Housing

Since the 1950s, significant numbers of Moroccans (estimated at over 4 million) have moved from the countryside to the urban centers to escape rural unemployment. Housing and sanitation, consequently, have become urban problems. The government is engaged in a low-cost housing program to reduce the slum areas, called *bidonvilles,* that have formed around the large urban centers, especially Casablanca and Rabat. Loans have been available for private home construction, and builders have also received financial and technical assistance from the government to build workers' housing.

EDUCATION

In 1995, the overall illiteracy rate was an estimated 56% (43.4% for men and 69% for women). The school system includes modern secular public institutions, traditional religious schools, and private schools. Nine years of compulsory primary education was made a law in 1962. In 1994, over 3 million pupils were in primary school and 1.3 million in secondary school. In vocational schools, there were 18,762 students. Girls leave school at a younger age than boys and are a minority in secondary, as well as primary, schools; they make up fewer than one-third of university students. The language of instruction in primary schools is Arabic during the first two years, and both Arabic and French are used for the next three years.

Morocco has six universities. Al-Qarawiyin University at Fès, founded in 859, is reputed to be the oldest university in the world. The first modern Moroccan university, the University of Rabat (now the Muhammad V University), was opened in 1957. Other universities are Muhammad bin 'Abdallah (founded 1974), in Fès; Hassan II (1975), Casablanca; Cadi Ayyad (1978), Marrakech; and Muhammad I (1978), Oujda. There are about two dozen colleges and conservatories. In 1994, enrollment at all higher level institutions was 250,919.

1999 KEY EVENTS TIMELINE

March

- The most powerful observatory in North Africa opens in Rabat, Morocco, with a planetarium seating 40 people.

April

- King Hassan II accepts that the families of dissidents detained in the 1960s and 1970s should be compensated.

May

- A high level delegation of Israelis visits Morocco to meet with the king and participate in the meetings of the World Union of Moroccan Jews.

June

- President Hosni Mubarak of Egypt meets with King Hassan II for the annual meeting of the Egyptian-Morocco committee.

July

- King Hassan II, 70, dies of a heart attack July 23. He ruled for 38 years and is succeeded by his son, Crown Prince Sidi Muhammad, 35, who will rule as King Mohammed VI. He is the 18th monarch of the 400 year-old Alawite dynasty.

August

- Algeria accuses Morocco of harboring Islamists who are bent on overthrowing the Algerian government, including those responsible for a massacre of 30 Algerians near the Moroccan border. Algeria closed the border between the two nations in 1994 when Moroccans imposed entry visa requirements on Algerians seeking to enter the country.

September

- Crown Prince Abdullah of Saudi Arabia pays official visits to Morocco and to Algeria, during which he suggests a direct meeting between the two neighbors to iron out differences.

- Abraham Serfaty, head of the banned Marxist-Leninist ''Ila al-Aman'' movement, who was removed to France in 1991 after serving 17 years in prison as a threat to the monarchy, writes to the new king for permission to return to Morocco, and permission is granted.

October

- King Mohammed VI opens the Moroccan parliament; the king stressed investment, education, and solutions to the unemployment problem in his speech.

November

- Without warning, King Muhammad VI dismisses Driss Basri, Minister of the Interior and long time power broker of Hassan II.

December

- The children of Mehdi Ben Barka, a Moroccan exile who disappeared in Paris and was allegedly tortured to death, are welcomed back to Morocco in an official reception at Rabat airport by two of the king's representatives and two cabinet ministers who were supporters of Ben Barka.

- King Mohammed makes a brief visit to Tunisia, where he meets with President Zine el-Abidine Ben Ali. The two leaders call for a summit meeting of Arab nations.

ANALYSIS OF EVENTS: 1999

BUSINESS AND THE ECONOMY

Morocco's economy is fragile. Agriculture accounts for 17 percent of its gross domestic product (GDP), and the economy has been hard hit due to a severe drought in 1999. Foreign debt servicing consumes more than a third of the government's revenues.

There are more than 2,000,000 people without jobs in a workforce of 10,000,000 and a population of 29,000,000. More than 12,000,000 Moroccans live below the poverty line. The economy is highly dependent on remittances—almost $2 billion a year—from Moroccans working in Europe. Due to its geographic position, Morocco acts as the gateway for illegal immigrants crossing the Straits of Gibraltar to enter Europe. It is estimated that Spain employs at least 700,000 illegal immigrants, which strains its relations with northern European members of the European Union. Spain still has control of two enclaves on the Moroccan coast—Ceuta and Melilla, which are the easiest entryways for the immigrants to Europe. Both Morocco and Spain attempt to give the appearance of working at stopping the illegal immigration. However, both economies are dependent on these workers: Spain for cheap labor and Morocco for the remittances they bring.

Morocco has rewritten its petroleum law to entice foreign oil exploration interest. Royal Dutch/Shell Group and Britain's Enterprise have responded. The new laws reduce the maximum state holding from 25 to 50 percent if a discovery is made, and exempt exploration companies from corporate tax for ten years from the first production. Energy purchases were expected to cost the nation nearly a billion dollars. Morocco is actively seeking foreign business in this sector. The rise in petroleum prices at the end of the year do not augur well for Moroccans, who pay very steep taxes—as much as 75 percent of the actual price—for petroleum products. However, these taxes account for more than 14% of the government's revenues.

GOVERNMENT AND POLITICS

Mohammed VI assumed power on his father's death in July. He is unmarried and has an international law degree from France. The new ruler has claimed that his role model is King Juan Carlos of Spain, a constitutional monarch. He is projecting a more liberal attitude than this father, though he works within the autocratic system designed by his father. In his early weeks in office, Mohammed VI allowed a long-time dissident in exile to return home, pardoned and released over 8,000 prisoners, and reduced the sentences of over 38,000 others imprisoned in Morocco. He named an official spokesman for the palace in order to have direct communication with the press. The king also set up a committee to consider compensation for the families of political activists who disappeared in the 1960s and 1970s when social unrest was very pronounced against his father, Hassan II. Mohammed VI's father had acknowledged the disappearance of 112 such people; human rights organizations place the number at closer to 500.

In addition, the new king had to resolve the power play going on between the prime minister, Abderrahmane Youssoufi and Driss Basri, his father's power broker and Minister of the Interior for 20 years. The decision was made in November, when the King summarily dismissed Basri from the government. Ahmed el Midaoui, a security official Basri had fired two years before, replaced him. This bold move should bring profound changes as it strikes at a security cabal of police, auxiliary forces, and local authorities which Basri had built and over which he presided.

Relations with Algeria since the April election of President Abdelaziz Bouteflika look to improve. However, a vociferous verbal attack against Morocco over the issue of Morocco's harboring of Islamist extremists bent on bringing down the Algerian government for the past seven years came in a speech by Bouteflika following a massacre of Algerians near the Moroccan border.

The ties between the two countries are also strained from the long-running issue of the fate of the Western Sahara, a former Spanish colony. Algiers supports the Polasario Front in its liberation struggle while Morocco claims to be the legitimate government of the former Spanish colony. A U.N. supervised referendum regarding the fate of the territory has been set and put off several times since 1992. It is now tentatively scheduled for July 2000. Algeria now insists that it is no longer involved in the dispute. The latest head of the peace process, Charles Dunbar of the United States, resigned in frustration in March. Dunbar claimed that the process is merely producing an expensive and never-ending series of negotiations while more than 100,000 Saharawis remain in exile, having fled the country when Morocco occupied it in 1975.

Morocco currently has 100,000 soldiers and ''emigrants'' in the territory. Under Hassan II the referendum was continually blocked because the Moroccan king only wanted a result that would be favorable to Morocco and not independence for the former Spanish colony. It remains to be seen how the new king will approach the issue. His dismissal of Driss Basri, who had coordinated the former King's administrative moves for the incorporation of Western Sahara into Morocco, could signal a profound change in Moroccan policy in that dispute. The new king has moved for a formation of commissions for greater consultation with the people of the Western Sahara and for economic development to produce jobs there. However, the changes he signals do not as yet indicate a willingness to forego his father's goal of Moroccan incorporation of the phosphate-rich territory at all cost.

CULTURE AND SOCIETY

Faced with high adult unemployment, Moroccans in poor rural areas frequently respond by sending their children to work at lower wages, which employers are more willing to pay. This severely impacts girls' access to education. The Moroccan government admits that there are well over 500,000 child laborers in the country. Many are sold by their parents for a monthly sum of $10 for as long as the child works in conditions that frequently approach slavery. Over 60 percent of the population is illiterate. Mohammed VI is emphasizing education in his policy statements.

In another sign that change may come about under the new ruler, King Mohammed VI appointed Morocco's first female ambassador in three decades—Aziza Bennani—as the country's permanent ambassador to UNESCO in Paris. The only previous appointment of a woman for such a high-ranking post was by the King's father, who appointed his sister as ambassador to the United Kingdom and to Italy.

Morocco is on a campaign to win the bid for hosting the 2006 World Cup. In its bid to FIFA, the international soccer federation, Morocco suggested that it should be the first African country to host the World Cup due to its geographic location, expertise, past organization of international events, infrastructure, and history in the sport.

A special education commission which Hassan II appointed has not resolved the issue of the recognition of Moroccan Berber languages. The native Tamazight is not recognized by the Moroccan constitutions of September 13, 1969 despite the fact that an estimated 50 percent of the population claim Berber languages as a mother tongue. Arabic remains the official language of Morocco.

DIRECTORY

CENTRAL GOVERNMENT

Head of State

King
Mohammed VI, Monarch

Prime Minister
Abderrahmane Youssoufi, Office of the Prime Minister, Palais Royal, Le Mochouar, Rabat, Morocco
PHONE: +212 (7) 763804; 761763; 762425
FAX: +212 (7) 769995; 769195

Ministers

Minister of Foreign Affairs and Co-operation
Mohamed Benaissa, Ministry of Foreign Affairs and Co-operation, Avenue Roosevelt, Rabat, Morocco
PHONE: +212 (7) 762841; 761125; 762550
FAX: +212 (7) 765508; 764679
E-MAIL: ministere@maec.gov.ma

Minister of State and Interior
Driss Basri, Ministry of State and Interior, Quartier Administratif, Rabat, Morocco
PHONE: +212 (7) 761861; 760301
FAX: +212 (7) 762056

Minister of Justice
Omar Azziman, Ministry of Justice, Place Mamounia, Rabat, Morocco
PHONE: +212 (7) 732941
FAX: +212 (7) 730772

Minister of Waqf and Islamic Affairs

Abdelkabir M'Daghri Alaouim, Ministry of Waqf and Islamic Affairs, Le Mchouar, Rabat, Morocco

PHONE: +212 (7) 766801

FAX: +212 (7) 760532; 760185; 765282

Minister of Country Planning, Environment, Town Planning, and Housing

Mohamed el-Yazghi, Ministry of Country Planning, Environment, Town Planning, and Housing

PHONE: +212 (7) 763539; 764863

FAX: +212 (7) 763510

Minister of Economy and Finance

Fathallah Oualalou, Ministry of Economy and Finance, Boulevard Mohammed V, Quartier Administratif, 10000 Rabat, Morocco

PHONE: +212 (7) 765504

FAX: +212 (7) 761575

E-MAIL: ministre@mfie.gov.ma

Minister of Agriculture, Rural Development and Maritime Fishing

Habib Malki, Ministry of Agriculture, Rural Development and Maritime Fishing, Quartier Administratif, Place Abdallah Chefchaouni, BP 607, Rabat, Morocco

PHONE: +212 (7) 760933; 760993; 760102

FAX: +212 (7) 763378

Minister of Industry, Commerce, and Handicrafts

Alami Tazi, Ministry of Industry, Commerce, and Handicrafts, Quartier des Ministries, Rabat-Chellah, Morocco

PHONE: +212 (7) 761868; 761508

FAX: +212 (7) 766265

E-MAIL: ministre@mcinet.gov.ma

Minister of Social Development, Solidarity, Employment, and Vocational Training

Khalid Alioua, Ministry of Social Development, Solidarity, Employment, and Vocational Training

PHONE: +212 (7) 761855; 760318

FAX: +212 (7) 768881

Minister of Tourism

Hassan Sebbar, Ministry of Tourism, Quartier Administratif, Rabat, Morocco

PHONE: +212 (7) 761701; 761702

FAX: +212 (7) 763633

POLITICAL ORGANIZATIONS

Partide l'Istiqlal (PI)

4, avenue Ibn Toumert, Bab el-Had, Rabat, Morocco

PHONE: +212 (7) 730951; 730952; 730953

FAX: +212 (7) 725354; 736129; 732183

TITLE: Secretary General

NAME: Abbas el-Fassi

Mouvement populaire (MP)

66, rue Patrice Lumumba, Rabat, Morocco

PHONE: +212 (7) 767320; 766431

FAX: +212 (7) 767537

TITLE: Secretary General

NAME: Mohamed Laensar

Union nationale des forces populaires (UNFP)

28, rue Magellan, Casablanca 01, Morocco

PHONE: +212 (2) 302023

FAX: +212 (2) 319301

TITLE: Secretary General

NAME: Abdellah Ibrahimi

Mouvement populaire democratique et constitutionnel (MPDC)

352, blvd. Mohamed V, Rabat, Morocco

PHONE: +212 (7) 734601

FAX: +212 (7) 319301

TITLE: Secretary General

NAME: Abdelkrim Khatib

Parti du progres et du socialisme

4, rue Ibn Zakour Quartier des Orangers, Rabat, Morocco

PHONE: +212 (7) 208672; 208673

FAX: +212 (7) 208674

TITLE: Secretary General

NAME: Ismail Alaoui

Union socialiste des forces popularies (USFP)

17, rue Oued Souss. Agdal, Rabat, Morocco

PHONE: +212 (7) 773902; 773903; 773905

FAX: +212 (7) 773901

TITLE: Secretary General

NAME: Abderrahmane el-Youssoufi

Rassemblement national des independants (RNI)

6, rue Laos, avenue Hassan II, Rabat, Morocco

PHONE: +212 (7) 721420; 721424

FAX: +212 (7) 733824
TITLE: President
NAME: Ahmed Osman

Parti national democrate (PND)

18, rue de Tunis-Hassan, Rabat, Morocco
PHONE: +212 (7) 732127; 730754
FAX: +212 (7) 720170
TITLE: General Secretary
NAME: Mohamed Arsalane el-Jadidi

Union constitutionelle (UC)

158, avenue des FAR, Casablanca, Morocco
PHONE: +212 (2) 313630; 312229; 441142
FAX: +212 (2) 441141
TITLE: General Secretary
NAME: Mohamed Arsalane el-Jadidi

Organisation de l'action democratique populaire (OADP)

29, avenue Lalla Yacout, Apt. N1, BP 15797, Casablanca, Morocco
PHONE: +212 (2) 278442
FAX: +212 (2) 278442
TITLE: General Secretary
NAME: Mohamed Bensaid Ait Idder

Mouvement national populaire (MNP)

avenue Imam Malik, rue el-Madani Belhoussni Souissi, Rabat, Morocco
PHONE: +212 (7) 753623
FAX: +212 (7) 759761
TITLE: General Secretary
NAME: Mahjoubi Aherdane

Parti de l'avant garde democratique et social (PAGDS)

avenue Imam Malik, rue el-Madani Belhoussni Souissi, Rabat, Morocco
PHONE: +212 (7) 200559
FAX: +212 (7) 708491
TITLE: Porte Parole
NAME: Ahmed Benjelloune

Mouvement democrate social (MDS)

avenue Imam Malik, rue el-Madani Belhoussni Souissi, Rabat, Morocco
PHONE: +212 (7) 709110; 709495
TITLE: General Secretary
NAME: Mahmoud Archane

Parti socialiste democratique (PSD)

43, rue Abou Fariss al-Marini, Rabat, Morocco
PHONE: +212 (7) 208571; 208572; 208573
FAX: +212 (7) 208573
TITLE: General Secretary
NAME: Aissa Ouardighi

Parti du front des forces democratiques (FFD)

13, blvd. Tarik Ibnou Ziad, Rabat, Morocco
PHONE: +212 (7) 661623; 661624; 661625
FAX: +212 (7) 208573
TITLE: General Secretary
NAME: Thami Khyari

Parti de l'action (PA)

113, avenue Allal Ben Abdellah, Rabat, Morocco
PHONE: +212 (7) 206661
FAX: +212 (7) 208573
TITLE: General Secretary
NAME: Mohammed el-Drissi

DIPLOMATIC REPRESENTATION

Embassies in Morocco

Algeria

46-48, rue Tarek lbn Ziad, BP 448, Rabat, Morocco
PHONE: +212 (7) 765591; 765092; 765474
FAX: +212 (7) 762237
TITLE: Ambassador
NAME: M'hamed Lakhdar Belaid

Angola

PHONE: +212 (7) 659239
FAX: +212 (7) 659238
TITLE: Ambassador
NAME: Luis Jos de Almeida

Argentina

12, rue Mekki Bittaouri, Souissi, Rabat, Morocco
PHONE: +212 (7) 755120; 754181
FAX: +212 (7) 755410
TITLE: Ambassador
NAME: Adolfo Enrique Nanclares

Austria

2, Zankat Tiddas, BP 135, Rabat, Morocco
PHONE: +212 (7) 764003; 761698
FAX: +212 (7) 765425
TITLE: Ambassador
NAME: Michael Fitz

Bangladesh
25, avenue Tarek Ibn Ziad, Rabat, Morocco
PHONE: +212 (7) 766731; 760963
FAX: +212 (7) 766729
TITLE: Ambassador
NAME: Muhammad Syed Hussain

Belgium
6, avenue de Marrakech, BP 163, Rabat, Morocco
PHONE: +212 (7) 764746
FAX: +212 (7) 767003
TITLE: Ambassador
NAME: André Fontaine

Brazil
3, rue Cadi Benjelloun, La Pinede, Rabat, Morocco
PHONE: +212 (7) 755151; 755219
TITLE: Ambassador
NAME: Antonio Sabino Contuaria Guimaraes

Bulgaria
4, avenue de Meknes, BP 1301, Rabat, Morocco
PHONE: +212 (7) 763201
TITLE: Ambassador
NAME: Georgi Benchev Karev

Burkina Faso
7, rue el-Bouziri-Agdal, BP 6484, 10101 Rabat, Morocco
PHONE: +212 (7) 675512; 675518
FAX: +212 (7) 675517
TITLE: Ambassador
NAME: Assimi Kouanda

Cameroon
20, rue du Rif, Souissi, BP 1790, Rabat, Morocco
PHONE: +212 (7) 754194
TITLE: Ambassador
NAME: Mahamat Paba Sale

Canada
13 bis, rue Jaafar Assadik, BP 709, Agdal, Rabat, Morocco
PHONE: +212 (7) 672880
FAX: +212 (7) 672178
TITLE: Ambassador
NAME: Mark Bailey

Central African Republic
42, Avenue Pasteur, BP 770, Agdal, Rabat, Morocco
PHONE: +212 (7) 732685; 734198
FAX: +212 (7) 672178
TITLE: Ambassador
NAME: Martin Koyou Kombele

Chile
35, av. Ahmed Balafrej, Souissi, Rabat, Morocco
PHONE: +212 (7) 636065
FAX: +212 (7) 672178

China
16, Charia Hadj Ahmed Balafrej, Souissi, Rabat, Morocco
PHONE: +212 (7) 754056
FAX: +212 (7) 757519
TITLE: Ambassador
NAME: An Guozheng

Colombia
29, av. Michlifen, Imm. Moulay Driss, 2Šme App., Agdal, Rabat, Morocco
PHONE: +212 (7) 670804; 670805
FAX: +212 (7) 670802
TITLE: Ambassador
NAME: Ximena Andrade de Casalino

Republic of Congo
34, avenue al-Nasr, Rabat, Morocco
PHONE: +212 (7) 734862

Côte d'Ivoire
21, rue de Tiddas, BP 192, Rabat, Morocco
PHONE: +212 (7) 763151
FAX: +212 (7) 762792
TITLE: Ambassador
NAME: Amadou Thiam

Croatia
73, rue Marnissa, Souissi, Rabat, Morocco
PHONE: +212 (7) 638824

Czech Republic
PHONE: +212 (7) 755421
FAX: +212 (7) 755420
TITLE: Ambassador
NAME: Marie Zajikova

Denmark
4, rue de Khemisset, BP 203, Rabat, Morocco
PHONE: +212 (7) 769293; 766986
FAX: +212 (7) 769709
TITLE: Ambassador
NAME: Troels Simon Peter Branner

Djibouti
31, rue Aljazair, Rabat, Morocco
PHONE: +212 (7) 731833; 731834
FAX: +212 (7) 706821
TITLE: Ambassador
NAME: Ahmed Amine Fathallah

Equatorial Guinea
30, avenue des Nations Unies, Agdal, Rabat, Morocco

PHONE: +212 (7) 774205; 774674

Finland
16, rue Khemisset, Rabat, Morocco
PHONE: +212 (7) 762312
FAX: +212 (7) 762352
TITLE: Charge d'Affaires
NAME: Kristi Westphalen

France
3, Zankat Sahnoun, Agdal, Rabat, Morocco
PHONE: +212 (7) 689700
TITLE: Ambassador
NAME: Michel de Bonnecorse

Gabon
PHONE: +212 (7) 751950; 751968
FAX: +212 (7) 757550
TITLE: Ambassador
NAME: Victor Afounouna

Germany
7, rue Madnine, BP 235, Rabat, Morocco
PHONE: +212 (7) 709662; 708375
FAX: +212 (7) 706851
TITLE: Ambassador
NAME: Herwing Bartels

Greece
23, rue d'Oujda, Tour Hassan, Rabat, Morocco
PHONE: +212 (7) 723839; 733446
FAX: +212 (7) 702270
TITLE: Ambassador
NAME: Kodellis Dionyssios

Guinea
15, rue Hamza, Agdal, Rabat, Morocco
PHONE: +212 (7) 674148; 673488
FAX: +212 (7) 672513
TITLE: Ambassador
NAME: Aly Kaba

Hungary
190 OLM, Souissi, BP 5026, Rabat, Morocco
PHONE: +212 (7) 750757; 757503
FAX: +212 (7) 754123
TITLE: Charge d'Affaires
NAME: Janos Terenyi

India
13, Charia Michlifen, Agdal, Rabat, Morocco
PHONE: +212 (7) 671339; 675974
FAX: +212 (7) 671269
TITLE: Ambassador
NAME: Indraht Singh Rathore

Indonesia
PHONE: +212 (7) 757860; 757861
FAX: +212 (7) 757859

TITLE: Ambassador
NAME: Iskandar Dinata

Iran
Route des Zaers, avenue Bir Kassem, Km 4,8, BP 490, Souissi, Rabat, Morocco
PHONE: +212 (7) 752167; 750353
FAX: +212 (7) 659118
TITLE: Ambassador
NAME: Jaafar Chemissane

Iraq
39, avenue Mehdi Ben Barka, Souissi, Rabat, Morocco
PHONE: +212 (7) 754466
FAX: +212 (7) 795745
TITLE: Ambassador
NAME: Abdeljabbar Omar Ghani Addouri

Israel
52, avenue Mehdi Ben Barka; Souissi, Rabat, Morocco
PHONE: +212 (7) 657680; 657682
FAX: +212 (7) 657683
TITLE: Chief of the Bureau of Liaison
NAME: David Dadon

Italy
2, avenue Driss Al Azhar, Rabat, Morocco
PHONE: +212 (7) 706597; 706792; 706912
FAX: +212 (7) 706882
TITLE: Ambassador
NAME: Emilio Franco DeStefanis

Japan
39, avenue Ahmed Balafrej, Souissi, Rabat, Morocco
PHONE: +212 (7) 631782
FAX: +212 (7) 750078
TITLE: Ambassador
NAME: Hiromi Sato

Jordan
65, Villa Ouafae, Cit OLM, Souissi II, Rabat, Morocco
PHONE: +212 (7) 751125; 759270
FAX: +212 (7) 758722
TITLE: Ambassador
NAME: Mohamed Hassan Soleimane Addaoudia

Kuwait
avenue Imam Malik, Km 4,3, Souissi, Rabat, Morocco
PHONE: +212 (7) 751775; 754588; 754623
FAX: +212 (7) 753591
TITLE: Ambassador
NAME: Souleyman Ibrahim el-Marjane

Lebanon
19, avenue de Fes, Hassan, Rabat, Morocco
PHONE: +212 (7) 761614; 760728
FAX: +212 (7) 760949
TITLE: Ambassador
NAME: Mostapha Hassan Mostapha

Liberia
Lotissement 7, Napabia, rue Oulad Frej, Souissi, Rabat, Morocco
PHONE: +212 (7) 638426

Libya
1, rue Chouaib Doukkali, Rabat, Morocco
PHONE: +212 (7) 769566
TITLE: Ambassador
NAME: Embarek Abdullah Turki

Malaysia
2, Villa Amin, avenue Marrakech, Rabat, Morocco
PHONE: +212 (7) 767389; 767423
FAX: +212 (7) 767819

Mali
56, Cit OLM, Souissi II, Rabat, Morocco
PHONE: +212 (7) 759125
FAX: +212 (7) 754742

Malta
12, rue Ghomara, Souissi, Rabat, Morocco
PHONE: +212 (7) 750897
FAX: +212 (7) 750897
TITLE: Ambassador
NAME: Claude Petiet

Mauritania
266, Quartier OLM, Rabat, Morocco
PHONE: +212 (7) 656678; 656679
FAX: +212 (7) 656680
TITLE: Ambassador
NAME: Mohamed Lamine Ould Yahya

Mexico
6, rue Kadi Mohamed Bebri, BP 1789, Souissi, Rabat, Morocco
PHONE: +212 (7) 631969
FAX: +212 (7) 768583
TITLE: Ambassador
NAME: Francisco Jos Cruz Gonzalez

Netherlands
40, rue de Tunis, BP 329, Rabat, Morocco
PHONE: +212 (7) 733512
FAX: +212 (7) 773333
TITLE: Ambassador
NAME: Hendrik Van Pesch

Niger
14 bis, rue Jabal al-Ayachi, Agdal, Rabat, Morocco
PHONE: +212 (7) 674615
FAX: +212 (7) 768583

Nigeria
70, avenue Omar Ibn al-Khattab, BP 347, Agdal, Rabat, Morocco
PHONE: +212 (7) 771856
TITLE: Ambassador
NAME: Mohamed Salah Abdelouahab

Norway
9, rue Khenifra, Agdal, Rabat, Morocco
PHONE: +212 (7) 764085

Oman
21, rue Hamza, Agdal, Rabat, Morocco
PHONE: +212 (7) 772788
FAX: +212 (7) 674567
TITLE: Ambassador
NAME: Mohammed Bin Salim al-Shanfari

Pakistan
11, rue Azrou, Hassan, Rabat, Morocco
PHONE: +212 (7) 766453; 762402
FAX: +212 (7) 766742
TITLE: Ambassador
NAME: Hassan Azmat

Palestine
4, rue Soussa, BP 387, Rabat, Morocco
PHONE: +212 (7) 766008; 769807
FAX: +212 (7) 767166
TITLE: Ambassador
NAME: Ouajih Hassan Ali Kacem Abou Marouane

Peru
16, rue Ifrane, Rabat, Morocco
PHONE: +212 (7) 723236; 733284
FAX: +212 (7) 702803
TITLE: Ambassador
NAME: Juan Enrique Arevalo

Poland
23, rue Oqbah, Agdal, BP 425, Rabat, Morocco
PHONE: +212 (7) 771173; 771791
FAX: +212 (7) 775320
TITLE: Ambassador
NAME: Piotr Szymanowski

Portugal
5, rue Thami Lamdouar, Souissi, Rabat, Morocco
PHONE: +212 (7) 756446
FAX: +212 (7) 756445

TITLE: Ambassador
NAME: Manuel Silva Pereira

Qatar
4, avenue Tarik Ibn Ziad, BP 1220, Rabat, Morocco
PHONE: +212 (7) 765681
FAX: +212 (7) 756445
TITLE: Ambassador
NAME: Mohamed Hassan

Romania
10, rue Ouazzane, Rabat, Morocco
PHONE: +212 (7) 738611; 724694
FAX: +212 (7) 700196
TITLE: Ambassador
NAME: Ioan Balin

Russia
Avenue Imam Malik, km 4, Rabat, Morocco
PHONE: +212 (7) 753609; 753527; 753509
FAX: +212 (7) 753590
TITLE: Ambassador
NAME: Kolotoucha Vassili Ivanovitch

Saudi Arabia
43, place de l'Unit Africaine, Rabat, Morocco
PHONE: +212 (7) 730171; 732794; 734827
FAX: +212 (7) 768587
TITLE: Ambassador
NAME: Abdelaziz Khodja

Senegal
17, rue Cadi Ben Hamadi Senhaji, Souissi, Rabat, Morocco
PHONE: +212 (7) 754171
FAX: +212 (7) 753590
TITLE: Ambassador
NAME: Doudou Diop

South Africa
34, rue des Saadiens Hassan, Rabat, Morocco
PHONE: +212 (7) 706760
FAX: +212 (7) 706756
TITLE: Charge d'Affaires
NAME: Johannes Reinhard Mostert

South Korea
41, avenue Mehdi Benbarka, Souissi, Rabat, Morocco
PHONE: +212 (7) 751767; 751966
FAX: +212 (7) 750189
TITLE: Ambassador
NAME: Dong Ho Kim

Spain
3, Zankat Madnine, Rabat, Morocco
PHONE: +212 (7) 707600; 707980

FAX: +212 (7) 707387
TITLE: Ambassador
NAME: Jorge Dezcallar Mazzaredo

Sudan
5, rue Ghomara, Souissi, Rabat, Morocco
PHONE: +212 (7) 752864; 752863
FAX: +212 (7) 752865
TITLE: Ambassador
NAME: Sadik Youssef Abou Akila

Sweden
159, avenue John Kennedy, Souissi, BP 428, Rabat, Morocco
PHONE: +212 (7) 759308; 759318; 759313
FAX: +212 (7) 758048

Switzerland
Square de Berkane, Hassan, BP 169, Rabat, Morocco
PHONE: +212 (7) 706974; 707512
FAX: +212 (7) 705749
TITLE: Ambassador
NAME: Henri Cuennet

Syria
Km 3,2, Route des Zaers, Souissi, BP 5158, Rabat, Morocco
PHONE: +212 (7) 757521; 755551
FAX: +212 (7) 757522
TITLE: Ambassador
NAME: Ali Hassan

Thailand
11, rue Tiddas, BP 4436, Rabat, Morocco
PHONE: +212 (7) 763328; 763365
FAX: +212 (7) 763920
TITLE: Ambassador
NAME: Naronk Khemayodhin

Tunisia
6, avenue de Fes, Rabat, Morocco
PHONE: +212 (7) 730636; 730576; 727866
FAX: +212 (7) 730637
TITLE: Ambassador
NAME: Mounji Bousnina

Turkey
7, avenue de Fes, Rabat, Morocco
PHONE: +212 (7) 762605; 762658
FAX: +212 (7) 704980
TITLE: Ambassador
NAME: Husein Naci Akinci

United Arab Emirates
11, blvd. al-Alaouiyine, Rabat, Morocco
PHONE: +212 (7) 730975; 730917; 730976
FAX: +212 (7) 724146; 724148

TITLE: Ambassador
NAME: Issa Hamad Abou Chihab

United Kingdom
17, boulevard de la Tour Hassan, BP 45, Rabat, Morocco
PHONE: +212 (7) 720905; 731403; 704532
FAX: +212 (7) 704531
TITLE: Ambassador
NAME: Anthony Michael Layden

United States
3, Zankat Madnine, Rabat, Morocco
PHONE: +212 (7) 758181; 762265
FAX: +212 (7) 750863
TITLE: Ambassador
NAME: Edward M. Gabriel

JUDICIAL SYSTEM
Supreme Court
Apellate Court
District Court
Islamic Court

FURTHER READING
Articles
"Breaching the Ramparts." *The Economist* (January 2, 1999).

"An Endless Dance in the Desert." *The Economist* (March 27, 1999).

"Morocco." *Africa Confidential* 40, 23 (November 19, 1999).

"Morocco's Humanitarian King." *The Economist* (July 31, 1999).

Internet
"A Long Way to Go Before Official Recognition." *North Africa Journal.* November 19, 1999. Available Online @ http://www.africanews.org/north/morocco/stories/19991119_feat4.html (December 5, 1999).

"As Petroleum Price Increases, Debate Focuses on the Tax Regime in Morocco." *North Africa Journal*, November 29, 1999. Available Online @ http://www.africanews.org/north/morocco/stories/19991129/19991129_feat3.html (December 5, 1999).

"Who is Driss Basri?" *North Africa Journal.* November 16, 1999. Available Online @ www.africanews.org/north/morocco/stories/19991116_feat2.html (December 5, 1999).

Zunes, Stephen. *"In Focus: Morocco and Western Sahara."* December 1998. Available Online @ www.igc.org/infocus/briefs/vol3/v3n42mor.html (December 4, 1999).

MOROCCO: STATISTICAL DATA

For sources and notes see "Sources of Statistics" in the front of each volume.

GEOGRAPHY

Geography (1)

Area:

Total: 446,550 sq km.

Land: 446,300 sq km.

Water: 250 sq km.

Area—comparative: slightly larger than California.

Land boundaries:

Total: 2,017.9 km.

Border countries: Algeria 1,559 km, Western Sahara 443 km, Spain (Ceuta) 6.3 km, Spain (Melilla) 9.6 km.

Coastline: 1,835 km.

Climate: Mediterranean, becoming more extreme in the interior.

Terrain: northern coast and interior are mountainous with large areas of bordering plateaus, intermontane valleys, and rich coastal plains.

Natural resources: phosphates, iron ore, manganese, lead, zinc, fish, salt.

Land use:

Arable land: 21%

Permanent crops: 1%

Permanent pastures: 47%

Forests and woodland: 20%

Other: 11% (1993 est.).

HUMAN FACTORS

Demographics (2A)

	1990	1995	1998	2000	2010	2020	2030	2040	2050
Population	24,685.1	27,460.8	29,114.5	30,205.4	35,638.1	40,839.3	45,448.9	49,263.7	52,068.6
Net migration rate (per 1,000 population)	NA	NA	NA	NA	NA	NA	NA	NA	NA
Births	NA	NA	NA	NA	NA	NA	NA	NA	NA
Deaths	NA	NA	NA	NA	NA	NA	NA	NA	NA
Life expectancy - males	63.8	65.4	66.5	67.2	70.3	72.9	75.0	76.5	77.7
Life expectancy - females	67.8	69.6	70.6	71.3	74.4	77.0	79.2	80.9	82.3
Birth rate (per 1,000)	31.3	28.0	26.4	25.2	21.1	17.9	15.6	14.2	13.1
Death rate (per 1,000)	7.4	6.6	6.2	6.0	5.3	5.2	5.7	6.9	8.3
Women of reproductive age (15-49 yrs.)	5,930.8	6,867.4	7,493.7	7,934.4	9,727.0	11,028.5	11,777.4	11,917.7	11,872.2
of which are currently married	NA	NA	NA	NA	NA	NA	NA	NA	NA
Fertility rate	4.4	3.7	3.3	3.1	2.5	2.2	2.1	2.0	2.0

Except as noted, values for vital statistics are in thousands; life expectancy is in years.

Health Personnel (3)

Total health expenditure as a percentage of GDP, 1990-1997[a]

Public sector 1.2

Private sector 2.4

Total[b] 3.6

Health expenditure per capita in U.S. dollars, 1990-1997[a]

Purchasing power parity 124

Total 49

Availability of health care facilities per 100,000 people

Hospital beds 1990-1997[a] 110

Doctors 1993[c] 34

Nurses 1993[c] 94

Health Indicators (4)

Life expectancy at birth

1980 58

1997 67

Daily per capita supply of calories (1996) 3,244

Total fertility rate births per woman (1997) 3.1

Maternal mortality ratio per 100,000 live births (1990-97) . . . . .370[f]

Safe water % of population with access (1995) 57

Sanitation % of population with access (1995) 68

Consumption of iodized salt % of households (1992-98)[a] . . . .

Smoking prevalence

Male % of adults (1985-95)[a] 40

Female % of adults (1985-95)[a] 9

Tuberculosis incidence per 100,000 people (1997) 122

Adult HIV prevalence % of population ages 15-49 (1997) 0.03

Infants and Malnutrition (5)

Under-5 mortality rate (1997) 72

% of infants with low birthweight (1990-97) 9

Births attended by skilled health staff % of total[a] . . .40

% fully immunized (1995-97)

TB 94

DPT 95

Polio 95

Measles 92

Prevalence of child malnutrition under age 5 (1992-97)[b] 10

Ethnic Division (6)

Arab-Berber 99.1%

Other 0.7%

Jewish 0.2%

Religions (7)

Muslim 98.7%

Christian 1.1%

Jewish 0.2%

Languages (8)

Arabic (official), Berber dialects, French often the language of business, government, and diplomacy.

EDUCATION

Public Education Expenditures (9)

Public expenditure on education (% of GNP)

1980 . . . . .6.1

1996 . . . . .5.3

Expenditure per student

Primary % of GNP per capita

1980 . . . . .15.6

1996 . . . . .14.3

Secondary % of GNP per capita

1980 . . . . .54.8

1996 . . . .

Tertiary % of GNP per capita

1980 . . . . .155.4

1996 . . . . .72.3[1]

Expenditure on teaching materials

Primary % of total for level (1996) 0.2

Secondary % of total for level (1996) 1.0

Primary pupil-teacher ratio per teacher (1996) 28

Duration of primary education years (1995) 6

Literacy Rates (11A)

In thousands and percent[1]	1990	1995	2000	2010
Illiterate population (15+ yrs.)	9,124	9,730	10,153	10,507
Literacy rate - total adult pop. (%)	38.6	43.7	48.4	57.4
Literacy rate - males (%)	52.0	56.6	60.7	68.0
Literacy rate - females (%)	25.6	31.0	36.3	47.0

GOVERNMENT & LAW

Political Parties (12)

Chamber of Representatives	No. of seats
Socialist Union of Popular Forces (USFP)	.57
Constitutional Union (UC)	.50
National Rally of Independents (RNI)	.46
Popular Movement (MP)	.40
Social Democratic Movement (MDS)	.32
Istiqlal Party (IP)	.32

National Popular Movement (MNP) 19
National Democratic Party (PND) 10
Popular Constitutional and Democratic Movement (MPCD) 9
Party of Progress and Socialism (PPS) 9
Democratic Forces Front (FFD) 9
Democratic Socialist Party (PSD) 5
Organization of Democratic and Popular Action (OADP) 4
Action Party (PA) 2
Democracy and Istiqlal Party (PDI) 1

Military Affairs (14B)

	1990	1991	1992	1993	1994	1995
Military expenditures						
Current dollars (mil.)	1,419	1,255	1,709	1,354	1,374	1,375
1995 constant dollars (mil.)	1,631	1,387	1,839	1,420	1,408	1,375
Armed forces (000)	195	195	195	195	195	195
Gross national product (GNP)						
Current dollars (mil.)	26,460	29,250	28,740	29,090	33,460	32,290
1995 constant dollars (mil.)	30,410	32,320	30,910	30,500	34,300	32,290
Central government expenditures (CGE)						
1995 constant dollars (mil.)	9,120	9,379	9,712	NA	10,210[e]	NA
People (mil.)	26.2	26.8	27.4	28.0	28.6	29.2
Military expenditure as % of GNP	5.4	4.3	5.9	4.7	4.1	4.3
Military expenditure as % of CGE	17.9	14.8	18.9	NA	13.8	NA
Military expenditure per capita (1995 $)	62	52	67	51	49	47
Armed forces per 1,000 people (soldiers)	7.5	7.3	7.1	7.0	6.8	6.7
GNP per capita (1995 $)	1,162	1,208	1,130	1,091	1,201	1,107
Arms imports[6]						
Current dollars (mil.)	220	60	90	70	110	50
1995 constant dollars (mil.)	253	66	97	73	113	50
Arms exports[6]						
Current dollars (mil.)	0	0	0	0	0	0
1995 constant dollars (mil.)	0	0	0	0	0	0
Total imports[7]						
Current dollars (mil.)	6,800	6,873	7,348	6,760	7,188	8,563
1995 constant dollars (mil.)	7,815	7,595	7,904	7,087	7,368	8,563
Total exports[7]						
Current dollars (mil.)	4,265	4,313	3,984	3,991	4,013	4,824
1995 constant dollars (mil.)	4,902	4,766	4,285	4,184	4,114	4,824
Arms as percent of total imports[8]	3.2	.9	1.2	1.0	1.5	.6
Arms as percent of total exports[8]	0	0	0	0	0	0

Government Budget (13A)

Year: 1995

Total Expenditures: 93,889 Millions of Dirhams

Expenditures as a percentage of the total by function:

General public services and public order 17.31

Defense 13.56

Education 16.55

Health 3.12

Social Security and Welfare 6.96

Housing and community amenities 36

Recreational, cultural, and religious affairs 92

Fuel and energy 69

Agriculture, forestry, fishing, and hunting 4.15

Mining, manufacturing, and construction ....-

Transportation and communication 4.33

Other economic affairs and services 77

Crime (15)

Crime rate (for 1994)

Crimes reported 227,296

Total persons convicted ....NA

Crimes per 100,000 population 855

Persons responsible for offenses

Total number of suspects 219,894

Total number of female suspects 38,637

Total number of juvenile suspects 989

LABOR FORCE

Labor Force (16)

Total (million) 7.4

Agriculture 50%

Services 26%

Industry 15%

Other 9%

Data for 1985.

Unemployment Rate (17)

16% (1997 est.)

PRODUCTION SECTOR

Electric Energy (18)

Capacity ....3.788 million kW (1995)

Production ....10.8 billion kWh (1995)

Consumption per capita ....411 kWh (1995)

Transportation (19)

Highways:

total: 60,626 km

paved: 30,556 km (including 219 km of expressways)

unpaved: 30,070 km (1996 est.)

Pipelines: crude oil 362 km; petroleum products 491 km (abandoned); natural gas 241 km

Merchant marine:

total: 40 ships (1,000 GRT or over) totaling 205,053 GRT/259,339 DWT ships by type: cargo 9, chemical tanker 6, container 2, oil tanker 3, refrigerated cargo 11, roll-on/roll-off cargo 8, short-sea passenger 1 (1997 est.)

Airports: 70 (1997 est.)

Airports—with paved runways:

total: 26

over 3,047 m: 11

2,438 to 3,047 m: 4

1,524 to 2,437 m: 7

914 to 1,523 m: 3

under 914 m: 1 (1997 est.)

Airports—with unpaved runways:

total: 44

2,438 to 3,047 m: 1

1,524 to 2,437 m: 11

914 to 1,523 m: 21

under 914 m: 11 (1997 est.)

Top Agricultural Products (20)

Barley, wheat, citrus, wine, vegetables, olives; livestock.

MANUFACTURING SECTOR

GDP & Manufacturing Summary (21)

Detailed value added figures are listed by both International Standard Industry Code (ISIC) and product title.

	1980	1985	1990	1994
GDP ($-1990 mil.)[1]	17,733	20,850	25,826	28,743
Per capita ($-1990)[1]	915	956	1,061	1,085
Manufacturing share (%) (current prices)[1]	17.8	19.4	20.0	20.7
Manufacturing				
Value added ($-1990 mil.)[1]	3,198	3,975	4,888	5,179
Industrial production index	100	104	120	130
Value added ($ mil.)	1,485	1,372	3,360	4,165
Gross output ($ mil.)	6,244	4,704	11,261	12,188
Employment (000)	176	227	307	393

	1980	1985	1990	1994
Profitability (% of gross output)				
Intermediate input (%)	77	71	71	68
Wages and salaries inc. supplements (%)	13	12	11	13
Gross operating surplus	10	16	18	20
Productivity ($)				
Gross output per worker	33,920	19,786	35,324	29,758
Value added per worker	7,801	5,664	10,141	9,769
Average wage (inc. supplements)	4,363	2,434	3,774	3,784
Value added ($ mil.)				
311/2 Food products	130	110	144	304
313 Beverages	62	126	408	588
314 Tobacco products	38	117	224	249
321 Textiles	202	172	315	414
322 Wearing apparel	32	45	228	336
323 Leather and fur products	15	11	24	20
324 Footwear	24	20	44	35
331 Wood and wood products	30	34	65	72
332 Furniture and fixtures	19	7	14	16
341 Paper and paper products	64	64	151	127
342 Printing and publishing	26	19	43	32
351 Industrial chemicals	127	166	403	464
352 Other chemical products	97	13	30	22
353 Petroleum refineries	114	90	248	365
354 Miscellaneous petroleum and coal products	NA	NA	NA	NA
355 Rubber products	34	38	60	71
356 Plastic products	20	17	40	48
361 Pottery, china and earthenware	6	2	6	6
362 Glass and glass products	10	5	7	7
369 Other non-metal mineral products	154	80	315	333
371 Iron and steel	7	4	56	56
372 Non-ferrous metals	8	4	25	25
381 Metal products	110	96	166	211
382 Non-electrical machinery	30	24	60	72
383 Electrical machinery	61	56	132	133
384 Transport equipment	62	49	140	148
385 Professional and scientific equipment	1	3	7	7
390 Other manufacturing industries	2	1	4	5

FINANCE, ECONOMICS, & TRADE

Economic Indicators (22)

National product: GDP—purchasing power parity—$107 billion (1997 est.)

National product real growth rate: -2.2% (1997 est.)

National product per capita: $3,500 (1997 est.)

Inflation rate—consumer price index: 3% (1997 est.)

Balance of Payments (23)

	1992	1993	1994	1995	1996
Exports of goods (f.o.b.)	5,010	4,936	5,541	6,871	6,886
Imports of goods (f.o.b.)	−7,473	−7,001	−7,648	−9,268	−8,997
Trade balance	−2,463	−2,065	−2,107	−2,397	−2,111
Services - debits	−2,920	−3,024	−3,124	−3,632	−3,482
Services - credits	2,417	2,274	2,238	2,247	2,549
Private transfers (net)	208	154	173	70	50
Government transfers (net)	2,325	2,141	2,096	2,191	2,366
Overall balance	−433	−521	−723	−1,521	−627

Exchange Rates (24)

Exchange rates:

Moroccan dirhams (DH) per US$1

January 1998	.9.822
1997	.9.527
1996	.8.716
1995	.8.540
1994	.9.203
1993	.9.299

Top Import Origins (25)

$9.7 billion (c.i.f., 1996)

Origins	%
mostly franc zone and Western Europe	NA

NA stands for not available.

Top Export Destinations (26)

$6.9 billion (f.o.b., 1996) Data are for 1996 est.

Destinations	%
European Union	.63
Japan	.7.7
India	.6.6
United States	.3.4
Libya	.3.4

Economic Aid (27)

Recipient: ODA, $297 million (1993). Note: $2.8 billion debt canceled by Saudi Arabia (1991).

Import Export Commodities (28)

Import Commodities	Export Commodities
Semiprocessed goods 26%	Food and beverages 30%
Capital goods 25%	Semiprocessed goods 23%
Food and beverages 18%	Consumer goods 21%
Fuel and lubricants 15%	Phosphates 17%
Consumer goods 12%	
Raw materials 4%	

MOZAMBIQUE

Republic of Mozambique
República Popular de Moçambique

CAPITAL: Maputo (formerly Lourenço Marques).

FLAG: The flag consists of broad stripes of green, black, and yellow, separated by narrow bands of white. Extending from the hoist is a red triangle; centered on the triangle is a yellow five-pointed star upon which is a white book over which are crossed the black silhouettes of a hoe and an AK47 rifle.

ANTHEM: Begins "Viva viva FRELIMO."

MONETARY UNIT: The Mozambique escudo (ME), linked until 1977 with the Portuguese escudo, was in June 1980 renamed the metical (MT); it is a paper currency of 100 centavos. There are coins of 1, 2, 5, 10, and 20 meticais, and notes of 50, 100, 500, and 1,000 meticais. MT1 = $0.00009 (or $1 = MT11,478.05).

WEIGHTS AND MEASURES: The metric system is in use.

HOLIDAYS: New Year's Day, 1 January; Heroes' Day, 3 February; Women's Day, 7 April; Workers' Day, 1 May; Independence Day, 25 June; Victory Day, 7 September; Day of Revolution, 25 September; Christmas, 25 December.

TIME: 2 PM = noon GMT.

LOCATION AND SIZE: Located on the southeastern coast of Africa, Mozambique (Moçambique) has an area of 801,590 square kilometers (309,496 square miles), slightly less than twice the size of the state of California. It has a total boundary length of 7,003 kilometers (4,351 miles).

CLIMATE: The wet season has monthly average temperatures between 27°C and 29°C (81°–84°F); the dry season has June and July temperatures averaging 18°–20°C (64°–68°F). The average annual rainfall is greatest, about 142 centimeters (56 inches), over the western hills and the central areas.

INTRODUCTORY SURVEY

RECENT HISTORY

Mozambique was occupied by Bantu peoples by about AD 1000. Later, trade developed with Arabs who crossed the Indian Ocean. The first Europeans in the area, the Portuguese, began to settle and trade on the coast early in the sixteenth century. During the seventeenth century, they set up plantations and estates. By the end of the nineteenth century, Portugal had made boundary agreements with its colonial rivals, the United Kingdom and Germany, and had suppressed much of the African resistance in the interior. After the Portuguese revolution of 1926, the influence of trading companies in Mozambique declined, and in 1951 it became an overseas province of Portugal.

On 25 June 1962, the Mozambique Liberation Front (FRELIMO) was formed and on 25 September 1964 began the armed struggle for independence. Samora Machel became president of FRELIMO in December 1970, after its first president, Eduardo Mondlane, was assassinated. Following the Portuguese revolution of 25 April 1974, Portuguese and FRELIMO representatives negotiated an independence agreement, and Mozambique became officially independent at midnight on 24–25 June 1975. Machel, who became the nation's first president, quickly affirmed Mozambique's support of the movement for African control of Rhodesia (now Zimbabwe), and on 3 March 1976, Mozambique closed its border with Rhodesia.

After independence, FRELIMO was transformed from a liberation movement into a

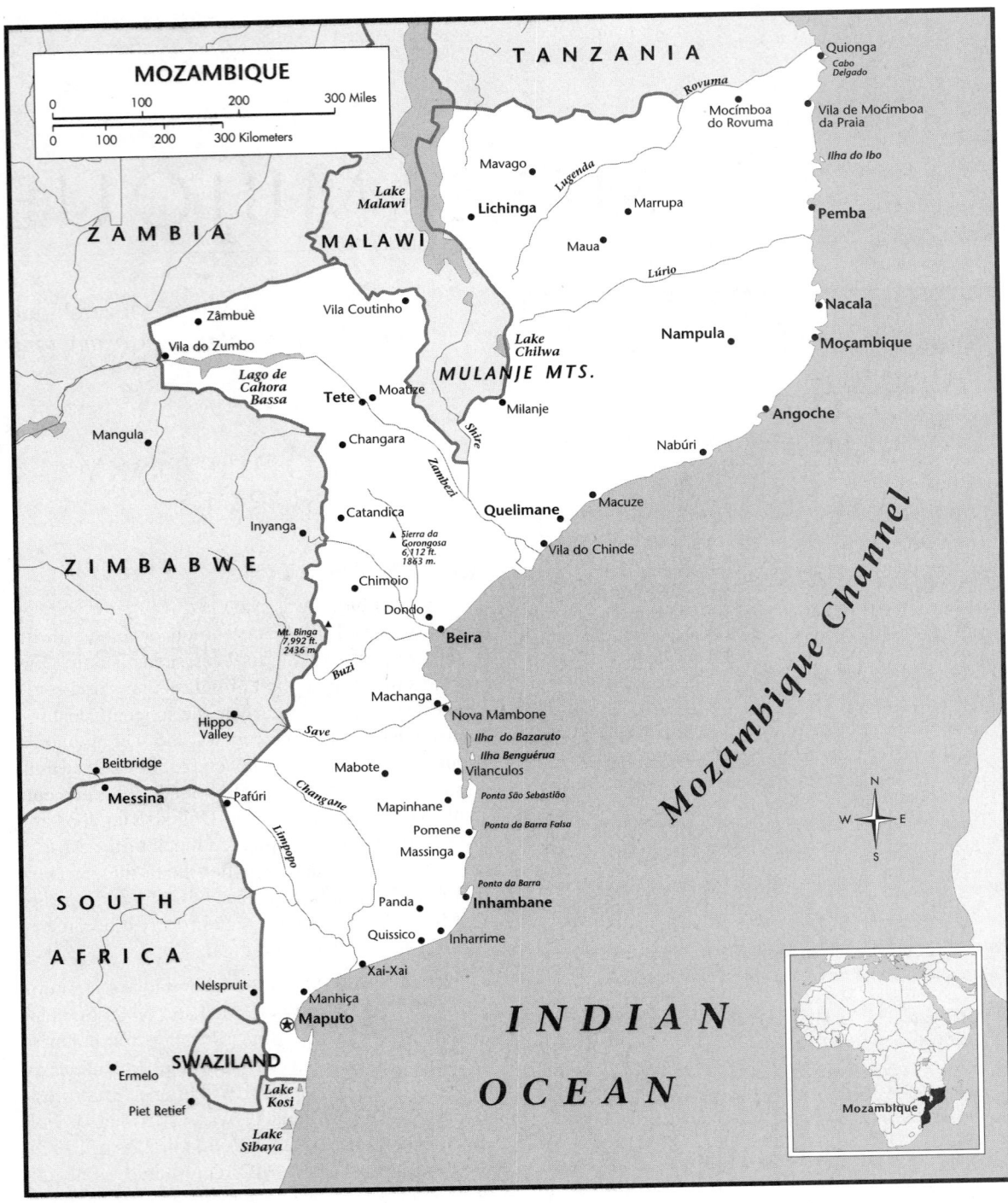

MOZAMBIQUE

| 0 | 100 | 200 | 300 Miles |
| 0 | 100 | 200 | 300 Kilometers |

TANZANIA

Quionga
Cabo Delgado

Rovuma

Moćimboa do Rovuma

Vila de Moćimboa da Praia

Lugenda

Mavago

Ilha do Ibo

Lichinga

Marrupa

Pemba

Maua

ZAMBIA

MALAWI

Lake Malawi

Lúrio

Zâmbuè

Vila Coutinho

Nacala

Vila do Zumbo

Lake Chilwa

Nampula

Moçambique

Lago de Cahora Bassa

Tete

Moatize

MULANJE MTS.

Mangula

Milanje

Shire

Angoche

Changara

Nabúri

Zambezi

Catandica

Quelimane

Macuze

Inyanga

▲ Sierra da Gorongosa 6,112 ft. 1863 m.

Vila do Chinde

ZIMBABWE

Chimoio

Dondo

Mt. Binga 7,992 ft. ▲ 2436 m.

Beira

Buzi

Machanga

Save

Nova Mambone

Ilha do Bazaruto

Hippo Valley

Ilha Benguérua

Beitbridge

Mabote

Vilanculos

Messina

Ponta São Sebastião

Pafúri

Changane

Mapinhane

Limpopo

Pomene

Ponta da Barra Falsa

Massinga

SOUTH

Ponta da Barra

AFRICA

Panda

Inhambane

Quissico

Inharrime

Nelspruit

Xai-Xai

Manhiça

INDIAN

Maputo

Ermelo

SWAZILAND

Lake Kosi

OCEAN

Piet Retief

Lake Sibaya

Mozambique Channel

Mozambique

Marxist-Leninist party dedicated to the creation of a Socialist state. A newly formed anti-government group opposed to FRELIMO's political stance and sympathetic to white interests, the Mozambique National Resistance (RENAMO), began to conduct a guerrilla rebellion with the backing of whites in Rhodesia. These activities continued into the 1980s and turned into a civil war. After the white government in Rhodesia fell and that country became Zimbabwe, RENAMO received substantial aid from South Africa and also had bases in Malawi.

On 19 October 1986, President Machel and 33 others were killed when their Soviet-built jetliner crashed inside South Africa. In August 1989, FRELIMO agreed to allow opposition parties to compete openly and legally. A peace treaty was finally signed on 4 October 1992, and a joint commission of government and RENAMO, along with a small UN monitoring force were named to carry out the agreement. Democratic elections were to be held within a year. In mid-1993, the national election was postponed until October 1994. Joaquim A. Chissano, FRELIMO leader and Mozambique's foreign minister since independence, won with 53.3% of the vote. The elections were monitored by 2,000 international observers for fairness.

GOVERNMENT

A revised constitution with a multiparty system of government came into force on 30 November 1990. The name of the country was changed from the People's Republic to the Republic of Mozambique. According to the 1990 constitution, the president is to be elected by universal adult vote for a five-year term. The Assembly of the Republic will replace the People's Assembly. Its deputies (between 200 and 250) are to be elected for five-year terms.

Judiciary

The formal justice system is divided into a civil/criminal system and a separate military justice system under joint supervision of the Ministries of Defense and Justice. The Supreme Court hears appeals from both systems. Local courts, part of the civil/criminal system, handle estate, divorce, and other social and family issues.

Political Parties

The Mozambique Liberation Front (Frente de Libertação de Moçambique—FRELIMO) was the sole legal political party until 1991. The new constitution in force in November 1990 legalized a multiparty system. FRELIMO and RENAMO (created as an armed rebel force) have been the most popular groups. Other parties include the Mozambican National Union (UNAMO), the Democratic Party of Mozambique (PADEMO), and the Mozambique National Movement (MONAMO).

DEFENSE

The armed forces in 1996 included 30,000 army personnel armed with 100 Soviet-made T-34, T-54, and T-55 tanks; a 750-member navy with three coastal patrol craft; and an air force of 4,000, with 43 MiG-21s and 4 armed helicopters.

ECONOMIC AFFAIRS

Mozambique is a poverty-stricken country with large debts. Civil war and droughts weakened Mozambique's economy in the 1980s, leaving it heavily dependent on foreign aid. However, recent shifts away from socialism and toward a market economy, as well as a resolution of the civil war, laid the foundation for an economic recovery. The economy grew by an average of 6% yearly between 1990 and 1996. International investment is increasing as stability returns, and an aggressive privatization program continues. Prospects for economic growth will depend heavily on good weather for farmers and a stable political situation.

Public Finance

The U.S. Central Intelligence Agency estimates that government revenues in 1992 totaled approximately $252 million and expenditures $607 million. External debt totaled $5 billion.

Income

In 1997 Mozambique's gross national product (GNP) was $14.6 billion at current prices, or about $800 per person, among the poorest in the world. Inflation was 52.2% per year during 1985–95, and the average annual real growth rate of the GNP per person was 3.6%.

Industry

Mozambique's industrial sector is primarily centered on the processing of locally produced raw materials, especially sugar, cashews, tea, and wheat. Brewing and textile production began in the 1980s, along with cement, fertilizer, and agricultural tool manufacturing.

Banking and Finance

The Mozambican branch of the defunct Portuguese National Overseas Bank was nationalized without compensation. By a decree of 23 May 1975, it was reconstituted as the Bank of Mozambique (Banco de Moçambique—BM). Functioning as a central bank, it serves as the government's banker and financial adviser, and as controller of monetary and credit policies. It is also an issuing bank, a commercial bank, and the state treasury; the bank manages Mozambique's external assets and acts as an intermediary in all international monetary transactions.

The bank has its headquarters at Maputo. In 1978, the government nationalized four of the five remaining private commercial banks (the Banco Standard Totta de Moçambique remains private).

In that year, a second state bank, the People's Investment Bank, was created and given responsibility for supervising a building society, the Mozambique Credit Institute (the industrial bank), and the National Development Bank.

After 1992, the government's economic reform program began to tackle the financial sector. Foreign banks were allowed to invest in Mozambican financial institutions, in 1994 interest rates were deregulated, and in 1995 the commercial activities of the central bank were assumed by a newly created institution, the Banco Comercial de Moçambique (BCM).

By 1996, the government had privatized the BCM and plans were afoot for the divestiture of the BPD (Banco Popular de Desenvolvimento), scheduled for early 1997. Portuguese interest in the BPD and other Mozambican banks has been strong.

Before 1992, Banco Standard Totta de Moçambique (BSTM) was the only private bank operating in the country. It has since been joined by Banco Português do Atlántico (BPA), Banco de Fomento e Exterior (BFE), and Banco Internacional de Moçambique (BIM), whose main shareholder is the Banco Comercial Português (BCP).

Economic Development

The government of Mozambique has abandoned its post-independence preference for a socialist organization of society, which it had tried to effect through the creation of cooperatives, state farms, and industries. In cooperation with the IMF, Mozambique is reforming its economy and preparing for a post-civil war period of economic growth. Progress has been slow, however, as inflation remains high (51% in 1995, down from 63% in 1994) and parastatals continue to control the telecommunications, electric power, transportation, and fuel sectors of the economy. Growth sectors include agriculture and related processing industries, transportation, and mining.

SOCIAL WELFARE

FRELIMO and its partner, the Organization of Mozambican Women, have widened educational and occupational opportunities for women and have pushed for a family law protecting women against desertion, abuse, and sexual harassment. Despite official policy and laws requiring equal rights for both sexes, there is still legal and social discrimination against women.

Healthcare

In 1985–95, only 39% of the population had access to health care services. The shortage of medical supplies and trained personnel has remained severe throughout Mozambique. In 1993, there was one doctor per 36,225 people. Estimated average life expectancy is only 45 years.

Housing

As of 1980, 63% of housing units were constructed of woven straw and 14% of cane and woodstick. Nearly 96% were without electricity and over half had no toilet facilities.

EDUCATION

Education is compulsory for seven years. In 1995, there were 4,149 primary schools with 24,575 teachers and 1,415,428 pupils. General secondary schools had 171,102 pupils. Eduardo Mondlane University is in Maputo. The country had an estimated adult illiteracy rate of 60% in 1995.

1999 KEY EVENTS TIMELINES

January

- The Presidents of Mozambique and South Africa, Joaquim Chissano and Nelson Mandela, inaugurate a monument to the memory of Samora Machel, Mozambique's first president, and the others who died with him in a plane crash at Mbuzini, South Africa on October 19, 1986.

February

- Track star Maria Mutola breaks her own 1996 indoor record for the 1,000-meter-run by almost half a second at the Gluben Galan meet in Stockholm.

March

- President Chissano gives his annual state of the nation address and declares the general situation of the country to be healthy, stable and at peace.

April

- The Enron Corp., a large U.S. oil and gas company, signs an agreement with the government to develop a gas, iron, and steel project that will be based at the Maputo port, using gas from the Pande field in southern Mozambique and iron ore from Phalaborwa in South Africa.

August

- The South African Development Community (SADC), chaired by President Chissano, holds a summit meeting of the 14-member group regarding regional conflicts, central bank gold sales (following Britain's May decision to sell more than half its gold reserves), and debt relief; their final communiqué calls for peace in the Democratic Republic of the Congo and officially gives their support to the Angolan government, currently fighting against UNITA (National Union for the Total Independence of Angola) rebels.

September

- President Chissano announces December 3–4 as dates for the country's second parliamentary and presidential elections.

- The Bank of Mozambique issues an initial forecast of 9.7 percent GDP growth rate for the Mozambique economy in 1999. The Bank attributes the continued strong showing of the economy to investment in large projects in the country, the devaluation of the South African rand, and the stability of the Mozambican currency.

November

- Britain's Queen Elizabeth II visits Mozambique where she is feted and thanked for her country's contributions to Mozambique's development and for Britain's support of debt relief for the country.

- The Queen opens a Trade and Investment Exhibition in Maputo.

- Boaventura Moises Machel, brother of the first president of independent Mozambique, the late Samora Machel, dies of AIDS, and for the first time a prominent family in Mozambique publicly announces that AIDS was the cause of their family member's death.

December

- Presidential and parliamentary elections take place in early December. The ruling party, FRELIMO, accuses the opposition RENAMO party of ballot-stuffing, though international observers say the elections are fair.

- On December 23, President Chissano is declared the election winner of another 5-year term, but opposition party members ask for a recount.

- UK Chancellor Gordon Brown reports that the UK is implementing a program to cancel millions of pounds of debt for some of the world's most indebted nations. The first four countries on the list, Uganda, Mozambique, Bolivia, and Mauritania, are expected to qualify for the debt forgiveness program by the end of January 2000.

ANALYSIS OF EVENTS: 1999

BUSINESS AND THE ECONOMY

Mozambique has had an economic turnaround since its 16-year civil war came to a conclusion and a democratically-elected government was put into place in 1994. Aid from many countries, the International Monetary Fund (IMF) and the World Bank has been forthcoming in response to the stabilization and privatization programs the country has put in place under pressure from the IMF. An IMF team in Mozambique in February/March projected rosy targets in growth of gross domestic product (9%) and inflation rate (less than 5.5 percent). Mozambique may be the first country to benefit from the "enhanced" version of the HIPC (Heavily Indebted Poor Countries) debt relief initiative, approved at the annual meeting of the IMF and World Bank boards, in October, 1999. This would result in the write-off of a large amount of debt. Both the IMF and the Paris Club of creditor nations have forgiven the bulk of Mozambique's external debt this year.

A point of major contention between Mozambique and the IMF has been over the issue of the cashew nut processing industry, and a similar disagreement is threatening to emerge over the sugar industry. IMF-imposed policies had led to the closure of 15 of the country's 16 major cashew nut processing factories and the laying off of 9,000 workers. In September the legislature moved to undo some of these policies, which the IMF has quietly admitted were not positive for the Mozambique economy. It remained to be seen whether the IMF would insist on the renunciation of protectionist tariffs for the national sugar and cashew nut industries.

As politics have changed in southern Africa, through the defeat of the rebel RENAMO force in Mozambique and the disbanding of the apartheid government in South Africa, the Temane natural gas field in Mozambique's southern province of

Inhambane now became attractive to foreign investors. This led to the construction of an international consortium of the Mozambique government and oil companies based in the United Arab Emirates, the United States, and South Africa to develop the field and the pipeline to the industrial center of South Africa. Two other gas fields and further exploration brought the expectation of a sound energy future for Mozambique's industrial expansion in the Maputo and Beira corridors. The government continued to seek debt relief, privatization, and foreign investment in major infrastructure projects in communications, transportation and heavy industry.

GOVERNMENT AND POLITICS

During 1999 the government was involved in implementing and responding to IMF requirements in order to obtain the credits and foreign investment needed to keep the economic revival alive. In addition, the government prepared for national legislature and presidential elections. Originally scheduled for October, the elections were rescheduled for December 3–4. International observers, including former U.S. president Jimmy Carter, declare the elections were fair, yet the ruling FRELIMO party accused RENAMO, the main opposition party, of ballot-stuffing.

On July 11, prior to the elections, opposition parties had reached an agreement to form a coalition around one candidate to contest the presidential elections. They chose RENAMO's Afonso Dhlakama to represent them. The parties involved in the coalition are: PUN (Party of National Unity), FAP (Popular Alliance Force), PPPM (Mozambique's Popular Party), ALIMO (Free Alliance of Mozambique), PUM (Mozambique's Unity Party) and PRD (Democratic Renewal Party), PVM (Mozambican Green Party), MONAMO (Mozambique's National Movement), PCN (Party of National Convention), and PALMO (Mozambique's Liberal Party). If successful they pledged to form a government of national unity.

Voter registration and electoral lists were finalized in September. As of September 20, 1999 there were 26 official political parties registered with the government. By law, all presidential candidates had to obtain notarized signatures of 10,000 registered voters. Mozambique's Supreme Court on 11 October rejected three candidates for December's presidential elections because they did not bring sufficient nominations. The candidates of the National Workers and Peasants Party (PANAOC),

the Democratic Party for the Liberation of Mozambique (PADELIMO), and the three party coalition UMO (Mozambican Opposition Union), all failed to provide enough signatures. The 10,000 signature requirement has come under attack due to the great difficulty minority parties have in reaching this total. There were three presidential candidates in the December elections: Joaquim Chissano of FRELIMO; Afonso Dhlakama of RENAMO; and Yaqub Sibindy of the Independent Party of Mozambique.

The government invited international election observation teams from several groups, including the Carter Center (U.S.) and the British Commonwealth, to which Mozambique was admitted as a member due to the fact that it is surrounded by nations with Commonwealth membership. A joint South African task force provided logistical support during the elections.

Campaigning was brisk by President Chissano and Mr. Dhalakama, with reports of violence in various localities. Dhlakama suggested financial chicanery on the part of Chissano and his party, FRELIMO, and Chissano charged Dhlakama and RENAMO with fomenting violence during campaigning as a desperation move in an unsuccessful in order to provide an excuse to withdraw and boycott the elections, as they did in 1994.

CULTURE AND SOCIETY

Despite real effort and much positive advancement, Mozambique continues to be one of the poorest countries in the world. Malaria is a major killer of children in Mozambique and is growing worse due to mosquito resistance to insecticides and parasite resistance to prophylactics. Mozambique had one of the highest maternal mortality rates in the world, at between 500 and 1,500 mothers' deaths for every 100,000 live births. In late 1998 and early 1999 the country again experienced a major cholera epidemic, with a higher death rate than the previous year, straining the resources of the health service. The Health Ministry grew increasingly concerned about the HIV infection rate, which is projected to reach close to 10% by the year 2000.

The government has begun a controversial, but voluntary, program of introducing local languages into primary education. Portuguese is increasingly the language of choice for Mozambicans, both at home and at work and school. Despite a major rebuilding effort, Mozambique's schools still suffer from the destruction caused by its 16-year civil war. The schools are in poor condition, the passing rate of children is low and the numbers of children who can continue into high school education is very small and quite inadequate to meet the needs of the country for an educated populace.

DIRECTORY

CENTRAL GOVERNMENT
Head of State

President
Joaquim Alberto Chissano, Office of the President, Avenida Julius Nyerere 2000, Caixa Postal 285, Maputo, Mozambique
PHONE: +258 491121
FAX: +258 492068

Prime Minister
Pascoel Manuel Mocumbi, Office of the Prime Minister, Praca da Marinha Popular, Maputo, Mozambique
PHONE: +258 426861
FAX: +258 426881

Ministers

Minister of Agriculture and Fisheries
Carlos Do Rosário, Ministry of Agriculture and Fisheries, Praça dos Herois, Moçambicanos, Maputo, Mozambique
PHONE: +258 460055
FAX: +258 460055

Minister of Culture, Youth and Sports
José Mateus Katupha, Ministry of Culture, Youth and Sports, Av. Patrice Lumumba 1217, Maputo, Mozambique
PHONE: +258 420068; 493977
FAX: +258 429700; 493077

Minister of Defense
Aguiar Real Mazula, Ministry of Defense, Av. Mártires da Machava 280,37, Maputo, Mozambique
PHONE: +258 493369; 492081
FAX: +258 491619

Minister of Education
Arnaldo Nhavoto, Ministry of Education, Av. 24 de Julho 167, 9° andar, Maputo, Mozambique
PHONE: +258 490830; 492829; 492006
FAX: +258 492160

Minister of Environmental Action Coordination
Bernardo Pedro Farraz, Ministry of Environmental Action Coordination, Av. Acordos de Lusaka 2115, Caixa Postal 2020, Maputo, Mozambique
PHONE: +258 466245
FAX: +258 465849
E-MAIL: micoa@ambinet.uem.mz

Minister of Foreign Affairs and Cooperation
Leonardo Santos Simão, Ministry of Foreign Affairs and Cooperation, Av. Julius Nyerere 4, Maputo, Mozambique
PHONE: +258 492258; 490222; 490223
FAX: +258 491460; 494070

Minister of Health
Aurélio Zilhão, Ministry of Health, Av. Eduardo Mondlane, Maputo, Mozambique
PHONE: +258 427131
FAX: +258 427133

Minister of Industry, Commerce, and Tourism
Oldemiro Baloi, Ministry of Industry, Commerce, and Tourism, Av. 25 de Setembro 86, Maputo, Mozambique
PHONE: +258 427204
FAX: +258 421305

Minister of the Interior
Almerino Manhenje, Ministry of the Interior, Av. Olof Palme 46/48, Maputo, Mozambique
PHONE: +258 420130
FAX: +258 420084

Minister of Justice
José Ibraimo Abudo, Ministry of Justice, Av. Julius Nyerere 33, Maputo, Mozambique
PHONE: +258 491613
FAX: +258 494264

Minister of Labor
Guilherme Luis Mavila, Ministry of Labor, Av. 24 de Julho 2351, 1° andar, Maputo, Mozambique
PHONE: +258 424400; 424072; 427051
FAX: +258 421881

Minister of Mineral Resources and Energy
John Kachamila, Ministry of Mineral Resources and Energy, Av. Fernão Magalhães 34, Maputo, Mozambique
PHONE: +258 429615; 425682
FAX: +258 427103

Minister of Planning and Finance
Tomáz Salomão, Ministry of Planning and Finance, Praça da Marinha Popular, Caixa Postal 272, Maputo, Mozambique
PHONE: +258 421303; 425071
FAX: +258 420137

Minister of Public Works and Housing
Roberto Costley-White, Ministry of Public Works and Housing, Av. Karl Marx 268, Maputo, Mozambique
PHONE: +258 420543; 430028
FAX: +258 421369

Minister of Social Action Coordination
Açucena da Costa Duarte, Ministry of Social Action Coordination, Rua de Tchamba 86, Caixa Postal 516, Maputo, Mozambique
PHONE: +258 742901; 490932
FAX: +258 490923

Minister of State Administration
Alfredo Gamito, Ministry of State Administration, Rua da Rádio Moçambique 112, Maputo, Mozambique
PHONE: +258 426666; 423335
FAX: +258 428565

Minister of Transport and Communications
Paulo Muxanga, Ministry of Transport and Communications, Av. Mártires de Inhaminga 336, Marputo, Mozambique
PHONE: +258 420223
FAX: +258 431028

POLITICAL ORGANIZATIONS

União Democrático-UD (Democratic Union)

TITLE: General Secretary
NAME: Antonio Palange

Frente da Libertação de Moçambique-FRELIMO (Front for the Liberation of Mozambique)

TITLE: Chairman
NAME: Joaquim Alberto Chissanó

Resistencia Nacional Moçambicana-RENAMO (Mozambique National Resistance)

TITLE: President
NAME: Afonso Dhlakama

DIPLOMATIC REPRESENTATION
Embassies in Mozambique

Algeria
Rua de Mukumbura, 121–125, Maputo, Mozambique
PHONE: +258 492070; 492203
FAX: +258 490582
TITLE: Ambassador
NAME: Abdelhamid Boubazine

Angola
Avenida Kenneth Kaunda, 783, Maputo, Mozambique
PHONE: +258 493691; 493139
FAX: +258 493930
TITLE: Ambassador
NAME: António José Condesse de Carvalho

Australia
Av. Julius Nyerere n° 794 9° E, Maputo, Mozambique
PHONE: +258 497329; 493072

Brazil
Av. Kenneth Kaunda n° 296, Maputo, Mozambique
PHONE: +258 492387; 492388; 492863
FAX: +258 490986
TITLE: Ambassador
NAME: Hélder Martins de Morais

Bulgaria
Av. do Zimbabwe n° 864–868, Maputo, Mozambique
PHONE: +258 491476; 490383
FAX: +258 491755

Canada
Av. Julius Nyerere, 1128, Maputo, Mozambique
PHONE: +258 492623; 492624; 492470
FAX: +258 492667
E-MAIL: canembas@ecanada.uem.mz
TITLE: Consul-General
NAME: Roberto Carr-Ribeiro

China
Av. dos Mártires da Machava n° 1309–4°, Maputo, Mozambique
PHONE: +258 491462; 491560
FAX: +258 491196
TITLE: Ambassador
NAME: Mi Shiheng

Congo
Av. Mártires da Machava, 385, Maputo, Mozambique

PHONE: +258 493779
FAX: +258 493779
NAME: Monsengo Bashwa Oshefwa

Cuba
Av. Kenneth Kaunda n° 492, Maputo, Mozambique
PHONE: +258 492444
FAX: +258 493673; 492700
TITLE: Ambassador
NAME: Evelino Dorta González

Denmark
Av. 24 de Julho n° 1500, Maputo, Mozambique
PHONE: +258 420172; 420173; 429052
FAX: +258 303526
TITLE: Consul
NAME: Peter Jul Larsen

Egypt
Av. Mao Tsé Tung n° 851 R/c, Maputo, Mozambique
PHONE: +258 491118; 491287
FAX: +258 491489
TITLE: Ambassador
NAME: Soad Mahmoud Shalaby

Finland
Av. Julius Nyerere n° 1128, Maputo, Mozambique
PHONE: +258 490518; 491663; 491660
FAX: +258 491662
TITLE: Ambassador
NAME: Ilari Rantakari

France
Av. Julius Nyerere n° 2361, Maputo, Mozambique
PHONE: +258 490444; 491693; 491694
FAX: +258 491727
E-MAIL: ambfrmoz@virconn.com
TITLE: Ambassador
NAME: Dedier Destremau

Germany
Rua Damião de Góis, 506, Maputo, Mozambique
PHONE: +258 492714; 492996; 490057
FAX: +258 492888
TITLE: Ambassador
NAME: Helmut Rau

India
Av. Kenneth Kaunda n° 167, Maputo, Mozambique
PHONE: +258 492437; 490717
FAX: +258 492364
E-MAIL: hcimpto@hcoi.uem.mz
TITLE: High Commissioner

NAME: Jaspal Singh

North Korea
Rua da Kaswende n° 167, Maputo, Mozambique
PHONE: +258 491482; 492934; 492675
TITLE: Ambassador
NAME: Ryang Gui Rak

South Africa
Av. Eduardo Mondlane no. 41-R/c, Maputo, Mozambique
PHONE: +258 490059; 490547; 490587
FAX: +258 493029; 492096
TITLE: High Commissioner
NAME: Mangisi C. Zitha

Spain
Rua Damião de Góis n° 347, Maputo, Mozambique
PHONE: +258 492025; 492027; 492030
FAX: +258 492055
TITLE: Ambassador
NAME: José Eugénio Salarich

United Kingdom
Av. Vladimir Lenine 310, Maputo, Mozambique
PHONE: +258 420111; 421695; 424635
FAX: +258 421666
TITLE: Bernard Jonathan Everett
NAME: High Commissioner

United States
Av. Kenneth Kaunda n° 193, Maputo, Mozambique
PHONE: +258 492797
FAX: +258 490114; 493695
TITLE: Ambassador
NAME: Brian Dean Curran

JUDICIAL SYSTEM
Supreme Court
Local Court

FURTHER READING
Articles
''Mozambique.'' *Africa Confidential* 40 (June 25, 1999).

''Mozambique.'' *Africa Confidential* 40 (September 10, 1999): 18.

''New Natural Gas Province Gets Ready Business.'' *Petroleum Economist* 66 (January 1999).

''Sida Bridges the Gap.'' *African Business* (July-August 1999).

Internet

Africa News. Available Online @ www.africanews.org/south/mozambique (November 25, 1999).

Mozambique News Agency. Available Online @ www.poptel.org.uk/mozambique-news/ (November 25, 1999).

MOZAMBIQUE: STATISTICAL DATA

For sources and notes see "Sources of Statistics" in the front of each volume.

GEOGRAPHY

Geography (1)

Area:

Total: 801,590 sq km.

Land: 784,090 sq km.

Water: 17,500 sq km.

Area—comparative: slightly less than twice the size of California.

Land boundaries:

Total: 4,571 km.

Border countries: Malawi 1,569 km, South Africa 491 km, Swaziland 105 km, Tanzania 756 km, Zambia 419 km, Zimbabwe 1,231 km.

Coastline: 2,470 km.

Climate: tropical to subtropical.

Terrain: mostly coastal lowlands, uplands in center, high plateaus in northwest, mountains in west.

Natural resources: coal, titanium, natural gas.

Land use:

Arable land: 4%

Permanent crops: 0%

Permanent pastures: 56%

Forests and woodland: 18%

Other: 22% (1993 est.).

HUMAN FACTORS

Demographics (2A)

	1990	1995	1998	2000	2010	2020	2030	2040	2050
Population	14,055.9	17,150.4	18,641.5	19,614.3	24,809.4	30,392.4	36,248.6	42,077.6	47,805.3
Net migration rate (per 1,000 population)	NA	NA	NA	NA	NA	NA	NA	NA	NA
Births	NA	NA	NA	NA	NA	NA	NA	NA	NA
Deaths	NA	NA	NA	NA	NA	NA	NA	NA	NA
Life expectancy - males	40.8	42.7	44.2	45.3	50.7	56.4	61.8	66.5	70.4
Life expectancy - females	43.1	45.0	46.5	47.6	53.3	59.1	64.7	69.8	74.1
Birth rate (per 1,000)	44.7	45.9	43.5	42.0	34.4	28.6	23.9	20.5	18.4
Death rate (per 1,000)	20.8	19.2	17.8	16.8	12.6	9.7	7.8	6.8	6.5
Women of reproductive age (15-49 yrs.)	3,320.4	4,026.9	4,394.1	4,641.1	6,101.1	7,988.2	9,876.2	11,548.3	12,711.1
of which are currently married	NA	NA	NA	NA	NA	NA	NA	NA	NA
Fertility rate	6.2	6.3	6.0	5.8	4.4	3.4	2.7	2.4	2.3

Except as noted, values for vital statistics are in thousands; life expectancy is in years.

Health Personnel (3)

Total health expenditure as a percentage of GDP,
1990-1997[a]

Public sector 4.6

Private sector . . . . .NA

Total[b] . . . . .NA

Health expenditure per capita in U.S. dollars,
1990-1997[a]

Purchasing power parity . . . . .NA

Total . . . . .NA

Availability of health care facilities per 100,000 people

Hospital beds 1990-1997[a] 90

Doctors 1993[c] . . . . .NA

Nurses 1993[c] . . . . .NA

Health Indicators (4)

Life expectancy at birth

1980 44

1997 45

Daily per capita supply of calories (1996) 1,799

Total fertility rate births per woman (1997) 5.3

Maternal mortality ratio per 100,000 live births
(1990-97) . . . . .1,100[c]

Safe water % of population with access (1995) 24

Sanitation % of population with access (1995) 23

Consumption of iodized salt % of households
(1992-98)[a] 62

Smoking prevalence

Male % of adults (1985-95)[a] . . . .

Female % of adults (1985-95)[a] . . . .

Tuberculosis incidence per 100,000 people
(1997) 255

Adult HIV prevalence % of population ages
15-49 (1997) 14.17

Infants and Malnutrition (5)

Under-5 mortality rate (1997) 208

% of infants with low birthweight (1990-97) 20

Births attended by skilled health staff % of total[a] . . .44

% fully immunized (1995-97)

TB 79

DPT 59

Polio 55

Measles 57

Prevalence of child malnutrition under age 5
(1992-97)[b] 26

Ethnic Division (6)

Indigenous tribal groups 99.66% (Shangaan Chokwe,
Manyika, Sena, Makua, and others), Europeans 0.06%,
Euro-Africans 0.2%, Indians 0.08%.

Religions (7)

Indigenous beliefs 50%

Christian 30%

Muslim 20%

Languages (8)

Portuguese (official), indigenous dialects.

EDUCATION

Public Education Expenditures (9)

Public expenditure on education (% of GNP)

1980 . . . . .4.4

1996 . . . .

Expenditure per student

Primary % of GNP per capita

1980 . . . .

1996 . . . .

Secondary % of GNP per capita

1980 . . . .

1996 . . . .

Tertiary % of GNP per capita

1980 . . . .

1996 . . . .

Expenditure on teaching materials

Primary % of total for level (1996) . . . .

Secondary % of total for level (1996) . . . .

Primary pupil-teacher ratio per teacher (1996) . . . . .58[1]

Duration of primary education years (1995) 5

Educational Attainment (10)

Age group (1980) . . . . .25+

Total population 4,242,819

Highest level attained (%)

No schooling[2] 81.0

First level

Not completed 18.1

Completed . . . . .NA

Entered second level

S-1 . . . . .0.8

S-2 . . . . .NA

Postsecondary 0.1

Literacy Rates (11A)

In thousands and percent[1]	1990	1995	2000	2010
Illiterate population (15+ yrs.)	5,158	5,298	5,700	6,040
Literacy rate - total adult pop. (%)	34.7	40.1	45.9	57.4
Literacy rate - males (%)	51.8	57.7	63.4	73.2
Literacy rate - females (%)	18.5	23.3	29.2	42.2

GOVERNMENT & LAW

Political Parties (12)

Assembly of the Republic	% of seats
Front for the Liberation of Mozambique (Frelimo)	44.33
Mozambique National Resistance (Renamo)	33.78
Democratic Union (DU)	5.15
Other	16.74

Military Affairs (14B)

	1990	1991	1992	1993	1994	1995
Military expenditures						
Current dollars (mil.)	77	107	91[e]	99	86	69
1995 constant dollars (mil.)	88	118	98[e]	103	88	69
Armed forces (000)	65	65	50	50	11	12
Gross national product (GNP)						
Current dollars (mil.)	831	913	899	1,131	1,217	1,284
1995 constant dollars (mil.)	955	1,009	967	1,186	1,247	1,284
Central government expenditures (CGE)						
1995 constant dollars (mil.)	NA	NA	581[e]	NA	NA	NA
People (mil.)	14.1	14.3	14.6	15.1	16.0	17.1
Military expenditure as % of GNP	9.2	11.7	10.1	8.7	7.0	5.4
Military expenditure as % of CGE	NA	NA	16.8	NA	NA	NA
Military expenditure per capita (1995 $)	6	8	7	7	5	4
Armed forces per 1,000 people (soldiers)	4.6	4.5	3.4	3.3	.7	.7
GNP per capita (1995 $)	68	70	66	78	78	75
Arms imports[6]						
Current dollars (mil.)	140	50	5	0	0	0
1995 constant dollars (mil.)	161	55	5	0	0	0
Arms exports[6]						
Current dollars (mil.)	0	0	0	0	0	0
1995 constant dollars (mil.)	0	0	0	0	0	0
Total imports[7]						
Current dollars (mil.)	878	899	855	955	1,140[e]	784
1995 constant dollars (mil.)	1,009	993	920	1,001	1,169[e]	784
Total exports[7]						
Current dollars (mil.)	126	162	139	132	147	169
1995 constant dollars (mil.)	145	179	150	138	151	169
Arms as percent of total imports[8]	15.9	5.6	.6	0	0	0
Arms as percent of total exports[8]	0	0	0	0	0	0

1993

Government Budget (13B)

Revenues . . . .$324 million

Expenditures . . . .$600 million

  Capital expenditures . . . .$310 million

Data for 1996 est.

LABOR FORCE

Labor Force (16)

80% engaged in agriculture. In 1993, 47% of the wage earners were employed in industry, 28% in transportation and communication; traditionally, a large number of Mozambicans work abroad.

Unemployment Rate (17)

Rate not available.

PRODUCTION SECTOR

Electric Energy (18)

Capacity . . . . .2.358 million kW (1995)

Production . . . . .465 million kWh (1995)

Consumption per capita . . . . .73 kWh (1995)

Transportation (19)

Highways:

total: 30,400 km

paved: 5,685 km

unpaved: 24,715 km (1996 est.) note: highway traffic impeded by land mines not removed at end of civil war

Waterways: about 3,750 km of navigable routes

Pipelines: crude oil (not operating) 306 km; petroleum products 289 km

Merchant marine:

total: 4 cargo ships (1,000 GRT or over) totaling 5,694 GRT/9,724 DWT (1997 est.)

Airports: 174 (1997 est.)

Airports—with paved runways:

total: 22

over 3,047 m: 1

2,438 to 3,047 m: 3

1,524 to 2,437 m: 10

914 to 1,523 m: 4

under 914 m: 4 (1997 est.)

Airports—with unpaved runways:

total: 152

2,438 to 3,047 m: 1

1,524 to 2,437 m: 16

914 to 1,523 m: 38

under 914 m: 97 (1997 est.)

Top Agricultural Products (20)

Cotton, cashew nuts, sugarcane, tea, cassava (tapioca), corn, rice, tropical fruits; beef, poultry.

FINANCE, ECONOMICS, & TRADE

Economic Indicators (22)

National product: GDP—purchasing power parity—$14.6 billion (1997 est.)

National product real growth rate: 8% (1997 est.)

National product per capita: $800 (1997 est.)

Inflation rate—consumer price index: 5.8% (1997)

MANUFACTURING SECTOR

GDP & Manufacturing Summary (21)

	1980	1985	1990	1992	1993	1994
Gross Domestic Product						
Millions of 1990 dollars	1,404	1,116	1,318	1,366	1,486	1,561
Growth rate in percent	2.46	−8.82	3.10	−0.85	8.84	5.00
Per capita (in 1990 dollars)	116.1	82.4	92.9	92.7	98.4	100.5
Manufacturing Value Added						
Millions of 1990 dollars	568	260	325	377	414	477
Growth rate in percent	3.25	−13.87	−1.04	3.74	9.70	15.25
Manufacturing share in percent of current prices	33.1	14.9	NA	NA	NA	NA

FINANCE, ECONOMICS,& TRADE

Balance of Payments (23)

	1991	1992	1993	1994	1995
Exports of goods (f.o.b.)	162	139	132	150	169
Imports of goods (f.o.b.)	−809	−769	−859	−917	−705
Trade balance	−646	−630	−727	−767	−536
Services - debits	−402	−444	−462	−510	−546
Services - credits	203	223	240	246	301
Private transfers (net)	502	499	503	565	339
Government transfers (net)	…	…	…	…	…
Overall balance	−344	−352	−446	−467	−445

Exchange Rates (24)

Exchange rates:

Meticais (Mt) per US$1

January 1998	11,635.0
1997	11,543.6
1996	11,293.8
1995	9,024.3
1994	6,038.6
1993	3,874.2

Top Import Origins (25)

$802 million (c.i.f., 1996 est.)

Origins	%
South Africa	.38
United States	NA
Japan	NA
Portugal	NA
France	NA

NA stands for not available.

Top Export Destinations (26)

$226 million (f.o.b., 1996 est.).

Destinations	%
Spain	NA
South Africa	NA
Japan	NA
Portugal	NA
United States	NA

NA stands for not available.

Economic Aid (27)

Recipient: ODA, $NA. NA stands for not available.

Import Export Commodities (28)

Import Commodities	Export Commodities
Food	Shrimp 40%
Clothing	Cashews
Farm equipment	Cotton
Petroleum	Sugar
	Copra
	Citrus

MYANMAR

CAPITAL: Yangon (formerly Rangoon).

FLAG: The national flag is red with a blue canton, within which 14 white stars encircle a rice stalk and an industrial wheel.

ANTHEM: *Kaba Makye* (Our Free Homeland).

MONETARY UNIT: The kyat (κ) is a paper currency of 100 pyas. There are coins of 1, 5, 10, 25, and 50 pyas and 1 kyat, and notes of 1, 5, 10, 25, and 100 kyats. κ1 = $0.16804 (or $1 = κ5.951).

WEIGHTS AND MEASURES: Both British and metric weights and measures are in general use, but local units are also employed.

HOLIDAYS: Independence Day, 4 January; Union Day, 12 February; Peasants' Day, 2 March; Defense Services Day, 27 March; Burmese New Year, 17 April; World Workers' Day, 1 May; Martyrs' Day, 19 July; Christmas, 25 December. Movable religious holidays include Full Moon of Tabaung, February or March; Thingyan (Water Festival), April; Full Moon of Kason, April or May; Waso (Beginning of Buddhist Lent), June or July; Thadingyut (End of Buddhist Lent), October; and Tazaungdaing, November.

TIME: 6:30 PM = noon GMT.

LOCATION AND SIZE: Situated in Southeast Asia, Myanmar has an area of 678,500 square kilometers (261,970 square miles), slightly smaller than the state of Texas, and a total boundary length of 8,134 kilometers (5,055 miles).

Myanmar's capital city, Yangon (formerly Rangoon), is located in the southern part of the country.

CLIMATE: Myanmar has a largely tropical climate with three seasons. Rainfall ranges from about 76 centimeters (30 inches) in central Myanmar to more than 500 centimeters (200 inches) in upper Myanmar during the monsoon season.

The mean annual temperature is 27°C (81°F); average daily temperatures in Yangon (Rangoon) range from 18° to 32°C (64°–90°F) in January, during the cool season, and from 24° to 36°C (75°–97°F) in April, during the hot season.

INTRODUCTORY SURVEY

RECENT HISTORY

In 1946, after the end of World War II, the sovereign Union of Burma came into being. In 1951 the nation held its first parliamentary elections. The decade of the 1950s brought an ambitious land reform program and an attempt to forge a neutral foreign policy. However, the country was faced with periodic communist rebellions and an off-and-on border dispute with China.

A coup in 1962 overthrew the government, and a military regime assumed control. The Socialist Republic of Burma was proclaimed on 3 January 1974. Under a new constitution, a president was elected, but the government continued to be dominated by the military. At this time, the country's only legal political organization was the Burma Socialist Program Party (BSPP). Meanwhile, a guerrilla war in border areas of the north and east continued through the 1980s. It was fought by the underground Burmese Communist Party and rebel ethnic groups.

When the military became dissatisfied with the government and the ruling BSPP party, it staged another military coup. On 18 September 1988 the army abolished the BSPP, took over the government, and imposed military rule under the State Law and Order Restoration Council (SLORC). The SLORC was headed by the army Chief of Staff, General Saw Maung. On 18 June 1989 the Saw Maung regime renamed Burma "Myanmar," the historic ethnic Burman name for the country.

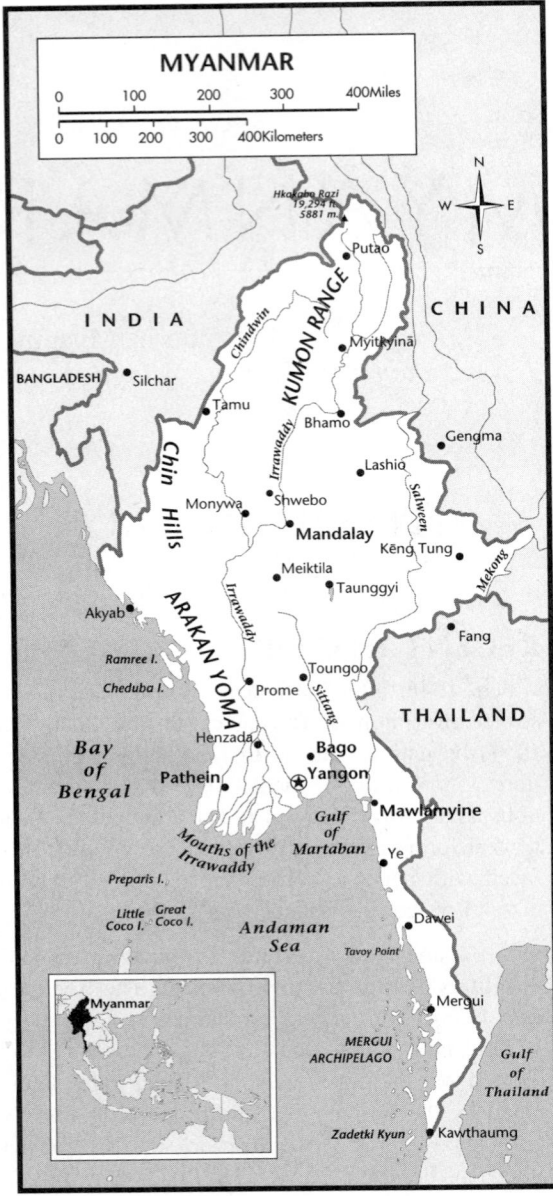

MYANMAR

0   100   200   300   400 Miles

0   100   200   300   400 Kilometers

Multiparty elections were held in May 1990, but the military refused to transfer power to the winning National League for Democracy (NLD). It announced in September 1990 that it intended to remain in power for five to ten more years.

In the early 1990s, the plight of dissident Aung San Suu Kyi, who was placed under house arrest in 1989, began receiving worldwide attention. In 1991 she was awarded the 1990 Sakharov Prize for Freedom of Thought by the European Parliament. On 10 December 1991 Aung San Suu Kyi's son, Alexander, accepted the 1991 Nobel Peace Prize on her behalf.

Another type of human rights violation in Myanmar that drew international attention was forced labor. It was reported that the SLORC used forced labor on tourist projects such as the reconstruction of the gold palace in Mandalay. Of Mandalay's 500,000 residents, each family had to contribute at least three days of free labor each month. The work lasted from dawn until evening and was so strenuous that it required several days of recovery. Forced labor was also used on many building projects and to carry supplies and munitions into malaria-infested areas for the military. Prison inmates were required to work every day. Many military families could be exempted, as could any family that agreed to pay a monthly fine of $6, about a week's wages for some families. Muslim refugees who fled Myanmar said that Muslims had to pay two to three times as much as others to escape labor.

Ever since Myanmar received its independence in 1948, the government has faced ethnic minorities fighting for autonomy. However, in 1991 the 600-member Palaung State Liberation Army and the 500-member Pa-O National Army rebel group signed truce agreements with SLORC, which served as models for settlements with other rebels. The Karens, Mons, and Karenni along the Thai border began talks with the military regime in early 1994. Eventually, the junta negotiated separate peace treaties with each rebel group.

As of mid-1994 the international community was still debating the most constructive approach to dealing with Myanmar. Many Asian countries argue that maintaining relations with Myanmar is more productive than isolating it. However, the United States has stuck to its hardline isolationist policy toward Myanmar to press for advancement of democracy and human rights. The United States

The takeover of the government by the military prompted dissent among the population. Among the most prominent dissidents was Aung San Suu Kyi. She rose to prominence by establishing a coalition party that opposed the military regime. In speeches and interviews she challenged the SLORC's record, characterizing it as one of economic and social degeneration. She also protested the SLORC's repressive laws and actions. Because of her actions, the government placed her under house arrest in 1989.

government still refers to Myanmar as Burma, the country's name prior to the military takeover.

In July 1995, the SLORC released dissident Aung San Suu Kyi from house arrest. She had been detained for six years. Most observers saw the SLORC's action as an attempt to gain international favor, and not as a sign that they were ready to loosen their grip on the country. Upon her release, Suu Kyi confirmed her commitment to democracy. The NLD planned to draft its own version of the constitution, and Suu Kyi planned pro-democracy rallies. Following mass student protests in December 1996, the government blamed Suu Kyi and returned her to house arrest. She was released again in July 1997. Rather than arrest her for her activities in 1998, the Myanmar military prevented her from attending opposition meetings. In one instance, they forced her to remain in her car for six days. They did allow her to return to Myanmar after a brief visit to see her dying husband, Michael Aris, in London.

Thousands of political opponents remained in prison during 1995 and 1996. The ruling leaders also faced renewed fighting with border insurgents, particularly the Karen National Union Army.

The Myanmar government has also come under considerable international criticism for its involvement in the country's massive drug trade. Myanmar is the world's largest producer of opium and heroin, and is a major producer of methamphetamines.

GOVERNMENT

A military coup in September 1988 brought the State Law and Order Restoration Council (SLORC) to power. SLORC abolished the previous government and the country was placed under martial law. On 18 September 1988 the official title of the state was changed to The Union of Myanmar. SLORC directs, supervises, and coordinates the work of the central and local government institutions.

In a multiparty election held 27 May 1990, the National League for Democracy (NLD) received 59.9% of the total vote and took 396 of the 485 contested seats. However, SLORC refused to hand over power to the NLD, instead insisting that a new constitution be drafted and approved by SLORC prior to the transfer of power.

Myanmar comprises seven states and seven divisions, further divided into 317 townships, which include villages and towns.

Judiciary

The British-style judicial system with which Myanmar began its independence, including a Supreme Court, was disbanded by the Revolutionary Council. Military tribunals which enforced orders issued by the State Law and Order Restoration Council (SLORC) were abolished in 1992. Ordinary courts now handle such cases. The Supreme Court appoints judges after approval by the SLORC. The judiciary is not independent.

Political Parties

With the military takeover of September 1988, the ruling Burma Socialist Program Party was formally abolished, and all governing authority was concentrated in the hands of the military. On 24 September 1988 the BSPP was reborn as the National Unity Party (NUP), inheriting the buildings and machinery of the old BSPP.

On 24 September 1988 the National League for Democracy (NLD), a coalition party, was formed in opposition to the military regime. The NLD won the 27 May 1990 elections by a landslide, electing 392 candidates; the NUP took 10 seats. NLD leader Aung San Suu Kyi was placed under house arrest on 20 July 1989 and was released in July 1995. The Democratic Alliance of Burma (DAB) is a coalition of 21 ethnic minorities and political dissident groups formed in 1988.

By March 1993 all but seven political parties had been deregistered by SLORC. Other political or pressure groups were the Kachin Independence Army (KIA), the United Wa State Army (UWSA), the Karen National Union (KNU), and several Shan factions including the Mong Tai Army (MTA).

DEFENSE

The armed forces play the major role in Myanmar's politics and administration; senior members of the government are officers who govern under martial law.

Myanmar's armed forces totaled an estimated 321,000 in 1995; military service for men and women is compulsory. The army, with 300,000 personnel, is organized in infantry battalions chiefly for internal security duties. The navy has 12,000–15,000 members, and the air force 9,000. The navy's ships include 30 gunboats and 36 river patrol craft. The air force has 91 combat aircraft, 10 transports, and 18 armed helicopters. Paramilitary forces total 85,250. Military expenditures were $1.9 billion in 1995.

ECONOMIC AFFAIRS

The military regime, SLORC, which took over Myanmar in 1988, proclaimed a market-oriented economic policy and invited foreign investment. Two trends have been apparent in the government's economic policies: the capture of revenues from short-term, quick turnover sources such as hardwoods, prospecting rights, and taxes on profits from illegal sources; and spending patterns that emphasize defense spending and acquisition of armaments.

Due to Myanmar's inability to stop the flow of drugs from its sector of the Golden Triangle, in February 1989 the United States removed Myanmar from a list of countries eligible to receive aid for combating the drug trade. Myanmar is the world's largest supplier of illegal opiates; in 1995 its opium accounted for 60% of worldwide production. About 60% of the heroin brought into the United States comes from Myanmar. Large quantities of smuggled consumer goods are sold in Myanmar's cities, where the black market thrives.

Myanmar receives no aid from United States or European Union (EU) programs and aid from Japan is run at a maintenance level. The International Monetary Fund (IMF), the World Bank, and the Asian Development Bank (ADB) extend no credit to Myanmar.

Public Finance

The government presents its budget in March for the April 1 March 31 fiscal year. The public sector budget typically shows an overall deficit. The government estimates that in the 1995–96 budget, military expenditures accounted for about 33% (down from almost 45% in 1995) of government spending and were equivalent to almost 10% of GDP.

The U.S. Central Intelligence Agency estimates that, in 1995, government revenues totaled approximately $5.3 billion and expenditures $10 billion. External debt totaled $5.5 billion.

The 1995 deficit was estimated at more than 6% of GDP. The deficit is financed by foreign debt, printing money, and borrowing from domestic banks. It is estimated that Burmese banks lend almost 80% of their money to the government and state enterprises.

Income

In 1997 the gross domestic product (GDP) was $55.7 billion, or about $1,190 per person.

Industry

Industry is geared largely to the processing of agricultural, mineral, and forest products. Principal industrial products are cement, steel, bricks and tiles, fertilizers, and processed foods. Consumer goods that were imported before 1962 and are now manufactured domestically include blankets, paper, glass products, bicycles, and water pumps. Other major consumer items manufactured are aluminum ware, jute and cotton cloth, pharmaceuticals, beverages, matches, and cigarettes. The assembly of television sets and motor vehicles is a recent development in Myanmar's industry.

Industrial products for 1995 included pig iron, 1,500 tons; crude steel, 25,000 tons; refined tin, 190 tons; and refined petroleum products, 5.3 million barrels.

Banking and Finance

Effective 23 February 1963, all 24 commercial banks in Myanmar—10 foreign and 14 indigenously owned—were nationalized and amalgamated into 4 state banks. In addition to the Central Bank of Myanmar, Union of Burma Bank, which serves as a central bank, the other state banks were the State Agricultural Bank, the State Commercial Bank, and the Industrial Bank. After subsequent reorganizations of the banking system, these became the Myanma Investment and Commercial Bank, Myanma Economic Bank, and the Myanma Foreign Trade Bank. Agricultural credit is provided by a separate Myanmar Agricultural and Rural Development Bank. Public savings increased sharply in 1977 after the banks raised interest rates. Efforts to attract the considerable liquidity in the hands of the public into the banking sector, and thence into investment, have not had much success. In recent years the expansion of bank savings has lagged well behind inflation.

By the end of 1994, licenses to open representative offices had been issued to 19 banks from overseas—six from Thailand, five from Singapore, three from Malaysia, and one each from France, Indonesia, Cambodia, Hong Kong, and Bangladesh. Since 1994 four private domestic banks have been permitted to conduct foreign exchange transactions for the first time. Various types of foreign exchange licenses have been issued recently to the private sector by the Central Bank. It issued seven authorized dealer licenses, three money changer licenses, 396 acceptor and holder licenses, and 66 FEC changer licenses in August 1994. Despite the liberalization of its economy, the country still lacks a capital market.

Money supply, as measured by M2, amounted to K235.7 billion in August 1996. In 1997, there were around 43 foreign banks with representative offices in Myanmar.

Economic Development

The major aim of Myanmar's government has been to rehabilitate, modernize, and diversify an economy that was extensively disrupted by World War II and that failed to develop from the 1940s through the 1960s. To this end, all foreign companies, all banks, the entire transport system, all foreign and much domestic trade, and all the main branches of industry have been nationalized. Some nationalized industries initially showed declines in output, while others were hard pressed to hold their own. By 1974, the government had no choice but to modify some of its more rigidly Socialist economic policies. A foreign investment ban imposed in the 1960s was relaxed, and foreign participation in mining was allowed for the first time in a dozen years. Privately owned businesses, to which the government had previously been unsympathetic, were allowed in specified fields. Economic development proceeded slowly under the four-year plan for 1974–78 and the 1978–82 development program, which was allocated 60% more funding than its predecessor and which achieved an annual growth rate exceeding 6%. The four-year plan for 1982–86, costing an estimated $5 billion, set an average annual growth target of 6.2%. The plan stressed infrastructural development, with particular emphasis on agriculture, construction, and energy production. The four-year plan for 1986–90 encouraged foreign investment.

In spite of the military government's commitment to the transformation of Myanmar's state-controlled economy to a market system, economic development has been limited by the government's failure to implement basic structural reforms. Such needed reforms include dismantling unproductive state-owned enterprises, establishing an independent state bank, making available private sector credit, controlling government spending, and adjustments to the official exchange rate. Basic infrastructure, transportation, telecommunications, and energy are inadequate. Because of the government's ongoing human rights abuses and for rea-

sons related to its narcotics exports, Myanmar recieves no financial assistance from the IMF, World Bank, or Asian Development Bank.

SOCIAL WELFARE

Although considerable advances have been made in health services, Myanmar's goal of establishing a welfare state has been limited by lack of public funds. In 1956, the government inaugurated a social security program that compensates workers for wage losses arising from sickness, injury, and maternity leave, provides free medical care, and establishes survivors' benefits. The program is funded by contributions from employers, employees, and the government. As yet, Myanmar does not have unemployment insurance, but workers are entitled to old age pensions.

Women have a high status in Myanmar's society and economic life. They may retain their maiden name after marriage, may obtain divorces without undue difficulty, and enjoy equal property and inheritance rights with men.

Myanmar's military government continues to engage in human rights abuses. The military uses forced labor as porters for the army. There is also widespread mistreatment of prisoners.

Healthcare

Until recent decades, few people in rural areas had the benefit of modern medicine. To correct this deficiency, the country's health services were reorganized by sending more doctors to rural areas and increasing the number of rural health centers. Doctors in private practice were inducted for two years of national service.

The progress of the health services is reflected in the reduction of the physician/ population ratio from 1 per 15,560 in 1960 to 1 per 3,578 by 1986. In 1986, Myanmar had 635 hospitals with 25,839 beds. There were 12,400 doctors in 1990.

Smallpox and plague have been practically eliminated as health hazards, and programs are under way to eradicate malaria and tuberculosis. However, gastrointestinal diseases such as typhoid, dysentery, and cholera remain widespread. In 1995, only 38% of the population had access to safe water. Another serious health problem is drug addiction, aggravated by the easy availability and low cost of opium. Under a drug abuse control program financed by the United States and the United Nations, a new 300-bed hospital for addicts was opened in 1982 at Thayetmyo; smaller facilities have been established in two dozen other towns.

Average life expectancy was 56 years in 1996. In 1990–95, 60% of the population had access to health care services.

Housing

Pre-war housing in Myanmar compared favorably with that in other Southeast Asian nations, but housing conditions have deteriorated. Urban dwellings are overcrowded and often unsafe.

EDUCATION

In 1994, Myanmar had 35,744 primary schools with 5.7 million students. Secondary schools had 69,411 teachers and 1.5 million students. Primary education lasts for 5 years, followed by 4 years of secondary education at the first stage and 2 years at the second stage.

Post-secondary institutions, including 18 teacher-training colleges, 6 agricultural institutes, 8 technical institutes, and 35 universities and colleges, enrolled a total of 235,236 students with 5,989 teaching staff in 1993. The Arts and Science Universities at Yangon (Rangoon) and Mandalay together enrolled about 19,500 students in the mid-1980s.

The Mass Education Council has attempted to increase literacy through special programs. The 1995 adult illiteracy rate was estimated at 17% (males, 11.3%; and females, 22.3%).

1999 KEY EVENTS TIMELINE

January

- The government reopens four medical colleges; other universities remain closed as a security measure.
- The Karen Nation Union, Myanmar's largest remaining rebel group, marks its 50th year of insurgency.

February

- Interpol's heroin suppression conference in Myanmar's capital, Yangon (formerly Rangoon) is boycotted by the U.S. and European countries.
- Dr. Ma Thida, writer and political prisoner, is released, but other dissidents are arrested.

March

- United Nations special investigator Rajsoomer Lallah reports on human rights violations in Myanmar.
- Michael Aris, husband of Myanmar's democracy movement leader, Aung San Suu Kyi, dies in London, denied a visa for a last visit to her.
- Burmese officials Gen. Than Shwe and Gen. Khin Nyunt meet with Thai Prime Minister Chuan Leekpai during a two day state visit in northern Thailand.

April

- A ceremony is held to celebrate completion of restoration work on the Shwedagon Buddhist pagoda. A few days later, a fire breaks out at the pagoda.

May

- Labor ministers of the Association of Southeast Asian Nations (ASEAN) hold their annual meeting in Myanmar.
- Following months of controversy, the European Union allows Myanmar to attend a ASEAN-EU Joint Cooperation Committee meeting.
- Karen environmental activist Ka Hsaw Wa wins the Goldman Environmental prize.

June

- Amnesty International releases reports on human rights violations against Myanmar's Shan, Karen and Karenni people.
- The International Labor Organization of the UN bars Myanmar from participation, due to its findings on forced labor in Myanmar.

July

- The government detains dissidents and family members, including a three year old girl, in the southern city of Pegu.
- Thai officials and the press decry the flow of heroin and amphetamines into Thailand from Myanmar.

August

- Australia's Human Rights Commissioner visits Myanmar in an effort to encourage the formation of a human rights organization.

September

- Low-key protests take place instead of the unrest called for by Burmese students on the "auspicious" date of 9/9/99.

- Two young British activists are arrested in Myanmar and given long prison terms.

October

- Armed Burmese youths seize the Burmese Embassy in Thailand, hold hostages, and escape in a helicopter.

- Angered at Thailand's handling of hostage situation, Myanmar shuts down all border trade with Thailand.

- UN Assistant Secretary-General Alvaro de Soto arrives for talks with the Burmese government and opposition.

November

- At an informal meeting in Manila, Philippines, six members of the Association of Southeast Asian Nations (ASEAN)—Brunei, Indonesia, Malaysia, Philippines, Singapore, and Thailand—agree to establish a free-trade zone by eliminating duties on most goods traded in the region by 2010. The remaining four newer and less-developed nation members—Cambodia, Laos, Myanmar, and Vietnam—will eliminate duties by 2015. Rice will be excluded from trade agreements, however.

ANALYSIS OF EVENTS: 1999

BUSINESS AND THE ECONOMY

Myanmar's economy struggled under a variety of pressures in 1999, as the currency, the kyat, plunged to a new low of 360 to the dollar at informal market rates, although the government refused to officially devalue the kyat. International lending institutions such as the World Bank and International Monetary Fund continued to refuse loans to Myanmar despite their meetings with government officials.

Foreign investment in Myanmar decreased to the lowest level in five years, according to government statistics, which cited a 70 percent drop in investment by Southeast Asian neighbors affected by the regional economic crisis. President Clinton renewed economic sanctions forbidding new U.S. investment in Myanmar. The primary foreign-funded infrastructure project, the Yadana natural gas pipeline, was beset by problems with power generating at its user end, Thailand, and was unable to come fully on-line. Exports continued in the garment industry, and new contracts were signed with mining firms. A Japan-Myanmar business council was formed to try to boost trade. Rice production and tourism, on which the government had pinned hard currency hopes, continued to slump. Myanmar's closure of the Thai border in October further disrupted trade, especially in fishing concessions.

GOVERNMENT AND POLITICS

Myanmar traditionally depended on the Association of South East Asian Nations (ASEAN) for prestige and support, and as a member was able to participate in a joint meeting of ASEAN and the European Union for the first time, in 1999. For the most part, however, Myanmar's human rights record led to its isolation and condemnation in the international arena. The State Peace and Development Council (SPDC), Myanmar's military government, sought to force resignations from the National League for Democracy (NLD), the party which had won a 1991 election, the results of which were not honored. Party members and other dissidents were detained for questioning or given prison terms. Calls for a dialogue between the SPDC and NLD leader Aung San Suu Kyi were unheeded. UN Assistant Secretary-General Alvaro de Soto visit to Myanmar was postponed by the SPDC but eventually took place, and he spoke with government officials and opposition leaders in an effort to encourage talks between the groups.

The UN's International Labor Organization (ILO) culminated a huge-scale investigation into the use of forced labor in Myanmar by passing a resolution to effectively bar Myanmar from participation in the ILO. The SPDC's campaigns of forced relocation and other human rights violations in ethnic minority regions were condemned by Amnesty International and the government. Australia's Human Rights Commissioner, Chris Sidoti, visited Myanmar to promote the formation of a human rights bureau there.

Although demonstrations called for by the opposition on the numerologically significant day of 9/9/99 largely failed to materialize inside Myanmar, the frustrations of political exiles took a dramatic turn with the seizure of Myanmar's embassy in Thailand in October. Myanmar's relations with its neighbor Thailand were strained by that event, and by Thai anger over Burmese production of heroin and methamphetamines that flowed into Thailand in 1999. China remained Myanmar's closest political ally and a significant trading partner, although the drug trade affected the Myanmar/China border as well. An Interpol conference about heroin suppression was held in Myanmar, but was boycotted by the U.S. and European countries, which accused the SPDC of involvement in money laundering for narcotics dealers.

CULTURE AND SOCIETY

Most colleges and universities in Myanmar remained shut down in 1999, as a measure to prevent student unrest. The press and other sources of information were tightly controlled by the SPDC. Myanmar's first Internet access was announced, but could be used only with government permission. In 1999, Khin Myo Chit, a veteran journalist known for her humorous essays, died; dissident writer Dr. Ma Thida was released after her long prison term; and prominent novelist Maung Tha Ya went into exile. A government-sponsored international tour by Burmese musicians was disrupted by demonstrations in Japan and England.

Myanmar's Health Ministry acknowledged the severity of the HIV/AIDS epidemic throughout the country, as the UN designated Myanmar an AIDS crisis zone. Substandard health care, malnutrition and child mortality remained severe problems in Myanmar.

Ka Hsaw Wa, an ethnic Karen activist, won the 1999 Reebok Human Rights Award and the Goldman Environmental Prize for his investigations of the situation in the gas pipeline region of southern Myanmar. A report by the U.S. State Department described religious persecution of Myanmar's Moslem Rohingya and Christian Chin ethnic minority groups.

DIRECTORY

CENTRAL GOVERNMENT
Head of State
Chairman of the State Peace and Development Council
Than Shwe, State Peace and Development Council

Prime Minister
Than Shwe, Office of the Prime Minister

Ministers
Minister of Agriculture and Irrigation
Nyunt Tin, Ministry of Agriculture and Irrigation
PHONE: +95 (1) 665587

Minister of Commerce
Kyaw Than, Ministry of Commerce

Minister of Communications, Post, and Telegraph
Win Tin, Ministry of Communications, Post, and Telegraph
PHONE: +95 (1) 292955

Minister of Construction
Saw Tun, Ministry of Construction
PHONE: +95 (1) 285899

Minister of Cooperatives
Aung San, Ministry of Cooperatives
PHONE: +95 (1) 277096

Minister of Culture
Win Sein, Ministry of Culture
PHONE: +95 (1) 277316

Minister of Defense
Than Shwe, Ministry of Defense

Minister of Education
Than Aung, Ministry of Education
PHONE: +95 (1) 286726

Minister of Electric Power
Tin Htut, Ministry of Electric Power

Minister of Energy
Lun Thi, Ministry of Energy
PHONE: +95 (1) 221060

Minister of Finance and Revenue
Khin Maung Thein, Ministry of Finance and Revenue
PHONE: +95 (1) 284763

Minister of Foreign Affairs
Win Aung, Ministry of Foreign Affairs
PHONE: +95 (1) 221529

Minister of Forestry
Aung Phone, Ministry of Forestry
PHONE: +95 (1) 663279

Minister of Health
Ket Sein, Ministry of Health
PHONE: +95 (1) 285896

Minister of Home Affairs
Tin Hlaing, Ministry of Home Affairs

PHONE: +95 (1) 549208

Minister of Hotels and Tourism
Saw Lwin, Ministry of Hotels and Tourism
PHONE: +95 (1) 287228; 286024; 285689;
275328

Minister of Immigration and Population
Saw Tun, Ministry of Immigration and
Population

Minister of Industry No. 1
Aung Thaung, Ministry of Industry No. 1
PHONE: +95 (1) 566064

Minister of Industry No. 2
Saw Lwin, Ministry of Industry No. 2
PHONE: +95 (1) 282826

Minister of Information
Kyi Aung, Ministry of Information
PHONE: +95 (1) 294827; 294812; 294645

Minister of Labor
Tin Aye, Ministry of Labor
PHONE: +95 (1) 278320

Minister of Livestock, Breeding, and Fisheries
Maung Maung Thein, Ministry of Livestock,
Breeding, and Fisheries
PHONE: +95 (1) 280398

Minister of Military Affairs
Tin Hla, Ministry of Military Affairs

Minister of Mines
Ohn Myint, Ministry of Mines
PHONE: +95 (1) 577316

Minister of National Planning and Economic Development
Soe Tha, Ministry of National Planning and
Economic Development
PHONE: +95 (1) 280816

Minister of Progress of Border Areas and National Races and Development Affairs
Thein Nyunt, Ministry of Progress of Border
Areas and National Races and Development
Affairs
PHONE: +95 (1) 285102

Minister of Rail Transport
Pan Aung, Ministry of Rail Transport
PHONE: +95 (1) 292772

Minister of Religious Affairs
Sein Htwa, Ministry of Religious Affairs

Minister of Science and Technology
U Thaung, Ministry of Science and Technology

Minister of Social Welfare, Relief, and Resettlement
Pyei Son, Ministry of Social Welfare, Relief,
and Resettlement

Minister of Sports
Sein Win, Ministry of Sports

Minister of Transport
Hla Myint Swe, Ministry of Transport

POLITICAL ORGANIZATIONS
Taingyintha Silonenyinyutye (National Unity Party)
NAME: Than Shwe

National Council of the Union of Burma (NCGUB)

Washington Office, 815 15th St NW, Suite 910,
Washington DC 20005, USA
PHONE: +(202) 3324300
FAX: +(202) 3937343
E-MAIL: ncgub@igc.apc.org
NAME: Sein Win

DIPLOMATIC REPRESENTATION
Embassies in Myanmar

Australia
88 Strand Road, Kyauktada Tsp., Yangon,
Myanmar
PHONE: +95 (1) 280965; 278307; 280234
FAX: +95 (1) 275521

China
94 Kayaybin Road, Dagon Tsp., Yangon,
Myanmar
PHONE: +95 (1) 221280; 221281; 221398
FAX: +95 (1) 227019

France
102 Fydaungsu Yeiktha Road, Dagon Tsp.,
Yangon, Myanmar
PHONE: +95 (1) 282122; 282418; 281759
FAX: +95 (1) 287759

Germany
32 Natmauk Street, Bahan Tsp., Yangon,
Myanmar
PHONE: +95 (1) 548951; 548952; 548953
FAX: +95 (1) 548899

India
545–547 Merchant Street, Kyauktada Tsp.,
Yangon, Myanmar
PHONE: +95 (1) 282550; 282552; 282933

FAX: +95 (1) 289562

Italy
3 Inya Myaing Road, Golden Valley, Bahan Tsp., Yangon, Myanmar
PHONE: +95 (1) 527100; 527101
FAX: +95 (1) 533670

Japan
100 Natmauk Road, Bahan Tsp., Yangon, Myanmar
PHONE: +95 (1) 549644; 549645; 549646
FAX: +95 (1) 549643

South Korea
97 University Avenue, Bahan Tsp., Yangon, Myanmar
PHONE: +95 (1) 527142; 527143; 527144
FAX: +95 (1) 532630

Russia
38 Sagawa Road, Dagon Tsp., Yangon, Myanmar
PHONE: +95 (1) 241955; 289730
FAX: +95 (1) 241953

Thailand
45 Pyay Road, 6 1/2 Mile, Hiaing Tsp., Myanmar
PHONE: +95 (1) 525670; 533082
FAX: +95 (1) 222784

United Kingdom
80 Strand Road, Kyauktada Tsp., Yangon, Myanmar
PHONE: +95 (1) 281700; 281702; 281703
FAX: +95 (1) 289566

United States
581 Merchant Street, Kyauktada Tsp., Yangon, Myanmar
PHONE: +95 (1) 282055; 282056; 282059
FAX: +95 (1) 280409

FURTHER READING

Books

Houtman, Gustaaf. ''Mental Culture in Burmese Crisis Politics: Aung San Suu Kyi and the National League for Democracy.'' Tokyo: Institute for the Study of Languages and Cultures of Asia and Africa, 1999.

MacLean, Rory. *Under the Dragon: Travels in a Betrayed Land*. London: HarperCollins, 1999.

Smith, Martin. *Myanmar: Insurgency and the Politics of Ethnicity*. London: Zed Books, 1999.

War in the Blood: Sex, Politics and AIDS in Southeast Asia. London: Zed Books, 1998.

Internet

''Waiting for Democracy.'' BBC Online, 6 August 1998. Available Online @ news2.thls.bbc.co.uk/hi/english/special_report/1998/08/98/Myanmar/newsid_145000/145416.stm (December 14, 1999).

''What Chance for Change?'' BBC Online, 6 August 1998. Available Online @ news2.thls.bbc.co.uk/hi/english/special_report/1998/08/98/Myanmar/newsid_146000/146014.stm (December 14, 1999).

MYANMAR: STATISTICAL DATA

For sources and notes see "Sources of Statistics" in the front of each volume.

GEOGRAPHY

Geography (1)

Area:

Total: 678,500 sq km.

Land: 657,740 sq km.

Water: 20,760 sq km.

Area—comparative: slightly smaller than Texas.

Land boundaries:

Total: 5,876 km.

Border countries: Bangladesh 193 km, China 2,185 km, India 1,463 km, Laos 235 km, Thailand 1,800 km.

Coastline: 1,930 km.

Climate: tropical monsoon; cloudy, rainy, hot, humid summers (southwest monsoon, June to September); less cloudy, scant rainfall, mild temperatures, lower humidity during winter (northeast monsoon, December to April).

Terrain: central lowlands ringed by steep, rugged highlands.

Natural resources: petroleum, timber, tin, antimony, zinc, copper, tungsten, lead, coal, some marble, limestone, precious stones, natural gas.

Land use:

Arable land: 15%

Permanent crops: 1%

Permanent pastures: 1%

Forests and woodland: 49%

Other: 34% (1993 est.).

HUMAN FACTORS

Demographics (2A)

	1990	1995	1998	2000	2010	2020	2030	2040	2050
Population	41,068.5	44,954.7	47,305.3	48,852.1	56,572.9	64,279.6	72,015.7	80,086.8	87,777.7
Net migration rate (per 1,000 population)	NA	NA	NA	NA	NA	NA	NA	NA	NA
Births	NA	NA	NA	NA	NA	NA	NA	NA	NA
Deaths	NA	NA	NA	NA	NA	NA	NA	NA	NA
Life expectancy - males	50.6	52.4	53.0	53.5	56.1	58.7	64.6	70.5	73.1
Life expectancy - females	53.6	55.4	56.1	56.5	61.6	64.3	70.6	76.9	79.6
Birth rate (per 1,000)	32.6	30.4	29.0	28.0	24.5	21.9	19.4	17.2	15.6
Death rate (per 1,000)	14.0	12.9	12.5	12.3	10.7	10.1	8.4	7.2	7.5
Women of reproductive age (15-49 yrs.)	10,149.0	11,271.4	11,983.2	12,468.3	14,810.7	16,867.9	18,894.3	20,552.2	21,652.0
of which are currently married	NA	NA	NA	NA	NA	NA	NA	NA	NA
Fertility rate	4.2	3.9	3.7	3.6	3.0	2.7	2.4	2.3	2.2

Except as noted, values for vital statistics are in thousands; life expectancy is in years.

Ethnic Division (6)

Burman 68%
Shan 9%
Karen 7%
Rakhine 4%
Chinese 3%
Mon 2%
Indian 2%
Other 5%

Religions (7)

Buddhist 89%
Christian 4%
 Baptist 3%
 Roman Catholic 1%
Muslim 4%
Animist beliefs 1%
Other 2%

Languages (8)

Burmese, minority ethnic groups have their own languages.

GOVERNMENT & LAW

Political Parties (12)

seats by party—	No. of seats
National League for Democracy (NLD)	.396
National Unit Party (NUP)	.10
Other	.79

Government Budget (13B)

Revenues . . . .$7.9 billion
Expenditures . . . .$12.2 billion
 Capital expenditures . . . .$5.7 billion

Data for FY96/97.

Military Affairs (14A)

Military age . . . . .18 years of age
Availability of manpower
 Males age 15-49 12,208,916
 Females age 15-49 (1998 est.) 11,983,225
Fit for military service
 Males 6,523,797
 Females (1998 est.) 6,387,291
Reaching military age annually
 Males 488,818
 Females (1998 est.) 469,850

Total expenditures (FY96/97 est.) . . . .$380 million
Expenditures as % of GDP . . . . .NA%

Both sexes liable for military service. NA stands for not available.

LABOR FORCE

Labor Force (16)

Total (million) 18.8
Agriculture 65.2%
Industry 14.3%
Trade 10.1%
Government 6.3%
Other 4.1%

Data for FY95/96 est. Distribution for FY88/89 est.

Unemployment Rate (17)

Rate not available.

PRODUCTION SECTOR

Electric Energy (18)

Capacity . . . . .1.212 million kW (1995)
Production . . . . .4.1 billion kWh (FY95/96 est.)
Consumption per capita . . . . .79 kWh (1995)

Transportation (19)

Highways:

total: 28,200 km

paved: 3,440 km

unpaved: 24,760 km (1996 est.)

Waterways: 12,800 km; 3,200 km navigable by large commercial vessels

Pipelines: crude oil 1,343 km; natural gas 330 km

Merchant marine:

total: 45 ships (1,000 GRT or over) totaling 561,786 GRT/742,450 DWT ships by type: bulk 15, cargo 18, chemical tanker 1, container 2, oil tanker 3, passenger-cargo 3, refrigerated cargo 1, vehicle carrier 2 note: a flag of convenience registry; includes ships of 2 countries: Japan owns 2 ships, US 3 (1997 est.)

Airports: 80 (1997 est.)

Airports—with paved runways:

total: 24

over 3,047 m: 3

2,438 to 3,047 m: 2

1,524 to 2,437 m: 12

914 to 1,523 m: 7 (1997 est.)

Airports—with unpaved runways:

total: 56

over 3,047 m: 1

1,524 to 2,437 m: 4

914 to 1,523 m: 19

under 914 m: 32 (1997 est.)

Top Agricultural Products (20)

Paddy rice, corn, oilseed, sugarcane, pulses; hardwood.

FINANCE, ECONOMICS, & TRADE

Economic Indicators (22)

National product: GDP—purchasing power parity—$55.7 billion (1997 est.)

National product real growth rate: 6% (1997 est.)

National product per capita: $1,190 (1997 est.)

Inflation rate—consumer price index: 30%-40% (1997 est.)

Exchange Rates (24)

Exchange rates:

Kyats (K) per US$1

January 1998	6.3941
1997	6.2418
1996	5.9176
1995	5.6670
1994	5.9749
1993	6.1570
unofficial 1998	310-350

Top Import Origins (25)

$1.4 billion (1996)

Origins	%
Japan	NA
Singapore	NA
China	NA
Thailand	NA
Malaysia	NA

NA stands for not available.

Top Export Destinations (26)

$693 million (1996).

Destinations	%
Singapore	NA
China	NA
Indonesia	NA
India	NA
Thailand	NA

NA stands for not available.

Economic Aid (27)

Recipient: ODA, $61 million (1993).

Import Export Commodities (28)

Import Commodities	Export Commodities
Machinery	Pulses and beans
Transport equipment	Teak
Construction materials	Rice
Food products	Rubber
Consumer goods	Hardwood

NAMIBIA

Republic of Namibia

CAPITAL: Windhoek.

FLAG: Top left triangle is blue, center diagonal band is red, and the bottom right triangle is green. Colors are separated by narrow white bands. On the blue triangle is a golden sun with twelve triangular rays.

ANTHEM: *Namibia Land of the Brave*, music and words by Axali Doeseb.

MONETARY UNIT: The South African rand (R) of 100 cents is in use; notes and coins are those of South Africa. R1 = $0.2874 (or $1 = R3.4795).

WEIGHTS AND MEASURES: The metric system is in use.

HOLIDAYS: New Year's Day, 1 January; Independence Day, 21 March; Easter, 1–4 April; Workers' Day, 1 May; Casinga Day, 4 May; Ascension Day, 12 May; Africa Day, 25 May; Heroes' Day, 26 August; Day of Goodwill, 7 October; Human Rights Day, 10 December; Christmas, 25–26 December.

TIME: 2 PM = noon GMT.

LOCATION AND SIZE: Namibia covers 824,290 square kilometers (318,260 square miles), slightly more than half the size of the state of Alaska. It has a total boundary length of 5,424 kilometers (3,370 miles).

Namibia's capital city, Windhoek, is in the center of the country.

CLIMATE: Namibia's climate is the driest in Africa, with sunny, warm days and cooler nights, especially during the winter months. The mean January temperature at Windhoek is 23°C (73° F). In winter, the mean temperature is 13°C (55°F). Much of Namibia experiences chronic drought. The annual rainfall, which mostly falls between December and March, generally averages only 2.5–15 centimeters (1–6 inches) in the south of the country, and some regions have gone 90 years without a drop of rain.

INTRODUCTORY SURVEY

RECENT HISTORY

After World War II (1939–45), South Africa tried to turn Namibia into its own province. In the 1950s, senators from South-West Africa sat in the South African parliament, and Windhoek was reduced to a provincial capital. The United Nations took South Africa before the International Court of Justice, but not until 1971 did the Court declare the South African occupation of Namibia illegal.

Meanwhile, in 1960, representatives of the native majority had formed the South-West Africa People's Organization (SWAPO) to seek independence and black majority rule. Beginning in 1966, but especially after 1977, SWAPO waged a guerrilla war. South Africa responded by building up its armed forces along Namibia's borders.

In 1978, South Africa accepted a Western-sponsored plan for an independent Namibia, but the plan proved difficult to implement in a way that satisfied all sides. It was not until April of 1989 that all sides finally agreed to a ceasefire and began the process of creating a new state.

Elections were held in November of 1989. SWAPO won 57% of the vote, the Democratic Turnahalle Alliance (DTA) received 29%, and a variety of ethnic-based parties received the rest. A new constitution was adopted on 9 February 1990, and Namibia became independent on 21 March 1990.

The SWAPO government (whose support comes chiefly from the Ovambo people of the north and from urban areas) has followed a policy of

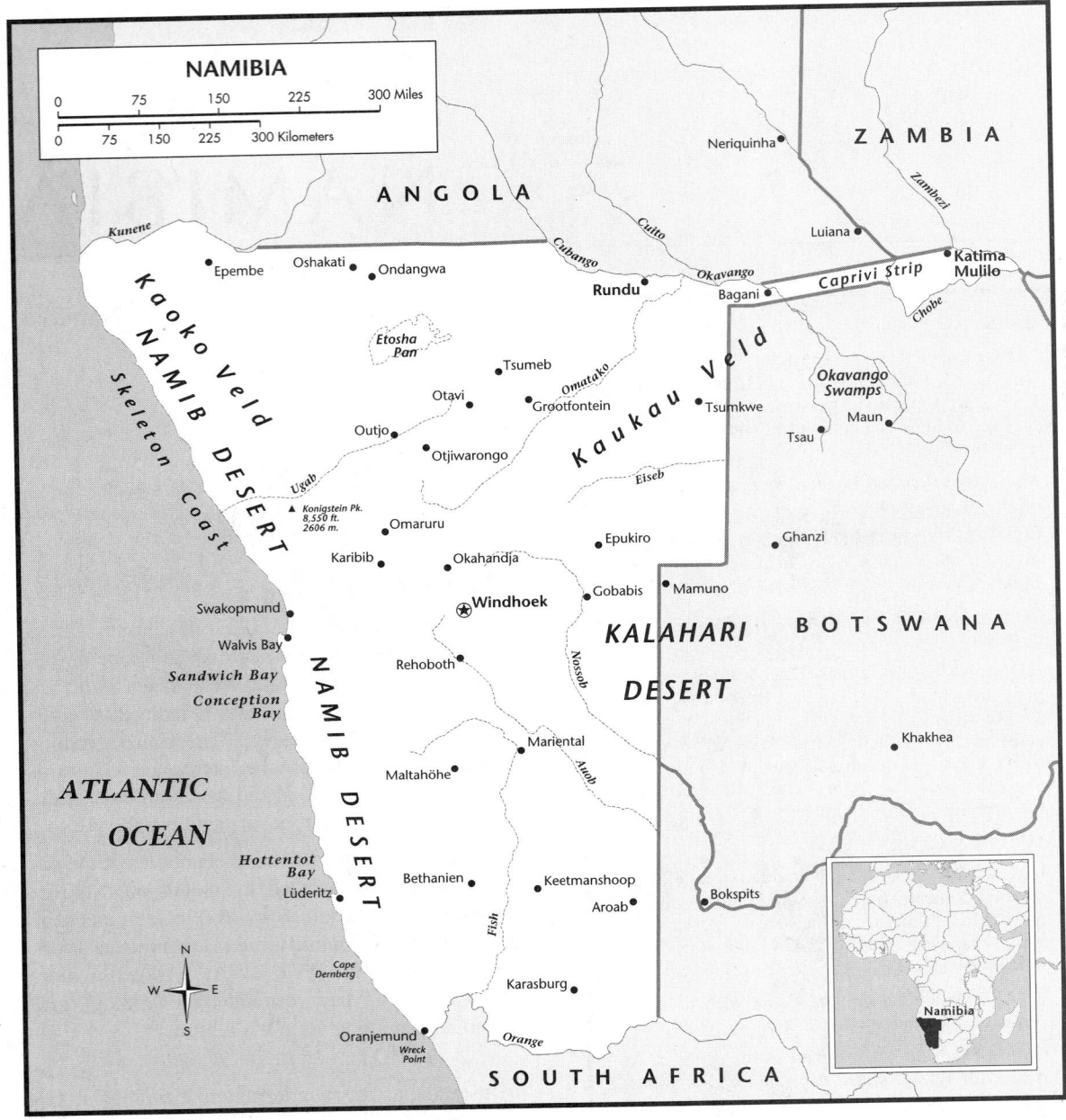

reconciliation with the white inhabitants and created a multiparty, nonracial democracy. In 1993, agreement was reached with South Africa to return Walvis Bay to Namibia, an act completed on 1 March 1994. Occasional border disputes with Angola disrupted the country. In mid-1994, a large section of the country's border was closed and Namibian guards had orders to shoot at any vehicles attempting to cross.

GOVERNMENT

The Namibia constitution adopted on 21 March 1990 is considered a model of democratic government. It provides for a two-chamber legislature, consisting of a National Assembly and a National Council. The Assembly consists of 72 elected deputies and six members appointed by the president. The Council is comprised of two members from each of 13 regions.

The president is elected by direct, popular vote. The president serves as head of state and commander-in-chief of the Defense Force. The term of office can be for no more than two five-year terms.

Judiciary

The formal court system is arranged on three levels: magistrates' courts, the High Court, and the Supreme Court. The Supreme Court serves as the highest court of appeals and also exercises constitutional review of legislation. The traditional courts handle minor criminal offenses such as petty theft and violations of local customs.

Political Parties

The South-West Africa People's Organization (SWAPO) is the largest political party. There are a number of ethnic parties, including the South-West African National Union (SWANU), largely representing the Herero; the white-led Democratic Turnhalle Alliance (DTA); the SWAPO-Democrats, a small Ovambo-based group; the Damara Council; and the Namibia Christian Democratic Party (a Kavango group).

In the 1994 National Assembly elections, SWAPO won 53 of 72 possible seats.

DEFENSE

Postwar national forces number 8,000 men in 8 mixed battalions and 100 men in naval patrol forces. There is a small national police force. Defense spending is $65 million (1995).

ECONOMIC AFFAIRS

Namibia's economy is dependent on a few primary exports, including minerals (diamonds, uranium, copper, lead, silver), livestock (both meat and hides), and fish, which, together, account for nearly 90% of exports. The economy is highly integrated with that of South Africa. Years of white rule have resulted in one of the most unequal income distributions on the African continent. However, a democratically elected government is now committed to developing previously neglected regions of the country.

Public Finance

The U.S. Central Intelligence Agency estimates that, in 1994, government revenues totaled approximately $941 million and expenditures $1.05 billion, including capital expenditures of $157 million. External debt totaled $385 million.

Income

In 1996 Namibia's gross national product (GNP) was $6.2 billion, or about $3,700 per person. For the period 1985–95, the average inflation rate was 10.5%, resulting in a real growth rate in GNP of 2.8% per person.

Industry

Namibia's industry is centered on meat and fish processing, with some production of basic consumer goods. There are furniture and clothing factories, metal and engineering works, assembly plants, and a cement plant. Historically, Namibia has been dependent on South African manufacturing.

Banking and Finance

Banking activities have recorded strong growth since independence in 1990, while the range of financial institutions operating in Namibia has begun to expand. Total assets of the four main commercial banks more than doubled in 1991–95 to $5.4 billion, and during 1995 bank lending to the private sector rose by 34% to n $4.7 billion as of end-December, 92% of total domestic credit, of which 41% comprised loans to individuals. There have been no banking failures since independence, but the regulatory regime inherited from South Africa is being brought more into line with international norms under a new banking institutions act that was due to come into effect in 1997.

First National Bank Namibia and Standard Bank Namibia, with assets totaling n $2 billion each as of end-1995, have the largest branch networks and remain wholly owned subsidiaries of their South African parent banks. The Commercial Bank of Namibia (CBN), a subsidiary of the Geneva-based Société Financière pour les Pays d'outre mer (SFOM) and South Africa's NEDCOR Bank, and Bank Windhoek, in which South Africa's ABSA Bank is the main shareholder, had assets of $1 billion each. In mid-1996, Bank Windhoek completed a merger with the Namib Building Society. The merger was originally to have included Namibia's biggest society, SWABOU, also with $1 billion in assets, which may revive its plans to convert to a bank. The City Savings and Investment Bank (CSIB), launched in 1994 as Namibia's first indigenously owned financial institution, had total assets of only $75 million at end-1995, and a single branch in Windhoek. Bank Industri Malaysia acquired a controlling interest shortly after CSIB was set up and following a mid-1996 recapitulation, activities may now be expanded.

Within four years, the Namibian Stock Exchange (NSE), which started operations in October 1992, has grown to become sub-Saharan Africa's second largest in terms of market capitalization, next to the Johannesburg Stock Exchange (JSE). The NSE is increasingly being used by local firms to raise capital for business expansions, while foreign investors are buying into Namibian equities through new listings and rights offers, which have been mainly over-subscribed. Some 95% of the NSE's overall market capitalization comprises dual-listings of South African parent groups of Namibian subsidiaries, accounting for 15 of the 26 listed shares in June 1996. However, local market capitalization more than doubled in the first half of 1996 to $2.4 billion.

Money supply, as measured by M2, amounted to $4.748 million in 1995. Total foreign reserves, excluding gold, were us $225.3 million at the end of 1995.

Economic Development

Namibia's government will continue to build and diversify its economy around its mineral reserves. Priorities include expanding the manufacturing sector, land reform, agricultural development in the populous north, and improved education and health opportunities. Transfer of Walvis Bay and 12 offshore islands to Namibia has returned to Namibia its deep-water port and 20% of its offshore rights.

SOCIAL WELFARE

The constitution promotes gender, racial, and regional equality. However, discrimination against women exists in both law and tradition. Indigenous San peoples have historically faced discrimination from Namibia's other ethnic groups. Namibia's whites have a substantially higher standard of living than its blacks. There is also a big difference in the living conditions between rural and urban Namibians.

Healthcare

In 1985 there were 64 hospitals and 130 clinics. In 1990, the population per physician was 4,315. Health services are provided through ethnically based government authorities, so the system is effectively segregated. In addition, most health care facilities are in the towns, which are largely white. Average life expectancy is 56 years, and 57% of the population has access to health care services.

Housing

There is a sharp contrast in housing standards between white and black Namibians. Most rural dwellings are self-constructed from local materials. In 1992 the backlog in housing units was estimated at 45,000 units.

EDUCATION

Education is compulsory for nine years between the ages of 7 and 16. In 1994, 367,669 Namibians were in primary and 101,974 pupils were in secondary schools. There is an Academy for Tertiary Education for adult students. Adult illiteracy is estimated at 62%. In 1994, there were 11,344 students in all higher level institutions.

1999 KEY EVENTS TIMELINE

February

- Namibian President Sam Nujoma meets Libyan leader Muammar Gaddafi after flying to Libya in violation of the 1992 UN air embargo.

March

- Kenyan President Daniel arap Moi arrives at Windhoek's airport Monday at the start of a three-day visit to Namibia.

- Ben Ulenga, a veteran member of the ruling South West Africa People's Organization and Namibia's former High Commissioner to the United Kingdom breaks away to form a new opposition party (the Congress of Democrats) to challenge SWAPO in general and presidential elections.

April

- The governments of Namibia, Botswana and Zimbabwe open the world's first legal ivory sale in a decade before a private audience of Japanese bidders in the capital Windhoek. Namibia offers 13.8 tons of stored ivory tusks for sale.

May

- Botswana and Namibia sign an agreement with UNHCR for voluntary repatriation of Namibian refugees in Botswana who fled separatist tensions in northern Namibia's Caprivi Strip.

June

- Nigerian President Olusegun Obasanjo discusses armed conflicts in Africa in the capital, Windhoek, with Namibian President, Sam Nujoma.

August

- Namibian separatists in the northern Caprivi region attack an army base and police station in the Caprivi regional capital, Katima Mulilo. At least 12 people are killed.

September

- President Sam Nujoma makes an official visit to Cuba at the invitation of President Fidel Castro.

November

- Presidential and legislative elections begin on November 30.

December

- The second and final day of presidential and legislative elections are held December 1, returning President Sam Nujoma to power with 77 percent of the vote, and his South West Africa People's Organisation (SWAPO) party to parliament with a majority.

- For the first time in President Nujoma's rule, an opposition party is created by Ben Ulenga, a former SWAPO leader who is now a leading SWAPO critic, introducing genuine party rivalry into Namibian politics.

- The World Court rules that an 1.4-square-mile uninhabited island, known as Kasikili or Sedudu, between Botswana and Namibia belongs to Botswana.

ANALYSIS OF EVENTS: 1999

BUSINESS AND THE ECONOMY

In 1999 Namibia's economy did not perform as well as it did following its 1989 independence from South Africa, when it was held up as an economic shining light in the region. October figures projected Namibia's economic growth rate at 4% for 1999. The economy, which was dependent on diamond mining, fishing, and agricultural commodity export, grew by only 2.6 percent in 1998. With a 3.1 percent population growth rate, this sluggish economic growth was worrisome. With an unchanging 35 percent unemployment rate Namibian citizens were voicing concerns about the ruling South West African People's Organization (SWAPO)'s handling of the economy, particularly considering its 1994 election promises focused on job production.

In the face of this bleak employment picture, the government allowed civil service jobs to more than double with 70,000 workers employed in a bloated government bureaucracy. The slightly higher 1999 economic growth rate came from better commodity prices and increased fish and diamond exports. Fish accounted for over 30 percent of exports in 1998. Trade with South Africa, home of its former apartheid-era rulers for 75 years, continues to dominate the country's trade statistics.

Namibia's 1999/2000 budget focused on poverty alleviation and investment. Namibia's business leaders indicated that foreign investors complained of red tape, strict labor laws, and unskilled workers. The budget was expected to spend 21 percent on education and 14 percent on health and social service. Defense was to receive 7.2 percent and police and finance 6.4 percent each. The budget foresaw a deficit of N $798.8 million, which the government planned to make up through foreign aid and by dipping into its account at the Bank of Namibia, and issuing government bonds and treasury bills. The budget made no provision for extra spending on the war in the Democratic Republic of the Congo, where Namibian forces (along with those of Angola and Zimbabwe) have been fighting since August 1998 against a Rwandan- and Ugandan-backed insurrection. The Namibian public was increasingly restless about their country's involvement in the quagmire.

A new container terminal in Walvis Bay embodied Namibia's attempt to become southern Africa's biggest Atlantic port, surpassing Cape Town. Observers expected that gas energy from the offshore Kudu Gas Fields might be the salvation of this economy which now imports about 70 percent of its power from South Africa.

GOVERNMENT AND POLITICS

The South West African People's Organization (SWAPO) government continued to experience difficulty from secessionist fighting in the Caprivi region of northern Namibia in 1999. More than 14 people died there in August 1999 in a battle between government forces and secessionists, who are primarily members of the Lozi/Barotse ethnic group seeking to unite with fellow Lozi in Zambia. There were reports of torture on the part of SWAPO forces, and the government did admit that ''mistakes'' were made in its handling of the rebellion.

Dating from the apartheid-era of South African rule, the Namibian political leadership had made public promises to concerning land reform. To date its success in this program had been marginal. The issue carried the threat of being quite explosive. The country had over 1.3 million peasants expecting to be settled on land owned by 6,000 commercial farms, a product of the pre-independence, white-controlled economy. More than 70 percent of the country's land was owned by a small number of primarily white people, many of whom were not resident in the country, while 80 percent of the Namibian people scraped by on the marginal 30 percent of the land that was left. The National Union of Namibia Workers, representing over 200,000 Namibians warned the government that it would take its memberships to the streets in protest marches throughout the country if the government did not expropriate land from the absentee owners. The constitution, however, prohibits confiscation of land. The threatened march had not materialized, but the issue continued to be highly volatile.

The country faced its third democratic elections since independence from South Africa in 1989. In the constitution established at independence, no president was allowed to rule for more than 10 years. SWAPO, whose fighters brought the country to independence after 30 years of struggle and who scored an impressive electoral win in the 1994 elections, used its overwhelming legislative majority to change the constitution to allow President Sam Nujoma to contest the elections for a third five-year term. This maneuver brought widespread criticism both within the country and internationally. The elections, held on November 30 and December 1 were for both the presidency and the 72-member National Assembly.

The Democratic Turnhalle Alliance was the major opposition party in 1994, but it remained tainted with its apartheid-era ties to white rule. For the 1999 elections, a third major party was formed in March 1999 after the defection from SWAPO of Ben Ulenga, 46, former member of the SWAPO central committee, trade unionist, and former Robben Island political prisoner for 15 years. The new party, the Congress of Democrats, criticized SWAPO for corruption, growing authoritarianism, an inflated government payroll—particularly at the cabinet level—and Namibia's entrance into the Congo conflict when it could ill afford the expense. There were five other minority parties that would not affect the outcome of the presidential vote.

Ninety invited international observers, from the European Union, the Southern African Development Community (SADC), the Organization of African Unity, SADC Electoral Commission's Forum, SADC Parliamentary Forum and the Southern African Students' Union, among others, were to witness the vote throughout the country.

CULTURE AND SOCIETY

Only about 46 percent of the Namibian population have gone beyond primary school level of education, and 15 percent have had no formal education at all. Only two percent of the population has reached the level of teachers' training, university or post-graduate work. The quality of teaching had been a problem and thus the poor performance of the educational system hampered the government's efforts to attract investment capital.

Officials continued to battle against HIV transmission, but it was estimated that already ten percent of the population was infected with the virus that caused AIDS.

As in former white settler colonies, Namibia battled the distrust between the races. Even the SWAPO leadership, according to opposition politicians, continued to refer to white citizens as ''white settlers'' and ''boers'' (the Afrikaans term for farmer). Opposition politicians suggest that the lack of reconciliation between the groups would continue to hinder the country's ability to move forward.

DIRECTORY

CENTRAL GOVERNMENT
Head of State

President
Sam Shafiishuma Nujoma, Office of the President, Robert Mugabe Avenue, Private Bag 13339, Windhoek, Namibia
PHONE: +264 (61) 220010
FAX: +264 (61) 221780; 221770

Prime Minister

Hage Gottfried Geingob, Office of the Prime Minister, Robert Mugabe Avenue, Private Bag 13338, Windhoek, Namibia
PHONE: +264 (61) 2879111
FAX: +264 (61) 226189

Ministers

Deputy Prime Minister

Hendrik Witbooi, Office of the Deputy Prime Minister, Robert Mugabe Avenue, Windhoek, Namibia

Minister of Agriculture, Water and Rural Development

Helmut Angula, Ministry of Agriculture, Water and Rural Development, Robert Mugabe Avenue, Private Bag 13184, Windhoek, Namibia
PHONE: +264 (61) 2029111
FAX: +264 (61) 229961

Minister of Basic Education and Culture

John Mutorwa, Ministry of Basic Education and Culture, Robert Mugabe Avenue, Windhoek, Namibia

Minister of Defense

Erikki Nghimtina, Ministry of Defense, Robert Mugabe Avenue, Windhoek, Namibia

Minister of Environment and Tourism

Phillemon Malima, Ministry of Environment and Tourism, Robert Mugabe Avenue, Private Bag 13346, Windhoek, Namibia
PHONE: +264 (61) 284 91 11
FAX: +264 (61) 229 936
E-MAIL: tourism@iwwn.com.na

Minister of Finance

Nangolo Mbumba, Ministry of Finance, Robert Mugabe Avenue, Windhoek, Namibia

Minister of Fisheries and Marine Resources

Abraham Iyambo, Ministry of Fisheries and Marine Resources, Metje Behnsen Building, Private Bag 13355, Windhoek, Namibia
PHONE: +264 (61) 240201
FAX: +264 (61) 232581

Minister of Foreign Affairs

Theo-Ben Gurirab, Ministry of Foreign Affairs, Robert Mugabe Avenue, Windhoek, Namibia

Minister of Health and Social Services

Libertine Amathila, Ministry of Health and Social Services, Robert Mugabe Avenue, Windhoek, Namibia

Minister of Higher Education, Technical Training, Science and Technology

Nahas Angula, Ministry of Higher Education, Technical Training, Science and Technology, Robert Mugabe Avenue, Windhoek, Namibia

Minister of Home Affairs

Jerry Ekandjo, Ministry of Home Affairs, Robert Mugabe Avenue, Windhoek, Namibia

Minister of Information and Broadcasting

Ben Amathila, Ministry of Information and Broadcasting, Robert Mugabe Avenue, Private Bag 13344, Windhoek, Namibia
PHONE: +264 (61) 222302
FAX: +264 (61) 222343

Minister of Justice

Ngarikutuke Tjirange, Ministry of Justice, Robert Mugabe Avenue, Windhoek, Namibia

Minister of Lands, Resettlement and Rehabilitation

Pendukeni Ithana, Ministry of Lands, Resettlement and Rehabilitation, Robert Mugabe Avenue, Windhoek, Namibia

Minister of Mines and Energy

Andimba Toiva Ya Toiva, Ministry of Mines and Energy, PO BOX 2895, Windhoek, Namibia
PHONE: +264 (61) 237925
FAX: +264 (61) 222638

Minister of Prisons and Correctional Services

Marco Hausiku, Ministry of Prisons and Correctional Services, Robert Mugabe Avenue, Windhoek, Namibia

Minister of Regional and Local Government and Housing

Nicky Iyambo, Ministry of Regional and Local Government and Housing, Robert Mugabe Avenue, Windhoek, Namibia

Minister of Trade and Industry

Hidipo Hamutenya, Ministry of Trade and Industry, Robert Mugabe Avenue, Private Bag 13340, Windhoek, Namibia
PHONE: +264 (61) 2849111
FAX: +264 (61) 229936

Minister of Works, Transport and Communications

Oskar Valentin Plichta, Ministry of Works, Transport and Communications, Robert Mugabe Avenue, Windhoek, Namibia

Minister of Youth and Sports
Richard Kapelwa-Kabajani, Ministry of Youth and Sports, Robert Mugabe Avenue, Windhoek, Namibia

POLITICAL ORGANIZATIONS

South West Africa People's Organization of Namibia (SWAPO)

NAME: Sam Nujoma

Democratic Coalition of Namibia (DCN)

NAME: Moses K. Katjiuongua

Democratic Turnhall Alliance (DTA)

TITLE: President
NAME: Mishake Muyongo

Monitor Action Group (MAG)

NAME: Kosie Pretorius

United Democratic Front (UDF)

NAME: Justus Garoeb

DIPLOMATIC REPRESENTATION

Embassies in Namibia

Finland
P.O. Box 3649, Independence Avenue, Sanlam Centre, 5th Floor, Windhoek, Namibia
PHONE: +264 (61) 221355
FAX: +264 (61) 221349
E-MAIL: finland@iafrica.com.na
TITLE: Ambassador
NAME: Kari Karanko

United States
14 Lossen Street, Ausspannplatz, Windhoek, Namibia
PHONE: +264 (61) 221601
FAX: +264 (61) 229792
TITLE: Ambassador
NAME: George F. Ward, Jr.

JUDICIAL SYSTEM

Magistrate's Court

High Court

Supreme Court

Traditional Court

Judicial Service Commission

FURTHER READING
Articles
''Namibia.'' *Africa Confidential* 40 (April 2, 1999).

''Namibia.'' *Africa Confidential* 40 (August 27, 1999).

''New Natural Gas Province Gets Ready Business.'' *Petroleum Economist* 66 (January 1999).

''Sida Bridges the Gap.'' *African Business* (July-August 1999).

Internet
Africa News Online. Available Online @ www.africanews.org/south/mozambique (November 25, 1999).

Namibia Online. Available Online @ www.republicofnamibia.com/ (November 30, 1999).

NAMIBIA: STATISTICAL DATA

For sources and notes see "Sources of Statistics" in the front of each volume.

GEOGRAPHY

Geography (1)

Area:

Total: 825,418 sq km.

Land: 825,418 sq km.

Water: 0 sq km.

Area—comparative: slightly more than half the size of Alaska.

Land boundaries:

Total: 3,824 km.

Border countries: Angola 1,376 km, Botswana 1,360 km, South Africa 855 km, Zambia 233 km.

Coastline: 1,572 km.

Climate: desert; hot, dry; rainfall sparse and erratic.

Terrain: mostly high plateau; Namib Desert along coast; Kalahari Desert in east.

Natural resources: diamonds, copper, uranium, gold, lead, tin, lithium, cadmium, zinc, salt, vanadium, natural gas, fish; suspected deposits of oil, natural gas, coal, iron ore.

Land use:

Arable land: 1%

Permanent crops: 0%

Permanent pastures: 46%

Forests and woodland: 22%

Other: 31% (1993 est.).

HUMAN FACTORS

Demographics (2A)

	1990	1995	1998	2000	2010	2020	2030	2040	2050
Population	1,409.1	1,543.9	1,622.3	1,674.1	1,915.1	2,154.2	2,517.0	3,090.5	3,757.1
Net migration rate (per 1,000 population)	NA	NA	NA	NA	NA	NA	NA	NA	NA
Births	NA	NA	NA	NA	NA	NA	NA	NA	NA
Deaths	NA	NA	NA	NA	NA	NA	NA	NA	NA
Life expectancy - males	43.5	42.0	41.7	41.6	39.2	43.7	57.9	72.0	76.5
Life expectancy - females	45.2	42.4	41.2	40.5	38.5	43.5	60.6	77.6	82.6
Birth rate (per 1,000)	38.6	36.6	35.8	35.4	33.6	30.8	28.4	24.9	21.1
Death rate (per 1,000)	19.0	19.6	19.8	20.0	21.9	18.3	9.4	3.9	3.2
Women of reproductive age (15-49 yrs.)	321.4	354.8	376.5	391.5	457.6	529.7	655.3	827.1	998.9
of which are currently married	NA	NA	NA	NA	NA	NA	NA	NA	NA
Fertility rate	5.5	5.2	5.0	4.9	4.3	3.8	3.3	2.9	2.6

Except as noted, values for vital statistics are in thousands; life expectancy is in years.

Health Personnel (3)

Total health expenditure as a percentage of GDP,
1990-1997[a]

Public sector 4.1

Private sector 3.4

Total[b] 6.8

Health expenditure per capita in U.S. dollars,
1990-1997[a]

Purchasing power parity 315

Total 127

Availability of health care facilities per 100,000 people

Hospital beds 1990-1997[a] . . . . .NA

Doctors 1993[c] 23

Nurses 1993[c] 81

Health Indicators (4)

Life expectancy at birth

1980 53

1997 56

Daily per capita supply of calories (1996) 2,168

Total fertility rate births per woman (1997) 4.9

Maternal mortality ratio per 100,000 live births
(1990-97) . . . . .220[d]

Safe water % of population with access (1995) 60

Sanitation % of population with access (1995) 42

Consumption of iodized salt % of households
(1992-98)[a] 59

Smoking prevalence

Male % of adults (1985-95)[a] . . . .

Female % of adults (1985-95)[a] . . . .

Tuberculosis incidence per 100,000 people
(1997) 527

Adult HIV prevalence % of population ages
15-49 (1997) 19.94

Infants and Malnutrition (5)

Under-5 mortality rate (1997) 75

% of infants with low birthweight (1990-97) 16

Births attended by skilled health staff % of total[a] . . .68

% fully immunized (1995-97)

TB 65

DPT 65

Polio 65

Measles 58

Prevalence of child malnutrition under age 5
(1992-97)[b] 26

Ethnic Division (6)

Black 86%

White 6.6%

Mixed 7.4%

Damara 7%

Nama 5%

Caprivian 4%

Bushmen 3%

Baster 2%

Tswana 0.5%

Religions (7)

Christian 80% to 90% (Lutheran 50% at least, other
Christian denominations 30%); Native religions 10% to
20%.

Languages (8)

English 7% (official), Afrikaans common language of
most of the population and about 60% of the white
population, German 32%, indigenous languages:
Oshivambo, Herero, Nama.

EDUCATION

Public Education Expenditures (9)

Public expenditure on education (% of GNP)

1980 . . . . .1.3[1]

1996 . . . . .9.1

Expenditure per student

Primary % of GNP per capita

1980 . . . .

1996 . . . . .15.5[1]

Secondary % of GNP per capita

1980 . . . .

1996 . . . . .33.8[1]

Tertiary % of GNP per capita

1980 . . . .

1996 . . . . .100.7[1]

Expenditure on teaching materials

Primary % of total for level (1996) . . . .

Secondary % of total for level (1996) . . . .

Primary pupil-teacher ratio per teacher (1996) . . . .

Duration of primary education years (1995) 7

Educational Attainment (10)

Age group (1991)[5] . . . . .25+

Total population 340,552

Highest level attained (%)

No schooling ....NA

First level

Not completed 49.1

Completed ....NA

Entered second level

S-1 ....43.8

S-2 ....NA

Postsecondary 4.0

Literacy Rates (11B)

Adult literacy rate

1980

Male ....—

Female ....—

1995

Male 78%

Female 74%

GOVERNMENT & LAW

Political Parties (12)

National Assembly	% of seats
South West Africa People's Organization (SWAPO)	73.89
Democratic Turnhalle Alliance of Namibia (DTA)	20.78
United Democratic Front (UDF)	2.72
Democratic Coalition of Namibia (DCN)	0.83
Monitor Action Group (MAG)	0.82

Military Affairs (14B)

	1990	1991	1992	1993	1994	1995
Military expenditures						
Current dollars (mil.)	41[e]	66[e]	63	60	56	64
1995 constant dollars (mil.)	47[e]	73[e]	68	62	57	64
Armed forces (000)	NA	8	8	8	8	8
Gross national product (GNP)						
Current dollars (mil.)	2,201	2,490	2,657	2,724	2,921	3,072
1995 constant dollars (mil.)	2,529	2,752	2,858	2,856	2,994	3,072
Central government expenditures (CGE)						
1995 constant dollars (mil.)	866	1,112	1,119	1,114	NA	NA
People (mil.)	1.4	1.5	1.5	1.5	1.6	1.6
Military expenditure as % of GNP	1.9	2.7	2.4	2.2	1.9	2.1
Military expenditure as % of CGE	5.4	6.6	5.6	5.5	NA	NA
Military expenditure per capita (1995 $)	33	50	45	41	36	39
Armed forces per 1,000 people (soldiers)	NA	5.5	5.4	5.2	5.1	4.9
GNP per capita (1995 $)	1,795	1,896	1,914	1,858	1,893	1,886
Arms imports[6]						
Current dollars (mil.)	0	0	0	0	10	5
1995 constant dollars (mil.)	0	0	0	0	10	5
Arms exports[6]						
Current dollars (mil.)	0	0	0	0	0	0
1995 constant dollars (mil.)	0	0	0	0	0	0
Total imports[7]						
Current dollars (mil.)	1,163	1,149	1,283	1,188	1,196	NA
1995 constant dollars (mil.)	1,337	1,270	1,380	1,245	1,226	NA
Total exports[7]						
Current dollars (mil.)	1,084	1,214	1,342	1,290	1,321	NA
1995 constant dollars (mil.)	1,246	1,341	1,444	1,352	1,354	NA
Arms as percent of total imports[8]	0.0	0	0	0	.8	NA
Arms as percent of total exports[8]	0.0	0	0	0	0	NA

Government Budget (13B)

Revenues . . . .$1.1 billion

Expenditures . . . .$1.2 billion

  Capital expenditures . . . .$193 million

Data for FY96/97 est.

Crime (15)

Crime rate (for 1997)

  Crimes reported 71,200

  Total persons convicted 38,400

  Crimes per 100,000 population 4,200

Persons responsible for offenses

  Total number of suspects . . . . .NA

  Total number of female suspects . . . . .NA

  Total number of juvenile suspects . . . . .NA

LABOR FORCE

Labor Force (16)

Total 500,000

Agriculture 49%

Industry and commerce 25%

Services 5%

Government 18%

Mining 3%

Data for 1994 est.

Unemployment Rate (17)

30% to 40%, including underemployment (1997 est.)

PRODUCTION SECTOR

Electric Energy (18)

Consumption per capita 584 kWh (1995). Imports electricity from South Africa.

Transportation (19)

Highways:

total: 64,799 km

paved: 7,841 km

unpaved: 56,958 km (1996 est.)

Merchant marine: none

Airports: 135 (1997 est.)

Airports—with paved runways:

total: 22

over 3,047 m: 2

2,438 to 3,047 m: 2

1,524 to 2,437 m: 15

914 to 1,523 m: 3 (1997 est.)

Airports—with unpaved runways:

total: 113

2,438 to 3,047 m: 2

1,524 to 2,437 m: 20

914 to 1,523 m: 70

under 914 m: 21 (1997 est.)

Top Agricultural Products (20)

Millet, sorghum, peanuts; livestock; fish.

FINANCE, ECONOMICS, & TRADE

Economic Indicators (22)

National product: GDP—purchasing power parity—$6.2 billion (1996 est.)

National product real growth rate: 3% (1996 est.)

National product per capita: $3,700 (1996 est.)

Inflation rate—consumer price index: 8% (1996 est.)

MANUFACTURING SECTOR

GDP & Manufacturing Summary (21)

	1980	1985	1990	1992	1993	1994
Gross Domestic Product						
Millions of 1990 dollars	1,981	1,848	2,129	2,288	2,244	2,365
Growth rate in percent	0.18	0.00	6.00	7.47	−1.93	5.41
Per capita (in 1990 dollars)	1,923.7	1,568.4	1,578.0	1,607.7	1,535.6	1,576.6
Manufacturing Value Added						
Millions of 1990 dollars	117	126	113	127	139	*142*
Growth rate in percent	−14.65	1.70	5.88	18.39	10.19	*2.10*
Manufacturing share in percent of current prices	4.6	4.6	6.1	6.1	8.9	*8.9*

FINANCE, ECONOMICS, & TRADE

Exchange Rates (24)

Exchange rates:

Nambian dollars (N$) per US$1

January 1998	.4.94193
1997	.4.60796
1996	.4.29935
1995	.3.62709
1994	.3.55080
1993	.3.26774

Top Import Origins (25)

$1.55 billion (f.o.b., 1996 est.)

Origins	%
United States	.NA
Puerto Rico	.NA

NA stands for not available.

Top Export Destinations (26)

$1.45 billion (f.o.b., 1996 est.) Data are for 1994.

Destinations	%
United Kingdom	.NA
South Africa	.NA
Spain	.NA
Japan	.NA

NA stands for not available.

Economic Aid (27)

Recipient: ODA, $NA. NA stands for not available.

Import Export Commodities (28)

Import Commodities	Export Commodities
Foodstuffs	Diamonds
Petroleum products and fuel	Copper
	Gold
Machinery and equipment	Zinc
Chemicals	Lead
	Uranium
	Cattle
	Processed fish
	Karakul skins

Balance of Payments (23)

	1992	1993	1994	1995	1996
Exports of goods (f.o.b.)	1,341	1,292	1,350	1,399	1,349
Imports of goods (f.o.b.)	−1,267	−1,216	−1,285	−1,511	−1,374
Trade balance	74	75	65	−112	−25
Services - debits	−697	−643	−628	−761	−690
Services - credits	371	457	477	625	535
Private transfers (net)	288	215	200	247	242
Government transfers (net)	51	25	20	31	21
Overall balance	87	130	133	31	84

NAURU

CAPITAL: There is no formal capital. The seat of government is in the district of Yaren.

FLAG: The flag has a blue background divided horizontally by a narrow gold band, symbolizing the equator. Below the band is a white 12-pointed star, representing the island's 12 traditional tribes.

ANTHEM: *Nauru Ubwema* (Nauru, Our Homeland).

MONETARY UNIT: The Australian dollar (A$) of 100 cents is the legal currency. A$1 = US$0.7008 (or US$1 = A$1.4269).

WEIGHTS AND MEASURES: Imperial weights and measures are used.

HOLIDAYS: New Year's Day, 1 January; Independence Day, 31 January; Angam Day, 26 October (a celebration of the day on which the population of Nauru reached the pre-World War II level); Christmas Day, 25 December; and Boxing Day, 26 December.

TIME: 11:30 PM = noon GMT.

LOCATION AND SIZE: Situated in the western Pacific, Nauru is the world's smallest independent island nation, with an area of 21 square kilometers (8.1 square miles), about one-tenth the size of Washington, D.C. It lies between two island groups, the Solomons and the Gilberts and its nearest neighbor is Banaba (formerly Ocean Island, now part of Kiribati).

CLIMATE: The average annual rainfall is about 45 centimeters (18 inches), but the amount varies greatly from year to year, and long droughts have been a repeated problem. Temperatures remain steady, between 24° and 33°C (75–91°F) year round, and relative humidity is also constant at about 80%.

INTRODUCTORY SURVEY

RECENT HISTORY

Nauru was flattened by Japanese bombings beginning in December 1941, and all its industrial plant and housing facilities were destroyed. The Japanese occupied the island from August 1942 until the end of the war three years later. Australian forces reoccupied Nauru in September 1945.

After World War II (1939–45), the island became a trust territory administered jointly by Australia, New Zealand, and the United Kingdom, who were to share the task of developing self-government on the island. On 31 January 1968, Nauru became the smallest independent republic in the world.

Since that time, Nauru has pursued a policy of isolation and nonalignment, although it does have a role in British Commonwealth affairs. In October 1982, Queen Elizabeth II visited the island, the first British monarch to do so. Nauru filed a claim in 1989 for compensation from Australia at the International Court of Justice for the loss of nearly all its topsoil from phosphate mining during the League of Nations mandate and the United Nations trusteeship. Australia agreed to pay A$107 million (about US$73 million) in August 1993 to settle the case.

In June 1992, Nauru signed both the Climate Change and Biodiversity Conventions. In July it hosted the 24th South Pacific Forum heads of government meeting, which focused on environmental issues. In 1993, Australia, New Zealand, and the

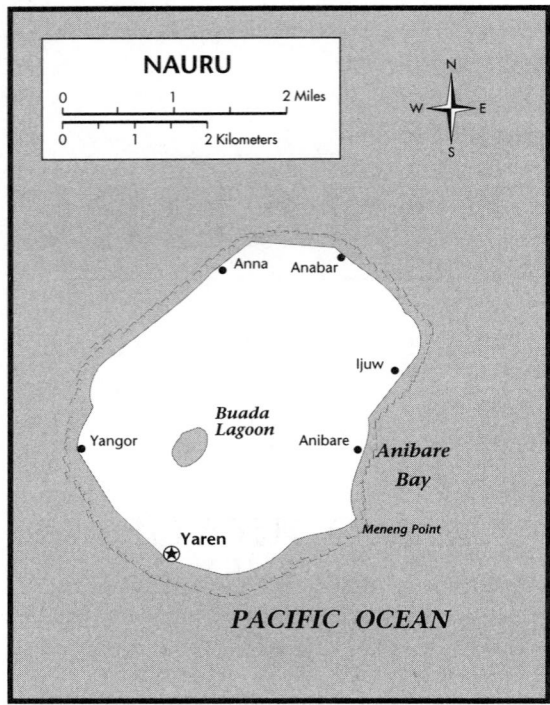

mates, will be exhausted by the early 2000s. By 1987, an estimated US$450 million had been set aside to support the country after the phosphates run out. However, the government has borrowed from the trust since 1990. In 1994, an audit revealed that $8.5 million was missing due to bad investments and corruption.

Aside from phosphates, Nauru has few domestic resources, and many food products and practically all consumer manufactures are imported.

Public Finance

Administrative costs in Nauru are met from the proceeds of phosphate sales, which are in decline as reserves approach exhaustion. In 1993, the governments of Nauru and Australia reached a us $73 million out-of-court settlement as restitution for Nauruan lands ruined by Australian phosphate mining. This payment assisted the government (which relies almost entirely on phosphate receipts for revenue) in facilitating economic diversification. The fiscal year extends from 1 July to 30 June. The U.S. Central Intelligence Agency estimates that, in 1993, government revenues totaled approximately $23.8 million and expenditures $69.2 million. External debt totaled $33.3 million.

Income

The gross domestic product (GDP) of Nauru was estimated to be $100 million in 1995, or $10,000 per person. Phosphates have given Nauruans one of the highest per person incomes in the Third World.

Industry

The phosphate industry is the only industry on the island.

Banking and Finance

The government-owned Bank of Nauru was founded in 1976. The Commonwealth Savings Bank of Australia and the Bank of New South Wales have branches in Nauru. The only commercial bank in the country is the Jefferson Bank and Trust Co. (1980). Most of the income from phosphates is invested in long-term funds overseas. There is no stock exchange.

Economic Development

Government policy is to exploit the phosphate deposits to the fullest extent for the highest returns. The government has diversified into aviation and shipping and plans to develop fishing and tourism. It has acquired the Grand Pacific Hotel on the Fijian Island of Suva and, in 1993, began work on a

United Kingdom agreed to pay Nauru a settlement for soil damage.

GOVERNMENT

Legislative power is held by the Parliament, composed of 18 members elected for a three-year term. Executive power is exercised by the president, who is also head of state.

Judiciary

The constitution provides for a Supreme Court, with a chief justice presiding. Cases are also heard in the District Court or Family Court. The Supreme Court is the supreme authority on the interpretation of the constitution.

Political Parties

The Democratic Party of Nauru, which aimed to curb the power of the presidency, became the only political party in Nauru in 1987. At the end of 1995, however, no political parties existed.

DEFENSE

Nauru has no armed forces. Although there is no formal agreement, Australia ensures its defense.

ECONOMIC AFFAIRS

The economy of Nauru has long been dependent on phosphates, which, according to recent esti-

F $18 million renovation of the facility. In 1993, Australia agreed to provide U.S. $73 million in compensation for pre-independence mining of phosphate to aid in restoring the extensive areas damaged by it.

SOCIAL WELFARE

Medical, dental, and hospital treatment and education are free. The government provides old age and disability pensions, and widows' and sickness benefits. Women face great social pressure to marry and raise families because Nauru's population was drastically reduced in World War II.

Healthcare

Tuberculosis, leprosy, diabetes, and vitamin deficiencies have been brought under control. Cardiovascular disease has become a major cause of illness and death. There are two modern hospitals, with a total of 207 beds and 10 doctors. Patients who need specialized care are flown to Australia.

Housing

Nearly all houses have electricity, and newer homes have a greater number of modern features.

EDUCATION

Attendance at school is compulsory for Nauruan children from 6 to 16 years old. In 1985 there were 1,451 students in seven government primary schools and 465 students in two secondary schools, with 142 teachers in all. There are scholarships available for higher education overseas, mainly in Australia and a university extension center connected to the University of the South Pacific.

1999 KEY EVENTS TIMELINE

January

- A Nauru government official says the number of the nation's public service employees will be reduced to half its current size by the year 2001. The island is preparing to live without phosphate riches, due to run out in 2003.

February

- Former President Lagumot Harris calls for the rehabilitation of Nauru's land, which have been devastated by phosphate mining.

April

- Renee Harris is elected by the Nauru Parliament as the new president of the island nation, defeating former President Bernard Dowiyogo by 10–7 vote.

May

- Nauru becomes a full member of the Commonwealth; it has a special member since its independence from Australia in 1968.

June

- The government signs new shipping contract that is expected to reduce freight costs from Australia, its main supplier.
- The national airline of Nauru reports its first operating profit in 30 years. Its projected earnings: $650,000.

July

- China abstains from voting when the Security Council of the United Nations considers Nauru's application for membership; the application is approved.

August

- The Chairman of the Nauru Rehabilitation Corporation says it will take another 20 to 25 years to rehabilitate the island. Nauru has been devastated by more than 80 years of phosphate mining.

September

- Nauru, along with Kiribati and Tonga, is admitted to the United Nations.
- Former Nauru president Lagumot Harris dies in Melbourne at age 61. He was chairman of the Nauru Rehabilitation Corporation at the time of his death.

ANALYSIS OF EVENTS: 1999

BUSINESS AND THE ECONOMY

In January, President Bernard Dowiyogo's government announced a series of economic reforms to prepare the nation for the time when it runs out of phosphates, its major source of income. The government said it would carry out its reforms with help from the Asian Development Bank.

Officials said the reform program would be painful, but essential to the survival of the country's economy. The government proposed the privatization of public companies, and said it would cut the number of government employees by half by 2001. In April, the government announced it was eliminating 400 jobs as part of its economic reform program. In time, 800 of 1,600 government jobs will be eliminated, saving Nauru about $2.2 million in salaries annually. The first 400 jobs would be eliminated in the country's public works, health and civil aviation departments. The government also has been considering the privatization of public enterprises, including its printing facilities. It also said it would seek private security companies to protect key island installations.

GOVERNMENT AND POLITICS

In 1999, Nauru, one of the world's smallest nations, joined the international community, first by becoming a full member of the Commonwealth in May, and a member of the United Nations in September. Nauru has a population of about 10,000 people living in an area of only 8.4 square miles.

As the country prepared to end its dependence on phosphates, political changes were taking place during 1999. In February, President Bernard Dowiyogo said Nauru needed political stability to make progress. The government, he said, was taking steps to create a more transparent democracy. The speech was intended to alleviate fears in his country, which was facing tough economic decisions. But Parliament gave him a no confidence vote in April. Rene Harris became the new president after defeating Dowiyogo by a 10–7 vote in Parliament. It was the seventh government in three years. Harris became a Member of Parliament in 1977, and held several government posts, including the chair of the Nauru Phosphate Corporation.

CULTURE AND SOCIETY

Before his death in September, the chairman of the Nauru Rehabilitation Corporation said it would take at least 20 to 25 years to rehabilitate Nauru, which was devastated by more than 80 years of phosphate mining. Lagumot Harris, who was 61 when he died, said rehabilitating Nauru would cost as much as $260 million, but the nation had no choice. The population, now estimated at about 10,000 people, was expected to more than double in the time it would take to rehabilitate the island. Thanks to phosphates, Nauru residents enjoyed some of the highest per capita incomes in the world for many years. But mining of the fossilized bird droppings also created a wasteland. Rehabilitating the island will not be easy. Native birds and vegetation have nearly disappeared. Even the national symbol, the frigate bird, has decreased in numbers. The Nauru people, accustomed to living an easy life will have to find new ways to earn a living. Phosphate deposits are expected to run out as early as 2003.

DIRECTORY

CENTRAL GOVERNMENT

Head of State

President
Bernard Dowiyogo, Office of the President
PHONE: +674 33100

Ministers

Minister of Education
Kennan Adeang, Ministry of Education
PHONE: +674 4443100
FAX: +674 4443178

Minister of External Affairs
Bernard Dowiyogo, Ministry of External Affairs

Minister of Finance
Reuben Kun, Ministry of Finance
PHONE: +674 4443140
FAX: +674 5554477

Minister of Health
Clinton Benjamin, Ministry of Health
PHONE: +674 4443166
FAX: +674 4443136

Minister of Development and Industry
Bernard Dowiyogo, Ministry of Development and Industry

Minister of Justice
Anthony Audoa, Ministry of Justice
PHONE: +674 4443160
FAX: +674 4443108

Minister of Public Service
Bernard Dowiyogo, Ministry of Public Service

Minister of Works, Community Services
Roy Degoregore, Ministry of Works, Community Services
PHONE: +674 4443177
FAX: +674 4443135

POLITICAL ORGANIZATIONS
Nauru Party
NAME: Bernard Dowiyogo

Democratic Party
NAME: Kennan Adeang

DIPLOMATIC REPRESENTATION
Embassies in Nauru

Australia
Civic Centre Orpo Box 6, Nauru Central Pacific
PHONE: +674 4443232; 4443233; 4443234
FAX: +674 4443227

China
Yaren, P.O. Box 294, Nauru Central Pacific
PHONE: +674 5554399
FAX: +674 5554594

JUDICIAL SYSTEM
Supreme Court
PHONE: +674 4443163
FAX: +674 4443140

FURTHER READING
Articles

"Air Nauru Records First Profit in 30 Years." Pacific Islands Development Program/East-West Center, Center for Pacific Islands Studies/University of Hawaii at Manoa, 28 June 1999.

"Former Nauru President Calls for Rehabilitation of Land." Pacific Islands Development Program/East-West Center, Center for Pacific Islands Studies/University of Hawaii at Manoa, 26 February 1999.

"Nauru Becomes Member of the United Nations." Reuters, 15 September 1999.

"Nauru to Cut 400 Government Jobs." Pacific Islands Development Program/East-West Center, Center for Pacific Islands Studies/University of Hawaii at Manoa, 5 April 1999.

"Nauru Public Service to be Cut by Half by 2001." Pacific Islands Development Program/East-West Center, Center for Pacific Islands Studies/University of Hawaii at Manoa, 26 February 1999.

"Shipping Rates Reduced Between Australia and Nauru." Pacific Islands Development Program/East-West Center, Center for Pacific Islands Studies/University of Hawaii at Manoa, 11 June 1999.

Books
Background Notes. Washington, D.C.: U.S. Government Printing Office, 1988, s.v. "Nauru."

Internet
"Big Tasks for a Small Island." BBC Online, 30 April 1999. Available Online @ news2.thls.bbc.co.uk/hi/english/world/asia-pacific/newsid_332000/332164.stm (December 13, 1999).

Nations of the Commonwealth: Nauru. Available Online @ www.tbc.gov.bc.ca/cwgames/country/Nauru/nauru.html (December 13, 1999).

Nauru Central Pacific. Available Online @ www.hideawayholidays.com.au/nauru.htm (December 13, 1999).

NAURU: STATISTICAL DATA

For sources and notes see "Sources of Statistics" in the front of each volume.

GEOGRAPHY

Geography (1)

Area:

Total: 21 sq km.

Land: 21 sq km.

Water: 0 sq km.

Area—comparative: about 0.1 times the size of Washington, DC.

Land boundaries: 0 km.

Coastline: 30 km.

Climate: tropical; monsoonal; rainy season (November to February).

Terrain: sandy beach rises to fertile ring around raised coral reefs with phosphate plateau in center.

Natural resources: phosphates.

Land use:

Arable land: NA%

Permanent crops: NA%

Permanent pastures: NA%

Forests and woodland: NA%

Other: 100% (1993 est.).

HUMAN FACTORS

Demographics (2B)

Population (July 1998 est.) 10,501

Age structure:

   0-14 years . . . . .NA

   15-64 years . . . . .NA

   65 years and over . . . . .NA

Population growth rate (1998 est.) 1.33%

Birth rate, 1998 est. (births/1,000 population) 18.03

Death rate, 1998 est. (deaths/1,000 population) 5.1

Net migration rate, 1998 est. (migrant(s)/1,000 population) 0.4

Infant mortality rate, 1998 est. (deaths/1,000 live births) 40.6

Life expectancy at birth (years):

   Total population 66.68

   Male 64.3

   Female (1998 est.) 69.18

Total fertility rate, 1998 est. (children born/woman) 2.08

Infants and Malnutrition (5)

Under-5 mortality rate (1997) 30

% of infants with low birthweight (1990-97) . . . . . .NA

Births attended by skilled health staff % of total[a] . . .NA

% fully immunized (1995-97)

   TB 78

   DPT 50

   Polio 36

   Measles 100

Prevalence of child malnutrition under age 5 (1992-97)[b] . . . . .NA

Ethnic Division (6)

Nauruan 58%

Other Pacific Islander 26%

Chinese 8%

European 8%

Religions (7)

Christian (two-thirds Protestant, one-third Roman Catholic).

Languages (8)

Nauruan (official, a distinct Pacific Island language), English widely understood, spoken, and used for most government and commercial purposes.

GOVERNMENT & LAW

Political Parties (12)

The legislative branch is a unicameral Parliament (18 seats; members elected by popular vote to serve three-year terms). No data on election results available.

Government Budget (13B)

Revenues . . . .$23.4 million

Expenditures . . . .$64.8 million

  Capital expenditures . . . . .NA

Data for FY95/96. NA stands for not available.

Military Affairs (14A)

Total expenditures . . . .$NA

Expenditures as % of GDP . . . . .NA%

NA stands for not available.

LABOR FORCE

Labor Force (16)

Unemployment Rate (17)

No unemployment.

PRODUCTION SECTOR

Electric Energy (18)

Capacity . . . . .10,000 kW (1995)

Production . . . . .30 million kWh (1995)

Consumption per capita . . . . .2,956 kWh (1995)

Transportation (19)

Highways:

total: 30 km

paved: 24 km

unpaved: 6 km (1996 est.)

Merchant marine: none

Airports: 1 (1997 est.)

Airports—with paved runways:

total: 1

1,524 to 2,437 m: 1 (1997 est.)

Top Agricultural Products (20)

Coconuts predominate.

FINANCE, ECONOMICS, & TRADE

Economic Indicators (22)

National product: GDP—purchasing power parity—$100 million (1993 est.)

National product real growth rate: NA%

National product per capita: $10,000 (1993 est.)

Inflation rate—consumer price index: -3.6% (1993)

Exchange Rates (24)

Exchange rates:

Australian dollars ($A) per US$1

January 1998 . . . . .1.5281

1997 . . . . .1.3439

1996 . . . . .1.2773

1995 . . . . .1.3486

1994 . . . . .1.3667

1993 . . . . .1.4704

Top Import Origins (25)

$21.1 million (c.i.f., 1991)

Origins	%
Australia	NA
United Kingdom	NA
NZ	NA
Japan	NA

NA stands for not available.

Top Export Destinations (26)

$25.3 million (f.o.b., 1991).

Destinations	%
Australia	NA
NZ	NA

NA stands for not available.

Economic Aid (27)

Recipient: ODA, $2.25 million from Australia (FY96/97 est.).

Import Export Commodities (28)

Import Commodities	Export Commodities
Food	Phosphates
Fuel	
Manufactures	
Building materials	
Machinery	

NEPAL

Kingdom of Nepal
Nepal Adhirajya

INTRODUCTORY SURVEY

RECENT HISTORY

The end of World War II (1939–45) brought the end to British rule on the South Asian subcontinent and caused deep stirrings of change in Nepal. Resentment grew against the autocratic despotism of the Ranas. A political reform movement began in 1947 with the founding of the Nepali Congress Party.

With Indian support, rebels began operations against the Rana government. Ultimately, with the guidance of Indian Prime Minister Nehru, a political compromise was reached that ended a century of hereditary Rana family rule and restored the monarchy. By late 1951 a new government took office, headed by Matrika Prasad Koirala, a founder of the Nepali Congress Party (NC).

The period after the fall of the Ranas was marked by a struggle between the government and the king for control of the country. In April 1959, King Mahendra Bir Bikram Shah proclaimed a democratic constitution providing for a constitutional monarchy, but suspended it and dissolved parliament less than 18 months later. In April 1962 he established an indirect, non-party system of rule through a system of panchayats (councils) leading up to a National Panchayat. However, five years later, the king, under Indian pressure, began gradually liberalizing his government.

In January 1972, Mahendra died suddenly and was succeeded by his 27-year-old son, Birendra Bir Bikram Shah Dev. The young monarch, who had

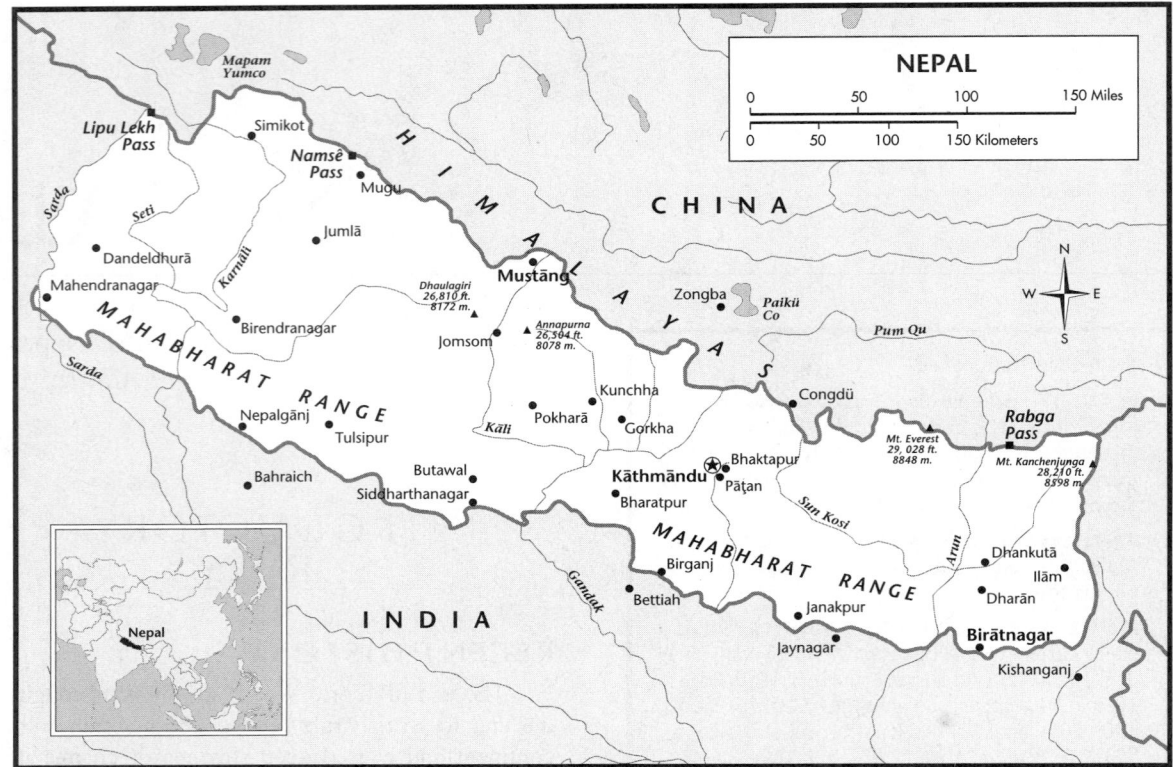

attended Harvard University in the United States, was committed to social reform. With the king promising further liberalization, the existing panchayat system was supported by 55% of the voters in May 1980. However, the king's failure to lift the ban on political parties angered his opposition.

Throughout the 1980s, opposition to the panchayat system, and to the ban on political parties, grew. After concessions by the king, a new constitution was adopted in November 1990. This constitution ended the panchayat era and restored multiparty democracy in a constitutional monarchy. In May 1991, the first open elections in 32 years were held. In the elections, the NC (Nepali Congress Party) won a majority in the new House of Representatives.

Nepal's foreign policies have remained generally neutral since World War II. It has maintained friendly relations with China and India, despite the occasional clash of policies on matters of trade. Nepal also has pursued friendly relations with the great powers and has received economic aid from India, the United States, the former Soviet Union, and the World Bank.

GOVERNMENT

The 1990 constitution established a constitutional monarchy in which the legislature consists of the king and two houses of parliament, the lower house called the House of Representatives and the upper house, the National Council. The House of Representatives has 205 members and the National Council 60.

The country is divided into 14 zones and 75 districts.

Judiciary

Each district has civil and criminal courts, as well as a court of appeals and 14 zone courts. There are five regional courts to which further appeals may be taken. At the top is the Supreme Court in Kathmandu, which is empowered to issue writs of habeas corpus and decide on the constitutionality of laws. The Supreme Court is the court of last resort, but the king may grant pardons and suspend, commute or remit sentences of any court. There are separate military courts, which deal only with military personnel.

Political Parties

The main party through Nepal's modern history has been the Nepali Congress Party (NC), which opposed and finally brought down King Mahendra's panchayat system of indirect government. The Communist Party of Nepal (CPN), reorganized as the United Marxist-Leninists (UML) is a leading opposition party in the parliament. The Rastriya Prajatantra Party (RPP) supports the monarchy. Most of the remaining seats in the lower house are in the hands of minor left/communist parties, including the United People's Front-Nepal (UPF/N), the Nepal Sadbhavana Party (NSP), and the National Democratic Party (DDP).

DEFENSE

Nepal maintains a small standing army of 42,800 regulars organized in 8 brigades. It maintains 11 air transports and helicopters. The army is made up mostly of hill people known as gurkhas, who are among the world's most renowned fighting men with extensive service in all parts of the globe in both world wars and several United Nations actions of this century. In 1995, Nepal spent an estimated $44 million on defense.

ECONOMIC AFFAIRS

The economy is based on agriculture, which engages about 90% of the labor force but is inefficiently organized and limited by a shortage of usable land in relation to population.

The industrial sector is still small and dominated by traditional handicrafts, spinning and weaving, and similar occupations. In 1989–90, Nepal weathered a major trade and transit dispute with India that suddenly placed potentially damaging tariffs on trade with its largest import supplier and external market.

Public Finance

For many years, government revenue was derived chiefly from privately owned land (amounting to about 30% of the country's area), customs duties, and forest and mining royalties. In 1955, however, because of increasing costs of development projects and administration, the government discarded the practice of adjusting the budgetary deficit by drawing on reserves and adopted a policy of raising additional revenue through taxation. Subsequently, a progressive income tax was introduced. Budget deficits grew steadily during the 1970s and 1980s, but were offset by foreign grants, domestic loans, foreign exchange borrowings, and transfers.

In 1995, government revenues totaled approximately $645 million and expenditures $1.05 bil-

lion. External debt totaled $2.3 billion, approximately 78% of which was financed abroad.

A shortfall in major cash crops and a widening trade deficit prompted the government to revise the 1996 budget with revenues projected at $743.3 million. To meet the revenue targets, taxes were increased on luxury items like imported liquor and cigarettes, and on petroleum and diesel fuel. The new budget called for a deficit of $289.6 million to be financed by loans, domestic borrowing, and sales of treasury bills and development bonds.

Income

In 1999, Nepal's gross national product (GNP) was $25 billion, or about $180 per person. For the period 1985–95 the average inflation rate was 11.6%, resulting in a real growth rate in GNP of 2.4% per person.

Industry

The carpet, garment, and spinning industries are the three largest industrial employers, followed by structural clay products, sugar and jute processing. Sugar production was 49,227 tons in 1995; jute goods, 20,187 tons; and soap, 23,477 tons. That year, 14.7 million meters of synthetic textiles and 5.06 million meters of cotton textiles were produced.

Production by heavy industries in 1995 included 326,839 tons of cement and 95,118 tons of steel rods.

Banking and Finance

Nepal's first commercial bank, the Nepal Bank Ltd., was established in 1937. The government owned 51% of the shares in the bank and controlled its operations to a large extent. Nepal Bank Ltd. was headquartered in Kathmandu, and had branches in other parts of the country.

Nepal's domestic banking system consists of the Nepal Rastra (National) Bank (NRB), the central bank, with its commercial subsidiary, the Rastriya Banijya (National Commercial) Bank; the Nepal Bank, three commercial banks; and state-owned banks for industrial and agricultural development—the Nepal Industrial Development Corp. (NIDC) and the Agricultural Development Bank of Nepal (ADBN). In 1984, Nabil, or Nepal Arab Bank, a joint venture with the UAE, was established. The French Indosuez Bank followed in 1986. The Rastra Bank was inaugurated by King Mahendra in 1956 as the central banking institution, with a capital of NR 10 million. Besides regulating the national currency, it issues notes of various denominations and assists in preparation of the government budget. The Rastra Bank may advance loans to industry if both the government and the bank consider the loan sound.

In May 1996, net foreign assets of government monetary authorities totaled $621.3 million. In 1994, the money supply, as measured by M2, totaled NR 72,696 billion. A vast expansion of paper currency resulted from the progressive monetization of the Nepalese economy and from the decree making Nepalese currency the only legal tender, thus abolishing the old dual currency system under which both Indian and Nepalese rupees circulated freely. In May 1986, the 30-year direct link between the Nepalese and Indian rupees was ended. Since then, the Nepalese rupee has floated against a group of international currencies, including the Indian rupee.

Since 1984, the government has allowed foreign banks to open offices in Nepal. Citibank opened an office in November 1984 to deal with foreign currency loans and short-term and trade finance, and to provide electronic banking facilities. Brindlays has set up a joint venture with Nepal Bank. The Bank of Dubai has set up the Nepal Arab Bank with the aim of channeling funds from Arab countries for industry, agriculture, and trade.

In the last few years several new banks have received permission from the government to operate on a joint venture basis and there has been rapid development of the financial sector as a result of the liberal economic policies adopted by the government. There has been a continuous increase in the number and size of banks, financial companies, and insurance companies.

The Nepal Bank of Ceylon, the biggest bank opened in the private sector through joint investments, was inaugurated at Siddharthanaga on 14 October 1996. In mid-December 1996, General Finance Ltd. went public by issuing 8,000 shares at NRs100 each.

The Nepal Rastra Bank directed all commercial banks to raise their capital to a minimum of NRs500 million by July 2001.

The Securities Exchange Center (SEC) was set up in 1981 under the control of the NRB and the NIDC, as a first step to setting up an organized stock exchange.

A stock exchange was established in 1984 in Kathmandu. Since 1964, the government has issued several series of 6% and 7% development bonds. On 4 January 1997, the Nepal Stock Exchange (NSE) suspended the share transactions of 23 companies for four months. The move was made after the companies failed to pay their annual fees to the NSE. This is the latest in a series of problems besetting the bourse. Only 11 out of the 90 listed companies published notices for annual general meetings for 1996–97. In 1995–96, only three companies submitted income and expenditure accounts to the exchange.

Economic Development

Planned economic development began in 1953 with construction of roads and airfields and of irrigation projects to bring more acreage under cultivation. In 1956, these projects were integrated into a five-year plan (1956–61) to assist existing industries, revive and expand cottage industries, encourage private investment, and foster technological training. After a plan for three years (1962–65), declared successful by the government, had run its course, a new plan (1965–70) was drawn up. This five-year program, which aimed at a 19% increase in national income, was the first to be framed within the context of the panchayat system, which was to serve as an important medium of project administration. The fourth plan (1970–75) and the fifth (1975–80) continued to emphasize infrastructural development, primarily in transportation, communications, electricity, irrigation, and personnel. The sixth development plan (1980–85) allocated nearly one-third of its total expenditure to agriculture and irrigation. However, money targeted for development projects was used for other purposes.

The objectives of the seventh plan (1986–90) were to increase production, create opportunities for employment, and fulfill basic needs. Of the total expenditure of NR 54.1 billion, 65% was to be used for investment, allocated as follows: agriculture, irrigation, and forestry, 30.6%; industry, mining, and electricity, 26%; transportation and communications, 17.7%; social services, 25.2%; and other sectors, 0.5%. Foreign aid was expected to fund about 70% of these projects.

In 1988 a structural adjustment program was initiated in response to accelerating inflation and burgeoning negative fiscal and balance of payment imbalances. Following further deterioration of macroeconomic indicators, especially in wake of the trade dispute with India and slippage in reform policy due to internal political tensions, the newly elected government in 1991 reemphasized its commitment to structural adjustment through a series of reforms affecting virtually all sectors of the economy. Immediate stress was placed on tax reform, easing import restrictions, lowering tariffs, and reunifying the exchange rate market to effect a currency devaluation. To streamline government investments in economic development, a list of priority development projects was drafted and public enterprises were transferred to private ownership, freeing government revenues for other budgetary items, including the social sector, drinking water, and rural infrastructure development.

Nepal's ninth five-year economic plan, scheduled for introduction in July of 1997, was expected to emphasize agriculture, liberal economic policies, and hydropower projects.

SOCIAL WELFARE

The government maintains a countrywide village development service, which endeavors to meet the villagers' needs for food, clothing, shelter, health services, and education. The Employee Provident Fund administers a program of old age, disability, and death benefits for government and corporate employees.

The new Constitution has increased opportunities for women, including equal pay for equal work, but few women hold formal jobs.

The abduction of young girls to be taken to India at work as prostitutes is a serious problem.

Healthcare

Although protected by mountain barriers, Nepal is in frequent danger from epidemics, notably cholera. Common illnesses are black fever (kala-azar), amoebic dysentery, eye diseases, typhoid, and venereal diseases. Malnutrition, contaminated water, and inadequate sanitation cause widespread health problems. Improved health programs in rural areas have helped control malaria, leprosy, and tuberculosis. Average life expectancy is about 57 years.

In 1990, there were 3 hospital beds per 100,000 inhabitants. The population per physician was 16,634 in 1993.

Housing

In the Kathmandu Valley, village houses are made of stone or mud bricks, with thatched roofs and raised eaves. Elsewhere, houses are often made of bamboo and reeds. Most houses have two stories, but some contain only two rooms, a sleeping room and a room for cooking. The well-constructed houses of the Sherpas are generally built of stone and timber, roofed with wooden slats. The latest available figures for 1980–88 show a total housing stock of nearly 3.1 million units with 5.6 people per dwelling.

EDUCATION

The number of illiterate persons is declining and was estimated in 1995 at 73% of adults (males, 59.1%; females, 86%). In 1993, there were 20,217 primary schools with 2.2 million pupils and 57,204 teachers. Secondary students numbered 910,114, with 25,881 teachers. In 1993, 102,018 students were enrolled in all higher level institutions.

1999 KEY EVENTS TIMELINE

January

- Nepal and India renew their transit treaty, allowing land-locked Nepal access to the Indian port of Calcutta.
- On January 24, King Birendra begins an official visit to India.

February

- In its annual survey the World Bank predicts a 2% growth rate for Nepal's economy; poor agricultural performance and low levels of investments are blamed.

April

- The country mourns the death of UML president Man Mohan Adhikari. Prime minister of the CPN-UML minority government after the 1994 elections, Adhikari was one of Nepal's leading political figures and a stalwart of the pro-democracy movement.

May

- The first phase of the general election begins on May 3; the second phase starts on May 17. Voter turnout is reported at 60%. Early returns indicate a victory for the Nepali Congress party.

July

- Prime Minister Bhattarai enlarges his cabinet to include thirty-two ministers.
- The government submits a budget for fiscal year 1999/2000.

September

- High level talks between Nepal and Bhutan are held over the issue of Bhutanese refugees in Nepal, but no progress is made towards an agreement on repatriating the refugees.

December

- Ten people are killed when a small Skyline Airways plane flying from Simra in the south to Kathmandu crashes into a mountain.

- Nepal bans the import of cars that do not not meet international carbon monoxide emission standards, because air pollution in Kathmandu is threatening tourism, a major part of the the country's economy.

ANALYSIS OF EVENTS: 1999

BUSINESS AND THE ECONOMY

Nepal is one of the world's poorest countries. Nearly half the population lives in poverty and unemployment is high. Agriculture is the main economic activity, providing occupation for 80% of the people and making up 41% of the nation's estimated $27 billion GDP for the year; 2.2% growth for this sector is expected in 1999. Nepal has vast hydropower resources, but harnessing their economic potential requires substantial infusions of foreign capital. Tourism is one of Nepal's biggest currency earners and has significant growth potential. The country is entirely dependent on foreign aid, which will provide nearly two-thirds of budgeted expenditures for 1999. Aid donors have called on the government to improve tax collections, practice austerity, and step up the pace of reform.

The 1999/2000 budget sets spending priorities for poverty alleviation, agricultural productivity, and infrastructure development. The financial sector is also targeted for reforms that will attract foreign investments.

GOVERNMENT AND POLITICS

A multiparty parliamentary democracy was established in 1990, ending thirty years of absolute monarchy. The first general elections under the new constitution were held in early 1991, resulting in a victory for the Nepali Congress (NC) party.

However, bickering within the NC brought down the government and prompted midterm elections in 1994 that returned a hung parliament. With neither of the two largest parties—the NC and the Communist Party of Nepal-United Marxist Leninist (CPN-UML)—winning a majority, smaller parties gained disproportionate influence in parliament. A succession of minority and coalition governments followed, each failing to survive opportunistic alliances and shifting loyalties among parties and politicians.

In 1998 the CPN-UML split in two: the UML and ML factions. The NC then formed a minority government with G.P. Koirala as prime minister. The short-lived NC-ML coalition collapsed in December 1998, and Koirala resigned but quickly forged a new alliance with the UML to stay on as prime minister. On January 13, 1999, this new government won a vote of confidence in parliament. Within days King Birendra accepted Koirala's request to dissolve parliament and hold elections in May. Surprising many observers, Koirala promised to step aside and let his long time protege and rival, Krishna Prasad Bhattarai, head the next government if the NC was returned to power. Analysts perceived this as a gambit to unite the party's competing factions. The NC's subsequent victory against a divided opposition gave the party a clear parliamentary majority, raising expectations for stable and effective government. The final tally had the NC with 111 seats and the UML as the main opposition with 71 seats in the 205-member parliament. Bhattarai was sworn in as prime minister on May 31, ending speculation that Koirala would renege on his promise.

The fresh electoral mandate, however, did not dispel skepticism about the NC's ability to preserve its fragile unity. Koirala remained a formidable presence in the NC, maintaining control of the party apparatus. It was rumored that Koirala would soon replace Bhattarai as prime minister, while Bhattarai insisted he would serve a full term. A growing rift between the two men was reported in the press, which claimed unhappiness in the Koirala camp over Bhattarai's initial cabinet that excluded Koirala supporters. Independent observers were also perplexed by Bhattarai's cabinet appointments, which favored old party "hacks" with unsavory reputations rather than the promised new faces. A long-awaited cabinet expansion on July 2 failed to satisfy Koirala, and there were rumblings of discontent with the government among his loyalists. Meanwhile, the UML elected its general secretary, Madhav Kumar Nepal, to lead the party in parliament.

At the same time, a 3-year old violent Maoist insurgency in western Nepal continued unabated, with the government drawing criticism from several quarters for alleged inaction. In September the government introduced legislation to strengthen domestic security provisions. This ''anti-terrorist'' bill has yet to be approved and is opposed by the UML. A Maoist-inspired general strike on October 7 shut down commerce, schools and transportation. The government's lack of progress in combating corruption and cronyism, and in tackling the country's social and economic problems has created dissatisfaction among some NC parliamentarians. A decision to raise fuel prices in November has also proved unpopular, and further weakened Bhattarai's sagging support in the NC.

CULTURE AND SOCIETY

Nepal is the world's only Hindu kingdom. The current monarch, King Birendra, traces his descent to a royal line dating to the eighteenth century. Nearly 90% of the Nepali people practice Hinduism, the nation's official religion. Buddhists are the largest religious minority. Many of Buddhism's important holy sites, including the Buddha's birthplace, are located in the mountain kingdom, and festivities and celebrations are held throughout the year. Although Nepal enjoys relative religious harmony, there are concerns that militant Hindu fervor could spread from neighboring India.

In early October Nepal hosted the South Asian Federation Games.

DIRECTORY

CENTRAL GOVERNMENT

Head of State

King
Birendra Bir Bikram Shah Dev

Prime Minister
Krishna Prasad Bhattarai, Office of the Prime Minister, Katmandu, Nepal
PHONE: +977 227955; 228555; 228460

Ministers

Minister of Education
Yog Prasad Upadhyay, Ministry of Education, Katmandu, Nepal
PHONE: +977 414690; 411499

Minister of Local Development, Women and Social Welfare
Chiranjibi Wagle, Ministry of Local Development, Women and Social Welfare, Katmandu, Nepal
PHONE: +977 523329; 241821

Minister of Works and Transport
Khum Bahadur Khadka, Ministry of Works and Transport, Katmandu, Nepal
PHONE: +977 262467

Minister of Water Resources
Gobinda Raj Joshi, Ministry of Water Resources, Katmandu, Nepal
PHONE: +977 227347

Minister of Agriculture
Chakra Prasad Bastola, Ministry of Agriculture, Katmandu, Nepal
PHONE: +977 225109

Minister of Foreign Affairs
Ram Sharan Mahat, Ministry of Foreign Affairs, Katmandu, Nepal
PHONE: +977 416001

Minister of Tourism and Civil Aviation
Bijay Kumar Gachchhadar, Ministry of Tourism and Civil Aviation, Katmandu, Nepal
PHONE: +977 225579; 246607

Minister of Housing and Physical Planning and Labor
Bal Bahadur K.C., Ministry of Housing and Physical Planning and Labor, Katmandu, Nepal
PHONE: +977 228670; 240764

Minister of Supplies
Prakash Man Singh, Ministry of Supplies, Katmandu, Nepal
PHONE: +977 525920

Minister of Youth, Sports and Culture
Sharad Singh Bhandari, Ministry of Youth, Sports and Culture, Katmandu, Nepal
PHONE: +977 262034; 521674

Minister of Forest and Soil Conservation
Mahantha Thakur, Ministry of Forest and Soil Conservation, Katmandu, Nepal
PHONE: +977 220160

Minister of General Administration
Siddharaj Ojha, Ministry of General Administration, Katmandu, Nepal
PHONE: +977 524623

Minister of Industry
Omkar Prasad Shrestha, Ministry of Industry, Katmandu, Nepal
PHONE: +977 229202

Minister of Home, Information and Communications
Purna Bahadur Khadka, Ministry of Home, Information and Communications, Katmandu, Nepal
PHONE: +977 224737; 228333

Minister of Health
Ram Baran Yadav, Ministry of Health, Katmandu, Nepal
PHONE: +977 262534

Minister of Finance
Mahesh Acharya, Ministry of Finance, Katmandu, Nepal
PHONE: +977 259809; 259924

Minister of Commerce
Ramkrishna Tamrakar, Ministry of Commerce, Katmandu, Nepal
PHONE: +977 224726; 523152

Minister of Law, Justice and Parliamentary Affairs
Tarini Datta Chataut, Ministry of Law, Justice and Parliamentary Affairs, Katmandu, Nepal
PHONE: +977 241577; 222874

Minister of Science and Technology
Surendra Prasad Chaudhary, Ministry of Science and Technology, Katmandu, Nepal
PHONE: +977 245434

Minister of Labor
Ram Bahadur Gurung, Ministry of Labor, Katmandu, Nepal
PHONE: +977 228291

Minister of Population and Environment
Bhakta Bahadur Balayar, Ministry of Population and Environment, Katmandu, Nepal
PHONE: +977 241591

Minister of Women and Social Welfare
Kamala Pant, Ministry of Women and Social Welfare, Katmandu, Nepal
PHONE: +977 535755

Minister of Education
Rajendra Kharel, Ministry of Education, Katmandu, Nepal
PHONE: +977 412804

Minister of Land Reform and Management
Gangadhar Lamsal, Ministry of Land Reform and Management, Katmandu, Nepal
PHONE: +977 221660

Minister of Information and Communication
Govinda Bahadur Shah, Ministry of Information and Communication, Katmandu, Nepal
PHONE: +977 242562

POLITICAL ORGANIZATIONS
Nepal Green Party
PO Box 890, Kalikasthan, Kathmandu, Nepal
PHONE: +977 411730
FAX: +977 419497
E-MAIL: greennp@wlink.com.np
NAME: Kuber Sharma

Janawadi Morcha
PO Box 890, Indrachowk, Itumbahal, Nepal
PHONE: +977 211033
FAX: +977 412418
NAME: Piruddhin Mir

Thapa (National Democratic Party)
Naxal, Kathmandu, Nepal
PHONE: +977 437057
FAX: +977 434441
NAME: Surya Bahadur

Nepal Communist Party (ML)
Bag Bazar, Kathmandu, Nepal
PHONE: +977 223827; 252950; 231957
FAX: +977 231957
NAME: Sahana Pradhan

Nepal Communist Party (United)
Dillibazar, Kathmandu, Nepal
PHONE: +977 430869
FAX: +977 411642
NAME: Bishnu Manandhar

Nepal Rastriya Congress
Lazimpat, Kathmandu, Nepal
PHONE: +977 411090
NAME: Dilli Raman Regmi

National People's Front

Mahaboudha, Kathmandu, Nepal
PHONE: +977 224226
NAME: Chitra Bahadur

Nepal Communist Party (UML)

PO Box 5471, Madan Nagar, Balkhu,
Kathmandu, Nepal
PHONE: +977 278081; 278082; 271872
FAX: +977 278084
NAME: Madhav Kumer

Nepal Communist Party (Verma)

Dillibazar, Kathmandu, Nepal
PHONE: +977 414997
NAME: Krishna Raj Venna

Nepal Sadbhawana Party

Shantinagar, New Banewhwor, Kathmandu,
Nepal
PHONE: +977 488068
FAX: +977 470797
NAME: Gajendra Narayan Singh

Nepali Congress

Bhansar Tole, Teku, Kathmandu, Nepal
PHONE: +977 246248; 226761; 227748
NAME: Girija Prasad Koirala

Rastirya Janata Parishad

Dillibazar, Kathmandu, Nepal
PHONE: +977 415150
NAME: Kirti Nidhi Bista

DIPLOMATIC REPRESENTATION

Embassies in Nepal

Australia
PO Box 879, Bansbari, Kathmandu, Nepal
PHONE: +977 417566; 413076; 411578

Austria
PO Box 146, Hattisar, Kathmandu, Nepal
PHONE: +977 410891

Bangladesh
Naxal, Bhagawati Bahal, PO Box 789,
Kathmandu, Nepal
PHONE: +977 414265; 414943

Belgium
Lazimpat, Kathmandu, Nepal
PHONE: +977 414760

Brazil
PO Box 2676, Kathmandu, Nepal
PHONE: +977 527223; 527261

Canada
c/o Canadian Cooperation Office, Lazimpat,
Kathmandu, Nepal
PHONE: +977 415398; 415391; 415193

China
PO Box 4234, Baluwatar, Kathmandu, Nepal
PHONE: +977 415383; 411740; 411958

Cyprus
PO Box 133, Kathmandu, Nepal
PHONE: +977 225490

Denmark
Lalita Niwas Road, PO Box 6332, Kathmandu,
Nepal
PHONE: +977 411409

Egypt
PO Box 792, Pulchowk, Lalitpur, Nepal
PHONE: +977 524844; 524812
FAX: +977 522975

Finland
PO Box 2126, Lazimpat, Kathmandu, Nepal
PHONE: +977 416636; 417221

France
PO Box 452, Lazimpat, Kathmandu, Nepal
PHONE: +977 413839; 412332

Germany
PO Box 226, Gyaneswor, Kathmandu, Nepal
PHONE: +977 412786; 416527
FAX: +977 416899

India
PO Box 292, Lainchour, Kathmandu, Nepal
PHONE: +977 411940; 410900; 410990
FAX: +977 413132
TITLE: Ambassador
NAME: Shri K. V. Rajan

Israel
Bishramalaya House, PO Box 371, Lazimpat,
Kathmandu, Nepal
PHONE: +977 411811; 413419

Italy
PO Box 1097, Baluwatar, Kathmandu, Nepal
PHONE: +977 412280; 412743
FAX: +977 413132

Japan
PO Box 264, Maharajgunj, Kathmandu, Nepal
PHONE: +977 414083

Maldives
PO Box 324, Durbar Marg, Kathmandu, Nepal
PHONE: +977 223045

Mexico
PO Box 989, Kantipath, Kathmandu, Nepal
PHONE: +977 414343

Myanmar
PO Box 2437, Chakupath, Lalitpur, Nepal
PHONE: +977 521788
FAX: +977 523402

Netherlands
PO Box 1966, Lagankhel, Kathmandu, Nepal
PHONE: +977 522915

New Zealand
PO Box 224, Dillibazar, Kathmandu, Nepal
PHONE: +977 412436

North Korea
Jhamsikhel, Lalitpur, Nepal
PHONE: +977 521084; 521855

Norway
PO Box 1045, Lagankhel, Kathmandu, Nepal
PHONE: +977 521646

Pakistan
G.PO Box 202, Panipokhari, Kathmandu, Nepal
PHONE: +977 411421

Philipines
PO Box 2640, Lazimpat, Kathmandu, Nepal
PHONE: +977 410213

Poland
Ganabahal, Kathmandu, Nepal
PHONE: +977 221101

Russia
PO Box 123, Baluwatar, Kathamandu, Nepal
PHONE: +977 411063; 412115

South Korea
PO Box 1058, Himshail, Tahachal, Red Cross
Marg, Kathmandu, Nepal
PHONE: +977 270172; 270417

Spain
Batisputali, Kathmandu, Nepal
PHONE: +977 472328

Sri Lanka
PO Box 8802, Baluwatar, Kathmandu, Nepal
PHONE: +977 419289; 413623

Sweden
Khichapokhari, Kathmandu, Nepal
PHONE: +977 220939

Switzerland
Jawalakhel, Kathmandu, Nepal
PHONE: +977 523168; 523468

Thailand
PO Box 3333, Jyoti Kendra, Thapathali,
Kathmandu, Nepal
PHONE: +977 213912; 213910

Turkey
Gyaneswor, Kathmandu, Nepal
PHONE: +977 412210

United Kingdom
PO Box 106, Lainchour, Kathmandu, Nepal
PHONE: +977 410583; 411281; 411590
TITLE: Ambassador
NAME: Ralph Frank

United States
PO Box 295, Panipokhari, Kathmandu, Nepal
PHONE: +977 411601; 411179; 412718
FAX: +977 419963

JUDICIAL SYSTEM
Supreme Court

FURTHER READING
Articles

Bijay, K.C. and P.N. Snowden. "Pricing Shares on a Nascent Market: The Nepal Stock Exchange 1994–96." *World Development* 27 (June 1999): 1083(1).

"The Gurkhas' New Fight." *The Economist* 352 (August 14, 1999): 34.

Kohrt, Brandon A. and Steven S. Schreiber. "Jhum-jhum: Neuropsychiatric Symptoms in a Nepali Village." *The Lancet* 353 (March 27, 1999): 1070(1).

"Mao Guns Again." *The Economist* 350 (February 13, 1999): 42(1).

"Nepal Chooses Telrad." *Israel Business Today* 13 (April 1999): 16(1).

"Nepal's Anti-Tobacco Measures." *The Lancet*, 353 (February 13, 1999): 569(1).

"Seventh Wonder." *The Economist* 351 (May 22, 1999): 45.

Shabad, Steven. "A Himalayan Mafia." *World Press Review* 46 (February 1999): 20(1).

Shabad, Steven. "A Maoist Insurgency." *World Press Review* 46 (June 1999): 22.

Shackley, Myra. ''The Himalayas: Masked Dances and Mixed Blessings.'' *UNESCO Courier* (July-August 1999): 28(2).

''A Shortage of Taxis in Nepal.'' *The Economist* 352 (August 7, 1999): 32.

''World Watch.'' *Time International* 153 (May 17, 1999): 18 + (1).

Internet

Explore Nepal. Available Online @ www.catmando.com/news/explore-nepal/ explrnpl.htm (November 17, 1999).

The People's Review. Available Online @ www. info-nepal.com/p-review/ (November 17, 1999).

NEPAL: STATISTICAL DATA

For sources and notes see "Sources of Statistics" in the front of each volume.

GEOGRAPHY

Geography (1)

Area:

Total: 140,800 sq km.

Land: 136,800 sq km.

Water: 4,000 sq km.

Area—comparative: slightly larger than Arkansas.

Land boundaries:

Total: 2,926 km.

Border countries: China 1,236 km, India 1,690 km.

Coastline: 0 km (landlocked).

Climate: varies from cool summers and severe winters in north to subtropical summers and mild winters in south.

Terrain: Terai or flat river plain of the Ganges in south, central hill region, rugged Himalayas in north.

Natural resources: quartz, water, timber, hydropower potential, scenic beauty, small deposits of lignite, copper, cobalt, iron ore.

Land use:

Arable land: 17%

Permanent crops: 0%

Permanent pastures: 15%

Forests and woodland: 42%

Other: 26% (1993 est.).

HUMAN FACTORS

Demographics (2A)

	1990	1995	1998	2000	2010	2020	2030	2040	2050
Population	19,333.1	21,965.6	23,698.4	24,920.2	31,627.0	38,858.5	46,340.5	53,757.9	60,661.3
Net migration rate (per 1,000 population)	NA	NA	NA	NA	NA	NA	NA	NA	NA
Births	NA	NA	NA	NA	NA	NA	NA	NA	NA
Deaths	NA	NA	NA	NA	NA	NA	NA	NA	NA
Life expectancy - males	54.3	56.8	58.0	58.9	63.0	66.6	69.7	72.3	74.4
Life expectancy - females	53.2	55.9	57.7	59.0	64.9	70.1	74.5	78.0	80.6
Birth rate (per 1,000)	38.8	36.6	35.7	35.0	30.0	25.2	21.9	18.9	16.7
Death rate (per 1,000)	12.9	11.3	10.4	9.9	7.7	6.3	5.6	5.5	5.9
Women of reproductive age (15-49 yrs.)	4,301.1	4,981.4	5,453.9	5,785.9	7,629.0	9,855.8	12,072.6	13,932.2	15,406.8
of which are currently married	NA	NA	NA	NA	NA	NA	NA	NA	NA
Fertility rate	5.6	5.2	4.9	4.7	3.8	3.1	2.7	2.4	2.2

Except as noted, values for vital statistics are in thousands; life expectancy is in years.

Health Personnel (3)

Total health expenditure as a percentage of GDP, 1990-1997[a]

Public sector 1.2

Private sector 3.8

Total[b] 5.0

Health expenditure per capita in U.S. dollars, 1990-1997[a]

Purchasing power parity 52

Total 10

Availability of health care facilities per 100,000 people

Hospital beds 1990-1997[a] 20

Doctors 1993[c] 5

Nurses 1993[c] 5

Health Indicators (4)

Life expectancy at birth

1980 48

1997 57

Daily per capita supply of calories (1996) 2,339

Total fertility rate births per woman (1997) 4.4

Maternal mortality ratio per 100,000 live births (1990-97) . . . . .1,500[c]

Safe water % of population with access (1995) 59

Sanitation % of population with access (1995) 23

Consumption of iodized salt % of households (1992-98)[a] 93

Smoking prevalence

Male % of adults (1985-95)[a] 69

Female % of adults (1985-95)[a] 13

Tuberculosis incidence per 100,000 people (1997) 211

Adult HIV prevalence % of population ages 15-49 (1997) 0.24

Infants and Malnutrition (5)

Under-5 mortality rate (1997) 104

% of infants with low birthweight (1990-97) . . . . . .NA

Births attended by skilled health staff % of total[a] 9

% fully immunized (1995-97)

TB 96

DPT 78

Polio 78

Measles 85

Prevalence of child malnutrition under age 5 (1992-97)[b] 47

Ethnic Division (6)

Newars, Indians, Tibetans, Gurungs, Magars, Tamangs, Bhotias, Rais, Limbus, Sherpas.

Religions (7)

Hindu 90%

Buddhist 5%

Muslim 3%

Other 2% (1981)

Only official Hindu state in the world, although no sharp distinction between many Hindu and Buddhist groups.

Languages (8)

Nepali (official), 20 other languages divided into numerous dialects.

EDUCATION

Public Education Expenditures (9)

Public expenditure on education (% of GNP)

1980 . . . . .1.8

1996 . . . . .2.8

Expenditure per student

Primary % of GNP per capita

1980 . . . . .14.6

1996 . . . .

Secondary % of GNP per capita

1980 . . . .

1996 . . . .

Tertiary % of GNP per capita

1980 . . . . .271.9

1996 . . . . .140.6[1]

Expenditure on teaching materials

Primary % of total for level (1996) 7.2

Secondary % of total for level (1996) . . . .

Primary pupil-teacher ratio per teacher (1996) . . . .

Duration of primary education years (1995) 5

Educational Attainment (10)

Age group (1991)[18] . . . . .6+

Total population 15,145,071

Highest level attained (%)

No schooling[2] 69.6

First level

Not completed 16.2

Completed . . . . .NA

Entered second level

S-1 . . . . .8.9

S-2 . . . . .2.0

Postsecondary 1.5

Literacy Rates (11A)

In thousands and percent[1]	1990	1995	2000	2010
Illiterate population (15+ yrs.)	8,308	9,149	10,088	12,009
Literacy rate - total adult pop. (%)	24.4	27.5	30.9	37.9
Literacy rate - males (%)	37.2	40.9	44.6	51.6
Literacy rate - females (%)	11.4	14.0	16.9	23.6

GOVERNMENT & LAW

Political Parties (12)

House of Representatives	% of seats
Nepali Congress Party (NCP)	.33
Communist Part of Nepal/United Marxist-Leninist (CPN/UML)	.31
National Democratic Party (NDP)	.18
Nepal Sadbhavana (Goodwill) Party	.3
Nepal Workers and Peasants Party (NWPP)	.1

Military Affairs (14B)

	1990	1991	1992	1993	1994	1995
Military expenditures						
Current dollars (mil.)	31	31	35	37	38	42
1995 constant dollars (mil.)	35	34	37	39	39	42
Armed forces (000)	35	35	35	35	35	40
Gross national product (GNP)						
Current dollars (mil.)	3,010	3,324	3,552	3,757	4,131	4,382
1995 constant dollars (mil.)	3,459	3,673	3,821	3,939	4,235	4,382
Central government expenditures (CGE)						
1995 constant dollars (mil.)	578	674	620	642	598	719
People (mil.)	19.1	19.6	20.0	20.5	21.0	21.6
Military expenditure as % of GNP	1.0	.9	1.0	1.0	.9	.9
Military expenditure as % of CGE	6.1	5.1	6.0	6.1	6.5	5.8
Military expenditure per capita (1995 $)	2	2	2	2	2	2
Armed forces per 1,000 people (soldiers)	1.8	1.8	1.7	1.7	1.7	1.9
GNP per capita (1995 $)	181	188	191	192	201	203
Arms imports[6]						
Current dollars (mil.)	10	0	0	0	10	0
1995 constant dollars (mil.)	11	0	0	0	10	0
Arms exports[6]						
Current dollars (mil.)	0	0	0	0	0	0
1995 constant dollars (mil.)	0	0	0	0	0	0
Total imports[7]						
Current dollars (mil.)	686	758	792	880	1,159	1,374
1995 constant dollars (mil.)	788	838	852	923	1,188	1,374
Total exports[7]						
Current dollars (mil.)	210	264	374	390	364	348
1995 constant dollars (mil.)	241	292	402	409	373	348
Arms as percent of total imports[8]	1.5	0	0	.9	0	0
Arms as percent of total exports[8]	0	0	0	0	0	0

Government Budget (13A)

Year: 1998

Total Expenditures: 57,991 Millions of Rupees

Expenditures as a percentage of the total by function:

General public services and public order . . . . . . .8.26[f]

Defense . . . . .4.53[f]

Education . . . . .13.98[f]

Health . . . . .6.62[f]

Social Security and Welfare . . . .

Housing and community amenities . . . . .5.88[f]

Recreational, cultural, and religious affairs . . . .-[f]

Fuel and energy . . . .

Agriculture, forestry, fishing, and hunting . . . . .6.07[f]

Mining, manufacturing, and construction . . . . . .1.40[f]

Transportation and communication . . . . .11.94[f]

Other economic affairs and services . . . .

Crime (15)

Crime rate (for 1997)

Crimes reported 9,350

Total persons convicted 5,100

Crimes per 100,000 population 44

Persons responsible for offenses

Total number of suspects 15,300

Total number of female suspects 625

Total number of juvenile suspects 75

LABOR FORCE

Labor Force (16)

Total (million) 10

Agriculture 81%

Services 16%

Industry 3%

Severe lack of skilled labor. Data for 1996 est.

Unemployment Rate (17)

Rate not available; substantial underemployment (1996).

PRODUCTION SECTOR

Electric Energy (18)

Capacity .292,000 kW (1995)

Production . . . . .980 million kWh (1996)

Consumption per capita . . . . .48 kWh (1996 est.)

Transportation (19)

Highways:

total: 7,700 km

paved: 3,196 km

unpaved: 4,504 km (1996 est.)

Airports: 45 (1997 est.)

Airports—with paved runways:

total: 5

over 3,047 m: 1

1,524 to 2,437 m: 3

914 to 1,523 m: 1 (1997 est.)

Airports—with unpaved runways:

total: 40

1,524 to 2,437 m: 2

914 to 1,523 m: 9

under 914 m: 29 (1997 est.)

Top Agricultural Products (20)

Rice, corn, wheat, sugarcane, root crops; milk, water buffalo meat.

MANUFACTURING SECTOR

GDP & Manufacturing Summary (21)

Detailed value added figures are listed by both International Standard Industry Code (ISIC) and product title.

	1980	1985	1990	1994
GDP ($-1990 mil.)[1]	1,950	2,477	3,099	3,739
Per capita ($-1990)[1]	131	146	161	175
Manufacturing share (%) (current prices)[1]	4.3	4.8	5.6	7.3
Manufacturing				
Value added ($-1990 mil.)[1]	84	120	163	270
Industrial production index	100	154	215	293
Value added ($ mil.)	91	179	269	388
Gross output ($ mil.)	513	661	656	979
Employment (000)	62	127	156	228
Profitability (% of gross output)				
Intermediate input (%)	82	73	59	60

	1980	1985	1990	1994
Wages and salaries inc. supplements (%)	4	6	10	9
Gross operating surplus	14	21	31	31
Productivity ($)				
Gross output per worker	7,409	4,756	4,068	3,963
Value added per worker	1,323	1,289	1,666	1,570
Average wage (inc. supplements)	300	313	400	387
Value added ($ mil.)				
311/2 Food products	38	59	38	70
313 Beverages	1	5	23	29
314 Tobacco products	17	26	40	37
321 Textiles	5	23	54	70
322 Wearing apparel	1	7	24	50
323 Leather and fur products	2	3	4	4
324 Footwear	—	1	1	7
331 Wood and wood products	2	4	3	7
332 Furniture and fixtures	4	3	2	4
341 Paper and paper products	—	1	3	6
342 Printing and publishing	1	3	2	4
351 Industrial chemicals	—	—	—	—
352 Other chemical products	2	8	13	17
353 Petroleum refineries	NA	NA	—	NA
354 Miscellaneous petroleum and coal products	NA	NA	—	NA
355 Rubber products	—	1	2	4
356 Plastic products	—	2	3	7
361 Pottery, china and earthenware	NA	NA	—	NA
362 Glass and glass products	NA	NA	NA	NA
369 Other non-metal mineral products	3	22	34	32
371 Iron and steel	3	4	8	8
372 Non-ferrous metals	NA	NA	—	NA
381 Metal products	1	5	8	17
382 Non-electrical machinery	NA	NA	—	NA
383 Electrical machinery	1	2	4	11
384 Transport equipment	NA	NA	—	NA
385 Professional and scientific equipment	—	—	—	—
390 Other manufacturing industries	10	1	3	3

FINANCE, ECONOMICS, & TRADE

Balance of Payments (23)

	1992	1993	1994	1995	1996
Exports of goods (f.o.b.)	376	397	369	350	389
Imports of goods (f.o.b.)	−752	−859	−1,159	−1,311	−1,495
Trade balance	−376	−462	−790	−961	−1,106
Services - debits	−242	−275	−327	−348	−275
Services - credits	307	362	614	723	791
Private transfers (net)	83	78	81	146	187
Government transfers (net)	46	74	71	84	76
Overall balance	−181	−222	−352	−356	−327

FINANCE, ECONOMICS, & TRADE

Economic Indicators (22)

National product: GDP—purchasing power parity—$31.1 billion (1997 est.)

National product real growth rate: 4.2% (1997 est.)

National product per capita: $1,370 (1997 est.)

Inflation rate—consumer price index: 7.5% (1997 est.)

Exchange Rates (24)

Exchange rates:

Nepalese rupees (NRs) per US$1

January 1998	63.265
1997	58.010
1996	56.692
1995	51.890
1994	49.398
1993	48.607

Top Import Origins (25)

$1.6 billion (c.i.f., 1997 est.)

Origins	%
India	NA
Singapore	NA
Japan	NA
Germany	NA

NA stands for not available.

Top Export Destinations (26)

$419 million (f.o.b., 1997 est.) but does not include unrecorded border trade with India.

Destinations	%
India	NA
United States	NA
Germany	NA
United Kingdom	NA

NA stands for not available.

Economic Aid (27)

Recipient: ODA, $411 million (FY97/98).

Import Export Commodities (28)

Import Commodities	Export Commodities
Petroleum products 20%	Carpets
Fertilizer 11%	Clothing
Machinery 10%	Leather goods
	Jute goods
	Grain

THE NETHERLANDS

CAPITAL: Constitutional capital: Amsterdam. Seat of government: The Hague (`s Gravenhage; Den Haag).

FLAG: The national flag, standardized in 1937, is a tricolor of red, white, and blue horizontal stripes.

ANTHEM: *Wilhelmus van Nassouwen (William of Nassau).*

MONETARY UNIT: The guilder (gulden; abbreviated f, designating the ancient florin) of 100 cents is a paper currency with one official exchange rate. There are coins of 5, 10, and 25 cents and 1, 2, 5, 10, and 50 guilders, and notes of 5, 10, 25, 50, 100, 250, and 1,000 guilders. f1 = $0.58962 (or $1 = f1.696).

WEIGHTS AND MEASURES: The metric system is the legal standard.

HOLIDAYS: New Year's Day, 1 January; Queen's Day, 30 April; National Liberation Day, 5 May; Christmas, 25–26 December. Movable religious holidays include Good Friday, Holy Saturday, Easter Monday, Ascension, and Whitmonday.

TIME: 1 PM = noon GMT.

LOCATION AND SIZE: Situated in northwestern Europe, the Netherlands has a total area of 37,330 square kilometers (14,413 square miles), of which inland water accounts for more than 2,060 square kilometers (795 square miles). The land area is 33,920 square kilometers (13,097 square miles). Comparatively, the area occupied by the Netherlands is slightly less than twice the size of the state of New Jersey. The Netherlands has a total boundary length of 1,478 kilometers (918 miles).

The capital city of the Netherlands, Amsterdam, is in the western part of the country.

CLIMATE: The Netherlands has a maritime climate, with cool summers and mild winters. The average temperature is about 2°C (36°F) in January and 19°C (66°F) in July, with an annual average of about 10°C (50°F). Average annual rainfall is about 76 centimeters (30 inches).

Kingdom of the Netherlands
Koninkrijk der Nederlanden

INTRODUCTORY SURVEY

RECENT HISTORY

The Netherlands successfully remained neutral during World War I (1914–18), and preserved its neutrality until the Germans overran the country during World War II (1939–45). Queen Wilhelmina (r.1890–1948) refused to surrender to the Germans, and instead fled to Britain with other officials of her government. Although Dutch resistance lasted only five days, destruction was widespread. Nearly the whole of downtown Rotterdam was wiped out, and other cities suffered great damage. The Dutch withstood severe repressions until their liberation by Allied forces in May 1945. Wilhelmina gave up the throne in 1948 and was followed by her daughter, Juliana (r.1948–80).

The East Indies, most of which had been under Dutch rule for over 300 years, were occupied by Japanese forces in 1942. In 1945, a group of Indonesians proclaimed an independent republic and resisted Dutch reoccupation. After four years of hostilities and following United Nations intervention, the Netherlands recognized the independence of Indonesia in December 1949.

Suriname (formerly Dutch Guiana), controlled by the Netherlands since 1815, became an independent nation on 25 November 1975. The Netherlands Antilles and Aruba continue to be dependent areas.

Reform of the social security system has been the major political issue in the 1990s, along with efforts to reduce public spending. A number of

radical social measures received parliamentary approval in recent years including conditions for administering euthanasia (causing death painlessly in terminal illnesses), legalization of prostitution, and laws banning discrimination.

Queen Juliana gave up the throne in 1980 in favor of her daughter, Beatrix. In 1966, Beatrix married Claus von Amsberg, a German diplomat, whose title remained Prince of the Netherlands when Beatrix became Queen. Their first-born son, Prince Willem-Alexander, is heir to the throne.

GOVERNMENT

The Netherlands is a constitutional monarchy, under the house of Orange-Nassau. Executive power is exercised by the crown and the cabinet, which must have the support of a majority in the parliament. The monarch acts as an adviser to the cabinet, may propose bills, and signs all bills approved by the legislature.

The Council of State, begun in 1532, is appointed by and presided over by the crown. It considers all legislation proposed by the crown or the cabinet before it is submitted to the parliament.

Legislative power is exercised jointly by the crown and the States-General (*Staten-Generaal*), a two-chamber parliament. The upper house (*Eerste Kamer*) consists of 75 members elected for four years by the provincial representative councils. The lower house (*Tweede Kamer*) has 150 members elected for four years directly by the people. All Dutch citizens who have reached the age of 18 years and live in the Netherlands can vote.

As of 1994, the country was divided into 12 provinces, each governed by a representative provincial council (*Provinciale Staten*).

Judiciary

There is no jury system, and the state rather than the individual acts as initiator of legal proceedings. Administrative justice is separate from civil and criminal justice and not uniform in dispensation. The supreme judiciary body is the High Court of the Netherlands (Court of Cassation). Its principal task is to supervise administration of justice and to review the judgments of lower courts.

There are five courts of appeal (gerechtshoven). The 19 district courts (arrondissementsrechtsbanken) provide first hearings of criminal cases and civil cases not handled by the 62 cantonal courts (kantonge-rechten), which handle petty criminal cases and civil cases involving sums of up to about $250. A single magistrate presides over most of these courts. There also are juvenile courts and special arbitration courts (for such institutions as the Stock Exchange Association and professional organizations).

Political Parties

Religion plays an important role in the political life of the Netherlands, and religiously oriented parties exercise considerable influence. However, since the mid-1960s the general trend has been toward a division into conservative and liberal parties, and religious parties have lost voter support.

The religious political party with the largest membership is the Catholic People's Party (Katholieke Volkspartij—KVP), which favors democratic government and a middle-of-the-road social policy. The Labor Party (Partij van de Arbeid—PvdA) has appealed mainly to national interests rather than to socialist ones, although it does favor state economic planning. The conservative People's Party for Freedom and Democracy (Volkspartij voor Vrijheid en Democratie—VVD)

has advocated free enterprise, separation of church and state, and individual liberties. The Democrats '66 (Democraten '66—D'66) emerged from discontent with the major political parties as a change-oriented party.

Smaller parties include the left-wing Pacifist Socialist Party (Pacifistisch Socialistische Partij–PSP), the Communist Party of the Netherlands (Communistische Partij van Nederland–CPN), the Farmers' Party (Boerenpartij–BP), and two very orthodox Calvinist groups: the State Reform Party (Staatkurdig Gerefoormeerde Partij–SGP) and the Reformed Political Association (Gerefoormeerd Politiek Verbond—GPV).

In 1991, the communists formally dissolved and joined a new left-wing alliance known as the Green Left (Groen Links).

As no single party commands a majority in the States-General, the governing cabinet is made up of various party representatives, according to their numerical strength.

In the legislative elections of May 1994, the PvdA took 37 of 150 seats; CDA, 34; VVD, 31; D'66, 24; and other parties, 24.

DEFENSE

Universal military training has been in force since the beginning of the twentieth century. All able bodied men reaching the age of 20 (about 43,000 a year) are subject to military training for 12 to 15 months. A small percentage of draftees, who make a request under the Conscientious Objectors Act, are required to undertake alternative service.

In 1995, the army (45,350, 30% draftees) consisted of 6 mechanized infantry brigades, 3 armored brigades, and corps troops assigned to the North Atlantic Treaty Organization (NATO). The navy had 14,000 officers and men, including 2,900 marines. The air force of 12,350 men contained 8 combat squadrons and 12 air defense squadrons, as well as transport and special auxiliary groups.

The police force numbers 3,600. The reserves for all services total 81,000, about 61,000 on short recall. The United States stations 1,580 troops in the Netherlands. The nation spent $8.5 billion on defense in 1995, or 3% of the gross domestic product.

ECONOMIC AFFAIRS

An industrial nation with limited natural resources, the Netherlands bases its economy on the importation of raw materials for processing into finished products for export. Food processing, metallurgy, chemicals, manufacturing, and oil refining are the principal industries.

Because of its geographic position on the sea, outstanding harbor facilities, and numerous internal waterways, the Netherlands has traditionally been a trading, transporting, and brokerage nation. The economy, being dependent on international trade, is sharply affected by economic developments abroad—including changes in prices of primary goods—over which the Netherlands has little or no control.

The domestic economy grew by an annual average of 3% during 1988–95. Inflation averaged about 2% per year during 1986–95.

Public Finance

Late in the year, the government submits to the lower house of the States-General its budget for the following calendar year. The government has gradually cut the deficit from 10% of GDP in 1983 to 2.75% in 1996, slightly below the 3% Maastricht criteria for European Economic and Monetary Union (EMU) in 1999. The deficit is largely financed by government bonds. Financing is also covered by issuing Dutch Treasury Certificates, which replaced a standing credit facility for short-term deficit financing with the Netherlands Central Bank. Under the Maastricht Treaty, the Netherlands Central Bank was abolished in 1994.

In 1995, government revenues totaled approximately $109.9 billion and expenditures $122.1 billion.

Income

In 1997, Netherland's gross national product (GNP) was $343.9 billion, or about $22,000 per person. For the period 1985–95, the average inflation rate was 1.7%, resulting in a real growth rate in (GNP) of 1.8% per person.

Industry

Since World War II, the high rate of population growth and the severing of economic ties with Indonesia have made the further development of industry important. The metallurgical industry in particular has made tremendous progress. The Philips Electrical Company at Eindhoven has become the greatest electrical products firm in Europe as well as one of the world's major exporters of electric bulbs and appliances. In 1996, Philips employed 273,000 people and had revenues of $41 billion. Unilever, a British-Dutch consumer products company, employed 306,000 in 1996 and had revenues of $52 billion.

The Royal Dutch/Shell Group had the world's highest corporate income in 1996, with revenues of $128 billion. Royal Dutch/Shell owns and operates one of the world's largest oil refineries at Curaçao, near Venezuela, and Rotterdam's suburb of Pernis has the largest oil refinery in Europe.

Industrial products include crude steel, pig iron, and pharmaceutical products. The Netherlands also produces cigarettes, beer, canned fish, cocoa and cocoa products, sugar, candies, biscuits, and potato flour.

Banking and Finance

The Netherlands Bank, nationalized in 1948, is the central bank. It issues the currency and regulates its value, establishes the rates of foreign exchange, issues money permits to foreigners, and supervises the privately owned banks. Since the 1950s, the Netherlands Bank has used reserve regulations and the central bank discount rate as instruments of monetary policy. The Dutch financial services industry has a long and distinguished history and has introduced many banking innovations to the world. Since the late 1980s, the sector has undergone a revolution. A common strategic desire to expand and to gain more financial strength, combined with deregulation of the financial market, prompted several bank mergers and the formation of financial conglomerates of banks and insurance groups. As a result, the number of dominant participants in the market has diminished to a handful, each providing the full range of financial services. The Netherlands Middenstands bank (NMB) and the state-owned Postbank merged to form the NMB Postbank in 1989, which in turn merged again with the Nationale Nederlanden insurance group to form the International Nederlanden Groep (ING) in 1991. The large ABN and Amro commercial banking groups joined up to form ABN-AMRO in 1990. VSB-bank, a conglomerate of savings banks, teamed up with the Ameu insurance group and Belgium's AG insurance group in 1990 to form the Dutch-Belgian Fortis group. Rabobank, a large cooperative group which specializes in the provision of agricultural credits and mortgage facilities but has been rapidly expanding its product portfolio in recent years, took a 50% share in the Robeco investment group in 1996.

At the end of 1995, official gold and foreign reserves, at $42.9 billion, accounted for 14.1% of total domestic liquidity.

The Netherlands has the oldest stock exchange in the world. The Amsterdam Stock Exchange (ASE); founded in the early 17th century, it is now one of the largest stock exchanges in operation. The issuance of new securities on the exchange is supervised by the Netherlands Bank, acting in cooperation with the commercial banks and stockbrokers.

The comparatively large share of foreign security listings and capital supply gives the ASE an international importance disproportionate to its size. Its strong international orientation is also reflected in the fact that its share of Europe's total market capitalization far outweighs the relative importance of the dutch economy. The multinational nature of the major Dutch companies, which has led to their shares being quoted on a number of international stock markets, means that stock price levels on the ASE are heavily influenced by developments elsewhere. The three largest companies, Royal Dutch Shell, Unilever, and ING, account for around 50% of total stock market capitalization.

In order to enhance the international competitiveness of the ASE, many reform measures have been taken in the past few years, with varying degrees of success. These include the introduction of a new electronic trading system open to foreign-based brokers, a division of the market into a wholesale and a retail segment, and a revamp of the exchange's organizational structure. Moreover, in early 1996, under pressure from the government, the stock exchange introduced an arrangement that aims to reduce the influence of the wide range of anti-takeover devices quoted corporations are permitted, which has long been considered as one of the exchange's most important shortcomings. Under the new arrangement, a prospective buyer who has gained 70% of a company's shares can turn to the Amsterdam Court of Justice after a period of 12 months.

On 1 January 1997, the Amsterdam Exchanges (AEX) were formed by the merger of the Amsterdam Stock Exchange (ASE) and the city's European Options Exchange (EDE). From approximately 680 at the end of January, the AEX index of 25 leading shares rose to 700 on 11 February 1997 and sped on to almost 775 by mid-March before suffering a correction prompted by the release of disappointing financial results by a brewing company, Grolsch, and fears of interest rate increases in the U.S.

Economic Development

The Netherlands government in the period since World War II has aimed at increased industrialization. To encourage industrialization, the maintenance of internal monetary equilibrium was vitally important, and the government has largely succeeded in this task. Successive governments pursued a policy of easy credits and a "soft" currency, but after the Netherlands had fully recovered from the war by the mid-1950s, a harder currency and credit policy came into effect. In the social sphere, stable relationships were maintained by a deliberate governmental social policy seeking to bridge major differences between management and labor. The organized collaboration of workers and employers in the Labor Foundation has contributed in no small measure to the success of this policy, and as a result, strikes (other than an occasional wildcat strike) are rare.

Successive wage increases helped bring the overall wage level in the Netherlands up to that of other EC countries by 1968. The Dutch government's policy, meanwhile, was directed toward controlling inflation while seeking to maintain high employment. In 1966, the government raised indirect taxes to help finance rising expenditures, particularly in the fields of education, public transportation, and public health. Further attempts to cope with inflation and other economic problems involved increased government control over the economy. Wage and price controls were imposed in 1970–71, and the States-General approved a measure granting the government power to control wages, rents, dividends, health and insurance costs, and job layoffs during 1974.

During the mid-1980s, the nation experienced modest recovery from recession; the government's goal was to expand recovery and reduce high unemployment, while cutting down the size of the annual budget deficit. The government has generally sought to foster a climate favorable to private industrial investment through such measures as preparing industrial sites, subsidizing or permitting allowances for industrial construction and equipment, assisting in the creation of new markets, granting subsidies for establishing industries in distressed areas, and establishing schools for adult training. In 1978, the government began, by means of a selective investment levy, to discourage investment in the western region (Randstad), while encouraging industrial development in the southern province of Limburg and the northern provinces of Drenthe, Friesland, and Groningen.

The Netherlands' largest economic development projects have involved the reclamation of land from the sea by construction of dikes and dams and by the drainage of lakes to create polders for additional agricultural land. The Zuider Zee project closed off the sea and created the freshwater Ijsselmeer by means of a 30 kilometers (19 mi.) barrier dam in 1932, and subsequently drained four polders enclosing about 165,000 hectares (408,000 acres). After a storm washed away dikes on islands in Zeeland and South Holland in 1953, killing some 1,800 people, the Delta project was begun. This project, designed to close estuaries between the islands with massive dams, was officially inaugurated in 1986; the cost was $2.4 billion. The Delta works include a storm surge barrier with 62 steel gates, each weighing 500 tons, that are usually left open to allow normal tidal flow in order to protect the natural environment. Another major engineering project was construction of a bridge and tunnel across the Western Schelde estuary in the south to connect Zeeland Flanders more directly with the rest of the country.

Dutch companies invested f6.9 billion in research and development by their own staff in 1995.

SOCIAL WELFARE

A widespread system of social insurance and assistance is in effect. Unemployment, accidents, illness, and disability are covered by insurance, which is compulsory for most employees and voluntary for self-employed persons. Maternity grants and full insurance for the worker's family are also provided, as are family allowances for children. There are also widows' and orphans' funds. A state pension is granted to all persons over 65. Women have equal legal status with men.

Healthcare

Under the Health Insurance Act, everyone with earned income of less than 50,900 guilders per year pays a monthly contribution in return for which they receive medical, pharmaceutical, and dental treatment and hospitalization. The state also pays for preventive medicine including vaccinations for children, and school dental services, medical research, and the training of health workers.

The general health situation has been excellent over a long period, helped by a rise in the standard of living, improvements in nutrition, hygiene, housing, and working conditions, and the expansion of public health measures. Average life expectancy is 78 years.

In 1992, there were 4.1 hospital beds per 1,000 people. As of 1993, there was 1 physician for every 398 people.

Major causes of death in 1992 were categorized as follows, per 100,000 inhabitants: (1) communicable diseases and maternal/perinatal causes; (2) noncommunicable diseases; and (3) injuries.

Housing

During World War II, more than 25% of Holland's 2 million dwellings were damaged. From 1945 to 1985, nearly 4 million dwellings were built. In 1985 alone, 98,131 dwellings were built. Most of the new units were subsidized by the national government. Subsidies are granted to municipalities, building societies, and housing associations, which generally build low-income multiple dwellings. The total number of housing units in 1996 was 6.4 million, averaging 2.42 residents per dwelling. About 90,000 new dwellings were built in 1996, of which 75% were one-family houses.

EDUCATION

Illiteracy is nearly nonexistent in the Netherlands. School attendance between the ages of 6 and 16 is compulsory. Secondary school is comprised of three types: general, secondary school, preuniversity—the athenaeum and the gymnasium, both lasting for six years; and vocational secondary school. Special education is provided to children with physical, mental, or social disabilities at special primary and secondary schools. In 1993, the Netherlands had 8,139 primary schools with 65,747 staff and 1.1 million students. At the secondary level, there were 88,229 teachers and 1.4 million students that year.

Vocational and university education is provided at the eight universities and five institutes (Hogescholen), which are equivalent to universities. These are funded entirely by the government. Facilities for adult education have been opened in various municipalities. In 1993, 512,403 students attended universities.

1999 KEY EVENTS TIMELINE

January

- The Netherlands is one of the eleven members of the European Union to adopt the euro as currency as of January 1, 1999. Although the euro becomes an official currency, national currencies in the eleven states will continue to circulate until 2002, when they will be replaced by the euro.

- Rotterdam harbor reports yet another record breaking year. More than 315 billion tons of imports and exports passed through the world's largest harbor in 1998.

- A majority of the Second Chamber (lower house) of the Dutch parliament indicates that it would be best if Crown Prince William Alexander resigns from the International Olympic Committee. Members of the Second Chamber react to the interim report of the IOC's own investigation that its members took bribes from cities hoping to host the Olympics.

February

- The Second Chamber of the Dutch parliament votes to repeal a 1911 law forbidding houses of prostitution. After January 1, 2000, brothels, which have been routinely tolerated and allowed to operate openly in the Netherlands, will be treated the same as any other legitimate business.

March

- Writer and Slavic studies specialist Karel van Reve dies at age 77 from Parkinson's disease. The author of several novels, van Reve had been a professor at Leiden University.

- The Social Democratic Party (PvdA) and Democrats '66 (D'66) lose seats in elections to provincial politics, while their coalition partner, the Liberal Party (VVD) and the Christian Democratic Appeal (CDA) gain seats. Green Left (GL), an opposition party to the left of the Social Democrats, wins more than 10% of the vote. The outcome narrows the support of the governing coalition in the indirectly elected First Chamber (upper house) of parliament.

- Dutch F–16 fighters support NATO allies in air attacks on Serbia and Kosovo.

April

- The trial of two former Libyan intelligence agents, accused of the 1989 bombing of Pan American flight 103 over Lockerbie, Scotland, opens at Camp Zeist in the Netherlands, a closed military base temporary ceded to the British.

- An outbreak of Legionnaire's disease at a floral show in Bovenkarspel, located north of Amsterdam, claims at least 21 lives out of 106 confirmed and 125 suspected cases.

- A parliamentary committee of inquiry investigating the manner in which Dutch cabinet ministers handled the 1992 crash of an El Al passenger jet into an Amsterdam apartment block indicate that several ministers (including some serving in the present cabinet) had provided the parliament with insufficient, untimely, and incorrect information about the crash.

- Football riots following Feyenoord (Rotterdam) football games prompt interior minister Bram Peper to demand measures allowing for the detention of prospective hooligans.

May

- Democrats' 66 withdraw from the Liberal-Democrats'66–Social Democratic cabinet following the narrow defeat of a constitutional amendment, which would have allowed ''corrective'' referenda to repeal statutes already passed into law. Corrective referenda are opposed by Liberal senators, such as former party leader Hans Wiegel. The cabinet continues with ''demissionaire,'' or caretaker status. A mediator is appointed to investigate whether the rift in the cabinet could be healed.

- Dutch banks accused of profiting from the sale of assets deposited into special accounts during the Nazi occupation of the Netherlands agree to compensate victims and their families.

- Belgian chickens and pork whose feed is believed to have been contaminated with dioxins are withdrawn from the Dutch and French markets.

June

- Following successful mediation efforts by Herman Tjeenk Willink, chairman of the First Chamber, the Kok cabinet resumes office. The Democrats' 66 backs off from its decision to resign when its coalition partners agree to support and secure the passage of a law permitting non-binding (advisory) referenda.

- Minister of Agriculture, Haijo Apoteker, resigns from the cabinet following allegations that he had failed to alert parliament and consumers to the risk of dioxins in pork.

- Elections to the European Parliament result in gains for both Green Left and the anti-EU Socialist Party (SP). Turnout is 29.9%.

- Liberal Party Leader Frits Bolkestein is designated to be the Dutch member of the new European Commission, headed by Romani Prodi. Bolkestein is responsible for the trade portfolio in the Prodi commission.

- The European Space Agency opens a full-scale model of a space station in Noordwijk. The station was designed to serve as a communications and training unit for future expeditions.

July

- Author Harry Mulisch receives the Libris Literature prize (value 100,000 guilders) for his novel, "The Procedure."

August

- The Dutch government moves to legalize euthanasia as well as make it available to children as young as twelve. Formalizing longstanding practices, euthanasia will be available to patients who voluntarily request it, who are in irrevocable pain, or for whom all other options have been exhausted.

September

- Minister of Agriculture Brinkhorst announces plans to drastically reduce the number of Dutch farms and livestock in order to comply with EU guidelines on the use of nitrates by 2003. Government plans include devices to prevent the overuse of fertilizer, funds to compensate farmers, and the restoration of land for other uses.

- The cabinet announces Taxation Plan 2001, a major overhaul reducing taxation on incomes and labor while raising value-added taxes and instituting separate categories of taxation for incomes, savings and investment, and sales and transactions. The intent is to stimulate environmentally friendly investment and position the Netherlands for increased participation in a global economy.

October

- An investigation of investment strategies in the province of South Holland concludes that elected and appointed officials had used provincial revenues to engage in extremely questionable banking practices in 1995. The inability to account for four billion guilders and the ensuring report results in the resignations of the appointed Queen's Commissioner (provincial administrator), and some members of the provincial cabinet and civil service.

- European Commission officials visit major banks in the Netherlands and Belgium to investigate alleged collusion in setting currency exchange fees.

- Two Dutch physicists, Gerardt Hooft and Martinus Veltman, share the 1999 Nobel prize for their work establishing mathematical theories for elementary particles of matter.

- Two of the three small opposition Calvinist parties, the Reformed Political Federation (RPF) and the Reformed Political Union (GPV), announce that they will work together in parliament with a view toward eventual merger.

- Karel Glastra van Loon received both the General Bank Literature Prize (100,000 guilders) and an award for young authors for his first novel, *De passievrucht* (The Passion Fruit).

December

- A 17-year-old Dutch school boy goes on a shooting rampage at his school, wounding four people, three seriously.

ANALYSIS OF EVENTS: 1999

BUSINESS AND THE ECONOMY

The Dutch economy continued to prosper in 1999. After years of budget cutting to reduce inflation and curtail annual deficits, the Dutch met EU targets for thein 1998, and along with ten other EU members adopted theon January 1, 1999. However, although larger firms now maintain accounts in euros, and some stores give prices in both guilders and euros, the locking in of exchange rates has had little visible effect on the Dutch economy.

More important influences on the Dutch economy flow from cooperation among trade union federations, businesses, and government, in place since the mid-1990s, as well as the success the Dutch have had in taking advantage of geographic location and educational skills to position themselves in emerging markets in services and distribution. Except for the 1970s, when polarization between trade unions and employers prevented it, the Netherlands has been known for cooperative labor relations in which unions work closely with employers and the government in order to maintain a competitive economy, employment, and an adequate standard of living. Particularly since 1993 trade unions federations and employers associations have worked together to keep wage increases below levels which might cause inflation while increasing flexibility and competitiveness. Their social partnership—dubbed the "polder model"—has brought a stream of visitors to the Netherlands in order to find out how it works. Unions typically forego a percentage of the wage increases they might otherwise demand in exchange for training programs, increased flexibility, and the creation of part-time jobs. Through the 1990s the Dutch have sustained steady rates of economic growth (2 to 3% per year), outperforming their trading partners and the EU average. Although unemployment and inactivity remain high among certain sectors of the population (immigrants with poor knowledge of Dutch) employers now complain about overheated labor markets and the difficulty of finding workers when they need them.

Despite ongoing complaints of too much regulation, large and small business have been thriving in this atmosphere. Dutch businesses are increasingly able to draw on a well-educated and increasingly flexible workforce. Particularly in banking and insurance, firms have merged in order to establish greater presence in international markets. Dutch firms are active both in the Netherlands and in foreign direct investment, particularly in the United States.

The Dutch economy does have its difficulties. An unusually large segment of the population has dropped out of the labor market because of either early retirement or apparent long-term disability. Changes in eligibility for long-term disability in the early 1990s have helped reduce the cost of such programs, but the restructuring of the delivery of other social welfare programs is still underway.

GOVERNMENT AND POLITICS

The current cabinet (Kok-II) is headed by Willem Kok, leader of the Social Democratic Party (PvdA) and former chairman of the Federation of Dutch Trade Unions (FNV). Kok is a widely respected leader who is more popular than his party. He became minister of Finance and vice-premier in 1989, when the PvdA joined the Christian Democrats in a center-left coalition. Kok became minister-president (premier) when a secular or "purple" coalition of the Social Democrats, Democrats '66, and Liberals (VVD) took office after the 1994 elections. Kok's first government was widely applauded for its success in fostering competition and reducing employment.

Following the 1998 elections Social Democrats, Democrats '66, and Liberals formed a second "purple" coalition. The second Kok cabinet has had difficulty achieving the same success as its predecessor. Despite careful selection the cabinet is more divided and less politically adept. Minor incidents have marred its record. In May 1999 the cabinet found itself temporarily relegated to caretaker status. Democrats '66 withdrew when cabinet proposals for a constitutional amendment permitting corrective referenda (able to repeal existing laws) failed in the First (or upper) Chamber by one vote, cast by former Liberal leader, Hans Wiegel. Difficulties within the cabinet were resolved when Democrats '66 agreed to return in exchange for prompt action on advisory referenda. Most observers expect the cabinet to survive a full four-year term. However, this is because of the absence of an alternative rather than out of a sense of common direction. Although dispirited, the government continues to steer a middle course—there is considerable continuity in the kinds of policies pursued by center-right and center-left cabinets through 1994 and by secular cabinets since then. The government is proceeding with plans to restructure both the tax system and the delivery of social welfare programs.

Although Liberals and Social Democrats differ on spending priorities, there is substantial agreement among the governing parties and the opposition Christian Democratic Appeal (CDA). The Socialist Party (SP) and the Green Left, however, offer different points of view. The Socialist Party is a small but growing force, willing to cater to white workers' fears and frustrations, particularly on the position of immigrants in Dutch society. Green Left is torn between an older style of oppositional politics and a desire to govern and ensure both a cleaner environment and a fairer distribution of wealth and power. On the right, the principal opposition comes from three small orthodox Calvinist parties, of which two have agreed to put aside their theological differences in order to cooperate in parliament. Center Democrats and other parties of the extreme right have had difficulty winning or sustaining support.

CULTURE AND SOCIETY

The Netherlands is a physically small but densely populated society fully plugged into the modern world. Land use is closely regulated, reflecting both the threat of water and population density. The Dutch have come up with a number of strategies to cope with crowding while continuing to live on a humane and tolerable scale. Rigorous land use policies hinder but do not prevent urban sprawl. In addition the Dutch have built a dense network of roads and a highly integrated system of public transportation. A liberal attitude toward vice has enabled authorities, past and present, to better monitor what is going on in areas such as prostitution and drugs.

Earlier immigrants from Indonesia or Dutch territories in the Caribbean are well integrated despite differences in racial background. More recent groups, particularly guest workers from the Mediterranean rim and refugees, are less well integrated and less able to function in Dutch society.

DIRECTORY

CENTRAL GOVERNMENT

Head of State

Queen

Beatrix Wilhelmina Armgard, Monarch, Cabinet of the Queen, korte Vijver Berg 3, NL-2513 AB The Hague, Netherlands
PHONE: +31 (70) 3308888
FAX: +31 (70) 3639307

Prime Minister

Wim Kok, Office of the Prime Minister

Ministers

Minister of Agriculture, Nature Management and Fisheries

Laurens-Jan Brinkhorst, Ministry of Agriculture, Nature Management and Fisheries, Bezuidenhoutseweg 73, Postal Box 20401, NL-2500 EK The Hague, Netherlands
PHONE: +31 (70) 3793911
FAX: +31 (70) 3815153

Minister of Defence

Frank de Grave, Ministry of Defence, Plein 4, Postal Box 20701, NL-2500 ES The Hague, Netherlands
PHONE: +31 (70) 3188188
FAX: +31 (70) 3187888

Minister for Development Cooperation

Eveline Herfkens, Ministry of Foreign Affairs, Bezuidenhoutseweg 67, Postal Box 20061, NL-2500 EB The Hague, Netherlands
PHONE: +31 (70) 3486486
FAX: +31 (70) 3484848

Minister for Economic Affairs

Annemarie Jorritsma née Lebbink, Ministry of Economic Affairs, Bezuidenhoutseweg 30, Postal Box 20101, NL-2500 EC The Hague, Netherlands
PHONE: +31 (70) 3798911
FAX: +31 (70) 3474081

Minister of Education, Culture and Science

Loek Hermans, Ministry of Education, Culture and Science, Europaweg 4, Postal Box 25000, NL-2700 LZ Zoetermeer, Netherlands
PHONE: +31 (79) 3232323
FAX: +31 (79) 3232330

Minister of Finance

Gerrit Zalm, Ministry of Finance, Korte Voorhout 7, Postal Box 20201, NL-2500 EE The Hague, Netherlands
PHONE: +31 (70) 3428000
FAX: +31 (70) 3427905

Minister for Foreign Affairs

Jozias van Aartsen, Ministry of Foreign Affairs, Bezuidenhoutseweg 67, Postal Box 20061, NL-2500 EB The Hague, Netherlands
PHONE: +31 (70) 3486486
FAX: +31 (70) 3484848

Minister for General Affairs

Wim Kok, Ministry of General Affairs, Binnenhof 20, Postal Box 20001, NL-2500 EA The Hague, Netherlands
PHONE: +31 (70) 3564100
FAX: +31 (70) 3564683

Minister of Health, Welfare and Sport

Els Borst-Eilers, Ministry of Health, Welfare and Sport, Parnassusplein 5, Postal Box 20350, NL-2500 EJ The Hague, Netherlands

PHONE: +31 (70) 3407911

FAX: +31 (70) 3407834

Minister of Housing, Spatial Planning and the Environment

Jan Pronk, Ministry of Housing, Spatial Planning and the Environment, Rijnstraat 8, Postal Box 20951, NL-2500 EZ The Hague, Netherlands

PHONE: +31 (70) 3393939

FAX: +31 (70) 3391352

Minister of the Interior and Kingdom Relations

Bram Peper, Ministry of the Interior and Kingdom Relations, Schedeldoekshaven 200, Postal Box 20011, NL-2500 EA The Hague, Netherlands

PHONE: +31 (70) 3026302

FAX: +31 (70) 3639153

Minister of Justice

Benk Korthals, Ministry of Justice, Schedeldoekshaven 100, Postal Box 20301, NL-2500 EH The Hague, Netherlands

PHONE: +31 (70) 3707911

FAX: +31 (70) 3707900

Minister for Major Cities and Integration

Roger van Boxtel, Ministry of the Interior and Kingdom Relations, Schedeldoekshaven 200, Postal Box 20011, NL-2500 EA The Hague, Netherlands

PHONE: +31 (70) 3026302

FAX: +31 (70) 3639153

Minister of Social Affairs and Employment

Klaas de Vries, Ministry of Social Affairs and Employment, Anna van Hannoverstraat 4, Postal Box 90801, NL-2509 LV The Hague, Netherlands

PHONE: +31 (70) 3334444

FAX: +31 (70) 3334040

Minister of Transport, Public Works and Water Management

Tineke Netelenbos, Ministry of Transport, Public Works and Water Management, Plesmanweg 1, Postal Box 20901, NL-2500 EX The Hague, Netherlands

PHONE: +31 (70) 3516171

FAX: +31 (70) 3517895

Plenipotentiary Minister of the Netherlands Antilles

E. Mendes de Gouveia, Cabinet of the Plenipotentiary Minister of the Netherlands Antilles, Badhuisweg 173–175, Postal Box 90706, NL-2509 LS The Hague, Netherlands

PHONE: +31 (70) 3066111

FAX: +31 (70) 3066110

Plenipotentiary Minister of Aruba

A. Croes, Cabinet of the Plenipotentiary Minister of Aruba, R.J. Schimmelpennincklaan 1, NL-2517 JN The Hague, Netherlands

PHONE: +31 (70) 3566200

FAX: +31 (70) 3451446

POLITICAL ORGANIZATIONS

Algemeen Ouderenverbond—Unie 55+-AOV-U55+ (General Elder People's League)

Tweede Kamer Unie55+ Fractie, Postbus 20018, NL-2500 EA, Gravenhage, Netherlands

PHONE: +31 (70) 3183825

FAX: +31 (70) 3182828

E-MAIL: unie55@pi.net

Centrumdemocraten (Centre Democrats)

Christen Democratisch Appel-CDA (Christian Democratic Appeal)

Tweede Kamer CDA-Fractie, Postbus 30805, NL-2500 GV, Gravenhage, Netherlands

PHONE: +31 (70) 3183020

FAX: +31 (70) 3182602

E-MAIL: cda@pi.net

Democraten 66 (Democrats 66)

Tweede Kamer D66-Fractie, Postbus 20018, NL-2500 EA, Gravenhage, Netherlands

PHONE: +31 (70) 3183066

FAX: +31 (70) 3183625

E-MAIL: lsd66@d66.nl

Groenen Links (Green Left)

Postbus 6192, NL-2001 HD Haarlem, Netherlands

PHONE: +31 (23) 5427370

FAX: +31 (23) 5144176

E-MAIL: info@degroenen.nl

TITLE: President
NAME: Ron van Wonderen

Natuurwetpartij Nederland (Dutch Natural Law Party)

Natuurwetpartij, Rivierenlaan 164, NL-8226 LH Lelystad, Netherlands
PHONE: +31 0320258181
FAX: +31 0320258858
E-MAIL: info@natuurwetpartij.nl

Partij van de Arbeid (Labour Party)

Tweede Kamer PvdA-Fractie, Postbus 20018, NL-2500 EA, Gravenhage, Netherlands
PHONE: +31 (70) 3183025
FAX: +31 (70) 3182797
E-MAIL: tkleden@pvda.nl

Reformatorische Politieke Federatie (Reformed Political Federation)

PHONE: +31 (70) 3182930
FAX: +31 (70) 3182933

Staatkundig Gereformeerde Partij-SGP (Reformed Political League)

Socialistische Partij (Socialist Party)

Vijverhofstraat 65, NL-3032 SC Rotterdam, Netherlands
PHONE: +31 (10) 2435555
FAX: +31 (10) 2435566
E-MAIL: sp@sp.nl

Volkspartij voor Vrijheid en Democratie (People's Party for Freedom and Democracy)

VVD Afdeling Nieuwegein, Kikvorsweide 3, NL-3437 VA Nieuwegein, Netherlands
PHONE: +31 (30) 6032931
E-MAIL: vvd@pen.nl

DIPLOMATIC REPRESENTATION

Embassies in Netherlands

Algeria
Van Stolklaan 173, NL-2585 JS The Hague, Netherlands
PHONE: +31 (70) 3522954

Argentina
Javastraat 20, NL-2585 AN The Hague, Netherlands
PHONE: +31 (70) 3654836

Australia
Carnegielaan 4, NL-2517 KH The Hague, Netherlands
PHONE: +31 (70) 3108200
TITLE: Ambassador
NAME: Ted Delofski

Austria
Van Alkemadelaan 342, NL-2597 AS The Hague, Netherlands
PHONE: +31 (70) 3245470

Belguim
Lange Vijverberg 12, NL-2513 AC The Hague, Netherlands
PHONE: +31 (70) 3123456

Bolivia
Nassaulaan 5/1, NL-2514 JS The Hague, Netherlands
PHONE: +31 (70) 3616707

Bosnia and Herzegovina
Van Bleiswijkstraat 118, NL-2582 LJ The Hague, Netherlands
PHONE: +31 (70) 3588505

Brazil
Mauritskade 19, NL-2514 HD The Hague, Netherlands
PHONE: +31 (70) 3469229

Bulgaria
Duinroosweg 9, NL-2597 KJ The Hague, Netherlands
PHONE: +31 (70) 3503051

Canada
Sophialaan 7, NL-2514 JP The Hague, Netherlands
PHONE: +31 (70) 3111600

Cape Verde
Koninginnegracht 44, 2514 AD The Hague, Netherlands
PHONE: +31 (70) 3469623

Cameroon
Amaliastraat 14, NL-2514 JC The Hague, Netherlands
PHONE: +31 (70) 3469715

Chile
Mauritskade 51, NL-2514 HG The Hague,
Netherlands
PHONE: +31 (70) 3642748

People's Republic of China
Adriaan Goekooplaan 7, 2517 JX The Hague,
Netherlands
PHONE: +31 (70) 3551515

Colombia
Groot Hertoginnelaan 14, NL-2517 EG The
Hague, Netherlands
PHONE: +31 (70) 3614545

Costa Rica
Laan Copes van Cattenburg 46, NL-2585 GB
The Hague, Netherlands
PHONE: +31 (70) 3544675

Côte d'Ivoire
Consulate of Ivory Cost, Rivierstaete, Amsteldijk
166, NL-1079 LH Amsterdam, Netherlands
PHONE: +31 (20) 6612444

Croatia
Amaliastraat 16, NL-2514 JC The Hague,
Netherlands
PHONE: +31 (70) 3633014

Cuba
Mauritskade 49, NL-2514 HG The Hague,
Netherlands
PHONE: +31 (70) 3606061

Cyprus
Jan van Nassaustraat 87, NL-2596 BR The
Hague, Netherlands
PHONE: +31 (70) 3284507

Czech Republic
Paleisstraat 4, NL-2514 JA The Hague,
Netherlands
PHONE: +31 (70) 3469712

Denmark
Koninginnegracht 30, NL-2514 AB The Hague,
Netherlands
PHONE: +31 (70) 3655830

Dominica
Consulate of Dominica, Labradordreef 18, NL-
3565 AN Utrecht, Netherlands
PHONE: +31 (30) 2615095

Dominican Republic
Consulate of the Dominican Republic, Van der
Veerelaan 45, NL-1181 PZ Amstelveen,
Netherlands
PHONE: +31 (20) 6471062

Ecuador
Surinamestraat 11, NL-2585 GG The Hague,
Netherlands
PHONE: +31 (70) 3463753

Egypt
Badhuisweg 92, NL-2587 CL The Hague,
Netherlands
PHONE: +31 (70) 3542000

El Salvador
Consulate of El Salvador, Het Witte Huis,
Wijnhaven 3–1, NL-3011 WG Rotterdam,
Netherlands
PHONE: +31 (10) 4133304

Estonia
Consulate of Estonia, Parkstraat 15, NL-2514 JD
The Hague, Netherlands
PHONE: +31 (70) 3456252

Ethiopia
Consulate of Ethiopia, Frederik Hendrikplein 1,
NL-2582 AT The Hague, Netherlands
PHONE: +31 (70) 3586944

Finland
Groot Hertoginnelaan 16, NL-2517 EG The
Hague, Netherlands
PHONE: +31 (70) 3469754

France
Smidsplein 1, NL-2514 BT The Hague,
Netherlands
PHONE: +31 (70) 3125800

Federal Republic of Germany
Groot Hertoginnelaan 18/20, NL-2517 EG The
Hague, Netherlands
PHONE: +31 (70) 3420600

Ghana
Laan Copes van Cattenburg 70, NL-2585 GD
The Hague, Netherlands
PHONE: +31 (70) 3062800

Greece
Amaliastraat 1, NL-2514 JC The Hague,
Netherlands
PHONE: +31 (70) 3638700

Honduras
Johan van Oldebarneveldtlaan 85, NL-2582 NK
The Hague, Netherlands
PHONE: +31 (70) 3523728

Hungary
Hogeweg 14, NL-2585 JD The Hague,
Netherlands
PHONE: +31 (70) 3500404

India
Buitenrustweg 2, NL-2517 KD The Hague,
Netherlands
PHONE: +31 (70) 3469771

Indonesia
Tobias Asserlaan 8, NL-2517 KC The Hague,
Netherlands
PHONE: +31 (70) 3108100

Iran
Duinweg 24, NL-2585 JX The Hague,
Netherlands
PHONE: +31 (70) 3548483

Iraq
Johan de Witlaan 16, NL-2517 JR The Hague,
Netherlands
PHONE: +31 (70) 3469683

Ireland
Dr. Kuyperstraat 9, 2514 BA The Hague,
Netherlands
PHONE: +31 (70) 3630993

Israel
Buitenhof 47, NL-2513 AH The Hague,
Netherlands
PHONE: +31 (70) 3760500
FAX: +31 (70) 3760555
E-MAIL: ambassade@israel.nl

Italy
Alexanderstraat 12, NL-2514 JL The Hague,
Netherlands
PHONE: +31 (70) 3469249

Japan
Tobias Asserlaan 2, NL-2517 KC The Hague,
Netherlands
PHONE: +31 (70) 3469544

Kenya
Nieuwe Parklaan 21, NL-2597 LA The Hague,
Netherlands
PHONE: +31 (70) 3504215

South Korea
Verlengde Tolweg 8, NL-2517 JV The Hague,
Netherlands
PHONE: +31 (70) 3586076

Kuwait
Carnegielaan 9, NL-2517 KH The Hague,
Netherlands
PHONE: +31 (70) 3603813

Latvia
Balistraat 88, NL-2585 XX The Hague,
Netherlands
PHONE: +31 (70) 3063934

Lebanon
Frederikstraat 2, NL-2514 LK The Hague,
Netherlands
PHONE: +31 (70) 3658906

Lithuania
Laan van Nieuw Oost Indie 27, NL-2593 BJ The
Hague, Netherlands
PHONE: +31 (70) 3855418

Luxembourg
Nassaulaan 8, NL-2514 JS The Hague,
Netherlands
PHONE: +31 (70) 3607516

Malawi
Consulate of Malawi, Lange Kerkdam 91, NL-
2242 BT Wassenaar, Netherlands
PHONE: +31 (70) 5114302

Malaysia
Rustenburgweg 2, NL-2517 KE The Hague,
Netherlands
PHONE: +31 (70) 3506506

Malta
Consulate of Malta, Baronielaan 59, NL-4818
PC Breda, Netherlands
PHONE: +31 (76) 5209043

Mexico
Nassauplein 17, NL-2585 EB The Hague,
Netherlands
PHONE: +31 (70) 3454058

Morocco
Oranjestraat 9, NL-2514 JB The Hague,
Netherlands
PHONE: +31 (70) 3469617

Myanmar
Consulate of Myanmar, Baronielaan 59, NL-
4818 PC Breda, Netherlands

PHONE: +31 (76) 5209054

New Zealand
Carnegielaan 10/ET4, NL-2517 KH The Hague,
Netherlands
PHONE: +31 (70) 3469324

Nicaragua
Zoutmanstraat 53/E, NL-2518 GM The Hague,
Netherlands
PHONE: +31 (70) 3630967

Nigeria
Wagenaarweg 5, NL-2597 LL The Hague,
Netherlands
PHONE: +31 (70) 3501703

Norway
Prinsessegracht 6A, NL-2514 AN The Hague,
Netherlands
PHONE: +31 (70) 3117611

Oman
Koninginnegracht 27, NL-2514 AB The Hague,
Netherlands
PHONE: +31 (70) 3615800

Pakistan
Amaliastraat 8, NL-2514 JC The Hague,
Netherlands
PHONE: +31 (70) 3648948

Paraguay
Consulate of Paraguay, Goudsesingel 8, 3e/3,
NL-3011 KA Rotterdam, Netherlands
PHONE: +31 (10) 4045541

Peru
Nassauplein 4, NL-2585 EA The Hague,
Netherlands
PHONE: +31 (70) 3653500

Philippines
Laan Copes van Cattenburch 125, NL-2585 EZ
The Hague, Netherlands
PHONE: +31 (70) 3648566

Poland
Alexanderstraat 25, NL-2514 JM The Hague,
Netherlands
PHONE: +31 (70) 3602806
FAX: +31 (70) 3602810
E-MAIL: ambhaga@polamb.nl
TITLE: Ambassador Extraordinary and
Plenipotentiary
NAME: Maria Wodzynska-Walicka

Portugal
Bazarstraat 21, NL-2518 AG The Hague,
Netherlands
PHONE: +31 (70) 3630217

Romania
Catsheuvel 55, NL-2517 KA The Hague,
Netherlands
PHONE: +31 (70) 3543796

Russia
Andries Bickerweg 2, NL-2517 JP The Hague,
Netherlands
PHONE: +31 (70) 3451300

Saudi Arabia
Alexanderstraat 19, NL-2514 JM The Hague,
Netherlands
PHONE: +31 (70) 3614391

Serbia
Groot Hertoginnelaan 30, NL-2517 EG The
Hague, Netherlands
PHONE: +31 (70) 3632397

Slovakia
Parkweg 1, NL-2585 JG The Hague, Netherlands
PHONE: +31 (70) 4167777

South Africa
Wassenaarseweg 40, NL-2596 CJ The Hague,
Netherlands
PHONE: +31 (70) 3924501

Spain
Lange Voorhout 50, NL-2514 EG The Hague,
Netherlands
PHONE: +31 (70) 3643814

Sri Lanka
Jakob de Graefflaan 2, NL-2517 JM The Hague,
Netherlands
PHONE: +31 (70) 3655910

Sudan
Laan Copes van Cattenburch 81, NL-2585 EW
The Hague, Netherlands
PHONE: +31 (70) 3605300

Suriname
Alexander Gogelweg 2, NL-2517 JH The Hague,
Netherlands
PHONE: +31 (70) 3650844

Sweden
Burgemeester van Karnebeeklaan 6, NL-2585
BB The Hague, Netherlands
PHONE: +31 (70) 4120200

Switzerland
Lange Voorhout 42, NL-2514 EE The Hague, Netherlands
PHONE: +31 (70) 3642831

Syria
Consulate of Syria, Laan van Meerdervoort 53/D, NL-2517 AE The Hague, Netherlands
PHONE: +31 (70) 3469795

Tanzania
Consulate of Tanzania, Parallelweg Z 215, NL-2914 LE Nieuwerkerk aan den Ijssel, Netherlands
PHONE: +31 180320939

Thailand
Laan Copes van Cattenburch 123, NL-2585 EZ The Hague, Netherlands
PHONE: +31 (70) 3452088

Tunisia
Gentsestraat 98, NL-2587 HX The Hague, Netherlands
PHONE: +31 (70) 3512251

Turkey
Jan Evertstraat 15, NL-2514 BS The Hague, Netherlands
PHONE: +31 (70) 3604912

United Kingdom
Lange Voorhout 10, NL-2514 ED The Hague, Netherlands
PHONE: +31 (70) 4270427

United States of America
Lange Voorhout 102, NL-2514 EJ The Hague, Netherlands
PHONE: +31 (70) 3109209
FAX: +31 (70) 3614688
TITLE: Ambassador
NAME: Cynthia P. Schneider

Uruguay
Mauritskade 33, NL-2514 HD The Hague, Netherlands
PHONE: +31 (70) 3609815

Vatican City
Carnegielaan 5, NL-2517 KH The Hague, Netherlands
PHONE: +31 (70) 3503363

Venezuela
2517 KH The Hague, Netherlands, NL-2514 JS The Hague, Netherlands
PHONE: +31 (70) 3651266

Yemen
Surinamestraat 9, NL-2585 GG The Hague, Netherlands
PHONE: +31 (70) 3653936

Zaire
Violenweg 2, NL-2597 KL The Hague, Netherlands
PHONE: +31 (70) 3547904

JUDICIAL SYSTEM
Court of Cassation
Hoge Raad
Kazerngstraat 52, 2514 CV The Hague, Netherlands
PHONE: +31 (70) 3611311
FAX: +31 (70) 3617484

Gerechtshof
J. v. Stolverglaan 2, 2595 CL The Hague, Netherlands
PHONE: +31 (70) 3813131

Juvenile Court
Special Arbitration Court

FURTHER READING
Articles
Ash, Toby. ''MEED Netherlands Special Report.'' *MEED (Middle East Economic Digest)*, 43, 21 (May 28, 1999): 21.

''Going Dutch. (Arguments Against a Bill in the Netherlands that Would Legalize Physician-Assisted Suicide).'' *The Wall Street Journal,* 6 October 1999, p. A22.

''The Netherlands: Legalizing Euthanasia.'' *The New York Times,* 11 August 1999, p. A6.

Books
Dun and Bradstreet Information Services. *D&B's Export Guide to the Netherlands.* Parsippany, N.J.: Dun and Bradstreet, 1994.

Goodin, Robert E., et al. *The Real Worlds of Welfare Capitalism.* New York: Cambridge University Press, 1999.

Huussen, Arend H., Jr. *Historical Dictionary of the Netherlands.* Lanham, Md.: Scarecrow Press, 1998.

Worldmark Yearbook 2000

Rochon, Thomas R. *The Netherlands: Negotiating Sovereignty in an Interdependent World.* Boulder, Colo.: Westview Press, 1999.

Van Zanden, J.L. *The Rise and Decline of Holland's Economy: Merchant Capitalism and the Labour Market.* New York: Manchester University Press, 1993.

Internet

''NL.'' *Netherlands Media.* Available Online @ www.nl-menu.nl/nlmenu.eng/media/home.html (November 15, 1999).

Royal Netherlands Embassy, Washington, D.C. Available Online @ www.netherlands-embassy.org/f_explorer.html (November 15, 1999).

NETHERLANDS: STATISTICAL DATA

For sources and notes see "Sources of Statistics" in the front of each volume.

GEOGRAPHY

Geography (1)

Area:

Total: 41,526 sq km.

Land: 33,889 sq km.

Water: 7,637 sq km.

Area—comparative: slightly less than twice the size of New Jersey.

Land boundaries:

Total: 1,027 km.

Border countries: Belgium 450 km, Germany 577 km.

Coastline: 451 km.

Climate: temperate; marine; cool summers and mild winters.

Terrain: mostly coastal lowland and reclaimed land (polders); some hills in southeast.

Natural resources: natural gas, petroleum, fertile soil.

Land use:

Arable land: 27%

Permanent crops: 1%

Permanent pastures: 31%

Forests and woodland: 10%

Other: 31% (1993 est.).

HUMAN FACTORS

Demographics (2A)

	1990	1995	1998	2000	2010	2020	2030	2040	2050
Population	14,951.5	15,459.0	15,731.1	15,878.3	16,241.7	16,084.9	15,490.7	14,385.3	12,974.2
Net migration rate (per 1,000 population)	NA	NA	NA	NA	NA	NA	NA	NA	NA
Births	NA	NA	NA	NA	NA	NA	NA	NA	NA
Deaths	75.2	NA	NA	NA	NA	NA	NA	NA	NA
Life expectancy - males	73.9	74.7	75.1	75.4	76.7	77.7	78.5	79.2	79.8
Life expectancy - females	80.2	80.6	81.0	81.3	82.6	83.6	84.5	85.2	85.8
Birth rate (per 1,000)	13.2	12.3	11.6	11.1	8.4	8.1	7.4	6.3	6.2
Death rate (per 1,000)	8.6	8.8	8.7	8.7	9.3	10.7	12.9	15.4	17.4
Women of reproductive age (15-49 yrs.)	3,966.6	4,026.1	3,970.3	3,937.1	3,794.1	3,390.0	3,017.1	2,682.7	2,272.4
of which are currently married	2,194.7	NA	NA	NA	NA	NA	NA	NA	NA
Fertility rate	1.6	1.5	1.5	1.5	1.4	1.3	1.3	1.3	1.3

Except as noted, values for vital statistics are in thousands; life expectancy is in years.

Health Personnel (3)

Total health expenditure as a percentage of GDP, 1990-1997[a]

Public sector 6.2

Private sector 2.4

Total[b] 8.5

Health expenditure per capita in U.S. dollars, 1990-1997[a]

Purchasing power parity 1,784

Total 1,978

Availability of health care facilities per 100,000 people

Hospital beds 1990-1997[a] 1130

Doctors 1993[c] . . . . .NA

Nurses 1993[c] . . . . .NA

Health Indicators (4)

Life expectancy at birth

1980 76

1997 78

Daily per capita supply of calories (1996) 3,259

Total fertility rate births per woman (1997) 1.5

Maternal mortality ratio per 100,000 live births (1990-97) . . . . .12[c]

Safe water % of population with access (1995) 99

Sanitation % of population with access (1995) 100

Consumption of iodized salt % of households (1992-98)[a] . . . .

Smoking prevalence

Male % of adults (1985-95)[a] 36

Female % of adults (1985-95)[a] 29

Tuberculosis incidence per 100,000 people (1997) 10

Adult HIV prevalence % of population ages 15-49 (1997) 0.17

Infants and Malnutrition (5)

Under-5 mortality rate (1997) 6

% of infants with low birthweight (1990-97) . . . . . .NA

Births attended by skilled health staff % of total[a] . . .NA

% fully immunized (1995-97)

TB . . . . .NA

DPT 95

Polio 95

Measles 96

Prevalence of child malnutrition under age 5 (1992-97)[b] . . . . .NA

Ethnic Division (6)

Dutch 96%

Moroccans, Turks, and other 4% (1988)

Religions (7)

Roman Catholic 34%

Protestant 25%

Muslim 3%

Other 2%

Unaffiliated 36% (1991)

Languages (8)

Dutch.

EDUCATION

Public Education Expenditures (9)

Public expenditure on education (% of GNP)

1980 . . . . .7.6

1996 . . . . .5.2[1]

Expenditure per student

Primary % of GNP per capita

1980 . . . . .13.9

1996 . . . .

Secondary % of GNP per capita

1980 . . . . .23.3

1996 . . . . .21.0[1]

Tertiary % of GNP per capita

1980 . . . . .73.4

1996 . . . . .47.6[1]

Expenditure on teaching materials

Primary % of total for level (1996) 3.1

Secondary % of total for level (1996) . . . .

Primary pupil-teacher ratio per teacher (1996) . . . .

Duration of primary education years (1995) 6

GOVERNMENT & LAW

Political Parties (12)

States General, Second Chamber	% of seats
Labor Party (PvdA)	.24.3
Christian Democratic Appeal (CDA)	.22.3
People's Party for Freedom and Democracy (VVD)	20.4
Democrats '66	.16.5
Other	.16.5

Government Budget (13A)

Year: 1997

Total Expenditures: 337.62 Billions of Guilders

Expenditures as a percentage of the total by function:

General public services and public order 9.26

Defense 3.86

Education 9.97

Health 14.79

Social Security and Welfare 37.38

Housing and community amenities 1.50

Recreational, cultural, and religious affairs 34

Fuel and energy 16

Agriculture, forestry, fishing, and hunting 99

Mining, manufacturing, and construction 32

Transportation and communication 3.47

Other economic affairs and services 1.18

Crime (15)

Crime rate (for 1997)

Crimes reported 1,217,300

Total persons convicted 206,900

Crimes per 100,000 population 7,800

Persons responsible for offenses

Total number of suspects 270,200

Total number of female suspects 27,000

Total number of juvenile suspects 45,900

Military Affairs (14B)

	1990	1991	1992	1993	1994	1995
Military expenditures						
Current dollars (mil.)	8,129	8,255	8,485	8,077	8,034	8,012
1995 constant dollars (mil.)	9,343	9,122	9,127	8,468	8,235	8,012
Armed forces (000)	104	104	90	86	77	67
Gross national product (GNP)						
Current dollars (mil.)	310,000	329,800	342,400	353,700	372,500	390,700e
1995 constant dollars (mil.)	356,300	364,400	368,300	370,900	381,900	390,700e
Central government expenditures (CGE)						
1995 constant dollars (mil.)	184,100	191,500	196,300	192,800	189,200	182,000
People (mil.)	15.0	15.1	15.2	15.3	15.4	15.5
Military expenditure as % of GNP	2.6	2.5	2.5	2.3	2.2	2.1
Military expenditure as % of CGE	5.1	4.8	4.6	4.4	4.4	4.4
Military expenditure per capita (1995 $)	625	605	601	554	535	518
Armed forces per 1,000 people (soldiers)	7.0	6.9	5.9	5.6	5.0	4.3
GNP per capita (1995 $)	23,830	24,190	24,270	24,280	24,830	25,240
Arms imports[6]						
Current dollars (mil.)	575	460	360	130	230	220
1995 constant dollars (mil.)	661	508	387	136	236	220
Arms exports[6]						
Current dollars (mil.)	200	100	180	250	230	230
1995 constant dollars (mil.)	230	111	194	262	236	230
Total imports[7]						
Current dollars (mil.)	126,100	125,900	134,600	124,700	141,400	175,100
1995 constant dollars (mil.)	144,900	139,100	144,800	130,800	145,000	175,100
Total exports[7]						
Current dollars (mil.)	131,800	133,600	140,300	139,100	155,600	194,700
1995 constant dollars (mil.)	151,400	147,700	151,000	145,900	159,500	194,700
Arms as percent of total imports[8]	.5	.4	.3	.1	.2	.1
Arms as percent of total exports[8]	.2	.1	.1	.2	.1	.1

LABOR FORCE

Labor Force (16)

Total (million) 6.6

Services 75%

Manufacturing and construction 23%

Agriculture 2%

Data for 1997. Percent distribution for 1996.

Unemployment Rate (17)

6.9% (1997)

PRODUCTION SECTOR

Electric Energy (18)

Capacity ....20.09 million kW (1996 est.)

Production ....82 billion kWh (1996 est.)

Consumption per capita ....4,968 kWh (1996 est.)

Transportation (19)

Highways:

total: 127,000 km

paved: 114,427 km (including 2,360 km of expressways)

unpaved: 12,573 km (1996 est.)

Waterways: 6,340 km, of which 35% is usable by craft of 1,000 metric ton capacity or larger

Pipelines: crude oil 418 km; petroleum products 965 km; natural gas 10,230 km

Merchant marine:

total: 453 ships (1,000 GRT or over) totaling 3,141,630 GRT/3,597,975 DWT ships by type : bulk 2, cargo 269, chemical tanker 33, combination bulk 2, container 44, liquefied gas tanker 16, livestock carrier 1, multifunction large-load carrier 7, oil tanker 28, passenger 6, refrigerated cargo 28, roll-on/roll-off cargo 11, short-sea passenger 3, specialized tanker 3 note: many Dutch-owned ships are also operating under the registry of Netherlands Antilles (1997 est.)

Airports: 28 (1997 est.)

Airports—with paved runways:

total: 19

over 3,047 m: 2

2,438 to 3,047 m: 8

1,524 to 2,437 m: 5

914 to 1,523 m: 3

under 914 m: 1 (1997 est.)

Airports—with unpaved runways:

total: 9

914 to 1,523 m: 3

under 914 m: 6 (1997 est.)

Top Agricultural Products (20)

Grains, potatoes, sugar beets, fruits, vegetables; livestock.

MANUFACTURING SECTOR

GDP & Manufacturing Summary (21)

Detailed value added figures are listed by both International Standard Industry Code (ISIC) and product title.

	1980	1985	1990	1994
GDP ($-1990 mil.)[1]	234,973	246,975	283,525	303,765
Per capita ($-1990)[1]	16,613	17,042	18,962	19,729
Manufacturing share (%) (current prices)[1]	18.7	18.6	20.1	*19.5*
Manufacturing				
Value added ($-1990 mil.)[1]	45,186	47,167	53,804	55,497
Industrial production index	100	104	119	123
Value added ($ mil.)	29,080	20,714	45,102	*47,829*
Gross output ($ mil.)	109,618	80,068	153,729	154,166
Employment (000)	944	797	780	*711*
Profitability (% of gross output)				
Intermediate input (%)	73	74	71	*69*
Wages and salaries inc. supplements (%)	*20*	*21*	*19*	*21*
Gross operating surplus	*7*	*5*	*10*	*10*
Productivity ($)				
Gross output per worker	109,994	87,795	157,847	*215,003*
Value added per worker	29,285	22,914	46,622	*69,616*
Average wage (inc. supplements)	*23,135*	*21,037*	*37,835*	*45,935*
Value added ($ mil.)				
311/2 Food products	4,562	2,896	6,037	*7,080*
313 Beverages	654	737	1,500	*1,900*

314 Tobacco products	282	775	1,848	*2,421*
321 Textiles	734	463	1,002	*1,045*
322 Wearing apparel	372	*134*	234	*204*
323 Leather and fur products	68	*34*	70	*62*
324 Footwear	118	51	72	*64*
331 Wood and wood products	594	234	477	*515*
332 Furniture and fixtures	418	164	362	*442*
341 Paper and paper products	805	660	1,618	*1,655*
342 Printing and publishing	2,480	1,446	3,217	*3,938*
351 Industrial chemicals	2,263	2,436	5,592	*3,897*
352 Other chemical products	913	902	1,846	*2,639*
353 Petroleum refineries	533	521	1,095	*985*
354 Miscellaneous petroleum and coal products	101	55	131	*119*
355 Rubber products	156	139	284	*265*
356 Plastic products	472	466	1,305	*1,528*
361 Pottery, china and earthenware	134	77	304	*373*
362 Glass and glass products	245	145	358	*392*
369 Other non-metal mineral products	893	*465*	1,016	*1,125*
371 Iron and steel	882	*798*	*1,502*	*1,345*
372 Non-ferrous metals	371	*329*	*607*	*521*
381 Metal products	2,455	1,293	2,904	*3,227*
382 Non-electrical machinery	2,369	1,628	3,552	*3,934*
383 Electrical machinery	3,687	2,656	5,286	*5,354*
384 Transport equipment	1,927	1,015	2,464	*2,194*
385 Professional and scientific equipment	237	146	308	*444*
390 Other manufacturing industries	356	49	111	*161*

FINANCE, ECONOMICS, & TRADE

Economic Indicators (22)

National product: GDP—purchasing power parity—$343.9 billion (1997 est.)

National product real growth rate: 3.25% (1997)

National product per capita: $22,000 (1997 est.)

Inflation rate—consumer price index: 2% (1997)

Exchange Rates (24)

Exchange rates:

Netherlands guilders, gulden, or florins (f.) per US$1

January 1998	2.0462
1997	1.9513
1996	1.6859
1995	1.6057
1994	1.8200
1993	1.8573

Balance of Payments (23)

	1992	1993	1994	1995	1996
Exports of goods (f.o.b.)	137,332	127,876	141,810	175,315	175,849
Imports of goods (f.o.b.)	−125,024	−110,972	−123,124	−153,213	−154,072
Trade balance	12,309	16,904	18,686	22,102	21,777
Services - debits	−67,021	−65,776	−67,560	−74,683	−75,179
Services - credits	66,486	66,901	72,139	83,170	85,318
Private transfers (net)	−3,379	−3,594	−4,236	−5,202	−5,506
Government transfers (net)	−977	−907	−1,041	−1,137	−1,152
Overall balance	7,417	13,529	17,988	24,250	25,259

Top Import Origins (25)

$1.791 trillion (c.i.f., 1997) Data are for 1996.

Origins	%
European Union	64
Germany	22
Belgium-Luxembourg	11
United Kingdom	10
Central and Eastern Europe	4
United States	8

Top Export Destinations (26)

$203.1 billion (f.o.b., 1997) Data are for 1996.

Destinations	%
European Union	80
Germany	29
Belgium-Luxembourg	13
United Kingdom	10
Central and Eastern Europe	4
United States	3

Economic Aid (27)

Donor: ODA, $2.9 billion (1997).

Import Export Commodities (28)

Import Commodities	Export Commodities
Raw materials and semifinished products	Manufactures and machinery
Consumer goods	Chemicals; processed food and tobacco
Transportation equipment	Agricultural products
Crude oil	
Food products	

NETHERLANDS ANTILLES

INTRODUCTORY SURVEY

RECENT HISTORY

The European discovery of the Windward Islands was made by Columbus in 1493, and that of the Leeward Islands (including Aruba) by a young Spanish nobleman, Alonso de Ojeda, who sailed with Amerigo Vespucci in 1499; hence the claim went to Spain. The Dutch fleet captured the Windward Islands in 1632 and the Leeward Islands in 1634. Peter Stuyvesant was the first governor. In 1648, St. Martin was peacefully divided between the Netherlands and France; this division still exists. During the colonial period, Curaçao was the center of the Caribbean slave trade. For a period during the Napoleonic wars (1807–15), Great Britain had control over the islands. Slavery was abolished in 1863. Under a 1954 statute, the Netherlands Antilles is a component of the Kingdom of the Netherlands, with autonomy in internal affairs.

GOVERNMENT

A governor, appointed by and representing the crown, heads the government, with a Council of Ministers as the executive body. The ministers are responsible to the Staten, a 23 member legislature (15 from Curaçao, 3 each from Bonaire and St. Martin, and 1 each from Saba and St. Eustatius). Members are elected by general suffrage of Dutch nationals aged 18 or older. A 1951 regulation established autonomy in local affairs for each of the then-existing island communities-Aruba, Curaçao, Bonaire, and the Leeward Islands-with responsibil-

ities divided between an elected island council, an executive council, and a lieutenant-governor. By agreements made in 1983, St. Martin, Saba, and Sint Eustatius have separate representation in the Staten, elect their own separate councils, and have their own lieutenant-governors and executive councils.

Judiciary

Cases are tried in a court of first instance and on appeal in the joint High Court of justice, with justices appointed by the crown.

DEFENSE

Defense is the responsibility of the Netherlands; a naval contingent is permanently stationed in the islands, and military service is compulsory. The Netherlands Antilles is an associate member of the EU.

ECONOMIC AFFAIRS

The prosperity of Curaçao is inseparably linked with its oil refineries. These were built there, beginning in 1918, chiefly because of the favorable location of the islands, their good natural ports and cheap labor, and the political stability of the territory. Tankers bring crude oil from Venezuela. The economic significance of the refineries is great, not only because of their output, but also because they provide employment and stimulate other economic activities, such as shipbuilding, metal industries, shipping, air traffic, and commerce in general. The government controls the price of basic foodstuffs and participates in the setting of rates to be charged for transportation and by privately owned utilities.

Public Finance

The currency unit is the Netherlands Antilles guilder, or florin (NAf) of 100 cents; NAf1 = $0.55866 (or $1 = roughly Nafl.79).

Industry

The GDP for 1994 was estimated at U.S. $1.92 billion, or U.S. $10,400 per capita. The unemployment rate (including Aruba) was 13.4% in 1993, and 60–70% of the work force was organized in labor unions. The principal agricultural products are sorghum, orange peel, aloes, groundnuts, yams, divi-divi, and some assorted vegetables. The fish catch in 1994 was 1,100 tons. Curaçao's favorable position at the crossing of many sea-lanes has stimulated commerce since the earliest days of European settlement. Transit trade benefits from Curaçao's improved harbors; Willemstad is a free port, as are the islands of Saba and St. Eustatius. In 1995, the IMF estimated Antillean exports at U.S. $1.7 billion and imports at U.S. $1.9 billion. Refined petroleum products are exported to the Netherlands and other countries from a refinery on Curaçao. Petroleum shipments dominated the country's foreign trade-refined petroleum accounted for about 98% of exports in 1993, while crude oil made up 64% of imports that year. In 1995, the U.S. was the market for 16.5% of exports; Dominican Republic, 11.2%; and the Netherlands, 5.9%. The U.S. provided 28.4% of imports in 1995, followed by the Netherlands ~16%) and Brazil (6%).

Banking and Finance

The Bank of the Netherlands Antilles (Bank van de Nederlandse Antillen) issues currency, holds official reserves, regulates banking system, and acts as the central foreign exchange bank. There are 14 authorized commercial banks and several savings and loan institutions that also handle financial matters. Netherlands Antilles Development Bank was created in 1981 to stimulate foreign investment in service industries. Tax treaties with the United States have encouraged U.S. individuals and businesses to shelter their funds in the islands.

Economic Development

Development aid from the Netherlands totals about $60 million annually.

SOCIAL WELFARE
Healthcare

There are six hospitals on Curaçao and four on the other islands.

EDUCATION

There are 74 nursery schools, 86 primary schools, secondary schools, 1 teacher-training college, and the University Institute of the Netherlands Antilles, on Curaçao (all excluding Aruba) all schools are government-supported. The language of instruction is Dutch in the Leeward Islands, except in the International School, where classes are taught in English; English is also used in the Windward Islands. The literacy rate is more than 95%, although education is not compulsory.

1999 KEY EVENTS TIMELINE

January

- *Science News* reports that the coral reef off Bonaire is suffering from disease and algae growth due to warm water and pollution.

- The Curacao Department of Tourism publishes a new twenty-page brochure to promote diving, snorkeling, and tourism on the island, with the theme ''Where the Fun Shines Night and Day.''

March

- A new $8.5 million terminal is opened by the Curacao Ports Authority to accommodate large cruise ships.

- A plan for a new sewage treatment plan is reportedly bogged down in government bureaucracy. An early plan, aimed at eliminating sewage problems from a waterfront area by 2002, was presented in October 1998, but the necessary approvals by government agencies have not yet been secured.

May

- From May 2–5, the Annual Caribbean Conference on Recycling and Waste Management takes place in Curacao. Known as ''ReCaribe '99,'' the conference combines sessions with an exhibition of the latest waste management technology from the Caribbean, South America, United States, and Europe.

September

- Brigade General Willem Prins is named commander of the Dutch naval forces in the Caribbean.

- The government of Bonaire approves a Nature Preservation Plan, and will consider designating a national park.

November

- Hurricane Lenny, with winds up to 145 miles per hour, causes damaging high tides and flooding.

ANALYSIS OF EVENTS: 1999

BUSINESS AND THE ECONOMY

Netherlands Antilles is comprised of the islands of Bonaire and Curacao, both of which rely heavily on tourism. The Port Authority of Curacao opened a new terminal, hoping to attract large cruise ships. Currently the unemployment rate is around 17% in Curacao, and the government hopes the island's investment in the port will attract more large cruise ships and the lucrative business they represent. The government estimates that a one-day docking by the world's largest cruise ships represents over $200,000 in revenue.

During the April conference on waste management and recycling held in Curacao, the Solid Waste Association of the Caribbean (SWAC) was established to promote the exchange of technology, and seek solutions to common problems.

GOVERNMENT AND POLITICS

Brigade General Willem Prins, the new commander for the Royal Dutch Marines for the Caribbean and for the Coast Guard of the Netherlands Antilles and Aruba, took command in September. Prins's predecessor, Commodore de Jager, had pledged to eradicate illegal drugs and drug trafficking.

DIRECTORY

CENTRAL GOVERNMENT

Head of State

Monarch
Beatrix Wilhelmina Armgard, Queen of the Netherlands

Governor
Jaime M. Saleh, Office of the Governor

Prime Minister
Miguel A. Pourier, Office of the Prime Minister

Ministers

Minister of Development Corporation, Health and Humanitarian Affairs
Laurenso Abraham, Ministry of Development Corporation, Health and Humanitarian

Minister of Economic Affairs, Labor and Social Affairs
Errol Goelo, Ministry of Economic Affairs, Labor and Social Affairs

Minister of Education, Culture, Youth and Sport Affairs
Philip Nieuw, Ministry of Education, Culture, Youth and Sort Affairs

Minister of Finance
Frank Mingo, Ministry of Finance

Minister of Justice
Rutsel Martha, Ministry of Justice

Minister of Traffic and Communication
Maurice Adriaans, Ministry of Traffic and Communication

Minister of Transportation
Leo Chance, Ministry of Transportation

POLITICAL ORGANIZATIONS

Antillean Restructuring Party (PAR)

Fokkerweg 26 Unit 3, Curaçao, Netherlands Antilles
PHONE: +599 (9) 4652566; 4652610
FAX: +599 (9) 4652622
E-MAIL: omi7@ibm.net
NAME: Miguel Pourier

Democratic Party of Bonair (PDB)

NAME: Broertje Janja

Democratic Party of Curacao (DP)

NAME: Augustin Diaz

Democratic Party of Sint Eustatius (DPSt.E)

NAME: Julian Woodley

Democratic Party of Sint Maarten (DPSt.M)

NAME: Sarah Westcott-Williams

Partido Nashonal di Pueblo-PNP (National People's Party)

TITLE: President
NAME: Maria Liberia-Peters

New Antilles Movement (MAN)

E-MAIL: dmartina@man.an
NAME: Don Dominico F. Martina

Nos Patria (NP)

NAME: Chin Behilia

Patriotic Movement of Sint Maarten (SPA)

NAME: Vance James

Patriotic Union of Bonaire (UPB)
Saba Democratic Labor Movement (SDLM)

NAME: Steve Hassell

Saba Unity Party (SUP)

NAME: Carmen Simmonds

Serious Alternative People's Party

Socialist Independent (SI)

NAME: George Hueck; Nelson Monte

St. Eustatius Alliance (SEA)

NAME: Ingrid Whitfield

Windward Islands People's Movement (WIPM-S)

NAME: Ray Hassell

Workers' Liberation Front (FOL)

NAME: Wilson (Papa) Godett

DIPLOMATIC REPRESENTATION

Embassies in Netherlands Antilles

Belgium

Hoek Caracasbaaiweg/Schottegatweg, PO Box 3037
PHONE: +599 (9) 4617003; 4613094
FAX: +599 (9) 4616569
TITLE: Consul
NAME: Ivan Moreno Jr.

Bolivia

Wolkstraat 16, Kamer 11, Netherlands Antilles
PHONE: +599 (9) 4612792
TITLE: Consul
NAME: Efrain Tauber

Brazil

Concordiastraat 52, Netherlands Antilles
PHONE: +599 (9) 4615222

Canada

Plaza Jojo Correa 2–4, Netherlands Antilles
PHONE: +599 (9) 4613515
TITLE: Consul
NAME: William H.L. Fabro

Chile

Gaituweg 35, Netherlands Antilles
PHONE: +599 (9) 7374333
FAX: +599 (9) 7367747
TITLE: Consul
NAME: Ramfis Anthony Gonzalez

Colombia

Wilhelminaplein 25, Netherlands Antilles
PHONE: +599 (9) 4614663
FAX: +599 (9) 4612680
TITLE: Consul
NAME: Fabio Contreras Forero

Costa Rica

K.R. 12–3–90 nr.91.002247, Reigerweg 15, Netherlands Antilles
PHONE: +599 (9) 7378428
TITLE: Consul-Generaal
NAME: Joseph J. Frankel

Denmark

Bonam Kaya D #135, Netherlands Antilles
PHONE: +599 (9) 7366686
FAX: +599 (9) 7366686
TITLE: Consul
NAME: Ole V. Hansen

Dominica

K.B. 27–7–83 nr.84, Louise de Colignylaan 22, Netherlands Antilles
PHONE: +599 (9) 7373478
TITLE: Consul
NAME: Dennis Oscar Riviere

Dominican Republic

K.B. nr., Van Goghstraat 31, Netherlands Antilles
PHONE: +599 (9) 7378063
TITLE: Consul-Generaal
NAME: Amin Rodriguez

El Salvador

Trompetbloemweg 30, Netherlands Antilles
PHONE: +599 (9) 7375411

Finland

K.B. 17–4–86 nr. 47, Cas Coraweg 74, Netherlands Antilles
PHONE: +599 (9) 4612104
TITLE: Consul
NAME: Helga Mensing

France

Ontarioweg 8, Netherlands Antilles
PHONE: +599 (9) 4614300
FAX: +599 (9) 4614819
TITLE: Consul
NAME: Dr. Jan Hendrik R. Beaujon

Grenada

Juan Domingoweg 63, Netherlands Antilles
PHONE: +599 (9) 8681446
TITLE: Consul
NAME: Dean G. Whiteman

Guatemala

K.B. nr. Angloweg 7, Netherlands Antilles
PHONE: +599 (9) 7375011
TITLE: Consul
NAME: Beulah N. Henriquez

Guyana
Hecubaweg 4, Netherlands Antilles
PHONE: +599 (9) 7379789
TITLE: Consul
NAME: Arnold Maria Ignatius Sankies

Great Britain
Jan Sofat 215, Netherlands Antilles
PHONE: +599 (9) 8695968
FAX: +599 (9) 8695964
TITLE: Consul
NAME: Edward Wilson

Haiti
Perseusweg 1, Netherlands Antilles
PHONE: +599 (9) 4612436
FAX: +599 (9) 4658180
TITLE: Consul-Generaal
NAME: Chantal Pilie Dominique

Honduras
Schottegatweg 215 E (O), Netherlands Antilles
PHONE: +599 (9) 4615951

India
Heerenstraat 4–B, Netherlands Antilles
PHONE: +599 (9) 4612262
FAX: +599 (9) 4614345
TITLE: Consul
NAME: D. Boolchand Nandwani

Israel
Trompetbloemweg 25, Netherlands Antilles
PHONE: +599 (9) 7373533
TITLE: Consul
NAME: Dr. Paul Ackerman

Italy
Nabij van Engelen 2a, Netherlands Antilles
PHONE: +599 (9) 7371561
FAX: +599 (9) 7371582
TITLE: Consul
NAME: K.M.D. Pruneti

Jamaica
K.R. 1–1–93 nr.93.008840, Habaaiweg 68,
Netherlands Antilles
PHONE: +599 (9) 4626561
TITLE: Consul
NAME: Rafaelito C. Hato

Japan
K.B.29–4–63 nr. 75, Schout bij Nacht
Doormanweg 71, Netherlands Antilles
PHONE: +599 (9) 4613075
TITLE: Consul
NAME: Lionel Capriles

Lebanon
Winston Churchillweg 159, Netherlands Antilles
PHONE: +599 (9) 8684799
TITLE: Consul
NAME: Abdallah Abdul Salam Dennaoui

Liberia
K.B 23–8–74 nr. 75, Angloweg 7, Netherlands
Antilles
PHONE: +599 (9) 7375011
TITLE: Consul
NAME: Heraclio M. Henriquez

Mexico
K.B. 7292/52 Scharlooweg 7, Netherlands
Antilles
PHONE: +599 (9) 4613651
TITLE: Consul
NAME: Morris E. Curiel

Norway
Plaza Jojo Correa 2–4, Netherlands Antilles
PHONE: +599 (9) 4611117
TITLE: Consul
NAME: Lionel Capriles II

Panama
Maduro Plaza, Dokweg 19, Netherlands Antilles
PHONE: +599 (9) 7371566
TITLE: Consul
NAME: Mercedes Carolina Saenz Diaz

Peru
Rijkseenheid Blvd, Netherlands Antilles
PHONE: +599 (9) 4613319
TITLE: Consul

Portugal
Schottegatweg West 351, Netherlands Antilles
PHONE: +599 (9) 8688333
TITLE: Consul
NAME: Eduardo Vieira Ribeiro

Spain
Comanchestraat 4, Netherlands Antilles
PHONE: +599 (9) 7369532
FAX: +599 (9) 7369072
TITLE: Vice-Consul
NAME: Damian Leo

Suriname
ITC-gebouw, kamer TM 1.24, Netherlands
Antilles
PHONE: +599 (9) 4636650
FAX: +599 (9) 4636450
TITLE: Consul Generaal
NAME: Radjendrakumar N. Sonny Hira

Sweden

Fransebloemweg 33, Netherlands Antilles
PHONE: +599 (9) 7375409
TITLE: Consul-Generaal
NAME: Henry Maduro

Trinidad and Tobago

Kaya Trinitaria #78, Netherlands Antilles
PHONE: +599 (9) 7371866
FAX: +599 (9) 7371864
TITLE: Consul
NAME: Louis C. Bergman

United States

J.B. Gorsiraweg 1, Netherlands Antilles
PHONE: +599 (9) 4612076
TITLE: Consul-Generaal
NAME: James Williams

Uruguay

Mahokstraat 7, Netherlands Antilles
PHONE: +599 (9) 4615395
FAX: +599 (9) 4615395
TITLE: Consul
NAME: Robert G. Willems

Venezuela

Handelskade 12, 2de Verdieping, Netherlands Antilles
PHONE: +599 (9) 4613100; 4613291
FAX: +599 (9) 4613179
TITLE: Consul-Generaal
NAME: Jose de Jesus Cortez Torres

JUDICIAL SYSTEM
Joint High Court of Justice

FURTHER READING
Articles

''Bonaire Government Approves Nature Plan.'' *Skin Diver* 48, 10 (October 1999): 84.

Kalosh, Anne. ''Cruising into the 21st Century?''. *Business Week* (January 18, 1999): 30B.

Marcus, Frances Frank. ''Doing What the Islands Do Best: A Survey of Caribbean Islands and their Different Attractions.'' *The New York Times,* 24 October 1999, p. TR10.

Raloff, Janet. ''Sea Sickness.'' *Science News* 155 (January 30, 1999): 72.

Books

Brushaber, Susan. *The Aruba, Bonaire and Curagao Alive Guide.* Edison, N.J.: Hunter Publishing, 1997.

Luntta, Karl. *Caribbean Handbook: The Virgin, Leeward, and Windward Islands.* Chico, Calif.: Moon Publications, 1995.

Sedoc-Dahlberg, Betty, ed. *The Dutch Caribbean: Prospects for Democracy.* New York: Gordon and Breach, 1990.

Internet

Caribbean Week. Available Online @ www.cweek.com (November 15, 1999).

Curacao Tourist Board. Available Online @ www.curacao-tourism (November 15, 1999).

NETHERLANDS ANTILLES: STATISTICAL DATA

For sources and notes see "Sources of Statistics" in the front of each volume.

GEOGRAPHY

Geography (1)

Area:

Total: 960 sq km.

Land: 960 sq km.

Water: 0 sq km.

Note: includes Bonaire, Curacao, Saba, Sint Eustatius, and Sint Maarten (Dutch part of the island of Saint Martin).

Area—comparative: more than five times the size of Washington, DC.

Land boundaries:

Total: 10.2 km.

Border countries: Guadeloupe (Saint Martin) 10.2 km.

Coastline: 364 km.

Climate: tropical; ameliorated by northeast trade winds.

Terrain: generally hilly, volcanic interiors.

Natural resources: phosphates (Curacao only), salt (Bonaire only).

Land use:

Arable land: 10%

Permanent crops: 0%

Permanent pastures: 0%

Forests and woodland: 0%

Other: 90% (1993 est.).

HUMAN FACTORS

Demographics (2A)

	1990	1995	1998	2000	2010	2020	2030	2040	2050
Population	188.8	198.9	205.7	209.9	226.4	237.9	244.5	244.0	237.9
Net migration rate (per 1,000 population)	NA	NA	NA	NA	NA	NA	NA	NA	NA
Births	NA	NA	NA	NA	NA	NA	NA	NA	NA
Deaths	NA	NA	NA	NA	NA	NA	NA	NA	NA
Life expectancy - males	72.0	71.4	72.0	72.4	74.1	75.5	76.6	77.5	78.3
Life expectancy - females	76.2	75.6	76.2	76.6	78.4	80.0	81.3	82.4	83.3
Birth rate (per 1,000)	19.1	19.1	17.6	16.6	13.1	12.5	11.2	10.1	9.7
Death rate (per 1,000)	6.4	6.9	6.6	6.6	6.9	8.1	9.6	11.3	12.7
Women of reproductive age (15-49 yrs.)	55.2	56.5	57.3	57.8	59.1	57.4	55.4	52.9	48.5
of which are currently married	NA	NA	NA	NA	NA	NA	NA	NA	NA
Fertility rate	2.1	2.2	2.1	2.0	1.8	1.8	1.8	1.7	1.7

Except as noted, values for vital statistics are in thousands; life expectancy is in years.

Ethnic Division (6)

Mixed black 85%

Carib Amerindian, white, East Asian . . . . .NA

Religions (7)

Roman Catholic, Protestant, Jewish, Seventh-Day Adventist.

Languages (8)

Dutch (official), Papiamento, a Spanish-Portuguese-Dutch- English dialect predominates, English widely spoken, Spanish.

EDUCATION

Educational Attainment (10)

Age group (1992)[8] . . . . .25+

Total population 111,592

Highest level attained (%)

No schooling 1.7

First level

Not completed 34.4

Completed . . . . .NA

Entered second level

S-1 . . . . .54.2

S-2 . . . . .NA

Postsecondary 8.8

GOVERNMENT & LAW

Political Parties (12)

States (Staten)	No. of seats
Antillean Restructuring Party (PAR)	.4
National People's Party (PNP)	.3
Democratic Party of Bonaire (PDB)	.2
New Antilles Movement (MAN)	.2
Labor Party People's Crusade (PLKP)	.3
Democratic Party of Sint Eustatius (DP-St. E)	.2
Workers' Liberation Front (FOL)	.2
Others	.4

Government Budget (13A)

Year: 1995

Total Expenditures: 655.1 Millions of Guilders

Expenditures as a percentage of the total by function:

General public services and public order . . . . .32.54[P]

Defense . . . .-[P]

Education . . . . .8.98[P]

Health . . . . .8.50[P]

Social Security and Welfare . . . . .12.94[P]

Housing and community amenities . . . . .2.64[P]

Recreational, cultural, and religious affairs . . . . . .85[P]

Fuel and energy . . . . .12[P]

Agriculture, forestry, fishing, and hunting . . . .-[P]

Mining, manufacturing, and construction . . . .-[P]

Transportation and communication . . . . .7.40[P]

Other economic affairs and services . . . . .3.34[P]

Military Affairs (14A)

Military age . . . . .20 years of age

Availability of manpower

Males age 15-49 (1998 est.) 52,845

Fit for military service

Males (1998 est.) 29,664

Reaching military age annually

Males (1998 est.) 1,456

Defense is the responsibility of the Kingdom of the Netherlands.

LABOR FORCE

Labor Force (16)

Total 89,000

Government 65%

Industry and commerce .28%

Data for 1983.

Unemployment Rate (17)

12.8% (1993)

PRODUCTION SECTOR

Electric Energy (18)

Capacity . . . . .200,000 kW (1995)

Production . . . . .840 million kWh (1995)

Consumption per capita . . . . .4,128 kWh (1995)

Transportation (19)

Highways:

total: 600 km

paved: 300 km

unpaved: 300 km (1992 est.)

Merchant marine:

total: 97 ships (1,000 GRT or over) totaling 894,479 GRT/1,230,865 DWT ships by type: bulk 4, cargo 32, chemical tanker 1, container 5, liquefied gas tanker 4, multifunction large-load carrier 19, oil tanker 6, passenger 1, refrigerated cargo 17, roll-on/roll-off cargo 8 note: a flag of convenience registry; includes ships of 2 countries: Belgium owns 9 ships, Germany 1 (1997 est.)

Airports: 5 (1997 est.)

Airports—with paved runways:

total: 5

over 3,047 m: 1

1,524 to 2,437 m: 2

914 to 1,523 m: 1

under 914 m: 1 (1997 est.)

Top Agricultural Products (20)

Aloes, sorghum, peanuts, vegetables, tropical fruit.

FINANCE, ECONOMICS, & TRADE

Economic Indicators (22)

National product: GDP—purchasing power parity—$2.4 billion (1997 est.)

National product real growth rate: -1.3% (1997 est.)

National product per capita: $11,500 (1997 est.)

Inflation rate—consumer price index: 3.6% (1997)

Exchange Rates (24)

Exchange rates: Netherlands Antillean guilders, gulden, or florins (NAf.) per US$1—1.790 (fixed rate since 1989)

Top Import Origins (25)

$1.4 billion (f.o.b., 1996 est.) Data are for 1993.

Origins	%
Venezuela	.26
United States	.18
Colombia	.6
Netherlands	.6
Japan	.5

Top Export Destinations (26)

$NA Data are for 1993.

Destinations	%
United States	.39
Brazil	.9
Colombia	.6

Economic Aid (27)

Recipient: ODA, $NA; the Netherlands Antilles received a $97 million Dutch aid package in 1996, making it the Netherlands' second largest aid recipient behind India. NA stands for not available.

Import Export Commodities (28)

Import Commodities	Export Commodities
Crude petroleum 64%	Petroleum products 98%
Food	
Manufactures	

NEW CALEDONIA

Territory of New Caledonia and
Dependencies

INTRODUCTORY SURVEY

RECENT HISTORY

New Caledonia was discovered in 1768 by Louis Antoine de Bougainville and was named by James Cook, who landed there in 1774. Local chiefs recognized France's title in 1844, and New Caledonia became a French possession in 1853. In 1946, it became a French overseas territory, and in 1958, its Assembly voted to maintain that status.

GOVERNMENT

Under 1976, 1984, and 1985 laws, New Caledonia is administered by an appointed high commissioner, an executive council, and a 46-seat Territorial Congress, consisting of the complete membership of the four regional councils. New Caledonia has two representatives in the French National Assembly and one in the Senate. The territory is divided into four administrative subdivisions, and there are 32 municipal communes.

ECONOMIC AFFAIRS
Industry

The economy is based on agriculture and mining. Coffee, copra, potatoes, cassava, corn, wheat, and fruits are the main crops, but agricultural production does not meet the domestic demand. New Caledonia is the fourth largest producer of ferronickel in the world, after Canada, Indonesia, and Russia. Nickel mining and smelting accounted for an estimated 25% of GDP and 80% of export earnings in 1995. Coffee, copra, and chromium make up most of the other exports. Trade is

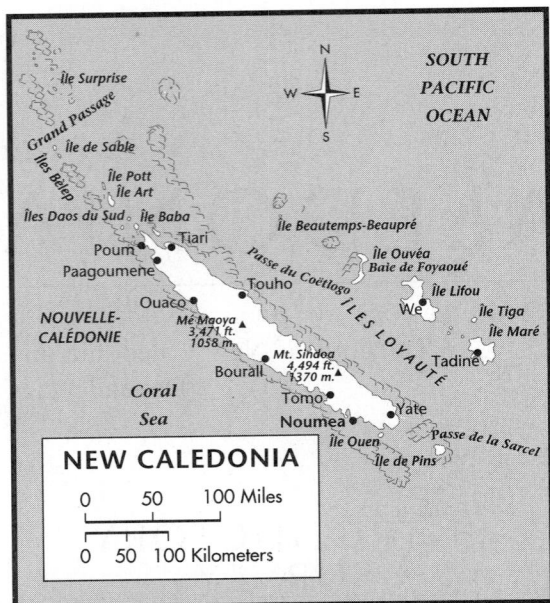

NEW CALEDONIA

0   50   100 Miles

0   50   100 Kilometers

mainly with France, Australia, Japan, and the United States. In 1992, exports totaled U.S. $477 million, imports totaled U.S. $926 million.

1999 KEY EVENTS TIMELINE

January

- The French Ministry of Finance establishes an exchange rate for the Pacific franc and the euro: one thousand Pacific francs will equal 8.38 euros.

- The New Caledonian delegation to the 7th Far East and South Pacific International Committee (FESPIC) games for handicapped persons in Bangkok, Thailand, includes twenty-two athletes; they rank eighth among the participating countries, winning twenty-five medals overall (fifteen gold, eight silver, two bronze).

May

- Elections are held for the first representatives to the New Caledonian Assembly as designated under the 1998 agreement.

June

- The first representatives to the New Caledonian Assembly elected in May are sworn in June 21 by French Minister of Overseas Territories Jean-Jacques. The Assembly replaces the High Com-

missioner, formerly appointed by the government of France.

August

- French two-star general Xavier André Stanislas de Zuchowicz arrives to assume command of the New Caledonia Armed Forces (FANC). De Zuchowicz is a former aide to President Jacques Chirac's military attachment.

September

- French Assistant Overseas Minister Jean-Jack Queyranne appoints Marie-Claude Tjibaou, the widow of the late pro-independence leader Jean-Marie Tjibaou, to a five-year term on the French Economic and Social Council (Conseil Economique et Social-CES) in Paris, France.

- A thirty-year old cagou bird, Houaïlou, is threatened with expulsion from the home where it lives. The cagou bird, New Caledonia's national symbol, emits a barking noise that is annoying to neighbors. Houaïlou was going to be moved to another location, but a public outcry and the gathering of 9,000 signatures by the New Caledonian Nature Protection Association may pressure the bird's owners to keep it where it is. Neighbors, however, may seek a court order to relocate the noisy bird.

- Seven couples waited in the capital of Nouméa on September 9, hoping to be married at nine o'clock, regarding the day (the ninth day of the ninth month, 1999) as lucky.

October

- New Caledonia hosts a squash tournament, the 9th Oceania Cup (known as the Pacific Cup until 1997) from October 4–9. Fifty players from the region compete in individual and team categories.

ANALYSIS OF EVENTS: 1999

BUSINESS AND THE ECONOMY

The economy of New Caledonia has suffered somewhat as the worldwide demand for steel has declined. New Caledonia, the world's fourth-largest producer of nickel, a key component of steel, has felt the decline sharply. To build a robust economy capable of supporting an independent New

Caledonia, new industries such as tourism and fishing must be developed.

GOVERNMENT AND POLITICS

In the first step toward fulfilling the referendum on independence scheduled for 2014 according to the Noame Accord (signed in November 1998), the first New Caledonian Assembly was sworn in. Anti-independence activists feel that this transition period will allow New Caledonians to realize the benefit of affiliation in France. Pro-independence activists, especially representatives of the Kanak community, regard the transition period as an opportunity to prepare politically and economically for complete autonomy without subsidies, currently around $880 million per year, or intervention from Paris.

Marie-Claude Tjibaou, chair of the Kanak Culture Development Agency and widow of the pro-independence leader Jean-Marie Tjibaou, was appointed to serve a five-year term on the French Economic and Social Council (Conseil Economique et Social-CES) in Paris, France. Her husband was murdered a decade ago by radicals within his own faction just one year after he had signed the historic Matignon Accords with anti-independence RPCR leader Jacques Lafleur and then-French Prime Minister Michel Rocard. In 1998, 72 percent of voters cast ballots in favor of the Noumea Accord, a peace agreement signed by French Prime Minister Lionel Jospin, Roch Wamytan, leader of the Kanak National Socialist Liberation Front (FLNKS), and Jacques Lafleur, head of the territory's anti-independence Rally for Caledonia in the Republic (RPCR).

General Xavier André Stanislas de Zuchowicz, a former aide to French President Jacques Chirac, was appointed to head the New Caledonia Armed Forces (FANC). De Zuchowicz is a two-star general and reported to be close to President Chirac. His appointment to service in New Caledonia fueled speculation that Chirac will spend the New Year in the French Pacific Territories.

CULTURE AND SOCIETY

During the 1980s French colonial settlers and New Caledonia's indigenous people, known as Kanaks, frequently engaged in violent conflicts. Nearly twenty years later, in 1998, representatives of France and the indigenous people signed an agreement, which will lead to a referendum on independence in 2014. Twenty-two athletes from New Caledonia are among the 2,600 representing thirty-six Asian and Pacific nations competing in the 7th Far East and South Pacific International Committee (FESPIC) games for handicapped persons in Bangkok, Thailand.

DIRECTORY

CENTRAL GOVERNMENT
Head of State

High Commissioner
Dominique Bur, Office of the High Commissioner, 1 avenue Foch, BP C05, 98844 Noumea, New Caledonia
PHONE: +687 266300
FAX: +687 272828

Offices

Chamber of Business
10 avenue James Cook, BP 4186, 98846 Noumea, New Caledonia
PHONE: +687 282337
FAX: +687 282729

Chamber of Agriculture
La Flottille, 3 rue A. Desmazures, BP 111, 98845 Noumea, New Caledonia
PHONE: +687 272056
FAX: +687 284587

Territorial Institute of Statistics
5 rue du General Gallieni, BP 823, 98 845 Noumea, New Caledonia
PHONE: +687 283156
FAX: +687 288148

French Office for Development
5 rue Barleux, BP J1, 98849 Noumea, New Caledonia
PHONE: +687 282088
FAX: +687 282413

Chamber of Commerce and Industry
15 rue de Verdun, BP M3, 98849 Noumea, New Caledonia
PHONE: +687 243100
FAX: +687 243131

Employment Agency
3 rue de la Somme, BP 497, 98845 Noumea, New Caledonia
PHONE: +687 281082
FAX: +687 272079

Economic and Social Committee of New
Caledonia
19 avenue Marechal Foch, BP 4766, 98847
Noumea, New Caledonia
PHONE: +687 278517
FAX: +687 278509

Pacific Society
Promenade Roger Laroque, Anse-Vata, BP D5,
98848 Noumea, New Caledonia
PHONE: +687 262000
FAX: +687 263818

Consultive Customs Consul
68 avenue J.Cook, Nouville, New Caledonia
PHONE: +687 242000
FAX: 687 249320

POLITICAL ORGANIZATIONS
Progressive Melanesian Union (UPM)
NAME: Edmond Nekiriai

Kanaka Socialist National Liberation Front (FLNKS)
NAME: Rock Wamytan

Kanak Socialist Liberation (LKS)
NAME: Nidoish Naisseline

New Caledonia National Party
NAME: Georges Chateney

Rally for Caledonia in the Republic (RPCR)
NAME: Jean-Louis Mir

Liberal Caledonian Movement
NAME: Jean Leques

JUDICIAL SYSTEM
Court of Appeal

FURTHER READING
Articles
''The Politics of Procrastination: Independence for New Caledonia may be Granted by France.'' *The Economist* 351, 8125 (June 26, 1999): 48.

Books
Aldrich, Robert. *France and the South Pacific Since 1940.* Honolulu: University of Hawaii Press, 1993.

New Caledonia: A Travel Survival Kit. 2nd ed. Berkeley, CA: Lonely Planet, 1990.

Internet
French Embassy in Suva. Available Online @ www.ambafrance.org.fj (November 15, 1999).

Pacific Island Report, University of Hawaii. Available Online @ pidp.ewc.hawaii.edu/PIReport/enter.htm (November 15, 1999).

NEW CALEDONIA: STATISTICAL DATA

For sources and notes see "Sources of Statistics" in the front of each volume.

GEOGRAPHY

Geography (1)

Area:

Total: 19,060 sq km.

Land: 18,575 sq km.

Water: 485 sq km.

Area—comparative: slightly smaller than New Jersey.

Land boundaries: 0 km.

Coastline: 2,254 km.

Climate: tropical; modified by southeast trade winds; hot, humid.

Terrain: coastal plains with interior mountains.

Natural resources: nickel, chrome, iron, cobalt, manganese, silver, gold, lead, copper.

Land use:

Arable land: 0%

Permanent crops: 0%

Permanent pastures: 12%

Forests and woodland: 39%

Other: 49% (1993 est.).

HUMAN FACTORS

Ethnic Division (6)

Melanesian 42.5%

European 37.1%

Wallisian 8.4%

Polynesian 3.8%

Indonesian 3.6%

Vietnamese 1.6%

Other 3%

Demographics (2A)

	1990	1995	1998	2000	2010	2020	2030	2040	2050
Population	168.3	184.6	194.2	200.5	229.6	255.5	278.0	295.4	307.6
Net migration rate (per 1,000 population)	NA	NA	NA	NA	NA	NA	NA	NA	NA
Births	NA	NA	NA	NA	NA	NA	NA	NA	NA
Deaths	NA	NA	NA	NA	NA	NA	NA	NA	NA
Life expectancy - males	68.8	70.7	71.7	72.4	75.2	77.1	78.4	79.3	79.9
Life expectancy - females	75.6	77.5	78.4	79.1	81.7	83.4	84.7	85.5	86.0
Birth rate (per 1,000)	23.3	22.0	21.1	20.3	17.0	15.5	14.0	12.9	12.4
Death rate (per 1,000)	5.2	4.9	4.8	4.8	5.1	5.8	6.8	7.9	9.4
Women of reproductive age (15-49 yrs.)	43.8	48.6	51.1	52.6	60.3	64.5	65.7	66.9	66.4
of which are currently married	NA	NA	NA	NA	NA	NA	NA	NA	NA
Fertility rate	2.8	2.6	2.5	2.4	2.2	2.1	2.0	2.0	2.0

Except as noted, values for vital statistics are in thousands; life expectancy is in years.

Religions (7)

Roman Catholic 60%

Protestant 30%

Other 10%

Languages (8)

French, 28 Melanesian-Polynesian dialects.

EDUCATION

Educational Attainment (10)

Age group (1989) . . . . .25+

Total population 69,922

Highest level attained (%)

No schooling[2] 6.5

First level

  Not completed 51.2

  Completed . . . . .NA

Entered second level

  S-1 . . . . .34.8

  S-2 . . . . .NA

Postsecondary 7.5

GOVERNMENT & LAW

Political Parties (12)

Territorial Congress	No. of seats
Rally for Caledonia in the Republic (RPCR)	22
Kanaka Socialist National Liberation Front (FLNKS)	12
A New Caledonia for All (UNCT)	9
Union Nationale pour l'Indepedance (UNI)	5
Developper Ensemble pour construire l'Avenir (DEPCA)	2
National Front (FN)	2
Rassemblement pour une Caledonie dans la France (RCF)	2
Other	2

Government Budget (13B)

Revenues . . . .$755.6 million

Expenditures . . . .$755.6 million

  Capital expenditures .NA

Data for 1995 est. NA stands for not available.

Military Affairs (14A)

Total expenditures . . . .$NA

Expenditures as % of GDP . . . . .NA%

Defense is the responsibility of France. NA stands for not available.

LABOR FORCE

Labor Force (16)

Total 70,044

Agriculture 32%

Industry 20%

Services 40%

Mining 8%

Data for 1988 Percent distribution for 1992.

Unemployment Rate (17)

15% (1994)

PRODUCTION SECTOR

Electric Energy (18)

Capacity .253,000 kW (1995)

Production . . . . .1.145 billion kWh (1995)

Consumption per capita . . . . .6,204 kWh (1995)

Transportation (19)

Highways:

total: 5,562 km

paved: 975 km

unpaved: 4,587 km (1993)

Merchant marine: none

Airports: 30 (1997 est.)

Airports—with paved runways:

total: 5

over 3,047 m: 1

914 to 1,523 m: 3

under 914 m: 1 (1997 est.)

Airports—with unpaved runways:

total: 25

914 to 1,523 m: 13

under 914 m: 12 (1997 est.)

Top Agricultural Products (20)

Vegetables; beef, other livestock products.

MANUFACTURING SECTOR

GDP & Manufacturing Summary (21)

	1980	1985	1990	1992	1993	1994
Gross Domestic Product						
Millions of 1990 dollars	1,079	1,070	1,600	1,812	1,813	1,869
Growth rate in percent	−0.40	4.51	−4.27	9.00	0.01	3.11
Per capita (in 1990 dollars)	7,542.8	6,900.2	9,523.8	10,476.1	10,357.6	10,499.8
Manufacturing Value Added						
Millions of 1990 dollars	98	78	112	123	121	123
Growth rate in percent	−4.64	−1.05	−4.27	6.02	−1.31	1.26
Manufacturing share in percent of current prices	5.8	4.7	NA	NA	NA	NA

FINANCE, ECONOMICS, & TRADE

Economic Indicators (22)

National product: GDP—purchasing power parity—$1.5 billion (1995 est.)

National product real growth rate: NA%

National product per capita: $8,000 (1995 est.)

Inflation rate—consumer price index: 1.7% (1996 est.)

Exchange Rates (24)

Exchange rates:

Comptoirs Francais du Pacifique francs (CFPF) per US$1

January 1998	110.60
1997	106.11
1996	93.00
1995	90.75
1994	100.93
1993	102.96

Linked at the rate of 18.18 to the French franc

Top Import Origins (25)

$930 million (c.i.f., 1996) Data are for 1996 est.

Origins	%
France	45
Australia	18
Singapore	7
New Zealand	6
Japan	4

Top Export Destinations (26)

$500 million (f.o.b., 1996) Data are for 1996 est.

Destinations	%
Japan	31
France	29
United States	12
Australia	7
Taiwan	6

Economic Aid (27)

Recipient: ODA, $NA. Note: important support from France. NA stands for not available.

Import Export Commodities (28)

Import Commodities	Export Commodities
Foods	Ferronickels
Transport equipment	Nickel ore
Machinery and electrical equipment	
Fuels	
Minerals	

NEW ZEALAND

INTRODUCTORY SURVEY

RECENT HISTORY

In 1907, New Zealand was made a dominion (a self-governing nation that recognizes the British monarchy) of the United Kingdom. In 1947, the New Zealand government formally claimed the complete independence available to self-governing members of the British Commonwealth. After World War II, New Zealand and U.S. foreign policies were increasingly intertwined. New Zealand was a founding member of the Southeast Asia Treaty Organization (SEATO) in 1954. New Zealand troops fought with United Nations (UN) forces in the Korea conflict and with U.S. forces in South Vietnam. The involvement in Vietnam touched off a national debate on foreign policy, however, and all New Zealand troops were withdrawn from the country by the end of 1971. New Zealand's military participation in SEATO was later terminated.

In 1984, a Labour government led by Prime Minister David Lange took office under a pledge to ban nuclear-armed vessels from New Zealand harbors. A United States request for a port visit by one of its warships was denied because of uncertainty as to whether the ship was nuclear-armed. The continuing ban put a strain on New Zealand's relations within the Australia-New Zealand-United States alliance (ANZUS), and in 1986 the United States suspended its military obligations to New Zealand under the ANZUS defense agreement. The United States also banned high-level contacts with the New Zealand government. The United States ended its ban on high-level contacts in March 1990.

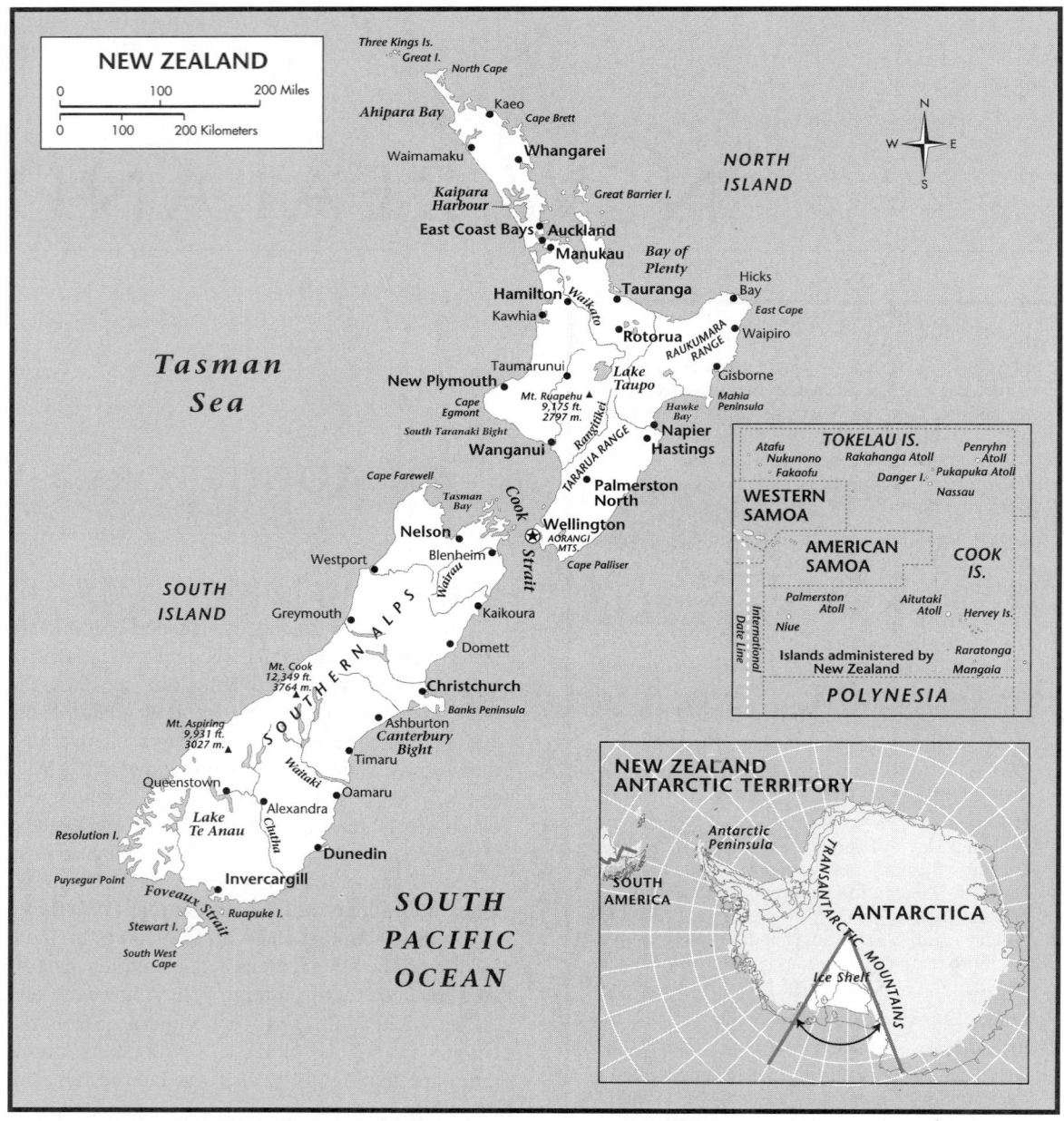

The native Maori people have claimed rights to all the country's coastline, 70% of the land, and half of the fishing rights. To answer these claims, a new Cabinet committee was formed in December 1989. The committee, including former Prime Minister Lange, worked with the 17-member Waitangi Tribunal, established in 1975 to consider complaints from Maoris. In 1996, the government settled a NZ$170 million agreement with the Waikato Tainui tribe on North Island for wrongfully taking the tribe's lands during the 1860s. Queen Elizabeth II signed the legislation, which contained an apology.

In February 1998, Auckland suffered from a power blackout that lasted for weeks, crippling commerce.

GOVERNMENT

New Zealand is an independent member of the Commonwealth of Nations. Like the United Kingdom, it is a constitutional monarchy. The head of state, the governor-general, is the representative of the crown. The governor-general is appointed for a five-year term.

Government is democratic and modeled on that of the United Kingdom. The single-chamber legislature, the House of Representatives, has 97 members. Each is elected by universal adult vote for a term of three years. Although there have been coalition governments, the two-party system usually operates. The party with a majority of members elected to the House of Representatives forms the government, the other party becoming the Opposition.

On his appointment, the prime minister, leader of the governing party, chooses 20 other ministers to form the cabinet. Each minister usually controls several government departments. Ministers are responsible to the House of Representatives for the operation of their departments.

In 1994, a coalition government lobbied to convert New Zealand into a republic, but the move was met with resistance from the National Party and public apathy.

The transition to a proportional voting system was introduced during the 1996 elections. Proportional representation means that each party is awarded seats according to its share of the overall vote, with a minimum set at 5%.

As of 1996, there were 93 county councils, 9 district councils, and 3 town districts.

Judiciary

Most civil and criminal cases are heard first in district courts. There is the right of appeal to the High Court, which is usually the court of first hearing for cases where a major crime or an important civil action is involved. Family courts were established in 1980 to hear cases involving domestic issues. The highest court, the Court of Appeal, rules on appeals only. There are also several special courts, such as the Arbitration Court, the Maori Land Court, and the Children and Young Persons Court. The judicial system is based on British common law. The judiciary is independent and impartial.

Political Parties

New Zealand's major parties are the Labour Party, formed in 1916, and the National Party, formed in 1935. In October 1990 the National Party, led by Jim Bolger, won a general election victory. Bolger's government made major cuts in New Zealand's welfare programs. The National

Party won reelection in the November 1993 general election, capturing 50 of 99 seats. In the 1996 election, Jim Bolger was elected as prime minister for a third term and a coalition government was formed by the National Party and the First Party. The National Party won 44 seats; Labour, 37; New Zealand First Party, 17; Alliance Party, 8; and United Party, 1.

DEFENSE

Service in the New Zealand regular armed forces is voluntary, but some white males (18–21) may be required to have military training for service in the territorial force (5,650).

In 1995, the army had a full-time regular force of 4,500 and 1,650 reserves; the navy had 2,150 regulars (300 women) and 1,050 reserves; and the air force had 3,220 regulars (600 women) and 1,050 reserves. The army has one active brigade (unit of troops), the navy 8 small surface combatants (combat-ready units) and 7 helicopters, and the air force 42 combat aircraft. Weapons are American and European. New Zealand has 35 service members working abroad in 6 different nations. The defense budget in 1996 was US$728 million.

ECONOMIC AFFAIRS

New Zealand's economy has traditionally been based on farming. The last decades, however, have seen the beginnings of heavy industry, and there has been a large expansion in light industries such as plastics, textiles, and footwear, mostly to supply the home market. In recent years there has been a trend toward the development of industries based on natural resources. The forest industry has greatly expanded. Pulp, log, and paper products are major exports.

The economy has been subjected to two major crises in 20 years: first, the loss of a large part of the British market for New Zealand's agricultural products when the United Kingdom joined the European Community in 1973; and second, limits placed on overspending by the government in the early 1980s, which enforced a 10-year program of controls. The program helped transform New Zealand from one of the most heavily protected and regulated economies to one of the most market-oriented and open in the world. By the mid-1990s, the domestic economy was growing at 5–6% per year and there were surpluses in the government's budget.

Public Finance

In 1994, in response to a decade of economic reforms that have opened the economy to foreign investment and triggered strong economic growth, the budget produced a surplus for the first time in 50 years. Government revenues totaled approximately U.S. $22.18 billion and expenditures U.S. $20.28 billion. External debt totaled U.S. $38.5 billion.

In 1995, public debt service dropped to U.S. $2.2 billion or 1.9% of GDP and 12% of expenditures. External debt accounted for 23% of total government debt. Interest on external debt equaled 3.5% of exports of goods and services plus investment income. The surpluses continued in 1996, but showed signs of weakness in 1997 as forecasts of slower economic growth and uncertainty over the intentions of the newly elected government prompted a drop in business confidence. Nevertheless, in June of 1997, the new government proposed a three-year program of increased spending on social programs and postponed a round of promised tax cuts.

Income

In 1997, New Zealand's gross national product (GNP) was US$63.4 billion, or about US$17,700 per person. For the period 1985–95, the average inflation rate was 3.9%, resulting in a real growth rate in GNP of 0.6% per person.

Industry

Industrial production has increased rapidly since the end of World War II. Plants include metal and petroleum processing, motor vehicle assembly, textiles and footwear, and a wide range of consumer appliances. The New Zealand Steel company manufactures billet slabs and ingots using domestically produced iron sands. Pacific Steel, which processes scrap metal, uses billets from New Zealand Steel. The Tiwai Point aluminum smelter, operated by an Australian-Japanese group, has an annual capacity of 244,000 tons.

The small but growing electronics industry produces consumer goods as well as commercial products such as digital gasoline pumps. Wool-based industries have traditionally been an important part of the economy, notably wool milling, the oldest sector of the textile industry. Other significant industrial areas include a diverse food-processing sector, tanneries, sheet glass, rubber, and plastics.

Banking and Finance

The Reserve Bank of New Zealand, established in 1933, exercises control over monetary circulation and credit. It is the bank of issue, handles all central government banking transactions, manages the public debt, and administers exchange control regulations. The Reserve Bank of New Zealand Amendment Act (1973) empowers the Bank to regulate credit from all sources and requires it to make loans (as the minister of finance may determine) in order to ensure continued full employment.

New Zealand's financial services sector is dominated by the commercial banks, leaving only a minor role for non-bank finance companies and savings institutions. In part this reflects the impact of deregulation since the mid-1980s. Before 1984, the financial sector was highly segmented with tight government controls on what different institutions could offer. (For example, only trading banks could offer checking accounts to clients.) The easing of regulations means that there are now only two formal categories of financial institution: registered banks and other financial institutions. However, both can offer a wide range of financial and banking services.

To be defined as a bank, a financial institution must register with the central Reserve Bank and meet a range of eligibility criteria, such as minimum capital adequacy, experience in the financial intermediation industry, and a commitment to stability of the financial system. The number of registered banks peaked at 24 in 1994, and in mid-1996 there were 16.

A number of bank mergers has increased the concentration of total banking assets in foreign ownership. Over 95% of total banking assets are foreign-owned, compared with 65% in 1990. The New Zealand banking industry is increasingly influenced by developments in Australia, since Australian banking groups control over two-thirds of banking assets in New Zealand; this share is unlikely to increase further, with the announcement in April 1996 of a conditional buy-out by Westpac Banking Corp. of Trust Bank, New Zealand's last domestically owned bank with a national branch network. The Post Office Savings Bank (established in 1865) has about 1,270 offices and agencies throughout New Zealand.

New Zealand is advantageously placed, since its trading day opens before the U.S. market closes and before the Asian and Australian markets open.

The main functions of the New Zealand Stock Exchange (NZSE) are to provide an orderly market for the trading and transfer of securities, to protect investors' interests, and to ensure that the market is fully informed. As of 1992, there were 38 corporate and partnership members of the NZSE.

The Stock Exchange Association of New Zealand, the forerunner to the NZSE, was founded in 1915.

The stock exchanges in Auckland, Wellington, Christchurch, Dunedin, and Invercargill are members of the New Zealand Stock Exchange (NZSE), with headquarters in Wellington. Official listing is granted to companies that comply with the Exchange's requirements. These do not impose qualifications as to share capital but do provide that the company must be of sufficient magnitude and its shareholding sufficiently well distributed to ensure a free market for its shares. Subject to the recommendation and approval of the stock exchange nearest to the registered offices, companies may secure unofficial listing for their shares. All transactions in shares quoted in the unofficial list are subject to special brokerage rates. In 1978, a five-member Securities Commission was established to oversee law and practice relating to securities.

Economic Development

Economic policy is established and directed by the government through taxation, Reserve Bank interest rates, price and monopoly controls, and import and export licensing. Import controls, introduced early in 1958, were further tightened in 1961 and 1973 to correct deficits in the balance of payments. Since then, the government has gradually liberalized import controls; in 1981, about 79% of private imports to New Zealand were exempt from licensing. An industrial restructuring program, begun in the mid-1970s, focuses on certain industries (e.g., textiles, footwear, automobiles, and electronics) whose domestic prices are much higher than those of foreign substitutes, with the aim of reducing the protection granted such products.

To help maintain economic stability, the government assists, and in some cases controls, various economic enterprises (agricultural distribution and marketing, commercial banking, and some insurance). In June 1982, in an effort to reduce inflation, the government announced a freeze on wages, prices, rents, and dividends. The freeze was lifted in March 1984, temporarily reimposed by a new Labour government, then terminated late in 1984.

Its termination, combined with a devaluation of the dollar, led to a resumption of high inflation. The government implemented severe monetary policies to reduce inflation in order to enhance a market- and export-led recovery from the October 1987 financial markets crash. The cost was a large increase in unemployment (from 7% to 10.4% of the labor force), but by 1991 inflation had been practically eliminated (2.2% for the year ending September 1991).

Since 1977, the New Zealand Planning Council has been charged with advising the government on economic, social, and cultural planning and in the coordination of planning. Working independently of the Planning Council, the Economic Monitoring Group, established in 1978, produces reports on economic trends.

In 1984/85, New Zealand contributed a total of NZ$61.4 million in technical and capital assistance and direct aid or loans to developing nations. An additional NZ$12.5 million was given in multilateral aid through the UN, the South Pacific Commission, ADB, and other organizations. The major recipients of development assistance are the nations of the South Pacific, who receive about 70% of New Zealand's bilateral aid and about 62% of its total overseas aid.

SOCIAL WELFARE

All persons in New Zealand are now protected economically for retirement and in the event of sickness, unemployment, and widowhood. Monetary benefits under the Social Security Act are paid for retirement, unemployment, sickness, and emergencies; and to widows, orphans, families, invalids, and minors. Medical benefits include medical, hospital, and pharmaceutical payments. A 1982 plan provides compensation for all workers injured in an accident, even if the injury did not occur at work.

New Zealand was the first country to grant full voting rights to women, and it celebrated the 100th anniversary of that event in 1993 with conferences and other activities.

Healthcare

New Zealand's health care system has been undergoing a restructuring since the mid-1980s. Area health boards, formed to combine primary and hospital care facilities for each region under a single administrative unit, were established in 1985. In 1991, the government announced plans to expand health care resources for those in financial need.

In 1993, there were 8,100 doctors (about 1 for every 608 people). Most physicians practice under the National Health Service, established by the Social Security Act of 1938, but private practice outside the scheme is permitted. In 1990, there were 344 hospitals with 30,000 beds (6.6 per 1,000 inhabitants).

Life expectancy at birth was 76 years in 1995. The principal causes of death are heart disease, cancer, and cerebrovascular diseases. Alcoholism is a significant public health problem in New Zealand. Estimates of the number of chronic alcoholics range upward from 53,000, and another 250,000 New Zealanders may be classified as excessive drinkers.

Housing

About 18,000 houses and apartments were built in New Zealand in 1992, when New Zealand's housing stock totaled 1.2 million. More than half the total housing stock has been constructed since 1957. The average weekly expense for rent and home ownership in 1995–96 was about NZ$127.

Most families own their own homes. The average private dwelling has three bedrooms, a living room, dining room, kitchen, laundry, bathroom, toilet, and garage. Most units are built of wood and have sheet-iron or tiled roofs.

EDUCATION

Education in New Zealand is compulsory for 10 years for children between 6 and 15, although most children attend school from the age of 5. The adult literacy rate is 99%. Most state schools are coeducational, but some private schools are not. New Zealand has 2,300 state primary schools and 60 privately owned schools. At the secondary level, there are 315 state-run schools and 15 private schools.

In 1994, 314,487 students attended primary schools, 404,563 students attended secondary schools, and 63,658 students were in vocational schools. For children in isolated areas, there is a public correspondence school. In some regions there are special state primary and secondary schools for Maori children, but most Maori children attend public schools.

There are six universities: the University of Auckland, University of Waikato (at Hamilton), Massey University (at Palmerston North), Victoria University of Wellington, University of Canterbury (at Christchurch), and University of Otago (at Dunedin). All universities offer courses in the arts, social sciences, commerce, and science.

An agricultural institution, Lincoln College, is associated with the University of Canterbury. Law is offered at Auckland, Waikato, Victoria, Canterbury, and Otago, and medicine at Auckland and Otago. The Central Institute of Technology, near Wellington, is the leading institution in a network of 24 polytechnic institutions. There are evening classes for adults interested in continuing their education at secondary schools, institutes, and community centers. University tuition fees are low, and financial assistance is given to applicants who have passed special qualifying examinations.

1999 KEY EVENTS TIMELINE

January

- Pirates invade the Southern Ocean off of Antarctica in search of the Patagonian toothfish.

February

- The Reserve Bank abandons ''monetary conditions index'' (MCI), previously used to set policy.

- The exchange rate falls, and interest rates peak at 10%.

- Te Kaha, a New Zealand frigate to patrol the pillage of toothfish, is dispatched in Antarctic waters.

- Parliament wraps up its first session of the year.

March

- The Reserve Bank sets an official cash rate to determine overnight interest rates in money markets.

- Six users of third generation oral contraceptives die due to venous thrombo embolism (VTE).

- Trinidad and Tobago sign a five year contract with the New Zealand Post to run their postal service.

May

- Conoco makes final preparations for drilling off the New Zealand coast.

- The United States threatens to impose tariffs on New Zealand's lamb trade, worth $140 million in 1998.

July

- Median housing is at NZ $167,000.

- U.S. President Bill Clinton mandates a three-year tariff that controls lamb imports. The New Zealand government appeals the tariff.

September

- The 7th annual Summit of Asia Pacific Economic Co-operation (APEC) is held.

- New Zealand evaluates a law regarding Asian boat people.

- A new free trade agreement is reached with Singapore.

- New Zealand launches a $26 million tourism campaign.

- The Coca-Cola Company seals an estimated $20 million deal to acquire Cadbury Schweppes' brands in New Zealand.

October

- Martin Donnelly, a renown New Zealand cricket player, dies at age 82.

November

- In a November 27 election, the Labour Party, the opposition party for the past nine years, wins 52 seats in parliament. The Labour Party, with 11 seats of the leftist Alliance party, Partner of Labour, wins the the majority in the 120-member parliament.

- Labour Party leader and prime minister-elect is Helen Clark. She and potential coalition partners reveal plans to legislate the Labour Party's promised tax increase by Christmas.

ANALYSIS OF EVENTS: 1999

BUSINESS AND THE ECONOMY

New Zealand's economy is heavily dependent on overseas trade. Traditionally a large portion of dairy, meat, and wool exports went to the United Kingdom. By the 1990s fishing, manufacturing, and tourism became more significant.

In the Asia Pacific market New Zealand is a liberal economy. The past fifteen years of successive governments have eliminated all domestic subsidies, export subsidies, and most tariffs. New Zealand has been held up as an economic model. Boasting among the lowest tax rates in the world, sound monetary and fiscal policies, and markets readily exposed to the world, New Zealand's economy is highly competitive.

The economy did suffer some hard knocks. Residual affects from the Asian financial crisis found New Zealand's exchange rate falling and its interest rate rising, the opposite of what the weakening economy needed. To combat the recession the Reserve Bank set an ''official cash rate'' to determine overnight interest rates in the money markets, intending this measure to create less volatile interest rates in the future.

In September the paper holdings sold to Fletcher Challenge Canada Ltd. (FCC) for C $3.6 billion created the biggest producer of groundwood papers in the Pacific Rim, with paper mills located in New Zealand. The transaction created a Pacific Rim powerhouse with assets of C $5 billion.

Another acquisition midyear found the Atlanta, Georgia-based Coca-Cola, Co. sealing an estimated U.S. $20 million deal for Cadbury Schweppes brands in New Zealand. Government regulators said they would not intervene.

Final preparations were made to drill off of Kaipara Harbor, including Conoco utilizing the Falcon Deepwater Frontier ultra drill ship to reach a well located 4,921 feet below water.

Also in 1999, Trinidad and Tobago signed a five-year contract with the New Zealand Post. Previously the service was losing around NZ $3 million a year, but it became eager to compete overseas and overcome the restrictions of New Zealand's legally protected monopoly.

Due to the November 1999 elections and rising interest rates, home buyers were not encouraged to take on large mortgages, but the housing market improved as the median house price reached NZ $167,000, up slightly over 1998's figures.

In addition, New Zealand's former prime minister Michael Moore has taken over as head of the World Trade Organization (WTO).

GOVERNMENT AND POLITICS

In July U.S. president Bill Clinton mandated a three-year tariff to control lamb trade from New

Zealand and Australia, worth $140 million in 1998. The order was supported by the U.S. International Trade Commission. New Zealand prime minister Jenny Shipley was urged to intervene, hoping to again witness the fairness shown by the Clinton administration in its ruling against the imposition steel import quotas.

The Environment Court of New Zealand dismissed all objections raised by a third party to the awarding of land use permits needed for drilling. The legal ruling removed the only obstacle to the venture. Target horizons included the Crown prospect to a total depth of about 13,000 feet. New Zealand presently produces U.S. $844 million in oil and gas that would otherwise be imported and has a funding package aimed at attracting oil explorers to the country. In 1999 the United States invested over $168 million in New Zealand petroleum exploration.

In Auckland in September twenty-one Asia Pacific Economic Cooperation (APEC) leaders prepared for a big summit. U.S. President Clinton and Chinese leader Jiang Zemin both attended, their first meeting since NATO accidentally bombed the Chinese embassy in Belgrade, Serbia. APEC's agenda was to lobby the World Trade Organization and push Europe toward adopting trading rules favorable to Asia Pacific nations. APEC leaders achieved a coup when Europe was forced to accept the marathon seven year Uruguay Round of trade talks, which began the process of dropping tariffs on agriculture and services. This progress, however, is a small step towards APEC's greater goal of economic reform. The forum continues to deal with the complexities of regional trade.

New Zealand held a general election in early December, aiming to prioritize the state welfare issues and resistance to tax increases.

The New Zealand Ministry of Health warned of the risks of venous thrombo embolism (VTE) in users of third generation oral contraceptives. The announcement followed coverage of six deaths and pharmaceutical company letters identifying the fatal contraindications to doctors.

CULTURE AND SOCIETY

Early 1999 revealed that the Southern Ocean fish stocks were being progressively depleted. Many fishing fleets sailed to ever more remote areas in an attempt to survive in the industry. New Zealand, however, tried to stop the plunder of one of the last great fishing grounds. Pirates were mak-

ing off with the Patagonian toothfish. Longliners—ships with lines of baited hooks—moved east to the Ross Sea, New Zealand's Antarctic dependency. Along with long range aircraft the frigate *Te Kaha* was dispatched to patrol. The toothfish commands high prices in Japan and the United States, but it was feared the Southern Ocean ground would soon be fished out. The effect on local seabirds would be devastating.

Socially in New Zealand, last spring found tensions mounting between pakeha (white) New Zealanders and the indigenous Maori, prompting some intellectuals to express fears of civil war. At the heart of the matter are the expanding Maori claims to taonga, or treasure. There are claims to gold, fruit, and even the nation's airwaves. Already 500 people have drawn salaries from the claims process.

The threat of boat people arriving in New Zealand had the nation reacting swiftly. A hasty law was passed to deal with the immigrants; however, the boatload of Chinese never appeared.

While New Zealand may hesitate to accept immigrants, it is quite welcoming to tourists. The Tourism Board announced a new $26 million campaign, and the music group Crowded House's global hit "Don't Dream It's Over" was chosen as the theme song. The marketing push aimed to increase New Zealand's tourism intake to 2.5 million by 2001, bringing $5 billion to the economy. Tourism is the country's biggest industry.

Well-known New Zealand cricket player Martin Donnelly died at 82. He was considered one of the best batsman to come from this country.

DIRECTORY

CENTRAL GOVERNMENT
Head of State

Monarch
Elizabeth II, Queen of England

Governor-General
Michael Hardie Boys

Prime Minister
Helen Clark, Office of the Prime Minister, Wellington, New Zealand
PHONE: +64 (04) 4719998
FAX: +64 (04) 4737045
E-MAIL: prime.minister@ministers.govt.nz

Ministers

Minister of Foreign Affairs and Trade
Donald McKinnon, Ministry of Foreign Affairs and Trade, Private Mail Bag 18901, Wellington 1001, New Zealand
PHONE: +64 (04) 4728877
FAX: +64 (04) 4729596

Minister of the Environment
Simon Upton, Ministry of the Environment, 84 Boulcott St., PO Box 10-362, Wellington, New Zealand
PHONE: +64 (04) 4734090
FAX: +64 (04) 4710195

Minister of Enterprise and Commerce
Max Bradford, Ministry of Enterprise and Commerce, Ministry of Commerce Building, 33 Bowen Street, Wellington, New Zealand
PHONE: +64 (04) 4720030
FAX: +64 (04) 4734638
E-MAIL: enterprise@ministers.govt.nz

Minister of Culture and Heritage
Marie Hasler, Ministry of Culture and Heritage, 4th Floor, Petherick Tower, 38-42 Waring Taylor St., Wellington, New Zealand
PHONE: +64 (04) 4994229
FAX: +64 (04) 4994490
E-MAIL: info@cultureandheritage.govt.nz

Minister of Health
Wyatt Creech, Ministry of Health, 133 Molesworth St., Wellington, New Zealand
PHONE: +64 (04) 4962000
FAX: +64 (04) 4962340
E-MAIL: MOH@moh.govt.nz

Minister of Food, Fiber, Biosecurity and Border Control
John Luxton, Ministry of Food, Fiber, Biosecurity and Border Control
E-MAIL: food@ministers.govt.nz

Minister of Finance
William Birch, Ministry of Finance
E-MAIL: finance@ministers.govt.nz

Minister of Social Services, Work and Income
Roger Sowry, Ministry of Social Services, Work and Income
E-MAIL: social.services@ministers.govt.nz

Minister of Maori Affairs
Tau Henare, Ministry of Maori Affairs, Te Puni Kokiri House, 143 Lambton Quay, Wellington, New Zealand
PHONE: +64 (04) 9226000
FAX: +64 (04) 9226299
E-MAIL: maori.affairs@ministers.govt.nz

Minister of Education
Nick Smith, Ministry of Education, 45-47 Pipitea Street, Thorndon, Wellington, New Zealand
PHONE: +64 (04) 4735544
FAX: +64 (04) 4991327
E-MAIL: communications@minedu.govt.nz

Minister of Conservation
Nick Smith, Ministry of Conservation
E-MAIL: vonservation@ministers.govt.nz

Minister of Accident Rehabilitation and Compensation Insurance
Murray McCully, Ministry of Accident Rehabilitation and Compensation Insurance
E-MAIL: acc@ministers.govt.nz

Minister of Sport, Fitness and Leisure
Murray McCully, Ministry of Sport, Fitness and Leisure

Minister of Justice
Tony Ryall, Ministry of Justice, Charles Fergusson Building, Bowen Street, Wellington, New Zealand
PHONE: +64 (04) 4949700
FAX: +64 (04) 4949701
E-MAIL: justice@ministers.govt.nz

Minister of State Owned Enterprises
Tony Ryall, Ministry of State Owned Enterprises

Minister of Youth Affairs
Tony Ryall, Ministry of Youth Affairs, PO Box 10-300 The Terrace, 48 Mulgrave Street, Wellington, New Zealand
PHONE: +64 (04) 4712158
FAX: +64 (04) 4712233
E-MAIL: info@youthaffairs.govt.nz

Minister of Transport
Maurice Williamson, Ministry of Transport, 38-42 Waring Taylor St, Wellington, New Zealand
PHONE: +64 (04) 4721253
FAX: +64 (04) 4733697
E-MAIL: transport@ministers.govt.nz

Minister of Research, Science, and Technology
Maurice Williamson, Ministry of Research, Science, and Technology, PO Box 5336, Wellington, New Zealand
PHONE: +64 (04) 4726400
FAX: +64 (04) 4711284
E-MAIL: info@morst.govt.nz

Minister of Communications
Maurice Williamson, Ministry of
Communications

Minister of Information Technology
Maurice Williamson, Ministry of Information
Technology

Minister of International Trade
Lockwood Smith, Ministry of International Trade
E-MAIL: international.trade@ministers.govt.nz

Minister of Tourism
Lockwood Smith, Ministry of Tourism

Minister of State Services
Simon Upton, Ministry of State Services
E-MAIL: state.services@ministers.govt.nz

Minister of Crown Research Initiatives
Simon Upton, Ministry of Crown Research
Initiatives

Minister of Courts
Georgina te Heuheu, Ministry of Courts, Level 3
Vogel Building, Aitken St, Wellington, New
Zealand
PHONE: +64 (04) 4948800
FAX: +64 (04) 4948820
E-MAIL: courts@ministers.govt.nz

Minister of Women's Affairs
Georgina te Heuheu, Ministry of Women's
Affairs, 48 Mulgrave St., Wellington, New
Zealand
PHONE: +64 (04) 4734112
FAX: +64 (04) 4720961
E-MAIL: mwa@mwa.govt.nz

Minister of Police
Clem Simich, Ministry of Police
E-MAIL: police@ministers.govt.nz

Minister of Immigration
Tuariki John Delamere, Ministry of Immigration
E-MAIL: immigration@ministers.govt.nz

Minister of Pacific Island Affairs
Tuariki John Delamere, Ministry of Pacific
Island Affairs, Level 1, Charles Fergusson Bldg.,
Ballantrae Place, Wellington, New Zealand
PHONE: +64 (04) 4734493
FAX: +64 (04) 4734301
E-MAIL: contact@minpac.govt.nz

Minister of Senior Citizens
David Carter, Ministry of Senior Citizens
E-MAIL: senior.citizens@ministers.govt.nz

Minister of Internal Affairs
Jack Elder, Ministry of Internal Affairs

E-MAIL: internal.affairs@ministers.govt.nz

Minister of Business Development
Peter McCardle, Ministry of Business
Development

Minister of Agriculture and Forestry
John Luxton, Ministry of Agriculture and
Forestry, Head Office-ASB Bank House,
101-103 The Terrace, Wellington, New Zealand
PHONE: +64 (04) 4744100
FAX: +64 (04) 4744244

Minister of Fisheries
John Luxton, Ministry of Fisheries, 101-103 The
Terrace, Wellington, New Zealand
PHONE: +64 (04) 4702600
FAX: +64 (04) 4702601
E-MAIL: info@fish.govt.nz

Minister of Revenue
William Birch, Ministry of Revenue

Minister of Tertiary Education
Max Bradford, Ministry of Tertiary Education

Minister of Defense
Max Bradford, Ministry of Defense, PO Box
5347, Lambton Quay, Wellington, New Zealand
PHONE: +64 (04) 4960999
FAX: +64 (04) 4960859
E-MAIL: communications@defence.govt.nz

Minister of Housing
Roger Sowry, Ministry of Housing, Level 12,
Vogel Building, Aitken Street, Wellington, New
Zealand
PHONE: +64 (04) 4722753
FAX: +64 (04) 4994744
E-MAIL: info@minhousing.govt.nz

Minister of Local Government
Maurice Williamson, Ministry of Local
Government

Minister of Statistics
Maurice Williamson, Ministry of Statistics

Minister of Disarmament and Arms Control
Donald McKinnon, Ministry of Disarmament and
Arms Control

Minister of Veterans Affairs
Donald McKinnon, Ministry of Veterans Affairs

Minister of Corrections
Clem Simrich, Ministry of Corrections

Minister of Racing
Clem Simrich, Ministry of Racing

Minister of Social Policy
Ministry of Social Policy, 39 Bowen Street,
Wellington, New Zealand
PHONE: +64 (04) 9163884
FAX: +64 (04) 9163910
E-MAIL: Philippa.White006@mosp.govt.nz

POLITICAL ORGANIZATIONS
New Zealand National Party

PO Box 1155, Wellington, New Zealand
PHONE: +64 (04) 4725211
FAX: +64 (04) 4781622
E-MAIL: hq@national.org.nz
NAME: Jenny Shipley

New Zealand Labor Party

PO Box 784, Wellington, New Zealand
E-MAIL: labour.party@parliament.govt.nz
TITLE: Leader
NAME: Helen Clark

New Zealand First Party

Parliament Buildings, Wellington, New Zealand
PHONE: +64 (04) 4719292
FAX: +64 (04) 4727751
E-MAIL: nzfirst@parliament.govt.nz
TITLE: Leader
NAME: Winston Peters

New Labor Party

TITLE: Leader
NAME: Jim Anderton

Green Party of Aotearoa

PO Box 11-652, Wellington, New Zealand
PHONE: +64 (04) 9388622
FAX: +64 (04) 9386251
TITLE: Co-Leaders
NAME: Jeannette Fitzsimons; Rod Donald

Mana Motuhake e Aotearoa (New Zealand Self-Government Party)

NAME: Sandra Lee

New Zealand Democratic Party

129 Onewa Road, Northcote, North Shore City,
New Zealand
PHONE: +64 (09) 4800364
FAX: +64 (09) 4800438
E-MAIL: nzdemocrats@hotmail.com
TITLE: President
NAME: Peter Kane

Liberal Party

TITLE: Co-Leaders
NAME: Hanmish Macintyre; Gilbert Myles

DIPLOMATIC REPRESENTATION
Embassies in New Zealand

Argentina
PO Box 5430, Lambton Qua, Wellington, New
Zealand
PHONE: +64 (04) 4728330
FAX: +64 (04) 4728331

Australia
72-78 Hobson Street, Thorndon, Wellington,
New Zealand
PHONE: +64 (04) 4736411
FAX: +64 (04) 4987103

Belgium
12th Floor, Axon House, 1-3 Willeston Street,
Wellington, New Zealand
PHONE: +64 (04) 4729558; 4729559
FAX: +64 (04) 4712764

Brazil
Level 9, Wool House, 10 Brandon Street,
Wellington, New Zealand
PHONE: +64 (04) 4733516
FAX: +64 (04) 4733517
E-MAIL: brasemb@ihug.co.nz

Canada
61 Moleworth Street, Wellington, New Zealand
PHONE: +64 (04) 4739577
FAX: +64 (04) 4712082

Chile
19 Bolton Street, Wellington, New Zealand
PHONE: +64 (04) 4716270
FAX: +64 (04) 4725324

China
2-6 Glenmore Street, Wellington, New Zealand
PHONE: +64 (04) 4721384
FAX: +64 (04) 4990419; 4721998

Cook Islands
56 Mulgrave Street, Wellington, New Zealand
PHONE: +64 (04) 4725126; 4725127
FAX: +64 (04) 4725121

El Salvador
1/644 Manukau Road, Epsom 1003, Auckland,
New Zealand
PHONE: +64 (025) 6254770
FAX: +64 (025) 6254710

Fiji

31 Pipitea Street, Thorndon, Wellington, New Zealand
PHONE: +64 (04) 4735401; 4735402

France

34-42 Manners Street, Wellington, New Zealand
PHONE: +64 (04) 3842555; 8027790; 8027791
FAX: +64 (04) 3842577; 3842579

Germany

90-92 Hobson Street, Thorndon, Wellington, New Zealand
PHONE: +64 (04) 4736063; 4736064
FAX: +64 (04) 4736069

India

10th Floor, FAI House, 180 Molesworth Street, Wellington, New Zealand
PHONE: +64 (04) 4736390; 4736391
FAX: +64 (04) 4990665

Indonesia

70 Glen Road, Kelburn, Wellington, New Zealand
PHONE: +64 (04) 4758697; 4758698; 4758699
FAX: +64 (04) 4759374

Iran

PO Box 10 249, The Terrace, Wellington, New Zealand
PHONE: +64 (04) 3862976; 3862983
FAX: +64 (04) 3863065

Israel

13th Floor, Equinox House, 111 The Terrace, Wellington, New Zealand
PHONE: +64 (04) 4722362; 4722368
FAX: +64 (04) 4990632

Italy

34-38 Grant Road, Thorndon, Wellington, New Zealand
PHONE: +64 (04) 4735339
FAX: +64 (04) 4727255

Japan

Majestic Centre, 100 Willis Street, Wellington, New Zealand
PHONE: +64 (04) 4731540
FAX: +64 (04) 4712951

Korea

Level 11, 2 Hunter Street, Wellington, New Zealand
PHONE: +64 (04) 4739073; 4739074
FAX: +64 (04) 4723865

Lithuania

28 Heather Street, Auckland, New Zealand

PHONE: +64 (025) 3796639
FAX: +64 (025) 3072911

Malaysia

10 Washington Avenue, Brooklyn, Wellington, New Zealand
PHONE: +64 (04) 3852439; 8010943
FAX: +64 (04) 3856973

Mexico

Level 8, GRE House, 111-115 Customhouse Quay, Wellington, New Zealand
PHONE: +64 (04) 4725555; 4725556
FAX: +64 (04) 4725800

Nauru

2nd Floor, 29 Union Street, Wellington, New Zealand
PHONE: +64 (04) 3091799
FAX: +64 (04) 3073113

Netherlands

Investment Center, Corner Ballance and Featherston Streets, Wellington, New Zealand
PHONE: +64 (04) 4716390
FAX: +64 (04) 4712923

Norway

61 Molesworth Street, Wellington, New Zealand
PHONE: +64 (04) 4712503
FAX: +64 (04) 4728023

Papua New Guinea

279 Willis Street, Wellington, New Zealand
PHONE: +64 (04) 3852474; 3852475; 3852476
FAX: +64 (04) 3852477

Peru

Level 8, Cigna House, 40 Mercer Street, Wellington, New Zealand
PHONE: +64 (04) 4998087
FAX: +64 (04) 4998087

Philippines

50 Hobson Street, Thorndon, Wellington, New Zealand
PHONE: +64 (04) 4729848; 4729921
FAX: +64 (04) 4725170

Poland

17 Upland Road, Kelburn, Wellington, New Zealand
PHONE: +64 (04) 4759433
FAX: +64 (04) 4759458

Portugal

Suite 1, 1st Floor, 21 Marion Street, Wellington, New Zealand
PHONE: +64 (04) 3859639
FAX: +64 (04) 3842534

Russia

57 Messines Road, Karori, Wellington, New Zealand
PHONE: +64 (04) 4766742
FAX: +64 (04) 4763843

Samoa

1A Wesley Road, Kelburn, Wellington, New Zealand
PHONE: +64 (04) 4720953; 4720954
FAX: +64 (04) 4712479

Singapore

17 Kabul Street, Khandallah, Wellington, New Zealand
PHONE: +64 (04) 4792076; 4792077
FAX: +64 (04) 4792315

South Africa

National Mutual Corporate Superannuation Services Ltd., 80 The Terrace, Wellington, New Zealand
PHONE: +64 (04) 4744953
FAX: +64 (04) 4710504

Spain

PO Box 71, Papkura, Auckland, New Zealand
PHONE: +64 (025) 2996019
FAX: +64 (025) 2989986

Sri Lanka

22 Bloomfield Terrace, Lower Hutt, New Zealand
PHONE: +64 5605817
FAX: +64 5665633

Sweden

13th Floor, Vogel Bldg., Aitken Street, Wellington, New Zealand
PHONE: +64 (04) 4999895
FAX: +64 (04) 4991464

Switzerland

Panama House, 22 Panama Street, Wellington, New Zealand
PHONE: +64 (04) 4721593; 4721594
FAX: +64 (04) 4996302

Thailand

2 Cook Street, Karori, Wellington, New Zealand
PHONE: +64 (04) 4768618; 4768619
FAX: +64 (04) 4763677

Turkey

15-17 Murphy Street, Thorndon, Wellington, New Zealand
PHONE: +64 (04) 4721292
FAX: +64 (04) 4721277

Tuvalu

PO Box 100-375, North Shore Mail Centre, Auckland, New Zealand
PHONE: +64 (025) 4106463; 2262133
FAX: +64 (025) 4106923

United Kingdom

44 Hill Street, Wellington, New Zealand
PHONE: +64 (04) 4950889
FAX: +64 (04) 4711974
TITLE: High Commissioner
NAME: Martin Williams

United States

29 Fitzherbert Terrace, Wellington, New Zealand
PHONE: +64 (04) 4722068
FAX: +64 (04) 4723537

Uruguay

7 Chisenhall Street, Karori, Wellington, New Zealand
PHONE: +64 (04) 4762275
FAX: +64 (04) 4762268

Vanuatu

50 Kelman Road, Kelston, Auckland, New Zealand
PHONE: +64 (025) 8181102

JUDICIAL SYSTEM

High Court

2 Molesworth St, PO Box 1091, Wellington, New Zealand
PHONE: +64 (04) 9158000
FAX: +64 (04) 9158434; 9158435

Court of Appeal

Cnr Molesworth and Aitken Streets, PO Box 1606, Wllington, New Zealand
PHONE: +64 (04) 9158000
FAX: +64 (04) 9158250

FURTHER READING
Articles

"Can the U.S. Still Lead on Trade?" *Asian Wall Street Journal*, 12 July 1999, p. 16(1).

"Coca Cola Takes Over Cadbury." *Tribune Business News*, 16 September 1999.

"Conoco is Making the Final Preparations for Drilling off New Zealand." *Offshore* 59, 5 (May 1999): 13(1).

"Costume Party—Leaders Prepare for Auckland Summit." *Newsweek International* (September 13, 1999): 45.

''New Zealand Drilling Cleared.'' *The Oil Daily*, 3 March 1999.

''New Zealand House Prices Rise from Year Ago Figures.'' *Asian Wall Street Journal*, 23 August 1999, p. 14(1).

''Renascent Nativism.'' *World Press Review* 46, (September 1999): 22.

''Stamp Duty.'' *The Economist* 351 (April 3, 1999): 53(1).

''Steel Cooking in Lamb Stew.'' *American Metal Market* (May 26, 1999): 12.

''U.S. Sheep Sector Gets Import Relief.'' *Feedstuffs* 71 (July 12, 1999): 3(1).

NEW ZEALAND: STATISTICAL DATA

For sources and notes see "Sources of Statistics" in the front of each volume.

GEOGRAPHY

Geography (1)

Area:

Total: 268,680 sq km.

Land: 268,670 sq km.

Water: 10 sq km.

Note: includes Antipodes Islands, Auckland Islands, Bounty Islands, Campbell Island, Chatham Islands, and Kermadec Islands.

Area—comparative: about the size of Colorado.

Land boundaries: 0 km.

Coastline: 15,134 km.

Climate: temperate with sharp regional contrasts.

Terrain: predominately mountainous with some large coastal plains.

Natural resources: natural gas, iron ore, sand, coal, timber, hydropower, gold, limestone.

Land use:

Arable land: 9%

Permanent crops: 5%

Permanent pastures: 50%

Forests and woodland: 28%

Other: 8% (1993 est.).

HUMAN FACTORS

Demographics (2A)

	1990	1995	1998	2000	2010	2020	2030	2040	2050
Population	3,298.9	3,507.6	3,625.4	3,697.9	4,028.8	4,325.7	4,530.0	4,599.3	4,561.2
Net migration rate (per 1,000 population)	NA	NA	NA	NA	NA	NA	NA	NA	NA
Births	NA	NA	NA	NA	NA	NA	NA	NA	NA
Deaths	26.5	NA	NA	NA	NA	NA	NA	NA	NA
Life expectancy - males	72.5	73.8	74.3	74.8	76.6	77.9	78.9	79.5	80.0
Life expectancy - females	78.6	79.9	80.9	81.6	83.1	84.2	85.0	85.6	86.0
Birth rate (per 1,000)	18.2	16.2	14.9	14.0	12.8	12.3	10.9	10.1	9.7
Death rate (per 1,000)	8.0	7.8	7.6	7.5	7.6	8.0	9.2	10.4	11.7
Women of reproductive age (15-49 yrs.)	860.5	909.9	926.0	935.5	1,006.5	1,034.7	1,007.8	985.9	920.1
of which are currently married	NA	NA	NA	NA	NA	NA	NA	NA	NA
Fertility rate	2.3	2.1	1.9	1.8	1.8	1.8	1.7	1.7	1.7

Except as noted, values for vital statistics are in thousands; life expectancy is in years.

Health Personnel (3)

Total health expenditure as a percentage of GDP,
1990-1997[a]

Public sector 5.9

Private sector 1.7

Total[b] 7.6

Health expenditure per capita in U.S. dollars,
1990-1997[a]

Purchasing power parity 1,309

Total 1,348

Availability of health care facilities per 100,000 people

Hospital beds 1990-1997[a] 730

Doctors 1993[c] 210

Nurses 1993[c] 1,249

Health Indicators (4)

Life expectancy at birth

1980 73

1997 77

Daily per capita supply of calories (1996) 3,405

Total fertility rate births per woman (1997) 1.9

Maternal mortality ratio per 100,000 live births
(1990-97) . . . . .25[c]

Safe water % of population with access (1995) 90

Sanitation % of population with access (1995) . . . .

Consumption of iodized salt % of households
(1992-98)[a] . . . .

Smoking prevalence

Male % of adults (1985-95)[a] 24

Female % of adults (1985-95)[a] 22

Tuberculosis incidence per 100,000 people
(1997) 5

Adult HIV prevalence % of population ages
15-49 (1997) 0.07

Infants and Malnutrition (5)

Under-5 mortality rate (1997) 7

% of infants with low birthweight (1990-97) 6

Births attended by skilled health staff % of total[a] . . .NA

% fully immunized (1995-97)

TB 20x

DPT 86

Polio 100

Measles 100

Prevalence of child malnutrition under age 5
(1992-97)[b] . . . . .NA

Ethnic Division (6)

New Zealand European 74.5%

Maori 9.7%

Other European 4.6%

Pacific Islander 3.8%

Asian and others 7.4%

Religions (7)

Anglican 24%

Presbyterian 18%

Roman Catholic 15%

Methodist 5%

Baptist 2%

Other Protestant 3%

Unspecified or none 33% (1986)

Languages (8)

English (official), Maori.

EDUCATION

Public Education Expenditures (9)

Public expenditure on education (% of GNP)

1980 . . . . .5.8

1996 . . . . .7.3

Expenditure per student

Primary % of GNP per capita

1980 . . . . .15.1

1996 . . . . .17.9

Secondary % of GNP per capita

1980 . . . . .13.6

1996 . . . . .23.8

Tertiary % of GNP per capita

1980 . . . . .59.8

1996 . . . . .45.8

Expenditure on teaching materials

Primary % of total for level (1996) 7.9

Secondary % of total for level (1996) . . . .

Primary pupil-teacher ratio per teacher (1996) 19

Duration of primary education years (1995) 6

Educational Attainment (10)

Age group (1991) . . . . .25+

Total population 1,992,354

Highest level attained (%)

No schooling 0.0

First level

Not completed 36.8

Completed . . . . .NA

Entered second level

S-1 . . . . .16.3

S-2 . . . . .7.8

Postsecondary 39.1

GOVERNMENT & LAW

Political Parties (12)

House of Representatives	% of seats
National Party (NP)	.34.1
New Zealand Liberal Party (NZLP)	.28.3
New Zealand First Party (NZFP)	.13.1
Alliance	.10.1
Association of Consumers and Taxpayers (ACT) . .	.6.17
United New Zealand (UNZ)	.0.91

Military Affairs (14B)

	1990	1991	1992	1993	1994	1995
Military expenditures						
Current dollars (mil.)	897	638	750	815	702	740
1995 constant dollars (mil.)	1,030	705	806	854	720	740
Armed forces (000)	11	11	11	11	10	10
Gross national product (GNP)						
Current dollars (mil.)	43,790	45,080	48,700	52,570	55,810	57,210[e]
1995 constant dollars (mil.)	50,320	49,820	52,380	55,110	57,210	57,210[e]
Central government expenditures (CGE)						
1995 constant dollars (mil.)	20,440	19,670	20,280	18,920	20,560	22,230
People (mil.)	3.3	3.3	3.4	3.4	3.5	3.5
Military expenditure as % of GNP	2.0	1.4	1.5	1.5	1.3	1.3
Military expenditure as % of CGE	5.0	3.6	4.0	4.5	3.5	3.3
Military expenditure per capita (1995 $)	312	211	239	249	208	211
Armed forces per 1,000 people (soldiers)	3.3	3.3	3.3	3.2	2.9	2.9
GNP per capita (1995 $)	15,250	14,930	15,490	16,100	16,500	16,310
Arms imports[6]						
Current dollars (mil.)	40	80	80	60	20	40
1995 constant dollars (mil.)	46	88	86	63	21	40
Arms exports[6]						
Current dollars (mil.)	0	0	0	0	0	0
1995 constant dollars (mil.)	0	0	0	0	0	0
Total imports[7]						
Current dollars (mil.)	9,501	8,381	9,202	9,636	11,910	13,960
1995 constant dollars (mil.)	10,920	9,261	9,898	10,100	12,210	13,960
Total exports[7]						
Current dollars (mil.)	9,488	9,898	9,824	10,540	12,180	13,740
1995 constant dollars (mil.)	10,900	10,610	10,570	11,050	12,490	13,740
Arms as percent of total imports[8]	.4	1.0	.9	.6	.2	.3
Arms as percent of total exports[8]	0	0	0	0	0	0

Government Budget (13A)

Year: 1997

Total Expenditures: 31,465 Millions of Dollars

Expenditures as a percentage of the total by function:

General public services and public order 9.60

Defense 2.98

Education 15.52

Health 15.88

Social Security and Welfare 39.90

Housing and community amenities 15

Recreational, cultural, and religious affairs 93

Fuel and energy 04

Agriculture, forestry, fishing, and hunting 1.13

Mining, manufacturing, and construction . . . .-

Transportation and communication 2.69

Other economic affairs and services 1.23

Crime (15)

Crime rate (for 1997)

Crimes reported 473,500

Total persons convicted 176,300

Crimes per 100,000 population 12,600

Persons responsible for offenses

Total number of suspects 195,100

Total number of female suspects 36,300

Total number of juvenile suspects 44,700

LABOR FORCE

Labor Force (16)

Total 1,634,500

Services 64.6%

Industry 25.0%

Agriculture 10.4%

Percentages for 1994. Total for September 1995.

Unemployment Rate (17)

5.9% (December 1996)

PRODUCTION SECTOR

Electric Energy (18)

Capacity . . . . .7.747 million kW (1995)

Production . . . . .33.696 billion kWh (1995)

Consumption per capita . . . . .9,889 kWh (1995)

Transportation (19)

Highways:

total: 92,200 km

paved: 53,568 km (including at least 144 km of expressways)

unpaved: 38,632 km (1994 est.)

Waterways: 1,609 km; of little importance to transportation

Pipelines: petroleum products 160 km; natural gas 1,000 km; liquefied petroleum gas or LPG 150 km

Merchant marine:

total: 16 ships (1,000 GRT or over) totaling 155,478 GRT/195,836 DWT ships by type: bulk 4, cargo 1, liquefied gas tanker 1, oil tanker 3, railcar carrier 1, roll-on/roll-off cargo 6 (1997 est.)

Airports: 111 (1997 est.)

Airports—with paved runways:

total: 44

over 3,047 m: 2

1,524 to 2,437 m: 8

914 to 1,523 m: 31

under 914 m: 3 (1997 est.)

Airports—with unpaved runways:

total: 67

1,524 to 2,437 m: 1

914 to 1,523 m: 23

under 914 m: 43 (1997 est.)

Top Agricultural Products (20)

Wheat, barley, potatoes, pulses, fruits, vegetables; wool, meat, dairy products; fish catch reached a record 503,000 metric tons in 1988.

MANUFACTURING SECTOR

GDP & Manufacturing Summary (21)

Detailed value added figures are listed by both International Standard Industry Code (ISIC) and product title.

	1980	1985	1990	1994
GDP ($-1990 mil.)[1]	36,487	42,371	43,657	47,092
Per capita ($-1990)[1]	11,721	13,049	12,993	13,337
Manufacturing share (%) (current prices) NA		21.7	20.7	18.0
Manufacturing				
Value added ($-1990 mil.)[1]	6,998	8,323	7,636	8,828

	1980	1985	1990	1994
Industrial production index	100	118	120	140
Value added ($ mil.)	4,756	4,657	6,923	8,251
Gross output ($ mil.)	14,790	15,399	23,433	27,804
Employment (000)	285	278	217	229
Profitability (% of gross output)				
Intermediate input (%)	68	70	70	70
Wages and salaries inc. supplements (%)	22	18	17	17
Gross operating surplus	10	12	12	12
Productivity ($)				
Gross output per worker	51,964	50,964	97,510	107,604
Value added per worker	16,711	15,414	28,808	32,618
Average wage (inc. supplements)	11,354	10,180	18,863	21,181
Value added ($ mil.)				
311/2 Food products	1,098	1,082	1,676	2,114
313 Beverages	110	93	216	249
314 Tobacco products	30	19	45	49
321 Textiles	222	193	232	248
322 Wearing apparel	185	170	202	192
323 Leather and fur products	45	46	54	52
324 Footwear	55	46	41	44
331 Wood and wood products	253	257	323	392
332 Furniture and fixtures	92	95	126	160
341 Paper and paper products	266	276	553	626
342 Printing and publishing	294	326	537	636
351 Industrial chemicals	140	134	249	289
352 Other chemical products	155	142	211	257
353 Petroleum refineries	26	−1	137	137
354 Miscellaneous petroleum and coal products	9	7	9	10
355 Rubber products	96	70	62	70
356 Plastic products	110	138	229	268
361 Pottery, china and earthenware	13	11	18	22
362 Glass and glass products	44	41	70	88
369 Other non-metal mineral products	114	127	169	174
371 Iron and steel	93	71	113	140
372 Non-ferrous metals	82	102	139	168
381 Metal products	371	404	480	629
382 Non-electrical machinery	235	264	340	404
383 Electrical machinery	239	200	260	341
384 Transport equipment	318	274	322	362
385 Professional and scientific equipment	14	20	24	30
390 Other manufacturing industries	45	48	86	100

FINANCE, ECONOMICS, & TRADE

Economic Indicators (22)

National product: GDP—purchasing power parity—$63.4 billion (1997 est.)

National product real growth rate: 2.5% (1997 est.)

National product per capita: $17,700 (1997 est.)

Inflation rate—consumer price index: 2% (1997 est.)

Exchange Rates (24)

Exchange rates:

New Zealand dollars (NZ$) per US$1

January 1998	1.7283
1997	1.5083
1996	1.4543
1995	1.5235
1994	1.6844
1993	1.8495

FINANCE, ECONOMICS, & TRADE

Balance of Payments (23)

	1992	1993	1994	1995	1996
Exports of goods (f.o.b.)	9,735	10,468	11,984	13,481	14,168
Imports of goods (f.o.b.)	−8,108	−8,749	−10,648	−12,584	−13,675
Trade balance	1,627	1,719	1,336	897	493
Services - debits	−5,645	−6,049	−8,008	−9,862	−10,023
Services - credits	2,520	3,128	4,267	5,314	5,029
Private transfers (net)	−56	−46	111	53	392
Government transfers (net)	184	178	178	179	161
Overall balance	−1,370	−1,070	−2,116	−3,419	−3,948

Top Import Origins (25)

$19.2 billion (1997 est.)

Origins	%
Australia	.21
United States	.18
Japan	.16
United Kingdom	.6

Top Export Destinations (26)

$18.5 billion (1997 est.).

Destinations	%
Australia	.19
Japan	.15
United Kingdom	.15
United States	.12

Economic Aid (27)

Donor: ODA, $98 million (1993).

Import Export Commodities (28)

Import Commodities	Export Commodities
Machinery and equipment	Wool
	Lamb
Vehicles and aircraft	Mutton
Petroleum	Beef
Consumer goods	Fish
Plastics	Cheese
	Chemicals
	Forestry products
	Fruits and vegetables
	Manufactures
	Dairy products
	Wood

NICARAGUA

Republic of Nicaragua
República de Nicaragua

CAPITAL: Managua.

FLAG: The national flag consists of a white horizontal stripe between two stripes of cobalt blue, with the national coat of arms centered in the white band.

ANTHEM: *Salve a ti, Nicaragua (Hail to You, Nicaragua).*

MONETARY UNIT: The gold córdoba (c$) is a paper currency of 100 centavos. There are coins of 5, 10, 25, and 50 centavos and 1 and 5 córdobas, and notes of 1, 2, 5, 10, 20, 50, 100, 500, 1,000, 5,000, 10,000, 20,000, 50,000, 100,000, 200,000, 500,000, 1,000,000, 5,000,000, and 10,000,000 córdobas. c$1 = us$0.11421 (or us$1 = c$8.756).

WEIGHTS AND MEASURES: The metric system is the legal standard, but some local units are also used.

HOLIDAYS: New Year's Day, 1 January; Labor Day, 1 May; Liberation Day (Revolution of 1979), 19 July; Battle of San Jacinto, 14 September; Independence Day, 15 September; All Saints' Day, 1 November; Christmas, 25 December. Movable religious holidays include Holy Thursday and Good Friday.

TIME: 6 AM = noon GMT.

LOCATION AND SIZE: Nicaragua, the largest of the Central American countries, has an area of 129,494 square kilometers (49,998 square miles), slightly larger than the state of New York. It has a total boundary length of 2,141 kilometers (1,330 miles).

Nicaragua's capital city, Managua, is located in the southwestern part of the country.

CLIMATE: Except in the central highlands, the climate is warm and humid. The mean temperature, varying according to altitude, is between 20° and 30°c (68° and 86°F). Average annual rainfall along the Mosquito Coast reaches 254–635 centimeters (100–250 inches). The highlands also have heavy rainfall. The Pacific coast averages over 200 centimeters (80 inches) a year.

INTRODUCTORY SURVEY

RECENT HISTORY

The guerrilla hero General Augusto César Sandino began organizing resistance to the American marine occupation force in 1927. American President Franklin D. Roosevelt created a foreign policy known as the "good neighbor" policy in 1933. The marines were pulled out for the last time. However, they left a legacy, having built the Nicaraguan National Guard, headed by Anastasio ("Tacho") Somoza García.

Officers of the National Guard shot Sandino after offering to negotiate a settlement with his forces. The National Guard was now unchallenged in Nicaragua, and three years later, Somoza unseated the liberal president Juan B. Sacasa and assumed the presidency. Somoza and his family were to rule Nicaragua directly or indirectly for the next 42 years.

Except for a three-year period between 1947 and 1950, Somoza was president until he was assassinated in 1956. His son, Luis Somoza Debayle, was president of congress and immediately became president under the constitution. In spite of a 1962 law attempting to limit the Somozas' hold on the government, the presidential election of February 1967 returned the Somozas to power after a four-year break. The victory for Anastasio Somoza, the younger brother of Luis, was overwhelming.

After drawing up a new constitution and declaring nine opposition parties illegal, Somoza won

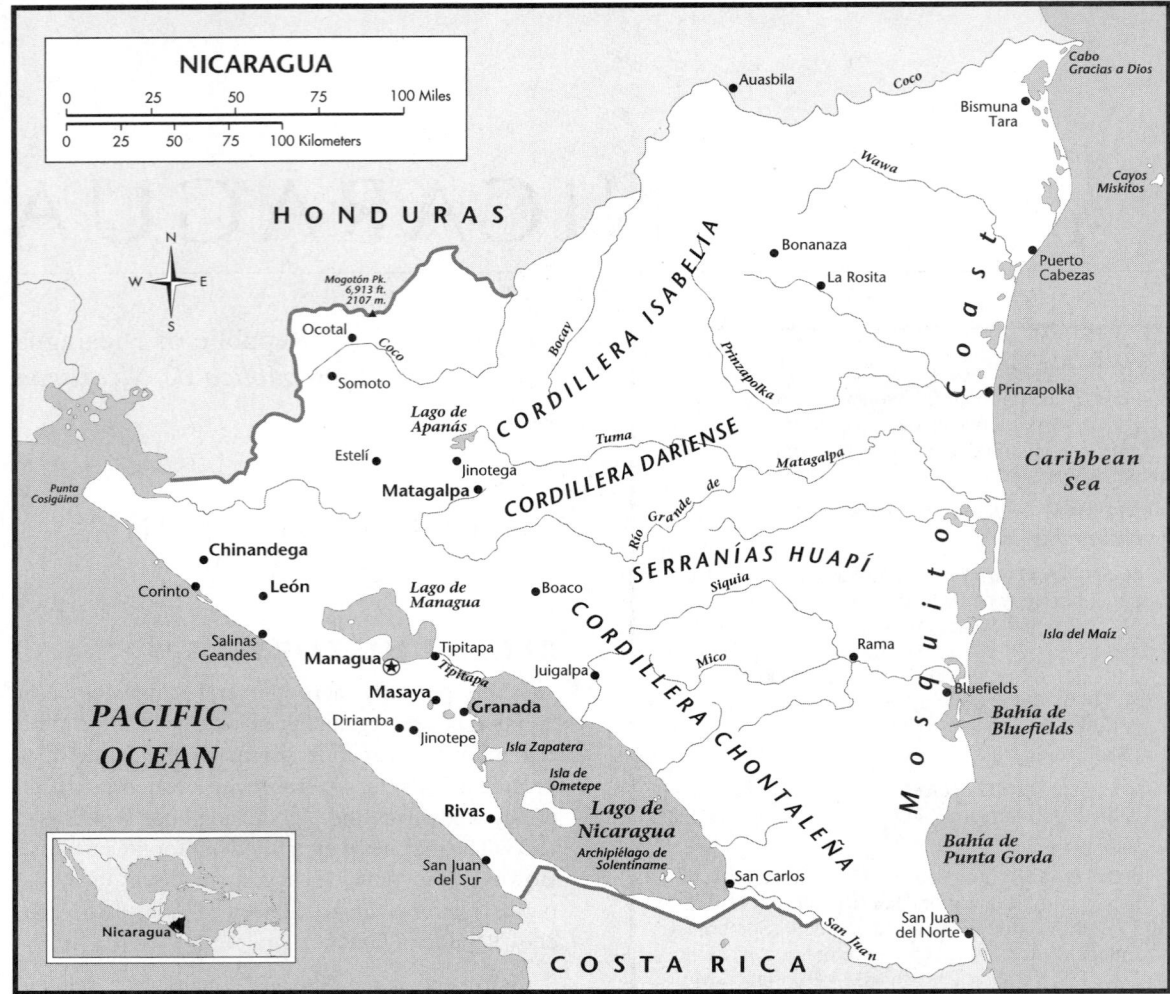

the September 1974 elections and remained president. While Somoza consolidated his hold on Nicaragua, a rebel organization, the Sandinista National Liberation Front (Frente Sandinista de Liberación Nacional–FSLN) began to agitate against his rule. Throughout the 1970s, opposition to Somoza grew, and American support began to dissolve.

By 1979, loss of support from the Church and the business community left Somoza without domestic allies. To make matters worse, the administration of President Jimmy Carter cut off military aid. In May 1979, the Sandinistas launched a final offensive. By July, Somoza had fled the country. By this time, an estimated 30,000–50,000 people had died in the fighting.

The Sandinistas engaged in an ambitious program to develop Nicaragua under leftist ideals. They dissolved the National Guard. However, the

Guard did not go away. In 1982 a number of anti-Sandinista guerrilla groups (broadly referred to as the ''contras''), consisting of former Guard members and Somoza supporters, began operating from Honduras and Costa Rica. As antigovernment activity increased, a state of emergency, proclaimed in March 1982, extended into 1987.

In April 1981, the administration of President Ronald Reagan began aiding the contras with funds channeled through the Central Intelligence Agency (CIA). Reagan was angered by the Sandinistas' support of the leftist guerrillas in El Salvador. However, the U.S. Congress proved reluctant to fund the Nicaraguan resistance. In 1986, it was revealed that U.S. government funds had been secretly diverted to provide aid to the contras. This was in violation of a U.S. congressional ban on such aid.

On the domestic scene, the Sandinistas' economic policies had not proven effective. The inflation rate reached 33,000% in 1988, and price controls led to serious food shortages. The Sandinistas continued to seek negotiated settlements for their internal strife.

In August 1987, Nicaragua signed the Arias peace plan for Central America. Nicaragua promised a cease-fire with the contras, a reduction in the armed forces, and amnesty for the rebels. In exchange, the Nicaraguans were to receive guarantees of nonintervention by outside powers.

The 1990 elections had a surprise winner—Violeta Chamorro, widow of a prominent newspaper publisher slain in 1978. Politically, Chamorro's situation was unstable. The Sandinistas were still in control of the military. Some former contras took to the field again, resuming their previous guerrilla tactics. Chamorro's own coalition, the National Opposition Union (UNO), proved shaky, and withdrew support from her government in 1993 after she attempted to call for new elections.

The political situation in Nicaragua was so shaky that international observers were called in for the October 1996 elections, as they had been in 1990. Arnoldo Alemán, the conservative former mayor of Managua and leader of the Liberal Constitutionalist Party (PLC) defeated Sandinista leader Daniel Ortega in Nicaragua's first peaceful transition of power in 100 years.

Hurricane Mitch, the worst Atlantic storm in two centuries, struck Nicaragua in late October 1998. According to estimates, the storm left approximately 2400 Hondurans dead and hundreds of thousands homeless. Most of the casualties occurred at the base of the Casitas Volcano where heavy rains caused mudslides. In addition, the hurricane left seventy percent of the roads impassable and seventy-one bridges either destroyed or damaged. In spite of the damage, recovery began quickly. Nearly all roads and bridges were repaired and in use by early 1999.

GOVERNMENT

The 1984 electoral reforms by the Sandinista government created an executive branch with a president elected for a six-year term by popular vote and assisted by a vice-president and a cabinet. The presidential term was shortened to five years in 1995. Legislative power is vested in a 93-member single-chamber National Constituent Assembly elected under a system of proportional representa-

tion for six-year terms. The nation is divided into 15 departments and 2 autonomous regions along the Atlantic coast.

Judiciary

The Supreme Court in Managua, whose justices are appointed by the National Assembly for six-year terms, heads the judicial branch. The judicial system consists of both civilian and military courts.

Political Parties

When the leftist Sandinista National Liberation Front (FSLN) came to power in July 1979, all political parties except those favoring a return to Somoza rule were permitted. Under the junta, Nicaragua's governing political coalition was the Patriotic Front for the Revolution (Frente Patriótico para la Revolución–FPR), formed in 1980.

The National Opposition Union (UNO) coalition headed by Violeta Chamorro in the early 1990s included the Conservatives and the Liberals, as well as several parties formerly aligned with the Sandinistas. By the mid-1990s, the UNO coalition had disbanded. The two dominant parties currently are the conservative Liberal Constitutionalist Party (PLC) and the left-wing FSLN.

DEFENSE

In 1995, the regular armed forces, a fusion of the Sandinista and Contra armies, numbered 17,000. The army had 15,000 personnel, the navy 800, and the air force 1,200 (with 15 armed helicopters). Nicaragua spent $34 million for defense in 1995.

ECONOMIC AFFAIRS

When President Violeta Chamorro took office in April 1990, she inherited a country in desperate economic trouble. It had the highest per-person foreign debt in the world, and inflation was climbing uncontrollably. The Chamorro administration introduced a strict economic stabilization program and worked to reestablish private enterprise (including the return of properties confiscated during the Sandinista era).

As a result of the strong decline in foreign debt, the country's economy began expanding. By 1996, the annual growth rate was 5.5%, the best performance since 1977.

Public Finance

Since the mid-1960s, government spending has consistently exceeded revenues. During the

Sandinista regime, detailed public finance budgets were not a priority. The U.S. Central Intelligence Agency estimates that, in 1994, government revenues totaled approximately $389 million and expenditures $551 million. External debt totaled $11.7 billion.

Income

In 1997, Nicaragua's gross national product (GNP) was $9.3 billion, or about $2,100 per person. For the period 1985–95, the average annual inflation rate was 963.7%, resulting in a decline in GNP of 5.8% per person.

Industry

Nicaraguan industry expanded during the 1970s but was severely disrupted by the civil war. In 1980, the manufacturing sector began to recuperate, but output declined again in 1985. Manufacturing is concentrated primarily in the areas of food and tobacco processing, beverages, petroleum refining, and chemicals. In 1996, the industrial sector accounted for 20% of the gross domestic product.

Banking and Finance

The banking system, nationalized in July 1979, is under the supervision of the comptroller general. The National Bank of Nicaragua, established in 1912, has been government-owned since 1940. In 1979, the bank was reorganized to become the National Development Bank. The Central Bank of Nicaragua (Banco Central de Nicaragua), established in 1961, is the bank of issue and also handles all foreign exchange transactions. As of 1979, deposits in foreign banks were prohibited, but in May 1985, the establishment of private exchange houses was permitted. In 1990, legislation was passed that allowed for the establishment of private banks.

By mid-1995, there were ten private banks operating. The state banks are the Banco Central de Nicaragua (the Central Bank), the Banco Nacional de Desarrollo, the Banco Nicaragüense de Industria y Comercio, and the Banco de Crédito Popular. In 1992, the Fondo Nicaragüense de Inversiones was given second-tier bank status. The new private banks are the Banco Mercantil, the Banco de la Producción, the Banco de Préstamos, the Banco de América Central, the Banco de Crédito Centroamericano, the Banco Intercontinent, the Banco de Exportación, the Banco del Café, the Banco Européo de Centroamérica, and the Banco del Campo.

The money supply, as measured by M2, was C1, 843.5 million at the end of 1994. Foreign reserves, at the end of 1996, amounted to $197 million. A small stock market has begun operations.

Economic Development

The Somoza government's 1975–79 National Reconstruction and Development Plan had as its major objective the improvement in living conditions through increased employment, continuing reconstruction of Managua, reduction in the economy's dependence on the external sector, acceleration of regional development, and strengthening of the country's role in CACM. The plan was disrupted by the civil strife in the late 1970s.

After the 1979 revolution, the government nationalized banking, insurance, mining, fishing, forestry, and a number of industrial plans. Although the government officially favored a mixed economy, in practice the private sector took second place in a development strategy that focused on public investment and control.

In response to the macroeconomic problems that arose in 1992, a series of measures were adopted by the Chamorro administration aimed at consolidating the stabilization process, increasing the competitiveness of exports and establishing a base for the promotion of growth.

Nicaragua now appears poised for rapid economic growth. However, long-term success at attracting investment, creating jobs, and reducing poverty depend on its ability to comply with an International Monetary Fund (IMF) program, resolve the thousands of Sandinista-era property confiscation cases, and open its economy to foreign trade.

SOCIAL WELFARE

A social insurance law enacted in 1956 provides for national compulsory coverage of employees against risks of maternity, sickness, employment injury, occupational disease, unemployment, old age, and death. Family allowance legislation enacted in 1982 provides benefits for children under the age of 15.

Women tend to hold traditionally low-paid jobs in the health, education, and textile sectors while occupying few management positions in the private sector. In 1995, however, Nicaragua had a female president and vice-president.

Healthcare

Slow progress in health care was made from the 1960s through the 1980s. Average life expectancy is 68 years. However, malnutrition and anemia remained common, goiter was endemic, and intestinal parasitic infections (a leading cause of death) afflicted over 80% of the population.

In 1990, there were 1.8 hospital beds per 1,000 inhabitants. In 1992, there was about one doctor for every 1,492 people, and 83% of the population had access to health care services.

Housing

Both urban and rural dwellers suffer from a dire lack of adequate housing. As a result of the 1972 earthquake, approximately 53,000 residential units were destroyed or seriously damaged in the Managua area. The Sandinistas launched housing-construction programs, but were hampered by a shortage of hard currency to pay for the construction equipment required.

EDUCATION

Primary and secondary education is free and compulsory between the ages of 6 and 13. In 1994, there were 765,972 pupils in 4,030 primary schools, with 20,626 teachers. In 1993, 203,888 students were enrolled in secondary schools.

Universities include the National Autonomous University of Nicaragua with campuses in Léon and Managua, the Central American University, and the Polytechnic University of Nicaragua. In 1992, there were 35,750 students in 16 institutions of higher learning, with 2,274 instructors.

1999 KEY EVENTS TIMELINE

January

- Two months after Hurricane Mitch hits Central America, 50 tons of supplies bound for Nicaragua, including medicine, remain undelivered in Los Angeles warehouses for lack of money.

- Nicaraguans use U.S.-trained sniff dogs to detect hidden anti-personnel land mines.

February

- President Arnoldo Aleman increased his net worth 3,800 percent in the last 10 years while working in government jobs, according to Nicaragua's comptroller. Aleman brands the report as "denigration, defamation, slander."

March

- President Bill Clinton kneels on parched earth imprinted with the outline of a little girl who died in a mudslide in Nicaragua, and tells the country it deserves world support. The country is still suffering in the aftermath of Hurricane Mitch.

April

- Nicaraguan army experts destroy the first 5,000 of 130,000 land mines in Nicaragua's military arsenal; 5,000 more are destroyed in August.

May

- National transportation strike to demand lower gasoline prices paralyses the nation. At least two are dead and more than 100 are arrested during the strike. The army is called to keep the peace. President Aleman is forced to give in to strikers' demands.

June

- Nicaragua asks the United States for a six-month extension on amnesty granted to its undocumented immigrants in the wake of Hurricane Mitch.

July

- Costa Rica and Nicaragua tussle over border and immigration.

- Nicaraguans observe the 20th anniversary of the Sandinista Revolution that toppled the 40-year Somoza dictatorship. Some wonder what went wrong, others remain happy that Sandinistas are no longer in power. More than 30,000 celebrate the anniversary in Managua.

September

- Nicaragua deports five members of a Corsican separatist group to face various charges in France.

- Less than a year after Hurricane Mitch, many Nicaraguans are forced from their homes by torrential rains.

- President Bill Clinton expands debt-relief plan for poor nations. He includes Nicaragua and Honduras in the list.

- Thousands of armed ex-contra rebels seize two key highway junctions and paralyze traffic through most of the country. They allow traffic to flow after President Aleman says he will deliver land titles promised to the contras during a 1990 peace agreement that ended Nicaragua's civil war.

October

- Torrential rain and floods knock down two bridges along the Pan-American Highway, blocking overland traffic throughout Central America, authorities in Honduras and Nicaragua said.

- President Arnoldo Aleman marries Maria Fernanda Flores Lanzas, a Miami school teacher who fled Nicaragua during the Sandinista regime.

- A drop in world coffee prices translates into losses of $506 million for Central America. Prices are not expected to rise until 2000.

December

- Nicaragua and Honduras meet for talks at the Organization of American States to seek a solution to a new territorial dispute. Nicaragua asks the International Court of Justice to settle the disagreement over the sea border.

ANALYSIS OF EVENTS: 1999

BUSINESS AND THE ECONOMY

In 1999, about 70 percent of Nicaragua's population lived in poverty, and more than half of the work force was unemployed or severely underemployed. Annual per capita income was $435, compared with $1,200 in 1979, when the Sandinistas toppled the Somoza dictatorship. Although the political extremes might argue over who was to blame, it was clear to all that Nicaragua was not living up to expectations. As a reporter from the Washington Post noted, ''Twenty years after the Marxist-led Sandinista National Liberation Front overthrew the Somoza dictatorship with some of the hemisphere's most ambitious promises of social and political reform—and nine years after the U.S.-backed conservatives were elected on the strength of still more promises—Nicaragua is poorer than ever and deeply splintered between the haves and have-nots.''

For Nicaragua's poorer classes, these hard facts recalled the bitterness of life under Somoza and the euphoria of the Sandinista era. On June 19, more than 30,000 Nicaraguans gathered in Managua to celebrate the 20th anniversary of the overthrow of the 40-year Somoza dictatorship. Even the sponsors, the Sandinista National Liberation Front, were surprised by the large turnout. For many Nicaraguans, there was little to celebrate. Despite years of fighting and attempted social reforms, the nation remained the second poorest in the hemisphere, just behind Haiti.

In September 1999 U.S. President Clinton announced that both Nicaragua and Honduras were to be included in a debt-relief plan for the poorer nations. This was welcomed news as a month later, in October, the Nicaraguan government announced a projected deficit of about $236 million for the year 2000. The government was expected to receive $590 million in revenues with projected expenditure of $821.5 million. Officials said the proposed budget set aside $125 million to pay foreign debts.

GOVERNMENT AND POLITICS

With the sluggish economy and growing polarization of wealth the nation's political foes have been forced to talk to each other. President Arnoldo Aleman, a conservative and wealthy businessman and leader of the ruling Liberal Alliance (a coalition of five right and centrist parties), has conducted closed-door meetings with Sandinista party leader Daniel Ortega, who remained a powerful politician despite presidential losses in 1990 and 1996. Reportedly, the two have conducted negotiations on changes in election laws and other constitutional issues, but many Nicaraguans believe the talks are simply an attempt by the two men to preserve power within their parties. In interviews, Aleman said he was not striking any deals with the Sandinistas, and never would. But he also acknowledged that the Sandinistas remained the second most powerful political movement in the country, and could not be ignored.

Aleman was under heavy pressure in 1999. His government capitulated to striking transport workers, and to thousands of armed ex-contra rebels who demanded land promised during a peace agreement that ended Nicaragua's civil war in 1990. He was forced to defend himself against allegations of corruption, and accusations that he used his government jobs and connections to increase his net worth by 3,800 percent in the last 10 years.

Aleman's aides charged that journalists paid by political opponents fueled many of the allegations against Aleman. To prove it, they distributed a list of more than 60 journalists who had received a total of more than $120,000 in government funds during the past fiscal year. Some critics said that Aleman had also manipulated the media, pointing to a published poll claiming that two-thirds of Nicaraguans supported the president. His private life did not escape scrutiny, facing criticism for putting matters of the heart before matters of the state. In October, he married Maria Fernanda Flores Lanzas, a Miami school teacher who fled Nicaragua during the Sandinista regime. He planned a lavish honeymoon in Venice. Through it all, Aleman continued to put a positive spin on the country's problems. ''Of all the countries in Central America, we are the most secure. There is no fear of crime. We respect elections. The army does not answer to the political parties. There is no hyperinflation, and growth is 6 to 7 percent,'' he told the *Washington Post*.

CULTURE AND SOCIETY

In March 1999 President Bill Clinton traveled to Central America to offer help after Hurricane Mitch devastated the area in October 1998. In Nicaragua, Clinton stopped at the site of a village destroyed by a mudslide triggered by the hurricane. At his feet, the parched earth was imprinted with the outline of a little girl, one of about 2,000 people who died in the mudslide. At that spot, he promised to help Nicaragua recover from the devastation.

A year after the hurricane little had changed in Nicaragua. Among the poorest nations in the world, many of its people remained in make-shift shelters built right after Mitch. The country was not prepared for another natural disaster, which came in mid September 1999 when torrential rains began drenching Central America. By October 3, with 11 dead and thousands displaced by high waters, the government of Nicaragua declared a national emergency. Authorities opened new shelters, delivered food, and helped evacuate about 4,000 people throughout the country. In Managua, the rising waters of Lake Nicaragua threatened 20 neighborhoods. In the middle of the lake, waters rose along the shores of Ometepe island, destroying homes and forcing their occupants to flee up Maderas volcano. The Coco River carried away houses in northeastern Nicaragua, where Mitch had already destroyed everything in sight. As the waters began to recede in mid-October, many Nicaraguans again began the difficult task of rebuilding their lives.

Even sports seemed to be under a cloud. In August, Nicaraguans were shocked to read that national boxing hero Alexis Argüello wanted to die after losing a battle against illicit drugs. An article in La Noticia newspaper claimed that the three-time world boxing champion tried to get a friend to inject him with lethal drugs to put him out of his misery. Adored by Nicaragua's young, Argüello had won 90 of his 96 career bouts.

Finally, the fact that Nicaragua's present seems to be mired in the past found its metaphor in the tedious and dangerous daily task of destroying anti-personnel mines. In 1999 a total of 10,000 mines were neutralized as part of an international agreement prohibiting their use. At the close of the civil war the combatants had left up to 130,000 mines buried throughout the countryside. Nicaragua also has been working with the Organization of American States to clear the area along the Nicaraguan-Honduran border, where another 70,000 mines remain buried. During 1999, dogs trained in the U.S. helped sniff for mines at a faster and safer pace, Nicaraguan authorities said.

DIRECTORY

CENTRAL GOVERNMENT
Head of State

President
Arnoldo Aleman Lacayo, Office of the President, Casa de Gobierno, Apdo. 2398, Managua, Nicaragua
PHONE: +505 2282803; 2833675
FAX: +505 2786202

Ministers

Minister of Public Works, the Economy and Commerce
Noel Sacasa Cruz, Ministry of Public Works, the Economy and Commerce, Edificio Central: Km. 6 carretera Masaya, Frente a Camino de Oriente, Apartado Postal No. 8, Managua, Nicaragua
PHONE: +505 2788712; 2775556; 2670003

Minister of Agriculture and Livestock
Mario de Franco Montalván, Ministry of Agriculture and Livestock, Km 8 1/2 Carretera a Masaya, Managua, Nicaragua
PHONE: +505 2760200; 2760202; 2760203

E-MAIL: fosemag@tmx.com.ni

Minister of Defense
Pedro Joaquín Chamorro Barrios; Jaime Cuadra
Somarriba, Ministry of Defense, Del Hotel
Intercontinental 2 c. al Sur, 1 c. Oeste, Managua,
Nicaragua
PHONE: +505 2663580; 2681950; 2684988
E-MAIL: midef@ibw.com.ni

Minister of Education, Culture and Sports
José Antonio Alvarado, Ministry of Education,
Culture and Sports, Centro Cívico, Managua,
Nicaragua
PHONE: +505 2650046; 2650144; 2650146

Minister of Government
Jaime Cuadra Somarriba, Ministry of
Government, Edificio Silvio Mayorga, Managua,
Nicaragua
PHONE: +505 2227538; 2282284; 2283678

Minister of Property and Public Finance
Esteban Duque Estrada, Ministry of Property and
Public Finance, Frente a la Asamblea Nacional,
Managua, Nicaragua
PHONE: +505 2227231; 2227232; 2227233

Minister of the Family
Humberto Belli Pereira, Ministry of the Family,
De la distribuidora Vicky 2 1/2 c. al Oeste,
Managua, Nicaragua
PHONE: +505 2781620; 2785637

Minister of Foreign Relations
Eduardo Montealegre, Ministry of Foreign
Relations, Barrio Altagracia Frente a Costado
Sur Restaurante los Ranchos, Managua,
Nicaragua
PHONE: +505 2666222; 2664097; 2664563

Minister of Health
Lombardo Martínez, Ministry of Health,
Complejo Nacional de Salud "Dra. Concepción
Palacios," Semáforos de Rubenia, 500 mts. al
Este, 2 c. al Sur, Managua, Nicaragua
PHONE: +505 2893482; 2893489; 2897441

Minister of Construction and Transportation
Yamileth Bonilla, Ministry of Construction and
Transportation, Frente al Estadio Nacional,
Managua, Nicaragua
PHONE: +505 2225111; 2225952; 2225955

**Minister of Environment and Natural
Resources**
Roberto Stadthagen, Ministry of Environment
and Natural Resources, Km. 12 1/2 Carretera
Norte, Managua, Nicaragua

PHONE: +505 2331111; 2331113

Minister of Labor
Wilfredo Navarro Moreira, Ministry of Labor,
Estadio Nacional 300 vs al Norte, Managua,
Nicaragua
PHONE: +505 2893482; 2893489; 2897441

POLITICAL ORGANIZATIONS

Partido Comunista de Nicaragua-PCdeN (Communist Party of Nicaragua)

Ciudad Jardín 0-30, Apdo. 4231, Managua,
Nicaragua
NAME: Eli Altamira Pérez

Partido Liberal Independiente-PLI (Liberal Independence Party)

Ciudad Jardín, F-29 Frente a Optica Selecta,
Managua, Nicaragua
NAME: Virgilio Godoy Reyes

Partido Nacional Conservador-PND (National Conservative Party)

Frente Costado Sur Galeria Internacional,
Managua, Nicaragua
NAME: Silviano Matamoros Lacayo

Alianza Popular Conservadora-APC (Conservative Popular Alliance Party)

Iglesia El Carmen, 2 c. al Norte, Managua,
Nicaragua
NAME: Francisco Anzoátegui Lacayo; Myriam
Argüello Morales

Frente Sandinista de Liberación Nacional-FSLN (Sandinista National Liberation Front)

PHONE: +505 2660845
FAX: +505 2661560
NAME: Daniel Ortega Saavedra

Partido Liberal-Pali (Liberal Party)

Restaurante Terraza, 1 c. Abajo, Apdo J-47,
Managua, Nicaragua
PHONE: +505 2663875
NAME: Andrés Zúñiga

Partido Social Cristiano Nicaragüense-PSCN (Nicaraguan Social Christian Party)

Iglesia Larreynaga, 1 1/2c. al Lago, Apdo 4774,
Managua, Nicaragua
NAME: Erick Ramírez

Partido Socialista Nicaragüense-PSN (Nicaraguan Socialist Party)

1er Callejón, Col. Mántica de Estatua Montoya, 1 c. al Norte, Managua, Nicaragua
PHONE: +505 2662321
FAX: +505 2662936
NAME: Gustavo Tablada Zelaya

Unión Demócrata Cristiana-UDC (Christian Democratic Union)

De Iglesia Santa Ana, 2 c. Abajo, Barrio Santa Ana, Apdo 3089, Managua, Nicaragua
PHONE: +505 2662576

Partido Liberal Constitucionalista (Liberal Constitutional Party)

Alianza Liberal Nicabox 498, P.O. Box 02-5640, Miami, Florida 33102-5640
PHONE: +(505) 2651125
FAX: +(505) 2650111
TITLE: President
NAME: Arnoldo Alemán

DIPLOMATIC REPRESENTATION
Embassies in Nicaragua

Belgium
Calle 27 de Mayofrente a gasolinera, Esso Edificio Targa Industrial, Apartado Postal 3397, Managua, Nicaragua
PHONE: +505 2223202
FAX: +505 2224660

Canada
Costado oriental de la Casa Nazareth, Una Quadra Arriba, Calle Noval, Apartado Postal 25, Managua, Nicaragua
PHONE: +505 2680433
FAX: +505 2680437

Denmark
Royal Danish Embassy, De Plaza España, 1c. Abajo, 2c. Al lago, 1/2c. Abajo, Apartado Postal 4942, Managua, Nicaragua
PHONE: +505 2680250
FAX: +505 2668095
E-MAIL: denmark@ns.tmx.com.niem

France
De la Iglesia el Carmen 1 cuadra 1/2 Abajo, Managua, Nicaragua

Italy
De la Estatua de Montoya 1 cuadra al Lago, Managua, Nicaragua

PHONE: +505 2666486; 2662961
FAX: +505 2663987

Japan
Plaza Espafia 1 cuadra abajo y 1 cuadra al lago, Bolonia, Apartado Postal 1789, Managua, Nicaragua

Russia
Apartado Postal 249, Las Colinas, Calle Vista Alegre 214, Managua, Nicaragua
PHONE: +505 2799544; 2799838; 2760131
FAX: +505 2760179

Taiwan
Embassy of the Republic of China, Planes de Altamira, Lotes #19 y 20 Frente de la Cancha de Tenis, Apartado Postal 4653, Managua, Nicaragua
PHONE: +505 2706054
FAX: +505 2674025

United Kingdom
Plaza Churchill Reparto 'Los Robles' Managua Apartado A-169, Managua, Nicaragua
PHONE: +505 2780014; 2780887
FAX: +505 2784085

United States
KM. 4 1/2 Carretera Sur, Managua, Nicaragua
PHONE: +505 2666010
FAX: +505 2666046

JUDICIAL SYSTEM
Supreme Court of Justice
Court of Appeals

FURTHER READING
Articles

"Americas Renew Focus on War's Ghosts: Land Mines." *The Seattle Times*, 11 January 1999.

"Clinton Urges World Support in Central America's Moment of Need." The Associated Press, 9 March 1999.

"More than 100,000 People Flee Floodwaters in Central America." *Los Angeles Times*, 26 September 1999.

"A Nation Tempered by Poetry." *Los Angeles Times*, 26 July 1999.

"Nicaragua: Focusing on a Resilient People in a Bright, Exuberant Country." *The Seattle Times*, 5 September 1999.

"Nicaragua Gives in to Transport Workers." *The Miami Herald*, 6 May 1999.

"In Nicaragua, News Handouts may be Money." *The Miami Herald*, 19 April 1999.

"Nicaraguan President Fends Off Accusations of Enrichment." *The Miami Herald*, 28 February 1999.

"Nicaraguans Plant the Seeds of Recovery." *Los Angeles Times*, 21 February 1999.

"Politicians' Bribes Exposed in Nicaragua." *The Seattle Times*, 11 April 1999.

"Taiwan Wins Central America Support for U.N." *The Seattle Times*, 11 August 1999.

"Twenty Years After the Revolution, Nicaraguans Wonder How it All Could Have Gone so Wrong." *The Miami Herald*, 18 July 1999.

"Twenty Years After the Sandinista Revolution: Regimes Change, Poverty Remains in Nicaragua." *The Washington Post*, 20 July 1999.

Internet

Central Intelligence Agency. *World Factbook, 1998*. Available Online @ www.odci.gov/cia/publications/factbook/ (December 13, 1999).

NICARAGUA: STATISTICAL DATA

For sources and notes see "Sources of Statistics" in the front of each volume.

GEOGRAPHY

Geography (1)

Area:

Total: 129,494 sq km.

Land: 120,254 sq km.

Water: 9,240 sq km.

Area—comparative: slightly smaller than New York State.

Land boundaries:

Total: 1,231 km.

Border countries: Costa Rica 309 km, Honduras 922 km.

Coastline: 910 km.

Climate: tropical in lowlands, cooler in highlands.

Terrain: extensive Atlantic coastal plains rising to central interior mountains; narrow Pacific coastal plain interrupted by volcanoes.

Natural resources: gold, silver, copper, tungsten, lead, zinc; timber; fish.

Land use:

Arable land: 9%

Permanent crops: 1%

Permanent pastures: 46%

Forests and woodland: 27%

Other: 17% (1993 est.).

HUMAN FACTORS

Demographics (2A)

	1990	1995	1998	2000	2010	2020	2030	2040	2050
Population	3,590.7	4,185.3	4,583.4	4,851.0	6,181.6	7,479.1	8,723.5	9,852.2	10,817.0
Net migration rate (per 1,000 population)	NA	NA	NA	NA	NA	NA	NA	NA	NA
Births	NA	NA	NA	NA	NA	NA	NA	NA	NA
Deaths	NA	NA	NA	NA	NA	NA	NA	NA	NA
Life expectancy - males	60.7	63.0	64.3	65.1	68.9	72.0	74.4	76.3	77.6
Life expectancy - females	65.1	67.7	69.1	70.1	74.2	77.6	80.2	82.1	83.6
Birth rate (per 1,000)	39.1	39.0	36.0	34.0	26.1	21.5	18.3	15.9	14.3
Death rate (per 1,000)	7.3	6.3	5.8	5.4	4.3	3.9	4.2	4.9	6.1
Women of reproductive age (15-49 yrs.)	822.8	995.5	1,113.9	1,196.5	1,617.3	2,074.1	2,407.4	2,602.3	2,661.1
of which are currently married	NA	NA	NA	NA	NA	NA	NA	NA	NA
Fertility rate	4.9	4.7	4.3	4.0	3.0	2.4	2.2	2.0	2.0

Except as noted, values for vital statistics are in thousands; life expectancy is in years.

Health Personnel (3)

Total health expenditure as a percentage of GDP, 1990-1997[a]

Public sector 5.3

Private sector 3.4

Total[b] 8.6

Health expenditure per capita in U.S. dollars, 1990-1997[a]

Purchasing power parity 174

Total 37

Availability of health care facilities per 100,000 people

Hospital beds 1990-1997[a] 180

Doctors 1993[c] 82

Nurses 1993[c] 56

Health Indicators (4)

Life expectancy at birth

1980 59

1997 68

Daily per capita supply of calories (1996) 2,328

Total fertility rate births per woman (1997) 3.9

Maternal mortality ratio per 100,000 live births (1990-97) . . . . .160[c]

Safe water % of population with access (1995) 62

Sanitation % of population with access (1995) 59

Consumption of iodized salt % of households (1992-98)[a] 98

Smoking prevalence

Male % of adults (1985-95)[a] . . . .

Female % of adults (1985-95)[a] . . . .

Tuberculosis incidence per 100,000 people (1997) 95

Adult HIV prevalence % of population ages 15-49 (1997) 0.19

Infants and Malnutrition (5)

Under-5 mortality rate (1997) 57

% of infants with low birthweight (1990-97) 9

Births attended by skilled health staff % of total[a] . . .61

% fully immunized (1995-97)

TB 100

DPT 94

Polio 100

Measles 94

Prevalence of child malnutrition under age 5 (1992-97)[b] 12

Ethnic Division (6)

Mestizo (mixed Amerindian and white) 69%

White 17%

Black 9%

Amerindian 5%

Religions (7)

Roman Catholic 95%

Protestant 5%

Languages (8)

Spanish (official). English- and Amerindian-speaking minorities on Atlantic coast.

EDUCATION

Public Education Expenditures (9)

Public expenditure on education (% of GNP)

1980 . . . . .3.4

1996 . . . . .3.7

Expenditure per student

Primary % of GNP per capita

1980 . . . . .8.2

1996 . . . . .11.4[1]

Secondary % of GNP per capita

1980 . . . . .15.5

1996 . . . .

Tertiary % of GNP per capita

1980 . . . . .25.8

1996 . . . .

Expenditure on teaching materials

Primary % of total for level (1996) . . . . .0.9[1]

Secondary % of total for level (1996) . . . .

Primary pupil-teacher ratio per teacher (1996) . . . . .38[1]

Duration of primary education years (1995) 6

Literacy Rates (11A)

In thousands and percent[1]	1990	1995	2000	2010
Illiterate population (15+ yrs.)	689	822	956	1,246
Literacy rate - total adult pop. (%)	64.0	65.7	67.2	69.9
Literacy rate - males (%)	63.1	64.6	65.9	68.2
Literacy rate - females (%)	64.8	66.6	68.4	71.6

GOVERNMENT & LAW

Political Parties (12)

National Assembly	% of seats
Liberal Alliance 46.03	
Sandinista National Liberation Front (FSLN) 36.55	
Nicaraguan Party of the Christian Road (PCCN) . .3.73	
National Conservative Party (PCN) 2.12	
Sandinista Renovation Movement (MRS) 1.33	

Government Budget (13A)

Year: 1994

Total Expenditures: 4,726.7 Millions of Gold Cordobas

Expenditures as a percentage of the total by function:

General public services and public order 17.61	
Defense 5.82	
Education 15.49	
Health 13.36	
Social Security and Welfare 14.70	
Housing and community amenities 3.30	
Recreational, cultural, and religious affairs 1.30	
Fuel and energy 26	
Agriculture, forestry, fishing, and hunting 2.70	
Mining, manufacturing, and construction . . . .-	
Transportation and communication 8.02	
Other economic affairs and services 46	

Military Affairs (14B)

	1990	1991	1992	1993	1994	1995
Military expenditures						
Current dollars (mil.)	198	45	38	34	33	34
1995 constant dollars (mil.)	228	49	41	36	34	34
Armed forces (000)	28	20	15	15	14	14
Gross national product (GNP)						
Current dollars (mil.)	1,262	1,172	1,231	1,308	1,268	1,576
1995 constant dollars (mil.)	1,450	1,295	1,324	1,371	1,300	1,576
Central government expenditures (CGE)						
1995 constant dollars (mil.)	793	493	547	535	605	654
People (mil.)	3.6	3.7	3.8	3.9	4.0	4.2
Military expenditure as % of GNP	15.7	3.8	3.1	2.6	2.6	2.2
Military expenditure as % of CGE	28.8	10.0	7.6	6.7	5.6	5.3
Military expenditure per capita (1995 $)	63	13	11	9	8	8
Armed forces per 1,000 people (soldiers)	7.8	5.4	3.9	3.8	3.5	3.4
GNP per capita (1995 $)	404	349	347	321	321	379
Arms imports[6]						
Current dollars (mil.)	70	80	5	5	0	0
1995 constant dollars (mil.)	80	88	5	5	0	0
Arms exports[6]						
Current dollars (mil.)	0	0	30	0	0	40
1995 constant dollars (mil.)	0	0	32	0	0	40
Total imports[7]						
Current dollars (mil.)	638	751	855	746	875	962
1995 constant dollars (mil.)	733	830	920	782	897	962
Total exports[7]						
Current dollars (mil.)	331	272	223	267	351	520
1995 constant dollars (mil.)	380	301	240	280	360	520
Arms as percent of total imports[8]	11.0	10.7	.6	.7	0	0
Arms as percent of total exports[8]	0	0	13.5	0	0	7.7

Crime (15)

Crime rate (for 1997)

Crimes reported 69,100

Total persons convicted 45,326

Crimes per 100,000 population . . . . .NA

Persons responsible for offenses

Total number of suspects 35,500

Total number of female suspects 3,350

Total number of juvenile suspects 5,350

LABOR FORCE

Labor Force (16)

Total (million) 1.5

Services 54%

Agriculture 31%

Industry 15%

Data for 1995 est.

Unemployment Rate (17)

16%; underemployment 36% (1996 est.)

PRODUCTION SECTOR

Electric Energy (18)

Capacity .457,000 kW (1995)

Production . . . . .1.76 billion kWh (1995)

Consumption per capita . . . . .416 kWh (1995)

Transportation (19)

Highways:

total: 18,000 km

paved: 1,818 km

unpaved: 16,182 km (1996 est.)

Waterways: 2,220 km, including 2 large lakes

Pipelines: crude oil 56 km

Merchant marine: none

Airports: 185 (1997 est.)

Airports—with paved runways:

total: 13

over 3,047 m: 1

2,438 to 3,047 m: 1

1,524 to 2,437 m: 3

914 to 1,523 m: 3

under 914 m: 5 (1997 est.)

Airports—with unpaved runways:

total: 172

1,524 to 2,437 m: 1

914 to 1,523 m: 27

under 914 m: 144 (1997 est.)

Top Agricultural Products (20)

Coffee, bananas, sugarcane, cotton, rice, corn, cassava (tapioca), citrus, beans; beef, veal, pork, poultry, dairy products.

MANUFACTURING SECTOR

GDP & Manufacturing Summary (21)

Detailed value added figures are listed by both International Standard Industry Code (ISIC) and product title.

	1980	1985	1990	1994
GDP ($-1990 mil.)[1]	4,790	4,945	4,232	4,349
Per capita ($-1990)[1]	1,710	1,531	1,151	1,017
Manufacturing share (%) (current prices)[1]	12.8	13.8	6.2	*17.9*
Manufacturing				
Value added ($-1990 mil.)[1]	374	389	260	*272*
Industrial production index	100	*120*	110	*115*
Value added ($ mil.)	242	982	*1,579*	*653*
Gross output ($ mil.)	612	1,587	*2,404*	*975*
Employment (000)	34	39	*47*	*56*
Profitability (% of gross output)				
Intermediate input (%)	60	38	*34*	*33*
Wages and salaries inc. supplements (%)	12	10	*11*	*12*
Gross operating surplus	28	52	*55*	*55*
Productivity ($)				
Gross output per worker	18,017	38,009	*47,856*	*16,343*
Value added per worker	7,131	23,515	*31,430*	*10,935*
Average wage (inc. supplements)	2,078	4,152	*5,725*	*2,084*
Value added ($ mil.)				
311/2 Food products	52	268	*393*	*152*

MANUFACTURING SECTOR

GDP & Manufacturing Summary (21)

	1980	1985	1990	1994
313 Beverages	48	227	421	178
314 Tobacco products	28	64	118	51
321 Textiles	9	70	102	40
322 Wearing apparel	4	23	44	18
323 Leather and fur products	2	6	12	4
324 Footwear	4	27	42	18
331 Wood and wood products	3	10	14	6
332 Furniture and fixtures	1	4	4	1
341 Paper and paper products	1	3	3	1
342 Printing and publishing	4	22	36	15
351 Industrial chemicals	11	23	31	13
352 Other chemical products	14	56	100	45
353 Petroleum refineries	35	78	111	47
354 Miscellaneous petroleum and coal products	—	1	2	1
355 Rubber products	1	6	11	5
356 Plastic products	4	20	29	12
361 Pottery, china and earthenware	—	2	—	—
362 Glass and glass products	—	1	1	1
369 Other non-metal mineral products	7	17	23	10
371 Iron and steel	—	1	2	1
372 Non-ferrous metals	—	—	—	—
381 Metal products	9	40	62	26
382 Non-electrical machinery	—	3	4	2
383 Electrical machinery	1	5	8	4
384 Transport equipment	1	3	4	2
385 Professional and scientific equipment	1	—	—	—
390 Other manufacturing industries	—	2	2	1

FINANCE, ECONOMICS, & TRADE

Economic Indicators (22)

National product: GDP—purchasing power parity—$9.3 billion (1997 est.)

National product real growth rate: 6% (1997 est.)

National product per capita: $2,100 (1997 est.)

Inflation rate—consumer price index: 11.6% (1996)

Balance of Payments (23)

	1992	1993	1994	1995	1996
Exports of goods (f.o.b.)	223	267	351	530	675
Imports of goods (f.o.b.)	−771	−659	−785	−865	−1,052
Trade balance	−548	−392	−433	−335	−377
Services - debits	−651	−591	−644	−584	−557
Services - credits	94	106	108	121	143
Private transfers (net)	258	186	193	230	262
Government transfers (net)	78	88	82	75	95
Overall balance	−769	−604	−694	−492	−435

FINANCE, ECONOMICS, & TRADE

Exchange Rates (24)

Exchange rates:

Gold cordobas (C$) per US$1

October 1997	9.76
1996	8.44
1995	7.55
1994	6.72
1993	5.62

Top Import Origins (25)

$1.1 billion (c.i.f., 1996)

Origins	%
Central America	NA
United States	NA
Venezuela	NA
Japan	NA

NA stands for not available.

Top Export Destinations (26)

$635 million (f.o.b., 1996).

Destinations	%
United States	NA
Central America	NA
Germany	NA
Canada	NA

NA stands for not available.

Economic Aid (27)

Recipient: ODA, $NA. NA stands for not available.

Import Export Commodities (28)

Import Commodities	Export Commodities
Consumer goods	Coffee
Machinery and equipment	Seafood
	Meat
Petroleum products	Sugar
	Gold
	Bananas

NIGER

Republic of Niger
République du Niger

INTRODUCTORY SURVEY

RECENT HISTORY

The French entered Niger at the close of the nineteenth century and pushed steadily eastward, encircling Lake Chad with military outposts by 1900. In 1901, they established Niger as a military district, part of a larger unit known as Haut-Sénégal et Niger. After putting down a Tuareg rebellion that began during World War I (1914–18), the French made Niger a colony in 1922. It had a governor but was administered from Paris. World War II (1939–45) barely touched Niger, since the country was too isolated to be of use to the French anti-Nazi forces.

On 19 December 1958, Niger's Territorial Assembly voted to become an independent state within the French Community. On 3 August 1960, the Republic of the Niger was proclaimed, and Hamani Diori became its first president.

Diori was able to stay in power throughout the 1960s and early 1970s. However, unrest developed as Niger suffered from the drought of the early 1970s. On 15 April 1974, the Diori government was overthrown by a military takeover led by Lieutenant Colonel Seyni Kountché, the former chief of staff. Kountché then assumed the presidency. The former president was put under house arrest from 1974 to 1980. Kountché died of a brain tumor in November 1987, and Colonel 'Ali Seybou (now Brigadier General), the army chief of staff, was appointed president.

The National Movement for the Development of Society (MNSD) was created in 1989 as Niger's

---

CAPITAL: Niamey.

FLAG: The flag is a tricolor of orange, white, and green horizontal stripes, with an orange circle at the center of the white stripe.

ANTHEM: *La Nigérienne.*

MONETARY UNIT: The Communauté Financière Africaine franc (CFA Fr) is a paper currency with one basic official rate based on the French franc (CFA Fr = 1 French franc). There are coins of 1, 2, 5, 10, 25, 50, 100, and 500 CFA francs, and notes of 50, 100, 500, 1,000, 5,000, and 10,000 CFA francs. CFA Fr1 = $0.00196 (or $1 = CFA Fr510.65).

WEIGHTS AND MEASURES: The metric system is the legal standard.

HOLIDAYS: New Year's Day, 1 January; Anniversary of 1974 military takeover, 15 April; Labor Day, 1 May; Independence Day, 3 August; Proclamation of the Republic, 18 December; Christmas, 25 December. Movable religious holidays include 'Id al-Fitr, 'Id al-'Adha', and Milad an-Nabi.

TIME: 1 PM = noon GMT.

LOCATION AND SIZE: A landlocked country, the Republic of the Niger is the largest state in West Africa, with an area of 1,267,000 square kilometers (489,191 square miles), slightly less than twice the size of the state of Texas. It has a total boundary length of 5,621 kilometers (3,492 miles). Niger's capital city, Niamey, is located in the southwestern part of the country.

CLIMATE: Niger, one of the hottest countries in the world, has three basic climatic zones: the Sahara desert in the north, the semidesert region to the south of the desert, and the Sudan in the southwest corner stretching across Niger and Chad.

The intense heat of the Saharan zone often causes the slight rainfall to evaporate before it hits the ground. At Bilma in the east, annual rainfall is only 2 centimeters (0.79 inches), compared with 63.6 centimeters (25 inches) at Niamey in the southwest. At Niamey, the average daily temperature fluctuates from 24°C (75°F) in January to 29°C (83°F) in July.

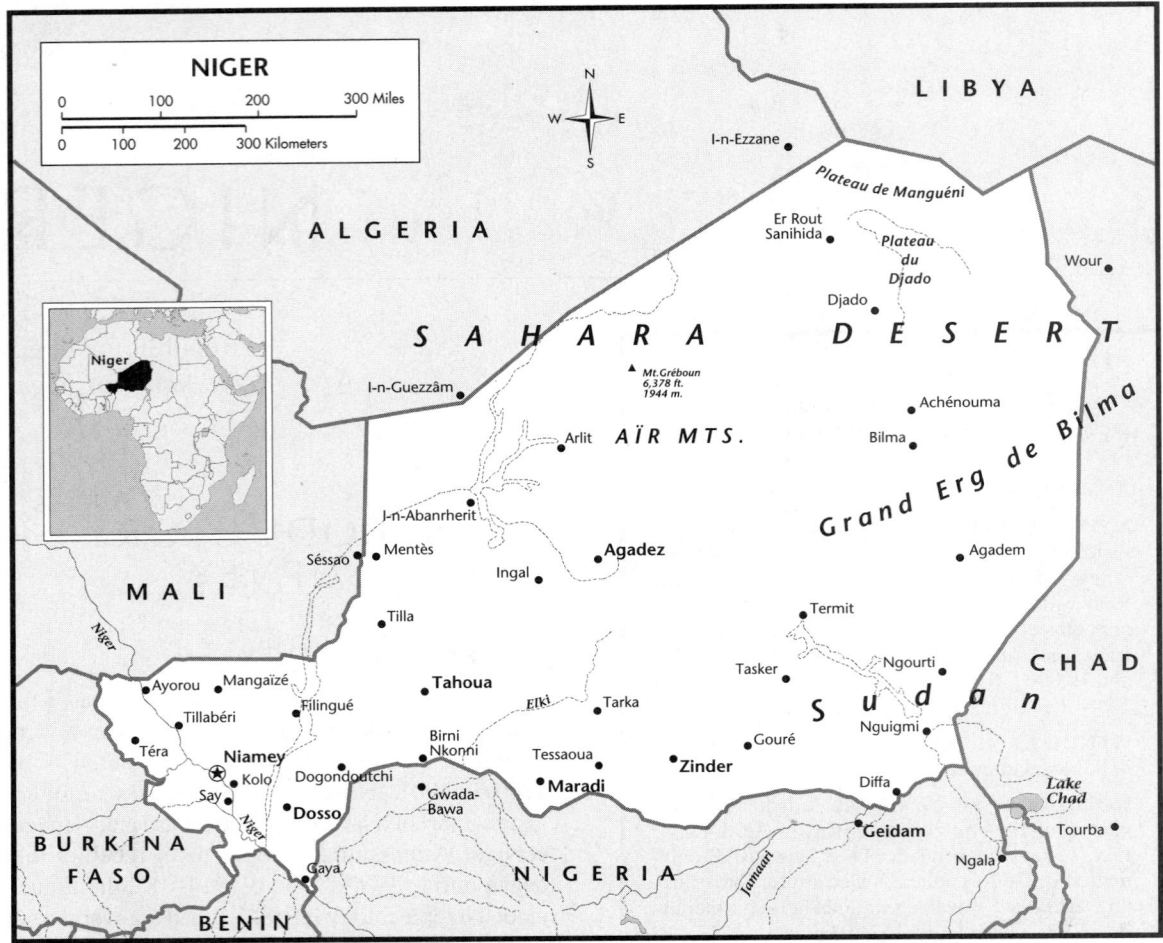

sole political party. Since then, however, there have been demands for multiparty democracy. The president agreed to the calling of a National Conference (July–October 1991) to prepare a new constitution. An interim government, headed by Amadou Cheiffou, was appointed. After the adoption of the new constitution in December 1992, a series of elections were held. In the elections, Mahamane Ousmane was elected president with 54% of the vote.

The new government has attempted to control a Tuareg rebellion in the north. It accuses Libya of encouraging the Tuaregs. Others accuse the Niger government of showing favoritism for members of the Zarma (or Djerma), one of the five major ethnic groups in Niger. High level talks, under the joint mediation of Algeria, Burkina Faso, and France, were resumed and led to a peace accord in April 1995.

After the legislative elections of January 1995, there was a power struggle for the cabinet appoint-

ments of the prime minister. The president and prime minister fought over policy and power during 1995. In January 1996, Colonel Ibrahim Bare Maïnassara led a military coup that removed the president and dissolved the Assembly. A civilian prime minister, Boukary Adji, was put in office within a month after the coup. In May 1996, a draft constitution was submitted for a national vote and was approved. A ban on political parties was ended and civil liberties were restored. Maïnassara was elected president with 52% of the vote in July 1996.

GOVERNMENT

A national conference from July to October 1991 drafted a new, multiparty democratic constitution that was approved on 26 December 1992. It established the Third Republic with a National Assembly of 83 deputies chosen by popular and competitive elections, a president likewise elected, and a prime minister elected by the Assembly. The new government was sworn in on 23 April 1993.

In January 1996, the government was overthrown with relatively little violence by Colonel Ibrahim Bare Maïnassara. Within six months, the regime had drafted and submitted a new constitution for national approval. The constitution was approved on 12 May 1996.

Judiciary

The 1992 constitution called for an independent judiciary. The Supreme Court is now the final court of appeals. Special courts deal with civil service corruption. There are also magistrates' courts, eight labor courts, and justices of the peace in 19 administrative districts. Traditional and customary courts hear cases involving divorce or inheritance. Customary courts are presided over by a legal practitioner with basic legal training who is advised about local tradition by a local official.

Political Parties

After the constitutional referendum of December 1992 introduced multiparty democracy, several new parties were formed.

Although the National Movement for the Development of Society (MNSD) is the largest party in the legislature (29 of 83 seats), it did not form the government. A short-lived coalition of nine parties known as the Alliance of the Forces of Change (AFC) controlled the National Assembly and the presidency. In January 1996 the military stepped in and dissolved the Assembly and overthrew the president. All political parties were banned until May, when a new constitution was approved.

DEFENSE

Niger's army numbered 5,200 in 1995. There were 100 personnel in the air force. France provides military advisers and is the chief source of military equipment. Niger spends $21 million on defense (1995).

ECONOMIC AFFAIRS

Niger is a dry, landlocked country with much of its territory located in the Sahara desert. The economy depends mainly on uranium mining, foreign aid, livestock raising, and farming.

In January 1994 France suddenly devalued the CFA franc, causing its value to drop in half overnight. The devaluation caused Niger's trade relationship with Nigeria to improve and it boosted revenue from exports.

Public Finance

Budgets are nominally balanced but only through the infusion of foreign loan funds and grants. Expenditures have been severely constrained because of the fall in receipts from the sale of uranium ore due to decline in world demand. The end of the uranium boom in the late 1980s left the public sector poorly equipped to adapt, as public expenditures had focused on infrastructure and construction projects at the expense of agricultural development. Consequently, heavy foreign debts were incurred.

The U.S. Central Intelligence Agency estimates that, in 1995, government revenues totaled approximately $188 million and expenditures $400 million, including capital expenditures of $125 million. External debt totaled $1.41 billion.

Income

In 1997 Niger's gross national product (GNP) was $6.3 billion at current prices, or about $670 per person. For the period 1985–95 the average inflation rate was 1.3%, resulting in a decline in GNP of 2.1% per person.

Industry

Manufacturing consists mainly of the processing of agricultural products and includes a groundnut (edible root) oil plant, rice mills, flour mills, cotton gins, and tanneries. A textile mill and cement plant are in operation, and light industries produce beer and soft drinks, processed meats, baked goods, soaps and detergents, perfume, plastic and metal goods, farm equipment, and construction materials.

Banking and Finance

The Central Bank of the West African States (Banque Centrale des États de l'Afrique de l'Ouest–BCEAO) is the bank of issue for Niger and other West African states. Niger has a monetary committee that reports to the BCEAO and works under BCEAO general rules but possesses autonomy in internal credit matters.

Two development banks remain following the collapse of the Banque de développement de la república du Niger (BDRN) in 1990: Crédit du Niger (CN), and the Caisse nationale du crédit agricole (CNCA). Three commercial banks collapsed in Niger between 1988 and early 1992: the Banque internationale pour le commerce et l'industrie-Niger (BICI-N); the Banque de crédit et de commerce (BCC), which the African Development Bank's Nigeria Trust Fund agreed to take over following the collapse of the parent bank, the Bank of Credit and Commerce International (BCCI); and the Banque Islamique du Niger (BIN), which closed in February 1992. Banque Meridien-BIAO du Niger was taken over in September 1995 in a combined purchased by Banque Belgolaise of Belgium, which took 35%, and Cofipa, a European investment group (15%), the remaining 50% of the equity being sold to private Nigerian interests. The bank changed its name to BIAO-Niger. The Banque arabe libyenne et nigérienne pour le commerce extérieur (Balinex) was rescued in March 1992 when Libya announced a CFA Fr746 million loan to increase its capital. Other commercial banks include the Nigeria International Bank Niamey, owned by Citibank, and the Banque Massraf Fayçal Al Islami-Niger.

Money supply, as measured by M2, amounted to CFA FR134.18 billion at the end of 1995.

Economic Development

Government development programs have had three basic aims: first, to diversify production of foodstuffs; second, to develop underground water resources; and third, to develop and improve the country's infrastructure. France is the leading bilateral aid donor.

SOCIAL WELFARE

The National Fund of Social Security provides pensions, family allowances, and workers' compensation for employees in the private sector. Civil servants participate in a national insurance fund and also receive family allowances.

Women are frequently denied educational and employment opportunities. Young girls have limited access to education.

Healthcare

In 1992, there were about 3 physicians per 100,000 people. There were 38 medical centers throughout the country. Only 30% of the population had access to health care services in 1993. The average life expectancy is 47 years.

Housing

Most government buildings and many houses in the metropolitan centers are essentially French in style. The Tuareg nomads live in covered tents, while the Fulani live in small collapsible huts made of straw mats.

EDUCATION

The adult illiteracy rate stood at 86% in 1995 (males: 79.1% and females: 93.4%). Schooling is compulsory for children aged 7–15. In 1993, there were 2,656 primary schools with 12,216 teachers and 394,063 pupils. In 1992, there were 80,009 pupils in secondary schools. Only 33% of secondary school students were female. In 1991, 4,513 students were enrolled in higher institutions, including the National School of Administration in Niamey, the University of Niamey, and the Islamic University of West Africa at Say.

1999 KEY EVENTS TIMELINE

January

- Opposition parties accuse President Ibrahim Mainassara of abusing his office and public funds, and of monopolizing state radio and television for political propaganda.

February

- The bodies of 150 members of the Democratic Revolutionary Front, Toubou nomads who disappeared last year, are found in eastern Niger.

- Local elections are disturbed by violence.

March

- Niger authorities meet with traditional healers to fight against desertification.

April

- Troops and tanks roll into the capital of Niamey, closing the country's borders.

- President Ibrahim Bare Mainassara is assassinated by his bodyguards at Niamey airport. Prime Minister Ibrahim Assane Mayaki calls his death a tragic accident.

- Daouda Malam Wanké, head of the Presidential Guard Unit, is named president of the interim government.

- The French government and international organizations cancel financial aid to Niger.

May

- Niger's government is completely restructured; former officials are put under house arrest and freedom of the press is restored.

June

- Toubou rebels, led by Issa Lamine, accuse the new government of failing to honor a peace agreement signed with the former administration.

- Authorities declare an official investigation of Mainassara's assassination.

July

- Writer Gremah Boucar wins one of Human Rights Watch's Hellman-Hammette grants.

- Army Chief of Staff Lieutenant Colonel Soumanu Zangruina is to be replaced, and the military restructured.

- A new constitution is created, providing amnesty to those involved in April's military coup and creating a basis for democratic elections. Voters support the constitution in a referendum.

September

- The World Bank freezes disbursements to Niger because of the country's $1.9 million debt on loan payments.

- General strikes take place in Niger. Doctors and journalists, who have not been paid in months, are among the participants.

October

- Elections are held to end military rule through the interim government.

November

- A run-off ballot is set because none of the seven candidates for president win a majority in the election.

December

- Tandja Mamadou is sworn in as president on December 22. He appoints Hama Amadou prime minister, a position Amadou previously held during 1995 under then-president Mahamane Ousmane.

ANALYSIS OF EVENTS: 1999

BUSINESS AND THE ECONOMY

Although the Republic of Niger is primarily a desert land, a small area along the southern border supports the country's main business in agriculture. Ninety percent of the population lives and works in and around the capital of Niamey and nearby towns, where trade in cattle and other produce takes place. Since the 1970s, when a large reserve of Uranium was found on Niger's soil, heavy mining has provided revenue, the supply of which has dwindled over the years. The majority of trade occurs with neighboring Nigeria, and the country's former colonial occupier, France.

Niger's currency is still pegged to the French Franc, called the CFA Franc, and the majority of foreign aid comes from France. With a yearly GDP of $970 per capita and very little foreign investment Niger needs all the financial support it can get. About half of the country's revenue comes from foreign aid, and even this was denied to the government after the April coup this year.

France, Japan, and the European Union halted trade and aid to Niger to protest its military rule until democratic elections were set up in October. The World Bank froze disbursements in September because of $1.9 million in unpaid loans. By November, however, the World Bank was again assisting Niger. With the implementation of civilian rule slated for the year 2000 there are hopes that additional aid will return, despite the country's history of military rule.

GOVERNMENT AND POLITICS

Former President Ibrahim Bare Mainassara came to power in 1996 during a coup d'état that ousted Niger's first democratically elected government. Mainassara's military administration was accused of abusing access to public funds and of using the state radio and television for political propaganda. Pro-democracy activists reported vote-rigging in February's local elections, and in the same month 150 members of an opposition party, the Democratic Revolutionary Front, led by Issa Lamine, were found massacred in eastern Niger.

The April coup and assassination of President Mainassara was carried out at Niamey's airport by the head of Mainassara's Presidential Guard Unit, Daouda Malam Wanké, and Niger's military. Mr. Wanké named himself head of the National Council for Reconciliation, which claimed the goal of bringing citizen rule back to Niger. The party came under extreme criticism for the assassination, prompting the new leaders to immediately set up a new constitution scheduled for a June referendum.

The constitution absolved the military of any wrongdoing in the coup and prepared for democratic presidential elections in October.

Mainasarra's Prime Minister, Ibrahim Assana Mayaki, retained his position after the coup, calling Mainasarra's death an "unfortunate accident." Mayaki will share power with the newly elected president, who will be chosen in November. The candidates in the election are Colonel Tandja Mamadou of the former ruling party and ex-prime minister Mahamadou Issafou. International observers have been satisfied by election conditions, returning some legitimacy to the governing body, but military rule will not end until 2000. In the meantime relations between Niger and Libya may sour—Yusuf Bashar, diplomat to Libya, was arrested for his friendship with the Libyan government and his loyalty to the assassinated president; he was later released. Libya lays claim to 19,400 square km of land in northern Niger.

CULTURE AND SOCIETY

The majority of Niger's population, about 75%, are Husa farmers on the southern border, while the rest are nomadic peoples of the desert. Recently government officials called upon traditional tribal healers to help in the fight against desertification, using native plants to save arable land. Though the land is rich with valuable minerals, including uranium, few wish to take the risks involved with mining in the Saharan desert.

The native cultures of Niger are also not very amenable to foreign enterprise and western ideals. Most citizens in Niger are Muslim, many of whom protested this year against government ratification of an international convention meant to eliminate discrimination against women, claiming that "women already have all the liberties permitted by Islam."

In Niger's society it is not only women who have been oppressed, but also political parties and writers opposing the ruling party. In 1999 Mr. Gremah Boucar was awarded one of Human Rights Watch's Hellman-Hammette, granted to those who are the target of political persecution grants. A number of pro-democracy movements have sprung up around the country since former President Mainassara came to power in a 1996 coup.

DIRECTORY

CENTRAL GOVERNMENT
Head of State

Head of State; Chairman of the National Reconciliation Council
Tandja Mamadou, Office of the National Reconciliation Council

Prime Minister
Hama Amadou, Office of the Prime Minister

Ministers

Minister of Agriculture and Animal Breeding
Tassiou Aminou, Ministry of Agriculture and Animal Breeding

Minister of Civil Service, Labor and Employment
Mahamane Ousmane, Ministry of Civil Service, Labor and Employment

Minister of Mines and Energy
Yahaya Bare, Ministry of Mines and Energy

Minister of Foreign Affairs and Cooperation
Aichatou Minaoudou, Ministry of Foreign Affairs and Cooperation

Minister of National Defense
Moussa Moumouni Djermakoye, Ministry of National Defense

Minister of National Education
Baringaye Ahmed Akilou, Ministry of National Education

Minister of Public Health
Sani Mamane, Ministry of Public Health

Minister of Water Resources and Environment
Ali Seyni Gado, Ministry of Water Resources and Environment

POLITICAL ORGANIZATIONS
Alliance for Democracy and Progress

TITLE: Chairman
NAME: Issoufou Bachard

Democratic and Social Convention (Rahama)

NAME: Mahamane Ousmane

Movement for Development and Pan-Africanism

TITLE: Chairman

NAME: Mai Manga Boucar

Niger Progressive Party-African Democratic Rally

NAME: Dandiko Koulodo

DIPLOMATIC REPRESENTATION
Embassies in Niger

United Kingdom
Niamey, Niger

JUDICIAL SYSTEM
Supreme Court

Court of Appeal

FURTHER READING
Articles
''The Military's Hold on Western Africa.'' *U.S. News World and Report*, 19 April 1999, p. 13–14.

''Niger's President Assassinated at Airport.'' *Jet* (3 May 1999): 23.

Books
Chilson, Peter. *Riding the Demon: On the Road in West Africa.* Athens, GA: University of Georgia Press, 1999.

Hill, Kathleen. *Still Waters in Niger.* Evanston, IL: TriQuarterly Books, 1999.

Maluwa, Tiyanjana. *International Law in Post-Colonial Africa.* Boston, MA: Kluwer Law International, 1999.

Internet
Africaonline. Available Online @ www.africaonline.com (October 28, 1999).

Africa News Online. Available Online @ www.africanews.org/west/mauritania/ (November 12, 1999).

Central Intelligence Agency. *World Factbook, 1998.* Available Online @ www.odci.gov/cia/ publications/factbook/mr.html (November 12, 1999).

Focus on Niger. Available Online @ www.txdirect.net/~jmayer/ton.html/ (November 15, 1999).

''General Strike Bites in Niger.'' BBC Online, 14 September 1999. Available Online @ news2.thls.bbc.co.uk/hi/english/world/africa/ newsid%5F447000/447065.stm (December 13, 1999).

Integrated Regional Information Network (IRIN). Available Online @ www.reliefweb.int/IRIN (October 28, 1999).

''More Changes Planned in Niger Military.'' BBC Online, 23 July 1999. Available Online @ news2.thls.bbc.co.uk/hi/english/world/africa/newsid%5F401000/401622.stm (December 13, 1999).

''Niger Election Goes to Run-Off.'' BBC Online, 20 October 1999. Available Online @ news2.thls.bbc.co.uk/hi/english/world/africa/newsid%5F480000/480574.stm (December 13, 1999).

''Niger Goes to the Polls.'' BBC Online, 16 October 1999. Available Online @ news2.thls.bbc.co.uk/hi/english/world/africa/newsid%5F477000/477199.stm (December 13, 1999).

''Polls Close in Niger.'' BBC Online, 17 October 1999. Available Online @ news2.thls.bbc.co.uk/hi/english/world/africa/newsid%5F477000/477874.stm (December 13, 1999).

''Seven Candidates Qualify for Niger Elections.'' BBC Online, 4 September 1999. Available Online @ news2.thls.bbc.co.uk/hi/english/world/africa/newsid%5F438000/438457.stm (December 13, 1999).

''Voters in Niger Back Democracy.'' BBC Online, 19 July 1999. Available Online @ news2.thls.bbc.co.uk/hi/english/world/africa/newsid%5F397000/397573.stm (December 13, 1999).

NIGER: STATISTICAL DATA

For sources and notes see "Sources of Statistics" in the front of each volume.

GEOGRAPHY

Geography (1)

Area:

Total: 1.267 million sq km.

Land: 1,266,700 sq km.

Water: 300 sq km.

Area—comparative: slightly less than twice the size of Texas.

Land boundaries:

Total: 5,697 km.

Border countries: Algeria 956 km, Benin 266 km, Burkina Faso 628 km, Chad 1,175 km, Libya 354 km, Mali 821 km, Nigeria 1,497 km.

Coastline: 0 km (landlocked).

Climate: desert; mostly hot, dry, dusty; tropical in extreme south.

Terrain: predominately desert plains and sand dunes; flat to rolling plains in south; hills in north.

Natural resources: uranium, coal, iron ore, tin, phosphates, gold, petroleum.

Land use:

Arable land: 3%

Permanent crops: 0%

Permanent pastures: 7%

Forests and woodland: 2%

Other: 88% (1993 est.).

HUMAN FACTORS

Demographics (2A)

	1990	1995	1998	2000	2010	2020	2030	2040	2050
Population	7,644.2	8,843.9	9,671.8	10,260.3	13,677.8	17,983.4	22,993.2	28,373.4	33,895.9
Net migration rate (per 1,000 population)	NA	NA	NA	NA	NA	NA	NA	NA	NA
Births	NA	NA	NA	NA	NA	NA	NA	NA	NA
Deaths	NA	NA	NA	NA	NA	NA	NA	NA	NA
Life expectancy - males	38.8	40.7	41.8	42.6	46.9	51.5	56.1	60.6	64.7
Life expectancy - females	37.6	39.8	41.2	42.2	47.7	53.8	60.1	66.0	71.3
Birth rate (per 1,000)	55.9	55.2	53.0	51.6	45.3	39.2	32.5	26.9	22.7
Death rate (per 1,000)	28.0	25.1	23.4	22.2	17.0	13.0	9.7	7.6	6.5
Women of reproductive age (15-49 yrs.)	1,750.6	2,013.0	2,176.3	2,296.0	3,079.4	4,208.1	5,658.7	7,415.1	9,131.8
of which are currently married	NA	NA	NA	NA	NA	NA	NA	NA	NA
Fertility rate	7.5	7.5	7.3	7.2	6.3	5.2	4.1	3.2	2.6

Except as noted, values for vital statistics are in thousands; life expectancy is in years.

Health Personnel (3)

Total health expenditure as a percentage of GDP,
1990-1997[a]

Public sector 1.6

Private sector . . . . .NA

Total[b] . . . . .NA

Health expenditure per capita in U.S. dollars,
1990-1997[a]

Purchasing power parity . . . . .NA

Total . . . . .NA

Availability of health care facilities per 100,000 people

Hospital beds 1990-1997[a] . . . . .NA

Doctors 1993[c] 3

Nurses 1993[c] 17

Health Indicators (4)

Life expectancy at birth

1980 42

1997 47

Daily per capita supply of calories (1996) 2,116

Total fertility rate births per woman (1997) 7.4

Maternal mortality ratio per 100,000 live births
(1990-97) . . . . .590[d]

Safe water % of population with access (1995) 48

Sanitation % of population with access (1995) 17

Consumption of iodized salt % of households
(1992-98)[a] 7

Smoking prevalence

Male % of adults (1985-95)[a] . . . .

Female % of adults (1985-95)[a] . . . .

Tuberculosis incidence per 100,000 people
(1997) 148

Adult HIV prevalence % of population ages
15-49 (1997) 1.45

Infants and Malnutrition (5)

Under-5 mortality rate (1997) 320

% of infants with low birthweight (1990-97) 15

Births attended by skilled health staff % of total[a] . . .15

% fully immunized (1995-97)

TB 44

DPT 28

Polio 28

Measles 42

Prevalence of child malnutrition under age 5
(1992-97)[b] 43

Ethnic Division (6)

Hausa 56%

Djerma 22%

Fula 8.5%

Tuareg 8%

Beri Beri (Kanouri) 4.3%

Arab, Toubou, and Gourmantche 1.2%

Last category includes about 1,200 French expatriates.

Religions (7)

Muslim 80%. Remainder indigenous beliefs and
Christians.

Languages (8)

French (official), Hausa, Djerma.

EDUCATION

Public Education Expenditures (9)

Public expenditure on education (% of GNP)

1980 . . . . .3.1

1996 . . . .

Expenditure per student

Primary % of GNP per capita

1980 . . . . .26.2[1]

1996 . . . .

Secondary % of GNP per capita

1980 . . . .

1996 . . . .

Tertiary % of GNP per capita

1980 . . . . .1,539.5[1]

1996 . . . .

Expenditure on teaching materials

Primary % of total for level (1996) . . . .

Secondary % of total for level (1996) . . . .

Primary pupil-teacher ratio per teacher (1996) 41

Duration of primary education years (1995) 6

Literacy Rates (11A)

In thousands and percent[1]	1990	1995	2000	2010
Illiterate population (15+ yrs.)	3,576	4,081	4,672	6,185
Literacy rate - total adult pop. (%)	11.6	13.6	15.9	21.4
Literacy rate - males (%)	18.2	20.9	23.8	30.5
Literacy rate - females (%)	5.2	6.6	8.3	12.7

GOVERNMENT & LAW

Political Parties (12)

National Assembly	No. of seats
National Union of Independents for Democratic Revival (UNIRD)	59
Nigerien Alliance for Democracy and Social Progress-Zaman Lahia (ANDPS-Zaman Lahia)	8
Union of Patriots, Democrats, and Progressives-Shamuwa (UPDP-Shamuwa)	4
Alliance for Democracy and Progress (ADP-AUMUNCI DARAJA)	3
Coalition of Independents	3
Union for Democracy and Social Progress-Amana (UDPS-Amana)	3
PMT-Albarka	2
Movement for Development and Pan-Africanism (MDP-Alkwali)	1

Government Budget (13B)

Revenues	$370 million
Expenditures	$370 million
Capital expenditures	$186 million

Data for including $160 million from foreign sources. Data for 1998 est.

Military Affairs (14B)

	1990	1991	1992	1993	1994	1995
Military expenditures						
Current dollars (mil.)	NA	21	21[e]	23	21	21
1995 constant dollars (mil.)	NA	23	22[e]	24	22	21
Armed forces (000)	5	5	5	5	7	9
Gross national product (GNP)						
Current dollars (mil.)	1,510	1,602	1,539	1,601	1,700	1,860[e]
1995 constant dollars (mil.)	1,735	1,770	1,655	1,678	1,743	1,860[e]
Central government expenditures (CGE)						
1995 constant dollars (mil.)	348	275[e]	NA	307[e]	NA	NA
People (mil.)	7.6	7.9	8.1	8.3	8.6	8.8
Military expenditure as % of GNP	NA	1.3	1.3	1.5	1.3	1.2
Military expenditure as % of CGE	NA	8.4	NA	7.9	NA	NA
Military expenditure per capita (1995 $)	NA	3	3	3	3	2
Armed forces per 1,000 people (soldiers)	.7	.6	.6	.6	.8	1.0
GNP per capita (1995 $)	227	225	204	201	203	210
Arms imports[6]						
Current dollars (mil.)	5	0	0	0	0	0
1995 constant dollars (mil.)	6	0	0	0	0	0
Arms exports[6]						
Current dollars (mil.)	0	0	0	0	0	0
1995 constant dollars (mil.)	0	0	0	0	0	0
Total imports[7]						
Current dollars (mil.)	389	355	306	309	234[e]	NA
1995 constant dollars (mil.)	447	392	329	324	240[e]	NA
Total exports[7]						
Current dollars (mil.)	283	307	262	225	232[e]	NA
1995 constant dollars (mil.)	332	339	282	236	238[e]	NA
Arms as percent of total imports[8]	1.3	0	0	0	0	NA
Arms as percent of total exports[8]	0	0	0	0	0	NA

LABOR FORCE

Labor Force (16)

Total 70,000

Agriculture 90%

Industry and commerce 6%

Government 4%

Total includes those who receive regular wages or salaries.

Unemployment Rate (17)

Rate not available.

PRODUCTION SECTOR

Electric Energy (18)

Capacity . . . . .63,000 kW (1995)

Production . . . . .170 million kWh (1995)

Consumption per capita . . . . .40 kWh (1995)

Imports about 200 million kWh of electricity from Nigeria.

Transportation (19)

Highways:

total: 10,100 km

paved: 798 km

unpaved: 9,302 km (1996 est.)

Waterways: Niger river is navigable 300 km from Niamey to Gaya on the Benin frontier from mid-December through March.

Airports: 27 (1997 est.)

Airports—with paved runways:

total: 9

2,438 to 3,047 m: 2

1,524 to 2,437 m: 6

914 to 1,523 m: 1 (1997 est.)

Airports—with unpaved runways:

total: 18

1,524 to 2,437 m: 1

914 to 1,523 m: 14

under 914 m: 3 (1997 est.)

Top Agricultural Products (20)

Cowpeas, cotton, peanuts, millet, sorghum, cassava (tapioca), rice; cattle, sheep, goats, camels, donkeys, horses, poultry.

MANUFACTURING SECTOR

GDP & Manufacturing Summary (21)

Detailed value added figures are listed by both International Standard Industry Code (ISIC) and product title.

	1980	1985	1990	1994
GDP ($-1990 mil.)[1]	2,680	2,251	2,481	2,462
Per capita ($-1990)[1]	480	341	321	278
Manufacturing share (%) (current prices)[1]	3.8	7.4	6.7	6.7
Manufacturing				
Value added ($-1990 mil.)[1]	87	141	163	184
Industrial production index	100	108	138	157
Value added ($ mil.)	31	20	29	18
Gross output ($ mil.)	90	59	92	58
Employment (000)	2	3	3	3
Profitability (% of gross output)				
Intermediate input (%)	65	64	66	66
Wages and salaries inc. supplements (%)	15	14	15	14
Gross operating surplus	20	22	20	20
Productivity ($)				
Gross output per worker	43,832	21,122	30,241	16,780
Value added per worker	15,137	7,639	10,466	5,896
Average wage (inc. supplements)	6,552	2,953	4,248	2,316
Value added ($ mil.)				
311/2 Food products	2	1	1	1
313 Beverages	7	6	8	5
314 Tobacco products	NA	NA	NA	NA
321 Textiles	6	5	8	5
322 Wearing apparel	1	1	1	1
323 Leather and fur products	1	—	1	—
324 Footwear	1	NA	NA	NA

GDP & Manufacturing Summary (21)

	1980	1985	1990	1994
331 Wood and wood products	—	—	—	—
332 Furniture and fixtures	—	—	—	—
341 Paper and paper products	—	—	—	—
342 Printing and publishing	2	*1*	*1*	*1*
351 Industrial chemicals	2	NA	NA	NA
352 Other chemical products	3	*3*	*4*	*3*
353 Petroleum refineries	NA	NA	NA	NA
354 Miscellaneous petroleum and coal products	NA	NA	NA	NA
355 Rubber products	NA	NA	NA	NA
356 Plastic products	1	NA	NA	NA
361 Pottery, china and earthenware	—	NA	NA	NA
362 Glass and glass products	NA	NA	NA	NA
369 Other non-metal mineral products	2	*1*	*2*	*1*
371 Iron and steel	NA	NA	NA	NA
372 Non-ferrous metals	NA	NA	NA	NA
381 Metal products	3	*1*	*2*	*1*
382 Non-electrical machinery	—	*1*	*1*	*1*
383 Electrical machinery	—	—	—	—
384 Transport equipment	NA	NA	NA	NA
385 Professional and scientific equipment	NA	NA	NA	NA
390 Other manufacturing industries	NA	NA	NA	NA

FINANCE, ECONOMICS, & TRADE

Economic Indicators (22)

National product: GDP—purchasing power parity—$6.3 billion (1997 est.)

National product real growth rate: 4.5% (1997 est.)

National product per capita: $670 (1997 est.)

Inflation rate—consumer price index: 5.3% (1996)

Exchange Rates (24)

Exchange rates:

CFA francs (CFAF) per US$1

January 1998	608.36
1997	583.67
1996	511.55
1995	499.15
1994	555.20
1993	283.16

Beginning 12 January 1994, the CFA franc was devalued to CFAF 100 per French franc from CFAF 50 at which it had been fixed since 1948.

Balance of Payments (23)

	1991	1992	1993	1994	1995
Exports of goods (f.o.b.)	351	347	300	227	288
Imports of goods (f.o.b.)	−418	−396	−312	−271	−306
Trade balance	−66	−49	−12	−45	−18
Services - debits	−237	−255	−216	−194	−205
Services - credits	70	77	56	46	39
Private transfers (net)	109	114	122	108	54
Government transfers (net)	−52	−46	−47	−41	−22
Overall balance	−176	−159	−97	−126	−152

Top Import Origins (25)

$374 million (c.i.f., 1996)

Origins	%
France	.24
Nigeria	.19
Cote d'Ivoire	NA
China	NA
Belgium-Luxembourg	NA

NA stands for not available.

Top Export Destinations (26)

$188 million (f.o.b., 1996).

Destinations	%
France	.41
Nigeria	.22
Burkina Faso	NA
Cote d'Ivoire	NA
Japan	.18

NA stands for not available.

Economic Aid (27)

Recipient: ODA; bilateral donors: France, Germany, EU, Japan.

Import Export Commodities (28)

Import Commodities	Export Commodities
Consumer goods	Uranium ore 67%
Primary materials	Livestock products 20%
Machinery	Cowpeas
Vehicles and parts	Onions
Petroleum	
Cereals	

NIGERIA

Federal Republic of Nigeria

INTRODUCTORY SURVEY

RECENT HISTORY

After World War II (1939–45), increasing pressures for self-government resulted in a series of short-lived constitutions. On 1 October 1960, Nigeria became a fully independent member of the British Commonwealth, and on 1 October 1963 it became a republic. Nnamdi Azikiwe was elected the first president of the Federal Republic of Nigeria.

Disagreements between regions led to a military takeover on 15 January 1966 and another takeover later that year which brought Lieutenant Colonel Yakubu Gowon to power as head of the military government. On 28 May 1967, Colonel Gowon assumed emergency powers as head of the Federal Military Government and announced changes in state borders throughout the country.

Rejecting the new arrangement, Eastern Region leaders announced on 30 May the independent Republic of Biafra. On 6 July, the federal government declared war on the new republic. By the time the war ended, on 12 January 1970, Biafra had been reduced to about one-tenth of its original area of 78,000 square kilometers (30,000 square miles), and a million or more persons had perished, many of disease and starvation.

In 1970, with the civil war ended, General Gowon promised a return to civilian rule, but then postponed it indefinitely. This helped lead to his overthrow on 29 July 1975. His successor, Brigadier Murtala Ramat Muhammad, strongly pursued

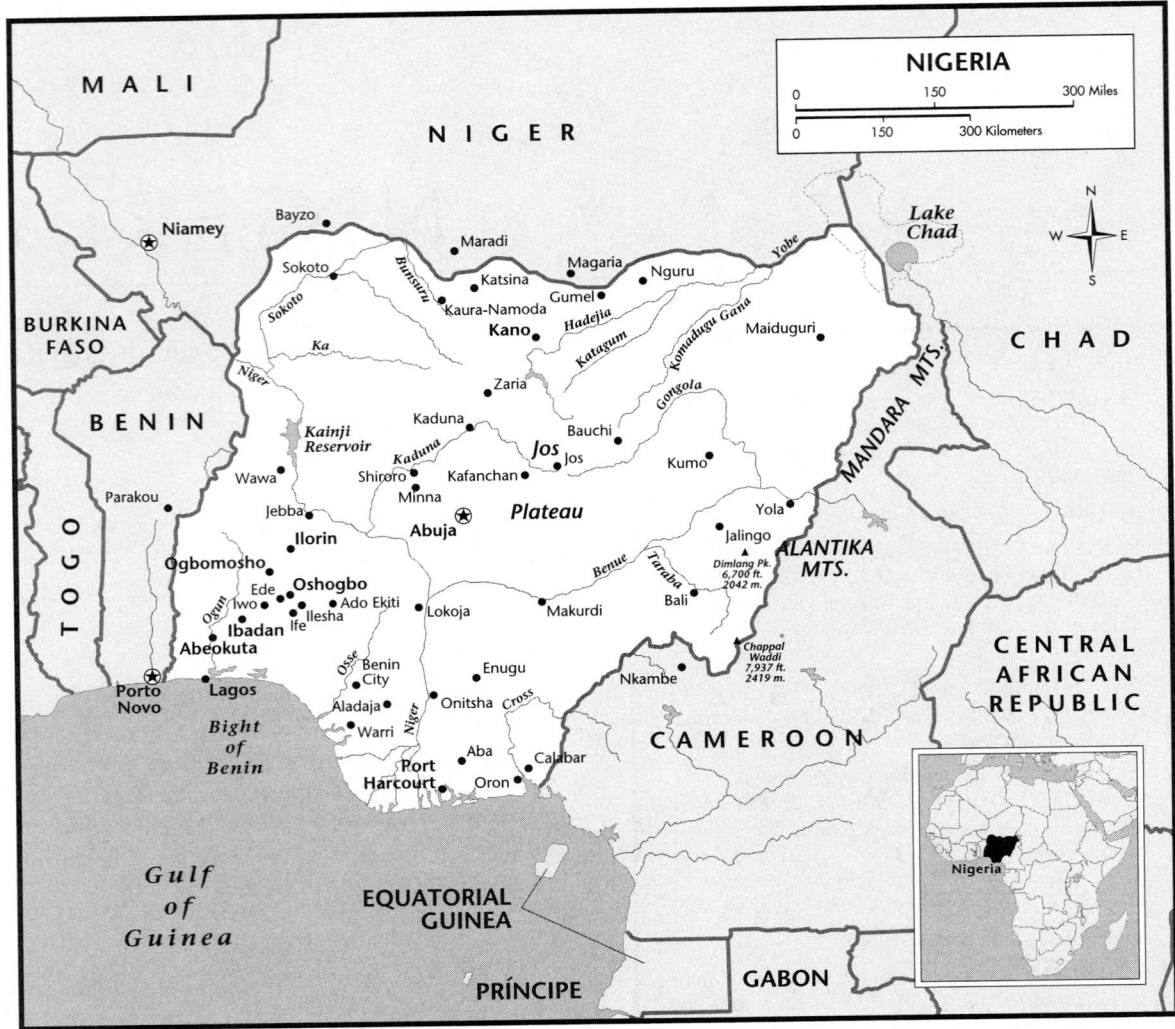

government reform but was assassinated in the course of a failed rebellion. He was replaced as head of the government by the former chief of staff of the armed forces, Lieutenant General Olusegun Obasanjo. In March 1976, Obasanjo established a 19-state federation. Political party activity was again permitted, and a new constitution took effect on 1 October 1979 and Alhaji Shehu Shagari became president. In August 1983, Shagari won re-election to a second term as president. In late December, however, he was removed from office in a military takeover.

The new military government, led by Major General Muhammadu Buhari, attracted growing public dissatisfaction and another takeover on 27 August 1985 brought Major General Ibrahim Badamasi Babangida to power. He assumed the title of president. Babangida promised a return to full civilian rule by 1992, local elections on a non-party basis, the creation of a governing assembly, the establishment of no more than two political parties, state elections, a national census, and finally presidential elections.

The change from military rule to a democratic civilian Third Republic was scheduled to be completed in 1992, but was blocked by crisis after crisis. Clashes between Muslims and Christians in 1991 and 1992 spread through northern cities. Hundreds were killed in the rioting and by the army seeking to control the riots.

Nonetheless, by January 1992, Nigerians geared up for the national presidential and legislative elections scheduled for later in the year. On 20 May 1992, the government banned all political, religious, and ethnic organizations other than the two approved political parties. Legislative elections were conducted on 4 July, but the ruling military council would not allow the people elected to the legislature to take office. Presidential elections were to follow, but again the military stood in the way. Political violence and charges of election fraud followed. In response, the military banned all 23 of the presidential candidates from future political competition.

The presidential election finally took place in 1993 amid controversy and great voter confusion. Chief M.K.O. Abiola apparently defeated his nearest rival 58.4% to 41.6%. But the military annulled the election a week later because of supposed irregularities, poor turnout, and legal complications.

Abiola, backed largely by the Yoruba people, demanded to be certified as president-elect. Civil unrest, especially in Lagos, followed. However, the military would not give up power. Under its latest strongman, General Sani Abacha, the corrupt military government crippled the Nigerian economy and drove the country into debt. In November 1993, Abacha took control and installed himself as head of state. He abolished all state and local governments, the national legislature, and political parties. In 1994, Abacha removed all civilians from his ruling council. Although the ban on political parties was lifted in June 1995, there were still restrictions on their operations. In April 1995 Abacha canceled a 1 January 1996 deadline for the return of civilian rule. In October 1995 he agreed to give up power to an elected government in 1998.

The execution of Ken Saro-Wiwa and eight others in November 1995 brought much criticism from the international community. Saro-Wiwa was the leader of the Movement for the Survival of the Ogoni People. Many observers believe he had been convicted of murder on trumped-up charges only because he led a group that opposed an oil-drilling deal in Nigeria's main oil-producing region. Nigeria was then suspended from the British Commonwealth. In May 1996 the government amended the law that had convicted Saro-Wiwa.

In February 1998, Nigeria led the West African intervention force that helped restore the elected government of Sierra Leone. Pope John Paul II visited Nigeria in March and appealed for human rights and democracy.

In June 1998, General Abacha died of a heart attack, and General Abdulsalam Abubakar assumed control, initially promoting a transition to democracy. On 7 July 1998, Abiola died of a heart attack in prison, on the eve of his expected release. There was public suspicion that his death was not natural, and riots broke out in Lagos, Ibadan, and Abeokuta, resulting in 19 deaths. Public fears of ethnic division grew, because Abiola was seen as a link between northern Hausas and southern Yorubas. Abubakar began releasing political prisoners and announced that the military would give up its power to an elected government in May 1999.

On February 27, 1999, Olusegun Obasanjo won the presidential elections over Olu Falae. Obasanjo is a former general who ruled the country from 1976 to 1979 when he became the first Nigerian military ruler to return power freely to an elected civilian government.

GOVERNMENT

The 1979 constitution established a federal system resembling that of the United States, with a directly elected president and vice-president and separate executive, legislative, and judicial branches. The military government that took command after the December 1983 takeover suspended the 1979 constitution, and it was still suspended after Abacha seized power on 17 November 1993. A military-dominated Provisional Ruling Council (PRC) rules by decree, and a 32-member Federal Executive Council manages government departments. In July 1998, the military government announced that it would yield power to an elected civilian government in May 1999. The elections held in February and were monitored by international observers who found them to be fair, overall.

Judiciary

The Supreme Court, its members appointed by the president, is the highest court in Nigeria. It hears appeals from the Federal Court of Appeals, which in turn hears appeals from the Federal High Court and state high courts. The Supreme Court also has original jurisdiction over constitutional disputes between the federal government and the states or between states. Customary and area courts exist to administer local laws and customs. In the northern states, Muslim law (Shari'ah) is administered in most courts. Decisions can be appealed to state courts.

Political Parties

Before the December 1983 takeover, two parties were permitted: a right-of-center National Republican Convention (NRC) and a left-of-center Social Democratic Party (SDP).

In November 1993, the military rulers suspended all partisan and political activities. Abacha's regime allowed no partisan political activity, but set up five political parties that it directly controlled. Under General Abubakar's transition to democracy, these parties will be disbanded and the people will have the right to organize their own political parties.

DEFENSE

The Nigerian armed forces are the largest in sub-Saharan Africa after South Africa, with 77,100 members in 1995. The army, with 62,000 members was divided into 10 brigades. The navy, with a total strength of 5,600, possessed 3 warships and 51 smaller craft. The air force, composed of 9,500 members, had 92 combat aircraft. Nigeria contributes about 5,000 troops to seven different peace-keeping operations, the majority in Liberia. Nigeria spent $1.2 billion on defense in 1995.

ECONOMIC AFFAIRS

Agriculture remains the basic economic activity for the great majority of Nigerians, although it accounts for only 28% of gross national product (GNP). The Nigerian economy, with a wealth of natural resources, offers great potential for economic growth. However, poor economic policy, political instability, and too much reliance on oil exports have created severe problems in the economy.

Crude oil accounts for 90% of exports and 80% of government revenue. In 1996, the World Bank reported that $2 billion in oil revenues from the early 1990s had been put in a secret government bank account.

Public Finance

The federal government is responsible for collecting taxes on income, profits, and property, as well as import and export taxes and excise duties. The petroleum sector provides about 70% of budgetary revenues. A large share of these revenues is redistributed to state governments. The budget is consistently in deficit.

Public investment flourished during the oil boom years of the 1970s. When the oil market prices collapsed in the 1980s however, the Nigerian government maintained its high level of spending, thus acquiring substantial foreign debt. Although privatization efforts began in 1986, increased government spending outside the official budget since 1990 has damaged public finance reform. As a result, the federal deficit increased from 2.8% of GDP in 1990 to 9% in 1992. Nigeria's medium- and long-term debt rose from US$14.6 billion in 1985 to US$32.5 billion in 1993.

The U.S. Central Intelligence Agency estimates that, in 1994, government revenues totaled approximately $2.7 billion and expenditures $6.4 billion, including capital expenditures of $1.8 billion.

Income

In 1996 Nigeria's gross national product (GNP) was $132.7 billion at current prices, or about $1,300 per person. For the period 1985–95 the average inflation rate was 33%, resulting in a real growth rate in GNP of 1.2% per person.

Industry

Industry accounts for about 53% of the gross national product (GNP). Nigeria only used 27.1% of its potential manufacturing capacity in 1994.

In 1996, Nigeria produced 140,000 barrels per day of refined petroleum products. The production represented only one-third of total capacity. Sabotage, fires, and maintenance and management problems have limited production.

The textile industry has shown the greatest growth since independence, and the country is practically self-sufficient in printed fabrics, blankets, and towels. Other areas of expansion include cement production (2.6 million tons in 1994), tire production, and furniture assembly. Other important industries include sawmills; cigarette factories; breweries; sugar refining; rubber, paper, soap, and detergent factories; footwear factories; pharmaceutical plants; tire factories; paint factories; and assembly plants for radios, record players, and television sets. Nigeria has five state-owned motor-vehicle assembly plants for Volkswagen, Peugeot, and Mercedes products. In 1995, Volkswagen announced the closing of its assembly plant in Lagos.

Banking and Finance

In 1892, Nigeria's first bank, the African Banking Corp., was established. The Nigerian banking system is patterned along British lines. Before World War II, two large British banks, the Bank of British West Africa and Barclays Bank, virtually monopolized Nigerian banking. After 1945, a number of African-owned banks entered the field; between 1946 and 1952, however, more than 20 such banks either failed or went into voluntary liquidation, primarily because of undercapitalization and rash loan policies. Banking ordinances have since been issued to correct this situation: in 1969, for example, the Banking Decree established minimum capital requirements for licensed banks, based on the total deposits. Licenses are mandatory.

The bank of issue is the Central Bank of Nigeria (CBN), established in 1958. The Central Bank regulates most commercial banking operations in Nigeria, but the federal Ministry of Finance has retained control of most international activities of the financial sector.

The 1969 Banking Decree requires that all banking institutions be incorporated in Nigeria, and a 1976 law gives the government 60% ownership of all foreign banks. Important additional sources of credit are provided by thrift and loan societies and by the branches of the National Development Corp. The Nigerian Industrial Development Bank (NIDB), established in 1964 in collaboration with the IFC and European, Japanese, and U.S. investment institutions, provides long- and medium-term financing to concerns in the industrial nonpetroleum, mining, and tourist sectors. The National Bank for Commerce and Industry helps finance smaller enterprises. Merchant banking has expanded rapidly since 1973, when the Union Dominican Trust Co. began operations. Other U.S., UK, and Japanese financial institutions have since set up merchant facilities in the country. In July 1990 the state banks were privatized. Beginning in 1990 the country allowed the establishment of foreign banks. Sixty percent of the foreign banks that are established in Nigeria must be held by Nigerian interests. In the same year the government began a program to establish 500 community banks.

The main clearing banks are the United Bank for Africa (with Banque Nationale de Paris and Bankers Trust Shareholdings), Union Bank of Nigeria, and First Bank of Nigeria (38% Standard Chartered). With a 1991 embargo on the licensing of banks still in force, the number of commercial banks in operation rose by only one in 1992 to 66 in 1995, while the number of merchant banks was unchanged at 54. Money supply, as measured by M2, was n 135.3 billion at the end of 1992. Total reserves, excluding gold, amounted to $11,305 million at the end of 1993.

The Nigerian (formerly Lagos) Stock Exchange (NSE) began operations on 1 July 1961, following passage of the Lagos Stock Exchange Act; the government promulgated regulations for the exchange and provided that all dealings in stock on behalf of principals be carried out only by members of the exchange. The government encourages public issues of shares by Nigerian companies in an effort to mobilize local capital for the country's development. The exchange, in Lagos, with branches in Kaduna and Port Harcourt, deals in government stocks and in shares of public companies registered in Nigeria. The stock exchange is managed by the Investment Co. of Nigeria. Since the provision of new investment incentives under the Nigerian Enterprises Promotion Decree of April 1974, activity on the stock exchange has increased. The Securities and Exchange Commission (SEC) has a dominant say in the markets, fixing prices of all new securities and regulating the prices of those already being traded. Transactions of 50,000 shares or more are subject to SEC approval.

In a bid to encourage foreign interest in the NSE, a computerized central securities clearing system (CSCS) was installed on 14 April 1997, although it got off to a quiet start. The custodian bank for the system is Nigeria International Bank/Citibank. The benefit of the system is that trades will be settled within one week and eventually within two days, compared with the long delays hitherto experienced in effecting share transfers after purchases and sales.

The market capitalization of the NSE grew from N280 billion at the end of 1996 to N370 billion on 27 March 1997.

On 21 April 1997, a CBN directive lifted the restrictions on equity ownership of individual and corporate investors in Nigerian banks. Under the new legislation, it is now possible for an individual or another corporation to own up to a 100% share in a bank. Prior to the directive, the maximum shareholding for an individual was just 10%, while for companies it was 30%. There is a requirement that commercial and merchant banks' minimum paid-up capital be raised to a uniform level of N500 million by the end of 1998.

Economic Development

The agriculture sector has been the focus of intense development interest in recent years, with food self-sufficiency the goal. In 1990, agriculture received 28% of the federal budget and was the subject of a separate three-year development plan involving public and private spending targets concentrating on the family farmer. The program includes price stabilization plans and schemes to revitalize the palm oil, cocoa, and rubber sub-sectors.

An integrated petrochemical industry is also priority. Using the output of the nation's refineries, Nigeria produces benzene, carbon black, and poly-propylene. The development of liquid natural gas facilities is expected to lead to the production of methanol, fertilizer, and domestic gas.

In the manufacturing sector, the government is backing a policy of local sourcing whereby locally produced raw materials are converted into finished products. The rehabilitation of the nation's trans-portation infrastructure is part of a three-year roll-ing investment plan begun in 1990.

SOCIAL WELFARE

There are two kinds of welfare services in Nigeria—those provided by voluntary agencies and those provided by the government. Workers are protected under the Labor Code Act (1958) and the Workmen's Compensation Act, which provides protection for workers in case of industrial acci-dents. Most companies also provide pension plans for their employees. Despite recent gains in the workplace, women have only a minor role in poli-tics.

Nigeria's human rights record worsened in 1995 by serious and systematic persecution of pro-democracy advocates. There were reports of people imprisoned without charge, torture, and killings outside the legal system.

Healthcare

According to 1992 data, primary care is largely provided through approximately 4,000 health cli-nics scattered throughout the country. There are 12 university teaching hospitals with about 6,500 beds. There is one doctor for every 5,191 people. Two-thirds of the population had access to health care services. Life expectancy is 53 years.

Malaria and tuberculosis are the most common diseases, but serious outbreaks of cerebrospinal meningitis still occur in the north. Just under half of all deaths are thought to be among children, who are especially vulnerable to malaria and account for 75% of registered malaria deaths. Schistosomiasis, Guinea worm, trachoma, river blindness, and yaws are also widespread. Progress, however, has been made in the treatment of sleeping sickness (trypa-nosomiasis) and leprosy.

Housing

Housing generally has not ranked high on the scale of priorities for social spending, and state governments have tended to rely upon local author-ities to meet the problem. Efforts at providing low-cost rural housing have been slight, despite the creation of the Federal Mortgage Bank of Nigeria in 1977, and shantytowns and slums are common in urban areas. The total number of housing units in 1992 was 25.7 million.

EDUCATION

The first six years of primary education were made compulsory in 1976. Recent years have seen a marked growth in educational facilities, but the overall adult illiteracy rate for the country was about 43% (males, 32.7%; females, 52.7%) in 1995.

Primary education begins in the local language but introduces English in the third year. In 1994 there were 16.2 million students in 38,649 primary schools. Secondary schools had 4.5 million stu-dents and 152,592 teachers. Technical education is provided by technical institutes, trade centers, and handicraft centers.

There are also 13 polytechnic colleges and 4 colleges of technology. In 1989, all higher level institutions combined had 19,601 teaching staff and 335,824 pupils.

1999 KEY EVENTS TIMELINE

January

- Results from the December 5 nationwide local elections show that the People's Democratic Party, opponents of the late General Sani Abacha, have won control of most of the 774 municipal governments being contested.

- General Abubakar announces new incentives in addition to tax holidays to local and foreign in-vestors engaged in the exploitation of Nigeria's gas resources.

- The military government predicts real GDP growth at 3%.

- Nigerians go to the polls to elect state governors and representatives to state assemblies.

- General Abubakar reaches an agreement with the IMF to allow IMF staff to monitor basic economic policy until June when an economic reform program for Nigeria will be negotiated.

February

- The All Peoples Party (APP) is unable to settle on a presidential candidate.

- Obasanjo (PDP) wins the presidential elections with 62% of the vote. His challenger, Olu Falae, receives 38%.

- Despite Falae's charges of election rigging, the Carter Center and the National Democratic Institute report no evidence that electoral abuses would have changed the overall results.

- Cattle dealers and fuel tanker drivers clash in Lagos, leaving 5 dead and more than 20 injured.

- The African Refugees Foundation (AREF) is being supported by the E.U. to organize a series of public activities under a democracy-in-peace initiative.

March

- Major oil producers reach a pricing agreement.

- The "Deep Offshore and Inland Basin Production Sharing Contracts Decree 1999," is signed, offering various incentives to operators-investors in the Nigerian oil industry.

- Obasanjo's visit to Yaoundé eases tensions over a maritime border dispute.

- The Naira begins significant depreciation.

- Nigeria wins bid to host 10th World Youth Championship, a three-week soccer fiesta scheduled to begin April 3.

- The U.S. Congressional Black Caucus backs a call for investigation into U.S. oil companies in Nigeria, which apparently are accepting extra-judicial killings and human rights abuses as the "cost of doing business" in Nigeria.

- A multi-million dollar development project is targeted for the delta region.

April

- The Commonwealth invites Nigeria to join.

- Schools close in teachers' strike.

- Niger Delta oil activists are killed.

- Diarrhea becomes the leading killer in the country.

- A human rights group expresses concern about the Constitution.

- The U.S. and Japan promise to resume aid to Nigeria.

- The new Constitution is said to be ready by the end of the month.

- Olu Falae closes his case against Obasanjo after a federal appeals court in Abuja rejects two pleas by the defeated presidential candidate.

- Nigeria and Central African Republic sign a trade pact during President Felix Patasse's two-day visit.

May

- An Islamic leader stresses the importance of religion.

- Obasanjo's vow to smash corruption is widely welcomed.

- Human rights groups send their wish lists to Obasanjo.

- Nigeria considers sanctions against Charles Taylor.

- Thirty are feared dead in communal fighting.

- Ghanaian fishermen demand compensation for oil spill.

- Commonwealth ban is lifted.

- Seventeen are reported killed in northeast cashes.

- Pressure group wants some foreigners out of the Niger Delta.

- The new Constitution becomes law.

- Top officials declare that the military must be modernized.

- Power is handed over officially to the new government. Some 20 heads of state attend Obasanjo's inauguration.

- The government seizes Abacha's assets.

June

- President Obasanjo delivers inaugural address June 4th.

- The Nigerian Senate approves seven more ministerial nominees.

- At least 10 people are killed in pipeline fire.

- Ethics code for ministers and advisers adopted.

- Cholera is reported in the north as living standards worsen around the country.

- Obasanjo agrees to send Nigeria peacekeepers to the DRC.

- Warri is declared a disaster zone. Obasanjo announces the creation of a new Delta development commission.

- A traditional ruler is kidnapped.

- The National Assembly opens.

- More than 120 senior officers are compulsorily retired, and 26 retire voluntarily.

- Some 200 civil servants, including 11 permanent secretaries are retired.

- The U.S. restores military ties with Nigeria.

- The E.U. lifts embargo against Nigeria, including travel restrictions and arms sales.

- Alscon aluminum smelter announces suspension of operations.

- The Nigerian women's soccer team in the U.S. attracts admiration for fanciful hair styles.

July

- The Speaker of the House forced to resign over allegations of age and certificate forgery. He is replaced by Ghali Umar Na'aba by election in the House.

- Kidnappings concern oil companies, while youths free 64 oil workers held hostage.

- Scores die in ethnic fighting. At least 70 reported killed in fighting between Hausa and Yoruba in Kano.

- Kidnapped pilots are freed.

- Guinea worm outbreak reported in the north.

- Phased withdrawal of troops from Sierra Leone planned.

- Nigeria asks the UN to be more active in Africa.

- The state announces plans to sell 60 public firms.

- A paid killing leaves former Minister of Sports, Tony Ikhazoboh, shot dead in his home.

August

- The police discover an arms factory in Ondo.

- More than 30 drown after a boat capsizes.

- A church and hotels are torched in Katsina.

- Plans are set to slash the military.

- A human rights group files 8,000 cases with the human rights panel.

- A multi-million dollar deal is made to electrify Lagos.

- The president of the Senate denies having a criminal past.

- Dozens are reported dead in a new outbreak of violence.

- Nigeria and Ghana sign gas pipeline project agreement.

September

- The government reintroduces universal basic education.

- Militants force the closure of a gas plant.

- The government enlists the FBI in search of $2.2 billion in loot.

- Four murders a day are recorded in Lagos.

- President Obasanjo requests churches help against corruption.

- Civil society welcomes a plan to clean up the police.

- The creation of five million jobs in one year is planned.

- Two thousand troops are pulling out of Sierra Leone.

October

- The threat of famine and starvation grows as Niger Delta flooding destroys farmland and forces people from their homes.

- The Nigerian government condemns the coup in Pakistan and severs military ties.

- Abacha's three sons are arraigned.

- Water spilling from a dam sweeps away settlements, killing many people.

- Ogoni refugees refuse to return home.

- Forty are suspected to have died from cholera in the northeastern state of Adamawa.

- Nigeria Liquefied Natural Gas (NLNG) scheduled to begin exporting LNG from Bonny Island in southeastern Nigeria.

- Tightened security around the president raises fears of a coup attempt.

November

- An angry President Olusegun Obasanjo charges the governor of Odi, a small town in the Niger Delta, with losing control of a situation wherein 12 policemen there were kidnapped then killed and warns him that action will be taken. Waiting until the governor is away attending a party conference, President Obasanjo orders troops to take over Odi; more than 300 soldiers storm the town, destroying buildings and killings dozens of local people.

- Riots break out in Lagos, beginning with a dispute between traders from Nigeria's two largest ethnic groups, the northern Hausas and southern Yorubas, over control of a food market. President Obasanjo blames a Yoruba nationalist group, Odua Peoples Congress (OPC), ordering police to arrest OPC members and shoot on site any who resisted; however, Lagos state officials back OPC claims that it was not involved.

December

- A report published to coincide with World AIDS Day warns that the HIV epidemic has reached an explosive stage in Nigeria.

- Nwamkwo Kanu, a soccer player, is named African Footballer of the Year.

ANALYSIS OF EVENTS: 1999

BUSINESS AND THE ECONOMY

The old adage, "a new broom sweeps clean," has given hope to observers looking for something positive in the shambles of the economy President Obasanjo has inherited. The national debt is somewhere between $26 to $31 billion, and real GDP growth in 1999 is expected to be around 1% due to low oil prices. Domestic investment and improved oil and gas revenue are expected to improve the picture in 2000, but until then, analysts are scrutinizing the new president's actions for signs that his government is serious about recovery.

Obasanjo has worried some analysts by delaying his outline for economic recovery. The government has approved plans for privatization of telecoms, which gives a strong indication of the government's commitment to divest. However, the twin scourges of mismanagement and corruption also threaten privatization. Obasanjo promised reductions in government spending by $1.1 billion in 1999. Furthermore, government contracts will be processed through federal and ministerial tender boards empowered to use transparent and competitive procedures. Corruption is estimated to add as much as 50% to the cost of contracts.

While industry is gloomy, energy should brighten the outlook in 1999 and 2000. A deterioration in operating conditions has reduced industrial capacity, lowered investment, and increased stocks of unsold goods. A lower purchasing capacity within the country reduced the demand for Nigerian goods internally. But Nigeria and Ghana signed a gas agreement in August, a follow-up to the agreement signed by Nigeria, Ghana, Benin, and Togo. The agreement is seen by many as a model for regional technical and commercial cooperation as it will save Ghana between 15,000 and 20,000 barrels of crude oil per day by using Nigerian gas to fire its power plants. A $400 million pipeline will convey Nigerian gas to industrial projects and provide electricity to Benin, Togo, and Ghana with eventual extension to Côte d'Ivoire.

GOVERNMENT AND POLITICS

The February multi-party elections, considered acceptably free and fair by international observer groups, have returned Nigeria to civilian rule after 15 years. This news, along with the democratic transfer of presidential power in South Africa, was perhaps the greatest cause for optimism on the continent in 1999. The new government compulsorily retired more than 120 senior military officers, and accepted the resignations of 26 more. Some 200 civil servants, including 11 permanent secretaries also retired. These purges, however, did not mask the appointment of many old faces to the cabinet, some of whom were believed to merit their positions, while others—cronies of Abacha—were compromise appointments.

The conviction of the former Speaker of the House of Representatives in July on two counts of perjury and forgery sent a message to elected officials that a new ethical standard would be enforced for public behavior. Salisu Buhari was caught falsifying his age, and among other things, forging a BA degree from the University of Toronto. Subsequent to the Buhari affair, the sweeping of the new broom resulted in a decision by the independent electoral commission to re-screen all assembly members to ascertain their ages and educational qualifications. In late July, the speaker of the house of representatives of the southeastern state of Abia became the first victim of impeachment by colleagues under the Fourth Republic.

Obasanjo's crusade against corruption remained a top governance priority in the country. General Abubakar's administration had investigated the wholesale theft of public funds under the previous government and recovered some of the country's stolen wealth. However, it did not prosecute the offenders, citing lack of sufficient evidence, and its last minute extra budgetary expenditures raised suspicions that looting of the public treasury had not been stopped. Obasanjo's former connection with the German NGO, Transparency International (TI), is expected to help him curb, though not eliminate routine corruption.

In foreign policy, the new government will probably enjoy good relations with the U.S. and the U.K. Nigeria will have a more difficult time playing regional policeman for ECOMOG because the National Assembly must approve deployment of troops in foreign countries. Two cabinet posts have been created to handle commerce in Africa, suggesting that Nigeria's Western-trade links may be reoriented toward its neighbors.

CULTURE AND SOCIETY

Despite high expectations for social change after 15 years of military rule, no one is deluded about the enormous socio-economic challenges ahead. It seems that many of the challenges to this society are not being met. Nigeria's more than 200 ethnic groups and 108 million people must make peace their priority. Ethnic clashes among Yoruba and Hausa in the northern city of Kano left more than 70 people dead. Law and order in many parts of country is only a chimera. Crumbling industrial infrastructure, urban pollution and crime, paid killings, the need for jobs, lack of access to decent health services, the threat of HIV/AIDS, and regional, religious, and ethnic rivalries are all at the heart of Nigeria's problems.

Estimates in per capita GNP show a decline to around $300 in 1999, well below the average for sub-Saharan Africa at $480. Sixty-six percent of the population is living below the poverty line. Only 50% of the population enjoys access to safe water, while child malnutrition is at 39%. On the other hand, 98% of the school age children are enrolled in primary school.

The delta region is perhaps highest on Nigeria's list of troubled areas. The oil it produces is the cash cow of the economy, but only 3% of this underground wealth returns home and services the needs of this region of the country. In May, the government made constitutional provisions to raise this amount to 13%, but Delta activists representing the six Delta states are demanding 50%. Ironically,

this year's abundant rains, responsible for record cotton and cereal harvests in the Sahel, have flooded the delta's farmlands, threatening famine and starvation, and leaving 300,000 people homeless.

The year 1999 saw a succession of riots, kidnappings of oil workers, seizures of oil facilities and violent clashes. In June there were at least 50 deaths, 82 injured people, and some 27 houses were burned, turning the southern city of Warri into a war zone. Bazookas, hand grenades, and automatic rifles were used to kill more than 200 people. The announcement in June of a multi-million dollar development initiative for the Delta, and new community cooperation programs initiated by the oil companies should improve the situation. Obasanjo has inaugurated a human rights abuses probe panel, which is investigating complaints stemming from the past 15 years.

A reform movement seems to be growing in Nigerian society, however, and changes have come when Nigerian churches, women's, and youth groups have demanded redress from business and government. Human rights organizations and activist groups are mushrooming around the country. The late Chief Abiola's daughter, Hafsat Abiola, has helped to found such a reform group, the Kudirat Initiative for Democracy (KIND), named after her mother. The organization is devoted to promoting democracy by strengthening civil society. A women's health and welfare group, CEDPA, has taken on gender equality issues and assumed advocacy roles by staging cooking strikes and marching on local government.

DIRECTORY

CENTRAL GOVERNMENT
Head of State

President
Olusegun Obasanjo, Office of the President

Vice President
Atiku Abubakar, Office of the Vice President

Ministers

Minister of Commerce in Africa
Engr. Bello, Ministry of Commerce in Africa

Minister of Communications
M. Arzika, Ministry of Communications

Minister of Culture and Tourism
Ojo Maduike, Ministry of Culture and Tourism

Minister of Defense
Yakubu Danjuma, Ministry of Defense

Minister of Education
Tande Adeniran, Ministry of Education

Minister of Environment
Hassan Adamu, Ministry of Environment

Minister of Health
Tim Menakaya, Ministry of Health

Minister of Information
Dapo Sarumi, Ministry of Information

Minister of Justice
Kanu Godwin Agabi, Ministry of Justice

Minister of Works and Housing
Tony Anenih, Ministry of Works and Housing

POLITICAL ORGANIZATIONS

All People's Party

NAME: Mahmud Warizi

People's Democratic Party

NAME: Soloman Lar

DIPLOMATIC REPRESENTATION

Embassies in Nigeria

Australia
2 Ozumba Mbadiwe Avenue, Victoria Island
ORPO Box 2427, Lagos, Nigeria
PHONE: +234 (1) 2618875
FAX: +234 (1) 2618703

Italy
8 Eleke Crescent, Victoria Island, Lagos, Nigeria
PHONE: +234 (1) 2621046
FAX: +234 (1) 2621050

United Kingdom
11 Eleke Crescent, Victoria Island (Private Bag 12136), Lagos, Nigeria
PHONE: +234 (1) 2619531
FAX: +234 (1) 2614021

JUDICIAL SYSTEM

Supreme Court

Federal Court of Appeal

FURTHER READING

Articles

DeLuca, Marshall. ''Nigeria Elects New President and Maybe a New Way of Life.'' *Offshore* (May 1999): 10.

''Former Military Ruler Olusegun Obasanjo Elected President of Nigeria; He Becomes First Elected President In 15 Years.'' *Jet* (March 15, 1999): 54.

''Nigerian Quagmire?'' *World Press Review* (March 1999): 19.

''Oil, Guns and Fury in the Delta.'' *Newsweek International* (March 8, 1999): 39.

''Protests Close Nigerian Plant.'' *The Oil Daily* 49 (September 24, 1999).

''Reaching for Your Machete.'' *The Economist* (July 31, 1999): 36.

Books

Africa on File. Facts on File, 1995, s.v. ''Nigeria.''

Falola, Toyin. *Violence in Nigeria: The Crisis of Religious Politics and Secular Ideologies.* Rochester, NY: University of Rochester Press, 1998.

Federal Republic of Nigeria, Federal Ministry of Information. *Nigeria 1991: Official Handbook.* Lagos: Emaconprint Ltd., 1991.

Ihonvbere, Julius Omozuanvbo. *Illusions of Power: Nigeria in Transition.* Trenton, NJ: Africa World Press, 1998.

Metz, Helen Chapin, ed. *Nigeria: A Country Study.* Washington, D.C.: U.S. Government Printing Office, 1992.

Osaghae, Eghosa E. *Crippled Giant: Nigeria Since Independence.* Bloomington: Indiana University Press, 1998.

Wright, Stephen. *Nigeria: Struggle for Stability and Status.* Boulder, Colo.: Westview Press, 1998.

Internet

Africa News Online. Available Online @ www.africanews.org/west/stories/1999_feat1.html (November 1, 1999).

Africaonline. Available Online @ www.africaonline.com (November 1, 1999).

NigeriaNews. Available Online @ www.nigerianews.net (November 1, 1999).

NIGERIA: STATISTICAL DATA

For sources and notes see "Sources of Statistics" in the front of each volume.

GEOGRAPHY

Geography (1)

Area:

Total: 923,770 sq km.

Land: 910,770 sq km.

Water: 13,000 sq km.

Area—comparative: slightly more than twice the size of California.

Land boundaries:

Total: 4,047 km.

Border countries: Benin 773 km, Cameroon 1,690 km, Chad 87 km, Niger 1,497 km.

Coastline: 853 km.

Climate: varies; equatorial in south, tropical in center, arid in north.

Terrain: southern lowlands merge into central hills and plateaus; mountains in southeast, plains in north.

Natural resources: petroleum, tin, columbite, iron ore, coal, limestone, lead, zinc, natural gas.

Land use:

Arable land: 33%

Permanent crops: 3%

Permanent pastures: 44%

Forests and woodland: 12%

Other: 8% (1993 est.).

HUMAN FACTORS

Demographics (2A)

	1990	1995	1998	2000	2010	2020	2030	2040	2050
Population	86,529.9	100,959.4	110,532.2	117,170.9	150,274.4	183,962.2	225,866.2	279,404.8	337,590.8
Net migration rate (per 1,000 population)	NA	NA	NA	NA	NA	NA	NA	NA	NA
Births	NA	NA	NA	NA	NA	NA	NA	NA	NA
Deaths	NA	NA	NA	NA	NA	NA	NA	NA	NA
Life expectancy - males	51.5	53.1	52.7	52.4	45.0	49.0	60.5	72.1	76.1
Life expectancy - females	53.6	55.7	54.4	53.7	47.6	51.9	65.1	78.2	82.5
Birth rate (per 1,000)	44.8	43.2	42.2	41.4	37.0	33.3	29.1	24.4	20.6
Death rate (per 1,000)	14.2	12.8	13.0	13.0	16.1	13.6	7.8	3.8	3.3
Women of reproductive age (15-49 yrs.)	18,952.9	22,194.4	24,388.9	25,856.8	33,967.3	44,355.3	58,469.2	75,737.0	91,697.8
of which are currently married	NA	NA	NA	NA	NA	NA	NA	NA	NA
Fertility rate	6.6	6.3	6.1	5.9	5.1	4.2	3.4	2.8	2.5

Except as noted, values for vital statistics are in thousands; life expectancy is in years.

Health Personnel (3)

Total health expenditure as a percentage of GDP, 1990-1997[a]

Public sector 0.2

Private sector 0.7

Total[b] 1.0

Health expenditure per capita in U.S. dollars, 1990-1997[a]

Purchasing power parity .11

Total 5

Availability of health care facilities per 100,000 people

Hospital beds 1990-1997[a] 170

Doctors 1993[c] 21

Nurses 1993[c] 142

Health Indicators (4)

Life expectancy at birth

1980 46

1997 54

Daily per capita supply of calories (1996) 2,609

Total fertility rate births per woman (1997) 5.3

Maternal mortality ratio per 100,000 live births (1990-97) . . . . .1,000[c]

Safe water % of population with access (1995) 50

Sanitation % of population with access (1995) 57

Consumption of iodized salt % of households (1992-98)[a] 98

Smoking prevalence

Male % of adults (1985-95)[a] 24

Female % of adults (1985-95)[a] 7

Tuberculosis incidence per 100,000 people (1997) 214

Adult HIV prevalence % of population ages 15-49 (1997) 4.12

Infants and Malnutrition (5)

Under-5 mortality rate (1997) 187

% of infants with low birthweight (1990-97) 16

Births attended by skilled health staff % of total[a] . . .31

% fully immunized (1995-97)

TB 29

DPT 21

Polio 25

Measles 38

Prevalence of child malnutrition under age 5 (1992-97)[b] 39

Ethnic Division (6)

Hausa, Fulani, Yoruba, Ibo, Kanuri, Ibibio, Tiv, Ijaw.

Religions (7)

Muslim 50%

Christian 40%

Indigenous beliefs 10%

Languages (8)

English (official), Hausa, Yoruba, Ibo, Fulani.

EDUCATION

Public Education Expenditures (9)

Public expenditure on education (% of GNP)

1980 . . . . .6.4[1]

1996 . . . . .0.9[1]

Expenditure per student

Primary % of GNP per capita

1980 . . . . .4.7[1]

1996 . . . .

Secondary % of GNP per capita

1980 . . . .

1996 . . . .

Tertiary % of GNP per capita

1980 . . . . .529.8[1]

1996 . . . .

Expenditure on teaching materials

Primary % of total for level (1996) . . . .

Secondary % of total for level (1996) . . . .

Primary pupil-teacher ratio per teacher (1996) . . . . .37[1]

Duration of primary education years (1995) 6

Literacy Rates (11A)

In thousands and percent[1]	1990	1995	2000	2010
Illiterate population (15+ yrs.)	26,562	26,075	25,171	22,278
Literacy rate - total adult pop. (%)	49.4	57.1	64.5	77.1
Literacy rate - males (%)	60.8	67.3	73.3	83.2
Literacy rate - females (%)	38.6	47.3	55.9	71.1

GOVERNMENT & LAW

Political Parties (12)

The legislative branch is a bicameral National Assembly, comprising a 109-member Senate and a 360-member House of Representatives. The National Assembly was suspended after the military takeover of 17 November 1993; in October 1995, the government announced a three-year program for transition to civilian rule; elections to the National Assembly took place 25 April 1998 for a term starting 1 October 1998; the election was substantially boycotted by the opposition and the legislature is unlikely to be representative of the electorate.

Government Budget (13B)

Revenues . . . .$13.9 billion

Expenditures . . . .$13.9 billion

  Capital expenditures . . . . .NA billion

Data for 1998 est. Data for 1998 est. NA stands for not available.

Military Affairs (14B)

	1990	1991	1992	1993	1994	1995
Military expenditures						
Current dollars (mil.)[3]	674[e]	662	513	631	793	NA
1995 constant dollars (mil.)[3]	775[e]	732	552	662	813	NA
Armed forces (000)	94	94	76	76	80	89
Gross national product (GNP)						
Current dollars (mil.)	72,090	80,770	85,690	87,170	93,820	95,340
1995 constant dollars (mil.)	82,850	89,260	17,060	91,390	96,170	95,340
Central government expenditures (CGE)						
1995 constant dollars (mil.)	21,320	20,170	17,060	33,430	23,090	NA
People (mil.)	86.5	89.2	92.0	94.8	97.7	100.8
Military expenditure as % of GNP	.9	.8	.6	.7	.8	NA
Military expenditure as % of CGE	3.6	3.6	3.2	2.0	3.5	NA
Military expenditure per capita (1995 $)	9	8	6	7	8	NA
Armed forces per 1,000 people (soldiers)	1.1	1.1	.8	.8	.8	.9
GNP per capita (1995 $)	958	1,001	1,002	964	984	946
Arms imports[6]						
Current dollars (mil.)	20	130	180	50	0	10
1995 constant dollars (mil.)	23	144	194	52	0	10
Arms exports[6]						
Current dollars (mil.)	0	0	0	0	0	0
1995 constant dollars (mil.)	0	0	0	0	0	0
Total imports[7]						
Current dollars (mil.)	5,686	9,031	8,119	7,508	6,511	29,990
1995 constant dollars (mil.)	6,537	9,979	8,733	7,871	6,674	29,990
Total exports[7]						
Current dollars (mil.)	13,670	12,260	11,890	9,916	9,368	34,180
1995 constant dollars (mil.)	15,710	13,550	12,790	10,400	9,603	34,180
Arms as percent of total imports[8]	.4	1.4	2.2	.7	0	0
Arms as percent of total exports[8]	0	0	0	0	0	0

LABOR FORCE

Labor Force (16)

Total (million) 42.844

Agriculture 54%

Industry, commerce, ...

and services 19%

Government 15%

Unemployment Rate (17)

28% (1992 est.)

PRODUCTION SECTOR

Electric Energy (18)

Capacity . . . . .5.881 million kW (1995)

Production . . . . .16.21 billion kWh (1996)

Consumption per capita . . . . .152 kWh (1995)

Transportation (19)

Highways:

total: 32,105 km

paved: 26,005 km (including 2,044 km of expressways)

unpaved: 6,100 km (1994 est.) note: many of the roads reported as paved may be graveled; because of poor maintenance, much of the road system is barely useable

Waterways: 8,575 km consisting of the Niger and Benue rivers and smaller rivers and creeks

Pipelines: crude oil 2,042 km; petroleum products 3,000 km; natural gas 500 km

Merchant marine:

total: 39 ships (1,000 GRT or over) totaling 379,210 GRT/643,851 DWT ships by type: bulk 1, cargo 14, chemical tanker 3, oil tanker 20, roll-on/roll-off cargo 1 (1997 est.)

Airports: 72 (1997 est.)

Airports—with paved runways:

total: 36

over 3,047 m: 6

2,438 to 3,047 m: 10

1,524 to 2,437 m: 10

914 to 1,523 m: 8

under 914 m: 2 (1997 est.)

Airports—with unpaved runways:

total: 36

over 3,047 m: 1

1,524 to 2,437 m: 1

914 to 1,523 m: 14

under 914 m: 20 (1997 est.)

Top Agricultural Products (20)

Cocoa, peanuts, palm oil, corn, rice, sorghum, millet, cassava (tapioca), yams, rubber; cattle, sheep, goats, pigs; fishing and forest resources extensively exploited.

MANUFACTURING SECTOR

GDP & Manufacturing Summary (21)

Detailed value added figures are listed by both International Standard Industry Code (ISIC) and product title.

	1980	1985	1990	1994
GDP ($-1990 mil.)[1]	28,357	27,329	35,462	39,666
Per capita ($-1990)[1]	394	329	412	366
Manufacturing share (%) (current prices)[1]	8.1	8.7	6.0	7.0
Manufacturing				
Value added ($-1990 mil.)[1]	1,537	1,427	1,779	1,559
Industrial production index	100	88	103	153
Value added ($ mil.)	2,422	1,726	3,682	3,165
Gross output ($ mil.)	4,740	3,534	6,148	5,516
Employment (000)	432	336	416	459
Profitability (% of gross output)				
Intermediate input (%)	49	51	40	43
Wages and salaries inc. supplements (%)	11	10	10	10
Gross operating surplus	40	39	50	48
Productivity ($)				
Gross output per worker	10,273	9,947	14,130	11,495
Value added per worker	5,260	4,872	8,697	6,800
Average wage (inc. supplements)	1,226	1,043	1,440	1,144
Value added ($ mil.)				
311/2 Food products	149	251	560	535
313 Beverages	267	205	424	484
314 Tobacco products	96	52	78	58
321 Textiles	231	233	490	353

GDP & Manufacturing Summary (21)

	1980	1985	1990	1994
322 Wearing apparel	3	1	*1*	*1*
323 Leather and fur products	12	23	*47*	*37*
324 Footwear	12	28	*60*	*55*
331 Wood and wood products	88	14	25	*16*
332 Furniture and fixtures	56	14	*33*	27
341 Paper and paper products	38	51	*118*	*108*
342 Printing and publishing	75	45	*105*	*103*
351 Industrial chemicals	30	9	*13*	8
352 Other chemical products	265	213	*452*	*354*
353 Petroleum refineries	*72*	-7	*36*	*31*
354 Miscellaneous petroleum and coal products	*6*	*-1*	*3*	*3*
355 Rubber products	26	31	*64*	*57*
356 Plastic products	98	49	*106*	*85*
361 Pottery, china and earthenware	—	2	*2*	*1*
362 Glass and glass products	24	7	*15*	*13*
369 Other non-metal mineral products	87	106	*225*	*176*
371 Iron and steel	3	17	*37*	*35*
372 Non-ferrous metals	33	*34*	*72*	*56*
381 Metal products	140	92	*199*	*160*
382 Non-electrical machinery	23	19	*42*	*34*
383 Electrical machinery	46	36	*78*	*62*
384 Transport equipment	526	193	*383*	*303*
385 Professional and scientific equipment	—	—	—	—
390 Other manufacturing industries	13	6	*11*	*8*

FINANCE, ECONOMICS, & TRADE

Economic Indicators (22)

National product: GDP—purchasing power parity—$132.7 billion (1996 est.)

National product real growth rate: 3.3% (1996 est.)

National product per capita: $1,300 (1996 est.)

Inflation rate—consumer price index: 12% (1997 est.)

Exchange Rates (24)

Exchange rates:

Naira (N) per US$1

December 1997	.21.886
1997	.21.886
1995	.21.895
1994	.21.996
1993	.22.065

Balance of Payments (23)

	1992	1993	1994	1995	1996
Exports of goods (f.o.b.)	11,791	9,910	9,459	9,355	14,103
Imports of goods (f.o.b.)	−7,181	−6,662	−6,511	−7,230	−5,621
Trade balance	4,611	3,248	2,948	2,125	8,482
Services - debits	−4,304	−6,061	−5,993	−6,572	−6,954
Services - credits	1,209	1,221	420	621	740
Private transfers (net)	731	21	−48	—	—
Government transfers (net)	22	791	546	703	824
Overall balance	2,269	−781	−2,128	−3,123	3,092

Top Import Origins (25)

$8 billion (c.i.f., 1996)

Origins	%
European Union	.50
United States	.12
Japan	.7

Top Export Destinations (26)

$15 billion (f.o.b., 1996) Data are for 1995.

Destinations	%
United States	.40
European Union	.21

Economic Aid (27)

Recipient: ODA, $NA. NA stands for not available.

Import Export Commodities (28)

Import Commodities	Export Commodities
Machinery	Petroleum and petroleum products 95%
Chemicals	Cocoa
Transportation equipment	Rubber
Manufactured goods	
Food and animals	

NIUE

CAPITAL: Alofi.

FLAG: The flag of Niue is yellow with the flag of the United Kingdom in the upper hoist-side quadrant; the flag of the UK bears yellow five-pointed stars—a large one on a blue disk in the center and a smaller one on each arm of the bold red cross.

MONETARY UNIT: 1 New Zealand dollar (NZ$) = 100 cents.

WEIGHTS AND MEASURES: The metric system is used.

HOLIDAYS: Takai, first week of the year; New Year's Day, 1 January; day after New Year's Day, 2 January; Waitangi Day, first Tuesday in February; Good Friday; Easter Monday; Anzac Day; Queen's Birthday, first Monday in June; Labor Day, fourth Monday in October; Christmas Day, 25 December; Boxing Day, 26 December; Provincial Anniversary Day; Peniamina Day; Annexation Day; and Constitution Day.

TIME: 1 AM = noon GMT.

LOCATION AND SIZE: An isolated coral island, Niue is 966 km (600 mi.) northwest of the southern Cook Islands, and located at 19°02'S and 169°52'W. Nieu became a British protectorate in 1900 and was annexed to New Zealand in 1901. Although Niue forms part of the Cook Islands, because of its remoteness and cultural and linguistic differences it has been separately administered. Niue has an area of 258 sq. km (100 sq. mi.).

CLIMATE: There is little temperature change throughout the year, with mean monthly temperatures ranging from 18°C (65°F) to 29°C (85°F). Average annual rainfall is 203 cm (80 inches), but is distributed unevenly throughout the year. Most rainfall occurs during the rainy season from December to April, when temperatures and humidity are higher and typhoons occasionally strike. Droughts occur periodically, so many buildings have water catchments to provide adequate water supply.

INTRODUCTORY SURVEY

RECENT HISTORY

Archaeological research and local oral tradition indicate initial settlement of the island by Samoans around 900 followed by Tongan conquest from the west in the sixteenth century. Modern Niuean language reflects affinities to both Samoan and Tongan. European influences began in 1774 when British explorer Captain James Cook landed on the island in 1774 naming it Savage Island because of a hostile reception. British missionaries began arriving in the 1830s but due to continued hostile receptions did not successfully settle until 1846. By 1900 Niue had become a British protectorate as part of the United Kingdom's Samoan holdings. The following year Britain annexed Niue to New Zealand as the westernmost island of New Zealand's Cook Island properties. In 1904 Niue was given a separate political identity from the Cook Islands with its own appointed commissioner and Island Council. The first popularly elected Niuean legislature replaced the Island Council in 1960. Establishment of local governmental leadership followed in 1966. Niue inhabitants, expected to number over 2,100 in 1999, remained overwhelmingly Polynesian in character.

GOVERNMENT

A self-governing parliamentary democracy, Niue adopted a new constitution in 1974 by passing the Niue Constitution Act. Niue increased control over domestic affairs but still remained in free association with New Zealand with Niueans en-

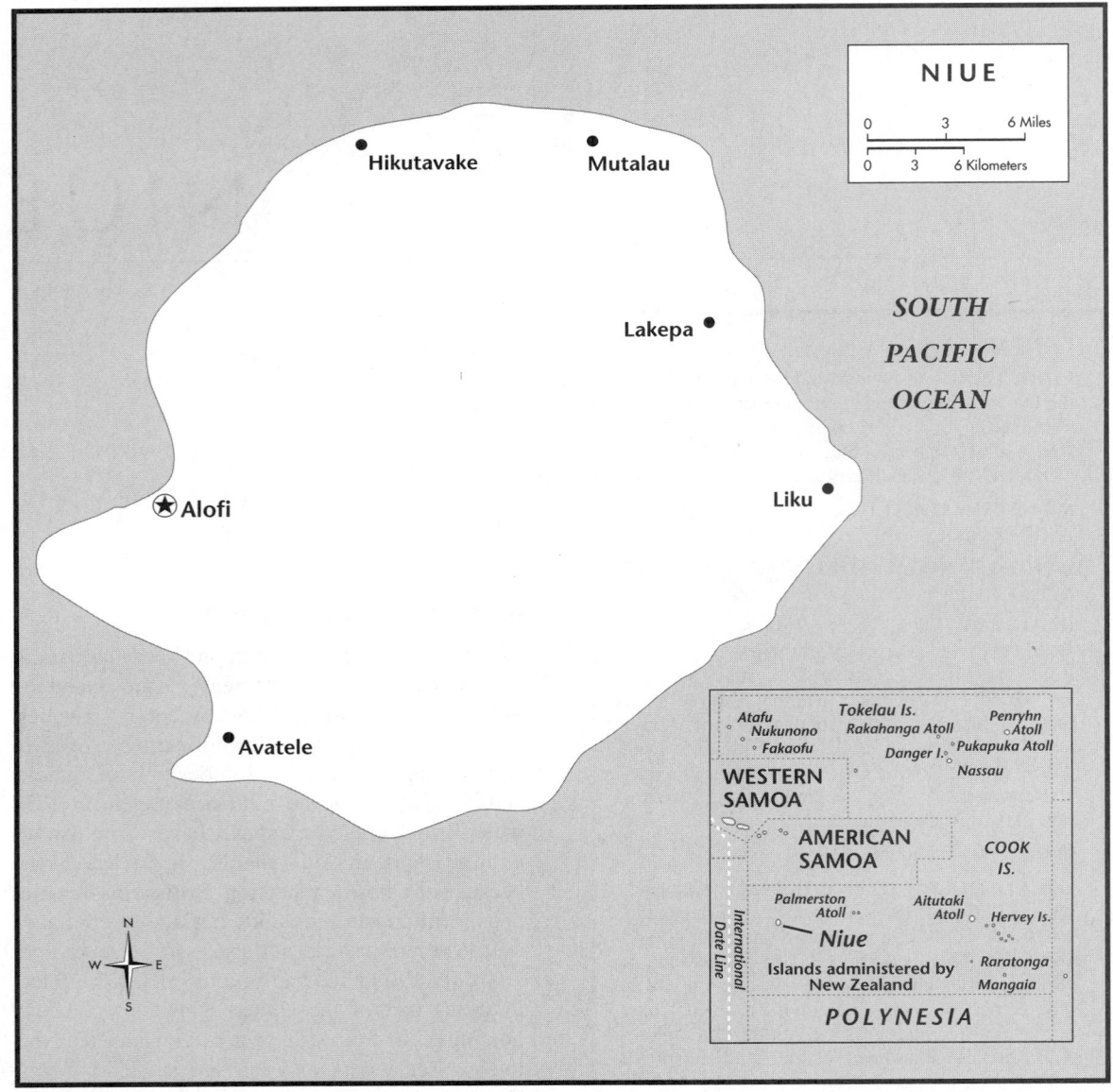

joying New Zealand citizenship. As a result, Niue is one of the smallest self-governing states in the world. The Niuean legislative branch is the unicameral Legislative Assembly located in Alofi, the capital and administrative center of the island. The British monarch remains head of state, which has been Queen Elizabeth II since 1952. The New Zealand High Commissioner represents New Zealand and United Kingdom in Niuean political affairs. A Premier elected by the Niuean Legislative Assembly serves three-year terms as the governmental leader. The first Premier, the popular Honorable Sir Robert R. Rex, served in office from 1974–92. The Assembly is composed of twenty members popularly elected with qualified voters being all resident adults over eighteen years of age. Six members are elected at large and the other represent fourteen villages. Three members of the Assembly are selected by the Premier to join the Premier in a four member cabinet. Each of the fourteen Niuean villages elect their own village council members to three-year terms. Niue is a member of the South Pacific Forum and the Pacific Community.

Judiciary

The Niuean legal system is based on English common law. Basic components are the Supreme Court of New Zealand, the Land Court, and the

High Court of Niue. The Land Court hears cases involving land titles. The Chief Justice of the High Court and judge for the Land Court visit the island on a quarterly basis. In their absence, locally appointed lay justices exercise limited criminal and civil jurisdiction. Appeals of High Court rulings are heard by a Court of Appeal, established in 1992.

Political Parties

The island's primary political party is the Niue People's Party (NPP), founded in 1987 and renamed in 1995.

DEFENSE

New Zealand remains responsible for Niue defense and foreign affairs. Niue does maintain a police force.

ECONOMIC AFFAIRS

One of the largest uplifted coral islands in the world, vegetation overall is scant despite the tropical climate. Less than a fourth of the island is capable of cultivation. Vulnerable to drought and cyclones, agriculture is primarily for local subsistence with only 8% of the island in permanent crops in 1993 and 4% in pasture. The fertile coastal strip is the primary part of the island intensively cultivated but is still largely held in traditional family patterns inhibiting more effective development. With work largely limited to family-owned plantations, the island suffers from substantial emigration of Niueans to New Zealand. A wide range of crops and livestock are raised for subsistence purposes. Some limited cash crops include passion fruit, pawpaw, coconuts, and limes. However, a 1989 hurricane destroyed Niue's coconut plantations leading to closure of the coconut cream processing plant. Another hurricane the following year destroyed the passion fruit and lime crops. Occasional droughts have posed additional challenges. Another important revenue source is sale of postage stamps to collectors.

In 1989 exports amounted to only U.S. $117,000 whereas imports totaled U.S. $4.1 million. In 1993 the government began seeking to establish a "tax haven" to attract some foreign business. In 1996 Niue made an unsuccessful bid to join the Asian Development Bank in an effort to spur investments in the island's economy.

Tourism is still little developed though the number of hotel rooms on the island increased in the mid-1990s. Limited air service also increased in

the early 1990's and a runway at Hanan International Airport was substantially lengthened in 1995. Just over 2,000 tourists, primarily from New Zealand, were visiting the island annually in the mid-1990s. New Prime Minister Sani Lakatani, leader of the NPP elected in early 1999, vowed to make tourism development a high priority.

Public Finance

With essentially no native export products, expenditures normally exceed revenues leaving Niue almost totally dependent on economic aid. In 1985 Niue's expenditures of $6.3 million exceeded revenues by almost $1 million. New Zealand, Niue's main trading partner, is the island's primary source of financial aid providing almost two-thirds of Niue's revenue, or $8.3 million in economic aid in 1995.

Income

In 1993 the gross domestic product (GDP) was U.S. $2.4 million with a per capita GDP of U.S. $1,200.

Industry

The extremely limited Niuean industry following demise of the coconut, passion fruit, and lime crops is focused on such products as honey, handicrafts, and leather goods. Tourism is yet to become a major component of the island's economy.

Banking and Finance

To facilitate on-island finance, the Development Bank of Niue, known as Fale Tupe Atihake Ha Niue, began operations in 1994.

SOCIAL WELFARE

With little industry, wage work is primarily limited to government service jobs largely subsidized by New Zealand aid. Public social service expenditures are extremely limited.

Healthcare

A twenty-four-bed government-supported hospital and dental clinic are located in Alofi. Life expectancy estimates in 1991 was 62.5 for males and 65.0 for females.

Housing

Most island residents live in small villages scattered along the coast. Following highly destructive hurricanes of 1959 and 1960, the government replaced the traditional lime-plastered, thatch-roofed houses with tin-roofed concrete-block structures. Many houses stand empty and villages only partially occupied from the outmigration of Niueans to New Zealand and elsewhere seeking greater economic opportunities. Out of a total of nearly 17,000 Niueans, only 2,600 actually lived on the island in the late 1990s.

EDUCATION

Niue enjoys a high literacy rate of approximately 95% of the total population. Education, which is free of charge, is compulsory for ten years between ages five and fourteen. One primary school and one secondary school are located on the island and the University of the South Pacific has an extension center on Niue. Approximately 10% of Niue's budget was dedicated to education in 1991.

1999 KEY EVENTS TIMELINE

June

- The migration of the southern humpback whale begins, and Niue is among the nesting areas of this huge aquatic mammal. Whales are seen in the waters around Niue from early June through September.

October

- Niue celebrates the twenty-fifth anniversary of its constitution.

- Independent members of the coalition government meet with the premier to voice their concerns over negotiations with a private company for air service to Niue.

- Four members of the Niue assembly-Toke T. Talagi, Hima Takelesi, Va'aiga Tukuitonga, and Billy Talagi—send a letter to the Niue Assembly Speaker on October 27 seeking a no confidence vote against the premier, Mr. Sani Lakatani, and his cabinet.

- Toke T. Talagi and Hima Takelesi tender their resignations as associate ministers.

November

- The National Assembly convenes in response to the request submitted in October for a vote of "no confidence." A meeting is expected to be called between November 2nd and 8th, as per the Constitution Act of 1974.

ANALYSIS OF EVENTS: 1999

BUSINESS AND THE ECONOMY

Niue, like its neighbors in the Pacific region, hopes to build up its tourism industry. Controversy, however, surrounds the mechanism for accomplishing it. Some in the government feel that Niue should develop its own airline to support tourism, while the premier and his cabinet favor contracting air service with a private company, Coral Air. The previous government had refused the Coral Air's proposal, but the current administration is proceeding with the deal. This controversy led to a request for a vote of "no confidence."

GOVERNMENT AND POLITICS

In October four independent members of the Niue Assembly submitted to the speaker of the assembly a request for a vote of "no confidence" (VONC). The four sought the vote over tension between the National Assembly and the premier and his cabinet over the deal with Coral Air. The independents propose that air service be developed by leasing planes and making a cooperative arrangement with another airline, such as Royal Tonga or Polynesian Airlines, with the assistance of New Zealand.

DIRECTORY

CENTRAL GOVERNMENT
Head of State

High Commissioner
Warren Searell

Premier
Sani Lakatani, Office of the Premier
PHONE: +683 4200
FAX: +683 4232

Ministers

Common Solicitor
Office of the Common Solicitor
PHONE: +683 4208
FAX: +683 4228

Minister of Planning and Development
Ministry of Planning and Development
PHONE: +683 4148

FAX: +683 4183

Minister of Administration
Ministry of Administration
PHONE: +683 4018
FAX: +683 4305

Minister of Agriculture, Forestry and Fisheries
Ministry of Agriculture, Forestry and Fisheries
PHONE: +683 4032
FAX: +683 4079

Minister of Common Affairs
Ministry of Common Affairs
PHONE: +683 4019
FAX: +683 4391

Minister of Education
Ministry of Education
PHONE: +683 4115
FAX: +683 4301

Minister of Justice and Land Titles
Ministry of Justice and Land Titles
PHONE: +683 4128
FAX: +683 4231

Minister of National Training and Development
Ministry of National Training and Development
PHONE: +683 4214
FAX: +683 4211

Minister of Police
Ministry of Police
PHONE: +683 4333
FAX: +683 4324

Minister of Telephone
Ministry of Telephone
PHONE: +683 4000

FAX: +683 4010

Minister of Treasury
Ministry of Treasury
PHONE: +683 4047
FAX: +683 4051

Minister of Public Works
Ministry of Public Works
PHONE: +683 4297
FAX: +683 4223

POLITICAL ORGANIZATIONS
Niue People's Action Party (NPP)

NAME: Young Vivian

DIPLOMATIC REPRESENTATION
Embassies in Niue

New Zealand
Tapeu Alofi, PO Box 78, Niue
PHONE: +683 4022
FAX: +683 4173

JUDICIAL SYSTEM
Supreme Court of New Zealand
High Court of Niue

FURTHER READING
Articles

"Vote of No Confidence in Niue Premier Lakatani and His Cabinet Planned." TalaNET News, 27 October 1999.

For sources and notes see "Sources of Statistics" in the front of each volume.

GEOGRAPHY

Geography (1)

Area:

Total: 260 sq km.

Land: 260 sq km.

Water: 0 sq km.

Area—comparative: 1.5 times the size of Washington, DC.

Land boundaries: 0 km.

Coastline: 64 km.

Climate: tropical; modified by southeast trade winds.

Terrain: steep limestone cliffs along coast, central plateau.

Natural resources: fish, arable land.

Land use:

Arable land: 19%

Permanent crops: 8%

Permanent pastures: 4%

Forests and woodland: 19%

Other: 50% (1993 est.).

HUMAN FACTORS

Demographics (2B)

Population (July 1998 est.) 1,647

Age structure:

0-14 years . . . . .NA

15-64 years . . . . .NA

65 years and over . . . . .NA

Population growth rate (1998 est.) . . . .-3.65%

Birth rate (births/1,000 population) . . . . .NA

Death rate (deaths/1,000 population) . . . . .NA

Net migration rate (migrant(s)/1,000 population) . . .NA

Infant mortality rate (deaths/1,000 live births) . . . . .NA

Life expectancy at birth:

Total population . . . . .NA

Male . . . . .NA

Female . . . . .NA

Total fertility rate (children born/woman) . . . . . . .NA

Infants and Malnutrition (5)

Under-5 mortality rate (1997) . . . . .NA

% of infants with low birthweight (1990-97) . . . . . .NA

Births attended by skilled health staff % of total[a] . . .NA

% fully immunized (1995-97)

TB 100

DPT 100

Polio 100

Measles 100

Prevalence of child malnutrition under age 5 (1992-97)[b] . . . . .NA

Ethnic Division (6)

Polynesian (with some 200 Europeans Samoans, and Tongans).

Religions (7)

Ekalesia Niue (Niuean Church) 75%—a Protestant church closely related to the London Missionary Society, Latter-Day Saints 10%, other 15% (mostly Roman Catholic, Jehovah's Witnesses, Seventh-Day Adventist).

Languages (8)

Polynesian closely related to Tongan and Samoan, English.

EDUCATION

Literacy Rates (11B)

Adult literacy rate

1980

  Male . . . . -

  Female . . . . -

1995

  Male . . . . -

  Female 99%

GOVERNMENT & LAW

Political Parties (12)

Legislative Assembly	No. of seats
Niue People's Action Party (NPP)	9
Independents	11

Government Budget (13B)

Revenues	$5.5 million
Expenditures	$6.3 million
Capital expenditures	NA

Data for 1985 est. NA stands for not available.

Military Affairs (14A)

Defense is the responsibility of New Zealand.

LABOR FORCE

Labor Force (16)

Total 450. Most work on family plantations; paid work exists only in government. Service, small industry, and the Niue Development Board. Data for 1992 est.

Unemployment Rate (17)

Rate not available.

PRODUCTION SECTOR

Electric Energy (18)

Capacity	1,000 kW (1995)
Production	.3 million kWh (1995)
Consumption per capita	1,633 kWh (1995)

Transportation (19)

Highways:

total: 234 km

paved: 0 km

unpaved: 234 km

Merchant marine: none

Airports: 1 (1997 est.)

Airports—with paved runways:

total: 1

1,524 to 2,437 m: 1 (1997 est.)

Top Agricultural Products (20)

Coconuts, passion fruit, honey, limes, taro, yams, cassava (tapioca), sweet potatoes; pigs, poultry, beef cattle.

FINANCE, ECONOMICS, & TRADE

Economic Indicators (22)

National product: GDP—purchasing power parity—$2.4 million (1993 est.)

National product real growth rate: NA%

National product per capita: $1,200 (1993 est.)

Inflation rate—consumer price index: 5% (1992)

Exchange Rates (24)

Exchange rates:

New Zealand dollars (NZ$) per US$1

January 1998	1.7283
1997	1.5082
1996	1.4543
1995	1.5235
1994	1.6844
1993	1.8495

Top Import Origins (25)

$4.1 million (c.i.f., 1989)

Origins	%
NZ	.59
Fiji	.20
Japan	.13
Samoa	NA
Australia	NA
United States	NA

NA stands for not available.

Top Export Destinations (26)

$117,500 (f.o.b., 1989).

Destinations	%
NZ	.89
Fiji	.NA
Cook Islands	.NA
Australia	.NA

NA stands for not available.

Economic Aid (27)

Recipient: ODA, $5.9 million from NZ (FY95/96).

Import Export Commodities (28)

Import Commodities	Export Commodities
Food	Canned coconut cream
Live animals	Copra
Manufactured goods	Honey
Machinery	Passion fruit products
Fuels	Pawpaw
Lubricants	Root crops
Chemicals	Limes
Drugs	Footballs
	Stamps
	Handicrafts

NORFOLK ISLAND

Territory of Norfolk Island

INTRODUCTORY SURVEY

RECENT HISTORY

British explorer Captain James Cook discovered the uninhabited island in 1774 and named it for the Duke of Norfolk. The Australian colony of New South Wales claimed Norfolk in 1788 and settled it with a small party including a few convicts. The island served as a penal settlement until 1814 and later from 1825 to 1855 when the penitentiary was finally abandoned. Shortly thereafter, almost 200 descendants of the mutineers from the *HMS Bounty* left the overcrowded Pitcairn Island and were resettled on Norfolk. The former Pitcairners established a unique society on Norfolk and one third of residents at the end of the 20th century still claim lineal descent from these early settlers. Under the Norfolk Island Act of 1913, Norfolk became a territory of the Commonwealth of Australia, however, the exact constitutional relationship with Australia has been continually disputed.

GOVERNMENT

Norfolk Island is administered as a territory under authority of the Commonwealth of Australia. No administrative divisions exist. The chief of state is the British monarch represented by the Governor-General of Australia. On the island the senior government representative of the United Kingdom and Australia is the Administrator, appointed by the Australian Governor-General and responsible to the Minister for Regional Services, Territories and Local Government.

The Norfolk Island Act of 1979 created a legislature, the Legislative Assembly, and an executive government, the Executive Council, enabling the island to govern its own internal affairs to the greatest practicable extent. The Legislative Assembly is comprised of nine members elected through an electoral process not more than three year terms. The Executive Council is made up of the executive members of the Legislative Assembly. The Executive Council includes five positions: (1) the President of the Legislative Assembly and Minister for Finance and Strategic Planning; (2) the Deputy President; (3) Minister for Community and Resource Management; (4) Minister for Tourism and Commerce; and, (5) Minister for Health and Immi-

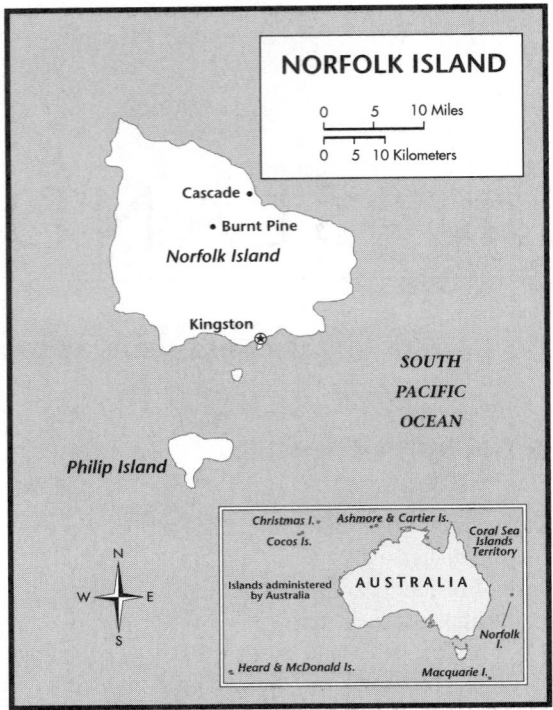

gration. Both bodies are lead by the President of the Legislative Assembly.

The Administrator must act with the advice of the Executive Council or the Australian Minister on every law proposed by the Assembly. The Administrator may give his approval, reserve the proposed law for the Governor-General's decision, or recommend amendments.

Judiciary

Norfolk Island's judiciary system includes a Supreme Court with appeals directed to the Federal Court of Australia and the Court of Petty Sessions exercising both civil and criminal jurisdiction. The legal system is based on local ordinances and the laws of Australia. Cases not covered by local or Australian law come under English common law.

Political Parties

No formal political parties exist on Norfolk Island. All those elected in 1997 were non-partisans.

DEFENSE

The Australian military provides defense protection to Norfolk Island backed by New Zealand and the United States through a security treaty.

ECONOMIC AFFAIRS

Since the 1960's tourism has been Norfolk Island's predominate industry. The operation of hotels and duty-free stores employ many islanders. As many as 30,000 tourist, many from New Zealand, visit annually. Prosperity brought to the island by tourism has allowed the agricultural sector to become self-sufficient in the areas of beef, poultry, and eggs. Fishing is important locally, but expansion is severely restricted by the lack of accessible harbors. Agricultural products grown in the fertile soil include Norfolk Island pine seed, Kentia palm seeds, cereals, fruits, and vegetables. Shipped all over the world, the seed of the Norfolk Island pine is a chief export. Forestry programs strive to increase the island's resource of pines and hardwoods.

In addition to the Norfolk Island pine seeds, exports include the Kentia palm, small quantities of avocados, and postage stamps. Imports of food, fuel, and consumer goods are brought in mainly for the tourist trade. Exploitation of the gas and oil fields in the island's exclusive economic zone was a hotly debated topic at the close of the 20th century.

Public Finance

Public revenue comes from tourism, custom duties, sale of postage stamps, liquor sales (a government monopoly), and company registration and license fees. In the fiscal year ending in June of 1996 custom duties accounted for 27% of the total revenue. Residents are not taxed on income earning within the territory.

Industry

Tourism is the chief industry followed by commercial cultivation of Norfolk Island pine seed and Kentia palm seed in the agricultural sector. The remainder of agricultural production is at the subsistence level with the goal of self-sufficiency.

Banking and Finance

The Commonwealth Banking Corporation and Westpac Banking Corporation Savings Bank, Ltd., both of Australia, provide banking services to the island.

SOCIAL WELFARE

The Legislative Assembly passed the Social Services Act of 1980 designed to implement a comprehensive scheme of social welfare benefits related to the scheme and benefits payable in mainland Australia.

Healthcare

Two doctors, a pharmacist and a 20-bed hospital provide medical care to the island.

Housing

Most housing is of timber construction. The island's older buildings and residences dating from the convict era are coral stone. Many larger buildings are in brick and stone.

EDUCATION

For children between the ages of six and fifteen education is free and compulsory and run by the New South Wales Department of Education. In 1997 one state school with 21 full-time teachers served 328 students from pre-school to secondary levels. Scholarships and bursaries were available for students who wished to continue their education in Australia.

1999 KEY EVENTS TIMELINE

January

- Greenwich University, incorporated on Norfolk Island in 1994, opens its doors for the first time as an accredited Australian University. The Greenwich University Act of 1998, extending Australian accreditation to Greenwich University, passed in December 1998.

February

- Twice-weekly flights from Sydney, Australia, to Norfolk Island are announced by the charter airline Air Nauru.

March

- Australia's Human Rights and Equal Opportunity Commission calls for new regulations that would remove Norfolk Island's authority over its immigration laws. The Commission suggests that the island's authority over planning and zoning laws is adequate to limit population growth.

July

- Norfolk Islanders appeal to the Australian Senate Legal and Constitutional Committee to reject laws that will force the island to conform with Australian electoral laws and modify its rigid immigration restrictions.

September

- A plane based on Norfolk Island and operated by Greenpeace, an environmental activist organization, unsuccessfully searched the ocean between Australia and New Caledonia for two days. The objects of its search were two ships, the Pintail and the Pacific Teal, reportedly traveling to Japan loaded with recycled plutonium (nuclear fuel). The ships, owned by the United Kingdom, were not located.

ANALYSIS OF EVENTS: 1999

BUSINESS AND THE ECONOMY

Many of the businesses on Norfolk Island have concentrated on planning for tourism related to millennium celebrations.

GOVERNMENT AND POLITICS

The government is actively resisting Australia's move to incorporate Norfolk Island more fully into compliance with Australian laws and regulations, to modify the island's tight controls on immigration, and to impose Australian authority over Norfolk Island elections. At present Norfolk Island is exempt from many Australian regulations, and officeholders and voters may hold citizenship in any country (Norfolk Island does not require Australian citizenship for its officeholders or voters). To participate in elections on Norfolk Island one must have spent at least 900 days on the island over four years of residence. Australia is proposing new regulations that would limit election participation—both for candidates and for voters—to Australia citizens. An estimated 20% of Norfolk Island's current voters would lose their right to vote under this regulation.

CULTURE AND SOCIETY

Many Norfolk Islanders seek to preserve their isolation and independence from Australia and to keep the limit on tourism that has enabled the island to foster a simple and relaxed lifestyle for its residents. As the Australian government considers steps to increase the island's integration into Australia and to expand its conformity to Australian laws, islanders are resisting loudly.

DIRECTORY

CENTRAL GOVERNMENT

Head of State

Administrator
A.J. Messner

President and Chief Minister
George Charles Smith, Office of the President

Head Administrator
A.J. Messner, Office of the Head Administrator
FAX: +61 (6723) 22681
E-MAIL: Tony.Messner@dotrs.gov.au

Ministers

Minister of Finance
George Smith, Ministry of Finance

Minister of Agriculture
Ernie Friend, Ministry of Agriculture
PHONE: +61 (6723) 22609
FAX: +61 (6723) 22609

Minister of Forestry
John (Fanny) Christian, Ministry of Forestry
PHONE: +61 (6723) 23195
FAX: +61 (6723) 23317

Minister of Tourism and Commerce
James Robertson, Ministry of Tourism and
Commerce

**Minister of Immigration and Resource
Management**
Cedrick Robinson, Ministry of Immigration and
Resource Management

Minister of Health
Geoff Gardner, Ministry of Health

JUDICIAL SYSTEM

Supreme Court

Supreme Court Registrar, Norfolk Island, South
Pacific 2895
PHONE: +61 (6723) 23691

FURTHER READING

Articles

''Air Nauru to Serve Norfolk Island from
Sydney.'' Pacnews, 1 February 1999.

Greene, Gervase. ''Islanders Prepare to Repel
'Invasion.''' *The Age* (July 5, 1999).

Internet

Norfolk Island. Available Online @ www.nf /
index.html (November 17, 1999).

Norfolk Island Travel Channel. Available Online
@ www.norfolkisland.nf (November 17,
1999).

NORFOLK ISLAND: STATISTICAL DATA

For sources and notes see "Sources of Statistics" in the front of each volume.

GEOGRAPHY

Geography (1)

Area:

Total: 34.6 sq km.

Land: 34.6 sq km.

Water: 0 sq km.

Area—comparative: about 0.2 times the size of Washington, DC.

Land boundaries: 0 km.

Coastline: 32 km.

Climate: subtropical, mild, little seasonal temperature variation.

Terrain: volcanic formation with mostly rolling plains.

Natural resources: fish.

Land use:

Arable land: NA%

Permanent crops: NA%

Permanent pastures: 25%

Forests and woodland: NA%

Other: 75% (1993 est.).

HUMAN FACTORS

Demographics (2B)

Population (July 1998 est.) 2,179

Age structure:

 0-14 years . . . . .NA

 15-64 years . . . . .NA

 65 years and over . . . . .NA

Population growth rate (1998 est.) . . . .−0.69%

Birth rate (births/1,000 population) . . . . .NA

Death rate (deaths/1,000 population) . . . . .NA

Net migration rate (migrant(s)/1,000 population) . . .NA

Infant mortality rate (deaths/1,000 live births) . . . . .NA

Life expectancy at birth:

 Total population . . . . .NA

 Male . . . . .NA

 Female . . . . .NA

Total fertility rate (children born/woman) . . . . . . .NA

Ethnic Division (6)

Descendants of the Bounty mutineers, Australian, New Zealander, Polynesians.

Religions (7)

Anglican 39%

Roman Catholic 11.7%

Uniting Church in Australia 16.4%

Seventh-Day Adventist 4.4%

None 9.2%

Unknown 16.9%

Other 2.4% (1986)

Languages (8)

English (official), Norfolk a mixture of 18th century English and ancient Tahitian.

GOVERNMENT & LAW

Political Parties (12)

The legislative branch is a unicameral Legislative Assembly (9 seats; members elected by electors who have nine equal votes each but only four votes can be given to any one candidate; members serve three-year terms). All seats are held by independents.

Government Budget (13B)

Revenues . . . .$4.6 million

Expenditures . . . .$4.8 million

 Capital expenditures . . . . .NA

Data for FY92/93. NA stands for not available.

Military Affairs (14A)

Defense is the responsibility of Australia.

LABOR FORCE

Labor Force (16)

Total 1,395. Data for 1991 est.

Unemployment Rate (17)

Rate not available.

PRODUCTION SECTOR

Electric Energy (18)

No data available.

Transportation (19)

Highways:

total: 80 km

paved: 53 km

unpaved: 27 km

Merchant marine: none

Airports: 1 (1997 est.)

Airports—with paved runways:

total: 1

1,524 to 2,437 m: 1 (1997 est.)

Top Agricultural Products (20)

Norfolk Island pine seed, Kentia palm seed, cereals, vegetables, fruit; cattle, poultry.

FINANCE, ECONOMICS, & TRADE

Economic Indicators (22)

No data available.

Exchange Rates (24)

Exchange rates:

Australian dollars ($A) per US$1

January 1998	1.5281
1997	1.3439
1996	1.2773
1995	1.3486
1994	1.3667
1993	1.4704

Top Import Origins (25)

$17.9 million (c.i.f., FY91/92)

Origins	%
Australia	NA
other Pacific island countries	NA
NZ	NA
Asia	NA
Europe	NA

NA stands for not available.

Top Export Destinations (26)

$1.5 million (f.o.b., FY91/92).

Destinations	%
Australia	NA
other Pacific island countries	NA
NZ	NA
Asia	NA
Europe	NA

NA stands for not available.

Economic Aid (27)

None.

Import Export Commodities (28)

Import Commodities	Export Commodities
NA	Postage stamps
	Seeds of the Norfolk Island pine and Kentia palm
	Small quantities of avocados

NORTHERN MARIANA ISLANDS

Commonwealth of the Northern Mariana Islands

INTRODUCTORY SURVEY

RECENT HISTORY

The Northern Mariana Islands (NMI) were first settled by peoples originating in Southeast Asia. Ferdinand Magellan stopped at the Marianas in 1521 during his first circumnavigation and named the islands the Ladrones, Spanish for Thieves. Claimed for Spain in 1565, permanent Spanish colonization began in 1668 and the islands were renamed the Marianas in honor of Mariana of Austria, the regent of Spain. The Spanish expanded their holdings north to include Guam. With the Spanish world weakening in the nineteenth century, NMI became embroiled in colonial battles. The United States seized Guam from Spain in 1898. Spain withdrew from the Pacific after selling the remaining Marianas to Germany. The division between Guam and NMI became permanent.

Japan took official possession of NMI following World War I with the signing of the Treaty of Versailles in 1919. At the outbreak of World War II, Japan seized Guam from the United States but the Americans recaptured Guam and took over all of the Mariana Islands by 1944. A year later one of the islands, Tinian, served as the base for the U.S. planes that dropped the atomic bombs on Hiroshima and Nagasaki.

In 1947 the United States signed a Trustee Agreement with the United Nations to administer NMI as a district within the Trust Territory of the Pacific Islands. In 1975 NMI voted for status as a U.S. Commonwealth Territory. The Northern Mariana Commonwealth Covenant was signed in 1976

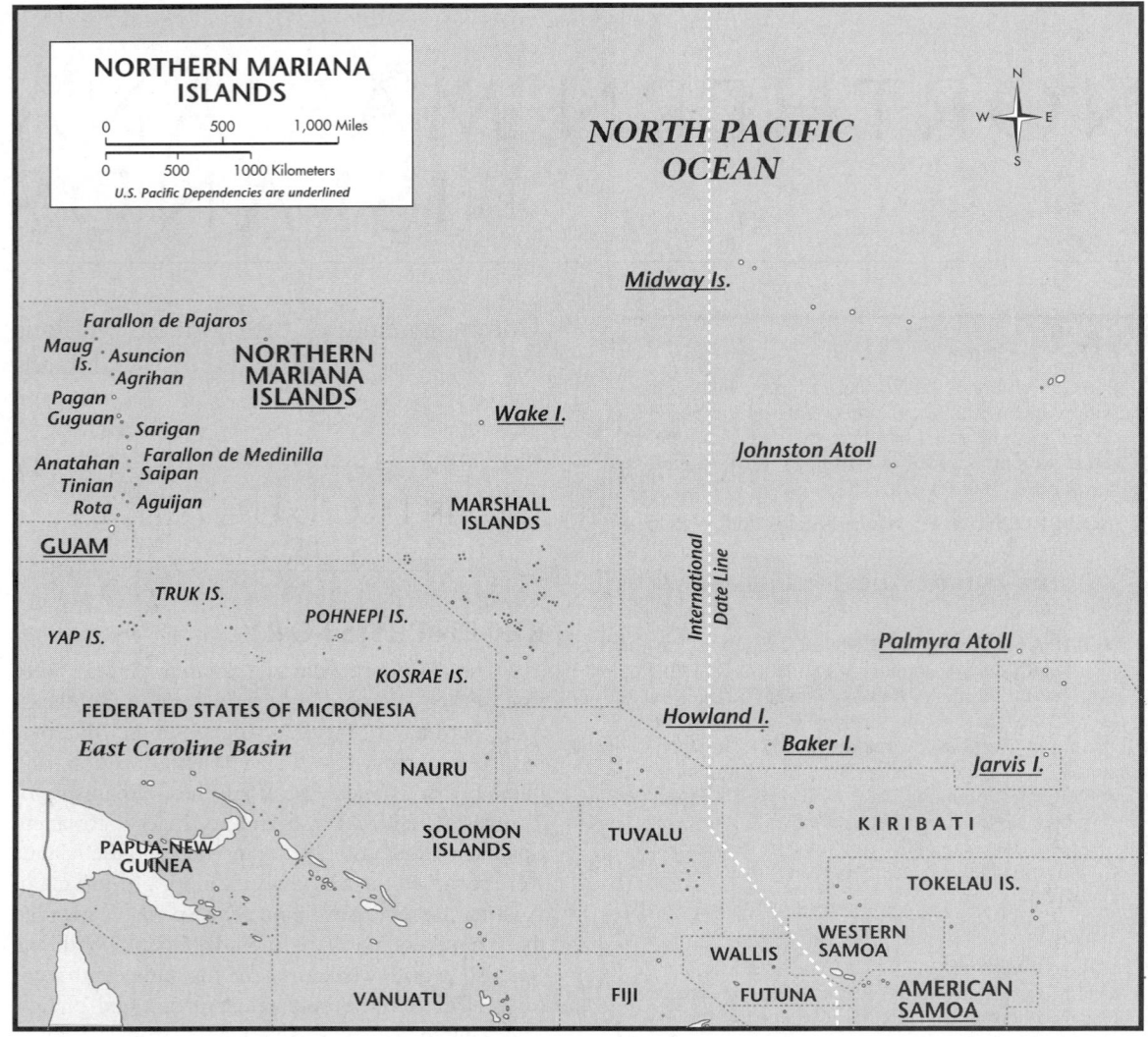

NORTHERN MARIANA ISLANDS

0   500   1,000 Miles

0   500   1000 Kilometers

U.S. Pacific Dependencies are underlined

NORTH PACIFIC OCEAN

Midway Is.

Farallon de Pajaros

Maug Is. •Asuncion

NORTHERN MARIANA ISLANDS

•Agrihan

Pagan
Guguan•   •Sarigan

Wake I.

Johnston Atoll

Anatahan• •Farallon de Medinilla
Tinian•   •Saipan
Rota•   •Aguijan

GUAM

MARSHALL ISLANDS

International Date Line

Palmyra Atoll

TRUK IS.

YAP IS.   POHNEPI IS.

KOSRAE IS.

FEDERATED STATES OF MICRONESIA

Howland I.

Baker I.

Jarvis I.

East Caroline Basin

NAURU

KIRIBATI

PAPUA-NEW GUINEA

SOLOMON ISLANDS

TUVALU

TOKELAU IS.

WESTERN SAMOA

WALLIS

VANUATU   FIJI   FUTUNA   AMERICAN SAMOA

and in 1977 U.S. President Jimmy Carter approved the NMI constitution providing for internal self-governing. Elections took place in 1977 for a governor, lieutenant governor, and bicameral legislature. The United States terminated the administration of the trusteeship in 1986 when NMI was formally admitted to U.S. commonwealth status. At that time a proclamation by U.S. President Ronald Reagan conferred U.S. citizenship on the island's residents.

The 1980s and 1990s saw a dramatic increase in population leading to social and economic problems. Persistent problems of an inadequate minimum wage coupled with reports of improper labor practices and poor treatment of alien workers in garment factories dominated the Marianas' political scene in the late 1990s.

GOVERNMENT

Northern Mariana Islands is a commonwealth in political union with the United States. The islands are divided into four municipalities—Northern Islands, Saipan, Rota, and Tinian. Although the President of the United States is the chief of state, the commonwealth has been self-governing since 1977 and elects a governor, lieutenant governor, and bicameral legislature by popular vote. Administrative headquarters are at Chalan Kanoa in Saipan. The governor and lieutenant governor are elected on the same ticket for four-year terms. Executive authority rests with the governor.

Legislative authority rests with the Northern Marianas commonwealth legislature. The bicameral legislature consists of a Senate and House of Representatives. The Senate has nine seats, three each from Saipan, Rota, and Tinian. Senators are elected for four year staggered terms. The House of Representatives has eighteen seats with members elected for two-year terms. Senate and House elections take place every two years.

The Commonwealth maintains an elected official, the ''resident representative,'' in Washington, D.C., but has no delegates in Congress.

Judiciary

The NMI judiciary includes the Commonwealth Supreme Court, which hears appeals from the Superior Court, the Superior Court, and a U.S. Territorial District Court in Saipan. U.S. federal law applies to the Commonwealth except in four areas: customs, taxation, immigration, and wages. The Commonwealth is not part of U.S. Custom Territory, enacts its own taxation laws, and federal minimum wage and immigration laws do not apply.

Political Parties

The two major political parties are the Republican and Democratic parties. In 1997 the Republicans held the governor and lieutenant governorships and retained a majority of the seats in the Senate and House of Representatives.

DEFENSE

The U.S. military provides defense protection to the Northern Mariana Islands.

ECONOMIC AFFAIRS

By 1998 the economy of the Commonwealth centered on tourism and garment manufacturing. The rapidly growing tourism industry employed 45% of the labor force and provided approximately 50% of the gross domestic product (GDP). Offering luxury hotels to the tourists, predominately Japanese, Korean, and American, Saipan and Rota are the main tourist centers. Large scale investment, primarily Japanese, resulted in major increases in hotel rooms and number of tourists throughout the 1980s and 1990s. North Mariana Islands are also opening up to the gambling market with a hotel casino complex on Tinian. Tourism earned U.S. $522 million in 1995. Closely tied to tourism is the construction industry, which provides employment for approximately 20% of the workforce building new facilities.

The lucrative garment industry rapidly expanded Commonwealth revenues in the 1990s. The garment factories, most run by Chinese or South Korean firms, operate with foreign contract workers predominately from China, Bangladesh, and the Philippines who are paid substantially less than the U.S. minimum wages. Garment exports earned approximately $419 million in 1995. Benefitting manufacturers, the exported garments may be stamped ''Made in the USA'' and are free of duties and quotas applied to products made in China and Korea.

Small-scale manufacturing of handicrafts including stone, clay, and glass products provided additional employment and revenue. The agricultural sector, concentrated in small holdings and including cultivation of fruits and vegetables, and cattle and pig ranches, employed only 2.2% of workers in 1992.

The principal export is garments and chief imports are petroleum products, automobiles and parts, food, and construction equipment. Heavy dependence on imports generally produces trade deficits.

The annual rate of inflation between 1990 and 1996 averaged 4.7%. The Northern Marianas are members of the Pacific Community and an associate member of the U.N. Economic and Social Commission for Asia and the Pacific.

Public Finance

Budgets revenues are derived from local revenues and from United States assistance. Although declining as local government revenues increase, the United States provides considerable financial assistance. For capital development, governmental operation, and other programs the United States provided $228 million between 1986 and 1992. For the fiscal years 1993–94 and 1995–96 the islands received $27.7 million. From fiscal year 1996–97 through 2002–03 the Commonwealth with matching local funding will receive $11 million for infrastructure development. In the fiscal year 1995 budget estimates predicted revenue of $217.1 million and total expenditures of $190.4 million.

Income

The gross domestic product (GDP) purchasing power parity was estimated at $524 million in 1996 and reflected United States spending. The 1994 GDP per capita purchasing power parity estimation was $9,300. Tourism and garment manufacturing are the only two major sources of income.

Industry

The predominate industrial activities include tourism, garment manufacturing, and construction.

Other industries include small scale manufacturing of handicrafts.

Banking and Finance

Banking centers in Saipan includes the Bank of Guam, Bank of Hawaii, Bank of Saipan, City Trust Bank, Development Bank, Hongkong and Shanghai Banking Corporation, Union Bank, and two savings and loan associations, First Savings and Loan of America and Guam Savings and Loan Bank.

SOCIAL WELFARE

Health and social welfare budgetary expenditures accounted for 18.4% of total government expenditure.

Healthcare

In the 1990s the Marianas operated the Commonwealth Health Center on Saipan. Smaller sub-hospitals were located on Tinuan and Rota. All other inhabited islands have health dispensaries. The single greatest factor straining the health system is rapid population growth of non-resident alien workers.

Housing

As a result of growth in population and the economy between 1980 and 1995, the number of housing units more than tripled from 1980 to 12,058 units in 1995. In 1995, 4,038 units were occupied by owners, and 5,219 by renters. Consisting of units government and businesses provide to expatriate workers, 2,081 units were occupied without payment of rent by occupants. Persons, generally alien workers, occupying group quarters as barracks and other structures numbered 9,703 down from the 1990 total of 11,489.

EDUCATION

School attendance for children ages six to sixteen is compulsory. In elementary and secondary schools instructional materials and courses offered are modeled after those in the United States but modified to meet the unique needs and characteristics of the islands.

All inhabited islands have primary schools. Public and church-operated secondary schools are located in Saipan. The student-teacher ratio is 20.9 to one by 1995 estimates.

A public junior college, College of the Northern Marianas, was established in 1976. Students also pursue post-secondary education at the University of Guam or in various institutions in Hawaii or the continental United States. Over 90% of students receive some form of federal student aid in addition to grants from the government of the North Marianas.

The total literacy rate was estimated to be 97% in 1980. In 1995 the Mariana's government budgetary expenditure for education was 19.6% of total expenditures.

1999 KEY EVENTS TIMELINE

January

- The Commonwealth celebrates its twenty-first anniversary as a separate political entity on January 9.

March

- Covenant Day is celebrated.

April

- Seventeen retailers are served with subpoenas for purportedly selling clothing made in Saipan sweatshops.
- The 1999 Electronics Expo is held.
- The 1999 Flame Tree Festival is held in Saipan from April 23–25.

May

- The Taste of the Marianas festival takes place.
- The 1999 CNMI Agricultural Fair is held in Saipan on May 29.

July

- Citizens of the Commonwealth celebrate Liberation Day on July 4.
- The International Festival of Cultures is held from July 17–18.

August

- PCBs are discovered in Tanapag.
- On August 6, the fifty-fourth anniversary of the atomic bombing of Hiroshima, Japan is commemorated. The "Enola Gay," the B-29 bomber that dropped the bomb, took off from Tinian Island in the Northern Mariana Islands.
- The 15th Annual Fishing Tournament is held in Saipan from August 21–22.

September

- The Marianas Visitors Authority sponsors Plumeria Dreams 1999: Island Wedding Fashion Show on September 11.

November

- Citizenship Day is celebrated on November 4.

ANALYSIS OF EVENTS: 1999

BUSINESS AND THE ECONOMY

Tourism continued to be an economic mainstay for the Commonwealth of the Northern Mariana Islands (CNMI) in 1999. The Mariana Visitors Authority dubbed 1999 "Visit the Marianas Year."

The Northern Mariana Islands Council for the Humanities held a series of Teacher Institutes focusing on Mariana's history. The Institute consisted of five sessions covering the history of the Spanish Colonial Era, the German period, the Japanese civilian period, the war years, and the history of the post-war years. Writers and historians from various Commonwealth institutions led the sessions.

In April seventeen retailers, including The Gap, J. Crew, Tommy Hilfiger, Wal-Mart, the Limited, Nordstrom, and others, were served with subpoenas for purportedly selling clothing made in sweatshops in Saipan. Three lawsuits were filed on behalf of young women employed in the sweatshops on the island.

GOVERNMENT AND POLITICS

On January 9 the Commonwealth celebrated its twenty-first anniversary as a separate political entity. On that day in 1978 the first governor of the Commonwealth of the Northern Mariana Islands, Carlos S. Camacho, was sworn into office.

One of the most significant holidays was celebrated in March. Covenant Day commemorates the establishment of the Commonwealth of the Northern Mariana Islands (CNMI) in political union with the United States of America. The Covenant was approved by a joint resolution of the U.S. Congress twenty-three years ago and defines the CNMI's distinctive relationship with the United States. Unlike lands that become part of the United States as states or territories—via occupation, sale, or surrender—the CNMI became part of the United States through a voluntary vote by the people of the CNMI.

Between April and August dozens of boatloads of illegal Chinese immigrants descended on Tinian. In October President Bill Clinton guaranteed the Marianas that it would receive payment for its assistance in providing food and shelter for the immigrants, who came seeking asylum. So far the CNMI has received $750,000 for aiding over 600 illegal immigrants.

During August an unsafe level of PCBs was found in the soil in Tanapag. The contamination was suspected of having occurred some fifty years ago. U.S. Army Corps of Engineers (ACE), the U.S. Environmental Protection Agency (EPA), the CNMI's Department of Environmental Quality (DEQ), and the Department of Public Health (DPH), among others, gave a presentation on the contamination in October. Among the topics for discussion was a draft report for further treatment of the PCB problem.

Also in October the CNMI government continued to request reimbursement from the United States for funds spent hosting citizens from the Freely Associated States, or FAS (the Federated States of Micronesia, the Marshall Islands, and Palau). Housing, education, and medical benefits have been provided for more than two years for nearly 5,000 FAS citizens, with no reimbursement to date provided by the federal government.

Public Law 11–88, an effort to control the display and sale of tobacco, particularly to minors, passed. In November two amendments were proposed for the election ballot. One was a constitutional amendment proposed by Senate Legislative Initiative 11–4 giving the CNMI government three departments of finance. The second amendment was proposed by Senate Legislative Initiative 11–1, allowing only people of Northern Mariana Island descent to vote on any changes to Article XII, affecting its protection against the alienation of land. The islands of Rota and Tinian also had local laws on the ballot. Both concerned gambling. Tinian's proposal suggested changes to its Casino Gaming Control Act, and Rota's proposed law called for the establishment, regulation, and control of casino gambling on the island.

CULTURE AND SOCIETY

The Mariana's Visitors Authority (MVA) sponsored the "Taste of the Marianas" in May at Memorial Park. Major hotels and restaurants offered samples of their cuisine for a small fee, while live music and a cook-off competition between hotel chefs were main attractions.

In mid-July the "International Festival of Cultures" was held. It featured a parade, live music, crafts, and edibles.

In sports, Rocball, a non-contact team net game similar to volleyball, continued to be one of the favorite athletic activities. It has been played in the CNMI since 1979.

DIRECTORY

CENTRAL GOVERNMENT

Head of State

President of the United States
William Jefferson Clinton, Office of the President of the United States, The White House, 1600 Pennsylvania Ave, Washington, D.C., United States

Governor
Pedro P. Tenorio, Office of the Governor, Capitol Hill, Saipan, MP 96950, Northern Marianas Islands
PHONE: +672 6642276
FAX: +672 6642290
E-MAIL: gov.frosario@saipan.com

Lieutenant Governor
Jesus R. Sablan, Office of the Lieutenant Governor, Capitol Hill, Saipan, MP 96950, Northern Marianas Islands
PHONE: +672 6642276
FAX: +672 6642290

Ministers

Minister of Finance
Lucy Nielsen, Ministry of Finance, Governor's Cabinet, Caller Box 10007 Saipan, MP 96950, Northern Marianas Islands
PHONE: +672 6641100
FAX: +672 6641115

Minister of Labor and Immigration
Mark Zachares, Ministry of Labor and Immigration, Governor's Cabinet, Caller Box 10007 Saipan, MP 96950, Northern Marianas Islands
PHONE: +672 6643154
FAX: +672 6643153

Minister of Health Services
Joseph P. Villagomez, Ministry of Health Services, Governor's Cabinet, Caller Box 10007 Saipan, MP 96950, Northern Marianas Islands
PHONE: +672 2348950
FAX: +672 2348930

Minister of Lands and Natural Resources
Jack A. Tenorio, Ministry of Lands and Natural Resources, Governor's Cabinet, Caller Box 10007 Saipan, MP 96950, Northern Marianas Islands
PHONE: +672 3229830
FAX: +672 3222633

Minister of Community and Cultural Affairs
Thomas A. Tebuteb, Ministry of Community and Cultural Affairs, Governor's Cabinet, Caller Box 10007 Saipan, MP 96950, Northern Marianas Islands
PHONE: +672 6642571; 2333343
FAX: +672 6642570

Minister of Public Safety
Charles W. Ingram Jr., Ministry of Public Safety, Governor's Cabinet, Caller Box 10007 Saipan, MP 96950, Northern Marianas Islands
PHONE: +672 2348536
FAX: +672 2342313

Minister of Public Works
John B. Cepeda, Ministry of Public Works, Governor's Cabinet, Caller Box 10007 Saipan, MP 96950, Northern Marianas Islands
PHONE: +672 2355827
FAX: +672 2356346

Minister of Commerce
Bernadita T. Palacios, Ministry of Commerce, Governor's Cabinet, Caller Box 10007 Saipan, MP 96950, Northern Marianas Islands
PHONE: +672 6643000
FAX: +672 6643067

Minister of Administration
Jose I. De Leon Guerrero, Ministry of Administration, Governor's Cabinet, Caller Box 10007 Saipan, MP 96950, Northern Marianas Islands
PHONE: +672 6642200
FAX: +672 6642210

Minister of Programs and Legislative Review

Gloria W. Hunter, Ministry of Programs and Legislative Review, Governor's Cabinet, Caller Box 10007 Saipan, MP 96950, Northern Marianas Islands

PHONE: +672 6642286

FAX: +672 6642313

Minister of Management and Budget

Virginia C. Villagomez, Ministry of Management and Budget, Governor's Cabinet, Caller Box 10007 Saipan, MP 96950, Northern Marianas Islands

PHONE: +672 6642265

FAX: +672 6642272

Minister of Finance and Budget

Mike S. Sablan, Ministry of Finance and Budget, Governor's Cabinet, Caller Box 10007 Saipan, MP 96950, Northern Marianas Islands

PHONE: +672 6642245

FAX: +672 6642242

Minister of Public Liaison

Gregorio C. Sablan, Ministry of Public Liaison, Governor's Cabinet, Caller Box 10007 Saipan, MP 96950, Northern Marianas Islands

PHONE: +672 6642233

FAX: +672 6642390

Minister of Policy and Research

Mike Malone, Ministry of Policy and Research, Governor's Cabinet, Caller Box 10007 Saipan, MP 96950, Northern Marianas Islands

PHONE: +672 6642225

FAX: +672 6642211

Minister of Women's Affairs

Maryann Tudela, Ministry of Women's Affairs, Governor's Cabinet, Caller Box 10007 Saipan, MP 96950, Northern Marianas Islands

PHONE: +672 2884102

FAX: +672 2880845

Minister of Indigenous Affairs

Ignacio Demapan, Minister of Indigenous Affairs, Governor's Cabinet, Caller Box 10007 Saipan, MP 96950, Northern Marianas Islands

PHONE: +672 6642480

FAX: +672 2881159

POLITICAL ORGANIZATIONS

Republican Party

NAME: Benigno R. Fitial

Democratic Party

JUDICIAL SYSTEM

The Supreme Court

P.O. Box 2165 CK, Saipan, MP 96950, Northern Marianas Islands

PHONE: +672 2369715

FAX: +672 2369701

E-MAIL: supreme.court@saipan.com

The Superior Court

P.O. Box 502179, Susupe, Saipan, MP 96950, Northern Marianas Islands

PHONE: +672 2369740

FAX: +672 2369741

E-MAIL: cnmi.superior.court@gtepacifica.net

Federal District Court

FURTHER READING

Articles

Lucentini, Jack. "17 Retailers Subpoenaed on Sweatshop Charges; Human Rights Activists Push Action for Saipan." *Journal of Commerce and Commercial* (May 4, 1999).

Saladores, Benhur C. "CNMI to Press for Reimbursement for Hosting FAS Citizens." *Saipan Tribune* (October 28, 1999).

———. "President Clinton Assures Guam and Northern Marianas Payment for Hosting Illegal Chinese Immigrants." *Saipan Tribune* (October 28, 1999).

Internet

Bruce Lloyd Media CNMI News. Available Online @ net.saipan.com/news/index.htm (November 9, 1999).

Commonwealth of the Northern Mariana Islands Home Page. Available Online @ www.saipan.com/ (November 10, 1999).

Law of the Commonwealth of the Northern Marianas Islands. Available Online @ cnmilaw.org/ (November 15, 1999).

Tighe, Ruth L. "On My Mind." Available Online @ net.saipan.com/cftemplates/omm/ archives.cfm (November 8, 1999).

NORTHERN MARIANA ISLANDS: STATISTICAL DATA

For sources and notes see "Sources of Statistics" in the front of each volume.

GEOGRAPHY

Geography (1)

Area:

Total: 477 sq km.

Land: 477 sq km.

Water: 0 sq km.

Note: includes 14 islands including Saipan, Rota, and Tinian.

Area—comparative: 2.5 times the size of Washington, DC.

Land boundaries: 0 km.

Coastline: 1,482 km.

Climate: tropical marine; moderated by northeast trade winds, little seasonal temperature variation; dry season December to June, rainy season July to October.

Terrain: southern islands are limestone with level terraces and fringing coral reefs; northern islands are volcanic.

Natural resources: arable land, fish.

Land use:

Arable land: 21%

Permanent crops: NA%

Permanent pastures: 19%

Forests and woodland: NA%

Other: NA%

HUMAN FACTORS

Demographics (2A)

	1990	1995	1998	2000	2010	2020	2030	2040	2050
Population	44.0	58.1	66.6	72.1	99.1	123.7	144.0	157.6	162.6
Net migration rate (per 1,000 population)	NA	NA	NA	NA	NA	NA	NA	NA	NA
Births	NA	NA	NA	NA	NA	NA	NA	NA	NA
Deaths	NA	NA	NA	NA	NA	NA	NA	NA	NA
Life expectancy - males	68.6	69.5	71.8	72.5	75.3	77.3	78.6	79.5	80.0
Life expectancy - females	75.5	76.2	78.4	79.0	81.6	83.4	84.7	85.5	86.0
Birth rate (per 1,000)	26.9	26.2	23.1	21.2	17.8	15.1	13.0	11.4	10.1
Death rate (per 1,000)	3.3	2.9	2.5	2.4	2.5	3.3	4.8	7.2	9.8
Women of reproductive age (15-49 yrs.)	14.4	20.5	24.0	26.2	35.3	38.2	39.1	38.5	35.7
of which are currently married	NA	NA	NA	NA	NA	NA	NA	NA	NA
Fertility rate	2.3	2.2	1.9	1.8	1.8	1.8	1.7	1.7	1.7

Except as noted, values for vital statistics are in thousands; life expectancy is in years.

Ethnic Division (6)

Chamorro, Carolinians and other Micronesians, Caucasian, Japanese, Chinese, Korean.

Religions (7)

Languages (8)

English, Chamorro, Carolinian. 86% of population speaks a language other than English at home.

GOVERNMENT & LAW

Political Parties (12)

Legislative branch is a bicameral Legislature consists of the Senate (9 seats; members are elected by popular vote to serve four-year staggered terms) and the House of Representatives (18 seats; members are elected by popular vote.

Government Budget (13B)

Revenues . . . .$190.4 million

Expenditures . . . .$190.4 million

  Capital expenditures . . . .$19.1 million

Data for FY94/95.

Military Affairs (14A)

Defense is the responsibility of the US.

LABOR FORCE

Labor Force (16)

7,476 total indigenous labor force; 2,699 unemployed; 22,560 foreign workers. Data for 1995.

Unemployment Rate (17)

14% (residents)

PRODUCTION SECTOR

Electric Energy (18)

No data available.

Transportation (19)

Highways:

total: 362 km (1991 est.)

paved: NA km

unpaved: NA km

Waterways: none

Merchant marine: none

Airports: 5 (1997 est.)

Airports—with paved runways:

total: 3

2,438 to 3,047 m: 1

1,524 to 2,437 m: 2 (1997 est.)

Airports—with unpaved runways:

total: 2

2,438 to 3,047 m: 1

under 914 m: 1 (1997 est.)

Top Agricultural Products (20)

Coconuts, fruits, vegetables; cattle.

FINANCE, ECONOMICS, & TRADE

Economic Indicators (22)

National product: GDP—purchasing power parity—$524 million (1994 est.) note: GDP numbers reflect US spending

National product real growth rate: NA%

National product per capita: $10,500 (1994 est.)

Inflation rate—consumer price index: 6.5% (1994 est.)

Exchange Rates (24)

Exchange rates: US currency is used

Economic Aid (27)

None.

Import Export Commodities (28)

Import Commodities	Export Commodities
Food	Garments
Construction equipment and materials	
Petroleum products	

NORWAY

Kingdom of Norway
Kongeriket Norge

INTRODUCTORY SURVEY

RECENT HISTORY

Although Norway remained neutral during World War I (1914–18), its merchant marine suffered losses. Norway proclaimed its neutrality during the early days of World War II (1939–45), but Norwegian waters were strategically too important for Norway to remain outside the war. On 9 April 1940, Germany invaded. The national resistance was led by King Haakon. In June 1940, Haakon escaped, taking the government with him. Then he established Norway's government-in-exile in England.

The government that remained in Oslo fell to Vidkun Quisling, a former Norwegian defense minister who had aided the German invasion. His name afterwards became a term in the Norwegian language for one who collaborates with the enemy. After the German surrender, he was arrested, convicted of treason, and shot. During the late 1940s, Norway abandoned its former neutrality, accepted aid from the United States, and joined the North Atlantic Treaty Organization (NATO). King Haakon died in 1957 and was succeeded by Olav V.

The direction of economic policy has been the major issue in Norway since World War II. Especially controversial have been the issue of taxation and the degree of government involvement in private industry. Economic planning has been introduced, and several state-owned enterprises established. Prior to the mid-1970s, Labor Party-

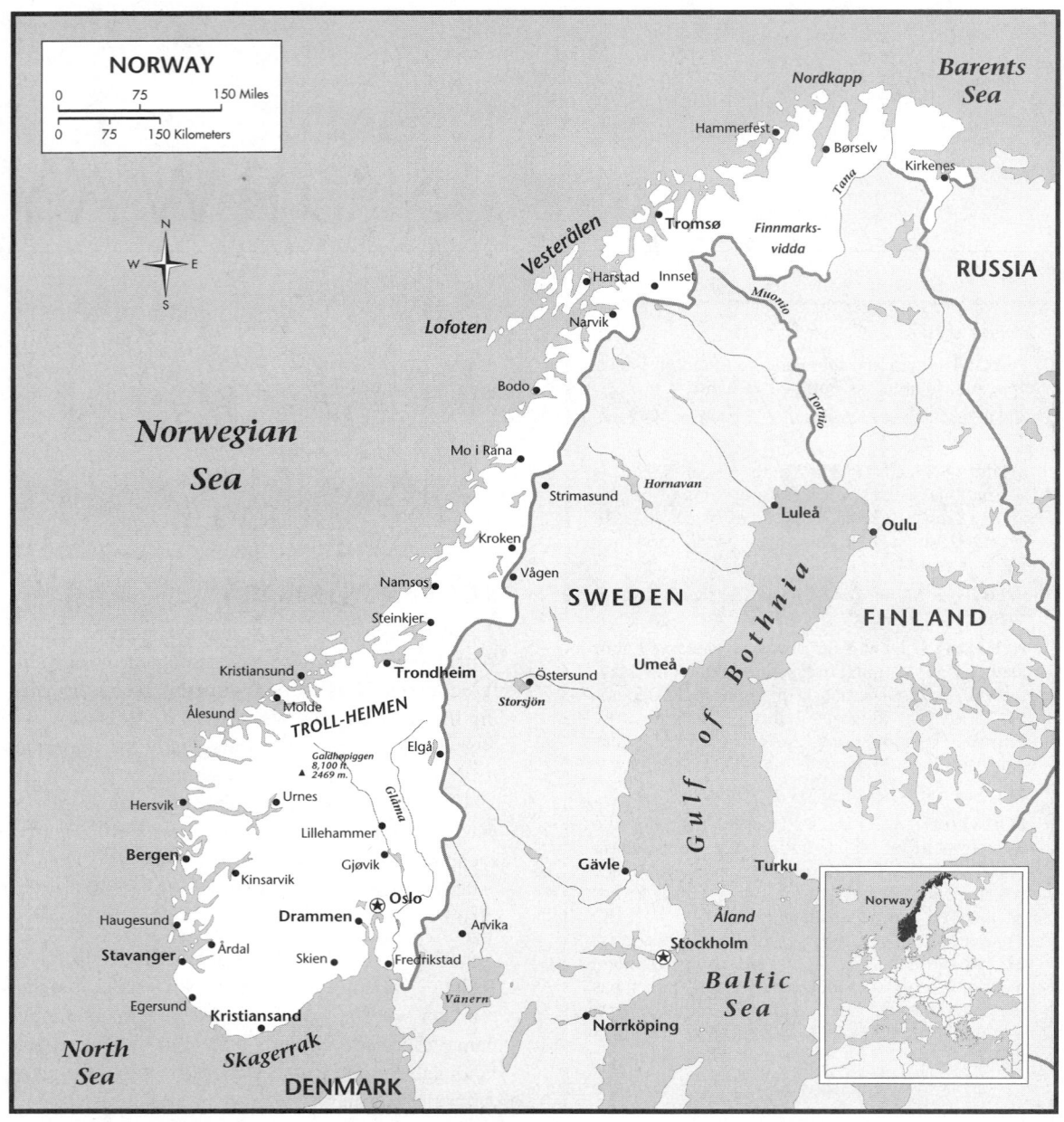

dominated governments enjoyed a broad public consensus for their foreign and military policies.

In November 1972, about 54% of Norwegians voting rejected Norway's entry into what was then the European Economic Community (EEC). The EEC, now the European Union (EU), is intended to make trade between European countries as easy as it is between Michigan and New York.

After the 1973 general elections, the Labor Party, which had been in favor of joining the EEC, found its control over the government had begun to weaken. The Labor Party, under the leadership of Gro Harlem Brundtland, lost control of the government to the Conservatives in the 1981 elections. Brundtland (b. 1939), at age 41, was the youngest woman ever to run a modern government. The Labor Party regained control in 1986, and Brundtland resumed her role as prime minister.

On 17 January 1991, King Harald took over the throne when his father died. The heir-apparent (next king) is Haakon Magnus (b. 1973), Harald's son.

The EU issue has remained controversial. In late November 1994, Norwegians again voted to reject membership in the EU, despite the fact that its neighbors, Sweden and Finland, would become members in January 1995. Those in favor of membership are primarily from urban areas, and are engaged in business or the professions. Those opposed, from coastal areas to the north and the western rural areas, feel that Norway is strong enough and rich enough in natural resources to remain independent. Of special concern is protection of the rich fishing grounds in Norway's territorial waters.

GOVERNMENT

Norway is a constitutional monarchy. The constitution of 17 May 1814, as amended, places executive power in the king and legislative power in the Storting. The sovereign (king or queen) must be a member of the Evangelical Lutheran Church of Norway, which he or she heads. A constitutional amendment in May 1990 allows females to take the throne. Royal power is exercised through a cabinet (the Council of State), consisting of a prime minister and at least seven other ministers of state.

Since the introduction of parliamentary rule in 1884, the Storting (parliament) has become the supreme authority, with complete control over finances and with power to override the monarch's veto under a specified procedure. The monarch is theoretically free to choose his or her own cabinet. In practice the Storting selects the ministers, who must resign if the Storting votes no confidence.

The Storting is made up of 165 representatives from 18 counties. Election for a four-year term is by direct voting. After election, the Storting divides into two sections by choosing one-fourth of its members to form the upper chamber Lagting, with the rest constituting the lower chamber Odelsting. The Odelsting deals with certain types of bills (chiefly proposed new laws) after the committee stage and forwards them to the Lagting. After approving bills, the Lagting sends them to the king for the royal assent (agreement).

Norway had 47 urban municipalities (bykommuner) and 407 rural municipalities (herredskommuner) in 1986. They are grouped into 18 counties (fylker), each governed by an elected county council.

Judiciary

Each municipality has a conciliation council, elected by the municipal council, to mediate in lesser civil cases so as to settle them, if possible, before they go to court. Cases receive their first hearing in town courts (byrett) and rural courts (herredsrett), which try both civil and criminal cases. Their decisions may be brought before a court of appeals (lagmannsrett); there are five such courts, at Oslo, Skien, Bergen, Trondheim, and Tromsø.

Appeals may be taken to the Supreme Court (Høyesterett) at Oslo, which consists of a chief justice and 17 judges, of whom 5 sit in a single case. Special courts include a Social Insurance Court and a Labor Disputes Court which handles industrial relations disputes.

Political Parties

The present-day Conservative Party (Høyre) was established in 1885. The Liberal Party (Venstre), founded in 1885, stresses social reform. Industrial workers founded the Labor Party (Arbeiderparti) in 1887 and, with the assistance of the Liberals, obtained the universal vote for men in 1898, and for women in 1913. The Social Democrats broke away from the Labor Party in 1921–22, and the Communist Party (Kommunistparti), made up of former Laborites, was established in 1923.

The Agrarian (Farmers) Party was formed in 1920. It changed its name to the Center Party (Senterparti) in 1958. The Christian People's Party (Kristelig Folkeparti), founded in 1933, and also known as the Christian Democratic Party, supports the principles of Christianity in public life.

Labor increased its support in the 1993 election, winning 67 seats. The Center Party became the second largest party while the Conservatives and other right-wing parties suffered a decline. The results were as follows: Labour Party (67), Center Party (32), Conservative Party (28), Christian People's Party (13), Socialist Left Party (13), Progress Party (10), and others (2).

DEFENSE

The monarch is supreme commander of the armed forces. About 16,900 draftees served in the armed forces of 30,000 officers and enlisted men in 1995. National service is required and universal, but exceptions may be made for religious reasons. Those exempted must serve for two years in the civil labor corps.

The army's total strength is 14,700 officers and men. The navy has a total of 6,400 men, including 1,000 men in the coastal artillery. The air force consists of 7,900 officers and men, with 80 combat aircraft. Reservists of all services number approximately 255,000, and the home guards has 79,000 men.

Norway is the host nation for the North Atlantic Treaty Organization (NATO) Allied Forces North, and provides troops for six peacekeeping operations. The nation spent $3.8 billion on defense in 1995.

ECONOMIC AFFAIRS

Norway, with its long coastline and vast forests, was traditionally a fishing and lumbering country. Since the end of World War I it has greatly increased its transport and manufacturing activities. The discovery since the late 1970s of major new oil reserves in the North Sea has had considerable impact on the Norwegian economy.

Foreign trade is a critical economic factor. Norway was especially sensitive to the effects of the worldwide recession of the early 1980s and is affected by variations in world prices, particularly those of oil, gas, and shipping. Since the early 1980s, Norway's exports have been dominated by petroleum and natural gas.

The economy grew by an annual average of 1.3% during 1989–91 and by 3.7% during 1992–94. In 1995, the economy grew by 3.7%, inflation was 2.5%, and unemployment was 8%.

Public Finance

Norway's fiscal year coincides with the calendar year. The U.S. Central Intelligence Agency estimates that, in 1995, government revenues totaled approximately $48.6 billion and expenditures $53 billion.

The government's stated policy is that the domestic private sector should cover the bulk of financing requirements related to Norway's external deficits. Since 1990, the government has allowed the private sector increased access to long-term foreign capital markets to facilitate improvements in the term-structure of its foreign debt.

Income

In 1997, Norway's gross national product (GNP) was $120.5 billion at current prices, or about $27,400 per person. For the period 1985–95 the average inflation rate was 3.1%, resulting in a real growth rate in GNP of 1.6% per person.

Industry

The most important export industries are oil and gas production, metalworking, pulp and paper, chemical products, and processed fish. Products traditionally classified as home market industries (electrical and nonelectrical machinery, casting and foundry products, textiles, paints, varnishes, rubber goods, and furniture) also make an important contribution.

Electrochemical and electrometallurgical products—aluminum, ferroalloys, steel, nickel, copper, magnesium, and fertilizers—are based mainly on Norway's low-cost electric power. Without any bauxite reserves of its own, Norway has thus been able to become a leading producer of aluminum (846,735 tons in 1995). Industrial output is being increasingly diversified.

About half of Norway's industries are situated in the area of Oslo's fjord. In 1991, 11,532 establishments in this area employed 298,982 persons.

Banking and Finance

The Bank of Norway was founded as a commercial bank in 1816; in 1949, all its share capital was acquired by the state. It is the central bank and the sole note-issuing authority. The bank discounts treasury bills and some commercial paper; trades in bonds, foreign exchange, and gold and silver; and administers foreign exchange regulations. The bank also receives money for deposit on current account but generally pays no interest on deposits. The head office is in Oslo, and there are 20 branches.

In 1938 there were 105 commercial banks, but mergers brought the total down to only 31 in 1974 and 21 in 1984. As of 1993, the total was down to 20. The three largest—the Norske Creditbank, Bergen Bank, and Christiania Bank og Kreditkasse—account for more than half of the total resources of the commercial banks. In 1988, a number of small savings banks and one medium-sized commercial bank, Sunnmorsbanken, became illiquid or insolvent. Most were rescued by merging with larger banks. After a slight improvement in 1989, however, banks' positions deteriorated again in 1990 following heavy losses sustained in the securities markets. As commercial property prices continued to fall, the position of the country's second and third largest commercial banks, Christiania and Fokus, became increasingly precarious. To prevent a loss of confidence in the banking system, the government established a Government Bank Insurance Fund in March 1991. Within months this was called upon to provide capital to support the country's three largest banks, two of which—Christiania and Fokus—were by then insolvent.

The banking system has gradually recovered from this crisis of the late 1980s and early 1990s.

At the end of 1995, total foreign exchange reserves (excluding gold) stood at $22.5 billion. Money supply, as measured by M2, amounted to Kr616.1 billion at the end of 1995.

Ten state banks and other financial institutions serve particular industries or undertakings, including agriculture, fisheries, manufacturing, student loans, mortgages, and others. Although savings banks also have been merging in recent years, there were still 133 private savings banks and many credit associations in 1993.

A law of 1961 contains measures to implement the principle that banking policies are to be based on social as well as economic and financial considerations. The government appoints 25% of the representatives on the board of every commercial bank with funds of over Kr100 million. Guidelines for these banks are worked out cooperatively with public authorities.

The stock exchanges of Norway are at Oslo (the oldest, founded 1818), Trondheim, Bergen, Kristiansund, Drammen, Stavanger, Ålesund, Haugesund, and Fredrikstad.

Economic Development

The government holds shares in a number of large enterprises: a minority of shares in most industrial establishments and all or controlling shares in some armaments factories, as well as in chemical and electrometallurgical companies, power stations, and mines. The government also participates in joint industrial undertakings with private capital, in enterprises too large or risky for private capital, and in establishments with shares formerly held by German interests. Government policy also aims at attracting foreign investment.

Rapid industrial development and exploitation of resources are major governmental goals, with special emphasis on northern Norway, where development has lagged behind that of the southern areas. The Development Fund for North Norway, established in 1952, together with a policy of tax concessions, resulted in progress there at a rate more rapid than that of the rest of the country. The exploitation of offshore oil and natural gas reserves has had a profound effect on Norway's economy in recent years. Increased oil revenues have expanded both domestic consumption and investment. The government has used oil revenues to ease taxes and increase public investment in regional development, environmental protection, social welfare, education, and communications. In 1992, Norway's offshore oil and taxes amounted to Kr32,299 million. Although the expansion of innovative oil development projects—such as the $4.2 billion Heidrun oil project —continues, Norway is looking to produce more natural gas than oil. The $5 billion Troll gas field, which was to begin production in 1996, is one such project.

A tax law permits industry and commerce to build up tax-free reserves for future investment, foreign sales promotion, and research. Designed to provide a flexible tool for influencing cyclical developments, the law's intent is to help ensure that total demand at any given time is sufficient to create full employment and strong economic growth. In the late 1970s, the government introduced combined price and wage agreements in an effort to restrain inflation and ensure real increases in buying power for consumers.

To stimulate industry, incentives are available for undertakings in the north as well as in other economically weak regions; companies may set aside up to 25% of taxable income for tax-free investment. Tariff incentives are available for essential imports. A Regional Development Fund grants low-interest, long-term loans to firms to strengthen the economy of low-income, high-unemployment areas anywhere in the country.

In 1991, the government introduced a three-year program to improve infrastructure and reduce unemployment. This plan was to spend nearly Kr10 billion, primarily for road and rail communications, with the money coming from budget cuts in other areas.

Norway has been active in aiding developing nations under the Norwegian Agency for International Development. The leading recipients are Tanzania, Mozambique, Zambia, Bangladesh, Nicaragua, and Ethiopia.

SOCIAL WELFARE

Norway has been a pioneer in the field of social welfare and is often called a welfare state. Accident insurance for factory workers was introduced in 1894 and compulsory health insurance in 1909. Sickness benefits, family allowances during hospitalization, and grants for funeral expenses are paid. Public assistance, available in Norway since

1845, supplements the foregoing programs. Social welfare has long included maternity benefits with free prenatal clinics.

The National Insurance Act, which came into effect in 1967, provides old-age pensions, rehabilitation allowances, disability pensions, widow and widower pensions, and survivor benefits to children. Workers' compensation covers both accidents and occupational diseases. Family allowance coverage, in force since 1946, is provided for children under the age of 16.

In spite of a 1978 law mandating equal wages for equal work by men and women, economic discrimination continues, and the average pay for women in industry is lower than that for men.

Healthcare

Since 1971, there has been a National Insurance Scheme. Hospital care is free of charge, but a minor sum is charged for medicine and primary health care.

In 1988, there were 1,200 health institutions, including 92 hospitals. In 1991, there were 15,533 hospital beds. In the same year, there were 13,826 doctors and 58,561 nurses.

Average life expectancy, among the highest in the world, is 78 years. Major causes of death in 1990 were: communicable diseases and maternal/perinatal causes; noncommunicable diseases; and injuries. In 1996, there were 518 cases of AIDS.

Housing

Housing problems were complicated by the destruction caused by World War II and postwar increases in the birthrate. Norway built more dwellings per 1,000 inhabitants than any other European country, completing between 31,000 and 42,000 units annually from 1967 through 1981. Construction of new dwellings has slowed in recent years, however; only 21,689 units were completed in 1991. As of 1990, Norway had a total of 1.8 million dwelling units. Since 1988, housing demand has fallen more than 50%.

EDUCATION

There is practically no adult illiteracy in Norway. The Basic Education Act of 1969 introduced a nine-year system of compulsory education for all children between the ages of 7 and 16. Local authorities generally provide school buildings and equipment and the central government contributes funds towards teachers' salaries and covers a considerable portion of the cost of running the schools.

Secondary school for students from 16 to 19 may involve theoretical studies, practical training, or a combination of both. Three-year general secondary schools (gymnasiums) prepare students to go on to a university. In the 1993 academic year, 380,315 students were enrolled in the gymnasiums and other secondary schools. It is possible for students to enter a university without having passed through a gymnasium.

Since 1976, the upper secondary school system has included vocational schools. These may be operated by the state, by local authorities, or by the industrial sector.

Norway's institutions of higher education include 215 colleges and 14 universities, with a total enrollment of 176,722 in 1993. The largest universities include the University of Oslo, the University of Bergen, the University of Trondheim, and the University of Troms. There are also specialized institutions such as the Agricultural University of Norway (near Oslo); the Norwegian School of Economics and Business Administration (Bergen); and the Norwegian College of Veterinary Medicine (Oslo) representing fields not covered by the universities.

1999 KEY EVENTS TIMELINE

January

- Norwegian metals manufacturer, Elkem A.S.A., a producer of aluminum and alloys for the steel industry, agrees to sell its manganese operations to the French firm, Eramet S.A., for 1.5 billion kroner ($201 million).

- Bakke Trine Bakke of Norway wins the World Cup in women's slalom for the first time in the competition held in St. Anton, Austria.

- At Innsbruck, Austria, Olympic champion Adne Soendral wins the 1,500-meter men's speed skating World Cup race, breaking the course record.

February

- In Vail, Colorado, Lasse Kjus of Norway wins a record fifth medal, becoming just the first skier in history to win five medals in a world championship competition. Only four skiers have won four medals in a world championship.

March

- Two of the country's largest financial groups agree to merge. The state-owned Postbanken will be purchased by Den Norske Bank A.S. for 4.5 billion Norwegian kroner, or $579.9 million, in stock and cash.

- Three United States music companies ask the Norwegian police to prosecute Fast Search and Transfer, a company that provides the Internet search engine, Lycos, Inc., with MP3 audio files. The U.S. companies allege that Fast Search and Transfer is infringing on copyrights.

- Bjarte Engen Vik of Norway wins the Nordic Combined World Cup by winning a 15-kilometer cross-country yesterday in Oslo.

- Twins Rune and Frode Kollerud, racing for University of Utah, finish first and second in the National Collegiate Athletic Association (NCAA) men's freestyle cross-country race at the N.C.A.A. Ski Championships in Rumford, Maine.

- Bjorn Daehlie of Norway wins his sixth overall Nordic World Cup title, taking the men's World Cup 15-kilometer classic style event at the Lahti (Finland) Ski Games.

- Lasse Kjus wins his first World Cup downhill title in Kvitfjell, Norway.

April

- The government dismisses the board of directors of the state oil company, Statoil.

- Nikita, a Caspian sturgeon given to Norway by the government of the then-USSR in the 1960s, dies when the salt level in his tank is accidentally raised to a lethal level. The aquarium plans to ask Russian president Boris Yeltsin for a replacement for the fish who was 38—not particularly old for a sturgeon.

- Europe's largest shipbuilding, Kvaerner S.A., announces that it will sell its shipyard in Norway and cut about 25,000 jobs there.

June

- Shareholders of the oil company Saga Petroleum A.S.A. accepts the nearly $5 billion bid from the two state-controlled oil companies, Norsk Hydro A.S.A. and Statoil. Saga Petroleum was a small, but rival, company to the two large government concerns.

July

- A Norwegian passenger ferry catches fire off the coast of Sweden. Thirteen hundred people were evacuated, but one elderly Norwegian perished in the disaster.

- Daredevil Thor Kappfjell, age thirty-two, is killed in a jump from a cliff in Norway. He gained notoriety by parachuting from the World Trade Center, Empire State Building, and the Chrysler Building in New York.

August

- Norway's whale hunters report a difficult season marked by angry protestors and lower demand for whale products by consumers.

September

- Two Scandinavian state-controlled telephone companies, Sweden's Telia A.B. and Norway's Telenor A.S. complete a merger that was announced in January; disputes over details of the merger took several months to resolve. The combined company, worth an estimated $18.6 billion, will be better able to compete in the European market, with over 50,000 employees and annual sales estimated at $10 billion.

- On September 30, Norway's embassy in Chile is surrounded by more than a hundred police officers because former guerilla member Marcela Rodriguez Valdevieso is inside seeking asylum in Norway. Rodriguez was sentenced to ten years in jail for her part in the 1990 murder of a Chilean policeman during a confrontation between guerillas attempting to free one of their members and police.

October

- Nearly 2,000 troops of the Norwegian Telemark Battalion take over responsibility for the region of Kosovo surrounding (but not including) the capital, Pristina. They assume the responsibilities formerly carried out by British forces, their allies in NATO; the British leaving the area on October 12.

November

- The Oslo Conference on November 1st and 2nd turns into a summit meeting. U.S. President Bill Clinton's attendance is considered an official state visit, and he is received by King Harald at the Royal Palace upon his arrival. Also attending are Russia's Prime Minister Vladimir Putin, Israel's Prime Minister Ehud Barak, Palestinian

President Yasir Arafat, Finland's President Martti Ahtisaari, and U.S. Foreign Secretary Madeleine Albright. The meeting is being held in honor of the late Israeli Prime Minister, Yitzak Rabin, to give new momentum to the Middle East peace talks.

- The high-speed express ferry boat Sleipner sinks in the North Sea, and at least twenty passengers drown and many survivors suffer hypothermia. King Harald and Prime Minister Kjell Magne Bondevik attend the memorial service for those who lost their lives.

- At a meeting in Istanbul, Russia promises to allow representatives of the Organisation for Security and Cooperation in Europe (OSCE) to visit Chechnya. OSCE Chairman, Norway's Foreign Minister Knut Vollebaek, and Russia's Foreign Minister Igor Ivanov are unable to agree on a date for Vollebaek's visit to Chechnya.

- Every year since 1947, Norway has given the city of London a Christmas tree as a thank-you gift for Londoners' assistance to Norwegians during World War II. Norway's 53rd Christmas tree for London, a twenty-one meter (65-foot) spruce, is cut by Oslo's mayor and the Mayor of Welstminster, London, from a forest on the outskirts of Oslo.

ANALYSIS OF EVENTS: 1999

BUSINESS AND THE ECONOMY

Unlike its Scandinavian neighbors Sweden and Finland, Norway has elected not to join the European Union. Since the 1960s when oil and gas were discovered off the Norwegian coast, petroleum products have been a key component of the Norwegian economy. Norway is second only to Saudi Arabia in the export of petroleum products.

The economy is strong, but growth has slowed to about one percent per year. The economy relies heavily on imports, especially of food, more than half of which must be imported. Although not a part of the European Union, nearly seventy percent of Norway's imports come from EU countries.

GOVERNMENT AND POLITICS

The government is planning for the future when petroleum reserves are depleted and the economy will no longer be able to support the current levels of government welfare.

CULTURE AND SOCIETY

The Sami, indigenous people of the northern region of Norway, Sweden, and Finland, seek autonomy. The United Nations Human Rights Commission has asked Norway for an explanation why the Sami have not yet been granted the right to self-determination. Norway has ratified the convention on civil and political rights, which gives all ethnic groups the right to self-determination. The president of the Sami Assembly, Svein Roald Nystø, charges that Norway is taking too long to implement the U.N. agreements on indigenous peoples.

DIRECTORY

CENTRAL GOVERNMENT
Head of State

King
Harald V, Monarch, Royal Palace, Det Kgl. Slott, Drammensveien 1, N-0010 Oslo, Norway
PHONE: +47 (22) 441920
FAX: +47 (22) 550880

Prime Minister
Kjell Magne Bondevik, Office of the Prime Minister, Akersgaten 42, PO Box 8001 Dep, 0030 Oslo, Norway
PHONE: +47 (22) 249090
E-MAIL: odin@ft.dep.telemax.no

Ministers

Minister of Cultural Affairs
Åslaug M. Haga, Ministry of Cultural Affairs, Akersgata 59 (R5), PO Box 8030 Dep, N-0030 Oslo, Norway
PHONE: +47 (22) 249090
FAX: +47 (22) 249550

Minister of Children and Family Affairs
Valgerd Svarstad Haugland, Ministry of Children and Family Affairs, Akersgt. 59 (R5), Postbox 8036 Dep, N-0030 Oslo, Norway
PHONE: +47 (22) 249090
FAX: +47 (22) 249515

Minister of Trade and Industry
Lars Sponheim, Ministry of Trade and Industry, Grubbegt. 8, PO Box 8148 Dep, N-0033 Oslo, Norway
PHONE: +47 (22) 243700; 249090

FAX: +47 (22) 249565

Minister of Foreign Affairs

Knut Vollebæk, Ministry of Foreign Affairs, 7. juni plass 1, Postbox 8114 Dep, N-0032 Oslo, Norway

PHONE: +47 (22) 243000; 243600

FAX: +47 (22) 249580; 249581

Minister of International Development and Human Rights

Hilde Frafjord Johnson, Ministry of International Development and Human Rights, 7. juni plass 1, Postbox 8114 Dep, N-0032 Oslo, Norway

PHONE: +47 (22) 243900

FAX: +47 (22) 249580; 249581

Minister of Fisheries

Peter Angelsen, Ministry of Fisheries, Grubbegt. 8, PO Box 8118 Dep, N-0032 Oslo, Norway

PHONE: + 47 (22) 246400; 249090

FAX: +47 (22) 249585

Minister of Finance and Customs

Gudmund Restad, Ministry of Finance and Customs, Akersgata 40 (blokk G), PO Box 8008 Dep, N-0030 Oslo, Norway

PHONE: + 47 (22) 244100

FAX: +47 (22) 249514

Minister of Agriculture

Kåre Gjnnes, Ministry of Agriculture, Akersgata 59 (R5), Postbox 8007 Dep, N-0030 Oslo, Norway

PHONE: +47 (22) 249100

FAX: +47 (22) 249555

Minister of Defense

Eldbjerg Lewer, Ministry of Defense, Myntgata 1, PO Box 8126 Dep, N-0032 Oslo, Norway

PHONE: +47 (22) 402001

FAX: +47 (22) 402323

Minister of Justice and Police

Odd Einar Drum, Ministry of Justice and Police, kersgt. 42 (blokk H), PO Box 8119 Dep, N-0032 Oslo, Norway

PHONE: +47 (22) 245100

FAX: +47 (22) 249540

Minister of Education, Research and Church Affairs

Jon Lilletun, Ministry of Education, Research and Church Affairs, Akersgt. 44 (blokk Y), Postbox 8119 Dep, N-0032 Oslo, Norway

PHONE: +47 (22) 247400

FAX: +47 (22) 249540

Minister of Transport and Communications

Dag Jostein Fjærvoll, Ministry of Transport and Communications, Akersgata 59 (R5), Postbox 8010 Dep, N-0030 Oslo, Norway

PHONE: +47 (22) 248100

FAX: +47 (22) 249570

Minister of Petroleum and Energy

Marit Arnstad, Ministry of Petroleum and Energy, Grubbegt. 8, PO Box 8148 Dep, N-0033 Oslo, Norway

PHONE: +47 (22) 246100

FAX: +47 (22) 249565

Minister of Health and Social Affairs

Magnhild Meltveit Kleppa, Ministry of Health and Social Affairs, Grubbegata 10, Postbox 8011 Dep, N-0030 Oslo, Norway

PHONE: +47 (22) 248400

FAX: +47 (22) 249576

Minister of the Environment

Guro Fjellanger, Ministry of the Environment, Myntgata 2, Postbox 8013 Dep, N-0030 Oslo, Norway

PHONE: +47 (22) 245700

FAX: +47 (22) 249560

Minister of Labour and Government Administration

Laila Dåvy, Ministry of Labour and Government Administration, Akersgata 59 (R5), Postbox 8004 Dep, N-0030 Oslo, Norway

PHONE: +47 (22) 244600

FAX: +47 (22) 242710

Minister of Local Government and Regional Development

Odd Roger Enoksen, Ministry of Local Government and Regional Development, Akersgata 59 (R5), Postx 8112 Dep, N-0032 Oslo, Norway

PHONE: +47 (22) 246800

FAX: +47 (22) 249545

POLITICAL ORGANIZATIONS

Det norske Arbeiderparti (Labor Party)

NAME: Thorbjorn Jagland

Hoyre (Conservative Party)

NAME: Jan Petersen

Senterpartiet (Center Party)

NAME: Anne Enger Lahnstein

Kristelig Folkeparti (Christian People's Party)

NAME: Valgerd Haugland

Sosialistisk Venstreparti (Socialist Left Party)

NAME: Kristin Halvorsen

Norges Kommunistiske Parti (Norwegian Communist Party)

NAME: KareAndre Nilsen

Fremskrittspartiet (Progress Party)

TITLE: Chairman
NAME: Carl I. Hagen

Venstre (Liberal Party)

NAME: Lars Sponheim

Rod Valgallianse (Red Electoral Alliance)

NAME: Aslak Sira Myhre

DIPLOMATIC REPRESENTATION

Embassies in Norway

Austria
Thomas Heftyesgt 19-21, 0244 Oslo, Norway
PHONE: +47 (22) 552348
FAX: +47 (22) 554361
NAME: Harald Wiesner

Chile
Meltzersgt. 5, 0244 Oslo, Norway
PHONE: +47 (22) 448955
FAX: +47 (22) 442421
E-MAIL: embchile@online.no
TITLE: Ambassador
NAME: Manuel Atria

Denmark
Olav Kyrres gate 7, N-0244 Oslo, Norway
PHONE: +47 (22) 540800
FAX: +47 (22) 554634
E-MAIL: anske@online.no
NAME: Ib Ritto Andreasen

Egypt
Drammensvn 90A, 0244 Oslo, Norway
PHONE: +47 (22) 200010
FAX: +47 (22) 562268
NAME: Magdy Abdel Moneim Hefny

Finland
Thomas Heftyes gate 1, 0244 Oslo, Norway
PHONE: +47 (22) 430400
FAX: +47 (22) 430629
E-MAIL: finland@online.no
NAME: Ole Norrback

France
Drammensvn 69, 0244 Oslo, Norway
PHONE: +47 (22) 441820
FAX: +47 (22) 563221
NAME: Patrick Henault

Greece
Nobelsgt. 45, 0244 Oslo, Norway
PHONE: +47 (22) 442728
FAX: +47 (22) 560072
E-MAIL: gremb@online.no
NAME: Ole Norrback

Hungary
Sophus Liesgt. 3, 0244 Oslo, Norway
PHONE: +47 (22) 552418
FAX: +47 (22) 447693
NAME: Arpad Hargita

Indonesia
Inkognitogt. 8, 0244 Olso Norway
PHONE: +47 (22) 441121
FAX: +47 (22) 553444
NAME: Amiruddin Noor

Italy
Inkognitogt. 7, 0244 Oslo, Norway
PHONE: +47 (22) 552233
FAX: +47 (22) 443436
NAME: Mario Quagliotti

Mexico
Drammensvn 108B, 0244 Oslo, Norway
PHONE: +47 (22) 431165
FAX: +47 (22) 444352
NAME: Gustavo Iruegas Evaristo

United Kingdom
Thomas Heftyesgate 8, 0244 Oslo, Norway
PHONE: +47 (22) 132700
FAX: +47 (22) 132741
E-MAIL: britemb@online.no
NAME: Richard Dales

United States
Drammensveien 18, 0244 Oslo, Norway
PHONE: +47 (22) 448550
FAX: +47 (22) 430777
E-MAIL: oslo@usis.no
NAME: David B. Hermelin

JUDICIAL SYSTEM

The Supreme Court

PO Box 8016 Dep, 0030 Oslo, Norway
PHONE: +47 (22) 035900
FAX: +47 (22) 332355

FURTHER READING

Articles

Beckman, Jeremy. "Void Looming for Norwegian Yards: Norway's Petroleum Industry." *Offshore* 59 (April 1999): 20.

"Modest Rule: Politics in Norway Remain Undramatic." *The Economist* 352 (August 14, 1999): 40.

"Norway Can Afford to Do Its Own Thing." *The Economist* 350 (January 23, 1999).

Omestad, Thomas. "Norway's Equally Good Life." *U.S. News and World Report* (December 7, 1998): 37.

Books

Matthews, Donald R. *Parliamentary Representation: The Case of the Norwegian Storting.* Columbus: Ohio State University Press, 1999.

Shaffer, William R. *Politics, Parties, and Parliaments: Political Change in Norway.* Columbus: Ohio State University Press, 1998.

Swaney, Deanna. *Norway.* Hawthorn, Aus.: Lonely Planet, 1999.

Internet

Norway Post. Available Online @ www.norwaypost.no/ (December 1, 1999).

NORWAY: STATISTICAL DATA

For sources and notes see "Sources of Statistics" in the front of each volume.

GEOGRAPHY

Geography (1)

Area:

Total: 324,220 sq km.

Land: 307,860 sq km.

Water: 16,360 sq km.

Area—comparative: slightly larger than New Mexico.

Land boundaries:

Total: 2,515 km.

Border countries: Finland 729 km, Sweden 1,619 km, Russia 167 km.

Coastline: 21,925 km (includes mainland 3,419 km, large islands 2,413 km, long fjords, numerous small islands, and minor indentations 16,093 km).

Climate: temperate along coast, modified by North Atlantic Current; colder interior; rainy year-round on west coast.

Terrain: glaciated; mostly high plateaus and rugged mountains broken by fertile valleys; small, scattered plains; coastline deeply indented by fjords; arctic tundra in north.

Natural resources: petroleum, copper, natural gas, pyrites, nickel, iron ore, zinc, lead, fish, timber, hydropower.

Land use:

Arable land: 3%

Permanent crops: NA%

Permanent pastures: 0%

Forests and woodland: 27%

Other: 70% (1993 est.).

HUMAN FACTORS

Demographics (2A)

	1990	1995	1998	2000	2010	2020	2030	2040	2050
Population	4,242.0	4,356.6	4,420.0	4,455.7	4,568.8	4,609.5	4,535.2	4,314.6	4,012.1
Net migration rate (per 1,000 population)	NA	NA	NA	NA	NA	NA	NA	NA	NA
Births	NA	NA	NA	NA	NA	NA	NA	NA	NA
Deaths	NA	NA	NA	NA	NA	NA	NA	NA	NA
Life expectancy - males	73.1	75.0	75.4	75.7	76.8	77.8	78.6	79.2	79.8
Life expectancy - females	80.1	80.8	81.2	81.5	82.7	83.7	84.5	85.2	85.8
Birth rate (per 1,000)	15.0	13.8	12.9	12.2	9.9	9.6	8.4	7.3	6.9
Death rate (per 1,000)	10.9	10.3	10.2	10.1	9.8	10.1	11.8	13.6	15.1
Women of reproductive age (15-49 yrs.)	1,055.7	1,073.6	1,062.9	1,058.8	1,060.8	1,014.6	938.3	867.0	750.2
of which are currently married	1,423.6	NA	NA	NA	NA	NA	NA	NA	NA
Fertility rate	2.0	1.9	1.8	1.7	1.6	1.5	1.4	1.4	1.3

Except as noted, values for vital statistics are in thousands; life expectancy is in years.

Health Personnel (3)

Total health expenditure as a percentage of GDP, 1990-1997[a]

Public sector 6.2

Private sector 1.3

Total[b] 7.5

Health expenditure per capita in U.S. dollars, 1990-1997[a]

Purchasing power parity 1,844

Total 2,622

Availability of health care facilities per 100,000 people

Hospital beds 1990-1997[a] 1330

Doctors 1993[c] . . . . .NA

Nurses 1993[c] . . . . .NA

Health Indicators (4)

Life expectancy at birth

1980 76

1997 78

Daily per capita supply of calories (1996) 3,350

Total fertility rate births per woman (1997) 1.9

Maternal mortality ratio per 100,000 live births (1990-97) . . . . .6[c]

Safe water % of population with access (1995) 100

Sanitation % of population with access (1995) 100

Consumption of iodized salt % of households (1992-98)[a] . . . .

Smoking prevalence

Male % of adults (1985-95)[a] 36

Female % of adults (1985-95)[a] 36

Tuberculosis incidence per 100,000 people (1997) 6

Adult HIV prevalence % of population ages 15-49 (1997) 0.06

Infants and Malnutrition (5)

Under-5 mortality rate (1997) 4

% of infants with low birthweight (1990-97) 4

Births attended by skilled health staff % of total[a] . . .NA

% fully immunized (1995-97)

TB . . . . .NA

DPT 92

Polio 92

Measles 93

Prevalence of child malnutrition under age 5 (1992-97)[b] . . . . .NA

Ethnic Division (6)

Germanic (Nordic, Alpine, Baltic), Lapps (Sami) 20,000.

Religions (7)

Evangelical Lutheran 87.8%

Other Protestant and Roman Catholic 3.8%

None 3.2%

Unknown 5.2% (1980)

Evangelical Lutheran is state church.

Languages (8)

Norwegian (official). Small Lapp- and Finnish-speaking minorities.

EDUCATION

Public Education Expenditures (9)

Public expenditure on education (% of GNP)

1980 . . . . .6.5

1996 . . . . .7.5

Expenditure per student

Primary % of GNP per capita

1980 . . . . .27.2

1996 . . . . .31.1[1]

Secondary % of GNP per capita

1980 . . . . .14.9

1996 . . . . .20.1[1]

Tertiary % of GNP per capita

1980 . . . . .38.1

1996 . . . . .48.0[1]

Expenditure on teaching materials

Primary % of total for level (1996) 2.0

Secondary % of total for level (1996) . . . .

Primary pupil-teacher ratio per teacher (1996) . . . .

Duration of primary education years (1995) 6

Educational Attainment (10)

Age group (1990) . . . . .16+

Total population 3,460,669

Highest level attained (%)

No schooling 0

First level

Not completed 0

Completed . . . . .NA

Entered second level

S-1 . . . . .37.3

S-2 . . . . .44.0

Postsecondary 18.7

GOVERNMENT & LAW

Political Parties (12)

Parliament	% of seats
Labor	.35
Center Party	.7.9
Conservatives	.14.3
Christian People's	.13.7
Socialist Left	.6
Progress	.15.3
Liberal Party	.4.4
Other parties	.1.6

Government Budget (13A)

Year: 1996

Total Expenditures: 375,393 Millions of Kroner

Expenditures as a percentage of the total by function:

General public services and public order 7.53

Defense 6.50

Education 6.84

Health 4.20

Social Security and Welfare 37.72

Housing and community amenities 1.36

Recreational, cultural, and religious affairs 1.23

Fuel and energy 35

Agriculture, forestry, fishing, and hunting 4.04

Continued on next page.

Military Affairs (14B)

	1990	1991	1992	1993	1994	1995
Military expenditures						
Current dollars (mil.)	3,133	3,195	3,680	3,566	3,812	3,508
1995 constant dollars (mil.)	3,600	3,530	3,958	3,738	3,907	3,508
Armed forces (000)	51	41	36	32	33	38
Gross national product (GNP)						
Current dollars (mil.)	94,840	100,300	106,000	112,500	120,900	128,000[e]
1995 constant dollars (mil.)	109,000	110,800	114,000	118,000	124,000	128,000[e]
Central government expenditures (CGE)						
1995 constant dollars (mil.)	52,270	57,110	62,190	61,960	59,660	NA
People (mil.)	4.2	4.3	4.3	4.3	4.3	4.4
Military expenditure as % of GNP	3.3	3.2	3.5	3.2	3.2	2.7
Military expenditure as % of CGE	6.9	6.2	6.4	6.0	6.5	NA
Military expenditure per capita (1995 $)	849	828	924	867	901	804
Armed forces per 1,000 people (soldiers)	12.0	9.6	8.4	7.4	7.6	8.7
GNP per capita (1995 $)	25,700	26,010	26,610	27,370	25,890	29,350
Arms imports[6]						
Current dollars (mil.)	430	340	320	140	120	140
1995 constant dollars (mil.)	494	376	344	147	123	140
Arms exports[6]						
Current dollars (mil.)	20	80	40	60	50	20
1995 constant dollars (mil.)	23	88	43	63	51	20
Total imports[7]						
Current dollars (mil.)	27,230	25,570	25,900	23,960	27,310	32,700
1995 constant dollars (mil.)	31,300	28,260	27,860	25,110	27,990	32,700
Total exports[7]						
Current dollars (mil.)	34,050	34,110	35,180	31,850	34,690	41,750
1995 constant dollars (mil.)	39,130	37,690	37,840	33,390	35,560	41,750
Arms as percent of total imports[8]	1.6	1.3	1.2	.6	.4	.4
Arms as percent of total exports[8]	.1	.2	.1	.2	.1	.0

GOVERNMENT & LAW

Government Budget (13A) cont.

Mining, manufacturing, and construction 43

Transportation and communication 4.89

Other economic affairs and services 2.78

Crime (15)

Crime rate (for 1997)

Crimes reported 431,600

Total persons convicted 172,600

Crimes per 100,000 population 9,750

Persons responsible for offenses

Total number of suspects 69,000

Total number of female suspects 11,000

Total number of juvenile suspects 25,500

LABOR FORCE

Labor Force (16)

Total (million) 2.13

Services 71%

Industry 23%

Agriculture, forestry, and fishing 6%

Data for 1993.

Unemployment Rate (17)

2.6% (year end 1997)

PRODUCTION SECTOR

Electric Energy (18)

Capacity . . . . .26.431 million kW (1995)

Production . . . . .121.375 billion kWh (1995)

Consumption per capita . . . . .26,547 kWh (1995)

Transportation (19)

Highways:

total: 91,323 km

paved: 65,753 km (including 106 km of expressways)

unpaved: 25,570 km (1996 est.)

Waterways: 1,577 km along west coast; 2.4 m draft vessels maximum

Pipelines: refined products 53 km

Merchant marine:

total: 762 ships (1,000 GRT or over) totaling 21,042,709 GRT/33,839,476 DWT

Airports: 102 (1997 est.)

Airports—with paved runways:

total: 65

over 3,047 m: 1

2,438 to 3,047 m: 11

1,524 to 2,437 m: 14

914 to 1,523 m: 11

under 914 m: 28 (1997 est.)

Airports—with unpaved runways:

total: 37

914 to 1,523 m: 5

under 914 m: 32 (1997 est.)

Top Agricultural Products (20)

Oats, other grains; beef, milk; livestock output exceeds value of crops; among world's top 10 fishing nations; fish catch of 2.33 million metric tons in 1994.

MANUFACTURING SECTOR

GDP & Manufacturing Summary (21)

Detailed value added figures are listed by both International Standard Industry Code (ISIC) and product title.

	1980	1985	1990	1994
GDP ($-1990 mil.)[1]	82,790	97,604	105,524	119,468
Per capita ($-1990)[1]	20,262	23,502	24,882	27,667
Manufacturing share (%) (current prices)[1]	17.3	15.3	14.6	NA
Manufacturing				
Value added ($-1990 mil.)[1]	14,041	15,028	14,437	15,609
Industrial production index	100	109	113	123
Value added ($ mil.)	9,339	7,660	13,504	13,714[1]
Gross output ($ mil.)	31,936	28,186	50,107	49,140
Employment (000)	354	312	271	251[1]
Profitability (% of gross output)				
Intermediate input (%)	71	73	73	72
Wages and salaries inc. supplements (%)	21	20	19	23
Gross operating surplus	8	7	8	4
Productivity ($)				
Gross output per worker	89,656	89,751	184,292	187,896

GDP & Manufacturing Summary (21)

	1980	1985	1990	1994
Value added per worker	26,217	24,391	49,684	*54,540*
Average wage (inc. supplements)	19,129	17,852	35,540	*45,828*
Value added ($ mil.)				
311/2 Food products	908	633	1,307	*1,798*
313 Beverages	292	296	660	*635*
314 Tobacco products	168	220	478	*572*
321 Textiles	213	126	191	*210*
322 Wearing apparel	101	59	58	*58*
323 Leather and fur products	18	9	16	*16*
324 Footwear	24	10	11	*12*
331 Wood and wood products	567	366	619	*466*
332 Furniture and fixtures	196	165	236	*211*
341 Paper and paper products	452	400	787	*610*
342 Printing and publishing	668	717	1,381	*1,381*
351 Industrial chemicals	452	422	811	*615*
352 Other chemical products	227	183	393	*452*
353 Petroleum refineries	103	24	195	*155*
354 Miscellaneous petroleum and coal products	53	59	63	*61*
355 Rubber products	51	39	58	*23*
356 Plastic products	170	147	278	*303*
361 Pottery, china and earthenware	26	18	27	*26*
362 Glass and glass products	55	50	77	*74*
369 Other non-metal mineral products	281	215	361	*283*
371 Iron and steel	385	276	347	*330*
372 Non-ferrous metals	743	550	826	*683*
381 Metal products	595	465	784	*762*
382 Non-electrical machinery	933	1,079	1,590	*1,902*
383 Electrical machinery	547	498	751	*814*
384 Transport equipment	1,000	555	1,028	*1,035*
385 Professional and scientific equipment	32	39	82	*116*
390 Other manufacturing industries	59	42	89	*114*

FINANCE, ECONOMICS, & TRADE

Economic Indicators (22)

National product: GDP—purchasing power parity—$120.5 billion (1997 est.)

National product real growth rate: 3.5% (1997 est.)

National product per capita: $27,400 (1997 est.)

Inflation rate—consumer price index: 2% (1997 est.)

Balance of Payments (23)

	1992	1993	1994	1995	1996
Exports of goods (f.o.b.)	35,162	31,989	35,002	42,282	49,950
Imports of goods (f.o.b.)	−25,860	−23,995	−27,509	−33,471	−36,035
Trade balance	9,303	7,995	7,493	8,811	13,915
Services - debits	−21,246	−19,633	−17,666	−19,849	−19,776
Services - credits	16,682	15,192	15,525	17,907	18,595
Private transfers (net)	−1,288	−1,082	−1,054	−1,255	−1,301
Government transfers (net)	−469	−320	−689	−791	−187
Overall balance	2,983	2,152	3,609	4,823	11,245

Exchange Rates (24)

Exchange rates:

Norwegian kroner (NKr) per US$1

January 1998	7.4875
1997	7.0734
1996	6.4498
1995	6.3352
1994	7.0576
1993	7.0941

Top Import Origins (25)

$35.1 billion (c.i.f., 1996) Data are for 1995.

Origins	%
European Union	71.0
Sweden	15.4
Germany	13.8
United Kingdom	9.7
Denmark	7.5
Netherlands	4.4
United States	6.6

Top Export Destinations (26)

$49.3 billion (f.o.b., 1996) Data are for 1995.

Destinations	%
European Union	77.2
UK	19.8
Germany	12.7
Netherlands	9.1
France	7.8
Sweden	9.8
United States	6.0

Economic Aid (27)

Donor: ODA, $1.014 billion (1993).

Import Export Commodities (28)

Import Commodities	Export Commodities
Machinery and equipment and manufactured consumer goods 54%	Petroleum and petroleum products 43%
Chemicals and other industrial inputs 39%	Metals and products 11%
Foodstuffs 6%	Foodstuffs (mostly fish) 9%
	Chemicals and raw materials 25%
	Natural gas 6.0%
	Ships 5.4%

OMAN

Sultanate of Oman
Saltanat 'Uman

CAPITAL BOX

CAPITAL: Muscat (Masqat).

FLAG: The flag is red with a broad stripe of white at the upper fly and green at the lower fly. In the upper left corner, white crossed swords overlay a ceremonial dagger.

ANTHEM: *Nashid as-Salaam as-Sutani (Sultan's National Anthem).*

MONETARY UNIT: The Omani riyal (RO), established in November 1972, is a paper currency of 1,000 baizas. There are coins of 2, 5, 10, 25, 50, 100, 250, and 500 baizas, and notes of 100, 250, and 500 baizas (the last two being replaced by coins) and 1, 5, 10, 20, and 50 riyals. RO1 = $2.60417 (or $1 = RO0.384).

WEIGHTS AND MEASURES: The metric system was adopted on 15 November 1974. The imperial and local system are also used.

HOLIDAYS: Accession of the Sultan, 23 July; National Day, 18 November; Sultan's Birthday, 19 November. Movable Muslim religious holidays include 'Id al-Fitr, 'Id al-'Adha', and Milad an-Nabi.

TIME: 4 PM = noon GMT. Solar time is also observed.

LOCATION AND SIZE: The Sultanate of Oman is the second-largest country on the Arabian Peninsula after Saudi Arabia, with an area officially estimated at 212,460 square kilometers (82,031 square miles), slightly smaller than the state of Kansas. The northernmost part of Oman, separated from the rest of the country by the United Arab Emirates, juts into the Strait of Hormuz. The total estimated boundary length is 3,466 kilometers (2,154 miles). The capital, Muscat, is in the northeastern part of the country.

CLIMATE: Annual rainfall varies from 10 centimeters (4 inches) in Muscat to up to 64 centimeters (25 inches) in Zufar. The climate generally is very hot, with temperatures reaching 54°C (129°F) in the hot season.

INTRODUCTORY SURVEY

RECENT HISTORY

The first sultanate (kingdom) was established in Muscat about 1775 and concluded its first treaty with the British in 1798. Weakened by political division, Muscat lost control of the interior in the second half of the nineteenth century. In 1920, the Treaty of Seeb was signed between the sultan (king of a Muslim state) of Muscat and the imam (Muslim leader) of Oman, placing Oman under the rule of the Sultan as an independent area. From 1920 to 1954 there was comparative peace.

In that year, Petroleum Development (Oman) Ltd., a British-managed oil company, won permission to maintain a small army, the Muscat and Oman Field Force (MOFF). In early 1955, MOFF, together with British troops, occupied all of Oman and expelled the imam. In 1962 the sultanate of Muscat was proclaimed an independent state. Oman joined the United Nations late in 1971.

The present sultan, Qabus bin Sa'id, changed the name of the country from Muscat and Oman to the Sultanate of Oman in 1970. He has presided over a broad modernization program, opening the country to the outside world while preserving political and military ties with the British. Oman dominates the Strait of Hormuz, which links the Gulf of Oman with the Persian Gulf. Its strategic importance drew Oman and the United States closer together during the Iran–Iraq war in the 1980s and the Gulf War in 1991. In 1994, there were reports that about 500 people critical of the government were arrested.

GOVERNMENT

Oman's sultan is an absolute monarch. The country has no constitution, legislature, or voting. The Majlis Ash-Shura, or Consultative Council, established in 1991, is seen as a first step toward popular participation in government. It has no legislative function, but can question cabinet members on their policies and plans.

On 6 November 1996 the sultan issued a decree providing for citizens' basic rights. The decree also established the Majlis Oman (Council of Oman) which includes a new Majlis al-Dawla (Council of State) and the current Consultative Council.

Oman is divided into three governates and 41 wilayats (districts).

Judiciary

Shari'a courts based on Islamic law administer justice, with the Chief Court at Muscat. Appeals from the Chief Court are made to the sultan, who exercises powers of clemency (mercy or leniency in setting punishment). The magistrate court, a criminal court, rules on violations of the criminal code.

In 1996, the sultan issued a basic law that recognized an independent jury. There are no jury trials.

Political Parties

There are no legal political parties nor, at present, is there any active opposition movement.

DEFENSE

Oman's armed forces, including some 3,700 foreign members and British advisors numbered 43,500 in 1995. The army had 25,000 members, the air force 4,100, and the navy 4,200. In 1995 Oman spent $1.8 billion on defense, or 16% of its gross domestic product.

ECONOMIC AFFAIRS

Since the mid-1970s most of the economy has revolved around oil. The petroleum industry accounted for 90% of exports in 1995, or about $3.6 billion. Based on current oil production, reserves should last some 17 years. In recent years, the production of natural gas has become a significant factor in the economy.

Public Finance

Deficits have been typical since 1982, and are financed by withdrawals from the State General Reserve Fund and external borrowing. Oman's oil resources and low foreign debt enable the government to easily borrow from abroad. Revenues expand largely on the vicissitudes of the world's oil market. When oil prices fell in 1986, the government responded with a 14% currency devaluation and postponement of development expenditures. The Persian Gulf crisis did not severely affect revenues in 1991.

The U.S. Central Intelligence Agency estimates that in 1995, government revenues totaled approximately $4.7 billion and expenditures $5.6 billion. External debt totaled $3 billion, approximately 74% of which was financed abroad.

Income

In 1997, Oman's gross national product (GNP) was $17.2 billion at current prices. The national product averaged about $8,000 per person. For the period 1985–95 the average inflation rate was slightly negative, at −0.2%, resulting in a real growth rate in GNP of 0.3% per person.

Industry

Besides oil, Oman's industries consist mostly of small scale food processing enterprises. Other industries manufacture non-metallic mineral products, wood products, and fabricated metal products.

Banking and Finance

The Central Bank of Oman, set up in April 1975, has powers to regulate credit and is authorized to make temporary advances to the government. Its assets in 1993 stood at $720.1 billion.

All commercial banks in the sultanate were given until 1993 to raise their paid up capital to RO 10 million for local banks and RO 3 million for foreign banks. The Central Bank of Oman advised all banks which were unable to comply with these new requirements to merge with other commercial banks. The Central Bank has been encouraging banks to merge in order to cut down on the oversupply of banking services. In 1995, there were seven local banks, three of which were the products of mergers or takeovers. Oman Arab Bank and Oman-European Bank merged in 1994. Commercial Bank of Oman and Oman Banking Corporation merged to form the Commercial Bank of Oman in 1993, and Bank of Muscat and al-Bank al-Ahli al-Omani began operations as Bank Muscat al-Ahli al-Omani the same year.

In 1995, there were 11 foreign banks licensed to operate in Oman. The largest of these was the British Bank of the Middle East (BBME), the first to establish itself in Oman in 1948. Other foreign banks include Grindlays, Standard Chartered, Habib Bank Zurich, Bank Melli Iran, Bank of Baroda, and Citibank. The banking sector has been under pressure to increase its proportion of Omani staff to 90%, but the deadline for such a move has been progressively delayed. Because of the proliferation of branches concentrated in coastal areas, commercial banks now have to open two branches in the interior for every branch opened along the coast.

In 1990, the Central Bank introduced new restrictions on banking activities. Banks were no longer allowed to deal in speculative futures transactions involving foreign exchange or precious metals. The government also introduced a depositor insurance fund to which all banks have to subscribe.

At the end of 1995, two of the three development banks announced plans to merge. The Oman Development Bank (ODB) was to merge with the Oman Bank for Agriculture and Fisheries (OBAF). Neither bank had financial problems and the merger was intended to create a stronger banking unit to face growing competition and finance an increasing number of projects. Both banks are joint-stock companies owned by the government and the private sector. The third development bank is the Oman National Housing Development Association, which was established in 1974, with the state and the BBME as shareholders. In 1977 it was replaced by the Oman Housing Bank (OHB). The OHB now has five branches.

An Omani stock market, the Muscat Securities Market (MSM), was officially established in 1988 but trading did not begin until the following year. By 1994 there were 86 banks and companies quoted on the exchange with a combined capitalization of $1.5 billion. The MSM has now established a link with the Bahrain Stock Exchange (BSE) where shares can be cross listed. A similar agreement with Kuwait is expected.

Total reserves, excluding gold, amounted to $1,254.2 million at the end of June 1995. Money supply, as measured by M2, totaled RO 1,511.9 million at the end of 1995.

Economic Development

Oman's second five-year plan (1981–85) suffered to some extent from the impact of declining oil prices in the early 1980s. The objectives of the third development plan (1986–90) were to encourage the private sector to play a larger role in the economy and to expand such areas as agriculture, fishing, manufacturing, and mining. The fourth five-year development plan (1991–95) aimed to achieve average annual GDP growth rates of just over 6% and the diversification of the sources of national income in order to reduce the dependence on the oil sector. The declared aim of the fifth five-year plan (1996–2000) is to achieve a balanced budget. To meet this goal the government plans to increase non-oil revenues, reduce public spending, enhance privatisation of the economy, and encourage foreign investment. The plan also calls for growth rates in the GDP of 4.6% and an increase in the non-oil sector's share of the economy from 60% to 69% of GDP by the year 2000.

SOCIAL WELFARE

Oman maintains a welfare program that provides old age pensions and disability and survivorship benefits to employed citizens between the ages of 15 and 59. Women have begun to enter professional areas such as medicine and communications in greater numbers in recent years.

Healthcare

There are 40 hospitals. In 1993, the population per physician was about 1,131. Average life expectancy is 71 years. In 1993, 89% of the population had access to health care services.

Housing

In 1989, 34% of all housing units were traditional Arabic houses, 30% were modern apartments, and 36% were detached houses.

EDUCATION

The adult literacy rate is estimated to be below 50%. In 1994, there were 425 primary schools with 301,999 students and 11,586 teachers, of whom 50% were women. In secondary schools, there were 9,449 teachers and 162,959 students. Sultan Qabus University opened in 1986. In 1991, all higher level institutions had 7,322 students.

1999 KEY EVENTS TIMELINE

January

- Omani Finance Minister Ahmad Abdul-Nabi Makki projects that Oman's budget deficit will double in 1999, based on oil prices of $9 per barrel.

- The foreign ministers of Oman, Egypt, Saudi Arabia, Syria, and Yemen meet in Cairo to discuss Iraq.

February

- Oman's Sultan, Qaboos bin Said, attends the funeral of King Hussein of Jordan.

March

- U.S. Defense Secretary William Cohen visits Oman and other Arab allies of the United States to explain American policy toward Iraq.

April

- South African President Nelson Mandela visits Oman to promote Omani investment in South Africa.

- King Abdullah of Jordan and Sultan Qaboos meet for talks in Oman.

- Sultan Qaboos signs an agreement with the president of the United Arab Emirates, Sheikh Zayed bin Sultan al-Nahyan, defining the borders between Oman and the emirate of Abu Dhabi.

October

- Omani Oil Minister Mohammad bin Hamad Seif al-Ramhi suggests extending global oil production cuts beyond their originally projected expiration in April 2000.

- U.S. Defense Secretary William Cohen includes Oman on his nine nation Middle East tour and meets Sultan Qaboos to discuss Israel and Iraq.

ANALYSIS OF EVENTS: 1999

BUSINESS AND THE ECONOMY

The economy of Oman, heavily dependent on its annual production of 900,000 barrels of crude oil, was adversely affected when the price of oil dropped below $10 per barrel in 1998, a 25-year low. In the first three quarters of 1998 Oman's gross domestic product (GDP) dropped by an annualized rate of 8.5%, and Omani oil production similarly fell by 32% in the same period. In January 1999 the Omani finance minister announced that the country's budget deficit was expected to double within the year. Seeking to offset the loss in oil revenue through other sources the government raised customs duties from 5% to 15%, corporate income taxes from 7.5% to 12%, and the cigarette tax from 75% to 100%, though it did not institute taxes on personal income or consumption. In March 1999 Oman joined the Organization of Petroleum Exporting Countries (OPEC), of which Oman is not a member, in agreeing to reduce global oil production by 2.1 million barrels of crude oil per day until April 2000. This was done in the hope of raising oil prices to $18 per barrel and stabilizing the oil market. In October 1999 the Omani oil minister recommended extending global oil production cuts beyond the date originally proposed for their expiration.

Oman has sought to diversify its economy and ease its dependence on oil. A gas liquefaction plant at Sur is slated for completion next year, though plans for a power station, an aluminum processing plant, a steel mill, and petrochemical and fertilizer plants at Salalah and Sohar, and the gas pipelines to fuel them, remain unrealized. While oil production constitutes less of Oman's GDP than was the case two decades ago, it is still the major source of revenue for the government and is the mainspring of the country's economy. Manufacturing still accounts for only 5% of the GDP.

The Omani government has made a move toward greater privatization. At the successful new port at Salalah a free zone will be built solely by private investors. The private sector will also finance a new airline to service Salalah, which is a tourist destination as well as a trade center. Legislation barring expatriates from certain sectors of the economy has encouraged private employment of Omani nationals, most of whom work for the government; and the industrial sector, comprised of 19% of Omani nationals in 1995, was 28% Omani in 1997. The increase is not significant on a large scale, however, and most Omanis tend to avoid work they consider too menial. In addition, some employers prefer foreign labor, which is less expensive and more easily utilized.

In October the undersecretary at the Ministry of Economy of Oman announced that the government and its ministries, as well as the banks and large corporations of Oman, had adapted their computer systems to accommodate the change to the year 2000.

GOVERNMENT AND POLITICS

Throughout 1999 Oman held to a middle-of-the-road stance of conciliation and compromise in Middle Eastern politics. In January Oman's foreign minister met with his counterparts from Egypt, Saudi Arabia, Syria, and Yemen at a closed meeting in Cairo to forge a position on the question of Iraq for the upcoming meeting of the 22-member Arab League later in the month. Iraq's foreign minister criticized the closed meeting as counterproductive to Arab unity.

In February Oman's Sultan, Qaboos bin Said, attended the funeral of King Hussein of Jordan, a gesture that expressed the close ties between Oman and Jordan. U.S. Defense Secretary William Cohen included Oman in his tour of Persian Gulf allies, which aimed to allay concerns about extended U.S. actions against Iraq. Newly enthroned King Abdullah of Jordan, accompanied by his prime minister and foreign minister, met with Qaboos in April to maintain the good relations between Jordan and Oman, which alone among the Gulf states refrained from criticizing Jordan for its non-oppositional stance toward neighboring Iraq during the Gulf War.

State visits continued in April when South African President Nelson Mandela spent three days in Oman. He met with high-level government ministers and business leaders to encourage commercial ties between Oman and South Africa. Later that same month Qaboos signed an agreement with the president of the United Arab Emirates defining the borders between Oman and the emirate of Abu Dhabi. In August an emissary of Oman delivered a letter from U.S. President Bill Clinton to Iranian President Mohammad Khatami in Tehran regarding securing Iran's cooperation in resolving the 1996 Khobar Towers bombing in Saudi Arabia. William Cohen once again visited Oman in October and met with Qaboos to discuss the Middle East peace process in light of Ehud Barak's election as Israeli prime minister and the future of Iran under Khatami's presidency. Qaboos was optimistic about the prospects of peace and saw Khatami as a tempering influence on Iran.

CULTURE AND SOCIETY

The government of Oman enlisted the aid of the World Wide Fund for Nature to ensure the survival of the Arabian oryx, a white antelope that lives in the Omani desert. The Arabian oryx had been saved once from near extinction in 1961. Captive breeding efforts resulted in a replenished population that was released into the wild in 1982, but by March 1999 the number of oryx had dwindled to one hundred from a count of four hundred wild animals in 1996. Poachers who sell the animals to private zoos have been blamed for the decimation of the herds. A conference in Abu Dhabi was part of a coordinated regional effort to reintroduce the animals into the wild once again. The Diwan of the Royal Court in Oman retains an Advisor for the Conservation of the Environment.

The World Health Organization sponsored the "Muscat Walk" in Muscat, the capital of Oman, to promote health consciousness among the Omani public. The 6-kilometer walk, originating at

Oman's Ministry of Health, was covered by Oman Television and attended by about one thousand people. Healthy food was served to walkers, who also received pamphlets on maintaining a healthy diet and lifestyle.

DIRECTORY

CENTRAL GOVERNMENT

Head of State

Sultan and Prime Minister
Qaboos bin Said al-Said, Office of the Prime Minister

Ministers

Deputy Prime Minister
Sayyid Fahad bin Mohamed al-Said, Office of the Deputy Prime Minister, PO Box 721, Muscat PC 113, Oman
PHONE: +968 736086
FAX: +968 738517

Minister of National Heritage and Culture
Faisal bin Ali bin Faisal al-Said, Ministry of National Heritage and Culture, PO Box 668, Muscat PC 113, Oman
PHONE: +968 602735
FAX: +968 602735

Minister of Oil and Gas
Mohammed bin Hamad bin Saif al-Ramahi, Ministry of Oil and Gas, PO Box 551, Muscat PC 113, Oman
PHONE: +968 60333
FAX: +968 696972

Minister of Higher Education
Yahya bin Mahfoudh al-Mantheri, Ministry of Higher Education, PO Box 82, Ruwi PC 112, Oman
PHONE: +968 693148
FAX: +968 513254

Minister of Interior
Sayyid Ali bin Hamoud al-Busaidi, Ministry of the Interior, PO Box 127, Ruwi PC 112, Oman
PHONE: +968 602244
FAX: +968 607145

Minister of Defense
Badr bin Saud bin Hareb al-Bu Saidi, Ministry of Defense, PO Box 113, Muscat PC 113, Oman
PHONE: +968 709199
FAX: +968 618205

Minister of Communications
Salim bin Abdullah al-Ghazali, Ministry of Communications, PO Box 648, Muscat PC 113, Oman
PHONE: +968 702233
FAX: +968 795266

Minister of Health
Ali bin Mohammed bin Moosa, Ministry of Health, PO Box 393, Muscat PC 113, Oman
PHONE: +968 602177
FAX: +968 601430

Minister of Water Resources
Hamed bin Said al-Aufi, Ministry of Water Resources, PO Box 2575, Ruwi PC 112, Oman
PHONE: +968 703552
FAX: +968 703553

Minister of Commerce and Industry
Maqbool bin Ali bin Sultan, Ministry of Commerce and Industry, PO Box 550, Muscat PC 113, Oman
PHONE: +968 799500
FAX: +968 796403

DIPLOMATIC REPRESENTATION

Embassies in Oman

Italy
Way 2411 House n.842 Qurum, Muscat, Oman
PHONE: +968 560968
FAX: +968 564846

United Kingdom
PO Box 300, Muscat, Oman 113
PHONE: +968 693077
FAX: +968 693087

United States
Muscat, Oman

JUDICIAL SYSTEM

Chief Court

Magistrate Court

FURTHER READING

Articles

"Arabian Flights." *The Economist* 351, 8114 (April 10, 1999): 61.

Caplan, Brian and James Romanow. "Fitting the Pieces into Place." *Euromoney* (March 1999): 19.

Gawdat, Bahgat. ''Education in the Gulf Monarchies: Retrospect and Prospect.'' *International Review of Education* 1999, vol. 45, no. 2, p. 127+.

Gorman, Martyn. ''Oryx Go Back to the Brink.'' *Nature* 398 (March 18, 1999): 190.

Paramand, Benedict. ''Spotlight on Oman: A Star Is Born on the Arabian Sea . . . But How Fast Will Change Come?'' *Business Week International* (June 21, 1999): 4.

Smith, Andrew. ''A Slippery Slope.'' *The Banker* 149 (August 1999): 65+.

''The Oryx: Life on a Tightrope.'' *Science* 284 (April 30, 1999): 737.

Books

Hawley, Donald. *Oman and Its Renaissance.* London; New Jersey: Stacey International, 1990.

Kechichian, Joseph A. *Oman and the World: the Emergence of an Independent Foreign Policy.* Santa Monica, Calif.: Rand, 1995.

Riphenberg, Carol J. *Oman: Political Development in a Changing World.* Westport, Conn.: Praeger, 1998.

Skeet, Ian. *Oman: Politics and Development.* New York: St. Martin's Press, 1992.

Internet

Ministry of Information, Sultanate of Oman. ''Omanet.'' Available Online @ www.omanet.com (November 2, 1999).

''Oman.'' *ArabNet.* Available Onlie @ www.arab.net/oman/oman_contents.html (November 2, 1999).

OMAN: STATISTICAL DATA

For sources and notes see "Sources of Statistics" in the front of each volume.

GEOGRAPHY

Geography (1)

Area:

Total: 212,460 sq km.

Land: 212,460 sq km.

Water: 0 sq km.

Area—comparative: slightly smaller than Kansas.

Land boundaries:

Total: 1,374 km.

Border countries: Saudi Arabia 676 km, UAE 410 km, Yemen 288 km.

Coastline: 2,092 km.

Climate: dry desert; hot, humid along coast; hot, dry interior; strong southwest summer monsoon (May to September) in far south.

Terrain: vast central desert plain, rugged mountains in north and south.

Natural resources: petroleum, copper, asbestos, some marble, limestone, chromium, gypsum, natural gas.

Land use:

Arable land: 0%

Permanent crops: 0%

Permanent pastures: 5%

Forests and woodland: NA%

Other: 95% (1993 est.).

HUMAN FACTORS

Demographics (2A)

	1990	1995	1998	2000	2010	2020	2030	2040	2050
Population	NA	2,130.8	2,363.6	2,532.6	3,519.9	4,679.7	5,951.4	7,227.1	8,453.2
Net migration rate (per 1,000 population)	NA	NA	NA	NA	NA	NA	NA	NA	NA
Births	NA	NA	NA	NA	NA	NA	NA	NA	NA
Deaths	NA	NA	NA	NA	NA	NA	NA	NA	NA
Life expectancy - males	NA	68.3	69.0	69.6	71.9	73.8	75.3	76.6	77.6
Life expectancy - females	NA	72.3	73.1	73.7	76.2	78.3	80.1	81.5	82.7
Birth rate (per 1,000)	NA	36.9	37.8	38.1	34.4	30.1	25.8	21.7	18.7
Death rate (per 1,000)	NA	4.7	4.4	4.2	3.8	3.8	4.1	4.4	4.4
Women of reproductive age (15-49 yrs.)	NA	402.4	460.3	496.6	710.4	1,045.5	1,445.5	1,867.4	2,229.1
of which are currently married	NA	NA	NA	NA	NA	NA	NA	NA	NA
Fertility rate	NA	6.2	6.1	6.1	5.4	4.3	3.3	2.6	2.3

Except as noted, values for vital statistics are in thousands; life expectancy is in years.

Health Personnel (3)

Total health expenditure as a percentage of GDP, 1990-1997[a]

Public sector 2.5

Private sector . . . . .NA

Total[b] . . . . .NA

Health expenditure per capita in U.S. dollars, 1990-1997[a]

Purchasing power parity . . . . .NA

Total . . . . .NA

Availability of health care facilities per 100,000 people

Hospital beds 1990-1997[a] 210

Doctors 1993[c] 120

Nurses 1993[c] 290

Health Indicators (4)

Life expectancy at birth

1980 60

1997 73

Daily per capita supply of calories (1996) . . . .

Total fertility rate births per woman (1997) 4.8

Maternal mortality ratio per 100,000 live births (1990-97) . . . .

Safe water % of population with access (1995) 88

Sanitation % of population with access (1995) 85

Consumption of iodized salt % of households (1992-98)[a] 65

Smoking prevalence

Male % of adults (1985-95)[a] . . . .

Female % of adults (1985-95)[a] . . . .

Tuberculosis incidence per 100,000 people (1997) 13

Adult HIV prevalence % of population ages 15-49 (1997) 0.11

Infants and Malnutrition (5)

Under-5 mortality rate (1997) 18

% of infants with low birthweight (1990-97) 8

Births attended by skilled health staff % of total[a] . . .91

% fully immunized (1995-97)

TB 96

DPT 99

Polio 99

Measles 98

Prevalence of child malnutrition under age 5 (1992-97)[b] . . . . .NA

Ethnic Division (6)

Arab, Baluchi, South Asian (Indian, Pakistani, Sri Lankan, Bangladeshi), African.

Religions (7)

Ibadhi Muslim 75%; Sunni Muslim, Shi'a Muslim, Hindu.

Languages (8)

Arabic (official), English, Baluchi, Urdu, Indian dialects.

EDUCATION

Public Education Expenditures (9)

Public expenditure on education (% of GNP)

1980 . . . . .2.1

1996 . . . . .4.4[1]

Expenditure per student

Primary % of GNP per capita

1980 . . . .

1996 . . . . .13.1[1]

Secondary % of GNP per capita

1980 . . . .

1996 . . . . .2.21[1]

Tertiary % of GNP per capita

1980 . . . .

1996 . . . . .27.4[1]

Expenditure on teaching materials

Primary % of total for level (1996) . . . .

Secondary % of total for level (1996) 0.9

Primary pupil-teacher ratio per teacher (1996) . . . . .26[1]

Duration of primary education years (1995) 6

Educational Attainment (10)

Age group (1996) . . . . .25+

Total population 461,115

Highest level attained (%)

No schooling[2] 71.7

First level

Not completed 11.5

Completed . . . . .NA

Entered second level

S-1 . . . . .5.9

S-2 . . . . .11.1

Postsecondary . . . . .NA

Literacy Rates (11B)

Adult literacy rate

1980

Male . . . .-

Female . . . .-

1995

Male 71%

Female 46%

GOVERNMENT & LAW

Political Parties (12)

The legislative branch is a bicameral Majlis Oman consists of an upper chamber (41 seats; members appointed by the Sultan; has advisory powers only) and a lower chamber (82 seats; members elected by limited suffrage, however, the Sultan makes final selections and can negate election results; body has some limited power to propose legislation, but otherwise has only advisory powers). There are no political parties.

Military Affairs (14B)

	1990	1991	1992	1993	1994	1995
Military expenditures						
Current dollars (mil.)	1,707	1,450	1,767	1,691	1,818	1,735
1995 constant dollars (mil.)	1,961	1,602	1,901	1,773	1,864	1,735
Armed forces (000)	32	29	35	35	31	36
Gross national product (GNP)						
Current dollars (mil.)	9,445	9,088	9,996	9,871	10,060	10,410
1995 constant dollars (mil.)	10,850	10,040	10,750	10,350	10,310	10,410
Central government expenditures (CGE)						
1995 constant dollars (mil.)	4,841	4,508	5,381	5,148	5,072	5,121
People (mil.)	1.8	1.8	1.9	2.0	2.0	2.1
Military expenditure as % of GNP	18.1	16.0	17.7	17.1	18.1	16.7
Military expenditure as % of CGE	40.5	35.5	35.3	34.4	36.7	33.9
Military expenditure per capita (1995 $)	1,120	880	1,006	903	915	822
Armed forces per 1,000 people (soldiers)	18.3	15.9	18.5	17.8	15.2	17.1
GNP per capita (1995 $)	6,199	5,518	5,688	5,274	5,067	4,935
Arms imports[6]						
Current dollars (mil.)	10	50	10	140	290	460
1995 constant dollars (mil.)	11	55	11	147	297	460
Arms exports[6]						
Current dollars (mil.)	0	0	0	0	0	0
1995 constant dollars (mil.)	0	0	0	0	0	0
Total imports[7]						
Current dollars (mil.)	2,678	3,190	3,765	4,109	3,910	4,242
1995 constant dollars (mil.)	3,078	3,525	4,050	4,307	4,008	4,242
Total exports[7]						
Current dollars (mil.)	5,501	4,865	NA	NA	NA	NA
1995 constant dollars (mil.)	6,322	576	NA	NA	NA	NA
Arms as percent of total imports[8]	.4	1.	.3	3.4	7.4	10.8
Arms as percent of total exports[8]	0	0	NA	NA	NA	NA

Government Budget (13A)

Year: 1997

Total Expenditures: 1,848.0 Millions of Rials

Expenditures as a percentage of the total by function:

General public services and public order 14.72

Defense 36.20

Education 14.60

Health 7.03

Social Security and Welfare 4.27

Housing and community amenities 6.77

Recreational, cultural, and religious affairs 1.93

Fuel and energy 4.41

Agriculture, forestry, fishing, and hunting 1.44

Mining, manufacturing, and construction 20

Transportation and communication 1.80

Other economic affairs and services 89

Crime (15)

Crime rate (for 1997)

Crimes reported 2,750

Total persons convicted 1,100

Crimes per 100,000 population 125

Persons responsible for offenses

Total number of suspects 2,050

Total number of female suspects 175

Total number of juvenile suspects 525

LABOR FORCE

Labor Force (16)

Total 780,500

Agriculture 37%

Data for 1997 est. Percent distribution for 1993 est.

Unemployment Rate (17)

Rate not available.

PRODUCTION SECTOR

Electric Energy (18)

Capacity ....1.744 million kW (1995)

Production ....7.8 billion kWh (1995)

Consumption per capita ....3,670 kWh (1995)

Transportation (19)

Highways:

total: 32,800 km

paved: 9,840 km (including 550 km of expressways)

unpaved: 22,960 km (1996 est.)

Pipelines: crude oil 1,300 km; natural gas 1,030 km

Merchant marine:

total: 3 ships (1,000 GRT or over) totaling 16,306 GRT/8,210 DWT ships by type: cargo 1, passenger 1, passenger-cargo 1 (1996 est.)

Airports: 138 (1997 est.)

Airports—with paved runways:

total: 6

over 3,047 m: 4

2,438 to 3,047 m: 1

914 to 1,523 m: 1 (1997 est.)

Airports—with unpaved runways:

total: 132

over 3,047 m: 2

2,438 to 3,047 m: 6

1,524 to 2,437 m: 57

914 to 1,523 m: 32

under 914 m: 35 (1997 est.)

Top Agricultural Products (20)

Dates, limes, bananas, alfalfa, vegetables; camels, cattle; annual fish catch averages 100,000 metric tons.

MANUFACTURING SECTOR

GDP & Manufacturing Summary (21)

	1980	1985	1990	1992	1993	1994
Gross Domestic Product						
Millions of 1990 dollars	4,477	9,000	10,521	12,184	12,668	12,542
Growth rate in percent	6.05	13.76	7.52	7.70	3.98	−1.00
Per capita (in 1990 dollars)	4,066.3	6,442.5	6,008.7	6,382.1	6,359.6	6,038.4
Manufacturing Value Added						
Millions of 1990 dollars	49	265	396	414	NA	NA
Growth rate in percent	19.05	20.39	14.58	4.23	NA	NA
Manufacturing share in percent of current prices	0.8	2.4	3.7	4.3	*4.3*	NA

FINANCE, ECONOMICS, & TRADE

Economic Indicators (22)

National product: GDP—purchasing power parity—$17.2 billion (1997 est.)

National product real growth rate: 3.5% (1997 est.)

National product per capita: $8,000 (1997 est.)

Inflation rate—consumer price index: 1% (1996 est.)

Exchange Rates (24)

Exchange rates: Omani rials (RO) per US$1—0.3845 (fixed rate since 1986)

Top Import Origins (25)

$4.8 billion (f.o.b., 1997 est.) Data are for 1996.

Origins	%
UAE	22% (largely reexports)
Japan	15
United Kingdom	15
France	6
United States	5

Top Export Destinations (26)

$7.6 billion (f.o.b., 1997 est.) Data are for 1996.

Destinations	%
Japan	29
South Korea	17
China	12
Thailand	11
United States	7

Economic Aid (27)

Recipient: ODA, $82 million (1993).

Import Export Commodities (28)

Import Commodities	Export Commodities
Machinery	Petroleum 75%
Transportation equipment	Reexports
Manufactured goods	Fish
Food	Processed copper
Livestock	Textiles
Lubricants	

Balance of Payments (23)

	1992	1993	1994	1995	1996
Exports of goods (f.o.b.)	5,555	5,365	5,542	6,065	7,339
Imports of goods (f.o.b.)	−3,627	−4,030	−3,693	−4,050	−4,385
Trade balance	1,928	1,336	1,849	2,015	2,954
Services - debits	−1,671	−1,594	−1,624	−1,684	−1,791
Services - credits	341	434	270	338	231
Private transfers (net)	−16	18	26	29	10
Government transfers (net)	−1,181	−1,384	−1,326	−1,498	−1,670
Overall balance	−599	−1,190	−805	−800	−266

PAKISTAN

Islamic Republic of Pakistan
Islami Jamhooria Pakistan

INTRODUCTORY SURVEY

RECENT HISTORY

In the early twentieth century, British power was increasingly challenged by the rise of nationalist mass movements. The Indian National Congress began to attract wide support in this century with its advocacy of non-violent struggle. But because its leadership style appeared, to many Muslims, to be uniquely Hindu, Muslims formed the All-India Muslim League to look after their interests.

On 14 August 1947, British India was divided into the two self-governing dominions of India and Pakistan. This division, known as partition, resulted in a mass movement of Hindus, Muslims, and Sikhs who found themselves on the "wrong" side of new international boundaries. More than 20 million people moved, and up to 3 million of these were killed.

The new Pakistan was a state divided into two wings: East Pakistan (with 42 million people crowded mainly into what had been the eastern half of India's Bengal province) and West Pakistan (with 34 million in a much larger territory that included the former Indian provinces of Baluchistan, Sind, the Northwest Frontier, and western Punjab). In between, the wings were separated by 1600 kilometers (1000 miles) of an independent, mainly Hindu, India.

From the capital in Karāchi, in West Pakistan, the leaders of the new state worked hard to establish a workable parliamentary government with broad acceptance in both East and West. Political

CAPITAL: Islamabad.

FLAG: The national flag is dark green, with a white vertical stripe at the hoist and a white crescent and five-pointed star in the center.

ANTHEM: The opening lines of the national anthem, sung in Urdu, are "Blessed be the sacred land, Happy be the bounteous realm, Symbol of high resolve, land of Pakistan, Blessed be thou citadel of faith."

MONETARY UNIT: The rupee (R) is a paper currency of 100 paisa. There are coins of 1, 2, 5, 10, 25, and 50 paisa and of 1 rupee, and notes of 1, 2, 5, 10, 50, 100, 500, and 1,000 rupees. R1 = $0.02493 (or $1 = R40.12).

WEIGHTS AND MEASURES: The metric system was introduced in 1966 and made mandatory as of 1 January 1979.

HOLIDAYS: Pakistan Day, 23 March; May Day, 1 May; Independence Day, 14 August; Defense of Pakistan Day, 6 September; Anniversary of Death of the Quaid-e-Azam, Mohammad Ali Jinnah, 11 September; Christmas and Birthday of the Quaid-e-Azam, 25 December. Religious holidays include 'Id al-Fitr, Id al-'Adha', 1st of Muharram, and Milad an-Nabi.

TIME: 5 PM = noon GMT.

LOCATION AND SIZE: Situated in southern Asia, Pakistan has an area of 803,940 square kilometers (310,403 square miles), slightly less than twice the size of the state of California. The total boundary length is 7,820 kilometers (4,870 miles). Pakistan's capital city, Islamabad, is located in the northern part of the country.

CLIMATE: Pakistan's climate is dry and hot near the coast, becoming progressively cooler toward the northeastern uplands. The winter season is generally cold and dry. By the end of June the temperature may reach 49°C (120°F). Between July and September, the monsoon (very heavy rainfall) provides an average rainfall of about 38 centimeters (15 inches) in the river basins and up to about 150 centimeters (60 inches) in the northern areas.

stability proved hard to achieve, with frequent declarations of martial law and states of emergency in the years following 1954.

In the years leading up to 1971, domestic politics in Pakistan were dominated by efforts to bridge the political and ethnic gap that—more than geography—separated East and West. The gap persisted despite their common feelings of anxiety about India and shared commitment to Islam. Economically more important, East Pakistan, governed as a single province, disliked national policies laid down in West Pakistan, dominated by Punjabis and recent refugees from northern and western India.

In 1958, the Army chief, General Mohammad Ayub Khan, seized control of Pakistan, imposing martial law and banning all political activity for several years. He later began policies designed to

reduce the political influence of East Pakistan in the government. Amid rising political tension in both East and West in 1968, Ayub was forced from office, and General Mohammad Yahya Khan, also opposed to greater independence for East Pakistan, assumed the presidency in 1969.

Yahya's attempt to restore popular government in the general elections of 1970 failed when the popular verdict supported greater independence for East Pakistan. The election results were ignored, and civil unrest in East Pakistan rapidly spread to become civil war. India, with more than a million refugees pouring into its West Bengal state, joined in the conflict in support of the rebellion in November 1971, tipping the balance in favor of East Pakistan. In early 1972, the country of Bangladesh was created from the ruins of East Pakistan.

The outcome of the civil war led to the resignation on 20 December 1971 of Yahya Khan and brought to the presidency Zulfikar Ali Bhutto, whose populist Pakistan Peoples Party (PPP) had won a majority of seats in West Pakistan. Bhutto quickly charted an independent course for West Pakistan, which became the Islamic Republic of Pakistan. He distanced Pakistan from former close ties with the United States and Europe, seeking a much more active role in the Third World, especially in the growing international Islamic movement. Bhutto began limited land reform, nationalized banks and industries, and obtained support among all parties for a new constitution adopted in 1973, restoring a strong prime ministership, which he then assumed.

In the following years, Bhutto grew more and more dictatorial, until he was finally removed from office by the army on 5 July 1977. General Mohammad Zia-ul-Haq partially suspended the 1973 constitution and imposed martial law, which was extended despite repeated broken promises to hold popular elections.

Zia expanded the role of Islamic values and institutions in society. When the Soviet Union invaded Afghanistan in 1979, he assumed a strong anti-communist leadership role and renewed close ties with the United States to enhance Pakistan's security. He also improved relations with India, including normalization of trade, transport, and other nonsensitive areas.

In the late 1980s, India canceled election results and dismissed the state government. This led to the beginning of an armed rebellion against Indian rule by Muslim militants in Kashmir, an Indian province which had been split uneasily between Indian and Pakistani influence since 1949. Indian repression and Pakistani support of the militants continue to threaten to spark new Indo-Pakistan conflict.

Zia was among 18 officials (including the American ambassador) killed in the crash of a Pakistan Air Force plane in 1988. In November of that year, Benazir Bhutto, Zulfikar's daughter, became prime minister but was removed from office two years later by president Ghulam Ishaq amid growing power struggles within the government.

In 1993, widespread government corruption was exposed, corrupt officials dismissed, and political reforms undertaken. Elections were held in October and the PPP, leading a coalition called the People's Democratic Alliance (PDA), returned to power, with Benazir Bhutto again prime minister. Farooq Leghari was elected president. In 1996, Leghari dismissed Bhutto and her cabinet and dissolved the National Assembly. Nawaz Sharif won the general election held in February 1997. In April 1997, Sharif fired Navy Chief Admiral Mansur-ul Haq, who was suspected of being corrupt and misusing funds. It marked the first time in 25 years that a military chief was removed by civilian government. The shake-up of the military resulted in the dismissal and imprisonment of several high-ranking officials. In early 1998, Pakistani officials began investigating allegations that during her time in office, Benazir Bhutto and her husband, Asif Ali Zardari, were involved in diverting over $100 million to foreign bank accounts managed by her family. The government estimated that the couple indirectly received $1.5 billion through illegal payments and bribes.

In May 1998, India conducted several underground nuclear test explosions, prompting international outcry. The tests were India's first since 1974. Later that month, Pakistan began its own nuclear tests, intensifying global fears of a nuclear arms race between Pakistan and India. In April 1999 Pakistan and India test-fired missiles capable of carrying nuclear warheads.

The economic sanctions that followed after Pakistan's nuclear tests devastated an already weak Pakistani economy. With the economic collapse, crime rates soared.

Despite the continued tension, both sides made an effort to improve relations. In February 1999, India and Pakistan re-opened scheduled bus service between their countries for the first time in thirty-four years. On the first trip, Indian prime minister Atal Bechari Vajpayee rode to Lahore for a meeting with Sharif. During their talks, the two leaders agreed to continue to reduce tension between their countries.

GOVERNMENT

Pakistan is governed under the constitution of 14 August 1973 (as amended) which declared Islam the state religion and provided for a president as official head of state and a prime minister as executive head of government. The parliament consists of a National Assembly of 217 members elected for five-year terms, plus 20 seats to be filled by vote of the elected members. The Senate has 84 members elected for six-year terms by the provincial assemblies and tribal councils, plus 3 seats reserved for the federal capital area.

Pakistan is divided into 4 provinces. Outside the provinces, there are 11 federally administered tribal land areas.

Judiciary

The Supreme Court has original, appeals, and advisory jurisdictions. Each province has a high court. Below the high courts are district and session courts, and below these are subordinate courts and village courts on the civil side and magistrates on the criminal side. Courts are subject to pressure from the executive branch partly because the president controls the appointments of judges. However, the Supreme Court has recently acted with a greater degree of independence by handing down a number of cases against the government. There are no jury trials in Pakistan.

Political Parties

The two main political parties are the Pakistan Muslim League (PML), led by Nawaz Sharif, and the Pakistan Peoples Party (PPP), led by Benazir Bhutto, daughter of the late Prime Minister Zulfikar Bhutto. Political alliances shift frequently in Pakistan. There are many local splinter groups that have been calling for the decentralization of power.

Both the PPP and the PML have competed successfully in forming governments in provincial assemblies only when they have recruited (or neutralized) strong regional parties, like the Awami National Party (ANP) in the Northwest Frontier Province and the Muhajir Quami Movement (MQM) in Sindh.

DEFENSE

In 1993, Pakistan's armed forces totaled 587,000. Its army of 520,000 was the world's ninth largest, comprising 2 armored divisions, 19 infantry divisions, and 40 brigades of specialized troops and supporting arms. The navy (22,000) had 9 submarines, 3 destroyers, and 13 patrol and coastal combatants with a small naval air arm. The air force, with a total strength of 45,000, had 430 combat aircraft. Paramilitary forces, including the Pakistan rangers, the frontier corps, a maritime security agency, a national guard, and local defense units, totaled 247,000. Military service is voluntary. Defense expenditures in 1995 were estimated at $3.6 billion, or 8% of gross domestic product.

ECONOMIC AFFAIRS

Despite steady expansion of industry during the 1980s, Pakistan's economy remains dominated by agriculture. At $480 in 1995, income per person has improved slightly since the mid-1980s when it was $400. Pakistan is generally poor in natural resources, although extensive reserves of natural gas and petroleum are being exploited. Iron ore, chromite, and low-quality coal are mined.

A growing debt, large government expenditures on public enterprises, low tax revenues, and high levels of defense spending contributed to serious financial deficits during the late 1980s. In response, in 1988 the government began a major economic reform program with World Bank and International Monetary Fund (IMF) support.

Rising inflation became a serious problem in the early 1990s, reaching 11.8% in 1990–91 and declining only somewhat to 9.2% in 1991–92. Severe floods in late 1992 weakened exports during 1992–93. In 1995, the government failed to follow recommendations by the International Monetary Fund (IMF) to pursue a more market-oriented economy, so the IMF suspended a $1.5 billion loan. By 1996, the economy was in the worst recession in 25 years. Tax receipts and export income were down, and the government's debt increased close to the point of default.

Public Finance

The fiscal year extends from 1 July to 30 June. The federal government frames two separate budgets: revenue (current account) and capital. Deficits have appeared since 1971–72, a combined result of the loss of revenues from East Pakistan, stepped-up defense expenditures, lax expenditure controls, and a low and inelastic tax base. Current expenditures (debt service, defense, administration) now consume over 70% of the budget; development needs (education, health, energy, and rural development) receive the remainder. Tax revenues have not kept pace with expenditure growth due to widespread evasion, corruption among tax officials, overreliance on foreign trade taxes, and a tax exemption for agricultural income, which comprises 25% of GDP.

The U.S. Central Intelligence Agency estimates that, in 1995, government revenues totaled approximately $11.9 billion and expenditures $12.4 billion. The budget deficit was hovering at about 6.2% of GDP in 1995 and 1996 and was projected to reach almost 7% in 1997. Interest payments on the accumulated debt threatened to bankrupt the government by mid-1997. As a condition for a $1.6 billion loan from the IMF and World Bank, the government agreed to reduce the deficit to 4% of GDP. To do so, the government is attempting to raise revenues by expanding the tax base beyond the 1% of Pakistanis who currently pay income tax. Other proposals include a reduction in government payrolls, improved tax administration, and an end to the tax exemption for agricultural income. Despite the dismal financial situation, the government has yet to reduce defense spending, which accounts for almost 25% of the budget.

Income

In 1997, Pakistan's gross national product (GNP) was $344 billion, or $2,600 per person. For the period 1985–95 the average inflation rate was 9.3%, resulting in a real growth rate in gross national product of 1.2% per person.

Industry

Despite steady overall industrial growth during the 1980s, manufacturing remains concentrated in cotton processing, textiles, food processing and petroleum refining. Small-scale and cottage industries employ about three-fourths of Pakistan's industrial workers and account for about one-fourth of its industrial production.

Cotton textile production is the most important of Pakistan's industries. Pakistan supplies its own cotton fabrics (314.9 million square meters/376.4 million square yards produced in 1993–94) and exports substantial quantities. Factories also produce synthetic fabrics, worsted yarn, and jute textiles. Cotton yarn production equalled 1.3 million tons in 1993–94. Jute textile output amounted to over 100,000 tons.

Other important industries include food processing, chemicals manufacture, and the iron and steel industries. In 1996, Pakistan's software industry had exports of $25 million.

Banking and Finance

The central banking institution is the State Bank of Pakistan (SBP), established in 1948 at Karachi and with branches in the larger cities. The government holds 51% of the bank's paid-up capital; 49% is held by corporations, societies, and individuals. The State Bank has exclusive responsibility for the issuance of currency; it is the financial agent of the central and provincial governments, and is responsible for the flotation and management of the public debt. In March 1996, the money supply, as measured by M2, amounted to R837.8 billion.

The nation's largest commercial banks were nationalized in 1974 and regrouped under five state banking institutions: the National Bank of Pakistan, Habib Bank, United Bank, Muslim Commercial Bank, and Allied Bank of Pakistan. The government-controlled banking system thus comprised all but a few of the nation's banks and accounted for a large share of total bank deposits and outstanding domestic credit. In 1981, in accordance with the Islamic condemnation of usury, virtually all banks opened special accounts for depositors who preferred, in lieu of interest, to share in the profits or losses from investments made with their money. In 1985, all savings accounts stopped yielding interest and converted to sharing in profit and loss. Pakistan instituted banking reform in 1991. The Muslim Commercial Bank and the Allied Bank of Pakistan Ltd. reverted to private ownership shortly thereafter. In 1991 banking licenses were granted to private commercial banks that wanted to establish foreign bank branches in the country. But major weaknesses persist and are particularly marked in the case of the four remaining government-run commercial banks, which account for the bulk of deposits and advances. The total assets of domestic commercial banks amounted to R1.77 trillion on 31 March 1996, up from R1.56 trillion a year earlier.

The portfolios of the 16 state-owned development finance institutions, which provide the bulk of long-term lending to industry and agriculture, likewise tend to be of poor quality. Their lending is less diversified and more risky than that of commercial banks, while their costs are higher and margins lower.

The state provides credit through the Agricultural Development Bank of Pakistan and the House Building Finance Corp. Industrial loans are made available through the Pakistan Industrial Credit and Investment Corp. (established in 1957), the Industrial Development Bank of Pakistan (1961), and the National Development Finance Corp. (1973).

There are stock exchanges at Lahore and Karachi, with the latter accounting for a major share of the business. In the nine months to end-March 1996, there were 33 new listings on the Karachi Stock Exchange, the largest of the country's three bourses, bringing the total to 775.

Economic Development

After the founding of the Pakistani state in 1947, the government's economic policy concentrated attention on developing an economic infrastructure, achieving self-sufficiency in food, and developing export industries. A major new land reform program introduced in March 1972 had resulted by March 1975 in the confiscation (for eventual redistribution) of 45.3% of all privately cultivated farmland. By November 1973, the government had nationalized industries in 10 major categories of production. In a third major step, most of the commercial banks were nationalized on 1 January 1974, resulting in control of more than 90% of all banking business by the State Bank and the five newly created units.

By the late 1970s, however, Pakistan's martial law government, claiming the nationalization program had stifled production and discouraged private investment, moved to restore private sector confidence by fostering economic stability and by redressing the balance of payments deficit, which was causing large overseas debt obligations. A new five-year plan (1978–83), Pakistan's fifth, reserved 48% of industrial investment for the private sector and set goals for an annual economic growth rate of 7.2%, a 4.2% rise in per capita income, and increases of 6% in agricultural output and 10% in industrial production. The plan was allocated a budget of $21 billion, of which 25% was to come from external sources. Indications were that the agricultural sector would meet its target, but that rising oil costs and the burden of providing for the Afghan refugees had impeded progress in other sectors.

The sixth five-year plan (1983–88), with a proposed outlay of R210 billion, envisioned further investments in water and power development, deregulation to increase private sector activity, and a new emphasis on provision of social services and infrastructural improvements for rural areas. Prime Minister Junejo announced a program for 1986–90, with an outlay of R70 billion, focusing on rural development, particularly in the areas of education, village electrification, potable water supply, roads, health care, and employment.

By the late 1980s, a number of structural factors resulted in increasingly critical fiscal and balance of payment deficits. With less than 30% of the budget devoted to infrastructural development and other needs in health and education, the prognosis for long-term social and economic development remained poor. In response, a medium-term structural reform program was developed under the government of Prime Minister Benazir Bhutto for implementation in 1989–91. Aimed at correcting fiscal and external imbalances, the program targeted a reform of the tax collection system, tighter government spending controls and monetary management, the privatization of state-owned industrial enterprises, banks and utilities, the phasing out of state monopolies in the transportation, insurance, telecommunications and energy sectors, and liberalization of investment and foreign exchange regulations. Implementation of the ambitious program proceeded under the government of Nawaz Sharif who assumed the prime minister's office in 1991. Results have been somewhat uneven thus far, with little effective improvements scored in the country's tax system or its fiscal and balance of payments deficits. While the rapid change of government in 1993 and ongoing political tensions appear to be dampening private investment somewhat, official assurances have been given that structural reform and privatization will continue.

Since the early 1950s through 1993, Pakistan is estimated to have received about $37 billion in aid disbursements, including both long-term and medium-term loans and grants, making it one of the largest recipients in the developing world. For the Indus Valley project, Pakistan received funding of more than $1.3 billion from the IBRD, IDA, ADB, U.S., UK, and other countries. In addition to U.S. aid (a six-year commitment of $4.02 billion made in 1988 with $2.1 billion disbursed by 1990), Pakistan has also received aid from Iran and the Arab states. New economic aid from the U.S. was halted in 1990, under the terms of a Congressional amendment requiring certification of Pakistan's status as a nuclear weapons-free country.

SOCIAL WELFARE

A social security scheme enacted in 1972 covers employees of firms with 10 or more workers. Social security coverage includes old age, disability, and survivor benefits, as well as sickness and maternity payments, workers' compensation, and unemployment benefits. Since 1973, cost-of-living allowances have been paid to workers earning less than minimum wage.

The government's Islamization program to promote social welfare in accordance with Islamic ideals was introduced in 1977. Islamic welfare taxes, the *zakat* and *ushr*, were levied to redistribute wealth. The ushr tax on landowners took effect in 1983. Islamic beliefs are taught in the public schools and reflected widely by the mass media. Laws against drinking alcoholic beverages, adultery, and lying have been strictly enforced.

The Women's Ministry, established in 1979, has sponsored some 7,000 centers in rural areas and urban slums to provide women with a basic education and to teach them such skills as livestock farming, midwifery, and secretarial work. Women face serious social and legal discrimination.

The use of child labor in Pakistan is widespread. Bonded child labor is illegal but still affects hundreds of thousands of children. In bonded labor, the employer keeps the child working to pay off a long-term debt of the parent.

Healthcare

Health facilities in Pakistan are inadequate, mainly due to a lack of resources and a high population growth rate. In 1993, 85% of the population had access to health care.

In 1992, there were 60,250 physicians and 20,000 registered homeopathic medical practitioners. Special attention has been given to the training of nurses, and several training centers are in operation. However, medical personnel ratios, though much improved, remain inadequate: 1 doctor per 1,923 persons and 1 nurse per 1,769 in 1993. The country had 1 hospital bed per 1,769 inhabitants that year. The vast majority of hospitals are located in urban areas.

Malaria, tuberculosis, intestinal diseases, venereal diseases, and skin diseases remain Pakistan's main public health problems. Drug addiction, especially among university students, is an increasing concern. Average life expectancy is estimated at 64 years.

Housing

The rapid increase in urbanization, coupled with the rising population, has added to the housing shortage in urban areas. About 25% of the people in large cities live in *katchi abadis* (shantytowns). The Public Works Department has built more than 8,000 units in Islamabad, Lahore, and Peshawar. In 1987, the National Housing Authority was created to coordinate the upgrading of the existing *katchi abadis* and prevent the growth of new ones. As of 1991, 171 *abadis* had been renovated, and 522 more were under development.

EDUCATION

In 1995, the illiteracy rate was 62% (males, 50%; females, 76%). As of 1993, there were 15.5 million primary school pupils and 5 million secondary school students. Girls attend separate schools at both primary and secondary levels.

In 1991, 1.7 million students were enrolled at institutions of higher learning. In 1995, there were 29 colleges and universities. An agricultural university was established in 1961 at Lyallpur (now Faisalābad). Two engineering and technological universities have been founded at Lahore (1961) and Islamabad (1966). Research institutions include the Institute of Islamic Studies at Lahore, the Iqbal Academy at Lahore, and the Pakistan Institute of International Affairs at Karāchi. Urdu and English are the languages of instruction.

Many adult literacy centers have been established in recent years. In addition, the People's Open University was established at Islamabad (1974) to provide mass adult education through correspondence and the communications media.

1999 KEY EVENTS TIMELINE

January
- Prime Minister Nawaz Sharif narrowly escapes a bomb attack on January 3rd; the next day, alleged Sunni militants kill several Shia worshippers in a mosque in Punjab.

February
- Demonstrations are held in Lahore against the government's attempts to intimidate the press.
- Islamics protest Indian prime minister Vajpayee's visit.
- On February 20, Sharif and Vajpayee hold talks near Lahore to defuse tensions between the two countries.

March
- The government announces new measures to revive the sagging economy.
- Foreign currency restrictions are relaxed and import duties are cut.

April
- Former prime minister Benazir Bhutto and her husband are convicted on corruption charges.

- Pakistan responds to Indian missile tests by test-firing its own upgraded Ghauri ballistic missile. Capable of delivering a nuclear warhead up to 1400 miles, the Ghauri is seen as placing most Indian cities within range of a Pakistani strike.

May

- India and Pakistan trade accusations over fighting in the Kargil region of Kashmir.

- Pakistan denies direct involvement of its forces and claims Kashmiri guerrillas are responsible for seizing territory on India's side of the LOC.

- Pakistan claims two Indian jets were shot down for violating its airspace over Kashmir.

June

- Fighting in Kargil escalates while India and Pakistan mobilize troops along their border.

- Diplomatic pressure on Pakistan mounts; on June 9th, the United States calls on Pakistan to remove the guerrillas.

July

- Prime Minister Nawaz Sharif and U.S. President Clinton hold talks in Washington on July 4.

- Pakistan agrees to withdraw guerrillas from Kargil.

- The IMF withholds new loans to Pakistan, citing the government's failure to implement tough economic reforms; the news depresses share prices in the nation's stock exchange.

August

- India shoots down a Pakistani naval patrol plane; Pakistan claims the action is unprovoked.

September

- The government imposes a 15% general sales tax.

October

- Army chief of staff General Pervez Musharraf ousts Sharif and takes control of Pakistan's government in a military coup.

- Musharraf offers reassurance that "the army does not intend to stay in power" and that civilian rule—and the constitution—will be reestablished at an unspecified time. He distances himself from Islamic extremists and says that he will pull back troops from the border with India.

November

- In what is assumed to be a warning, six rockets are set off close to the American embassy, an American library, and a building that houses some United Nations offices; authorities search for the rocketeers, as well as a motive.

- Nawaz Sharif, ousted as prime minister in a military coup in October, appears before an anti-terrorist court that will try him on charges relating to his alleged attempt on the day of the coup to divert new ruler General Pervez Musharraf's plane from the Karachi airport, where it was scheduled to land a flight from Sri Lanka. Although the plane landed safely, the charges of attempted murder, kidnapping, and hijacking are punishable by life imprisonment or death.

December

- Pakistan's military ruler General Pervez Musharraf announces the establishment of 100 courts to try the corrupt and those with delinquent bank loans.

- The new military regime announces plans to send troops to de-silt the country's irrigation system in an effort to speed reforms.

- A man admits to sexually molesting and killing over 100 boys, saying he carried out the crimes because the police failed to investigate an attack that had been perpetrated against him.

- On December 8, prosecutors charge former prime minister Nawaz Sharif with hijacking, kidnapping, attempted murder, and plotting to wage war against the state. Later in December, a murder case is registered against former prime minister Benazir Bhutto (and five others), relating to charges that she ordered police to fire on members of the Islamic fundamentalist Jamaat-I-Islami party in 1996.

ANALYSIS OF EVENTS: 1999

BUSINESS AND THE ECONOMY

Pakistan's struggling economy received little cheer in 1999. Fiscal indecision and post-nuclear test economic sanctions dried up foreign investments while budget and trade deficits soared. According to some reports, unemployment reached an all time high in 1999 accompanied by nearly 8 percent inflation rate. Projected gross domestic product (GDP) growth was 3.4 percent and is expected to further decline in 2000. Under this scenario, the country will remain heavily dependent on foreign assistance. This assistance is uncertain after the coup in which the military brought down the government in October 1999.

In early 1999, Pakistan faced a severe payments crisis and was on the verge of defaulting on its $32 billion foreign debt. The U.S. lifted some sanctions, clearing the way for the International Monetary Fund (IMF) to negotiate a bailout package of $1.5 billion with Pakistan. The agreement stipulated that Pakistan had to implement market reforms to stabilize its finances. Key demands included cuts in budget deficits and improved tax collections.

Although the IMF disbursed $575 million in January, it delayed an additional disbursement of $280 million in the summer to express displeasure with the government's inaction on promised reforms. Prior to fresh talks with the IMF in September, the government announced a new sales tax, but widespread protests forced a retreat. A dispute over energy pricing between the government and Hubco, a privately owned power company, continued in 1999. This dispute has discouraged foreign investments and also put Pakistan at odds with the World Bank and the IMF.

GOVERNMENT AND POLITICS

For most of its independent existence, Pakistan has been ruled by the military. In the 1990s, however, popularly elected civilian governments were in charge. In 1997, Nawaz Sharif became prime minister after his party, the Muslim League, captured 134 seats in the 217-seat parliament. As prime minister, Sharif consolidated power, but in the process, alienated the political parties, MQM and ANP, that had previously supported his government. Moreover, Sharif replaced the country's president and supreme court chief justice with political loyalists. Critics charged these actions weakened the institutional checks and balances on Sharif's authority. In 1998, he even humbled the military, forcing army chief, General Jehangir Karamat, into early retirement for demanding that the army have a say in the government's decisions. Sharif appointed General Pervez Musharraf to the post, bypassing more senior army officers. Reportedly, Sharif expected General Musharraf, who ap-

parently lacked a power base within the military's dominant ethnic culture, to be more pliable.

Musharraf, however, had enough power to carry out a surprise coup against Sharif in October. Promising to restore local democracy within a year, Musharraf has suspended parliament and the constitution. He also announced a multi-point plan aimed at reviving the country's economy. The plan includes an increase in current taxes and the introduction of new taxes, outlines to improve investor confidence, and deregulation efforts. Despite international calls that Musharraf announce a timetable for returning the country to democracy, he has refused and instead focused on his plans to revive the nation politically and economically.

Pakistan and neighboring India have been at odds over Muslim majority Kashmir for more than 50 years. Both claimed the territory. Pakistan controlled the western third while India administered the rest as its state of Jammu and Kashmir. A "line of control" (LOC) serves as the de facto border between the two sides. Since 1989, Indian and Pakistani troops have waged a low intensity conflict along this border, shelling each other's positions. Also, Muslim militants, allegedly armed and inspired by Pakistan, have conducted a violent campaign against Indian rule in Jammu and Kashmir.

Attempts to resolve the Kashmir dispute are at an impasse. Both countries refuse to budge from their hard-line demands. The absence of a settlement prevents the normalization of India-Pakistan relations. In 1998, the two countries revealed their nuclear weapons capability in a series of underground nuclear tests. India enjoys vast superiority over Pakistan in conventional weapons. Pakistan justifies its nuclear weapons as deterrence against possible Indian aggression. Arguably, these weapons can stabilize or destabilize the Kashmiri standoff.

The year 1999 proved to be an eventful but troubled time for Pakistan. The domestic security situation worsened because of increased ethnic and religious violence. National security was endangered by ill-conceived belligerence in Kashmir, and the economy fell into a tailspin. Prime Minister Sharif's inability to provide credible leadership eventually led to his ouster in an October military coup. Early in the year, Sharif escaped an assassination attempt while traveling to his family estate. His government also received a setback when the Supreme Court ruled against military courts set up to expedite justice in Sindh. The ruling deprived the government of a key instrument in the exercise of federal authority to stem violence in the province. A government tax probe of the country's leading newspaper raised concerns that Sharif was attempting to muzzle the press.

In February, Sharif hosted his Indian counterpart, Vajpayee, in talks aimed at defusing aggravated tensions over nuclear testing. Both men agreed to measures reducing the likelihood of an accidental nuclear exchange, and held out prospects for a quick resumption of dialogue on normalizing relations. Optimism evaporated in May when India accused Pakistani infiltrators of crossing the LOC and seizing Indian territory in Kargil. Pakistan denied the charge, claiming only Kashmiri militants were involved. India launched a strong military response against the intruders, ruling out any negotiated compromises. Intense diplomatic activity followed, as the two countries appeared to be blundering towards a larger war. World opinion favored India's version of events, and Pakistan came under increasing diplomatic pressure to pull back the infiltrators. In July, Pakistan agreed to urge the 'militants' retreat. Still, the two countries remained in a confrontational mode, highlighted by sporadic clashes in Kashmir and the downing of a Pakistani naval aircraft by Indian jets.

The Kargil episode raised vexing questions about Sharif's leadership and motives, and the army's role. Sharif's credibility declined among Pakistanis, especially Islamic nationalists, who accused him of caving in to U.S. pressure. In September, massive anti-government demonstrations, orchestrated by a reinvigorated and newly united opposition, demanded Sharif's resignation. Reportedly, the army was unhappy with the government's Kargil capitulation and rumors circulated of a rift between Sharif and General Musharraf. In early October, while Musharraf was abroad, Sharif dismissed him as army chief. The general returned and, with the army's backing, confined Sharif to house arrest and declared himself in charge. Subsequently, in November, Sharif was officially placed under arrest and charged with serious offenses.

CULTURE AND SOCIETY

Pakistan's estimated population of 138 million is overwhelmingly Muslim. Islam is the state religion and underpins the country's cultural and social life. A common religion has not prevented ethnic conflict. Punjabi domination has led to unrest among Sindhi and Baluchi minorities. In Sindh province, relations between native Sindhis and immigrants from India known as Mohajirs are tense and frequently violent. The Sharif government proposed making shari'a, or Islamic law, supreme, prompting violence between the country's Sunni Muslim majority and Shia Muslim minority. The latter fear discrimination under Sunni interpretations of shari'a. Women's groups and secularists are also concerned about Islamist fervor's impact on social freedoms and opportunities.

DIRECTORY

CENTRAL GOVERNMENT
Head of State

Chief Executive
Pervez Musharraf, Office of the Chief Executive, Constitution Ave, Islamabad, Pakistan

POLITICAL ORGANIZATIONS
Awami National Party (ANP)
NAME: Ajmal Khan Khattak

Baluchistan National Party (BNP)
Jamiat Ulema-i-Pakistan-JUP (Islamic Movement of Pakistan)

Mansoorah, Multan Rd., Lahore 54700, Pakistan
PHONE: +92 (042) 5419520; 7844605
FAX: +92 (042)_7832194
E-MAIL: info@jamaat.org
TITLE: President
NAME: Qazi Hussain Ahmad

Mohajir Quami Mahaz-MQM (Mohajir National Movement, Altaf faction)
NAME: Altaf Hussain

National People's Party (NPP)
NAME: Ghulam Mustafa Jatoi

Pakhtun Khawa Mill Awami Party-PKMAP (Pakhtun Khwa National People's Party)
NAME: Mahmood Khan Achakzai

Pakistan Muslim League Functional Group (PML-F)
NAME: Pir Pagaro

Pakistan Muslim League Junejo faction (PML-J)

NAME: Hamid Nasir Chattha

Pakistan Muslim League Nawaz Sharif faction (PML-N)

NAME: Nawaz Sharif

Pakistan People's Party (PPP)

Zardari House-8, Street 19, Sector F-8/2,
Islamabad, Pakistan
PHONE: +92 (51) 282781 282782
FAX: +92 (51) 282741
E-MAIL: info@ppp.org.pk
TITLE: Chair
NAME: Benazir Bhutto

Jamhoori Watan Party-JWP (Republican Nation Party)

NAME: Akbar Khan Bugti

DIPLOMATIC REPRESENTATION

Embassies in Pakistan

Afghanistan
8 St #90, G-6/3 Islamabad, Pakistan
PHONE: +92 826505
FAX: +92 824504

Albania
231 St #18, F-10/2, Islamabad, Pakistan
PHONE: +92 290730; 290740
FAX: +92 290750

Algeria
107 St #9, E-7 Islamabad, Pakistan
PHONE: +92 206631
FAX: +92 820912

Argentina
20 Hill Rd., F-6/3 Islamabad, Pakistan
PHONE: +92 821242
FAX: +92 825564

Australia
Diplomatic Enclave No. 2, Islamabad, Pakistan
PHONE: +92 824345

Austria
13, St #1, F-6/3 Islamabad, Pakistan
PHONE: +92 279237; 279238
FAX: +92 828366

Bangladesh
1, St #5, F-6/3, Islamabad, Pakistan
PHONE: +92 279267

FAX: +92 279266

Belgium
14 St #17, F-7/2, Islamabad, Pakistan
PHONE: +92 827091; 277753
FAX: +92 822358

Bosnia
1, School Rd., F-8/3, Islamabad, Pakistan
PHONE: +92 261041; 261003
FAX: +92 261004

Brazil
Attaturk Avenue, G-6/3 Islamabad, Pakistan
PHONE: +92 279690; 279691
FAX: +92 823034

Brunei Darussalam
16 St #21, F-6/2 Islamabad, Pakistan
PHONE: +92 823038; 823783; 823372
FAX: +92 823138

Bulgaria
6-11 Diplomatic Enclave, Islamabad, Pakistan
PHONE: +92 279196
FAX: +92 279195

Canada
Diplomatic Enclave, G-5 Islamabad, Pakistan
PHONE: +92 279100; 279102; 2791003
FAX: +92 279110

China
Diplomatic Enclave, Islamabad, Pakistan
PHONE: +92 822540; 817279
FAX: +92 821116

Croatia
70 Margala Rd., F-7/2 Islamabad, Pakistan
PHONE: +92 827662; 827649
FAX: +92 827645

Czech Republic
49, St #27, F-6/2 Islamabad, Pakistan
PHONE: +92 274304

Denmark
9, 90th St., G-6/3 Islamabad, Pakistan
PHONE: +92 824722
FAX: +92 823483

Egypt
38-51 U.N. Boulevard DE, G-5/4 Islamabad,
Pakistan
PHONE: +92 279550; 820180
FAX: +92 279552

Finland
11 St #90, G-6/3 Islamabad, Pakistan
PHONE: +92 828426; 822136; 822318
FAX: +92 828426; 828427

France
Diplomatic Enclave, G-5 Islamabad, Pakistan
PHONE: +92 278730; 278731; 278932
FAX: +92 822583; 825389

Germany
Diplomatic Enclave, Ramna 5, Islamabad,
Pakistan
PHONE: +92 279430
FAX: +92 279436

Greece
6 Margala Rd, F-7/3 Islamabad, Pakistan
PHONE: +92 822558; 825186
FAX: +92 825161

Hungary
12, Margala Rd., F-6/3 Islamabad, Pakistan
PHONE: +92 823352; 823353
FAX: +92 825256

India
Diplomatic Enclave, G-5, Islamabad, Pakistan
PHONE: +92 272676

Indonesia
Diplomatic Enclave 1, St#5, Islamabad, Pakistan
PHONE: +92 206656
FAX: +92 829145

Iran
222-238, St # 2, G-5/1, DE, Islamabad, Pakistan
PHONE: +92 276210
FAX: +92 8244839

Iraq
57, St #48, F-8/4 Islamabad, Pakistan
PHONE: +92 253391; 253392; 253393
FAX: +92 253394

Italy
54, Margala Rd., Shalimar 6/3, Islamabad,
Pakistan
PHONE: +92 828982
FAX: +92 829026

Japan
53-70, Ramna 5/4, DE, Islamabad, Pakistan
PHONE: +92 279320; 279330
FAX: +92 279320

Jordan
131 St #14, E-7 Islamabad, Pakistan
PHONE: +92 823459; 823460
FAX: +92 823207

Kazakstan
2 St#4, F-8/3 Islamabad, Pakistan
PHONE: +92 262926; 262924
FAX: +92 262926

Kenya
10 St #9, F-7/3 Islamabad, Pakistan
PHONE: +92 279540; 279542
FAX: +92 279541

Korea
9 St #18, F-8/2 Islamabad, Pakistan
PHONE: +92 279385; 279386; 279387
FAX: +92 279391

Kuwait
1, 2 and 24, DE Islamabad, Pakistan
PHONE: +92 279413

Lebanon
6 St #27, Shalimar 6/2, Islamabad, Pakistan
PHONE: +92 278338
FAX: +92 826410

Libya
12, Margala Rd., F-8/3 Islamabad, Pakistan
PHONE: +92 255066

Malaysia
78 Margala Rd., F-6/2 Islamabad, Pakistan
PHONE: +92 279574
FAX: +92 824761

Mauritius
27, St #26, F-6/2 Islamabad, Pakistan
PHONE: +92 824657; 824658; 828985
FAX: +92 824656

Morocco
6, Gomal Rd., E-7 Islamabad, Pakistan
PHONE: +92 820565
FAX: +92 822745

Myammar
12/1 St #13, F-7/2 Islamabad, Pakistan
PHONE: +92 822460; 828818
FAX: +92 828819

Nepal
11 St #84, G-6/4 Islamabad, Pakistan
PHONE: +92 828838; 278051
FAX: +92 928839

Netherlands
2nd Floor PIA Building Blue Area, Islamabad,
Pakistan
PHONE: +92 279510; 279511; 279512
FAX: +92 279512

Nigeria
6 St #22, F-6/2 Islamabad, Pakistan
PHONE: +92 823542; 823547
FAX: +92 824104

Norway
25 St #19, F-6/2 Islamabad, Pakistan

PHONE: +92 279720; 279721; 279722
FAX: +92 279729

Oman
53 St #48, F-8/4 Islamabad, Pakistan
PHONE: +92 254925; 254469
FAX: +92 255074

Palestine
486-B, St #9, F-10/2, Islamabad, Pakistan
PHONE: +92 291185
FAX: +92 294703

Philippines
8, St #60, F-7/4 Islamabad, Pakistan
PHONE: +92 824933; 822720
FAX: +92 277389

Poland
24, G-5/4, DE II, Islamabad, Pakistan
PHONE: +92 279491; 279492
FAX: +92 825442

Portugal
40 A, Main Margala Rd., F-7/2 Islamabad, Pakistan
PHONE: +92 279530; 279531
FAX: +92 279532

Qatar
20, Khayaban-e-Iqbal, F-6/3 Islamabad, Pakistan
PHONE: +92 826483; 826484
FAX: +92 820868

Romania
13, St #88, G-6/3 Islamabad, Pakistan
PHONE: +92 826514; 826515
FAX: +92 826515

Russia
Diplomatic Enclave, Ramna 4, Islamabad, Pakistan
PHONE: +92 278670; 278671
FAX: +92 826552

Saudi Arabia
14 Hill Rd., F-6/3 Islamabad, Pakistan
PHONE: +92 820156; 820150; 821056
FAX: +92 278816

Serbia
14 St #87, G-6/3 Islamabad, Pakistan
PHONE: +92 829556; 829557
FAX: +92 820956

Somalia
21 St #56, F-6/4 Islamabad, Pakistan
PHONE: +92 263383; 279789; 279790
FAX: +92 826117

South Africa
48 Margala Rd., F-8/2 Islamabad, Pakistan
PHONE: +92 262354; 262356; 250318
FAX: +92 250114

Spain
St #6, Ramna 5, DE, Islamabad, Pakistan
PHONE: +92 279480
FAX: +92 279489

Sri Lanka
St #52, F-6/4 Islamabad, Pakistan
PHONE: +92 828735
FAX: +92 828751

Sudan
7, St #1, G-6/3 Islamabad, Pakistan
PHONE: +92 827068, 828710
FAX: +92 827073

Sweden
4, St #5, F-6/3 Islamabad, Pakistan
PHONE: +92 828712; 828713; 828714
FAX: +92 825284

Switzerland
St #6, DE G-5/4 Islamabad, Pakistan
PHONE: +92 279291
FAX: +92 279286

Syria
30 Hill Rd., F-6/3 Islamabad, Pakistan
PHONE: +92 279470; 279471
FAX: +92 279472

Thailand
10, St #33, F-8/1 Islamabad, Pakistan
PHONE: +92 280586; 254697; 280909
FAX: +92 256730

Tunisia
221, St #21, E-7 Islamabad, Pakistan
PHONE: +92 827869; 827870
FAX: +92 827871

Turkey
58 Attaturk Ravenue, G-6/3 Islamabad, Pakistan
PHONE: +92 278748; 278749
FAX: +92 278752

Turkmenistan
22-A, F-7/1, Nazim-ud-Din Road, Islamabad, Pakistan
PHONE: +92 274913
FAX: +92 278799

United Arab Emirates
1-22 DE University Rd., Islamabad, Pakistan
PHONE: +92 279052; 278053; 279054

United Kingdom
PHONE: +92 822131; 822132; 822133
FAX: +92 823439

United States
Diplomatic Enclave, Ramna 5, Islamabad, Pakistan
PHONE: +92 826161; 826162; 826163
FAX: +92 276427

Uzbekistan
6 St #29, F-7/1 Islamabad, Pakistan
PHONE: +92 820779
FAX: +92 278128

Yemen
138 St #14, E-7 Islamabad, Pakistan
PHONE: +92 821146; 821147
FAX: +92 279567

JUDICIAL SYSTEM
Supreme Court
Federal Court

FURTHER READING
Articles

"The Battle for India." *The Economist* 352 (August 14, 1999): 31.

"Bhutto Brought to Book: Convicted of Graft and Sentenced to Jail, Pakistan's Former Prime Minister May Face the End of Her Rocky Political Career." *Time International* 153 (April 26, 1999): 29.

Bokhair, Farhan. "Pakistan Vows to Get Tough with Loan Defaulters." *The Banker* 149 (September 1999): 10.

"Eurobonds." *The Economist* 350 (February 13, 1999): 71(1).

"Ever More Dangerous in Kashmir." *The Economist* 351 (June 19, 1999): 32.

"Minutes of Glory." *The Economist* 351 (April 17, 1999): 44.

"More Taxing." *The Economist* 352 (September 4, 1999): 43.

"Pakistan: The Battle Plan." *The Economist* 353 (October 23, 1999): 42.

"Pakistan: Put Them in Irons." *The Economist* 353 (November 13, 1999): 41.

"Pakistan's Violence." *The Economist* 350 (January 9, 1999): 36.

"The Proxy War." *The Economist* 352 (August 21, 1999): 33.

Qureshi, Fazel, et al. "Bittersweet Revenge." *Newsweek International,* 25 October 1999, p. 40.

"Women's Woes." *The Economist* 352 (August 14, 1999): 32.

Internet

Daily Pakistan News. Available Online @ www.daily-pakistan-news.com/ (November 23, 1999).

PAKISTAN: STATISTICAL DATA

For sources and notes see "Sources of Statistics" in the front of each volume.

GEOGRAPHY

Geography (1)

Area:

Total: 803,940 sq km.

Land: 778,720 sq km.

Water: 25,220 sq km.

Area—comparative: slightly less than twice the size of California.

Land boundaries:

Total: 6,774 km.

Border countries: Afghanistan 2,430 km, China 523 km, India 2,912 km, Iran 909 km.

Coastline: 1,046 km.

Climate: mostly hot, dry desert; temperate in northwest; arctic in north.

Terrain: flat Indus plain in east; mountains in north and northwest; Balochistan plateau in west.

Natural resources: land, extensive natural gas reserves, limited petroleum, poor quality coal, iron ore, copper, salt, limestone.

Land use:

Arable land: 27%

Permanent crops: 1%

Permanent pastures: 6%

Forests and woodland: 5%

Other: 61% (1993 est.).

HUMAN FACTORS

Demographics (2A)

	1990	1995	1998	2000	2010	2020	2030	2040	2050
Population	113,914.1	126,404.1	135,135.2	141,145.3	170,751.4	198,723.1	223,671.4	244,337.7	260,246.7
Net migration rate (per 1,000 population)	NA	NA	NA	NA	NA	NA	NA	NA	NA
Births	NA	NA	NA	NA	NA	NA	NA	NA	NA
Deaths	NA	NA	NA	NA	NA	NA	NA	NA	NA
Life expectancy - males	55.8	57.4	58.2	58.8	61.2	63.5	65.6	67.6	69.4
Life expectancy - females	56.7	58.9	60.0	60.6	63.9	66.9	69.7	72.3	74.6
Birth rate (per 1,000)	41.8	37.1	34.4	32.6	25.7	21.2	17.7	15.6	14.1
Death rate (per 1,000)	13.0	11.5	10.7	10.2	8.4	7.6	7.5	8.1	9.1
Women of reproductive age (15-49 yrs.)	24,860.5	28,113.0	30,662.8	32,653.7	43,675.7	53,498.8	60,763.4	63,863.6	63,554.3
of which are currently married	NA	NA	NA	NA	NA	NA	NA	NA	NA
Fertility rate	6.2	5.4	4.9	4.6	3.2	2.4	2.1	2.0	2.0

Except as noted, values for vital statistics are in thousands; life expectancy is in years.

Health Personnel (3)

Total health expenditure as a percentage of GDP, 1990-1997[a]

Public sector 0.8

Private sector 2.7

Total[b] 3.5

Health expenditure per capita in U.S. dollars, 1990-1997[a]

Purchasing power parity 45

Total 13

Availability of health care facilities per 100,000 people

Hospital beds 1990-1997[a] 70

Doctors 1993[c] 52

Nurses 1993[c] 32

Health Indicators (4)

Life expectancy at birth

1980 55

1997 62

Daily per capita supply of calories (1996) 2,408

Total fertility rate births per woman (1997) 5.0

Maternal mortality ratio per 100,000 live births (1990-97) . . . . .340[c]

Safe water % of population with access (1995) 62

Sanitation % of population with access (1995) 39

Consumption of iodized salt % of households (1992-98)[a] 19

Smoking prevalence

Male % of adults (1985-95)[a] 27

Female % of adults (1985-95)[a] 4

Tuberculosis incidence per 100,000 people (1997) 181

Adult HIV prevalence % of population ages 15-49 (1997) 0.09

Infants and Malnutrition (5)

Under-5 mortality rate (1997) 136

% of infants with low birthweight (1990-97) 25

Births attended by skilled health staff % of total[a] . . .18

% fully immunized (1995-97)

TB 90

DPT 74

Polio 74

Measles 74

Prevalence of child malnutrition under age 5 (1992-97)[b] 38

Ethnic Division (6)

Punjabi, Sindhi, Pashtun (Pathan), Baloch, Muhajir (immigrants from India and their descendants).

Religions (7)

Muslim 97%

Sunni 77%

Shi'a 20%

Christian, Hindu, and other 3%

Languages (8)

Punjabi 48%, Sindhi 12%, Siraiki (a Punjabi variant) 10%, Pashtu 8%, Urdu (official) 8%, Balochi 3%, Hindko 2%, Brahui 1%, English (official and lingua franca of Pakistani elite and most government ministries), Burushaski, and other 8%.

EDUCATION

Public Education Expenditures (9)

Public expenditure on education (% of GNP)

1980 . . . . .2.0

1996 . . . . .3.0

Expenditure per student

Primary % of GNP per capita

1980 . . . . .8.7

1996 . . . .

Secondary % of GNP per capita

1980 . . . .

1996 . . . . .127.4

Tertiary % of GNP per capita

1980 . . . . .521.2[1]

1996 . . . .

Expenditure on teaching materials

Primary % of total for level (1996) . . . .

Secondary % of total for level (1996) . . . .

Primary pupil-teacher ratio per teacher (1996) . . . .

Duration of primary education years (1995) 5

Educational Attainment (10)

Age group (1990)[19] . . . . .25+

Total population . . . . .NA

Highest level attained (%)

No schooling 73.8

First level

Not completed 9.7

Completed . . . . .NA

Entered second level

S-1 . . . . .5.8

S-2 . . . . .8.2

Postsecondary 2.5

Literacy Rates (11A)

In thousands and percent[1]	1990	1995	2000	2010
Illiterate population (15+ yrs.)	44,805	48,693	53,690	64,623
Literacy rate - total adult pop. (%)	34.2	37.8	41.8	49.9
Literacy rate - males (%)	46.3	50.0	54.0	61.6
Literacy rate - females (%)	20.9	24.4	28.6	37.6

GOVERNMENT & LAW

Political Parties (12)

National Assembly	No. of seats
Pakistan Muslim League, Nawaz Sharif faction (PML/N)	30
Pakistan People's Party (PPP)	17
Awami National Party (ANP)	7
Mutahida Qaumi Movement, Altaf faction (MQM/A)	6
Jamhoori Watan Party (JWP)	5
Baluch National Party (BNP)	4
Jamiat Ulema-i-Islami, Fazlur Rehman group (JUI/F)	2
Pakistan Muslim League, Junejo faction (PML/J)	2
Balochistan National Movement/Mengal Group (BNM/M)	1
Pakhtun Khwa Milli Awami Party (PKMAP)	1
Tehrik-I-Jafria Pakistan (TJP)	1
Independents	6
Vacant	5

Military Affairs (14B)

	1990	1991	1992	1993	1994	1995
Military expenditures						
Current dollars (mil.)	3,120	3,228	3,796	3,776	3,933	3,740
1995 constant dollars (mil.)	3,586	3,567	4,083	3,958	4,032	3,740
Armed forces (000)	550	565	580	580	540	587
Gross national product (GNP)						
Current dollars (mil.)	44,080	47,530	52,140	54,410	57,230	60,930
1995 constant dollars (mil.)	50,650	52,520	56,090	57,040	58,660	60,930
Central government expenditures (CGE)						
1995 constant dollars (mil.)	12,320	12,990	14,640	15,270	15,220	14,770
People (mil.)	113.9	116.9	118.9	120.9	123.7	126.4
Military expenditure as % of GNP	7.1	6.8	7.3	6.9	6.9	6.1
Military expenditure as % of CGE	29.1	27.5	27.9	25.9	26.5	25.3
Military expenditure per capita (1995 $)	31	31	34	33	33	30
Armed forces per 1,000 people (soldiers)	4.8	4.8	4.9	4.8	4.4	4.6
GNP per capita (1995 $)	445	449	472	472	474	482
Arms imports[6]						
Current dollars (mil.)	925	220	450	550	290	480
1995 constant dollars (mil.)	1,063	243	484	577	297	480
Arms exports[6]						
Current dollars (mil.)	40	80	30	5	10	20
1995 constant dollars (mil.)	46	88	32	5	10	20
Total imports[7]						
Current dollars (mil.)	7,376	8,439	9,379	9,500	8,889	11,460
1995 constant dollars (mil.)	8,477	9,325	10,090	9,960	9,112	11,460
Total exports[7]						
Current dollars (mil.)	5,589	6,528	7,317	6,688	7,365	7,992
1995 constant dollars (mil.)	6,423	7,214	7,870	7,012	7,550	7,992
Arms as percent of total imports[8]	12.5	2.6	4.8	5.8	3.3	4.2
Arms as percent of total exports[8]	.7	1.2	.4	.1	.1	.3

Government Budget (13B)

Revenues . . . .$9.6 billion

Expenditures . . . .$13.6 billion

  Capital expenditures . . . . .NA

Data for FY96/97. NA stands for not available.

LABOR FORCE

Labor Force (16)

Total (million) 37.8

Agriculture 47%

Mining and manufacturing 17%

Services 17%

Other 19%

Data for 1998.

Unemployment Rate (17)

Rate not available.

PRODUCTION SECTOR

Electric Energy (18)

Capacity . . . . .13.169 million kW (1995)

Production . . . . .58.1 billion kWh (1997)

Consumption per capita . . . . .436 kWh (1997)

Transportation (19)

Highways:

total: 224,774 km

paved: 128,121 km

unpaved: 96,653 km (1996 est.)

Pipelines: crude oil 250 km; petroleum products 885 km; natural gas 4,044 km (1987)

Merchant marine:

total: 24 ships (1,000 GRT or over) totaling 416,875 GRT/684,580 DWT ships by type: bulk 5, cargo 15, container 3, oil tanker 1 (1997 est.)

Airports: 115 (1997 est.)

Airports—with paved runways:

total: 80

over 3,047 m: 11

2,438 to 3,047 m: 20

1,524 to 2,437 m: 31

914 to 1,523 m: 15

under 914 m: 3 (1997 est.)

Airports—with unpaved runways:

total: 35

over 3,047 m: 1

1,524 to 2,437 m: 8

914 to 1,523 m: 8

under 914 m: 18 (1997 est.)

Top Agricultural Products (20)

Cotton, wheat, rice, sugarcane, fruits, vegetables; milk, beef, mutton, eggs.

MANUFACTURING SECTOR

GDP & Manufacturing Summary (21)

Detailed value added figures are listed by both International Standard Industry Code (ISIC) and product title.

	1980	1985	1990	1994
GDP ($-1990 mil.)[1]	21,941	29,767	39,464	47,984
Per capita ($-1990)[1]	257	290	324	351
Manufacturing share (%) (current prices)[1]	14.6	15.9	17.4	17.5
Manufacturing				
Value added ($-1990 mil.)[1]	2,889	4,411	6,096	7,671
Industrial production index	100	132	152	194
Value added ($ mil.)	2,423	3,236	4,394	5,719
Gross output ($ mil.)	7,144	10,132	13,354	17,193
Employment (000)	452	493	539	582
Profitability (% of gross output)				
Intermediate input (%)	66	68	67	67
Wages and salaries inc. supplements (%)	7	6	7	7
Gross operating surplus	27	26	26	26
Productivity ($)				
Gross output per worker	14,606	20,484	24,677	29,441
Value added per worker	4,953	6,545	8,121	9,804
Average wage (inc. supplements)	1,122	1,323	1,754	2,139
Value added ($ mil.)				
311/2 Food products	431	580	697	954
313 Beverages	45	74	80	106
314 Tobacco products	300	372	447	579

	1980	1985	1990	1994
321 Textiles	483	562	816	963
322 Wearing apparel	7	18	75	116
323 Leather and fur products	41	35	27	33
324 Footwear	4	3	34	47
331 Wood and wood products	4	9	15	20
332 Furniture and fixtures	3	6	5	6
341 Paper and paper products	39	33	47	57
342 Printing and publishing	24	36	41	50
351 Industrial chemicals	127	281	300	397
352 Other chemical products	156	230	318	412
353 Petroleum refineries	158	45	260	340
354 Miscellaneous petroleum and coal products	9	17	33	43
355 Rubber products	28	41	41	46
356 Plastic products	12	21	21	29
361 Pottery, china and earthenware	5	8	15	16
362 Glass and glass products	11	17	31	43
369 Other non-metal mineral products	171	199	347	489
371 Iron and steel	99	342	296	409
372 Non-ferrous metals	1	1	1	1
381 Metal products	38	33	42	49
382 Non-electrical machinery	43	80	79	104
383 Electrical machinery	78	98	140	176
384 Transport equipment	97	83	156	199
385 Professional and scientific equipment	6	6	12	15
390 Other manufacturing industries	11	11	17	19

FINANCE, ECONOMICS, & TRADE

Economic Indicators (22)

National product: GDP—purchasing power parity—$344 billion (1997 est.)

National product real growth rate: 3.1% (1997 est.)

National product per capita: $2,600 (1997 est.)

Inflation rate—consumer price index: 11.8% (FY96/97)

Exchange Rates (24)

Exchange rates:

Pakistani rupees (PRs) per US$1

January 1998	44.050
1997	41.112
1996	36.079
1995	31.643
1994	30.567
1993	28.1

Annual average of official rate; parallel market rate is higher

Balance of Payments (23)

	1991	1992	1993	1994	1995
Exports of goods (f.o.b.)	6,381	6,881	6,761	7,083	8,317
Imports of goods (f.o.b.)	−8,642	−9,671	−9,336	−9,311	−11,195
Trade balance	−2,262	−2,790	−2,574	−2,228	−2,878
Services - debits	−3,559	−4,149	−4,228	−4,339	−5,039
Services - credits	1,597	1,625	1,628	1,893	2,035
Private transfers (net)	619	378	333	355	274
Government transfers (net)	2,345	3,068	1,955	2,514	2,276
Overall balance	−1,261	−1,868	−2,887	−1,804	−3,333

Top Import Origins (25)

$11.4 billion (FY96/97)

Origins	%
European Union	NA
Japan	NA
United States	NA
China	NA

NA stands for not available.

Top Export Destinations (26)

$8.2 billion (FY96/97).

Destinations	%
European Union	NA
United States	NA
Hong Kong	NA
Japan	NA

NA stands for not available.

Economic Aid (27)

Recipient: $2.2 billion from all bilateral and multilateral sources (FY96/97).

Import Export Commodities (28)

Import Commodities	Export Commodities
Petroleum	Cotton
Petroleum products	Textiles
Machinery	Clothing
Transportation equipment	Rice
Vegetable oils	Leather
Animal fats	Carpets
Chemicals	

PALAU

CAPITAL: Koror, Koror Island.

FLAG: The flag, adopted 1 January 1981, is light blue, with a yellow disc set slightly off center toward the hoist.

ANTHEM: *Belau er Kid.*

MONETARY UNIT: The U.S. dollar is the official medium of exchange.

WEIGHTS AND MEASURES: British units are used, as modified by U.S. usage.

HOLIDAYS: New Year's Day, 1 January; Youth Day, 15 March; Senior Citizens Day, 5 May; Constitution Day, 9 July; Labor Day, 1st Monday in September; United Nations Day, 24 October; Thanksgiving Day, 4th Thursday in November; Christmas, 25 December.

TIME: 8 PM = noon GMT.

LOCATION AND SIZE: Palau (also known as Belau) consists of the Palau group of Pacific islands, in the western Caroline Islands, and four remote islands to the southwest. The country consists of more than 200 islands, with a total land area of 441 square kilometers (170.4 square miles), ranking 178 out of 192 in size among the world's nations.

CLIMATE: The annual mean temperature is 28°C (82°F) in the coolest months. There is high precipitation throughout the year—up to 380 centimeters (150 inches)—and a relatively high humidity of 82%.

INTRODUCTORY SURVEY

RECENT HISTORY

As part of the Carolinian archipelago, the islands were sighted by European navigators as early as the 16th century. In 1686, the Spanish explorer Francisco Lezcano named Yap Island (now in the Federated States of Micronesia) ''La Carolina'' after King Charles II of Spain. The name was later generalized to include all the islands. Spanish sovereignty was established in 1885. In 1899, after Spain's defeat in the Spanish-American War of 1898, Palau, with the rest of the Carolines, was sold to Germany. At the outbreak of World War I in 1914, the islands were taken by the Japanese. As a member of the League of Nations, Japan was given a mandate over Palau in 1920, and Koror was developed as an administrative center of Japanese possessions in the north Pacific.

In 1947, following occupation by U.S. forces in World War II, Palau became part of the UN Trust Territory of the Pacific Islands, which was administered by the U.S. After the adoption of a constitution in 1980, Palau became a self-governing republic in 1981. Since 1982, the republic has been involved in negotiating a Compact of Free Association (CPA) with the U.S. Negotiations were stalled because the 1980 constitution prohibits the placement of nuclear weapons, and the U.S. has wanted to use the islands as a military site. In June 1985, President Haruo Remelil was assassinated; Vice-President Alfonso Oiterang served as acting president until August 1985, when he was defeated by Lazarus E. Salii. President Salii committed suicide in August 1988. Kuniwo Nakamura was elected president in November 1992. On 1 October 1994 Palau became an independent nation in free association with the US; under the CPA the U.S. is responsible for Palau's defense. In 1995, Palau entered into diplomatic talks with the United States, Japan and Taiwan.

A new capital is under construction in eastern Babelthuap, about 20 km northeast of Koror.

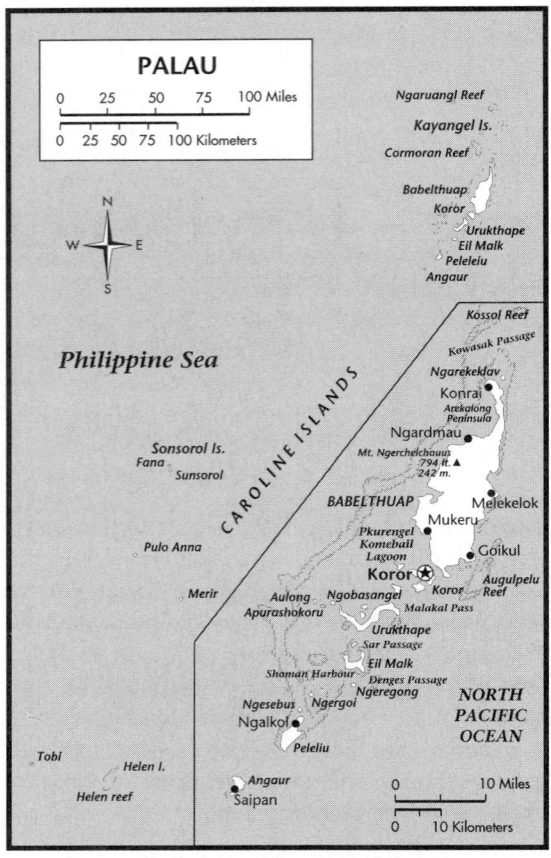

GOVERNMENT

The government comprises three branches: the executive, the legislative, and the judicial. The executive branch is headed by the president, who is elected by popular vote for not more than two terms of four years each. The president is assisted by a cabinet of ministers, one of whom is the vice president and is also elected by popular vote. A council of chiefs, based on Palau's clan system, advises the president on traditional and customary matters.

The legislative branch, known as the Olbiil Era Kelulau, or National Congress, is a bicameral form of legislature, comprising 14 senators and 16 delegates. The senators, elected for four-year terms, are apportioned throughout Palau on the basis of population and traditional regional political groupings. The delegates are elected from each of the 16 states and have the same four-year term as the senators.

In November 1992 Kuniwo Nakamura was elected Palau's new president, with 50.7% of the vote. Palau's vice president, Tommy E. Remengesau, Jr., was also elected at that time.

Each of Palau's 16 states has a government headed by a governor, who is popularly elected, in most cases, for a four-year term. The members of the state legislatures are popularly elected for a four-year term, although in a few states, the term of office is limited to two years. The states are empowered to make their own laws, which must not be in conflict with the national constitution or any existing laws.

Judiciary

The Supreme Court is the highest court in the land. Other courts include the National Court, which, although constitutionally mandated, was not operational as of 1987, and the lower court system, consisting of the Court of Common Pleas. In October 1990 U.S. Interior Secretary Manuel Lujan issued an order granting the Interior Department in Washington the power to veto laws and reverse decisions by Palau's courts. This reassertion of legal authority by the United States was partially in response to the decade of unsuccessful negotiations concerning a plan for eventual self-government.

The Constitution provides for an independent judiciary and the government respects this provision in practice. Palau has an independent prosecutor and an independent public defender system.

Political Parties

Palau has one political party, Palau Nationalist Party.

DEFENSE

The U.S. is responsible for defense. Palau has no armed forces and does not have U.S. armed forces within its borders except for a small contingent of U.S. Navy Seabees who undertake civil action projects.

ECONOMIC AFFAIRS

The economy has a narrow production base as a result of limited natural resources and few skilled personnel. The services sector consists largely of government administration and trade. Large gaps exist between government revenues and expenditures and between imports and exports. These gaps are financed largely by assistance from the U.S. Unemployment is a major problem. Recently, expansion of air travel in the Pacific has fueled growth of the tourist sector. Tourist arrivals were up 56% in 1996, while hotel accommodations are expected to double. A new airport was just completed recently.

Public Finance

Revenues include grants from the U.S. and domestic revenues from taxes and other fees. The U.S. Central Intelligence Agency estimates that in 1995, government revenues totaled approximately $17 million and expenditures $57 million. External debt totaled $100 million.

Income

The U.S. Central Intelligence Agency (CIA) maintains statistics on gross domestic product (GDP), defined as the value of all final goods and services produced within a nation in a given year. According to CIA estimates, the purchasing power parity of GDP in 1995 was $81.8 million or $5,000 per capita. The economy is heavily subsidized by the U.S. government.

Industry

Manufacturing plays a limited role in the economy. A copper processing plant is located in Malakal. Concrete blocks are manufactured, utilizing imported cement, and there is a small-scale sawmill industry.

Agricultural production belongs almost entirely to the nonmonetary, or subsistence, sector. Most households outside Koror are fully or partially engaged in subsistence agriculture. Staple subsistence crops include taros, cassavas, sweet potatoes, bananas, and papayas. Commercial produce is marketed mainly in Koror, consisting mostly of copra and coconut oil, vegetables, and a wide variety of tropical fruits.

Livestock is limited to pigs, chickens, ducks, cattle, and goats. Pigs and chickens are raised by most households. Several small commercial egg-producing operations supply eggs to the Koror market. The Livestock Branch of the Division of Agriculture maintains breeding herds of pigs, cattle, and goats.

Palau's marine resources are rich and diverse. Subsistence fishing within the reef is a major activity and dominates market production. The total catch was 1,500 tons in 1994. Deep-sea fishing for pelagic species resulted in a tuna catch of 80 tons in 1994. Seasonal trochus harvesting for shell button manufacture is an important source of income for most fishermen. Other marine resources include pearls, shrimp, ornamental fish, seaweed (agar), and mollusks. Palau is known for having some of the best diving, snorkeling, and sport fishing areas in the world.

Forestry resources consist of coastal mangrove, coconut and pandanus palms, and rain forest species in upland areas. Palau is heavily dependent on imported forestry products, including furniture and lumber for house construction. The government's forestry station at Nekken on Babeldaob Island, of which more than half of the 1,257 ha (3,105 acres) consists of natural forest, provides primarily mahogany seedlings to farmers. Palau imported $1.1 million in forest products during 1995.

Crystalline calcite from glistening limestone caves was first quarried as long as 1,500–2,000 years ago. The doughnut-shaped finished carved products would be transported by canoe some 250 miles to Yap (now part of the Federated States of Micronesia), and used as currency.

The Koror state government engages in commercial production of dredged coral from the Palau lagoon, with a production capacity of 800 cu m per day. Other states are also involved in coral dredging. A private company supplies aggregates for concrete from crushed basalt rock and beach sand.

Banking and Finance

In 1993, there were five commercial banks. Two are branches of foreign banks, the Bank of Hawaii and the Bank of Guam; the other, a local bank which started in 1985, is the Bank of Palau.

Economic Development

The government's first 5-year national development plan (1987–91) was the first phase of its 15-year development program and it is currently entering the last years of the plan. The plan focuses on the development of a private sector production based economy, efficient public sector management, development of natural resources to earn foreign exchange, personnel development, regional development, and environmental preservation.

SOCIAL WELFARE

Social organization is based on the maternal kin group, or clan. Villages ideally consist of ten clans, with the leader of the highest ranking clan serving as village chief. Rapid socioeconomic change has given rise to a range of social problems for communities and social groups, particularly youth. Most social development activities in the areas of health and education are funded by U.S. government programs.

A system of old age, disability and survivor's pensions was first introduced in 1967. This program covers all gainfully employed persons, and provides old age pensions after the age of 60. This program is financed by 4% contributions from employees, which is matched by an equal contribution from employers.

Healthcare

Hospital services are provided by the Mac-Donald Memorial Hospital in Koror, which has 60 beds. Medical services in Koror are also provided by the Belau Medical Clinic and the Seventh-Day Adventist Eye Clinic. The population of Palau in 1995 was 17,000. Only 300 births were reported in 1995. The infant mortality rate was 251 per 1,000 in 1995. Immunization rates for children under one were as follows: diphtheria, pertussis and tetanus (100%); polio (100%); measles (100%); and hepatitis B (100%) in 1995, No measles or polio were reported in 1995. Only 1 case of AIDS was reported in 1996.

Housing

There were 2,501 occupied houses in 1986, of which 72% were located in Koror and the adjacent state of Airai. Most house walls are constructed from metal sheets, wood, or concrete blocks, and roofs are of corrugated material. About 80% of all houses have water and electricity.

EDUCATION

Education is free and compulsory for all Palauan children aged 6–14. In 1990, there were 369 students in private high school in and 1,756 in public schools. The Palau High School in Koror, the only public high school, enrolls 64% of the total secondary school enrollment. In 1990, 445 secondary students attended private schools and 165 were in public schools. Postsecondary education is provided by the College of Micronesian Occupational College (MOC) in Koror. The adult literacy rate is 98%.

1999 KEY EVENTS TIMELINE

January

- A controversial minimum wage law goes into effect.

February

- Palau opens an embassy in Tokyo, Japan.

March

- Palau joins other Asia-Pacific nations in a plea for aid to resolve the millennium computer bug problem.

April

- The annual Palau fishing derby is held.

May

- South Korea and Palau agree to increase trade between the two nations.

June

- A Pacific Free Trade Area is endorsed by trade ministers of the South Pacific Forum.
- Palau's president, Kuniwo Nakamura, has an historic visit with South African leader Nelson Mandela.

July

- The Sydney 2000 Olympic Organizing Committee announces that the Olympic Torch will travel through Palau.

August

- President Nakamura signs an ethics-in-government law.

September

- Residents of Palau receive tsunami warnings after a large earthquake hits Taiwan.

October

- Palau hosts the 30th South Pacific Forum.

December

- Palau establishes diplomatic relations with Taiwan.

ANALYSIS OF EVENTS: 1999

BUSINESS AND THE ECONOMY

In January Senate President Isidoro Rudimch warned that Palau was living in an artificial economy because it relied too heavily on aid from the United States. In addition, the World Bank reported in May that Palau's protectionist environment curtailed foreign investment, and it called for the loosening of restrictions to spur investments. Palau's efforts for much of the year have been aimed at expanding its economic base and encouraging growth. Trade ministers of the South Pacific Forum, of which Palau is a member, endorsed the proposal for a Pacific Free Trade Area (FTA) which would create a regional market of six million people. The FTA allows goods produced in the fourteen island countries to be traded freely. In November Palau aviation officials continued negotiations with Air Macau to become Palau's national airline carrier.

Tourism, fishing, and agriculture continued to be the major economic industries in the small republic. The Palau Visitor's Authority reported an annual increase of 19% in visitor traffic from North America, Guam, and the Northern Mariana Islands. There was also an increase in travel from Japan and Europe. As a result President Kuniwo Nakamura announced that Palau will have 1,500 hotel rooms by the year 2000.

In agriculture there was great concern from government officials over rising sea levels, which contributed to the ruin of taro crops in thirteen of Palau's sixteen states. The National Emergency Management Office was forced to seek technical help from other nations in an effort to salvage the crops.

The fishing industry experienced several developments. In January President Nakamura threatened to cut off diplomatic ties with the Philippines because of continuing poaching by Filipino fishermen in Palau's exclusive economic zone. The Philippines sent a delegation to Palau in September to address President Nakamura's concerns.

The Palau Conservation Society released a report in May detailing the decline in the local tuna industry. The report noted a decrease in revenues from tuna of 35% to 45%. Also in May Micronesia, the Marshall Islands, and Palau signed a memorandum of understanding on fisheries management. The memorandum made the three island nations more efficient in managing marine assets and enforcing fisheries laws. Korean and Palauan trade officials signed an agreement in April allowing Korean fishing boats to catch tuna within Palau's territorial waters.

GOVERNMENT AND POLITICS

A controversial minimum wage law went into effect on January 1, 1999. The new law set the minimum wage at $2.50 per hour, but it exempted foreign workers. President Nakamura supported the new law and believed it would have a positive impact on labor practices. The president also signed into law an ethics-in-government bill intended to affirm the integrity of the electoral system and the fairness and honesty of government officials.

In March President Nakamura directed the Minister of Justice to begin a crackdown on the unauthorized use of government vehicles, which had become a major issue with citizens. There was also a strong movement in the Palau Congress to change the present bicameral Congress (House of Representatives and Senate) to a unicameral form of government, reducing the cost of government. Such a proposal would eventually be put to the people in a vote, possibly in November 2000.

The Republic of Palau hosted the 30th South Pacific Forum in October. Over three hundred foreign delegates, observers, and media members attended the Forum. President Kuniwo Nakamura, also the incoming Chairman of the South Pacific Forum, formally invited United Nations Secretary General Kofi Annan to attend the meeting. The South Pacific Forum is an organization of sixteen Pacific nations concerned with the economic and political stability and viability of the region. The Forum considered issues on climate and sea level change, regional security and law enforcement, fisheries, and the United Nations Special Session on Small Island Developing States. Palau also hosted the First Micronesian Traditional Leaders' Conference in July.

CULTURE AND SOCIETY

The coral reefs surrounding the islands of Palau attract diving enthusiasts from around the world. There were, however, reports from the National Oceanic and Atmospheric Administration (NOAA) and Greenpeace revealing that the reefs are dying off because of increased surface water temperatures and climate change brought on by the burning of fossil fuels. NOAA reported that the islands of Palau have been especially hard hit by ''coral bleaching.'' The Greenpeace report predicted that the vast majority of the coral reefs would be dead in forty to seventy years. In a related development, Japan announced plans to build a global research and protection center in Palau to study the area's coral reefs.

The International Olympic Committee voted to give Palau full National Olympic Committee status. With this announcement Palau will participate in the Sydney 2000 Olympic torch relay. The torch will arrive in Palau on May 23, 2000, and will be carried by one hundred Palauan torchbearers. Before the Olympic torch leaves Palau a lighting ceremony of a community cauldron will take place in Koror, the Palauan capital.

Members of the Pacific Arts Association from Palau and other Pacific island nations, Europe, and the United States attended a meeting in October at the Field Museum in Chicago, Illinois, to honor Dr. Philip Dark, editor of the *Pacific Arts Journal* for the last twenty-five years.

Roman Tmetuchl, the leader of Palau's independence and free association movements, died at age 73. Tmetuchl chaired the Palau Political Status Commission in the mid-1970s and was instrumental in the development of the Compact of Free Association that was approved by voters in 1994.

DIRECTORY

CENTRAL GOVERNMENT
Head of State

President
Kuniwo Nakamura, Office of the President, PO Box 100, Koror, Palau

Vice President and Minister of Administration
Tommy E. Remengesau, Jr., Office of the Vice President, PO Box 100, Koror, Palau

Ministers

Minister of Education
Billy G. Kuartei, Ministry of Education

Minister of Commerce and Trade
Okada Techitong, Ministry of Commerce and Trade

Minister of Health
Masao M. Ueda, Ministry of Health

POLITICAL ORGANIZATIONS
Palau Nationalist Party

NAME: Polycarp Basilius

DIPLOMATIC REPRESENTATION
Embassies in Palau

United States
PO Box 6028, Koror, Palau 96940
PHONE: +680 4882920; 4882990

FAX: +680 4882911
TITLE: Ambassador
NAME: Thomas C. Hubbard

JUDICIAL SYSTEM
The Supreme Court
PO Box 248, Koror, Palau 96940

National Court
Court of Common Pleas

FURTHER READING
Articles

"Air Macau may Become Palau's National Carrier." *Pacific Islands Report* (November 3, 1999).

"Annual Palau Fishing Derby April 10–11." *Pacific Islands Report* (February 12, 1999).

Camp, Roya. "Palau Trailblazer Tmetuchl Dead at 73." *Pacific Islands Report* (July 3, 1999).

"Embassy of Palau Opens in Tokyo." *Pacific Islands Report* (February 2, 1999).

Field, Michael. "Pacific Leaders Reluctantly Yield to Global Forces at Palau Pacific Islands Forum Summit." *Pacific Islands Report* (October 4, 1999).

"Forum Officials Met in Palau on Regional Issues." *Pacific Islands Report* (October 1, 1999).

"FSM, Palau, and Marshall Islands Sign Memorandum of Understanding on Fisheries Management." *Pacific Islands Reports* (May 31, 1999).

"Greenpeace Warns about Coral Destruction in Pacific." *Pacific Islands Report* (July 6, 1999).

Knight, Danielle. "Warmer Oceans Destroying Coral Reefs." *Asia Times Online* (January 8, 1999).

"Olympic Torch Relay to Travel through Palau, the Newest Member of the IOC." *Pacific Islands Report* (June 29, 1999).

"Palau and Korea move to Increase Trade." *Pacific Islands Report* (May 18, 1999).

"Palau Senate President Rudimch Warns of Living in Artificial Economy." *Pacific Islands Report* (January 19, 1999.

"Palau Threatening to Cut Ties with Philippines." *Pacific Islands Report* (January 12, 1999).

"Palau's Tuna Industry in Bad Shape." *Pacific Islands Report* (May 27, 1999).

"President Nakamura Signs Palau Ethics in Government Law." *Pacific Islands Report* (August 5, 1999).

Sayson, Malou L. "Unicameral Palau Legislature under Consideration." *Pacific Islands Report* (January 4, 1999).

Taiko, Amy. "Palau Minimum Wage Law goes into Effect." *Pacific Islands Report* (December 28, 1998).

"Traditional Micronesian Leaders meet in Palau." *Pacific Islands Report* (June 17, 1999).

"World Bank says Palau has Unfriendly Investment Environment." *Pacific Islands Report* (May 28, 1999).

Internet

Welcome to Pacific Islands Development Center. Available Online @ http://pidp.ewc.hawaii.edu/ (Accessed November 13, 1999).

PALAU:
STATISTICAL DATA

For sources and notes see "Sources of Statistics" in the front of each volume.

GEOGRAPHY

Geography (1)

Area:

Total: 458 sq km.

Land: 458 sq km.

Water: 0 sq km.

Area—comparative: slightly more than 2.5 times the size of Washington, DC.

Land boundaries: 0 km.

Coastline: 1,519 km.

Climate: wet season May to November; hot and humid.

Terrain: varying geologically from the high, mountainous main island of Babelthuap to low, coral islands usually fringed by large barrier reefs.

Natural resources: forests, minerals (especially gold), marine products, deep-seabed minerals.

Land use:

Arable land: NA%

Permanent crops: NA%

Permanent pastures: NA%

Forests and woodland: NA%

Other: NA%

HUMAN FACTORS

Demographics (2A)

	1990	1995	1998	2000	2010	2020	2030	2040	2050
Population	15.2	17.0	18.1	18.8	21.7	23.5	25.0	25.9	26.4
Net migration rate (per 1,000 population)	NA	NA	NA	NA	NA	NA	NA	NA	NA
Births	NA	NA	NA	NA	NA	NA	NA	NA	NA
Deaths	NA	NA	NA	NA	NA	NA	NA	NA	NA
Life expectancy - males	63.9	63.9	64.5	64.9	66.8	68.6	70.2	71.6	72.9
Life expectancy - females	70.2	70.2	70.8	71.2	73.1	74.9	76.4	77.8	79.1
Birth rate (per 1,000)	21.4	23.4	21.3	21.8	16.8	15.6	15.1	13.7	13.0
Death rate (per 1,000)	8.9	8.4	7.9	7.7	7.3	8.4	10.1	11.5	11.7
Women of reproductive age (15-49 yrs.)	3.6	4.4	4.8	5.0	5.5	5.6	5.7	6.1	6.2
of which are currently married	NA	NA	NA	NA	NA	NA	NA	NA	NA
Fertility rate	2.8	2.9	2.6	2.7	2.5	2.3	2.1	2.0	2.0

Except as noted, values for vital statistics are in thousands; life expectancy is in years.

Infants and Malnutrition (5)

Under-5 mortality rate (1997) 34

% of infants with low birthweight (1990-97) 8

Births attended by skilled health staff %
of total[a] . . . . .NA

% fully immunized (1995-97)

TB 0

DPT 91

Polio 90

Measles 83

Prevalence of child malnutrition under age 5
(1992-97)[b] . . . . .NA

Ethnic Division (6)

Palauans are a composite of Polynesian, Malayan, and
Melanesian races.

Religions (7)

Christian (Catholics, Seventh-Day Adventists,
Jehovah's Witnesses, the Assembly of God, the
Liebenzell Mission, and Latter-Day Saints), Modekngei
Religion (one-third of the population observes this
religion which is indigenous to Palau).

Languages (8)

English (official in all of Palau's 16 states), Sonsorolese
(official in the state of Sonsoral), Angaur and Japanese
(in the state of Anguar), Tobi (in the state of Tobi),
Palauan (in the other 13 states).

EDUCATION

Literacy Rates (11B)

Adult literacy rate

1980

Male . . . .-

Female . . . .-

1995

Male . . . .-

Female 97%

GOVERNMENT & LAW

Political Parties (12)

The legislative branch is a bicameral Parliament; it
consists of the Senate (14 seats; members elected by
popular vote on a population basis to serve four-year
terms) and the House of Delegates (16 seats—one from
each state members elected by popular vote to serve four-
year terms). No data are available on election results.

Government Budget (13B)

Revenues . . . .$52.9 million

Expenditures . . . .$59.9 million

Capital expenditures . . . . .NA

Data for 1997 est. NA stands for not available.

Military Affairs (14A)

Total expenditures . . . .$NA

Expenditures as % of GDP . . . . .NA%

Defense is the responsibility of the US. NA stands for not
available.

LABOR FORCE

Unemployment Rate (17)

7%

PRODUCTION SECTOR

Electric Energy (18)

Capacity . . . . .62,000 kW (1995)

Production . . . . .195 million kWh (1995)

Consumption per capita . . . . .11,704 kWh (1995)

Transportation (19)

Highways:

total: 61 km

paved: 36 km

unpaved: 25 km

Merchant marine: none

Airports: 3 (1997 est.)

Airports—with paved runways:

total: 1

1,524 to 2,437 m: 1 (1997 est.)

Airports—with unpaved runways:

total: 2

1,524 to 2,437 m: 2 (1997 est.)

Top Agricultural Products (20)

Coconuts, copra, cassava (tapioca), sweet potatoes.

FINANCE, ECONOMICS, & TRADE

Economic Indicators (22)

National product: GDP—purchasing power parity—
$160 million (1997 est.) note: GDP numbers reflect US
spending

National product real growth rate: 10% (1997 est.)

National product per capita: $8,800 (1997 est.)

Inflation rate—consumer price index: NA%

Exchange Rates (24)

Exchange rates: US currency is used.

Top Import Origins (25)

$72.4 million (f.o.b., 1996).

Origins	%
United States	NA

NA stands for not available.

Top Export Destinations (26)

$14.3 million (f.o.b., 1996).

Destinations	%
United States	NA
Japan	NA

NA stands for not available.

Economic Aid (27)

Recipient: ODA, $NA. Note: the Compact of Free Association with the US, entered into after the end of the UN trusteeship on 1 October 1994, will provide Palau with up to $700 million in US aid over 15 years in return for furnishing military facilities. NA stands for not available.

Import Export Commodities (28)

Import Commodities	Export Commodities
NA	Trochus (type of shellfish)
	Tuna
	Copra
	Handicrafts

PANAMA

Republic of Panama
República de Panamá

INTRODUCTORY SURVEY

RECENT HISTORY

In the decades following World War II (1939–45), the question of sovereignty over the Canal Zone was a persistent source of conflict in Panamanian politics. In 1964, riots broke out in the Canal Zone when Panamanians protested American neglect of a 1962 joint Panama–U.S. flag-flying agreement. From then on, Panama sought sovereignty over the Canal Zone.

In October 1968, National Guard Brigadier General Omar Torrijos Herrera deposed the elected president and established a dictatorship.

Final agreement on the future of the canal and the Canal Zone came on 7 September 1977. General Torrijos and U.S. president Jimmy Carter signed the Panama Canal Treaty. The treaty recognized Panama's sovereignty over the Canal Zone, but granted the United States rights to operate, maintain, and manage the canal through 31 December 1999. After that date, ownership of the canal itself would revert to Panama.

In addition, a so-called Neutrality Treaty guaranteed the neutrality of the canal and denied the United States the right of intervention into Panamanian affairs. The treaties were ratified by popular vote in Panama on 23 October 1977. After prolonged debate and extensive amendment the treaties were also passed by the U.S. Senate in March and April 1978.

Torrijos resigned as head of government in 1978 but continued to rule behind the scenes as

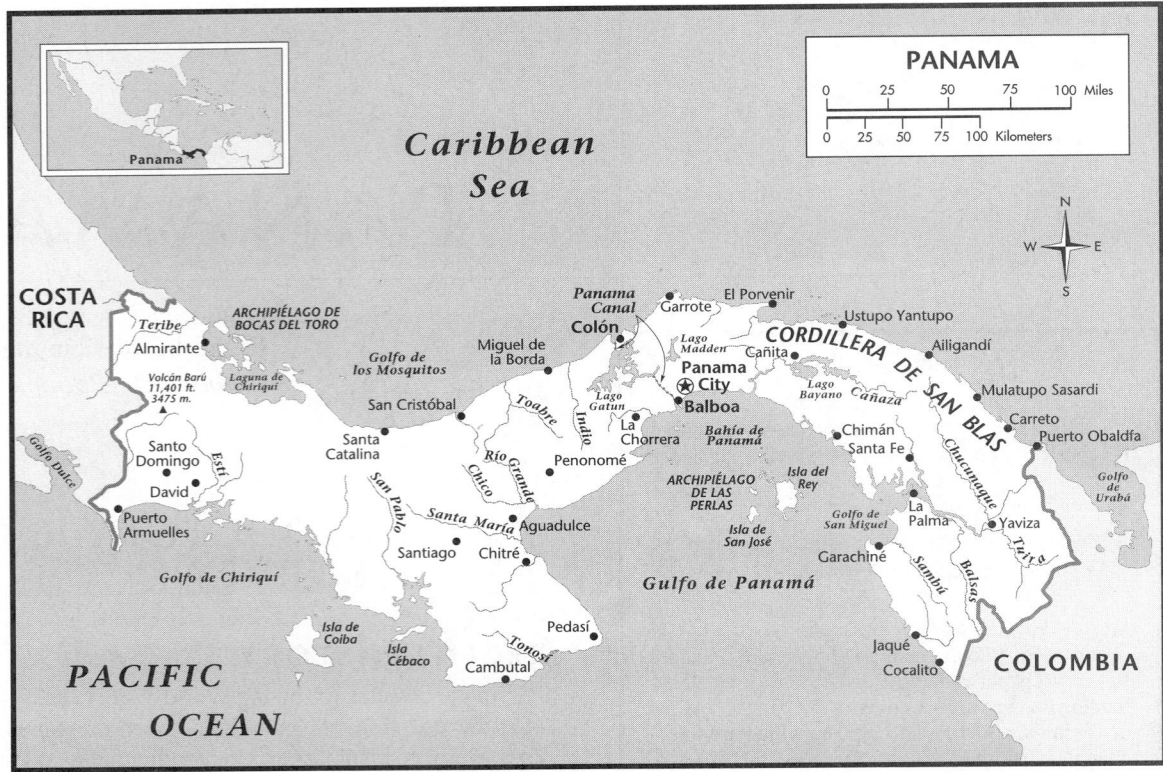

National Guard commander until his death in a plane crash on 31 July 1981. Over the next few years, the National Guard, now renamed the Panama Defense Forces (PDF), came under the influence of General Manuel Noriega, as a succession of civilian governments followed each other.

By 1987, Noriega had been accused by close associates and the United States of falsifying the 1984 election results, drug trafficking, giving aid to the Colombian and Salvadoran rebels, and providing military secrets to Cuba. The United States Senate approved legislation cutting off aid to Panama in December 1987. In February 1988, Noriega was indicted in U.S. courts for drug trafficking. Throughout 1988 and 1989, both the United States and Panamanian opposition struggled to oust Noriega, who clung to power.

In December 1989, after a series of moves including a trade embargo by the United States calculated to bring down the Noriega regime, Noriega declared war on the United States and ordered attacks on U.S. military personnel. President George Bush responded quickly, ordering the U.S. military into Panama. Noriega surrendered and was sent to the United States for trial.

The administration of Guillermo Endara, who became president after the downfall of Noriega, was widely criticized for the continuing poor economic conditions. In May 1994, a new president, Ernesto Pérez Balladares was elected. In 1995, government reform of the labor code set off widespread strikes and rioting. Balladares's economic reforms failed to produce significant improvements by 1996. In addition, several political parties were charged with accepting money from drug traffickers.

GOVERNMENT

Under the constitution of 1972, Panama is a republic in which the president, assisted by a cabinet, exercises executive power. Legislative power is vested in the unicameral Legislative Assembly. The 67 members are elected for five-year terms by direct popular vote. All Panamanians 18 years of age or over have the right to vote.

Panama is divided into 9 provinces, each subdivided into 65 municipal districts.

Judiciary

Judicial authority rests with the Supreme Court, which is composed of 9 magistrates. There are 4 superior courts, 18 circuit courts, and at least

1 municipal court in each district. At the local level, two types of administrative judges, "corregidores" and "night" (or "police") judges, hear minor civil and criminal cases involving sentences under one year.

The 1996 amendment to the constitution abolished the standing military and provided for a temporary special police force to protect the borders. The Judicial Technical Police perform criminal investigations to support public prosecutors.

Political Parties

The coalition that came to power in 1990 consisted of President Guillermo Endara's Arnulfista Party, led by Dr. Arnulfo Escalona; the National Liberal Republican Movement (MOLIRENA), led by second vice-president Guillermo Ford; and the Christian Democratic Party (PDC), led by first vice-president Ricardo Arias. Later, Arias broke from the coalition and the PDC, which controlled the Legislative Assembly.

With the election of Ernesto Pérez Balladares to the presidency in May 1994, the Democratic Revolutionary Party (PRD) returned to power. The PRD had been closely linked with the country's former military regime.

DEFENSE

The new National Police Force numbers 11,000, supported by a maritime service (350 staff, 3 patrol boats) and air service (350 staff, 14 aircraft and helicopters). The United States maintains a garrison of 10,500 in the Canal Zone.

ECONOMIC AFFAIRS

In the early 1990s, Panama rebounded from a severe recession brought about by the United States embargo and subsequent military invasion, aimed at bringing down General Manuel Noriega, who was responsible for an increase in drug trafficking. By 1992, Panama's economic growth was among the strongest in the Western Hemisphere. In 1993, the economy continued to grow, but at a slower pace.

Panama's economy is based on well-developed service industries, including the Panama Canal, banking, insurance, and government. Panama does not print any money and, therefore, lacks an independent monetary policy. The U.S. dollar is the legal tender in the nation.

Public Finance

The U.S. Central Intelligence Agency estimates that, in 1995, government revenues totaled approximately $1.86 billion and expenditures $1.86 billion. External debt totaled $6.7 billion.

Income

In 1997, Panama's gross national product (GNP) was $18 billion at current prices, or about $6,700 per person. For the period 1985–95, the average annual inflation rate was 1.7%, resulting in a decline in GNP of 0.4% per person.

Industry

Industry, generally light, consists principally of food-processing and alcoholic beverage production, ceramics, tropical clothing, cigarettes, hats, furniture, shoes, soap, and edible oils. The government encourages industrialization by granting special tax breaks to new enterprises and imposing protective duties on competing foreign manufacturers. The Industrial Development Bank promotes small industries and provides credit on a long-term basis.

Banking and Finance

Panama was considered the most important international banking center in Latin America in the late 1980s. In 1970 only 28 banks operated in Panama's international banking center; by 1987 there were 120, with assets of nearly $39 billion. The growth in Panama's offshore banking has contributed to the country's relative prosperity and accentuated the importance of the service sector in the economy. As an example of offshore banking, the Central Bank of India established an office in Panama in the late 1970s to finance its trade with Brazil. Since 1983, the year of the onset of Latin America's financial crisis, the Panamanian banking sector has contracted, both in number of banks and total assets. Some recovery was recorded in 1990. In 1990 there were 100 banks in Panama. Sixty of the banks in Panama have general licenses, 30 banks have international licenses, 18 foreign banks have representative offices, and two banks were government owned. The National Bank of Panama (Banco Nacional de Panamá–BNP), founded in 1904, is the principal official (but not central) bank and also transacts general banking business. Banking activities are supervised by the National Banking Commission (Comisión Bancaria Nacional–CBN). Private banks include branches of U.S., Japanese, Latin American, and other foreign firms. Liberalized banking regulations and use of the dollar have made Panama one of Latin America's major offshore banking centers.

The normalization of relations with the U.S. following the U.S. invasion in December 1989 led to an immediate improvement in public finances, and by 1992, they were in modest surplus, which was maintained in the following two years.

The balboa is fully convertible with the dollar at a fixed rate of 1:1, and there is no central bank. The government cannot, therefore, implement a monetary policy. Most monetary developments are exogenously determined by the balance of payments. Money supply, as measured by M2, amounted to B 5,223.9 million at the end of 1995.

Panama's banking center has allegedly been the main money-laundering point for proceeds from international drug-trafficking. In March 1994, it was decreed that persons entering Panama must declare money or financial instruments in excess of $10,000. For deposits and withdrawals in excess of this amount from local banking institutions, a form would have to be filled in providing details about the person carrying out the transaction.

Panama's international stock exchange, the Bolsa de Valores de Panama, began operations in June 1990. In 1995, there were a total of 102 listed companies, of which 96 were local and 6 foreign entities. Panama's Central de Custodia de Valores (Panaclear) began operations in November 1996. A rating agency was expected to begin operations by early 1997.

Economic Development

The Panamanian economy is the most stable, and among the more prosperous in the region. But the economy is highly segmented between its dynamic, internationally oriented service sector and the domestically oriented sector, which is beset with policy-induced rigidities and low productivity. Factor markets are also segmented by policies that drive up the cost of labor and lower the cost of capital. About 14% of the labor force is unemployed despite the preponderance of services in the economy, low growth of the economically active population and relatively slow rural-urban migration. The protected poor performance of the economy has impeded job creation, and contributed to high poverty levels and income inequality.

Despite Panama's relatively high per capita income, two-fifths of the population lives in poverty. Income distribution is highly skewed and has become much more regressive in the past decade. In

1979, the poorest 20% of the population received 4% of income; in 1989, that share had plunged to 2%, leaving Panama with one of the most unequal distributions in the hemisphere. The government's strategy for mitigating poverty and inequality rests primarily on reviving sustainable growth; its economic program emphasizes reforms that will mitigate the bias against employment creation, increase agricultural productivity, and reduce the high cost of the basic consumption basket.

SOCIAL WELFARE

The Social Security Fund provides medical service and hospitalization, maternity care, pensions for disability and old age, and funeral benefits. Children are cared for through a child welfare institute, which operates under the Ministry of Labor and Social Welfare. The government has made efforts to integrate the Amerindian population of the eastern Caribbean coast through land grants, basic education, and improved transportation. The social security system covered more than 1 million persons in the mid-1980s.

While Panama has a relatively high rate of female enrollment in higher education, many female graduates are still forced to take low-paying jobs. Only 4% of the country's managerial positions are occupied by women.

Healthcare

Public health services include free health examinations and medical care for the needy, health education, sanitation inspection, hospital and clinic construction, and nutrition services. In 1993, 82% of the population had access to health care services.

Malaria has been controlled and the yellow-fever mosquito practically eliminated. Today, the principal causes of death are cancer, heart disease, cerebrovascular disease, pneumonia and bronchopneumonia, and enteritis and diarrhea. In some areas of Panama, poor sanitation, inadequate housing, and malnutrition still constitute health hazards. Average life expectancy is 74 years.

Housing

Housing in urban areas has been a permanent problem since U.S. construction in the Canal Zone brought a great influx of migrant laborers into Colón and Panamá (Panama City). In the early 1980s, however, the shortage of low-income housing remained acute, particularly in Colón. In 1980–88, total housing units numbered 448,000 with 4.9 people per dwelling.

EDUCATION

In 1995, illiteracy was estimated at 9% of the adult population (males, 8.6%; females, 9.8%). Education is free and compulsory for children aged 7 through 15. In 1994, there were 2,791 primary schools with 364,934 students. At the secondary schools there were 209,929 students.

Universities include the state-run University of Panama and Santa María la Antigua. In 1994, at all institutions of higher learning, there were 4,291 teaching staff with 70,327 students enrolled.

1999 KEY EVENTS TIMELINE

January

• Panamanian airlines order 8 new 737-700 planes at an estimated cost of $400 million.

February

• Mireya Moscoso, the widow of former president Arnulfo Arias, is seen as the favorite candidate to win the May presidential elections. Moscoso would be the first woman to occupy that position.

March

• Martín Torrijos, the presidential candidate of the ruling Democratic Revolutionary Party whose father signed the 1977 agreement with U.S. President Jimmy Carter allowing Panama to regain control of the canal by December 31, 1999, is heavily campaigning for the presidential election.

April

• Panama is reported to be considering asking the U.S. for the extradition of former strongman General Manuel Noriega. Noriega was deposed in 1989 when the U.S. invaded the island. He currently faces a long prison term in the United States for drug-related charges.

May

• Mireya Moscoso, the widow of former president Arnulfo Arias and candidate of the Arnulfista Party, wins the presidential elections and becomes Panama's first woman to hold the highest elected office in the nation.

June

• There is growing international concern over Panama's ability to run the canal after the U.S. turns it over on December 31, 1999.

July

• President-elect Moscoso announces her intention of revising the constitution to reduce the power and influence of political parties and the military.

• Ending a long military presence in Panama, the U.S. closes its last military base on the island.

• President-elect Moscoso announces her cabinet.

• The vice-president-elect visits China over growing concerns that China will become involved in the running of the canal once the United States turns it over to Panama on December 31, 1999.

August

• Panama celebrates 85 years of operating the canal.

September

• Mireya Moscoso is inaugurated as president of Panama as concerns grow about Panama's ability to operate the canal after 1999.

November

• Panama takes control of the Howard Air Force Base, the last U.S. air force base on its soil, and announces plans to offer the facility for development.

• Panamanian police question Panama Canal security in an investigation of the hijacking of two helicopters amid reports that they were seized by Colombian guerillas.

December

• Former U.S. president Jimmy Carter visits Panama as part of a formal delegation transferring the Panama Canal from U.S. to Panamanian control.

• The American agency the Panama Canal Commission becomes the Panama Canal Authority, officially transferring control of the Panama Canal officially from U.S. to Panama on December 31.

ANALYSIS OF EVENTS: 1999

BUSINESS AND THE ECONOMY

Panama's main engine of growth during the 20th century has been the Panama Canal. As one of the most impressive engineering achievements of humankind, the canal has allowed Panama to become a financial center in Central America. Most Panamanians work in canal-related activities, with the service sector accounting for a large segment of Panama's economy. The presence of U.S. military personnel throughout most of the century also allowed for the direct transfer of funds from the United States to Panama. However, as the century ends and the deadline for the final transfer of control of the canal from the U.S. to Panama draws near, Panama faces important challenges to secure and consolidate its privileged position as a financial center in the region. In accordance with the Carter-Torrijos agreement signed in 1977, the United States, represented in the handover ceremony by former president Jimmy Carter, turned ownership and control of the canal over to Panama on December 31, 1999. Beginning 2000, Panama will be solely responsible for the operations and maintenance of the canal. Rumors have surfaced that China is interested in providing technical and financial support to the government of Panama, but in a visit to the United States, Panamanian president Mireya Moscoso affirmed that only Panamanians would run the canal. It remains to be seen if Panama will be able to provide the efficient service needed to meet the growing demand for the use of the canal. It is expected that Panama will bring in foreign experts to improve the canal operations and to plan for future upgrades and improvements that are badly needed.

GOVERNMENT AND POLITICS

Mireya Moscoso was elected Panama's president in May. She defeated ruling party candidate Martín Torrijos. Moscoso is the first woman to be elected president in Panama. The election was marked by president Pérez Balladares's attempt to reform the constitution to allow for presidential re-election. When the effort failed, Torrijos and Moscoso campaigned hard to attract many disenchanted Panamanians. Torrijos is the son of former strongman Omar Torrijos, the man who ruled Panama from 1961 until his death in 1981. Torrijos signed the agreement with the U.S. that paved the way for the peaceful transfer of the Canal from the United States to Panama on Dec 31, 1999. Moscoso is the widow of former president and populist leader Arnulfo Arias. Arias was overthrown by Torrijos in 1969 and then sought asylum in the United States. Moscoso returned to Panama after the U.S. invaded the island and removed strongman Manuel Noriega. The election had an important historical component, but discontent with the current Pérez Balladares government also hurt Torrijos chances.

Upon taking office in August, Moscoso vowed to lead a successful transition over the control of the canal. Panama had national celebrations on December 15, when control of the canal was formally handed over from the U.S. to Panama. Problems persist, however, as social tensions increase as a result of high unemployment and growing inequality. Moscoso is expected to face difficulties after the celebration of the canal turnover ends in 2000. It is unlikely that she will back the effort currently underway in Panama to request the extradition of former strongman Manuel Noriega, presently serving sentence in the United States, to face criminal charges in Panama. President Moscoso has vowed to fight corruption, but she will probably not seek after those who ruled the country in the 1980s.

CULTURE AND SOCIETY

Panama came into existence as a country because of the canal. The United States has had military and civilian presence in the canal since the country first declared independence in 1903. When the last military forces abandoned Panama in 1999, the symbolic meaning for the nation was enormous. The turnover of control of the canal on December 31, 1999 will also represent a founding moment for Panama. For the first time in its history, Panama will have full military and territorial control over the entire land. It is unclear whether Panama will be successful in running the canal or whether the U.S. will be asked back to help operate the canal, but for the first time in their history, Panamanians will have an opportunity to act as a fully independent country. The presence of U.S. military personnel and technical experts who worked in the canal during this century will result in a more permanent American influence in Panama's daily life. English is widely spoken in the country and the U.S. dollar is the preferred currency in most private and public sector business. The official withdrawal of U.S. troops and the turnover of the canal to Panama will not bring to an end American influence in that Central American country.

DIRECTORY

CENTRAL GOVERNMENT
Head of State

President
Mireya Moscoso, Office of the President, President's Office, 3rd Ave., near the Cathedral, Panama
PHONE: +507 (011) 2279600

Ministers

Minister of Agricultural Development
Manuel Miranda, Ministry of Agriculture Development
PHONE: +507 (011) 2325043; 2325150

Minister for Canal Affairs
Jorge Eduardo Ritter, Ministry for Canal Affairs

Minister of Commerce and Industry
Raul Hernandez, Ministry of Commerce and Industries
PHONE: +507 (011) 2274222; 2271222

Minister of Education
Pablo Thalassinos, Ministry of Education
PHONE: +507 (011) 2622200; 2622645

Minister of Finance and Treasury
Miguel Heras, Ministry of Finance and Treasury

Minister of Foreign Relations
Jorge Eduardo Ritter, Ministry of Foreign Relations
PHONE: +507 (011) 2288644

Minister of Government and Justice
Mariela Sagel, Ministry of Government and Justice
PHONE: +507 (011) 2122000

Minister of Health
Aida de Rivera, Ministry of Health
PHONE: +507 (011) 2253540

Minister of Housing
Gerardo Solis, Ministry of Housing
PHONE: +507 (011) 2627692; 2627222

Minister of Labor and Social Welfare
Reynaldo Rivera, Ministry of Labor and Social Welfare
PHONE: +507 (011) 2255763

Minister of Planning and Economic Policy
Guillermo Chapman, Ministry of Planning and Economic Policy

Minister of Presidency
Olmedo Miranda, Ministry of Presidency

Minister of Public Works
Luis Blanco, Ministry of Public Works
PHONE: +507 (011) 2325333

Minister of Women, Youth, Family, and Childhood
Leonor Calderon, Ministry of Women, Youth, Family, and Childhood
PHONE: +507 (011) 2610254; 2790686

POLITICAL ORGANIZATIONS
Partido Renovación Civilista-PRC (Civic Renewal Party)
NAME: Tomas Herrera

Movimiento de Renovación Nacional-MORENA (National Renovation Movement)
NAME: Pedro Vallerino

Movimiento Liberal Republicano Nacionalista-MOLIRENA (Nationalist Republican Liberal Movement)
Calle Venezuela, entre Vía España y Calle 50 Ciudad de Panamá, Panamá
NAME: Delia Cardenas
PHONE: +507 (0110 2135928; 2135929
FAX: +507 (011) 2656004
E-MAIL: molirena@hotmail.com

Partido Demócrata Cristiano-PDC (Christian Democratic Party)
NAME: Ruben Arosemena

Alianza Democrática-AD (Democratic Alliance)
Partido Arnulfista-PA (Arnulfista Party)
NAME: Mireya Moscoso de Gruber

Partido Liberal Auténtico-PLA (Authentic Liberal Party)
NAME: Arnulfo Escalona

Unión Democrática Independiente-UDI (Independent Democratic Union)
NAME: Jacinto Cardenas

Partido Liberal Nacional (National Liberal Party)

NAME: Roberto Aleman Zubieta

Movimiento Papa Egoró-MPE (Papa Egoró Movement)

NAME: Gloria Young

Pueblo Unido-PU (United People)

Partido Revolucionario Democrática-PRD (Democratic Revolutionary Party)

NAME: Gerardo Gonzalez

Partido Laborista-PALA (Labor Party)

NAME: Carlos Lopez Guevara

Partido Liberal Republicano-PLR (Liberal Republican Party)

NAME: Rodolfo Chiari

DIPLOMATIC REPRESENTATION

Embassies in Panama

Argentina
Calles 50 y 53, Urbanización Obarrio, Panamá City, Panamá
PHONE: +507 (011) 2646989

Bolivia
Calle 50, 78 Panamá City, Panamá
PHONE: +507 (011) 2690274

Brazil
Edificio El Dorado, Piso 1 Calle E Méndez, 24C Alegre, Panamá City, Panamá
PHONE: +507 (011) 2635322; 2635540

Canada
PHONE: +507 (011) 2649731; 2647115
FAX: +507 (011) 2638083

China
Edificio Grobman, Piso 6 Calle Manuel M Icaza, 12 Panamá City, Panamá
PHONE: +507 (011) 2649266
FAX: +507 (011) 2231134; 2234159

Costa Rica
Calle Gerardo Ortega, Panamá City, Panamá
PHONE: +507 (011) 2642980

Cuba
Avenidas Cuba y Ecuador, Panamá City, Panamá
PHONE: +507 (011) 2270359; 2275277
FAX: +507 (011) 2256681

Chile
Calle E Méndez y Vía España, Panamá City, Panamá
PHONE: +507 (011) 2239748

Ecuador
Calle Manuel Icaza, 12 Panamá City, Panamá
PHONE: +507 (011) 2642654
FAX: +507 (011) 2230159

El Salvador
Avenida Manuel Espinosa Batista, Panamá City, Panamá
PHONE: +507 (011) 2233020

France
Plaza de Francia, Panamá City, Panamá
PHONE: +507 (011) 2287824

Germany
Republica Federal Edificio Bancomer, Piso 6 Calles 50 y 53, Panamá City, Panamá
PHONE: +507 (011) 2637733; 2641147
FAX: +507 (011) 2236664

Greece
Consulate of Greece, Calle M Urbanizacion El Paical, Panamá City, Panamá
PHONE: +507 (011) 2602705

Japan
Edificio Sede Propia, Calles 50 y 60-E Obarrio, Panamá City, Panamá
PHONE: +507 (011) 2636155
FAX: +507 (011) 2636019

Korea
Calle 51E, Ricardo Arias, Campo Alegre, Edificio Plaza P.B., Panamá City, Panamá
PHONE: +507 (011) 2648203; 2648360
FAX: +507 (011) 2648825

Libya
Avenida Balboa y Calle 32, Panamá City, Panamá
PHONE: +507 (011) 2273342

Malta
Calle Elvira Méndez, Panamá City, Panamá
PHONE: +507 (011) 2649538

Mexico
Edificio Bancomer, Piso 5 Calle 50 y 53, Panamá City, Panamá
PHONE: +507 (011) 2635021

Nicaragua
Calle José de San Martín, 31 Panamá City, Panamá
PHONE: +507 (011) 2230981

Peru

Calles Elvira Méndez y 52, Panamá City,
Panamá

PHONE: +507 (011) 2231112

Russia

Edificio Omega, Piso 7 Avenida Samuel Lewis,
Panamá City, Panamá

PHONE: +507 (011) 2641408; 2641635

FAX: +507 (011) 2641558

Spain

Frente al Parque Porras Avenida 6, 44 Panamá
City, Panamá

PHONE: +507 (011) 2694018

FAX: +507 (011) 2276284

Uruguay

Avenida Justo Arosemena y Calle 32, 4 Panamá
City, Panamá

PHONE: +507 (011) 2259087

United States

Calle 37 y Avenida Balboa, Apartado 6959, 5
Panamá City, Panamá

PHONE: +507 (011) 2271777

FAX: +507 (011) 2271964

Venezuela

Torre Banco Union, Piso 5 Avenida Samuel
Lewis, Panamá City, Panamá

PHONE: +507 (011) 2691244

FAX: +507 (011) 2691916

JUDICIAL SYSTEM

Supreme Court of Justice

Dirección de Prensa y Relaciones Públicas,
Panamá City, Panamá

PHONE: +507 (011) 2627158; 2625641

FAX: +507 (011) 2625956

FURTHER READING

Articles

"Another Torrijos." *The Economist* (March 27,
1999).

"Frank Goes to Panama." *The Economist*
(January 16, 1999).

"Giving Up The Ship? The Looming Handover
of the Panama Canal has Fired Some Serious
Separation Anxiety in the U.S." *Time* 154, 10
(September 6, 1999): 48+.

"Mireya Moscoso." *U.S. News and World
Report* 127, 10 (September 13, 1999): 11.

"Panama–An Old Canal's New Life." *The
Economist* (June 12, 1999).

"Panama–Awaiting the Lady." *The Economist*
(August 28, 1999).

Internet

Embassy of Panama in Tokyo Available Online
@ embassy.kcom.ne.ip/panama/top.htm
(November 17, 1999).

Presidencia de la Republica de Panama
Available Online @ www.presidencia.gob.pa/
(November 17, 1999).

PANAMA: STATISTICAL DATA

For sources and notes see "Sources of Statistics" in the front of each volume.

GEOGRAPHY

Geography (1)

Area:

Total: 78,200 sq km.

Land: 75,990 sq km.

Water: 2,210 sq km.

Area—comparative: slightly smaller than South Carolina.

Land boundaries:

Total: 555 km.

Border countries: Colombia 225 km, Costa Rica 330 km.

Coastline: 2,490 km.

Climate: tropical; hot, humid, cloudy; prolonged rainy season (May to January), short dry season (January to May).

Terrain: interior mostly steep, rugged mountains and dissected, upland plains; coastal areas largely plains and rolling hills.

Natural resources: copper, mahogany forests, shrimp.

Land use:

Arable land: 7%

Permanent crops: 2%

Permanent pastures: 20%

Forests and woodland: 44%

Other: 27% (1993 est.).

HUMAN FACTORS

Demographics (2A)

	1990	1995	1998	2000	2010	2020	2030	2040	2050
Population	2,387.9	2,608.8	2,735.9	2,821.1	3,232.7	3,618.7	3,958.3	4,228.2	4,418.4
Net migration rate (per 1,000 population)	NA	NA	NA	NA	NA	NA	NA	NA	NA
Births	NA	NA	NA	NA	NA	NA	NA	NA	NA
Deaths	9.8	NA	NA	NA	NA	NA	NA	NA	NA
Life expectancy - males	70.2	71.2	71.7	72.1	73.7	75.0	76.2	77.1	77.8
Life expectancy - females	75.6	76.7	77.3	77.7	79.5	81.0	82.2	83.2	84.0
Birth rate (per 1,000)	26.5	22.8	22.0	21.4	18.3	16.2	14.6	13.5	12.8
Death rate (per 1,000)	5.3	5.2	5.1	5.1	5.3	5.9	6.8	8.0	9.4
Women of reproductive age (15-49 yrs.)	604.2	673.9	711.4	737.8	860.3	928.9	966.5	983.3	981.9
of which are currently married	364.1	NA	NA	NA	NA	NA	NA	NA	NA
Fertility rate	3.1	2.7	2.6	2.5	2.2	2.1	2.0	2.0	2.0

Except as noted, values for vital statistics are in thousands; life expectancy is in years.

Health Personnel (3)

Total health expenditure as a percentage of GDP, 1990-1997[a]

Public sector 4.7

Private sector 2.0

Total[b] 6.7

Health expenditure per capita in U.S. dollars, 1990-1997[a]

Purchasing power parity 457

Total 199

Availability of health care facilities per 100,000 people

Hospital beds 1990-1997[a] 2.50

Doctors 1993[c] 119

Nurses 1993[c] 98

Health Indicators (4)

Life expectancy at birth

1980 70

1997 74

Daily per capita supply of calories (1996) 2,556

Total fertility rate births per woman (1997) 2.6

Maternal mortality ratio per 100,000 live births (1990-97) . . . . .55[c]

Safe water % of population with access (1995) 84

Sanitation % of population with access (1995) 90

Consumption of iodized salt % of households (1992-98)[a] 92

Smoking prevalence

Male % of adults (1985-95)[a] . . . .

Female % of adults (1985-95)[a] . . . .

Tuberculosis incidence per 100,000 people (1997) 57

Adult HIV prevalence % of population ages 15-49 (1997) 0.61

Infants and Malnutrition (5)

Under-5 mortality rate (1997) 20

% of infants with low birthweight (1990-97) 8

Births attended by skilled health staff % of total[a] . . .84

% fully immunized (1995-97)

TB 99

DPT 95

Polio 99

Measles 92

Prevalence of child malnutrition under age 5 (1992-97)[b] 6

Ethnic Division (6)

Mestizo 70%

Amerindian and mixed (West Indian) 14%

White 10%

Amerindian 6%

Mestizo is mixed Amerindian and white.

Religions (7)

Roman Catholic 85%

Protestant 15%

Languages (8)

Spanish (official), English 14%. Many Panamanians are bilingual.

EDUCATION

Public Education Expenditures (9)

Public expenditure on education (% of GNP)

1980 . . . . .4.9

1996 . . . . .4.6[1]

Expenditure per student

Primary % of GNP per capita

1980 . . . . .12.3

1996 . . . .

Secondary % of GNP per capita

1980 . . . . .11.5

1996 . . . .

Tertiary % of GNP per capita

1980 . . . . .29.8

1996 . . . . .41.1[1]

Expenditure on teaching materials

Primary % of total for level (1996) 1.8

Secondary % of total for level (1996) . . . .

Primary pupil-teacher ratio per teacher (1996) . . . .

Duration of primary education years (1995) 6

Educational Attainment (10)

Age group (1990)[11] . . . . .25+

Total population .1,035,339

Highest level attained (%)

No schooling 11.7

First level

Not completed 20.2

Completed 21.8

Entered second level

S-1 . . . . .12.6

S-2 . . . . .16.4

Postsecondary 13.2

Literacy Rates (11A)

In thousands and percent[1]	1990	1995	2000	2010
Illiterate population (15+ yrs.)	169	161	155	134
Literacy rate - total adult pop. (%)	88.8	90.8	92.1	94.4
Literacy rate - males (%)	89.4	91.4	92.7	95.0
Literacy rate - females (%)	88.3	90.2	91.5	93.8

GOVERNMENT & LAW

Political Parties (12)

Legislative Assembly	No. of seats
Democratic Rebolutionary Party (PRD)	32
Solidarity Party (PS)	4
Labor Party (PALA)	1
Arnulfista Party (PA)	14
Papa Egoro Movement (MPE)	6
Nationalist Republican Liberal Movement (MOLIRENA)	4
Authentic Liberal Party (PLA)	3
Civic Renewal Party (PRC)	3
National Liberal Party (PLN)	2
Christian Democratic Party (PDC)	1
Independent Democratic Union (UDI)	1
National Renovation Movement (MORENA)	1

Military Affairs (14B)

	1990	1991	1992	1993	1994	1995
Military expenditures						
Current dollars (mil.)	69	77	80	95	101	97
1995 constant dollars (mil.)	80	86	86	99	104	97
Armed forces (000)	11	12	11	11	11	12
Gross national product (GNP)						
Current dollars (mil.)	4,359	5,477	5,557	6,119	6,639	7,083
1995 constant dollars (mil.)	5,009	6,052	5,977	6,415	6,806	7,083
Central government expenditures (CGE)						
1995 constant dollars (mil.)	1,319	1,541	1,512	1,776	1,942	NA
People (mil.)	2.4	2.4	2.5	2.5	2.6	2.6
Military expenditure as % of GNP	1.6	4.1	1.4	1.5	1.5	1.4
Military expenditure as % of CGE	6.0	5.5	5.7	5.6	5.3	NA
Military expenditure per capita (1995 $)	33	35	35	39	40	37
Armed forces per 1,000 people (soldiers)	4.6	4.9	4.4	4.4	4.3	4.6
GNP per capita (1995 $)	2,098	2,487	2,411	2,542	2,712	2,712
Arms imports[6]						
Current dollars (mil.)	5	5	0	0	0	0
1995 constant dollars (mil.)	6	6	0	0	0	0
Arms exports[6]						
Current dollars (mil.)	0	0	10	5	0	0
1995 constant dollars (mil.)	0	0	11	5	0	0
Total imports[7]						
Current dollars (mil.)	1,539	1,695	2,024	2,188	2,404	2,511
1995 constant dollars (mil.)	1,769	1,873	2,177	2,294	2,464	2,511
Total exports[7]						
Current dollars (mil.)	340	358	502	553	583	625
1995 constant dollars (mil.)	391	396	540	580	598	625
Arms as percent of total imports[8]	.3	.3	0	0	0	0
Arms as percent of total exports[8]	0	0	2.0	.9	0	0

Government Budget (13A)

Year: 1996

Total Expenditures: 2,255.3 Millions of Balboas

Expenditures as a percentage of the total by function:

General public services and public order 13.08
Defense 4.49
Education 16.80
Health 20.61
Social Security and Welfare 20.67
Housing and community amenities 4.54
Recreational, cultural, and religious affairs 63
Fuel and energy 03
Agriculture, forestry, fishing, and hunting 1.49
Mining, manufacturing, and construction 18
Transportation and communication 1.71
Other economic affairs and services 1.23

Crime (15)

Crime rate (for 1997)

Crimes reported 19,800
Total persons convicted 12,600
Crimes per 100,000 population 725

Persons responsible for offenses

Total number of suspects 6,050
Total number of female suspects 575
Total number of juvenile suspects 225

LABOR FORCE

Labor Force (16)

Total (million) 1.044
Government and community services 31.8%
Agriculture, hunting, and fishing 26.8%
Commerce, restaurants, and hotels 16.4%
Manufacturing and mining 9.4%
Construction 3.2%
Transport and communications 6.2%
Finance, insurance, and real estate 4.3%

Shortage of skilled labor, but an oversupply of unskilled labor. Data for 1997 est.

Unemployment Rate (17)

13.1% (1997 est.)

PRODUCTION SECTOR

Electric Energy (18)

Capacity . . . . .957 million kW (1995)
Production . . . . .3.6 billion kWh (1995)
Consumption per capita . . . . .1,355 kWh (1995)

Transportation (19)

Highways:

total: 11,100 km

paved: 3,730 km (including 30 km of expressways)

unpaved: 7,370 km (1996 est.)

Waterways: 800 km navigable by shallow draft vessels; 82 km Panama Canal

Pipelines: crude oil 130 km

Merchant marine:

total: 4,350 ships (1,000 GRT or over) totaling 89,622,112 GRT/137,529,188 DWT ships by type: bulk 1,240, cargo 1,033, chemical tanker 195, combination bulk 67, combination ore/oil 19, container 426, liquefied gas tanker 175, livestock carrier 9, multifunction large-load carrier 5, oil tanker 524, passenger 40, passenger-cargo 6, railcar carrier 1, refrigerated cargo 296, roll-on/roll-off cargo 101, short-sea passenger 40, specialized tanker 15, vehicle carrier 158 note: a flag of convenience registry; includes ships from 76 countries among which are Japan 1,236, Greece 418, Hong Kong 273, South Korea 247, Taiwan 227, China 185, Singapore 119, US 112, Switzerland 85, and Indonesia 60 (1997 est.)

Airports: 109 (1997 est.)

Airports—with paved runways:

total: 40

over 3,047 m: 1

2,438 to 3,047 m: 1

1,524 to 2,437 m: 5

914 to 1,523 m: 14

under 914 m: 19 (1997 est.)

Airports—with unpaved runways:

total: 69

914 to 1,523 m: 17

under 914 m: 52 (1997 est.)

Top Agricultural Products (20)

Bananas, rice, corn, coffee, sugarcane, vegetables; livestock; fishing (shrimp).

MANUFACTURING SECTOR

GDP & Manufacturing Summary (21)

Detailed value added figures are listed by both International Standard Industry Code (ISIC) and product title.

	1980	1985	1990	1994
GDP ($-1990 mil.)[1]	4,672	5,383	5,009	6,559
Per capita ($-1990)[1]	2,396	2,484	2,089	2,537
Manufacturing share (%) (current prices)[1]	9.7	8.2	7.8	*8.1*

	1980	1985	1990	1994
Manufacturing				
Value added ($-1990 mil.)[1]	428	421	407	*534*
Industrial production index	100	108	102	*133*
Value added ($ mil.)	477	551	591	*767*
Gross output ($ mil.)	*1,473*	1,765	1,703	*2,217*
Employment (000)	*31*	36	37	*44*
Profitability (% of gross output)				
Intermediate input (%)	*68*	69	65	65
Wages and salaries inc. supplements (%)	*9*	*13*	*13*	14
Gross operating surplus	*23*	*18*	*21*	*21*
Productivity ($)				
Gross output per worker	*46,753*	*48,651*	*45,211*	*49,762*
Value added per worker	*15,159*	15,183	16,311	*17,427*
Average wage (inc. supplements)	*4,241*	*6,270*	*6,133*	*6,959*
Value added ($ mil.)				
311/2 Food products	155	171	205	*254*
313 Beverages	52	53	69	*84*
314 Tobacco products	26	30	27	*35*
321 Textiles	4	3	6	*6*
322 Wearing apparel	31	26	34	*48*
323 Leather and fur products	4	1	3	*3*
324 Footwear	7	9	5	*7*
331 Wood and wood products	8	7	4	*5*
332 Furniture and fixtures	8	11	7	*9*
341 Paper and paper products	20	33	48	*33*
342 Printing and publishing	22	29	29	*39*
351 Industrial chemicals	4	9	6	*9*
352 Other chemical products	26	42	42	*60*
353 Petroleum refineries	*28*	*23*	*16*	*34*
354 Miscellaneous petroleum and coal products	—	—	*1*	2
355 Rubber products	2	2	2	2
356 Plastic products	12	21	23	*34*
361 Pottery, china and earthenware	—	—	—	—
362 Glass and glass products	*1*	7	7	*7*
369 Other non-metal mineral products	31	26	19	*41*
371 Iron and steel	5	*4*	*2*	5
372 Non-ferrous metals	2	*3*	*2*	*4*
381 Metal products	19	20	17	*24*
382 Non-electrical machinery	1	1	1	—
383 Electrical machinery	3	4	3	*5*
384 Transport equipment	4	13	6	*5*
385 Professional and scientific equipment	1	2	3	*4*
390 Other manufacturing industries	*2*	*3*	*3*	*7*

FINANCE, ECONOMICS, & TRADE

Economic Indicators (22)

National product: GDP—purchasing power parity—$18 billion (1997 est.)

National product real growth rate: 3.6% (1997 est.)

National product per capita: $6,700 (1997 est.)

Inflation rate—consumer price index: 1.2% (1997)

Exchange Rates (24)

Exchange rates: balboas (B) per US$1—1.000 (fixed rate)

Top Import Origins (25)

$2.95 billion (c.i.f., 1997 est.) Data are for 1996.

Origins	%
Germany	26.5
Italy	10.4
Russia	7.3
United Kingdom	6.3
Netherlands	4.8
France	4.4

Panama

Top Export Destinations (26)

$592 million (f.o.b., 1997 est.).

Destinations	%
United States	37
European Union	NA
Central America and Caribbean	NA

NA stands for not available.

Economic Aid (27)

Recipient: NA. NA stands for not available.

Import Export Commodities (28)

Import Commodities	Export Commodities
Capital goods 21%	Bananas 43%
Crude oil 11%	Shrimp 11%
Foodstuffs 9%	Sugar 4%
Consumer goods	Clothing 5%
Chemicals	Coffee 2%

Balance of Payments (23)

	1992	1993	1994	1995	1996
Exports of goods (f.o.b.)	5,104	5,417	6,044	6,104	5,889
Imports of goods (f.o.b.)	−5,480	−5,751	−6,295	−6,679	−6,518
Trade balance	−375	−334	−251	−575	−630
Services - debits	−2,451	−2,342	−2,454	−3,034	−2,566
Services - credits	2,353	2,329	2,578	3,112	2,984
Private transfers (net)	122	123	67	69	66
Government transfers (net)	82	80	82	86	86
Overall balance	−270	−143	22	−343	−60

PAPUA NEW GUINEA

CAPITAL: Port Moresby.

FLAG: The flag is a rectangle, divided diagonally. The upper segment is scarlet with a yellow bird of paradise; the lower segment is black with five white stars representing the Southern Cross.

ANTHEM: *O, Arise All You Sons.*

MONETARY UNIT: The kina (ᴋ) of 100 toea is linked with the Australian dollar. There are coins of 1, 2, 5, 10, 20, and 50 toea and 1 kina, and notes of 2, 5, 10, 20, and 50 kina. ᴋ1 = us$0.74906 or us$1 = ᴋ1.335.

WEIGHTS AND MEASURES: The metric system is the legal standard.

HOLIDAYS: New Year's Day, 1 January; Queen's Birthday, 1st Monday in June; Remembrance Day, 23 July; Independence Day, 16 September; Christmas, 25 December; Boxing Day, 26 December. Movable religious holidays include Good Friday and Easter Monday.

TIME: 10 PM = noon GMT.

LOCATION AND SIZE: Situated to the north of Australia, Papua New Guinea has a total land area of 461,690 square kilometers (178,259 square miles), slightly larger than the state of California. Mainland Papua New Guinea occupies the eastern portion of the island of New Guinea, the second-largest island in the world. It shares the island with its western neighbor, a province of Indonesia. Papua New Guinea has a total boundary length of 5,972 kilometers (3,711 miles).

Papua New Guinea's capital city, Port Moresby, is located on the country's southern coast.

CLIMATE: Annual rainfall varies widely with the monsoon pattern, ranging from as little as 100 centimeters (40 inches) at Port Moresby to as much as 750 centimeters (300 inches) in other coastal regions. Most of the lowland and island areas have daily mean temperatures of about 27°C (81°F), while in the highlands temperatures may fall to 4°C (39°F) at night and rise to 32°C (90°F) in the daytime. Relative humidity is uniformly high in the lowlands at about 80%.

Independent State of Papua New Guinea

INTRODUCTORY SURVEY

RECENT HISTORY

Papua New Guinea appears to have been settled by 14,000 BC, with migrations first of hunters and later of agriculturists probably coming from the Asian mainland by way of Indonesia. Early communities had little contact with each other because of rough terrain and so maintained their independence, as well as their individual languages and customs.

New Guinea was first sighted by Spanish and Portuguese sailors in the early 16th century and was known prophetically as Isla del Oro (Island of Gold). The western part of the island was claimed by Spain in 1545 and named New Guinea for a fancied resemblance of the people to those on the West African coast. (''Papua'' is a Malay word for the typically frizzled quality of Melanesian hair.) Traders began to appear in the islands in the 1850s, and the Germans sought the coconut oil trade in northern New Guinea about that time. The Dutch and the British had earlier agreed on a division of their interests in the island, and from 1828, the Dutch began to colonize the western portion.

Although the British flag was hoisted on various parts of eastern New Guinea, annexation was not ratified by the British government. Some Australian colonists were eager to see New Guinea become a British possession for trade, labor, gold mining, and missionary reasons; however, it was not until 1884, after an abortive Australian annexation attempt and under fear of German ambitions in the area, that Britain established a protectorate over

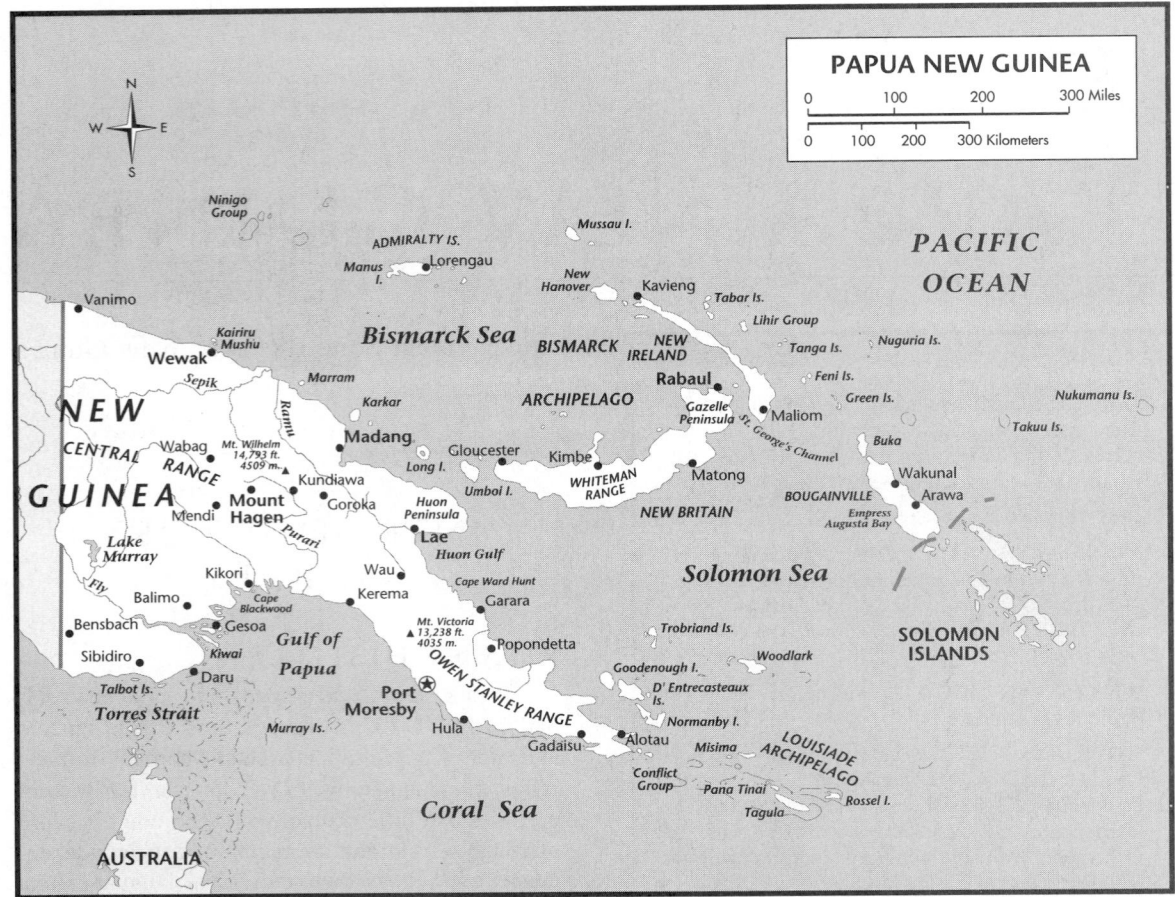

the southern coast of New Guinea and adjacent islands. The Germans followed by laying claim to three different parts of northern New Guinea. British and German spheres of influence were delineated by the Anglo-German Agreement of 1885. Germany took control of the northeastern portion of the island, as well as New Britain, New Ireland, and Bougainville, while Britain took possession of the southern portion and the adjacent islands.

British New Guinea passed to Australian control in 1902 and was renamed the Territory of Papua in 1906. German New Guinea remained intact until the outbreak of war in 1914, when it was seized by Australian forces. Although the territories retained their separate identities and status, they were administered jointly by Australia from headquarters at Port Moresby. In 1921, the former German New Guinea was placed under a League of Nations mandate administered by Australia; in 1947, it became the Trust Territory of New Guinea, still administered by Australia but now subject to the surveillance of the UN Trusteeship Council.

Both territories were merged into the Territory of Papua and New Guinea in 1949. A Legislative Council, established in 1953, was replaced by the House of Assembly in 1964. Eight years later, the territory was renamed Papua New Guinea, and on 1 December 1973, it was granted self-government. Separatist movements in Papua in 1973 and secessionist activities on the island of Bougainville in 1975 flared briefly and then died out, though debates over citizenship and land-reform provisions were vigorous until the passage of a constitution in 1975. Papua New Guinea achieved complete independence on 16 September 1975, with Michael Somare as prime minister of a coalition government.

Somare was voted out of office in 1980 but reelected in 1982; subsequently, he put through a constitutional change giving the central government increased authority over the provincial governments. Soon after, he suspended three provincial administrations for financial mismanagement. Somare also had to contend with social unrest, which culminated in June 1985 in a state of emergency after a prolonged wave of violent crime in Port Moresby. At the same time, his Pangu Pati was split by his deputy, Paias Wingti, who then founded a new party, the People's Democratic Movement (PDM). In November 1985, Somare was again voted out of office on a no confidence motion, and Wingti formed a cabinet. Though unrest continued, with serious riots in the Highlands in 1986, elections in mid-1987 returned Wingti to office at the head of a shaky five-party coalition.

Wingri's government was defeated in a no confidence vote in July 1988; a coalition government led by Rabbie Namaliu replaced the PDM government. A secessionist crisis on Bougainville dominated domestic politics during 1990–91. The Bougainville Revolutionary Army (BRA) declared the island of Bougainville to be independent from Papua New Guinea in May 1990, and in response government forces landed on the north of Bougainville in April 1991. Namaliu adjourned parliament early in 1991 to avoid a vote of no-confidence over the Bougainville crisis. Paias Wingti, the leader of the People's Democratic Movement (PDM), was reelected prime minister in July 1992 as the leader of a new coalition government with the support of the People's Progress Party, and the League for National Advancement.

During 1993 the government continued to extend its control over Bougainville, partly because of popular revulsion against human rights violations by members of the BRA. In September 1994, rebel troops withdrew to the surrounding hills of the Bougainville copper mine allowing government forces to reclaim it. In 1995, the prime minister halted cease-fire talks. The eight-year-old secessionist movement continued throughout 1997 and 1998.

In 1997, reformist premier Bill Skate, governor of Port Moresby, was elected by members of PNG's 109-seat parliament, defeating Michael Somare, who was also defeated for the post of parliamentary speaker by John Pundari, who is a member of Pangu. Skate represents Julius Chan who lost his seat in the elections but who supported Skate's selection as premier. Chan had hired a group of mercenaries to put down the rebellion in Bougainville, angering Brig. Gen. Jerry Sinigirok. Sinigirok was dismissed by Chan, a decision which led to rioting by 2,000 Sinigirok loyalists. Ultimately Chan made the decision to step aside pending a judicial inquiry into the hiring of mercenaries.

Chan had been elected prime minister on 30 August 1994.

GOVERNMENT

Papua New Guinea is an independent, parliamentary democracy in the Commonwealth of Nations, with a governor-general representing the British crown. Under the 1975 constitution, legislative power is vested in the National Parliament (formerly the House of Assembly) of 109 members, including 20 representing provincial electorates and 89 from open electorates, serving a term of up to five years. Suffrage is universal and voting compulsory for adults at age 19. The government is formed by the party, or coalition of parties, that has a majority in the National Parliament, and executive power is undertaken by the National Executive Council, selected from the government parties and chaired by the prime minister. The government has constitutional authority over the Defense Force, the Royal Papua New Guinea Constabulary, and intelligence organizations. Papua New Guinea is divided into 20 provinces, including the National Capital District. Each province has its own government, headed by a premier. In addition, there are more than 160 locally elected government councils.

Judiciary

The legal system is based on English common law. The Supreme Court is the nation's highest judicial authority and final court of appeal. Other courts are the National Court; district courts, which deal with summary and nonindictable offenses; and local courts, established to deal with minor offenses, including matters regulated by local customs.

The Papua New Guinea government has undertaken a process of legal reform under which village courts have been established to conserve and reactivate traditional legal methods. Special tribunals deal with land titles and with cases involving minors. An Ombudsman Commission has been established to investigate and refer to the public prosecutor cases involving abuse of official authority.

The Constitution declares the judiciary independent of executive, political, or military authority. It also provides a number of procedural due process protections including the right to legal counsel for criminal defendants.

Political Parties

Several parties have emerged in Papua New Guinean politics. In the House of Assembly elected in 1973, the Pangu Pati, headed by Michael Somare, formed a coalition government with the People's Progress Party, and Somare became prime minister. Opposition parties at the time were the United Party, which maintains a strong following in the Highlands, and the Papua Besena Party, which stands for the secession of Papua from Papua New Guinea and has had fluctuating support even on its home ground.

Generally, party allegiances have been fluid, and regional and tribal politics have had an important impact on political events. No fewer than eight parties have been founded since 1978. One of them, the People's Democratic Movement, formed in 1985 by dissident members of the Pangu Pati, won 18 seats in the 1987 elections, while the Pangu Pati captured 25. Parties that participated in the 1997 elections were the Pangu Pati, People's National Congress, the People's Progress Party, and the People's Democratic Movement.

DEFENSE

The main armed force is the Papua New Guinea Defense Force, which in 1995 had 3,700 men, 4 large patrol boats, 6 landing craft, and no armed aircraft. The Papua New Guinea Police Force is an armed constabulary with a strength of about 4,600. Australia provides 100 advisors and engineers to contribute to the upkeep of the military forces. Defense costs $60 million a year (1995) or 1.6 percent of gross domestic product.

ECONOMIC AFFAIRS

Economic activity is concentrated in two sectors, agriculture and mining. The subsistence sector, which occupies more than two-thirds of the working population, produces livestock, fruit, and vegetables for local consumption; agricultural products for export include copra, palm oil, coffee, cocoa, and tea. Rubber production has declined in recent years, and in the mid-1980s, coffee crops were threatened by the spread of coffee rust fungus through Western Highlands Province. New mining operations have compensated for the 1989 closure of the Bougainville mine, which had been a chief foreign exchange earner since the early 1970s. Currently, the main gold and silver mines are located at Ok Tedi in the Star Mountains, on Misima Island, and at Porgera. Oil and natural gas have been discovered in Southern Highlands Province. Forestry and fishing hold increasing importance.

Economic growth, which averaged 3.7% in the late 1980s, rose to 9% in 1991, 11.8% in 1992, and 16.6% in 1993. The growth was driven by a mineral and petroleum boom centered in the Highlands region. Growth slowed to 3% in 1994, 2.9% in 1995, and 1.6% in 1996 and 1997 due to an anticipated drop in production from Papua New Guinea's aging mines and oil fields. To halt the economic decline, the government awarded a lease to private developers for the $800 million Lihir gold project. In addition, construction projects involving airports, highways, disaster rehabilitation, development of the Gobe oil field, and a petroleum refinery are planned or being implemented. These projects, together with the onset of new production at the mine, are expected to generate a GDP growth rate of 4.5% in 1998.

Public Finance

Despite the government's efforts to hold down public expenditures, there was a budgetary deficit all through the 1980s. Shortfalls are covered by the Mineral Resources Stabilization Fund and by supplementary foreign grants and loans. The U.S. Central Intelligence Agency estimates that in 1995, government revenues totaled approximately $1.86 billion and expenditures $1.9 billion. External debt totaled $3.2 billion.

Income

The World Bank and the U.S. Central Intelligence Agency (CIA) both maintain statistics on national income. World Bank figures are for gross national product (GNP), defined as the value of all goods and services produced within a nation in a given year, plus income earned abroad, minus income earned by foreigners from domestic production. CIA figures are for gross domestic product (GDP), defined as the value of all final goods and services produced within a nation in a given year.

According to World Bank estimates, in 1995 Papua New Guinea had a GNP of $4.98 billion resulting in a per capita GNP of $1,160. For the ten year period 1985 to 1995, the average annual real growth rate of per capita GNP was 2.1%. During that same period, the average annual inflation rate was 4.6%. According to CIA estimates, the purchasing power parity of GDP in 1995 was $10.2 billion or $2,400 per capita. The CIA estimates that in 1995 the inflation rate for consumer prices was

15% and that the real growth rate of GDP was negative 3%.

Company incomes are taxed at a rate of 25% to 50%. Additional profits tax is calculated on the net profits of mining and petroleum companies at a rate of 35% to 50%. In addition, progressive tax rates are applied to individuals' wages and salaries, with taxes automatically withheld from paychecks. Tax rates range from 10% to 35%. Land and property taxes, estate and death taxes, gift taxes, stamp taxes, excise taxes, and sales taxes are also imposed.

A general levy of 7.5% is charged on all imports, except on supplies for the government, the missions, and the Bougainville copper project. An export tax is levied on numerous items, such as agricultural products, logs, and minerals.

Industry

The industrial sector, constrained by the small domestic market and the population's low purchasing power, is largely undeveloped. Industries are concentrated in industrial metals, timber processing, machinery, food, drinks, and tobacco. Manufacturing accounts for about 9% of GDP. Handicraft and cottage industries have expanded. A government-sponsored program assists Papua New Guineans in setting up businesses and purchases equity in existing firms. It has also encouraged small-scale import-substitution operations.

Agriculture in Papua New Guinea is divided into a large subsistence sector and a smaller monetary sector for export. Agriculture's importance has steadily declined since 1985, when it made up 33.8% of GDP. In 1995, agriculture only contributed about 25% to GDP. About 85% of the population engages in subsistence agriculture. Subsistence crops include yams, taro, and other staple vegetables. Cash crops are increasing in rural areas, stimulated by government-financed development programs. Production by small farmers of coffee, copra, cocoa, tea, and oil palm is important for export, although production on plantations, which are usually foreign owned, is also significant. Such plantations are gradually being sold back to nationals. Exports of cocoa, coffee, palm oil, and copra are expected to increase over the next few years. Principal crops and 1995 output (in tons) included sweet potatoes, 450,000; sugar cane, 300,000; copra, 120,000; coffee, 65,000; cocoa, 30,000; and rubber; 4,000. Papua New Guinea grows very little rice, the staple food for many of its inhabitants. A single Australian company imports over 150,000 tons per year to satisfy demand.

Livestock in 1995 included an estimated 1,030,000 hogs, 4,000 sheep, and 3 million chickens. That same year there were 110,000 head of cattle, and production was being encouraged with the aim of achieving self-sufficiency in meat supplies. Local poultry and beef production is sufficient to almost meet domestic demand. Beef imports are subject to quota controls. The farming of crocodiles, whose hides are exported, has also been expanded.

In many coastal parts of Papua New Guinea, fishing is of great economic importance. The government is involved in the development of fishing through supply of freezers and of transport and research facilities. The total catch in 1994 was 27,000 tons, 52% from inland fishing. Fish exports in 1994 were valued at $111.1 million, down from $141.6 million in 1991.

Forests and woodlands covered about 93% of the land area in 1994. Exploitable forests account for roughly 40% of the total land area and include a great variety of hardwood and softwood species. The total roundwood production in 1995 was 8,772,000 cu m, as compared with about 7,058,000 cu m in 1981. About 63% of all the timber cut in 1995 was used for fuel; production of sawn timber was estimated at 218,000 cu m. Plywood, hardwoods, and logs are regularly exported to Japan, New Zealand, Australia, and Europe.

In 1888, gold was discovered on Misima Island, marking the start of the history of mining on Papua New Guinea. As of 1995, the country was the sixth largest exporter of gold in the world. Prior to World War II, gold mining contributed 75% of Papua New Guinea's export earnings. This proportion declined greatly in subsequent years, but gold exports still accounted for 40% of the total export value in 1995. Gold production in 1995 was estimated at about 52,635 kg.

In 1971/72, the Bougainville copper mine, one of the richest in the world, began to export copper ores and concentrates, which amounted to almost 220,000 tons in 1988 when the mine was still in full operation. The mine closed in 1989 because of civil unrest caused by Bougainville Revolutionary Army militants. All copper production now comes from the Ok Tedi mine in the Star Mountains near the Indonesian border. The Ok Tedi mine was the world's eighth largest individual copper mine in

1995. In 1995, production at this mine amounted to 212,737 tons. In the same year, production of silver totaled 65,226 kg.

Mineral exploration is being expanded. Bauxite is known to exist on Manus Island, in the Admiralty Islands, and on New Ireland island. Additionally, lead, manganese, molybdenum, zinc, limestone, and phosphate guano and rock deposits are present. Major deposits of chromite, cobalt, and nickel are believed to be recoverable at a site on the Ramu River northeast of Ok Tedi. Reserves on Lihir Island in New Ireland Province have been estimated to contain some 613 tons of recoverable gold, and deposits at Porgera, near Ok Tedi, are considered to hold another 400 tons.

Banking and Finance

The Bank of Papua New Guinea, the country's central bank, was established in 1973, and the currency, the kina, was first issued in April 1975. The kina is backed by a standby arrangement with Australia, and the value of the kina is tied to the Australian dollar. The money supply, as measured by M3, was K2,312.6 million at the end of 1996.

The Papua New Guinea Banking Corp. was set up in 1973 to take over the savings and trading business of the former Australian-government-owned bank operating in Papua New Guinea. It competes with seven other private commercial banks, three of which are subsidiaries of Australian banks. Liquidity increased over the first six months of 1996, with total liquid assets held by the commercial banks standing at K999.3 million at the end of June 1996. There is no securities exchange in Papua New Guinea.

Economic Development

The bulk of foreign investment is in the mining and petroleum sector. Statistics on foreign equity holdings for 1995 show that Australia was the largest investor with K1,446 million, followed by the UK with K160 million and the U.S. with K91 million. Overall, foreign equity holdings fell from 55% of GDP in 1990 to 33% in 1994, primarily due to the completion of major mining and petroleum projects. In 1995, developers RTZ and Niugini Mining were awarded a lease for the $800 million Lihir gold project raising foreign equity holdings to 37% of GDP.

The Investment Promotion Authority (IPA), established in June of 1992, facilitates and certifies foreign investment. Corruption, civil unrest, and bureaucratic delays, however, frustrate the process.

A number of free trade zones are in the early stages of development.

The fundamental purposes of Papua New Guinea's economic strategy have been distilled into the nation's eight aims: a rapid increase in the proportion of the economy under the control of Papua New Guineans; a more equal distribution of economic benefits; decentralization of economic activity; an emphasis on small-scale artisan, service, and business activity; a more self-reliant economy; an increasing capacity for meeting government spending from locally raised revenue; a rapid increase in the equal and active participation of women in the economy; and governmental control and involvement in those sectors where control is necessary to achieve the desired kind of development.

SOCIAL WELFARE

A social security system, called the National Provident Fund, was formed in 1981 and covers persons employed by firms with 25 or more workers, providing old age, disability, and survivor benefits. In 1995, this program was financed by 5% contribution of earnings from employees, and 7% of payroll from employers. Retirement is set at age 55, or at any age with 15 years of contributions. Benefits are provided as a lump sum, and include total contributions plus interest. Workers' compensation is provided by employers through direct provision of benefits or insurance premiums. Rural communities traditionally assume communal obligations to those in need.

Despite a constitution guaranteeing them equal rights, women remain second-class citizens due to traditional patterns of discrimination. Village courts tend to enforce these patterns, and intertribal warfare often involves attacks on women. Polygamy is common, and the tradition of paying a bride-price persists. The government is working to improve the status of women, and has instituted an Office of Women's Affairs.

Healthcare

Government policy is to distribute health services widely and to provide comprehensive medical care, both preventive and curative. In 1990, there were 3.4 hospital beds per 1,000 people. Medical personnel in 1990 included 301 doctors and 2,447 nurses. In the same year, the population per physician was 12,870, and the population per nursing professional was 1,180. In 1992, there were 8 doctors per 100,000 people, with a nurse to doctor ratio of 8.1. In the years between 1985 and 1995, 96% of the population had access to health care services. Adequate sanitation and safe water are available to 22% and 28% of the population respectively.

The main health problems are malaria, tuberculosis, leprosy, and venereal disease. Significant malnutrition occurs in some areas, and pneumonia and related respiratory infections are major risks. In 1990, there were about 275 reported cases of tuberculosis per 100,000 inhabitants. There were 66,797 cases of malaria, 5,335 cases of tuberculosis, and 6,821 measles cases in 1994. The increased incidence of malaria has been linked to importation from neighboring islands. Immunization rates for children up to one year old were fairly high in 1994: tuberculosis, 91%; diphtheria, pertussis, and tetanus, 66%; polio, 66%; and measles, 39%. While undernutrition remains the main nutritional problem, dramatic changes have occurred in some groups with exposure to Westernized diets. Diabetes in the highland populations is low but has been documented to be as high as 16% in major cities of Papua New Guinea.

The country's population in 1994 was 4.2 million, with a birth rate in 1990–95 of 33.4 per 1,000 people, with only 4% of married women aged 15 to 49 using contraception. There were 139,000 births in 1994.

The infant mortality rate decreased from 110 deaths per 1,000 live births in 1974 to 64 in 1995. In 1990 23% of all births were low birth weight babies. The general mortality rate was 10.7 per 1,000 people in 1990–95, and the maternal mortality rate was 800 per 100,000 live births in 1991–93. Life expectancy was 55.8 years in 1990–1995. Total health care expenditures in 1990 were $142 million.

Housing

Traditional housing in rural areas appears to be adequate, but in urban areas there are acute shortages because of migration. In most urban areas, squatter settlements have been established. New housing (923 dwellings in 1984) has fallen far short of meeting the demand, especially for medium- and low-cost units. As of 1988, the housing stock totaled 555,000, and the number of people per dwelling averaged 5.8.

EDUCATION

Education in Papua New Guinea is not compulsory, and in the mid-1980s only one-third of the population was literate. The present government aims at upgrading and improving the quality of education. Children attend state-run community schools for primary education and provincial and national high schools for secondary education. After grade 6, they are tested and screened for continuing their studies in provincial high school. After grade 10, students have to qualify through an examination to enter one of the four national senior high schools, where they attend grades 11 and 12. After grade 10, students may enter one of the many technical or vocational schools which train them in various careers and skills, depending on their interests. The adult illiteracy rate in 1995 was 27.8% (male: 19%, female: 37.3%). In 1995, 2,790 primary schools had a total enrollment of 525,995 students.

In addition to the National Government System, there is an international School System which ends at high school. Fees are considerably higher than the government run schools and the curriculum is based on the British system. There are also privately run preschools and primary schools.

The University of Papua New Guinea in Port Moresby offers degrees in law, science, medicine and arts. The University of Technology in Lae offers degrees in technical subjects such as engineering, business, architecture, and forestry.

1999 KEY EVENTS TIMELINE

January

- A British tourist is rescued after surviving twenty-two days lost and alone in the remote rain forest of Papua New Guinea.

February

- A small commercial passenger plane crashes, killing all eleven people aboard.

March

- A clan fight leaves thirty-five people dead and dozens injured.

April

- A Roman Catholic archbishop calls on Papua New Guinea's prime minister to resign, warning a popular uprising is possible if he doesn't.

- A tropical deluge floods Papua New Guinea's remote Western Province, leaving up to 30,000 villagers short of food, clean water, and medical supplies.

- An earthquake with an estimated magnitude of 7.4 strikes off the coast of Papua New Guinea. There were no immediate reports of damage or injuries.

June

- A plane carrying seventeen people crashes in mountainous terrain in Papua New Guinea's highlands.

July

- Papua New Guinea establishes diplomatic ties with Taiwan. It is a symbolic victory for Taiwan over the People's Republic of China, but it creates political problems for Papua New Guinea. Prime Minister Bill Skate allegedly established the ties for a promised $2 million loan.

- China protests Papua New Guinea's decision to open diplomatic ties with rival Taiwan. China implies it is prepared to sever relations if the Papuan government does not reverse its decision.

- Papua New Guinea's Prime Minister Bill Skate announces his resignation, as parliament prepares for a no-confidence vote. His decision to establish diplomatic ties with Taiwan proves to be his undoing.

- Former central bank governor Mekere Morauta wins overwhelming approval as Papua New Guinea's new prime minister.

- Morauta announces his country will not establish diplomatic ties with Taiwan, ending the dispute with China.

August

- The government of Papua New Guinea sends a high level delegation to China to secure financial support.

- The World Wide Fund for Nature calls for the closure of a giant copper mine in Papua New Guinea, calling the project an environmental disaster. The government claims the country will suffer economically if it closes the mine.

October

- The local office of Transparency International, which fights corruption around the world, says government corruption in Papua New Guinea has led to poor health care and dilapidated schools. It urges the public to take a tough stance against corruption.

November

- The World Bank confirms a $300 million aid package, tied to economic reforms.

- A warning is issued to Australians that potentially menacing crocodiles in search of new breeding grounds are leaving Papua New Guinea for northern Australia.

December

- Five prospective bank robbers are killed by police in Port Moresby.

ANALYSIS OF EVENTS: 1999

BUSINESS AND THE ECONOMY

In August the World Wide Fund for Nature called for the closure of a major copper mine in Papua New Guinea, stating that the project was an environmental disaster. That left Papuans facing a tough decision. Closing the mine would hurt the economy, but leaving it open could hurt even more in the long run. The environmental group claimed the open caste Ok Tedi mine in the mountains of western Papua New Guinea has polluted rivers, caused flooding, and destroyed forests. The company that manages the mine said it was reconsidering its role because waste management procedures were not working. The chief executive for Broken Hill Proprietary Company Limited admitted they should not have become involved in the mining operation.

Prime Minister Mekere Morauta asked the World Bank to help assess the impact of the mine's closure, which could seriously damage the country's fragile economy. The mine accounts for about 20% of the island's export income and 10% of its annual gross domestic product. "A comprehensive, independent and balanced approach is necessary," Mekere told the press.

The government also announced in August that it was sending a high level delegation to the People's Republic of China to secure financial support. Mekere's government is trying to borrow money from world agencies as well as other governments. The delegation was expected to visit Japan and South Korea.

GOVERNMENT AND POLITICS

Prime Minister Bill Skate spent most of the first half of 1999 under accusations of corruption and links to Papua New Guinea's notorious street gangs, known as ''rascals.'' Skate's political problems were exacerbated in the first week of July, when he announced the establishment of diplomatic relations with Taiwan. The announcement triggered an international furor that threatened to hurt relations with several countries. Australian officials said Papua New Guinea had placed its own economic future at risk and was dragging the region into the sovereignty dispute between Taiwan and the People's Republic of China.

Taiwan reportedly offered Papua New Guinea $2 million in economic aid, but Australia pointed out that the island's exports to Taiwan amounted to only $11 million per year, while trade with China was six times larger. China was deeply offended with Papua New Guinea's decision to open diplomatic ties with Taiwan, which it regards as a rogue province. Chinese officials suggested they were prepared to sever relations if the Papuan government did not reverse its decision. Facing a critical shortfall in its budget and experiencing an inflation rate of over 20%, Papua New Guinea could not afford to make a diplomatic blunder.

Skate's actions triggered a quick response at home, where parliament prepared to vote him out of office. Skate offered his resignation, saying he was stepping down in an effort to restore political stability and business confidence. He said his resignation was not related to the China/Taiwan issue. Skate became prime minister after a general election in 1997. He campaigned on an anti-corruption ticket, but was embarrassed that same year when news videotapes showed him allegedly authorizing a bribe, boasting of ordering a murder, and bragging that he was the ''godfather'' of rascal gangs.

Parliament, by a 99 to 5 vote, elected Mekere Morauta as the new prime minister. After being sworn in Mourata stated that the nation's future was not going to be easy. He announced he would restart loan negotiations with the World Bank and the International Monetary Fund and continue the peace process in the secessionist conflict on Bougainville. Morauta also promised to review the Taiwan deal. The island didn't have to wait long for his ruling. Within his first week in power Morauta withdrew his country's diplomatic recognition of Taiwan after reviewing documents signed by former prime minister Skate. China welcomed the decision, charging Taiwan with pursuing money diplomacy.

CULTURE AND SOCIETY

Rabaul, Papua New Guinea, was nearly destroyed by a volcanic eruption in 1994, but its residents refuse to leave despite government pressure. When the eruption was over several feet of ash covered the buildings that were not destroyed and thousands of people were forced to leave their homes. Rabaul, once a picturesque harbor town located in a sheltered bay, is surrounded by the forested slopes of volcanic hills. The residents of Rebaul make their homes in the only settlement in the world built entirely within the rim of an active volcano. The government, however, wants them to move, and is building new homes and schools in safer areas along the coast. The government also refuses to spend money on rebuilding Rabaul, yet many residents have returned, dug out their homes and businesses, and tried to settle back into a normal life. The town, boasting a new mayor, has no electricity, but it continues to prevail in the shadow of the volcano. Meanwhile seismic monitors keep tabs on the nearby Tavurvur volcano, which is expected to erupt again.

In July 1998 another natural disaster affected the nation. One of the world's worst tsunamis hit several villages in Papua New Guinea, killing over 2,000 people. Many homes have been rebuilt, but the villagers, once a seafaring people, have moved inland, ''too frightened of the sea which once provided their living and their way of life,'' the BBC reported.

DIRECTORY

CENTRAL GOVERNMENT
Head of State

Queen
Elizabeth II, Monarch

Governor-General

Sir Silas Atopare, The Visitor Office,
Buckingham Palace, London SW1A 1AA,
England
PHONE: +44 (0171) 8391377
FAX: +44 (0171) 9309625

Prime Minister

Mekere Morauta, Office of the Prime Minister,
PO Box 6605, Morauta House, N.C.D., Boroko,
Papua New Guinea
PHONE: +675 3276792
FAX: +675 3276787
E-MAIL: primeminister@pm.gov.pg

Ministers

Deputy Prime Minister, Minister for Home Affairs, Women, Youth and Churches

John Pundari, Office of the Deputy Prime
Minister, Ori Lavi Haus, Nita Street, PO Box
7354, Boroko, Papua New Guinea
PHONE: +675 3254566
FAX: +675 3251230

Minister of Agriculture and Livestock

Ted Diro, Ministry of Agriculture and Livestock,
Spring Garden Road, PO Box 417, Konedobu,
Papua New Guinea
PHONE: +675 3231848
FAX: +675 3230563

Minister of Bougainville Affairs

Michael Somare, Ministry of Bougainville
Affairs, PO Box 343, Waigani 131, 3rd Floor,
Morauta Haus, Waigani, NCD, Papua New
Guinea
PHONE: +675 3276760
FAX: +675 3258038

Minister of Defense

Alfred Pogo, Ministry of Defense, Murray
Barracks FMB, Boroko 111, Papua New Guinea
PHONE: +675 3242480
FAX: +675 3256117

Minister of Education

John Waiko, Ministry of Education, PO Box 446
Waigani, P.S.A. Haus, Port Moresby, NCD,
Papua New Guinea
PHONE: +675 3254648
FAX: +675 3013555

Minister of Lands and Physical Planning

Fabian Pok, Ministry of Lands and Physical
Planning, PO Box 5665 Boroko, Aopi Centre,
Tower 2, Waigani, Port Moresby, NCD, Papua
New Guinea
PHONE: +675 3013116
FAX: +675 3013139

Minister of Petroleum and Energy

Tommy Tomscoli, Ministry of Petroleum and
Energy, PO Box 1993, Port Moresby, 3rd Floor,
NIC Haus, Champion Parade, Port Moresby,
Papua New Guinea
PHONE: +675 3201199
FAX: +675 3201141

Minister of Police and Correctional Services

Mathias Karani, Ministry of Police and
Correctional Services, PO Box 85, Konedobu,
Part Moresby, NCD, Papua New Guinea
PHONE: +675 3226100
FAX: +675 3226113

Minister of Provincial and Local Governments

Andrew Kumbakor, Ministry of Provincial and
Local Governments, PO Box 1287, Boroko,
NCD, Papua New Guinea

Minister of Rural Development, Environment and Conservation

William Ebenosi, Ministry of Rural
Development, Environment and Conservation,
PO Box 6601, Boroko 111, Kumul Avenue,
Waigani, Port Moresby, NCD, Papua New
Guinea
PHONE: +675 3011607
FAX: +675 3011691

Minister of Trade and Industry

Michael Nali, Ministry of Trade and Industry,
Heduru Haus, Waigani Drive, Waigani, Papua
New Guinea
PHONE: +675 3255311
FAX: +675 3254482

Minister of Transport and Civil Aviation

Bart Philemon, Ministry of Transport and Civil
Aviation, Jacksons Airport PO Box 684, Boroko
111, Papua New Guinea
PHONE: +675 3244400
FAX: +675 3251919

Minister of Works

Mao Zeming, Ministry of Works, PO Box 1489,
Port Moresby 121, Port Moresby, NCD, Papua
New Guinea
PHONE: +675 3222500
FAX: +675 3200236

Senior Minister of State

Peter Waieng, Ministry of State

Minister of Corporatization and Privatization
Ron Ganarafo, Ministry of Corporatization and Privatization

Minister of Fisheries
Ron Ganarafo, Ministry of Fisheries

Minister of Foreign Affairs
Michael Somare, Ministry of Foreign Affairs

Minister of Forests
Michael Ogio, Ministry of Forests

Minister of Housing
John Kamb, Ministry of Housing

Minister of Justice
Kilroy Genia, Ministry of Justice

Minister of Labor, Employment, Culture and Tourism
Herowa Agiwa, Ministry of Labor, Employment, Culture and Tourism

Minister of Mining
John Kaputin, Ministry of Mining

Minister of Planning and Implementation
Moi Avei, Ministry of Planning and Implementation

Minister of Public Service
Philemon Embel, Ministry of Public Services

POLITICAL ORGANIZATIONS

People's Progress Party (PPP)

TITLE: National Chairman
NAME: Julius Chan

People's Democratic Movement (PDM)

TITLE: Parliamentary Leader
NAME: Paias Wingti

People's Action Party (PAP)

TITLE: Party Leader
NAME: Akoka Doi

People's National Congress

TITLE: Leader
NAME: Bill Skate

Pangu Pati (Papua New Guinea United Party)

TITLE: Party Leader
NAME: Chris Haiveta

Melanesian Alliance (MA)

TITLE: Chairman

NAME: John Momis

National Party (NP)

TITLE: Party Leader
NAME: Michael Mel

Christian-Democratic Party

Movement for Greater Autonomy

National Alliance Party (NAP)

Peoples Resources Awareness Party (PRAP)

People's Unity Party

United Party (UP)

TITLE: Party Leader
NAME: Paul Torato

DIPLOMATIC REPRESENTATION

Embassies in Papua New Guinea

United Kingdom
PHONE: +675 3251677
FAX: +675 3253547
TITLE: Ambassador
NAME: Brian B. Low

United States
Douglas Street, PO Box 1492, Port Moresby, Papua New Guineaa
PHONE: +675 3211455
FAX: +675 3213423
TITLE: Ambassador
NAME: Arma Jane Karaer

JUDICIAL SYSTEM

Supreme Court

National Court

FURTHER READING

Articles

''Australia Anxious Over Taiwan/PNG Link.'' *BBC Online Network*, 6 July 1999.

''China Warns Papua New Guinea Over Taiwan Ties,'' The Associated Press, 6 July 1999.

''Death Sentence: The World's Languages are Disappearing at an Unprecedented Rate,'' *The Guardian*, 25 October 1999.

''Eleven Killed in Plane Crash in Papua New Guinea,'' The Associated Press, 3 February 1999.

"Fears for Health After PNG Flooding," *BBC Online Network*, 26 April 1999.

"Life Under the Volcano," *BBC Online Network*, 8 August 1999.

"Ocean Sensors Warn of Tsunami Death Waves," *The Guardian of London*, 8 May 1999.

"Papua New Guinea Cancels Taiwan Recognition Deal," The Associated Press, 21 July 1999.

"Papua New Guinea Seeks Chinese Financial Support," *BBC Online Network*, 23 August 1999.

"PM Quits in Papua New Guinea," *The Guardian of London*, 8 July 1999.

"PNG Pays Up To Mercenaries," *BBC Online Network*, 1 May 1999.

"Strong Earthquake Reported Off Papua New Guinea," The Associated Press, 5 April 1999.

"Thirty-five Dead in Papua New Guinea Fighting," The Associated Press, 3 March 1999.

"Taiwan, Papua New Guinea Set Up Diplomatic Ties," The Associated Press, 5 July 1999.

"Thousands Affected By Floods in Remote Area of Papua New Guinea," The Associated Press, 20 April 1999.

"Tidal Devastation: One year later," *BBC Online Network*, 16 July 1999.

PAPUA NEW GUINEA: STATISTICAL DATA

For sources and notes see "Sources of Statistics" in the front of each volume.

GEOGRAPHY

Geography (1)

Area:

Total: 462,840 sq km.

Land: 452,860 sq km.

Water: 9,980 sq km.

Area—comparative: slightly larger than California.

Land boundaries:

Total: 820 km.

Border countries: Indonesia 820 km.

Coastline: 5,152 km.

Climate: tropical; northwest monsoon (December to March), southeast monsoon (May to October); slight seasonal temperature variation.

Terrain: mostly mountains with coastal lowlands and rolling foothills.

Natural resources: gold, copper, silver, natural gas, timber, oil, fisheries.

Land use:

Arable land: 0.1%

Permanent crops: 1%

Permanent pastures: 0%

Forests and woodland: 92.9%

Other: 6%

HUMAN FACTORS

Demographics (2A)

	1990	1995	1998	2000	2010	2020	2030	2040	2050
Population	3,823.4	4,294.8	4,599.8	4,811.9	5,925.5	7,044.4	8,140.5	9,161.4	10,049.4
Net migration rate (per 1,000 population)	NA	NA	NA	NA	NA	NA	NA	NA	NA
Births	NA	NA	NA	NA	NA	NA	NA	NA	NA
Deaths	NA	NA	NA	NA	NA	NA	NA	NA	NA
Life expectancy - males	54.0	56.0	57.2	58.0	61.8	65.2	68.2	70.9	73.0
Life expectancy - females	55.6	57.7	59.0	59.8	63.9	67.7	71.1	74.1	76.7
Birth rate (per 1,000)	34.7	33.2	32.4	31.6	26.7	22.6	19.8	17.3	15.6
Death rate (per 1,000)	11.2	10.2	9.6	9.3	7.8	6.9	6.6	6.8	7.4
Women of reproductive age (15-49 yrs.)	855.6	1,004.0	1,093.0	1,154.8	1,495.1	1,864.6	2,152.0	2,376.6	2,521.3
of which are currently married	NA	NA	NA	NA	NA	NA	NA	NA	NA
Fertility rate	5.1	4.6	4.3	4.1	3.3	2.7	2.4	2.2	2.1

Except as noted, values for vital statistics are in thousands; life expectancy is in years.

EDUCATION

Educational Attainment (10)

Age group (1980) . . . . .25+
Total population 1,135,783
Highest level attained (%)
No schooling 82.6
First level
Not completed 8.2
Completed 5.0
Entered second level
S-1 . . . . .3.9
S-2 . . . . .0.3
Postsecondary . . . . .NA

Literacy Rates (11A)

In thousands and percent[1]	1990	1995	2000	2010
Illiterate population (15+ yrs.)	731	724	710	668
Literacy rate - total adult pop. (%)	68.1	72.2	75.9	82.3
Literacy rate - males (%)	77.8	81.0	83.7	88.0
Literacy rate - females (%)	57.4	62.7	67.6	76.3

GOVERNMENT & LAW

Military Affairs (14B)

	1990	1991	1992	1993	1994	1995
Military expenditures						
Current dollars (mil.)	100	75	85	127	139	107
1995 constant dollars (mil.)	115	83	92	133	142	107
Armed forces (000)	4	4	4	NA	4	5
Gross national product (GNP)						
Current dollars (mil.)	4,511	5,201	5,680	6,934	7,490	7,429
1995 constant dollars (mil.)	5,185	5,747	6,110	7,270	7,678	7,429
Central government expenditures (CGE)						
1995 constant dollars (mil.)	1,939	2,111	2,170	2,498	2,436	1,901[e]
People (mil.)	3.8	3.9	4.0	4.1	4.2	4.3
Military expenditure as % of GNP	2.2	1.4	1.5	1.8	1.9	1.4
Military expenditure as % of CGE	5.9	3.9	4.2	5.3	5.8	5.6
Military expenditure per capita (1995 $)	30	21	23	32	34	25
Armed forces per 1,000 people (soldiers)	1.0	1.0	.9	NA	1.0	1.2
GNP per capita (1995 $)	1,356	1,468	1,525	1,773	1,829	1,730
Arms imports[6]						
Current dollars (mil.)	10	10	60	0	0	0
1995 constant dollars (mil.)	11	11	65	0	0	0
Arms exports[6]						
Current dollars (mil.)	0	0	0	0	0	0
1995 constant dollars (mil.)	0	0	0	0	0	0
Total imports[7]						
Current dollars (mil.)	1,194	1,614	1,485	1,299	1,521	1,451
1995 constant dollars (mil.)	1,372	1,783	1,597	1,362	1,559	1,451
Total exports[7]						
Current dollars (mil.)	1,144	1,338	1,810	2,491	2,640	2,654
1995 constant dollars (mil.)	1,315	1,479	1,947	2,611	2,706	2,654
Arms as percent of total imports[8]	.8	.6	4.0	0	0	0
Arms as percent of total exports[8]	0	0	0	0	0	0

GOVERNMENT & LAW

Government Budget (13A)

Year: 1994

Total Expenditures: 1,630.23 Millions of Kina

Expenditures as a percentage of the total by function:

General public services and public order . . . . . .11.69[f]

Defense . . . . .3.33[f]

Education . . . . .17.59[f]

Health . . . . .8.88[f]

Social Security and Welfare . . . . .66[f]

Housing and community amenities . . . . .3.54[f]

Recreational, cultural, and religious affairs . . . . .1.43[f]

Fuel and energy . . . . .3.04[f]

Agriculture, forestry, fishing, and hunting . . . . . .8.19[f]

Mining, manufacturing, and construction . . . . . .1.51[f]

Transportation and communication . . . . .8.60[f]

Other economic affairs and services . . . . .4.49[f]

MANUFACTURING SECTOR

GDP & Manufacturing Summary (21)

	1980	1985	1990	1992	1993	1994
Gross Domestic Product						
Millions of 1990 dollars	2,827	3,015	3,221	3,945	4,514	4,672
Growth rate in percent	−2.29	3.60	−3.00	11.81	14.44	3.50
Per capita (in 1990 dollars)	915.9	876.0	839.0	982.0	1,098.4	1,111.1
Manufacturing Value Added						
Millions of 1990 dollars	411	458	388	486	531	589
Growth rate in percent	−0.42	3.01	−22.77	8.04	9.34	10.95
Manufacturing share in percent of current prices	10.5	11.0	12.4	9.4	8.8	8.8

FINANCE, ECONOMICS, & TRADE

Balance of Payments (23)

	1992	1993	1994	1995	1996
Exports of goods (f.o.b.)	1,948	2,604	2,651	2,670	2,530
Imports of goods (f.o.b.)	−1,323	−1,135	−1,325	−1,262	−1,513
Trade balance	625	1,470	1,326	1,408	1,017
Services - debits	−1,111	−1,207	−1,031	−1,153	−1,240
Services - credits	389	340	258	344	464
Private transfers (net)	255	172	167	182	124
Government transfers (net)	−63	−129	−150	−107	−52
Overall balance	95	646	569	674	313

PARAGUAY

Republic of Paraguay
República del Paraguay

INTRODUCTORY SURVEY

RECENT HISTORY

Federico Chávez ruled from 1949 until 1954. In May 1954, General Alfredo Stroessner, commander-in-chief of the armed forces, used his cavalry to seize power. With help from the United States, he brought financial stability to an economy racked by runaway inflation, but he used terrorist methods in silencing all opposition. Stroessner won a third presidential term in February 1963, despite the constitutional stipulation that a president could be reelected only once.

Stroessner ran for reelection in 1968, 1973, 1978, 1983, and 1988, all with only token opposition permitted. On 17 September 1980, the exiled former dictator of Nicaragua, Anastasio Somoza Debayle, who had been granted asylum by the Stroessner government, was assassinated in Asunción, and Paraguay broke off relations with Nicaragua.

During the 1980s, Stroessner relaxed his hold on Paraguay. The state of siege, which had been renewed every three months since 1959, was allowed to lapse in April 1987. However, allegations of widespread human rights abuses continued.

On 3 February 1989, Stroessner's 35-year dictatorship came to an end at the hand of General Andrés Rodríguez, second in command of the Paraguayan military. Immediately after the coup, Rodríguez announced that elections would be held in May. With only three months to prepare, little

opposition was mounted, and Rodríguez won easily with 75.8% of the vote.

There followed an immediate easing of restrictions on free speech and organization. Labor unions were recognized and opposition parties allowed to operate freely. Rodríguez promised and delivered elections in 1993. In an unprecedented transfer of political power from one elected government to another, Juan Carlos Wasmosy was elected to the presidency.

Wasmosy began to push for reforms toward a market-oriented economy. The plan included the sale of state-owned enterprises. The economy, however, was slow to respond to the reforms. In 1998, Raúl Cubas Grau was elected president, marking the first time in Paraguay's history that an elected civilian succeeded another as president. Cubas claimed that corruption by the previous administration had cost the economy $2 billion since 1996.

GOVERNMENT

Paraguay is a republic, with substantial powers conferred on the executive branch. The president, who is directly elected for a five-year term, is commander-in-chief of the military and conducts foreign affairs. He appoints the 11-member cabinet, most administrators, and justices of the Supreme Court. He is advised by the Council of State, consisting of the cabinet ministers, the president of the National University, the archbishop of Asunción, the president of the Central Bank, and representatives of other sectors and the military.

The 1967 constitution provided for a two-chamber legislature, consisting of the 36-member Senate and the 72-member Chamber of Deputies. Representatives must be at least 25 years of age and are elected for five-year terms. Voting is by secret ballot and is compulsory for all citizens between 18–60 years of age.

Paraguay is divided into 19 departments subdivided into districts, which, in turn, comprise municipalities and rural districts (*partidos*).

Judiciary

The five-judge Supreme Court exercises both original and appeals jurisdiction. There are four appeals tribunals: civil/commercial, criminal, labor, and juvenile. There are special appeals chambers for civil and commercial cases and criminal cases. Each rural district (*partido*) has a judge appointed by the central government to settle local disputes and to try accused persons and sentence those found guilty.

Political Parties

Since the end of the War of the Triple Alliance, two parties have dominated politics—the National Republican Association (Asociación Nacional Republicana), generally known as the Colorado Party, and the Liberal Party.

DEFENSE

Paraguay's armed forces numbered 20,200 (12,900 draftees) in 1995, with about 14,900 in the army, 3,600 in the navy (including 900 marines), and 1,700 in the air force. Paraguay has compulsory military service of 18–24 months for all males between the ages of 18 and 20. Expenditures of the Ministry of Defense were $107 million in 1995.

ECONOMIC AFFAIRS

Landlocked Paraguay has a limited economy based principally on agriculture, livestock production, forestry, and the basic processing of materials. In recent years, the relative importance of agriculture has declined, and the value of services has risen; however, cattle-raising remains a key economic activity. There is also a large underground economy.

During the 1970s and 1980s, Paraguay suffered from runaway inflation. An economic reform package was introduced in the early 1990s. It included judicial reform, keeping down government expenses, loosening controls over the exchange rate, and privatizing state-owned enterprises.

Public Finance

The public sector account balance deteriorated in the early 1990s to a deficit equivalent to 2.5% of GDP in 1992 (from a surplus of 7% of GDP in 1988). In the late 1980s, improved revenue collection and rising income from the new Itaipú power plan were largely responsible for favorable public sector account balances. In 1991/92, however, decreased tax collections (from newly-implemented tariff reforms) and large current expenditures increases (from escalating wages and pensions) caused the deficit to widen.

The U.S. Central Intelligence Agency estimates that, in 1995, government revenues totaled approximately $1.25 billion and expenditures $1.66 billion. External debt totaled $1.38 billion, approximately 93% of which was financed abroad.

Income

In 1997, Paraguay's gross national product (GNP) was $21.9 billion at current prices, or about $3,900 per person. For the period 1985–95 the average annual inflation rate was 24.9%, resulting in a real growth rate in GNP of 1.1%.

Industry

Among Paraguay's industrial strengths are the processing of agricultural, animal, and forestry products, mainly for export, and small-scale manufacturing of consumer goods for local needs. Most manufacturing is done in the Asunción area, but some plants are located near the source of the raw material used by the particular industry.

Food-processing plants include slaughterhouses, flour mills, sugar mills, oil mills for the production of cottonseed and peanut oils for domestic consumption, as well as castor, tung, coco, and palm oils for export. Related industries process the by-products of oil extraction, and mills produce yerba maté. There are numerous sawmills. A considerable but decreasing number of hides are also produced for export.

Although there is a considerable textile industry, imports still run high. Products for domestic consumption include pharmaceutical and chemical goods, finished wood and furniture, brick and tiles, cigars and cigarettes, candles, shoes, matches, soap, and small metal goods.

Banking and Finance

The Central Bank of Paraguay (BCP) was founded in 1952 as a state-owned, autonomous agency charged with establishing the government's monetary credit and exchange policies. Recommendations in early 1961 by an economic mission of the IDB and IBRD led to the establishment of the National Development Bank to provide an effective source of medium- and long-term agricultural and industrial credits. Savings and loan institutions are regulated by the superintendent of banks.

In 1995, there were 35 banks operating in Paraguay, of which nine had opened since 1990. During the same period the number of finance companies nearly doubled to 68. The increase in the number of banks and finance companies, out of all proportion to the size of the economy, is generally believed to be related to the rapid increase in "hot money" flows through Paraguay associated with drug smuggling. In late 1995, the Central Bank announced a freeze on the opening of new banks and finance companies on the grounds that the local market is saturated.

Foreign-owned banks account for about half of total deposits, and the two largest banks—Banco de Asunción and Citibank—are foreign-owned.

Paraguay's first stock market began trading in October 1993. By January 1996, 30 local companies were registered to operate on the exchange, and a further 27 were in the process of registration. All companies had a minimum paid-up capital of $50,000. However, the tradition of family ownership and almost universal practice of "double accounting" for tax evasion purposes places limits on the growth of a capital market.

Total foreign reserves, excluding gold, amounted to $978.3 million at the end of July 1996. Money supply, as measured by M2, was G2,825 billion at the end of 1995.

Economic Development

To a considerable extent, Paraguay has a government-controlled economy; government agencies fix prices, control distribution, regulate production and exportation, and exercise monopolistic rights over much of the economy. In recent decades, and particularly since the IMF stabilization program went into effect in the late 1950s, some controls have been loosened. In the wake of the free exchange system have come moves to eliminate government subsidies, such as that for wheat. In agriculture there is an annual plan for acreage quotas, but the principal problem has been one of meeting the quotas rather than of the surpluses. The establishment of the National Development Bank has created a source of medium- and long-term credits favorable to agriculture and industry. Price controls and marketing quotas are particularly significant to the cattle industry. Paraguay has sought to develop closer economic ties with Brazil, the US, and Western European nations, largely to reduce the country's dependence on trade with Argentina.

Economic planning is the responsibility of the Technical Planning Secretariat for Economic and Social Development, established in 1962. The first national plan covered 1965–66; the second, 1967–68. The third plan, a medium-term, five-year program for 1969–73, was replaced by a 1972–77 development scheme calling for a 26% increase in public investment in agriculture. Regional development, also given high priority, was to be accomplished through Paraguay's utilization of its water resources in the Itaipú hydroelectric project; a parallel development program for the Alto Paraná region was retarded by delays in the Yacyretá power project. The 1977–81 development plan aimed to achieve a more equitable distribution of social resources. A plan announced in September 1986 provided for comprehensive reform in exchange rates and in investment and fiscal policies.

SOCIAL WELFARE

Social insurance includes free medical, surgical, and hospital care for the worker and dependents; maternity care and cash benefits; sickness and accident benefits; retirement pensions at age 60; and funeral benefits. Unemployment insurance does not exist, but severance pay is provided. Domestic violence and workplace sexual harassment remain serious problems for women.

Healthcare

Hospital and medical facilities are generally concentrated in Asunción and other towns. In 1995, there was 1 hospital bed for every 762 people. In 1993 there was 1 doctor per 1,231 people. Approximately 60% of the population has access to health care services. In 1990–96, only 42% of the population had access to safe water and 41% had adequate sanitation.

Average life expectancy is 71 years. The principal causes of death are bacillary dysentery and other intestinal diseases, heart disease, pneumonia, and cancer.

Housing

Between 1982 and 1988, the number of housing units rose to 755,000 with five people per dwelling. In 1973, a National Housing Bank was established to finance low-income housing development.

EDUCATION

As of 1995, the estimated illiteracy rate was 8%, 6.5% for males and 9.4% for females. Elementary education is compulsory and free between the ages of 7 and 14. In 1994, there were 5,319 public and private primary schools, with 835,089 students; and 240,906 students at the secondary level.

Universities include the National University of Paraguay and Nuestra Señora de la Asunción Catholic University. Total university and higher institution enrollment in 1993 was 42,654 students.

1999 KEY EVENTS TIMELINE

March

- Gunmen assassinate Vice President Luis Maria Argaña, spinning the country into chaos. Argaña was a political enemy of President Raúl Cubas. Argaña wanted to impeach the president for defying Supreme Court orders to send failed coup leader Lino Oviedo back to prison.

- Supporters and opponents of President Cubas clash in Asunción. Six people are killed, and more than two hundred are injured.

- Under mounting pressure, Cubas resigns and turns power over Luis González Macchi, the head of the Senate.

- Argentina grants asylum to Oviedo, who is wanted for the murder of Argaña. Cubas flees to Brazil.

- President González Macchi swears in the country's first coalition government since 1946. He says he will not rest until Oviedo faces justice.

May

- The government announces that it will forcibly retire more than two hundred army officers who have close ties to Oviedo.

- One person is killed and fifteen are injured when protesters demand the resignation of a small town mayor with close ties to Oviedo.

- Diplomatic relations between Paraguay and Uruguay sour after Paraguayan officials criticize Uruguay for giving political asylum to Cubas's colleagues.

- Paraguayan golfer Carlos Franco shoots a final round 6 under par 66 to win his first title in the PGA Tour, a two-shot victory in the $2.6 million Compaq Classic.

July

- Brazil wins the America's Cup soccer tournament in Paraguay.

September

- Some Paraguayan legislators send a letter of apology to Argentinean President Carlos Menem. A Paraguayan senator criticized Argentina for giving asylum to Oviedo, claiming the former general was planning another coup from the neighboring country.

October

- According to officials in Argentina, Paraguayan fugitive Lino Oviedo will be allowed to remain in that country.

December

- Oviedo leaves Argentina where he has been living in exile and returns to live in hiding in Paraguay.

ANALYSIS OF EVENTS: 1999

BUSINESS AND THE ECONOMY

Relations between the Mercosur trade bloc members, Brazil, Argentina, Uruguay, and Paraguay, were at an all time low in 1999. And Paraguay, upset with its partners for giving political asylum to Lino Oviedo, Raúl Cubas, and some of their supporters, was in the middle of most disputes. Some Paraguayans have openly talked about leaving the Mercosur trade bloc. Privately, officials from other member nations would not likely stop Paraguay from leaving.

Paraguay is considered one of the most corrupt nations in the world, and its political instability has prevented Mercosur from pushing ahead with common institutions. Earlier in the year the U.S. State Department gave Paraguay a failing grade on its anti-drug efforts. The report said criminals have turned the country into a haven for smuggling and money laundering.

Instability has hurt economic growth as well, and Paraguay found itself in a deep recession in 1999, with its GDP expected to shrink by 3%. Some of the hardest hit by the economic downturn were tobacco, sugar, and soybean growers, as well as meatpackers. Thousands marched in Asunción in May to pressure the government to refinance credit lines worth $100 million.

GOVERNMENT AND POLITICS

Paraguay's fragile democracy has been under constant siege since dictator Alfredo Stroesnner was ousted from office in 1989 after thirty-five years in power. In the 1990s Paraguayans made some progress, and their democracy withstood several challenges, including a failed coup led by General Lino Oviedo in 1996.

By March 1999 a specter of chaos had enveloped the nation, and Paraguayans feared an imminent military coup. The troubles actually began in May, when Raúl Cubas reportedly won the cleanest presidential elections in the country's history with over 50% of the vote. Whatever goodwill Cubas had managed to build up in the nation quickly evaporated after he released his friend Oviedo from jail. Oviedo was serving a ten-year sentence for his part in the failed 1996 coup attempt and had been a source of constant problems for Paraguay. Citizens were outraged at Cubas's action, but the worse was yet to come. In March gunmen assassinated Vice President Luis Maria Argaña, a political enemy of both Cubas and Oviedo.

Argaña had called for the impeachment of President Cubas for defying Supreme Court orders to send Oviedo back to prison. Argaña was involved in a power struggle with Cubas and Oviedo for control of the Colorado Party, the most powerful political party in the nation. Oviedo, who wanted to become the party's president, stood in Argaña's way. Hours before his death on March 23 Argaña won a court battle to regain control of the party headquarters, which had been taken over by Oviedo's supporters a week earlier.

Oviedo and Cubas condemned the assassination, but almost immediately came under suspicion for their rival's death. A day after Argaña's murder Paraguay's lower house of Congress impeached Cubas for abuse of power. Argaña became a martyr in the battle for democracy. Three days after the assassination supporters and opponents of Cubas clashed in Asunción, leaving six people dead and over two hundred injured. Tanks rolled through the streets as authorities tried to bring the country under control. Cubas resigned two days later, before the Senate took an impeachment vote, and fled to Brazil. Oviedo sought political asylum in Argentina. One of Argaña's close allies, Luis González Macchi, became Paraguay's new president.

Despite Macchi's ties to the Stroessner regime thousands of Paraguayans celebrated the transfer of power and, seemingly, the survival of their fragile democracy. Macchi said he would not rest until Oviedo was returned to prison. Safely in asylum, Oviedo now created international problems for Paraguay, which claimed he was planning a coup from Argentina. Relations with Uruguay and Argentina quickly deteriorated. Lino Oviedo remains a painful distraction and a threat to Paraguay's future.

CULTURE AND SOCIETY

The America's Cup (Copa America) is one of soccer's most important Latin American trophies. Paraguay, as host of the 1999 event, was a favorite in the event. The tournament was held between June 29 and July 18. As many as 80,000 foreigners were expected to flock to Paraguay, which was hosting the most important sporting event in its history. Paraguay, with its difficult political, social, and economic problems, provided 15,000 police officers to protect the fans and the twelve participating teams.

The 1999 America's Cup was criticized by visiting journalists as the worst in the event's history. Organizers attempted to charge three times the actual value of the tickets, scaring away fans, and when the best teams played the stadiums were dangerously swelled with fans. In the end, perennial favorite Brazil defeated Uruguay, 3-0, in the finals.

Consolation for Paraguayan sports fans came in golf. Paraguayan Carlos Franco, who finished tied for sixth in the Masters, won his first PGA tournament in May. Franco shot a final round 6 under par 66 for a two-shot victory in the $2.6 million Compaq Classic in New Orleans, Louisiana.

DIRECTORY

CENTRAL GOVERNMENT
Head of State

President, Luis Angel González Macchi, Office of the President

Ministers

Minister of Agriculture and Livestock, Amancio Oscar Denis Sanchez

Ministry of Agriculture and Livestock
Presidente Franco 472, Asuncion, Paraguay
PHONE: +595 (21) 449614
FAX: +595 (21) 497965

Minister of Education and Worship
Nicanor Duarte Frutos, Ministry of Education and Worship, Chile 128 esq., Humaita y Piribebuy, Asuncion, Paraguay
PHONE: +595 (21) 443078
FAX: +595 (21) 443919

Minister of Finance and Economy
Federico Zayas, Ministry of Finance and Economy, Chile 128 esq., Palmas, Asuncion, Paraguay
PHONE: +595 (21) 440010
FAX: +595 (21) 448283

Minister of Foreign Relations
Jose Felix Fernandez Estigarribia, Ministry of Foreign Relations, Juan E. O'Leary y Presidente Franco, Asuncion, Paraguay
PHONE: +595 (21) 494593
FAX: +595 (21) 493910

Minister of Industry and Commerce
Guillermo Caballero Vargas, Ministry of Industry and Commerce, Avda Espana 323, Asuncion, Paraguay
PHONE: +595 (21) 204638
FAX: +595 (21) 213529

Minister of Interior
Walter Bower Montalto, Ministry of Interior, Estrella y Montevideo, Asuncion, Paraguay
PHONE: +595 (21) 493661
FAX: +595 (21) 448446

Minister of Justice and Labor
Silvio Ferreira, Ministry of Justice and Labor, G.R. de Francia y Estados Unidos, Asuncion, Paraguay
PHONE: +595 (21) 493515
FAX: +595 (21) 208469

Minister of National Defense
Nelson Argana, Ministry of National Defense, Avda Mariscl Lopez y Vice-President Sanchez, Asuncion, Paraguay
PHONE: +595 (21) 204771
FAX: +595 (21) 211583

Minister of Public Health and Social Welfare
Martin Chiola, Ministry of Public Health and Social Welfare, Avda Pettirossi y Brasil, Asuncion, Paraguay
PHONE: +595 (21) 207328
FAX: +595 (21) 206700

Minister of Public Works and Communications
Jose Alberto Planas, Ministry of Public Works and Communications, Oliva y Alberdi, Asuncion, Paraguay
PHONE: +595 (21) 444411
FAX: +595 (21) 444421

POLITICAL ORGANIZATIONS
Encuentro Nacional (EN)

Senador Long 370. esquina Del Maestro, Asunción, Paraguay
PHONE: +595 (21) 610699; 610701
FAX: +595 (21) 610699

Partido Liberal Radical Auténtico-PLRA (Authentic Radical Liberal Party)

Mariscal López, 1750, Asunción, Paraguay
PHONE: +595 (21) 244867; 204869
FAX: +595 (21) 204867
NAME: Domingo Laino

Asociación Nacional Republicana Partido Colorado-ASNPC (National Republican Association Colorado Party)

Asociación Nacional Republicana Junta de Gobierno, 25 de Mayo 842, C/Tacuary, Asunción, Paraguay
PHONE: +595 (21) 444137; 498669
FAX: +595 (21) 444210
E-MAIL: anr@uninet.com.pry
TITLE: Acting President
NAME: Bader Rachid Lichi

Christian Democratic Party (PDC)

Colon 871, Casilla 1318, Asuncion, Paraguay
NAME: Miguel Montaner

Febrerista Revolutionary Party (PRF)

Casa del Pueblo, Manduvira 552, Asunción, Paraguay
PHONE: +595 (21) 94041
NAME: Carlos Maria Ljubetic

DIPLOMATIC REPRESENTATION
Embassies in Paraguay

Argentina
Dirección Av. Espana y Peru, Asuncion, Paraguay
PHONE: +595 (21) 210320; 210321; 210322
FAX: +595 (21) 211029
E-MAIL: embarpy@pla.net.py

Belgium
Belgian Consulate, Ruta II, Kur 17,5, Capiata (Asuncion), Paraguay
PHONE: +595 (21) 282081
FAX: +595 (21) 282082

Brazil
Calle Coronel Irrazabal esq. Avda. Mariscal López, Asuncion, Paraguay
PHONE: +595 (21) 214466, 214534; 214680
FAX: +595 (21) 212693

Costa Rica
San Jose 447, Casilla 1936, Asuncion, Paraguay
PHONE: +595 (21) 213535

Germany
Av. Venezuela 241, Casilla 471, Asunción, Paraguay
PHONE: +595 (21) 214009
FAX: +595 (21) 212863
E-MAIL: 100566.2610@compuserve.com

Israel
Edif. San Rafael, 8, Yegros 437, Asuncion, Paraguay
PHONE: +595 (21) 495097
FAX: +595 (21) 496355
E-MAIL: israel@quanta.com.py

Italy
Calle Luis Morales 680, Luis de Leon, Asuncion, Paraguay
PHONE: +595 (21) 207429
FAX: +595 (21) 212630
E-MAIL: ambasu@quanta.com.py

Peru
Avda Mariscal Lopez 648, Casilla 433, Asuncion, Paraguay
PHONE: +595 (21) 200949

FAX: +595 (21) 212980

Spain
Yegros 437, Asuncion, Paraguay
PHONE: +595 (21) 90686

United Kingdom
Calle Presidente Franco, 706, P.O. Box 404, Asuncion, Paraguay
PHONE: +595 (21) 444472; 496068
FAX: +595 (21) 446385

United States
1776 Mariscal Lopez Ave, Casilla Postal 402, Unit 4711 APO AA 34036 0001, Asuncion, Paraguay
PHONE: +595 (21) 213715
FAX: +595 (21) 213728

Uruguay
25 de Mayo 1894 esq. General Aquino, Asuncion, Paraguay
PHONE: +595 (21) 25391
FAX: +595 (21) 23970

Vatican City
Apostolic Nunciature, Calle Ciudad del Vaticano, entre 25 de Mayo y Caballero, Casilla 83, Asuncion, Paraguay
PHONE: +595 (21) 215139
FAX: +595 (21) 212590
E-MAIL: nunciopy@pla.net.py

Venezuela
Edif. Delime II, 1, Juan E. O'Leary esq., Eduardo Victor Haedo, Apdo 94, Asuncion, Paraguay
PHONE: +595 (21) 44242

JUDICIAL SYSTEM
The Supreme Court
Consejo de la Magistratura

FURTHER READING
Articles

''Paraguay: Certifiable on the War on Drugs.'' *The Economist* (March 6, 1999): 36.

''Paraguay: Fratricide.'' *The Economist* (March 27, 1999): 38.

''Paraguay Lawmakers Trying to Impeach President.'' *The Seattle Times*. 25 March 1999.

''President Quits in Paraguay Turmoil.'' *The Seattle Times*. 29 March 1999.

"Paraguay, Bolivia Restart Gas Trade Discussions." *The Oil Daily*. 10 June 1999.

"Paraguay Mired in Corruption Investigations." *World Press Review* (June 1999): 23.

"Paraguay's General in his Asylum." *The Economist* (September 11, 1999): 40.

"Rivers of Blood." *Newsweek International* (April 5, 1999): 30.

"The Americas: The Woes of Three Uncertain Mini-Democracies." *The Economist* (April 3, 1999): 29.

"Troops Quell Impeachment Rioters in Paraguay," The Associated Press, 28 March 1999.

Books

Nickson, R. Andrew. *Historical Dictionary of Paraguay*. 2nd ed., Metuchen, N.J.: Scarecrow Press, 1993.

Paraguay, 1994 Post Report. rev. ed. Washington, D.C.: Dept. of State, 1994.

Trade Policy Review: Paraguay. Geneva, Switzerland: World Trade Organization, 1997.

Internet

Latin World. "Paraguay." Available Online @ http://www.latinworld.com/countries/paraguay/sur/paraguay/index.html (November 17, 1999).

Washington Post. "Paraguay." Available Online @ http://www.washingtonpost.com/wp-srv/inatl/longterm/worldref/country/paraguay.htm (November 17, 1999).

PARAGUAY: STATISTICAL DATA

For sources and notes see "Sources of Statistics" in the front of each volume.

GEOGRAPHY

Geography (1)

Area:

Total: 406,750 sq km.

Land: 397,300 sq km.

Water: 9,450 sq km.

Area—comparative: slightly smaller than California.

Land boundaries:

Total: 3,920 km.

Border countries: Argentina 1,880 km, Bolivia 750 km, Brazil 1,290 km.

Coastline: 0 km (landlocked).

Climate: subtropical; substantial rainfall in the eastern portions, becoming semiarid in the far west.

Terrain: grassy plains and wooded hills east of Rio Paraguay; Gran Chaco region west of Rio Paraguay mostly low, marshy plain near the river, and dry forest and thorny scrub elsewhere.

Natural resources: hydropower, timber, iron ore, manganese, limestone.

Land use:

Arable land: 6%

Permanent crops: 0%

Permanent pastures: 55%

Forests and woodland: 32%

Other: 7% (1993 est.).

HUMAN FACTORS

Demographics (2A)

	1990	1995	1998	2000	2010	2020	2030	2040	2050
Population	4,236.1	4,876.2	5,291.0	5,579.5	7,157.3	8,959.6	10,927.0	12,963.2	15,000.7
Net migration rate (per 1,000 population)	NA	NA	NA	NA	NA	NA	NA	NA	NA
Births	NA	NA	NA	NA	NA	NA	NA	NA	NA
Deaths	NA	NA	NA	NA	NA	NA	NA	NA	NA
Life expectancy - males	68.4	69.7	70.3	70.7	72.6	74.2	75.6	76.7	77.6
Life expectancy - females	72.6	73.7	74.3	74.7	76.6	78.2	79.7	80.9	81.9
Birth rate (per 1,000)	34.6	33.2	32.2	31.5	28.5	25.9	23.3	21.1	19.2
Death rate (per 1,000)	5.9	5.5	5.3	5.2	4.7	4.6	4.8	5.3	5.7
Women of reproductive age (15-49 yrs.)	1,002.9	1,163.1	1,266.0	1,341.0	1,735.4	2,190.3	2,681.8	3,188.6	3,659.2
of which are currently married	NA	NA	NA	NA	NA	NA	NA	NA	NA
Fertility rate	4.6	4.4	4.3	4.2	3.8	3.4	3.1	2.8	2.6

Except as noted, values for vital statistics are in thousands; life expectancy is in years.

Health Personnel (3)

Total health expenditure as a percentage of GDP, 1990-1997[a]

Public sector 1.8

Private sector 3.3

Total[b] 5.1

Health expenditure per capita in U.S. dollars, 1990-1997[a]

Purchasing power parity 173

Total 86

Availability of health care facilities per 100,000 people

Hospital beds 1990-1997[a] 60

Doctors 1993[c] 67

Nurses 1993[c] 10

Health Indicators (4)

Life expectancy at birth

1980 67

1997 70

Daily per capita supply of calories (1996) 2,485

Total fertility rate births per woman (1997) 3.8

Maternal mortality ratio per 100,000 live births (1990-97) . . . . .190[d]

Safe water % of population with access (1995) 39

Sanitation % of population with access (1995) 32

Consumption of iodized salt % of households (1992-98)[a] 79

Smoking prevalence

Male % of adults (1985-95)[a] 24

Female % of adults (1985-95)[a] 6

Tuberculosis incidence per 100,000 people (1997) 73

Adult HIV prevalence % of population ages 15-49 (1997) 0.13

Infants and Malnutrition (5)

Under-5 mortality rate (1997) 33

% of infants with low birthweight (1990-97) 5

Births attended by skilled health staff % of total[a] . . .61

% fully immunized (1995-97)

TB 87

DPT 82

Polio 82

Measles 61

Prevalence of child malnutrition under age 5 (1992-97)[b] . . . . .NA

Ethnic Division (6)

Mestizo 95%

White plus Amerindian 5%

Mestizo is mixed Spanish and Amerindian.

Religions (7)

Roman Catholic 90%. Mennonite and other Protestant denominations.

Languages (8)

Spanish (official), Guarani.

EDUCATION

Public Education Expenditures (9)

Public expenditure on education (% of GNP)

1980 . . . . .1.5

1996 . . . . .3.9

Expenditure per student

Primary % of GNP per capita

1980 . . . .

1996 . . . . .10.9

Secondary % of GNP per capita

1980 . . . .

1996 . . . . .12.0

Tertiary % of GNP per capita

1980 . . . .

1996 . . . . .91.0

Expenditure on teaching materials

Primary % of total for level (1996) . . . .

Secondary % of total for level (1996) . . . .

Primary pupil-teacher ratio per teacher (1996) 21

Duration of primary education years (1995) 6

Educational Attainment (10)

Age group (1992) . . . . .15+

Total population 2,427,485

Highest level attained (%)

No schooling 7.0

First level

Not completed 38.4

Completed 22.8

Entered second level

S-1 . . . . .12.8

S-2 . . . . .12.2

Postsecondary 6.6

Literacy Rates (11A)

In thousands and percent[1]	1990	1995	2000	2010
Illiterate population (15+ yrs.)	239	235	229	213
Literacy rate - total adult pop. (%)	90.7	92.1	93.4	95.4

In thousands and percent[1]	1990	1995	2000	2010
Literacy rate - males (%)	92.5	93.5	94.4	95.9
Literacy rate - females (%)	88.8	90.6	92.3	94.9

GOVERNMENT & LAW

Political Parties (12)

Chamber of Deputies	No. of seats
Colorado Party	.38
Authentic Radical Liberal Party (PLRA)	.33
National Encounter (EN)	.9

Government Budget (13A)

Year: 1993

Total Expenditures: 1,559,382 Millions of Guaranies

Expenditures as a percentage of the total by function:

General public services and public order 20.70

Defense 10.69

Education 22.07

Health 7.33

Social Security and Welfare 16.25

Housing and community amenities 44

Recreational, cultural, and religious affairs ....-

Fuel and energy 2.52

Agriculture, forestry, fishing, and hunting 5.39

Mining, manufacturing, and construction 08

Transportation and communication 8.50

Other economic affairs and services ....-

Military Affairs (14B)

	1990	1991	1992	1993	1994	1995
Military expenditures						
Current dollars (mil.)	85	119	130	107	101	121
1995 constant dollars (mil.)	97	132	140	113	104	121
Armed forces (000)	16	16	16	16	15	12
Gross national product (GNP)						
Current dollars (mil.)	6,667	7,047	7,250	7,763	8,205	8,789
1995 constant dollars (mil.)	7,661	7,787	7,798	8,138	8,411	8,789
Central government expenditures (CGE)						
1995 constant dollars (mil.)	704	922	1,059	1,050	NA	1,660[e]
People (mil.)	4.7	4.8	4.9	5.1	5.2	5.4
Military expenditure as % of GNP	1.3	1.7	1.8	1.4	1.2	1.4
Military expenditure as % of CGE	13.9	14.3	13.2	10.7	NA	7.3
Military expenditure per capita (1995 $)	21	27	28	22	20	23
Armed forces per 1,000 people (soldiers)	3.4	3.3	3.2	3.2	2.9	2.2
GNP per capita (1995 $)	1,647	1,626	1,582	1,605	1,613	1,640
Arms imports[6]						
Current dollars (mil.)	5	0	10	10	10	0
1995 constant dollars (mil.)	6	0	11	10	10	0
Arms exports[6]						
Current dollars (mil.)	0	0	0	0	0	0
1995 constant dollars (mil.)	0	0	0	0	0	0
Total imports[7]						
Current dollars (mil.)	1,352	1,460	1,422	1,689	2,370	2,851[e]
1995 constant dollars (mil.)	1,554	1,613	1,530	1,771	2,429	2,851[e]
Total exports[7]						
Current dollars (mil.)	959	737	657	725	817	886[e]
1995 constant dollars (mil.)	1,102	814	707	760	837	886[e]
Arms as percent of total imports[8]	.4	0	.7	.6	.4	0
Arms as percent of total exports[8]	0	0	0	0	0	0

Crime (15)

Crime rate (for 1997)

Crimes reported 25,200

Total persons convicted 13,700

Crimes per 100,000 population 500

Persons responsible for offenses

Total number of suspects 19,900

Total number of female suspects 4,300

Total number of juvenile suspects 3,100

LABOR FORCE

Labor Force (16)

Total (million) 1.8

Agriculture 45%

Data for 1995 est.

Unemployment Rate (17)

8.2% (urban) (1996 est.)

PRODUCTION SECTOR

Electric Energy (18)

Capacity . . . . .6.533 million kW (1995)

Production . . . . .40.05 billion kWh (1995)

Consumption per capita . . . . .577 kWh (1995)

Exported about 36.96 billion kWh of electricity to Brazil.

Transportation (19)

Highways:

total: 29,500 km

paved: 2,803 km

unpaved: 26,697 km (1996 est.)

Waterways: 3,100 km

Merchant marine:

total: 19 ships (1,000 GRT or over) totaling 26,442
GRT/32,510 DWT ships by type: cargo 14, chemical
tanker 1, oil tanker 3, roll-on/roll-off 1 (1997 est.)

Airports: 948 (1997 est.)

Airports—with paved runways:

total: 10

over 3,047 m: 3

1,524 to 2,437 m: 3

914 to 1,523 m: 4 (1997 est.)

Airports—with unpaved runways:

total: 938

over 3,047 m: 1

1,524 to 2,437 m: 29

914 to 1,523 m: 353

under 914 m: 555 (1997 est.)

Top Agricultural Products (20)

Cotton, sugarcane, soybeans, corn, wheat, tobacco,
cassava (tapioca), fruits, vegetables; beef, pork, eggs,
milk; timber.

MANUFACTURING SECTOR

GDP & Manufacturing Summary (21)

Detailed value added figures are listed by both International
Standard Industry Code (ISIC) and product title.

	1980	1985	1990	1994
GDP ($-1990 mil.)[1]	3,889	4,352	5,265	5,896
Per capita ($-1990)[1]	1,240	1,178	1,220	1,221
Manufacturing share (%) (current prices)[1]	16.5	16.2	17.3	15.5
Manufacturing				
Value added ($-1990 mil.)[1]	721	761	910	977
Industrial production index	100	113	133	104
Value added ($ mil.)	575	659	769	782
Gross output ($ mil.)	1,312	1,395	1,408	1,743
Employment (000)	143	129	156	159
Profitability (% of gross output)				
Intermediate input (%)	NA	NA	NA	NA
Wages and salaries inc. supplements (%)	NA	NA	NA	NA
Gross operating surplus	NA	NA	NA	NA
Productivity ($)				
Gross output per worker	9,131	10,794	8,915	10,718
Value added per worker	4,132	5,119	4,991	4,872
Average wage (inc. supplements)	NA	NA	NA	NA
Value added ($ mil.)				
311/2 Food products	170	219	235	242
313 Beverages	43	56	62	76
314 Tobacco products	6	7	7	6
321 Textiles	44	42	54	57
322 Wearing apparel	2	3	3	2
323 Leather and fur products	7	14	16	16

	1980	1985	1990	1994
324 Footwear	18	20	25	27
331 Wood and wood products	95	96	106	142
332 Furniture and fixtures	6	8	9	13
341 Paper and paper products	—	1	1	—
342 Printing and publishing	24	36	26	34
351 Industrial chemicals	4	6	6	6
352 Other chemical products	10	10	8	6
353 Petroleum refineries	94	51	68	41
354 Miscellaneous petroleum and coal products	—	—	—	—
355 Rubber products	—	—	—	—
356 Plastic products	6	16	18	14
361 Pottery, china and earthenware	—	—	—	—
362 Glass and glass products	1	2	3	4
369 Other non-metal mineral products	26	23	31	23
371 Iron and steel	—	—	—	—
372 Non-ferrous metals	1	4	6	10
381 Metal products	9	15	15	10
382 Non-electrical machinery	1	1	2	2
383 Electrical machinery	—	1	1	1
384 Transport equipment	5	10	8	5
385 Professional and scientific equipment	1	1	1	1
390 Other manufacturing industries	2	17	58	43

FINANCE, ECONOMICS, & TRADE

Economic Indicators (22)

National product: GDP—purchasing power parity—$21.9 billion (1997 est.)

National product real growth rate: 2.6% (1997 est.)

National product per capita: $3,900 (1997 est.)

Inflation rate—consumer price index: 6.2% (1997)

Exchange Rates (24)

Exchange rates:

Guaranies (G) per US$1

January 1998	2,528.8
1997	2,191.0
1996	2,062.8
1995	1,970.4
1994	1,911.5
1993	1,744.3

Top Import Origins (25)

$2.5 billion (c.i.f., 1996 est.) Data are for 1995.

Origins	%
Brazil	.29
United States	.22
Argentina	.14
Hong Kong	.9

Balance of Payments (23)

	1990	1991	1992	1993	1994
Exports of goods (f.o.b.)	1,382	1,121	1,081	1,500	1,871
Imports of goods (f.o.b.)	−1,636	−1,868	−1,951	−2,711	−3,148
Trade balance	−254	−747	−869	−1,211	−1,277
Services - debits	−579	−662	−720	−740	−872
Services - credits	604	1,012	955	1,074	1,358
Private transfers (net)	44	59	27	35	35
Government transfers (net)	12	14	7	7	7
Overall balance	−172	−324	−600	−834	−749

Top Export Destinations (26)

$1.1 billion (f.o.b., 1997 est.) Data are for 1997.

Destinations	%
Brazil	.48
Netherlands	.22
Argentina	.9
United States	.4
Uruguay	.3
Chile	.2

Economic Aid (27)

Recipient: ODA, $38 million (1993).

Import Export Commodities (28)

Import Commodities	Export Commodities
Capital goods	Cotton
Consumer goods	Soybeans
Foodstuffs	Timber
Raw materials	Vegetable oils
Fuels	Meat products
	Coffee
	Tung oil 2%

PERU

Republic of Peru
República del Perú

INTRODUCTORY SURVEY

RECENT HISTORY

Peru entered the twentieth century with a constitutional democratic government and a stable economy. A period of moderate reform came to an end in 1919, when Augusto Leguía y Salcedo, who had served as constitutionally elected president during 1908–12, took power in a military coup.

In opposition to Leguía's dictatorship, the leftist American Popular Revolutionary Alliance (APRA) was formed in 1924. In 1930, the worldwide depression reached Peru. There was an uprising of Apristas (members of APRA) in 1932, but the military and its conservative allies successfully contained it. World War II (1939–45) brought the eruption in 1941 of a border war with Ecuador, which was resolved in Peru's favor. (The nearly 200-year-old border dispute still has not been settled to the satisfaction of both countries.)

In 1945, APRA was legalized by President Manuel Prado y Ugartache. Over the next 20 years, Peru had a series of governments. Civilian regimes were terminated prematurely by military coups in 1948, 1962, and 1968. The 1948 coup was followed by eight years of military rule under General Manuel A. Odría.

The 1968 coup inaugurated 10 years of military government, which implemented socialist-style economic reforms. The military also reached out to Peru's long-neglected Amerindian population, making Tupac Amaru (leader of an Amerindian revolt against the Spanish) a national

---

CAPITAL: Lima.

FLAG: The national flag consists of red, white, and red vertical stripes, with the coat of arms centered in the white band.

ANTHEM: *Himno Nacional*, beginning "Somos libres, seámoslo siempre" ("We are free; let us remain so forever").

MONETARY UNIT: The nuevo sol (ML), a paper currency of 100 céntimos, replaced the inti on 1 July 1991 at a rate of I1,000,000 = ML1, but, in practice, both currencies are circulating. There are coins of 1, 5, 10, 20, and 50 céntimos and 1 nuevo sol, and notes of 10, 20, 50, and 100 nuevos soles and 10,000, 50,000, 100,000, 500,000, 1,000,000, and 5,000,000 intis. ML1 = $0.38911 (or $1 = ML2.57).

WEIGHTS AND MEASURES: The metric system is the legal standard.

HOLIDAYS: New Year's Day, 1 January; Labor Day, 1 May; Day of the Peasant, half-day, 24 June; Day of St. Peter and St. Paul, 29 June; Independence Days, 28–29 July; Santa Rosa de Lima (patroness of Peru), 30 August; Battle of Anzamos, 8 October; All Saints' Day, 1 November; Immaculate Conception, 8 December; Christmas, 25 December. Movable holidays include Holy Thursday and Good Friday.

TIME: 7 AM = noon GMT.

LOCATION AND SIZE: Peru is South America's third-largest country, with an area of 1,285,220 square kilometers (496,226 square miles), slightly smaller than the state of Alaska. It has a total boundary length of 9,354 kilometers (5,812 miles). Peru's capital city, Lima, is located on the Pacific coast.

CLIMATE: Average temperatures range from 21°C (70°F) in January to 15°C (59°F) in June at Lima, on the coast. At Cusco, in the mountains, the range is only from 12°C (54°F) to 9°C (48°F), while at Iquitos, in the Amazon region, the temperature averages about 32°C (90°F) all year round. In the eastern jungle, precipitation is heavy. Rainfall is often meager near the coast, but cool ocean breezes produce a sea mist called *garúa*.

PERU

| 0 | 100 | 200 | 300 | 400 Miles |
| 0 | 100 | 200 | 300 | 400 Kilometers |

symbol, and recognizing Quechua as an official national language.

Peru returned to civilian government with the elections of 1980, in which former president Fernando Belaúnde Terry was returned to office. During Belaúnde's administration, a small guerrilla group, Shining Path (Sendero Luminoso) began operating openly in the Andes. The government's campaign against terrorism, beginning in May 1983 and continuing through 1985, resulted in the disappearance of thousands, charges of mass killings, and the granting of unlimited power to the armed forces.

The election of 1985 was historic in two ways: it was the first peaceful transfer of power in 40 years, and it brought into office the first president from APRA since the party's founding. The economic policies of the new president, Alán García Pérez, were initially successful, but Peru's economic troubles persisted. After an initial boom, industrial production began to sag, and food shortages became common. By 1990, inflation had climbed to four-digit levels.

Meanwhile the Shining Path escalated its attacks, coming down from the mountains and striking at urban and suburban targets around Lima and

Callao. In response, García authorized a set of brutal counter-rebel campaigns.

By 1990, neither APRA nor the AP (the Popular Action Party of Belaúnde) had popular support. In a surprise turn of events, Alberto Fujimori, the son of Japanese immigrants, defeated conservative novelist Mario Vargas Llosa by 57% to 34%. Fujimori immediately imposed a set of harsh economic measures designed to curb inflation. These policies caused a great deal of economic disruption but did reduce inflation to pre-1988 levels.

Fujimori moved aggressively to combat the Shining Path and other guerrilla groups, but violence continued, human rights deteriorated, and the military became stronger. Fujimori also became more and more isolated politically. In April 1992, he shut down Congress and refused to recognize any judicial decisions. However, this *autogolpe* (''self-coup'') received widespread popular approval and, most importantly, the military supported Fujimori's moves. A border war with Ecuador in 1995 (in which both sides claimed victory) boosted Fujimori's popularity to help him win a second term.

In December 1996, 14 Tupac Amaru rebels seized the Japanese embassy and held dozens of people hostage. In April 1997, military commandos stormed the embassy and killed all of the Tupac Amaru guerillas. Only one hostage died in the raid, as a result of a heart attack.

After the end of the hostage crisis, protests erupted when Fujimori fired three Constitutional Tribunal judges. They had rejected his request to serve a third presidential term.

GOVERNMENT

Under the 1979 constitution, the president was popularly elected for a five-year term and could not be reelected to a consecutive term. The National Congress consisted of a 60-member Senate and a 180-member Chamber of Deputies. All elected legislators had five-year terms.

After the *autogolpe* (President Fujimori's 1992 seizure of all government power), the constitution was suspended. The Constituent Assembly soon amended the 1979 constitution to allow a president to run for a second consecutive term. The document is still under revision.

Peru is divided into 148 provincial subdivisions.

Judiciary

Peru's highest judicial body, the 16-member Supreme Court, sits at Lima and has national jurisdiction. The nine-member Court of Constitutional Guarantees rules on human rights cases. Superior courts, sitting in the departmental capitals, hear appeals from the provincial courts, which are divided into civil, penal, and special chambers.

As of 1993, approximately 70% of the judges and prosecutors had been appointed by President Fujimori after his seizure of all government powers in 1992, and they never were confirmed by Congress. Despite constitutional reforms, many accused persons (especially those accused of drug trafficking or terrorism) may spend months or even years in prison before they are brought to trial.

Political Parties

In recent times, Peru's two main political parties have been the American Popular Revolutionary Alliance (Alianza Popular Revolucionaria Americana—APRA) and The Popular Action Party (Partido de Acción Popular, or AP).

APRA was begun in 1924 as a movement of and for Latin American workers. Outlawed in 1931 and again in 1948, and legalized in 1956, APRA has traditionally opposed the military. In 1985, for the first time, an APRA candidate, Alán García Pérez, won the presidency. APRA is boycotting any political arrangement under current president Alberto Fujimori.

The Popular Action Party (AP) was founded in 1956. Originally a reform party, it competed with APRA for the support of those favoring change in Peru. The AP won the presidency in 1963 and 1980, with Fernando Belaúnde Terry as its candidate both times.

The Popular Christian Party (Partido Popular Cristiano—PPC), the main party on the right, holds eight Assembly seats in the Fujimori government.

The largest active guerrilla party is Shining Path (Sendero Luminoso), a communist group founded in 1964. Also active is the smaller MRTA/MIRA, formed from a merger of the Tupac Amaru Revolutionary Movement (Movimiento Revolucionario Tupac Amaru—MRTA) and the Movement of the Revolutionary Left (MIR).

DEFENSE

Two years of military service are obligatory and universal, but only a limited number of men between the ages of 20 and 25 are drafted. There are 188,000 army reservists.

The total strength of the armed forces in 1995 was 125,000 (including 74,500 draftees). Army personnel numbered 85,000, navy 25,000 (including 3,000 marines), and air force 15,000. About 66,000 men make up the national police. In 1995, Peru spent approximately $817 million on defense.

The armed forces, advised by 50 Russians, contend with approximately 5,000–8,000 armed guerrillas of the Shining Path and 500 terrorists of the Tupac Amaru movement.

ECONOMIC AFFAIRS

Since World War II, the Peruvian economy has developed rapidly, exhibiting a rate of growth that has been among the highest in Latin America. The strength of Peru's economy lies in its natural resources. Silver and gold were the prized commodities of colonial Peru. In more recent times, lead, copper, zinc, iron ore, and petroleum have become important exports.

In the early 1990s, the Peruvian economy came out of recession, as a result of an increase in foreign investment. In 1996, the economy grew by 2.8%, marking the fourth year in a row for real economic growth. The government has continued to reduce the annual rate of inflation. Annual inflation went down from 7,000% in 1990 to 40% in 1993 to 11.8% in 1996.

Public Finance

The central government publishes an annual budget representing the government's consolidated accounts (including budgetary and extrabudgetary transactions). Indirect taxes, including import and export duties, constitute the major source of government revenues. In the early 1970s, the number of state enterprises increased rapidly, which led to increased public-sector spending. As the revenues from state enterprises lagged behind expenditures, the budget deficit increased to about 10% of GDP during 1975–77, as compared to 1.7% during 1970–72. As a result of a fiscal stabilization program, the deficit was reduced to 6.5% of GDP in 1978, and to 2.5% in 1985.

In 1990, the Fujimori administration began to pursue tighter fiscal policies and attempted to avoid domestic financing of the deficit. The consolidated public sector deficit, which in 1990 was 6.5% of GDP, fell to 2.5% by 1992, despite the suspension of most foreign financing after the 5 April coup.

The IMF program allowed a foreign-financed deficit of 2.9% of GPD in 1993 for increased social sector spending and investment in infrastructure. However, with lower than expected foreign financing and tax collection, the deficit that could be maintained while meeting the public sector external debt obligations was only equivalent to about 2% of GDP. By August 1993, the government had gained $452 million through the privatization of fifteen state enterprises.

The U.S. Central Intelligence Agency estimates that, in 1995, government revenues totaled approximately $8.5 billion and expenditures $9.3 billion. External debt totaled $22.4 billion.

Income

In 1997, Peru's gross national product (GNP) was $110.2 billion at current prices, or about $4,420 per person. For the period 1985–95, the average annual inflation rate was 398.5%, resulting in a decline in GNP of 1.6% per person.

Industry

Smelting and refining are among Peru's most important industries. There are also a number of foundries, cement plants, automobile assembly plants, and plants producing sulfuric acid and other industrial chemicals.

The expansion of the fish meal industry led to the creation of many related industries—factories for the production of cans, paper, jute bags, and nylon fishnet. Once a major exporter of the natural fertilizer guano, Peru now produces synthetic fertilizers high in nitrogen and related industrial chemicals.

Banking and Finance

The Central Reserve Bank, the sole bank of issue, was established in Lima in 1931 to succeed the old Reserve Bank. Also created in 1931 was the Superintendency of Banks and Insurance, an agency of the Ministry of Finance, which defines procedure and obligations of banking institutions and has control of all banks. The government-owned National Bank (Banco de la Nación) not only acts as the government's tax collector and financial agent, but also is Peru's largest commercial bank. Another government agency, the Caja de Ahorros, provides secured loans to low-income borrowers.

Peru's banking sector has grown rapidly as a result of the economic recovery and capital inflows into the financial system. A decade ago, in 1987, the president of Peru was contemplating nationalizing the entire system. Shortly after his election, Mr. Fujimori decreed the abolition of the state's development and mortgage credit banks. Today, only the development finance corporation, Cofide, still exists, but as a second-tier bank channeling funds from other institutions and without the powers to raise financing on its own account. Along with the subsidized state development banks, a host of savings and loans cooperatives have disappeared, victims of financial mismanagement, hyperinflation, and embezzlement. With them went the savings of many lower- and middle-class Peruvians, who have been left with a distrust of the financial system.

Financial operations and assets remain concentrated: four banks account for almost three-quarters of all deposits in the system. Even though deposits in the banking system have almost doubled since 1990, Peru is severely underbanked. Total deposits in mid-1996 were ML27 billion, around 18% of GDP, approximately one-third of the ratio in neighboring Chile, for example. Foreign reserves, excluding gold, totaled $10,417 million in September 1996. Money supply, as measured by M2, amounted to ML24,875 million at the end of 1995.

The privately owned Lima Stock Exchange (Bolsa de Valores de Lima–BVL) regulates the sale of listed securities. It began a long bull run in 1992 as the economy stabilized and progress towards pacification was made. After falling by 17% in dollar terms in 1995, the dollar value of the index grew in 1996 until the third quarter. The gains, however, were almost completely wiped out by the hostage crisis at the end of the year. At the end of 1996, 234 companies were listed on the BVL, and the market capitalization was $13.7 billion.

Economic Development

After World War II, President Odria discontinued import licensing and certain price controls and enacted the Mining Code of 1950, the Petroleum Law of 1952, and the Electrical Industry Law of 1955, all with a view to reassuring sources of foreign and domestic capital of reasonable taxation and an adequate rate of earnings under liberal exploitation concessions. Given this stimulus to capital ventures, the economy expanded, and new exports, such as iron and coal, were developed.

After the coup of 1968, Peru's military rulers sought a profound restructuring of the country's economic life. The overall objectives were the establishment of effective state control of natural resources and redistribution of foreign participation; creation of manageable balance among governmental, private, and foreign sectors; and redistribution of productive sources more broadly throughout the population. Nationalization, coupled with a redistribution of ownership and management authority in major enterprises, was the cornerstone of the new policy from its incipient stages in 1968 though 1975. A five year plan was announced in December 1968, emphasizing a reorientation from an agricultural to an industrial economy and stressing the expropriation of large estates, with redistribution of land to peasants in the sierra. In early 1969, tax and credit incentives for the formation of cooperatives and the consolidation of smaller land-holding were enacted. In nonagricultural sectors, the government began, in 1969, selective nationalization of major foreign holding in the mining, petroleum, and infrastructure sectors. In several areas, a government presence was asserted through the creation of state-owned commercial enterprises, the most notable of which included Induperu, in industry; Mineroperu, in mining; Pescaperu, in fishing; Petroperu, in petroleum; Entelperu, in telecommunications; and COFIDE (Corporacion Financiera de Desarrollo), in investment.

Industrial enterprises in general were required to adopt profit-sharing and co-ownership schemes for their employees. Although strict limits were placed on foreign participation in Peruvian industry, such investments were not ruled out in principle, and in 1974, the government acted to guarantee fair settlement for U.S. holdings expropriated during 1968–73.

On 28 July 1974, the government announced its Inca Plan (which may actually have been drawn up before the 1969 coup), a master plan that envisioned eventual transformation of all economic entities along prescribed socialist lines. Three types of enterprises were to be permitted to operate in Peru: state-owned enterprises, worker-owned collectives (industrial communities), and social-property companies (entities managed by workers but financed by the state). In late 1975, the Central Bank set up a line of credit to aid the formation of social-property companies through the National Fund for Social Property. The Agrarian Bank, which had been created in July, was authorized to handle the credit requirements of the reorganized agricultural sector, as well as to ease the transformation of cooperatives and farmers' associations, many of which had existed for only a few years, into social-property entities. The order of priorities for industry placed basic industries—notably steel, nonferrous metals, chemicals, fertilizers, cement, and paper—at high rung, followed by manufacturers of capital good, such as machine tools, and industrial research. Reinvestment of profits was stressed throughout.

In the mid-1970s, the regime began to moderate the rigid price control system instituted in its formative years. The prices of petroleum and basic consumer goods were increased, while wage increases were fixed and agricultural subsidies removed. In September 1975, the sol was devalued and financial controls were imposed to help stem inflation (reaching 40% in 1975) and to ease the trade imbalance. The Tupac Amaru Development Plan, announced in 1977, limited the structural reforms of the Inca Plan, calling for economic decentralization and encouragement of foreign investment. In the late 1970s, a number of state-controlled enterprises were sold, and worker participation was curtailed. The civilian leaders who came to power in 1980 sought to reduce government participation in the economy and to improve the efficiency of state enterprises. Import tariffs and export taxes were reduced, and a new investment program for 1980–85 emphasized power and irrigation projects and the construction of housing and health care facilities. These attempts to revitalize the economy were hampered by the worldwide recession and by the soft market of Peru's commodity exports. In response, the Garcia Administration reverted to an interventionist policy, imposing import controls and regulating foreign-exchange availability, as well as influencing the financial sector by threatening to nationalize the banks.

The decade of the 1990s, with an Administration in favor of a market economy, has attracted more investment into Peru's economy. With foreign capital flowing in recent years, Peru was poised for economic recovery. Privatization and the rapidly growing economy are providing the government with funds to spend on infrastructure and social programs.

In August of 1990, the government began to implement an economic program based on an (1) economic stabilization plan, (2) a structural reform program and (3) a set of initiatives aimed at reintegrating the Peruvian economy into the international economic system. As a direct result economic growth in 1993, 1994 and 1995 was quite strong. However, growth slowed significantly in 1996 as the Peruvian economy entered a new phase of its growth cycle.

The economic stabilization plan focuses on achieving an inflation rate comparable to international levels, and fostering an environment favorable for savings, investment and sustained economic growth. The plan is based on strict fiscal discipline in accordance with an austere monetary policy.

Lastly, the reinsertion of Peru into the international financial system, beginning in 1991, is intended to restore normal relations between the country and its international creditors. Up to the present, Peru has normalized its relations with multilateral bodies and the Paris Club and is in the process of doing the same with the commercial banks.

SOCIAL WELFARE

Workers receive benefits covering disability, medical attention, hospitalization, maternity, old age, retirement, and widows' and orphans' benefits. Working mothers are entitled to maternity leave of 90 days at 100% pay.

Women are often kept from leadership roles in the public and private sectors by the force of tradition, although they are legally equal under the constitution.

Human rights violations have been committed by the government, Shining Path terrorists, and the Tupac Amaru Revolutionary Movement.

Healthcare

Although Peru has made significant advances toward reducing epidemic disease, improving sanitation, and expanding medical facilities, much remains to be done. Health services are concentrated around metropolitan Lima. There was one physician per 943 people in 1993, and about 75% of the population had access to health care services. In 1990, there were 32,434 hospital beds at a rate of 1.5 per 1,000 people.

Leading causes of death in 1990 were communicable diseases and maternal/perinatal causes, noncommunicable diseases, and injuries. There were about 26,000 war-related deaths in Peru from 1983 to 1992. Average life expectancy is estimated at 68 years.

Housing

Successive governments since the 1950s have recognized the importance of slum clearance and public housing programs in combating disease and high mortality rates. Most housing development programs carried out by the government and by private enterprise have been in the Lima area. In rural areas, a conservative estimate of the housing shortage runs to a minimum of 700,000. The total housing stock numbered 4.9 million in 1985.

EDUCATION

Education is free and compulsory for children aged 6 to 15. In 1995, the adult illiteracy rate was estimated at 11% (5.5% for men and 17% for women). A 1972 law established Quechua and Aymará as languages of instruction for non-Spanish-speaking Amerindians, especially in the lowest grades.

In 1994 there were 31,315 primary schools, with over 4 million pupils and 145,795 teachers. The number of secondary school students in 1994 was almost 2 million, with 100,698 teachers. The total higher education enrollment in 1994 reached 755,929. There is a national university in practically every major city; the oldest is the National University of San Marcos of Lima, originally founded in 1551.

1999 KEY EVENTS TIMELINE

January

- Latin Americans of Japanese descent interned in American labor or detention camps during World War II will get a letter of apology from President Clinton under a settlement approved this month.

- U.S. officials hail an "astonishing" drop in coca cultivation in Peru and Bolivia. But plantings of the illicit crop were skyrocketing in Colombia.

- President Alberto Fujimori reshuffles his cabinet. Victor Joy Way Rojas replaces Alberto Pandolfi arbulú as prime minister.

May

- Fujimori and Ecuadorian President Jamil Mahuad formally end a border dispute dating from 1941. The accord gives Ecuador property rights to a small piece of Peruvian territory and navigation rights on some Peruvian rivers.

June

- Shining Path guerrillas are blamed for nine deaths in two separate ambushes. Eighteen people have died in four attacks across the country in one week's time.

July

- Two American women imprisoned for three years in a Peruvian prison for trying to smuggle cocaine have been paroled. Jennifer Davis, 22, and her former roommate from California, Krista Barnes, were released from the Chorrillos women's prison near Lima.

- Peruvian authorities capture the last national leader of the country's Shining Path rebel movement. The arrest of Oscar Ramirez Durand, 46, known as "Comrade Feliciano," comes at a good time for embattled President Alberto Fujimori.

- Hundreds of construction workers and pensioners march to the presidential palace to protest the government's economic policies and Fujimori's possible re-election bid.

August

- President Alberto Fujimori proposes a law authorizing his armed forces to draft fresh recruits in case Colombia's war with leftist rebels spills into Peru's northeast jungle border.

- Peru asks Colombia to rescind former president Alan Garcia's political asylum status, claiming he called for a coup in his homeland.

- The presidents of Ecuador and Peru agree to build roads and bridges through a border region that has been closed by disputes and wars for more than half a century. Hundreds of people stage a protest against a new trade deal between the two countries. They jeer and throw stones as the two presidents drive through the town of Iquitos.

- Peru's flagship carrier Aeroperu, which ceased flights in March with $174 million in debts, was grounded for good after creditors voted to liquidate its assets.

September

- Firefighters contained a blaze that destroyed more than 220 acres of Manu National Park, considered the most diverse center of wildlife and fauna on the planet.

- The Inter-American Court of Human Rights rejects Peru's bid to withdraw from its jurisdiction. The court will continue to summon Peruvian officials to declare in reported abuses.

October

- Alberto Bustamante Belaúnde is appointed head of Fujimori's cabinet. The new prime minister says his main job is to guarantee "clarity" in the April 2000 presidential elections.

- Shining Path rebels kill five Peruvian soldiers during clash. In the meantime, jailed rebels go on a hunger strike.

- Thousands of Peruvians take to the streets in the country's major cities to protest President Fujimori's economic policies. They tell him not to run for office a third time.

November

- At least 46 people are reported missing after an avalanche buries homes in village in the northern Andes.

ANALYSIS OF EVENTS: 1999

BUSINESS AND THE ECONOMY

Peru's economy was battered by El Niño storms, worldwide economic problems, and low mineral prices in 1998, when growth averaged 1 percent. By 1999, mining, fishing and agriculture had improved. Yet the government scaled back its prediction of 4.5–5.5 percent growth. With the economy only expanding by 2.5 percent in the first seven months of the year, Fujimori's government projected 3 percent growth for 1999.

Peru's economy grew by 32 percent between 1993 and 1996 with Fujimori's free-market reforms. But the privatization of state companies left thousands of Peruvians out of work. The country's unions were weakened by anti-labor legislation under Fujimori, but they found some strength to protest his free-market reforms after they failed to generate jobs or reduce poverty. In April, unions and other organizations called for a one-day strike hoping to send a strong message to Fujimori not to run for a third term.

In August, the Inter-American Development Bank said it would loan Peru $311 million to modernize the nation's capital markets, and expand credit to small companies and poor families.

GOVERNMENT AND POLITICS

President Alberto Fujimori has built his reputation on his toughness against terrorism. The authoritarian leader mugged for the cameras when Abimael Guzman, the intellectual leader of the Shining Path guerrillas, was captured in 1992. His victories against the terrorists, his tough talk and daring, and his unwillingness to compromise with the extreme left led to his re-election in 1995.

By early 1999, Fujimori would not confirm if he would run for a third term in the April 2000 presidential elections. His approval ratings were at an all-time low in nine years in office, dragged down by a two-year recession and widespread unemployment that had one of two Peruvians living in poverty. His ratings perked up in July, when a beaming Fujimori posed in front of cameras to announce the capture of Oscar Ramirez Durand, the last national leader of Peru's Shining Path guerrillas.

A week earlier, Fujimori had withdrawn his country from the Inter-American Court of Human Rights, the hemisphere's top judicial body. In well-publicized attacks, Fujimori rejected the court's finding that a Peruvian military court was unfair to four Chilean nationals sentenced to life in prison for terrorist activities. No one could teach Peru lessons about human rights, he said. Following Durand's arrest, Fujimori declined to discuss with the United States the fate of an American woman's life sentence for treason in Peru.

The tough rhetoric worked at home, where his approval ratings went up as high as 50 percent by October. But the international community was not impressed, least of all the United States, which has supported Fujimori. In June, members of the U.S. House of Representatives said they were concerned at the "erosion of democracy and the rule of law" in Peru. A Senate subcommittee said it should be consulted before the White House gave any more American intelligence to Peru. In September, the Inter-American Court of Human Rights rejected Peru's bid to withdraw from its jurisdiction, and said it would continue to summon Peruvian officials to declare in reported abuses.

Despite his widely visible postures on terrorism, Fujimori was coy about his intentions to seek a third term. But his actions, and veiled messages— "power fascinates me," he told the media—

pointed to a vigorous campaign. Early in the year, Fujimori's government promised to reactivate the economy, create jobs and fight poverty—although how was never specified. A third term for the presidency, which will be decided in April 2000, is legally questionable. The Constitution prohibits a third term, but Fujimori's supporters in Congress circumvented the law, and approved a measure that would allow Fujimori to run for election a third time. Supreme Court justices who disagreed were dismissed.

Yet, Fujimori's shield of invincibility is showing some cracks. In April, leftist-led unions, students and other organizations called for a one-day strike. It was effective in Lima, but not as well received in the countryside, where Fujimori remains popular by distributing aid during critical times. By June, students opposed to Fujimori had collected half of 500,000 signatures to create a new national party. The problem for the opposition is the lack of a viable candidate to challenge the president. Opposition parties are weak and divided, and only two names, Lima mayor Alberto Andrade, and former chief of the social security institute Luis Castañeda, have come up as possible candidates. Former president Alan Garcia, who fled the country in 1992, and faces corruption charges, keeps coming up as a possible candidate. Fujimori's supporters are making sure that won't happen. In August, Peru asked Colombia to rescind Garcia's political asylum status, claiming he called for a coup in his homeland. That same month, Congress approved a law banning any former office-holder facing criminal charges from running for election. It seemed that little stood in the way for Fujimori.

CULTURE AND SOCIETY

Many Peruvians and other Latin Americans of Japanese ancestry were interned in American labor or detention camps during World War II. Little was known about them, but some measure of justice was restored in 1999. Latin Americans of Japanese descent were to get a letter of apology from U.S. President Bill Clinton under a settlement approved in January. The settlement provides for payments of $5,000 each, but only half the aging former internees were expected to get any money. More than 2,200 ethnic Japanese were taken from their homes in 13 Latin American countries and taken to camps in Louisiana, Texas and elsewhere. "I think for me and my family it does give a sense of finality," Kazuo Matsubayashi, 62, of Salt Lake City, told the Associated Press. He was taken captive in Lima in 1943, when he was five years of age.

The ancient history of the indigenous people of Peru continues to fascinate the world, which is why any new discovery is welcome news not just to archeologists. In September, American explorer Gene Savoy reported finding the lost city of Conturmarca. He has already been credited with discovering major indigenous ruins in Peru's rain forests. Savoy spent a month in Peru's high cloud forest, where he said he found the remains of the Chachapoyas, tall warriors defeated by the Incas shortly before the arrival of the Spaniards in 1532. The Incas often used the Chachapoyas as bodyguards. In another discovery, archeologists said they found 16 ancient tombs dating from the Inca empire in a 500-year-old stone temple that overlooks the historic city of Cuzco. The tombs contained skeletons believed to be royal members.

While the news of these discoveries was well received, it also caused some concern. In August, the government's cultural chief said the theft of ancient treasures had become a major problem, second only to drug trafficking.

DIRECTORY

CENTRAL GOVERNMENT
Head of State

President
Alberto Kenyo Fujimori, Office of the President

Prime Minister
Alberto Bustamante Belaúnde, Office of the Prime Minister

Ministers

Minister of Agriculture
Rodolfo Munante Sanguinetti, Ministry of Agriculture, Pje. Zela S/N Jesús María, Lima 11, Peru
PHONE: +51 (1) 4333034; 4332271
FAX: +51 (1) 4314771
E-MAIL: postmast@oia.minag.gob.pe

Minister of Defense
Julio Salazar Monroe, Ministry of Defense

Minister of Economy and Finance
Jorge Baca Campodonico, Ministry of Economy and Finance, Jr. Junín 319, Lima 1, Peru
PHONE: +51 (1) 4273930
FAX: +51 (1) 4282509

E-MAIL: postmaster@mef.gob.pe

Minister of Education
Domingo Palermo, Ministry of Education, Calle Van de Velde N° 160, San Borja, Lima, Perú
PHONE: +51 (1) 4353900
E-MAIL: postmaster@minedu.gob.pe

Minister of Energy and Mines
Daniel Hokama Tokashiki, Ministry of Energy and Mines

Minister of Fisheries
Ludwig Meier Cornejo, Ministry of Fisheries, 96 Calle Uno Oeste, N° 50, Urb. Corpac, San Isidro, Lima, Peru
PHONE: +51 (1) 2243336; 2243329

Minister of Foreign Affairs
Fernando de Trazegnies, Ministry of Foreign Affairs

Minister of Industry, Tourism, Integration, and International Trade Negotiations
Gustavo Caillaux, Ministry of Industry, Tourism, Integration, and International Trade Negotiations, Calle Uno 50, San Isidro, Lima, Peru
PHONE: +51 (1) 2243347

Minister of Interior
Jose Villanueva Ruesta, Ministry of Interior

Minister of Justice
Alfredo Quispe Correa, Ministry of Justice, Scipión Llona 350, Miraflores, Lima 18, Perú
PHONE: +51 (1) 4404310; 4417320
E-MAIL: webmaster@wwwminjus.gob.pe

Minister of Labor and Social Promotion
Jorge Domingo Gonzalez Izquierdo, Ministry of Labor and Social Promotion, Av. Salaverry 655, Jesús María, Lima, Peru
PHONE: +51 (1) 4332512; 3307382
FAX: +51 (1) 4242622
E-MAIL: prodlab@mtps.gob.pe

Minister of Presidency
Tomas Gonzalez Reatuegui, Ministry of Presidency

Minister for Promotion of Women and Human Development
Miriam Schenone, Ministry for the Promotion of Women and Human Development, Jr. Camaná 616, Lima, Peru
PHONE: +51 (1) 4289800
FAX: +51 (1) 4261665
E-MAIL: postmaster@lima.promudeh.gob.pe

Minister of Public Health
Mario Costa Bauer, Ministry of Public Health, Av. Salaverry cuadra 8 S/N, Jesús María, Lima, Peru
E-MAIL: webmaster@minsa.gob.pe

Minister of Transport, Communications, Housing, and Construction
Antonio Paucer Carbajal, Ministry of Transport, Communications, Housing, and Construction, Av. 28 de Julio # 800, Lima, Peru
PHONE: +51 (1) 4337800

POLITICAL ORGANIZATIONS

Unión Nacional Odriísta (UNO)
TITLE: Leader
NAME: Fernando Noriega

Renovación (National Renewal)
TITLE: Leader
NAME: Rafael Rey Rey

Renacimiento Andino (Andean Rebirth)
E-MAIL: renandino@wanka.net.pe
TITLE: Leader
NAME: Ciro Gálvez Herrera

Partido Revolucionario de los Trabajadores-PRT (Revolutionary Workers' Party)
Plaza 2 de Mayo 38, Apdo 2449, Lima 100 Peru
TITLE: Leader
NAME: Hugo Blanco

Partido Popular Cristiano-PPC (Popular Christian Party)
Avda Alfonso Ugarte 1484, Lima, Peru
PHONE: +51 (1) 4238723
FAX: +51 (1) 4236582

Partido Obrero Revolucionario Marxista-Partido Socialista de los Trabajadores (Marxist Revolutionary Workers' Party-Socialist Workers' Party)
Jirón Apurimac 465, Lima 1, Peru
PHONE: +51 (1) 4280443
TITLE: Leader
NAME: Ricardo Napuri

Partido Liberal-PL (Liberal Party)
TITLE: Leader
NAME: Miguel Cruchaga

Partido Demócrata Cristiano-PDC (Christian Democratic Party)

PHONE: +51 (1) 4238042
TITLE: Leader
NAME: Carlos Blancas Bustamante

Partido Comunista de Peru-PCP (Communist Party of Peru)

TITLE: Leader
NAME: Ruben Abimael Guzman Reinoso

Nueva Mayoría (New Majority)

TITLE: Leader
NAME: Jaime Yoshiyama Tanaka

Movimiento de Bases Hayistas-MBH (Hayist Movement)

Pasaje Velarde 180, Lima, Peru
TITLE: Leader
NAME: Andrés Townsend Ezcurra

Izquierda Unida-IU (Unified Left)

Avda Grau 184, Lima 23, Peru
TITLE: Leader
NAME: Gustavo Mohome

Izquierda Socialista (Socialist Left)

TITLE: Leader
NAME: Alfonso Barrantes Lingán

Coordinación Democrática (Democratic Coordinator)

TITLE: Leader
NAME: Jose Barba Caballero

Confluencia Socialista (Socialist Alliance)

TITLE: Leader
NAME: Jose Barba Caballero

Cambio 90 (Change 90)

TITLE: Leader
NAME: Alberto Fujimori

Alianza Popular Revolucionaria Americana-APRA (American Popular Revolutionary Alliance)

Avda Alfonso Ugarte 1012, Lima 5, Peru
PHONE: +51 (1) 4313909
TITLE: Leader
NAME: Armando Villanueva del Campo

Acción Popular-AP (Popular Action)

Paseo Colón 218, Lima 1, Peru
PHONE: +51 (14) 404907
TITLE: Leader
NAME: Fernando Belaúnde Terry

Izquierda Nacionalista (Nationalist Left)

TITLE: Leader
NAME: Pedro Reynaldo Cáceres Velásquez

DIPLOMATIC REPRESENTATION

Embassies in Peru

Argentina
Av. 28 de Julio Nro. 828, Lima 01, Peru
PHONE: +51 (1) 4339966
FAX: +51 (1) 4330769

Canada
Calle Libertad No. 130, 18-1126 Miraflores, Lima 18, Peru
PHONE: +51 (1) 4444015
FAX: +51 (1) 4444347

People's Republic of China
Jr. José Granda No. 150, Apartado Postal 395, Lima 27, Peru
PHONE: +51 (1) 4429458
FAX: +51 (1) 4429467

France
Av. Arequipa No. 3415, Apartado Postal 607, Lima 27, Peru
PHONE: +51 (1) 2217837
FAX: +51 (1) 4213693

Germany
Av. Arequipa No. 4210, Lima 18, Peru
PHONE: +51 (1) 4224919
FAX: +51 (1) 4226475

India
Magdalena del Mar, Lima 17, Perú
PHONE: +51 (1) 4602289
FAX: +51 (1) 4610374
E-MAIL: postmaster@indoperu.org.pe

Italy
Av. Gregorio Escobedo No. 298, Apartado Postal 11-0490, Lima 11, Peru
PHONE: +51 (1) 4632727
FAX: +51 (1) 4635317

Japan
Av. San Felipe Nro. 356, Apartado Postal 3708, Lima 11, Peru
PHONE: +51 (1) 4630000

FAX: +51 (1) 4630302

Russia
Av. Salaverry No. 3424, Lima 27, Peru
PHONE: +51 (1) 2640036
FAX: +51 (1) 2640130

United Kingdom
Edif. Pacífico-Washington, Natalio Sánchez No. 125, Piso 12, Apartado Postal 854, Lima 01, Peru
PHONE: +51 (1) 4334738
FAX: +51 (1) 4334735

United States
Avenida Encalada, Cuadra 17, Monterrico, P.O. Box 1995, Lima, Peru
PHONE: +51 (1) 4343000
FAX: +51 (1) 4343037
TITLE: Ambassador
NAME: Dennis C. Jett

JUDICIAL SYSTEM

Constitutional Court

Supreme Court of Justice

National Council of the Judiciary

FURTHER READING

''A Third Term for Fujimori,'' *The Economist* (April 17, 1999): 40.

''Explorer Says He's Found Ancient Lost City in Peru,'' *The Seattle Times* news services, 26 September 1999.

''Flowers and an Easter Week Procession Honor the Lord of Earthquakes,'' *The Seattle Times*, 31 January 1999.

''Fujimori Won't Discuss American's Life Sentence with U.S. Envoy,'' The Associated Press, 22 July 1999.

''Hot Debate Rages over Machu Picchu Facilities,'' *The Seattle Times* news services, 15 August 1999.

''Jungle Wired in Peru: Scientists Put Expedition Online for Students,'' *The Seattle Times* news services, 4 March 1999.

''Peru: Outlaw,'' *The Economist* (July 10, 1999): 32.

''Two American Women Paroled From Prison in Peru,'' *The Seattle Times*, 29 July 1999.

''What the Pottery Shards Tell Us About the Incas,'' *The Seattle Times* news services, 26 August 1999.

PERU: STATISTICAL DATA

For sources and notes see "Sources of Statistics" in the front of each volume.

GEOGRAPHY

Geography (1)

Area:

Total: 1,285,220 sq km.

Land: 1.28 million sq km.

Water: 5,220 sq km.

Area—comparative: slightly smaller than Alaska.

Land boundaries:

Total: 6,940 km.

Border countries: Bolivia 900 km, Brazil 1,560 km, Chile 160 km, Colombia 2,900 km, Ecuador 1,420 km.

Coastline: 2,414 km.

Climate: varies from tropical in east to dry desert in west.

Terrain: western coastal plain (costa), high and rugged Andes in center (sierra), eastern lowland jungle of Amazon Basin (selva).

Natural resources: copper, silver, gold, petroleum, timber, fish, iron ore, coal, phosphate, potash.

Land use:

Arable land: 3%

Permanent crops: 0%

Permanent pastures: 21%

Forests and woodland: 66%

Other: 10% (1993 est.).

HUMAN FACTORS

Demographics (2A)

	1990	1995	1998	2000	2010	2020	2030	2040	2050
Population	21,988.9	24,562.6	26,110.5	27,135.7	32,122.0	36,904.0	41,285.2	44,987.4	47,899.4
Net migration rate (per 1,000 population)	NA	NA	NA	NA	NA	NA	NA	NA	NA
Births	NA	NA	NA	NA	NA	NA	NA	NA	NA
Deaths	NA	NA	NA	NA	NA	NA	NA	NA	NA
Life expectancy - males	63.6	66.4	67.7	68.5	72.0	74.6	76.6	78.0	78.9
Life expectancy - females	68.0	71.1	72.3	73.2	76.9	79.7	81.8	83.4	84.5
Birth rate (per 1,000)	31.7	28.4	26.7	25.5	21.1	18.4	16.0	14.4	13.4
Death rate (per 1,000)	7.2	6.2	5.8	5.6	5.1	5.1	5.6	6.6	7.8
Women of reproductive age (15-49 yrs.)	5,377.2	6,146.9	6,630.3	6,934.9	8,490.6	9,720.6	10,509.6	10,946.2	10,981.3
of which are currently married	NA	NA	NA	NA	NA	NA	NA	NA	NA
Fertility rate	4.1	3.6	3.3	3.1	2.6	2.3	2.1	2.0	2.0

Except as noted, values for vital statistics are in thousands; life expectancy is in years.

Health Personnel (3)

Total health expenditure as a percentage of GDP, 1990-1997[a]

Public sector 2.2

Private sector 1.5

Total[b] 3.7

Health expenditure per capita in U.S. dollars, 1990-1997[a]

Purchasing power parity 156

Total 80

Availability of health care facilities per 100,000 people

Hospital beds 1990-1997[a] 140

Doctors 1993[c] 73

Nurses 1993[c] 49

Health Indicators (4)

Life expectancy at birth

1980 60

1997 69

Daily per capita supply of calories (1996) 2,310

Total fertility rate births per woman (1997) 3.2

Maternal mortality ratio per 100,000 live births (1990-97) . . . . .280[c]

Safe water % of population with access (1995) 66

Sanitation % of population with access (1995) 61

Consumption of iodized salt % of households (1992-98)[a] 93

Smoking prevalence

Male % of adults (1985-95)[a] 41

Female % of adults (1985-95)[a] 13

Tuberculosis incidence per 100,000 people (1997) 265

Adult HIV prevalence % of population ages 15-49 (1997) 0.56

Infants and Malnutrition (5)

Under-5 mortality rate (1997) 56

% of infants with low birthweight (1990-97) 11

Births attended by skilled health staff % of total[a] . . .56

% fully immunized (1995-97)

TB 98

DPT 98

Polio 97

Measles 94

Prevalence of child malnutrition under age 5 (1992-97)[b] 8

Ethnic Division (6)

Amerindian 45%

Mestizo 37%

White 15%

Black, Japanese, Chinese, and other 3%

Mestizo is mixed Amerindian and white.

Religions (7)

Roman Catholic

Languages (8)

Spanish (official), Quechua (official), Aymara.

EDUCATION

Public Education Expenditures (9)

Public expenditure on education (% of GNP)

1980 . . . . .3.1

1996 . . . . .2.9

Expenditure per student

Primary % of GNP per capita

1980 . . . . .7.2

1996 . . . .

Secondary % of GNP per capita

1980 . . . . .11.4[1]

1996 . . . .

Tertiary % of GNP per capita

1980 . . . .

1996 . . . .

Expenditure on teaching materials

Primary % of total for level (1996) 0.7

Secondary % of total for level (1996) 2.4

Primary pupil-teacher ratio per teacher (1996) . . . . .28[1]

Duration of primary education years (1995) 6

Educational Attainment (10)

Age group (1993) . . . . .25+

Total population 9,394,681

Highest level attained (%)

No schooling 16.4

First level

Not completed 34.7

Completed . . . . .NA

Entered second level

S-1 . . . . .27.2

S-2 . . . . .NA

Postsecondary 20.5

Literacy Rates (11A)

In thousands and percent[1]	1990	1995	2000	2010
Illiterate population (15+ yrs.)	1,847	1,736	1,627	1,286
Literacy rate - total adult pop. (%)	86.3	88.7	90.7	94.1
Literacy rate - males (%)	93.0	94.5	95.7	97.7
Literacy rate - females (%)	79.5	83.0	85.7	90.5

GOVERNMENT & LAW

Political Parties (12)

Democratic Constituent Congress	% of seats
Change 90-New Majority (C90/NM) 52.1	
Union for Peru (UPP) 14	
11 Other parties 33.9	

Government Budget (13B)

Revenues . . . .$8.5 billion
Expenditures . . . .$9.3 billion
  Capital expenditures . . . .$2 billion
Data for 1996 est.

Military Affairs (14B)

	1990	1991	1992	1993	1994	1995
Military expenditures						
Current dollars (mil.)	683[e]	488[e]	750	782	847	989
1995 constant dollars (mil.)	784[e]	539[e]	807	819	868	989
Armed forces (000)	125	123	112	112	112	115
Gross national product (GNP)						
Current dollars (mil.)	37,280	40,300	40,720	44,120	51,260	56,930
1995 constant dollars (mil.)	42,840	44,540	73,800	46,250	52,550	56,930
Central government expenditures (CGE)						
1995 constant dollars (mil.)	5,990	5,907	7,344	7,756	7,231	10,590
People (mil.)	21.8	22.3	22.7	23.2	23.7	24.1
Military expenditure as % of GNP	1.8	1.2	1.8	1.8	1.7	1.7
Military expenditure as % of CGE	13.1	9.1	11.0	10.6	12.0	9.3
Military expenditure per capita (1995 $)	36	24	35	35	37	41
Armed forces per 1,000 people (soldiers)	5.7	5.5	4.9	4.8	4.7	4.8
GNP per capita (1995 $)	1,961	1,998	1,925	1,993	2,221	2,363
Arms imports[6]						
Current dollars (mil.)	60	70	60	40	60	280
1995 constant dollars (mil.)	69	77	65	42	62	280
Arms exports[6]						
Current dollars (mil.)	0	0	0	0	0	0
1995 constant dollars (mil.)	0	0	0	0	0	0
Total imports[7]						
Current dollars (mil.)	3,470	4,195	4,860	4,858	6,691	9,224
1995 constant dollars (mil.)	3,988	4,636	5,228	5,093	6,859	9,224
Total exports[7]						
Current dollars (mil.)	3,231	3,329	3,484	3,515	4,555	5,575
1995 constant dollars (mil.)	3,713	3,679	3,748	3,685	4,669	5,575
Arms as percent of total imports[8]	1.7	1.7	1.2	.8	.9	3.0
Arms as percent of total exports[8]	0	0	0	0	0	0

Crime (15)

Crime rate (for 1994)

Crimes reported ....NA

Total persons convicted ....NA

Crimes per 100,000 population ....NA

Persons responsible for offenses

Total number of suspects 117,245

Total number of female suspects 6,592

Total number of juvenile suspects ....NA

LABOR FORCE

Labor Force (16)

Total 7.6 million. Agriculture, mining and quarrying, manufacturing, construction, transport, services. Data for 1996 est.

Unemployment Rate (17)

8.2%; extensive underemployment (1996)

PRODUCTION SECTOR

Electric Energy (18)

Capacity ....4.187 million kW (1995)

Production ....15.6 billion kWh (1995)

Consumption per capita ....648 kWh (1995)

Transportation (19)

Highways:

total: 72,800 km

paved: 7,353 km

unpaved: 65,447 km (1996 est.)

Waterways: 8,600 km of navigable tributaries of Amazon system and 208 km of Lago Titicaca

Pipelines: crude oil 800 km; natural gas and natural gas liquids 64 km

Merchant marine:

total: 8 ships (1,000 GRT or over) totaling 68,752 GRT/100,213 DWT ships by type: bulk 1, cargo 7 (1997 est.)

Airports: 244 (1997 est.)

Airports—with paved runways:

total: 43

over 3,047 m: 6

2,438 to 3,047 m: 15

1,524 to 2,437 m: 12

914 to 1,523 m: 8

under 914 m: 2 (1997 est.)

Airports—with unpaved runways:

total: 201

over 3,047 m: 2

2,438 to 3,047 m: 2

1,524 to 2,437 m: 24

914 to 1,523 m: 73

under 914 m: 100 (1997 est.)

Top Agricultural Products (20)

Coffee, cotton, sugarcane, rice, wheat, potatoes, plantains, coca; poultry, red meats, dairy products, wool; fish catch of 6.9 million metric tons (1990).

MANUFACTURING SECTOR

GDP & Manufacturing Summary (21)

Detailed value added figures are listed by both International Standard Industry Code (ISIC) and product title.

	1980	1985	1990	1994
GDP ($-1990 mil.)[1]	37,452	36,703	33,427	40,093
Per capita ($-1990)[1]	2,162	1,880	1,548	1,718
Manufacturing share (%) (current prices)[1]	20.2	25.3	28.8	*21.6*
Manufacturing				
Value added ($-1990 mil.)[1]	11,917	10,721	9,745	12,005
Industrial production index	100	86	78	95
Value added ($ mil.)	4,985	3,918	7,366	*6,895*
Gross output ($ mil.)	12,977	9,573	14,186	*16,751*
Employment (000)	273	263	285	*260*
Profitability (% of gross output)				
Intermediate input (%)	62	59	48	*59*
Wages and salaries inc. supplements (%)	*7*	6	*10*	*11*
Gross operating surplus	*32*	35	*42*	*31*
Productivity ($)				
Gross output per worker	47,484	36,350	49,727	*63,981*
Value added per worker	18,242	14,877	25,821	*26,374*
Average wage (inc. supplements)	*3,150*	2,154	*4,941*	*6,865*
Value added ($ mil.)				
311/2 Food products	767	402	1,077	*1,026*

	1980	1985	1990	1994
313 Beverages	379	303	545	831
314 Tobacco products	84	61	59	60
321 Textiles	466	352	647	543
322 Wearing apparel	65	52	133	75
323 Leather and fur products	56	20	32	19
324 Footwear	41	20	26	26
331 Wood and wood products	81	32	39	45
332 Furniture and fixtures	42	19	30	38
341 Paper and paper products	156	77	135	73
342 Printing and publishing	100	80	151	200
351 Industrial chemicals	215	158	237	192
352 Other chemical products	289	193	427	484
353 Petroleum refineries	192	1,154	1,409	1,444
354 Miscellaneous petroleum and coal products	6	1	5	2
355 Rubber products	62	51	74	51
356 Plastic products	89	90	144	152
361 Pottery, china and earthenware	15	8	10	13
362 Glass and glass products	47	15	37	55
369 Other non-metal mineral products	129	113	204	254
371 Iron and steel	192	123	177	101
372 Non-ferrous metals	604	172	930	528
381 Metal products	188	113	180	202
382 Non-electrical machinery	156	58	116	97
383 Electrical machinery	211	111	235	124
384 Transport equipment	278	106	219	127
385 Professional and scientific equipment	14	10	21	19
390 Other manufacturing industries	58	25	66	115

FINANCE, ECONOMICS, & TRADE

Economic Indicators (22)

National product: GDP—purchasing power parity—$110.2 billion (1997 est.)

National product real growth rate: 7.3% (1997 est.)

National product per capita: $4,420 (1997 est.)

Inflation rate—consumer price index: 6.7% (1997 est.)

Exchange Rates (24)

Exchange rates:

Nuevo sol (S) per US$1

January 1998	2.750
1997	2.664
1996	2.453
1995	2.253
1994	2.195
1993	1.988

Balance of Payments (23)

	1992	1993	1994	1995	1996
Exports of goods (f.o.b.)	3,661	3,516	4,598	5,591	5,897
Imports of goods (f.o.b.)	−4,002	−4,123	−5,596	−7,761	−7,897
Trade balance	−341	−607	−997	−2,170	−2,000
Services - debits	−3,247	−3,236	−3,708	−4,484	−4,233
Services - credits	1,040	1,046	1,407	1,709	1,979
Private transfers (net)	74	65	62	25	16
Government transfers (net)	372	431	575	617	631
Overall balance	−2,102	−2,301	−2,662	−4,303	−3,607

Top Import Origins (25)

$9.2 billion (f.o.b., 1996) Data are for 1996.

Origins	%
United States	31
Colombia	7
Chile	6
Venezuela	6
United Kingdom	6

Top Export Destinations (26)

$5.9 billion (f.o.b., 1996) Data are for 1996.

Destinations	%
United States	20
Japan	7
United Kingdom	7
China	7
Germany	5

Economic Aid (27)

Recipient: ODA, $363 million (1993).

Import Export Commodities (28)

Import Commodities	Export Commodities
Machinery	Copper
Transport equipment	Zinc
Foodstuffs	Fishmeal
Petroleum	Crude petroleum and byproducts
Iron and steel	Lead
Chemicals	Refined silver
Pharmaceuticals	Cotton
	Coffee

PHILIPPINES

Republic of the Philippines
Republika ng Pilipinas

INTRODUCTORY SURVEY

RECENT HISTORY

On 8 December 1941, Japan invaded the Philippines, which then became the site of the most bitter and decisive battles fought in the Pacific during World War II (1939–45). By May 1942, the Japanese had achieved full possession of the islands. United States forces, led by General Douglas MacArthur, recaptured the Philippines in early 1945, following the Battle of Leyte Gulf, the largest naval engagement in history. In September 1945, Japan surrendered.

On 4 July 1946, the Republic of the Philippines was inaugurated, with Manuel A. Roxas y Acuña as its first president. Both casualties and damage in the Philippines from World War II were extensive, and rehabilitation was the major problem of the new state. Communist guerrillas, called Hukbalahaps, were threatening the republic, and their revolutionary demands were countered by land reforms and military action.

In 1965, Ferdinand Edralin Marcos was elected president, and reelected in 1969 by a record majority of 62%. Unable to run for a third term in 1973, President Marcos placed the entire country under martial law, charging that the nation was threatened by a ''full-scale armed insurrection and rebellion.'' Marcos arrested many of his political opponents, some of whom remained in detention for years.

Throughout the 1970s, Marcos tightened his control of the government through purges of op-

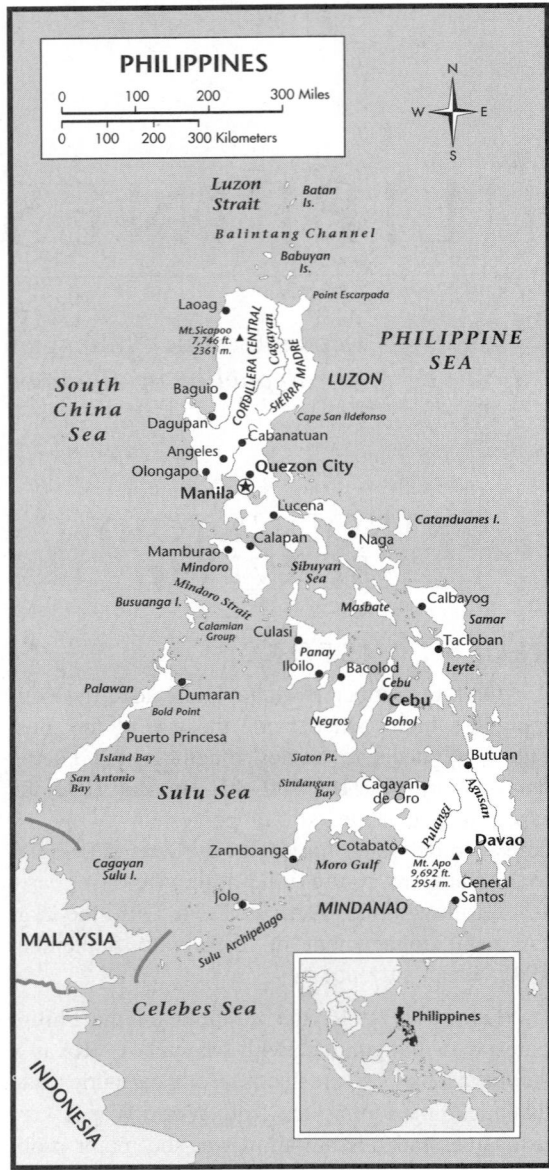

Aquino, Jr., a long-time critic of Marcos, was shot at the Manila airport which was later named in his honor. Aquino was assassinated as he returned from self-exile in the United States to lead the opposition in the 1984 legislative elections.

In 1985, political pressures were mounting on Marcos. He was forced to call for an election in February 1986. Later that month a military revolt grew into a popular rebellion that ousted the long-time leader. United States President Ronald Reagan offered Marcos asylum, and Marcos went into exile in Hawaii.

On 25 February 1986, Corazon Aquino, widow of Benigno Aquino, assumed the presidency. On 11 May 1987, she was elected in the first free elections in nearly two decades, held under a new constitution. On 20 December 1987 one of the worst ocean disasters in history occurred when an overcrowded passenger ship collided with an oil tanker off Mindoro Island and at least 1,500 people perished. On 28 September 1989 former president Ferdinand Marcos died in Honolulu. Aquino refused to allow him to be buried in the Philippines.

Under pressure from communist rebels, Aquino removed U.S. military bases from the Philippines in 1989. In September 1990 Aquino said it was time to consider an ''orderly withdrawal'' of U.S. forces from the Philippines. Within a year the Philippines was struck by three major natural disasters. In July 1990 an earthquake measuring 7.7 on the Richter scale struck. The epicenter was 55 miles north of Manila and more than 1,600 people were killed. A super-typhoon devastated the central islands in November 1990. An even more destructive natural disaster occurred on 12 June 1991 when Mount Pinatubo (in Zambales province near Olangapo), a volcano dormant for more than 500 years, violently erupted. The Philippine economy suffered again in 1995, when a typhoon badly damaged the rice crop. The amount of rice lost that season was triple the amount lost from the Mt. Pinatubo eruption.

On 30 June 1992 Fidel Ramos succeeded Corazon Aquino as president of the Philippines. Ramos, a Methodist and the Philippine's first non-Catholic president, considers the country's population growth rate as an obstacle to development. Catholics have protested the Ramos administration's birth control policies and the public health promotion of prophylactics to limit the spread of AIDS.

ponents, promotion of favorites, and delegation of leadership of several key programs—including the governorship of metropolitan Manila—to his wife, Imelda Romualdez Marcos.

Although Marcos made headway against the southern guerrillas, his human-rights abuses cost him the support of the powerful Roman Catholic Church. Pope John Paul II came to Manila in February 1981 and protested the violation of basic human rights. In June 1981, Marcos was elected for a new six-year term as president under an amended constitution preserving most of the powers he had exercised under martial rule. In 1983 Benigno S.

Internal violence by the Muslim population continued in the 1980s and 1990s. In January 1994 the government signed a ceasefire agreement with the Moro National Liberation Front ending 20 years of guerrilla war. However, in January 1996 Philippines police uncovered a plot by Muslim terrorists to assassinate Pope John Paul II during his visit to Manila that month. Muslim rebels in Mindanao raided the town of Ipil in April 1996, killing 57 people and burning the business district.

Conflicting claims to the Spratly Islands in the South China Sea are a source of tension between the Philippines and the People's Republic of China.

GOVERNMENT

Under the constitution of 11 February 1987, the Philippines is a democratic republican state. Executive power is vested in a president elected by popular vote for a six-year term, with no eligibility for reelection. The president is assisted by a vice-president, elected for a six-year term, with eligibility for one immediate reelection, and a cabinet, which can include the vice-president.

Legislative power rests with a two-chamber legislature. The Senate has 24 members elected for six-year terms. A House of Representatives is elected from single-member districts for three-year terms. In 1995, 204 members were elected. Up to 50 more may be appointed by the president.

In 1991, the Philippines was divided into 73 provinces and approximately 1,500 municipalities. Each municipality was further divided into communities (barangays).

Judiciary

Under the 1973 constitution, the Supreme Court, composed of a chief justice and 14 associate justices, was the highest judicial body of the state, with supervisory authority over the lower courts. The entire court system was modified in 1981, with the creation of new regional courts of trials and of appeals. Philippine courts function without juries.

The Constitution calls for an independent judiciary, and defendants in criminal cases are afforded the right to counsel.

Political Parties

After assuming the presidency in 1986, Corazon Aquino formally organized the People's Power Movement (Lakas Ng Bayan), the successor to the party of her late husband, Benigno Aquino. In the congressional elections of May 1987, Aquino's popularity gave her party a sweep in the polls, making it the major party in the country.

In 1993 there were over a dozen recognized political organizations and six parties organized in opposition to the government.

On 26 August 1994, President Fidel Ramos announced a new political coalition that would produce the most powerful political group in the Philippines. Ramos's Lakas–National Union of Christian Democrats (Lakas/NUCD) teamed with the Democratic Filipino Struggle (Laban ng Demokratikong Pilipino, Laban).

DEFENSE

The all-volunteer active armed forces numbered 107,500 in 1995, and reserves 131,000. The army, with 68,000 members, had 8 infantry divisions and 6 specialized brigades. The navy had a total of 23,000 members (including 9,000 marines). The coast guard had 2,000 personnel, with 1 frigate (warship) and 42 patrol and coastal combatants. The air force had a strength of 16,500, with 43 combat aircraft and 104 armed helicopters. The Philippine national police totaled 40,500, and the Citizen Armed Forces had 60,000 personnel. Estimated defense expenditures in 1995 were $1.2 billion.

ECONOMIC AFFAIRS

The Philippines is primarily an agricultural nation, raising crops for domestic use and export. It is the world's largest producer of coconuts and manila hemp (abacá). Manufacturing, which has expanded and diversified since political independence, depends on imported raw materials. Mining, once centered on gold, is now diversified, with chromite, copper, and iron providing important earnings. The economy is heavily dependent on foreign trade.

Throughout 1990–92 slow economic growth plagued the Philippines. Inadequate transport and communications networks and prolonged drought reduced industrial and agricultural expansion. Widespread unemployment and underemployment characterize the Philippine labor market. High rates of labor migration abroad (686,137 in 1992) provided some relief and accounted for a substantial portion of the country's foreign exchange earnings.

Since 1990 the most visible problem for the economy has been the shortage of electric power. In 1992 the water level of a lake in Mindanao fell, causing a 50% reduction in the power supply to Mindanao. In Manila, the industrial hub, power outages would last from four to six hours per day. In 1993 the inflation rate continued to decline and the return to economic growth accelerated, growing by 5.7% in 1996.

Public Finance

The principal sources of revenue are income taxes, taxes on sales and business operations, and excise duties. Infrastructural improvements, defense expenditures, and debt service continue to lead among the categories of outlays.

The government's commitment to fiscal balance resulted in a budget surplus for the first time in two decades in 1994. The surplus was achieved by higher taxes, privatization receipts, and expenditure cuts. The budget again showed a surplus in 1995 when government revenues totaled approximately $14.1 billion and expenditures $13.6 billion. External debt totaled $41 billion, approximately 33% of which was financed abroad. In 1996, 31% of government revenues was spent on social services, 26.5% on economic services, 9% on defense, 17% on general public service, 0.5% on net lending, and 16% on interest payments.

Income

In 1995, Philippines' gross national product (GNP) was $244 billion at current prices, or about $3,200 per person. For the period 1985–95 the average inflation rate was 9.8%, resulting in a real growth rate in GNP of 1.5% per person.

Industry

By the 1990s, 50% of manufacturing production was concentrated in the metropolitan Manila area, and 20% was in the nearby regions of Southern Tagalog and Central Luzon. Although small- and medium-sized businesses accounted for 80% of manufacturing employment, they accounted for only 25% of the value of manufactured goods. Industry accounted for about 32% of the domestic economy in 1996. The leading manufactured goods (by value) are foods, petroleum and coal, chemicals, electrical machinery, beverages, transport equipment, basic metals, and footwear.

Banking and Finance

The Philippine banking structure consists of the government-owned Central Bank of the Philippines (created in 1949), which acts as the government's fiscal agent and administers the monetary and banking system, and (as of late 1994) of some 38 commercial banks, of which 4 were foreign.

Other institutions include 786 rural banks, 38 private development banks, 7 savings banks, 10 investment houses, and 2 specialized government banks. The largest commercial bank, the Philippine National Bank (PNB), is a government institution with over 194 local offices and 12 overseas branches. It supplies about half the commercial credit, basically as agricultural loans. The government operates about 1,145 postal savings banks and the Development Bank of the Philippines, the Land Bank of the Philippines, and the Philippine Amanah Bank (for Mindanao). The money supply as of 1995, as measured by M2, stood at P 959.83 billion.

Philippine stock exchanges are self-governing, although the Philippine Securities and Exchange Commission, established in 1936, has supervisory power over registrants. The country's two stock exchanges, Manila and Makati (both in the capital), were formally merged in the Philippines Stock Exchange in March 1993. A computer link-up was effected a year later, although the two retained separate trading floors until November 1995. Only 206 companies were listed as of early 1996. But the process of privatization is expected to push up listings, while domestic participation in the equity market is being specifically promoted by new regulations due to be implemented in 1996 requiring that all initial public offerings reserve a 10% tranche for small investors.

Ecomomic Development

Beginning in 1972, the main tenets of the Marcos government's economic policies, as articulated through the National Economic Development Authority, included substantial development of infrastructure, particularly through the use of labor-intensive rather than capital-intensive (i.e., mechanized) methods, and a shift in export emphasis from raw materials to finished and semifinished commodities. The policies of the Aquino administration have stressed labor-intensive, small- and medium-scale agricultural projects and extensive land reform. In addition, wealth believed to have been amassed by President Marcos was actively being pursued all over the world. Long range planning has followed a series of economic plans, most of them covering five-year periods. The development program for 1967–70 aimed to increase the growth rate of per capita income from the 0.9% level in 1961–65 to 2.4%; to increase national income by 5.7% per year during the plan period, and to reduce the unemployment rate from 13% (1965) to 7.2% (1970). The government invested $3.5 billion in integrating the traditional and modern sectors of the economy. Marcos's first long-range plan following the 1972 declaration of martial law was a four-year (1974–77) infrastructural development program calling for a total outlay of P 21,500 million; of the total, 35% was to be expended on transportation, 33% on energy and power, 20% on water resources, 10% on education, health, and welfare, and 2% on telecommunications. A 1974–78 plan, announced in late 1975, envisioned a total outlay of P 38,000 million (after inflation, a lower figure than the previous plan's). Energy was to be the major focus of the new plan, with 34% of expenditures, followed by transportation, 30%; water resources, 23%; social programs, 7%; and other sectors, 6%. The goals of the 1978–82 plan included an 8% annual growth in GNP, rural development, tax incentives for export-oriented industries, continued self-sufficiency in grain crops despite rapid population growth, and accelerated development of highways, irrigation, and other infrastructure. The 1983–87 plan called for an annual expansion of 6.2% in GNP, improvement of the rural economy and living standards, and amelioration of hunger.

Under the Aquino administration the goals of the 1987–92 plan were self-sufficiency in food production, decentralization of power and decision making, job creation, and rural development. Economic performance for real growth fell far short of plan targets by 25% or more. Structural changes to provide a better investment climate were carried out. The Foreign Investment Act of 1991 liberalized the environment for foreign investment. An Executive Order issued in July 1991 reduced the number of tariff levels over five years and reduced the maximum duty rate from 50% to 30%. Quantitative restrictions were removed from all but a few products. The foreign exchange market was fully deregulated in 1992.

A new six-year medium-term development plan for 1993–98 was presented by the government in May 1993. The plan stressed people empowerment and international competitiveness within the framework of sustainable development. To do this, the government planned to disperse industries to regions outside the metropolitan Manila area. The plan also called for technological upgrading of production sectors, poverty alleviation, and human/social development. Over the six year period, agriculture's share of GDP was expected to decline from 23% to 19% of GDP while industry's share was to increase from 34% to 39%.

SOCIAL WELFARE

The government social program includes the settlement of landless families in new areas, building of rural roads, schools, and medical clinics, and the distribution of relief supplies to the needy.

The Social Security System (SSS) covers employees of private firms in industrial and agricultural production. Government employees are covered under the Government Service Insurance System (GSIS). The system's benefits include compensation for confinement due to injury or illness, pensions for temporary incapacity, insurance payments to families in case of death, old age pensions, and benefits to widows and orphans.

A medical care plan (Medicare) provides hospital, surgical, medicinal, and medical-expense benefits to members and their dependents. Women are eligible for paid maternity leaves of six weeks for the first four births.

The government has actively promoted family planning, and despite opposition from Roman Catholic traditionalists (including Pope John Paul II in his February 1981 visit), the program has met with significant success.

Most, but not all, of the legal rights enjoyed by men are extended to women. Restrictions on property ownership were removed by a 1992 law.

Healthcare

In 1991, there were 1,663 hospitals and 31,375 physicians. There was about 1 doctor per 8,330 people in 1992. Nearly 75% of the population had access to health care services in 1992.

Pulmonary infections (tuberculosis, pneumonia, bronchitis) are prevalent, but malaria is virtually unknown in larger cities and is being eliminated in the countryside. Malnutrition remains a health problem, despite government assistance in the form of Nutripaks, consisting of native foods such as mung beans and powdered shrimp, made available for infants, children, and pregnant women. Average life expectancy is about 66 years.

Housing

Tens of thousands of *barrios* (districts) are scattered throughout the Philippines, each consisting of a double row of small cottages strung out along a single road. Each cottage is generally built on stilts and has a thatched roof, veranda, and small yard. From 1984 to 1987, an annual average of about 103,150 units were built by private builders with minimal assistance from the government. The total number of dwellings in 1992 was 10.6 million.

EDUCATION

Education is free and compulsory in the primary schools and is coeducational. English is the main medium of instruction, although Pilipino or the local dialect is used for instruction in the lower primary grades. In 1995, about 5% of adults were illiterate (men, 5%; women, 5.7%).

In 1994, 35,671 primary schools had an enrollment of 10.9 million students and secondary schools had 4.8 million students.

The University of the Philippines is the leading institution of higher learning. In addition, there are some 50 other universities, including the University of Santo Tomás, founded in 1611 and run by Dominican friars. In 1993, universities and all higher level institutions had 1.6 million students.

1999 KEY EVENTS TIMELINE

January

- At least 458 people are injured from firecracker accidents and from stray bullets during raucous New Year's Eve celebrations in the Philippines.

- Over twenty people die when a bus plunges off a road into a deep ravine just south of Baguio in the northern Philippines. The accident occurs on January 21 in heavy fog.

February

- The first execution in twenty-three years is carried out on February 5 when Leo Echegaray, 38, a house painter convicted of raping his 10-year-old stepdaughter, dies by lethal injection.

- Rebels of the Maoist New People's Army in Mindanao abduct Army Brigadier General Victor Obillo and Captain Eduardo Montealto on February 18.

March

- The Jimmy Carter Work Project '99 builds nearly three hundred homes in one week at sites throughout the Philippines, with the main work site located in Maragondon, Cavite. Thousands of volunteers from corporate sponsors, schools, and overseas converge on the sites to compete the work during the week of March 21–27.

April

- In an effort to avoid a diplomatic row with the People's Republic of China, the Philippine government refuses to grant Taiwan's president, Lee Teng-hui, permission to visit Manila.

- An April 29 grenade attack in the Rapu Rapu islands in the northern Philippines kills at least twelve people at a dance club.

May

- Philips Semiconductor inaugurates a $300 million chip plant on May 7 at the Light Industry and Science Park II in Calamba, Laguna.

- On May 15 residents of Lucban, Tayabas, and other towns in Quezon Province celebrate the annual Pahiyas Festival by decorating their homes and businesses with produce from the region.

- A Chinese fishing vessel sinks on May 23 after a collision with a Philippine naval vessel off the disputed Scarborough Shoal.

- In an historic eighteen to five vote the Senate approves the Visiting Forces Agreement (VFA) between the Philippines and the United States government.

June

- Japan's Nippon Telegraph and Telephone purchases 15% of Philippine Long Distance Telephone.

- Apo Anno, a 500-year-old mummy, is reinterred June 21 in the burial caves of Benguet. The remains had been removed in 1918. Manila's National Museum agreed to return the mummy to the people of Benguet in northern Luzon.

- Mt. Mayon, the country's most restive volcano, explodes with steam and ash on June 22, forcing thousands to flee their homes.

- President Estrada signs the landmark Clean Air Act on June 23. The act is described by the environmental activist organization Greenpeace as "an environmental milestone" for the Philippines.

July

- The Philippine government executes three men on July 8 for the murder of a policeman.

- A Chinese fishing vessel sinks July 19 after colliding with a Philippine naval ship near the Kalayaan Island Group (KIG) in the South China Sea, raising tensions once again between Beijing and Manila.

- Supt. Alfredo Siwa, former chief of police of Baliuag, Bulacan, becomes the first senior police officer in the country to be sentenced by a lower court to die from lethal injection for killing a star witness.

- The *Manila Times* closes on July 25 after protracted struggle with President Estrada.

- Communist guerrillas increase their attacks on government forces following the collapse of peace talks in late May.

August

- Heavy monsoon rains in early August set off a landslide in the Cherry Hill housing project in Antipolo, outside metropolitan Manila, destroying hundreds of homes and leaving 75 people missing or dead. At least 160 die throughout the country due to two weeks of torrential rains.

- In Manila on August 20 thousands of protestors, led by former president Corazon (Cory) Aquino and Archbishop Jaime Cardinal Sin, demonstrate against President Estrada's proposed amendments to the constitution.

September

- President Estrada announces the discovery of hydrocarbon oil and gas by the Philippine National Oil Company Exploration Corp. in Maguindanao.

- Corazon Aquino and Archbishop Jaime Cardinal Sin continue their protest rallies against proposed changes to the constitution.

- The *Manila Times* is relaunched on September 21 under new, less combative ownership.

November

- Panfilo Lacson is appointed as the new police chief, warning his crooked colleagues, the Philippino police force infamous for corruption, that any criminality on the part of the country's police will be met with swift and severe reprisal.

- The ten member countries of the Association of South-East Asian Nations (ASEAN) meet in Manila with Japan, China, and South Korea; discussion focused on forming a common market with a unified currency. Six members—Brunei, Indo-

nesia, Malaysia, Philippines, Singapore, and Thailand—agree to establish a free-trade zone by eliminating duties on most goods traded in the region by 2010. The remaining four newer and less-developed nation members—Cambodia, Laos, Myanmar (Burma), and Vietnam—will eliminate duties by 2015. Rice will be excluded from trade agreements, however.

ANALYSIS OF EVENTS: 1999

BUSINESS AND THE ECONOMY

During 1999 the Philippines continued its shift from an economy based on agricultural produce and sweatshop factory output to an economy anchored by the assembly of computer chips and other electronic goods, many of them computer peripherals. Several resources within the country explain this change, including tax breaks, skilled but inexpensive workers, and political stability.

Fifty chip assemblers and computer component makers have contributed $6.6 billion to the country since 1994. Intel has a $550 million Pentium assembly and testing center in the country. Philips Semiconductors inaugurated a $300 million faculty in May of this year. Other technology companies with major investments include Acer, Toshiba, Hitachi, Fujitsu, Cypress Semiconductor, and Amkor Technology. In fact, a World Bank study published in February said that the Philippines has one of the world's most technologically advanced export structures.

After experiencing a .5% reduction in economic growth in 1998, primarily the result of the continued effects of the Asian economic crisis and bad weather caused by El Niño and La Niña, the economy improved through the first two quarters of 1999 at a rate of 2.9%. Double-digit export growth continued with merchandise exports increasing by 13.7% during the first seven months of the year.

GOVERNMENT AND POLITICS

The Visiting Forces Agreement and the constitutional changes advocated by President Joseph Estrada were two issues that dominated much of the political debate in 1999. Both issues inspired much debate and controversy in the Philippine government and across society.

A wide array of political forces, including Bagong Alyansang Makabayan (New Patriotic Alliance) and the Catholic Bishops Conference of the Philippines, strongly opposed the Visiting Forces Agreement (VFA), which they claimed one-sidedly favored the United States at the expense of the Filipino people. They vehemently argued against ratification of the agreement by the Senate, claiming that the VFA would give the U.S. military the opportunity to bring nuclear weapons into the Philippines without prior declaration, a violation of the Philippine constitution. In addition, they argued the agreement was ambiguous about what manner of military operations U.S. forces would be allowed to undertake in the Philippines. The opposition was also concerned about the extraterritoriality rights granted to U.S. military personnel under the agreement, which allowed that personnel could commit crimes against Filipino citizens, and, if on certified official duty, have immunity from Philippine courts and laws. Despite the strong opposition the Senate overwhelmingly ratified the VFA in May.

The second emotional issue to dominate the country's political debate was the on-going attempt by the Estrada administration to push the Constitutional Corrections for Development process. The opposition to this move included former President Corazon Aquino and the Catholic Bishops Conference of the Philippines. They led to two large opposition rallies on July 21 and August 20. The Estrada administration countered with a huge pro-change demonstration at an El Shaddai gathering, also on August 20.

The government argued for amendments in the economic provisions of the constitution, hoping to make it more attuned to global developments. It claimed that a number of rigid provisions existed in the present constitution that inhibited taking actions necessary to address important concerns in the country's modern economy. The administration also argued against the mass demonstrations, claiming that mass action at a time when the country's economy shows signs of positive growth could only have a destabilizing effect.

Manila Archbishop Jaime Cardinal Sin spoke for the opposition and said the government could achieve economic development through legislation, not a constitutional assembly. He called for reform that would combat corruption, mediocre public service, and the restoration of trust in public offices.

CULTURE AND SOCIETY

Tension between supporters and detractors of President Joseph Estrada has led to several conflicts tension within the government. President Estrada has rewarded close friends and supporters with both official and unofficial positions in his government, and his opponents claim this practice has undermined the constitutional process.

One of the most bitter conflicts over the past year has been between the Estrada administration and the news media, particularly the *Manila Times* and the *Manila Daily Inquirer*. In July the *Manila Times* closed after a legal attack by the government, which argued that the *Times* had libeled President Estrada. The president also publicly snubbed John Gokongweis, the owner, causing a loss of face and public humiliation for Mr. Gokongweis. The newspaper closed, and the president turned the brunt of his anger against the *Manila Daily Inquirer*, using his friends in the entertainment business to withhold advertising dollars to force the paper to change. The *Manila Times* was later purchased by new owners and reopened in September. The standoff between the media and the president continues.

Another controversy involving the president concerns his plans to abolish the Presidential Commission on Good Government (PCGG). Estrada undermined the Commission's attempts to prosecute cases against former Philippine president Ferdinand Marcos, his wife, and their cronies by expressing a clear willingness to settle pending cases filed by the PCGG. Estrada claims his motivation is to move forward and focus on the country's economic development; his detractors claim Estrada is providing more avenues for his cronies to gain greater control of the economy. The charge of allowing close business and political allies to take control of segments of the economy has awakened fears among millions of Filipinos that President Estrada may try to follow the example of former president Ferdinand Marcos.

DIRECTORY

CENTRAL GOVERNMENT
Head of State

President
Joseph Ejercito Estrada, Office of the President, Malacanang Palace, Jose P. Laurel St., Manila, Philippines

PHONE: +63 (2) 7356201
FAX: +63 (2) 7421641
E-MAIL: erap@erap.com

Departments

Executive Secretary
Ronaldo B. Zamora, Office of the Executive
Secretary, 2nd Floor, New Executive Bldg JP
Laurel St., San Miguel 1005, Manila, Philippines
PHONE: +63 (2) 7356023; 7333608
FAX: +63 (2) 7421643

Secretary of National Defense
Orlando Mercado, Department of National
Defense, 3rd Floor, DND Building, Camp
Aguinaldo, Quezon City, Philippines
PHONE: +63 (2) 9116193; 9116183
FAX: +63 (2) 9116213

Secretary of Agrarian Reform
Horacio R. Morales, Jr., Department of Agrarian
Reform, Rm. 209, PTS Building, Diliman 1100,
Quezon City, Philippines
PHONE: +63 (2) 9283979; 9283573
FAX: +63 (2) 9283968
E-MAIL: HoracioM@dar.gov.ph

Secretary of Agriculture
William Dollente Dar, Department of
Agriculture, DA Building, Eliptical Road,
Diliman, Quezon City, Philippines
PHONE: +63 (2) 9262288
FAX: +63 (2) 9262288; 9288751
E-MAIL: webmaster@dfa.gov.ph

Secretary of Budget and Management
Benjamin Diokno, Department of Budget and
Management, 2nd Floor, DBM Building 3,
General Solano St., San Miquel, Manila,
Philippines
PHONE: +63 (2) 7354887; 7354936
FAX: +63 (2) 7424173

Secretary of Education, Culture and Sports
Andrew Gonzales, Department of Education,
Culture and Sports, University of Life Building,
Meralco Ave., Bo. Ugong 1600, Pasig City,
Philippines
PHONE: +63 (2) 6227208; 6337228
FAX: +63 (2) 6320805

Secretary of Energy
Francisco Viray, Department of Energy,
Philippine National Petroleum Center, PNCP
Completx, Merritt Rd., Fort Bonifacio, Makati
City, Philippines
PHONE: +63 (2) 8442850; 8178603

FAX: +63 (2) 8178603

Secretary of Environment and Natural Resources
Rey Antonio Cerilles, Department of
Environment and Natural Resources, DENR
Building, Visayas Ave., Quezon City,
Philippines
PHONE: +63 (2) 9296633
FAX: +63 (2) 9204352

Secretary of Finance
Edgardo Espiritu, Department of Finance, 5th
Floor, Executive Tower Building, Vito Cruz co.
Mabini St., Malate 1004, Manila, Philippines
PHONE: +63 (2) 5234255; 5236051
FAX: +63 (2) 5219495

Secretary of Foreign Affairs
Domingo L. Siazon, Jr., Department of Foreign
Affairs, DFA Building, 2330 Roxas Blvd.,
Pasay, Metro Manila, Philippines
PHONE: +63 (2) 8318955; 8318970
FAX: +63 (2) 8321597

Secretary of Health
Felipe Estrella, Department of Health, San
Lazaro Compound, Rizal Ave., Santa Cruz,
Manila, Philippines
PHONE: +63 (2) 7438301
FAX: +63 (2) 7116055

Secretary of Justice
Serafin Cueveas, Department of Justice, Padre
Faura St., Ermita, Manila, Philippines
PHONE: +63 (2) 5218344; 5213721
FAX: +63 (2) 5211614

Secretary of Interior and Local Government
Joseph Ejercito Estrada, Department of Interior
and Local Government, PNCC Building, EDSA
Corner Reliance Street, Mandaluyong, Metro
Manila, Philippines
PHONE: +63 (2) 6318777; 6318722
FAX: +63 (2) 6318831

Secretary of Labor and Employment
Bienvenido Laguesma, Department of Labor and
Employment, Rm. 107, Executive Bldg., San
Jose Street, Intramuros, Manila, Philippines
PHONE: +63 (2) 5272118; 5272116
FAX: +63 (2) 5273499

Secretary of National Economic and Development Authority
Felipe Medalla, Department of National
Economic and Development Authority, NEDA
Building, Amber Ave., Pasig City, Philippines

PHONE: +63 (2) 6313716; 6313723
FAX: +63 (2) 6313747

Secretary of Public Works and Highways
Gregorio R. Vigilar, Department of Public
Works and Highways, DPWH Bldg., Bonifacio
Dr., Port Area 1002, Manila, Philippines
PHONE: +63 (2) 5274111; 5275616
FAX: +63 (2) 5275635

Secretary of Science and Technology
William G. Padolina, Department of Science and
Technology, General Santos Ave., Bicutan
Taguig 1604, Metro Manila, Philippines
PHONE: +63 (2) 8372939
FAX: +63 (2) 8372937

Secretary of Social Welfare and Development
Gloria Macapagal-Arroyo, Department of Social
Welfare and Development, Constitution Hills
1100, Quezon City, Philippines
PHONE: +63 (2) 9317916; 9318068
FAX: +63 (2) 9310149

Secretary of Trade and Industry
Jose T. Pardo, Department of Trade and
Industry, Industry and Investment Bldg., 385 Gil
J. Puyat Ave., Makati 1200, Philippines
PHONE: +63 (2) 8953515; 8976734

Secretary of Tourism
Gemma Cruz-Araneta, Department of Tourism,
DOT Bldg., TM Kalaw St., Agrifina Circle,
Rizal Park, Manila, Philippines
PHONE: +63 (2) 5241751; 5244760
FAX: +63 (2) 5217374

Secretary of Transportation and Communications
Vicente Rivera, Department of Transportation
and Communications, Philcomcen Bldg., Ortigas
Ave., Pasig 1600, Philippines
PHONE: +63 (2) 7267106; 7267125
FAX: +63 (2) 7269985

POLITICAL ORGANIZATIONS

Laban ng Masang Pilipino

Lakas ñg Edsa (People's Power)
TITLE: President
NAME: Raul Manglapus

National Union of Christian Democrats
TITLE: Secretary-General
NAME: Jose de Venecia

United Muslim Democratic Party

Nationalist People's Coalition
NAME: Eduardo Cojuangco

Partido Liberal (Liberal Party)
NAME: Raul Daza

Laban ñg Demokratikong Pilipino (Struggle for a Democratic Philippines)
NAME: Edgardo Angara

Partido ñg Demokratikong Pilipino-PDP (Philippines Democratic Party)
NAME: Jose Cojuangco

People's Reform Party
NAME: Miriam Defensor-Santiago

DIPLOMATIC REPRESENTATION

Embassies in the Philippines

Argentina
6th Floor, A.C.T. Tower Condominium, 135
Sen. Gil Puyat Avenue, Salcedo Village, Makati,
Metro Manila, Philippines
PHONE: +63 (2) 8936091; 8108301
TITLE: Ambassador
NAME: Juan Luis Garibaldi

Australia
1st-5th Floors, Dona Salustiana Dee Ty Tower,
104 Paseo de Roxas, Makati, Metro Manila,
Philippines
PHONE: +63 (2) 7502850
TITLE: Ambassador
NAME: John Edward Buckley

Austria
4th Floor, Prince Building, 117 Rada Street,
Legaspi Village, Makati, Metro Manila,
Philippines
PHONE: +63 (2) 8179191; 8174992; 8174993
TITLE: Ambassador
NAME: Wolfgang Jilly

Bangladesh
2nd Floor, Universal-Re Building, 106 Paseo de
Roxas corner Perea Street, Legaspi Village,
Makati, Metro Manila, Philippines
PHONE: +63 (2) 8175010; 8175001
TITLE: Ambassador
NAME: Reazul Hossain

Belgium
Multinational Bancorporation Centre, 9th Floor,
6805 Ayala Avenue, Makati, Metro Manila,
Philippines
PHONE: +63 (2) 8451869; 8451874
TITLE: Ambassador
NAME: Roland Van Remoortele

Brazil
6th Floor, RCI Building, 105 Rada Street,
Legaspi Village, Makati, Metro Manila,
Philippines
PHONE: +63 (2) 8928181; 8928182
TITLE: Ambassador
NAME: Luiz Mattoso Maia Amado

Brunei Darussalam
11th Floor, Ayala Wing, Bank of the Philippine
Islands Building, Ayala Avenue corner Paseo de
Roxas, Makati, Metro Manila, Philippines
PHONE: +63 (2) 8162836
TITLE: Ambassador
NAME: Dato Paduka Haji Yahya Bin Haji Harris

Canada
9th and 11th Floors, Allied Bank Centre, 6754
Ayala Avenue, Makati, Metro Manila,
Philippines
PHONE: +63 (2) 8670001
TITLE: Ambassador
NAME: John Treleaven

Chile
6th Floor, Dona Salustiana D.T. Tower, 104
Paseo de Roxas, Legaspi Village, Makati, Metro
Manila, Philippines
PHONE: +63 (2) 8160395; 8103149
TITLE: Ambassador
NAME: Sergio Silva

China
4896 Pasay Road, Dasmarinas Village, Makati,
Metro Manila, Philippines
PHONE: +63 (2) 8443148; 8437715
TITLE: Ambassador
NAME: Fu Ying

Colombia
18th Floor, Aurora Tower, Araneta Center,
Quezon City, Metro Manila, Philippines
PHONE: +63 (2) 9113101
TITLE: Ambassador
NAME: Miguel Duran Ordonez

Cuba
101 Aguirre cor. Trasierra Streets, Cacho
Gonzales Building, Penthouse, Legaspi Village,
Makati, Metro Manila, Philippines

PHONE: +63 (2) 8171192
TITLE: Ambassador
NAME: Francisco Ramos

Czech Republic
1267 Acacia Road, Dasmarinas Village, Makati,
Metro Manila, Philippines
PHONE: +63 (2) 8129254

Denmark
6th Floor, Salustiana D. Ty Tower, 104 Paseo de
Roxas corner Perea Street, Legaspi Village, 1226
Makati, Metro Manila, Philippines
PHONE: +63 (2) 8940086
TITLE: Ambassador
NAME: Bjarne Bladbjerg

Egypt
2229 Paraiso corner Banyan Streets, Dasmarinas
Village, Makati, Metro Manila, Philippines
PHONE: +63 (2) 8439220
TITLE: Ambassador
NAME: Nabil Zaki

Finland
21st Floor, Far East Bank Center, Sen. Gil Puyat
Avenue, Makati, Metro Manila, Philippines
PHONE: +63 (2) 8915011
TITLE: Ambassador
NAME: Pertti Majanen

France
The Pacific Star Building, 16th Floor, Makati
Avenue corner Sen. Gil Puyat Extension,
Makati, Metro Manila, Philippines
PHONE: +63 (2) 8101981
TITLE: Ambassador
NAME: Gilles Chouraqui

Germany
6th Floor, Solid Bank Building, 777 Paseo de
Roxas, Makati, Metro Manila, Philippines
PHONE: +63 (2) 8924906
TITLE: Ambassador
NAME: Wolfgang Gottelmann

India
2190 Paraiso Street, Dasmarinas Village, Makati,
Metro Manila, Philippines
PHONE: +63 (2) 8430101; 8430102
TITLE: Ambassador
NAME: C.P. Ravindranathan

Indonesia
185 Salcedo Street, Legaspi Village, Makati,
Metro Manila, Philippines
PHONE: +63 (2) 8925061
TITLE: Ambassador

NAME: Abu Hartono

Iran
4th Floor, Don Jacinto Building, Salcedo corner dela Rosa Streets, Legaspi Village, Makati, Metro Manila, Philippines
PHONE: +63 (2) 8921561
TITLE: Ambassador
NAME: Mohammad Raeisi

Iraq
2261 Avocado Street, Dasmarinas Village, Makati, Metro Manila, Philippines
PHONE: +63 (2) 8439838; 8133067
TITLE: Ambassador
NAME: Salah Nouri Hitemi al-Samarmad

Israel
23rd Floor, Trafalgar Plaza, H.V. de la Costa Street, Salcedo Village, Makati, Metro Manila, Philippines
PHONE: +63 (2) 8925329
TITLE: Ambassador
NAME: Ilan Baruch

Italy
6th Floor, Zeta Building, 191 Salcedo Street, Legaspi Village, Makati, Metro Manila, Philippines
PHONE: +63 (2) 8924531
TITLE: Ambassador
NAME: Graziella Simbolotti

Japan
2627 Roxas Boulevard, Pasay City 1300, Philippines
PHONE: +63 (2) 5515710

Korea
10th Floor, The Pacific Star Building, Makati Avenue, Makati, Metro Manila, Philippines
PHONE: +63 (2) 8116139
TITLE: Ambassador
NAME: Shin Sung-Oh

Kuwait
6th Floor, Morning Star Building, 347 Sen. Gil J. Puyat Avenue, Makati, Metro Manila, Philippines
PHONE: +63 (2) 8977751
TITLE: Ambassador
NAME: Fahd Salem al-Ajmi

Laos
34 Lapu-Lapu Street, Magallanes Village, Makati City, Philippines
PHONE: +63 (2) 8335759
TITLE: Ambassador

NAME: Sengchanh Soukhaseum

Libya
2416 Bouganvilla Street, Dasmarinas Village, Makati, Metro Manila, Philippines
PHONE: +63 (2) 8442045; 8442046
TITLE: Ambassador
NAME: Rajab Abdulaziz Azzarouq

Malaysia
107 Tordesillas Street, Salcedo Villag, Makati, Metro Manila, Philippines
PHONE: +63 (2) 8174581
TITLE: Ambassador
NAME: Abdul Aziz Mohammed

Malta
6th Floor, Cattleya Condominium, 235 Salcedo Street, Legaspi Village, Makati, Metro Manila, Philippines
PHONE: +63 (2) 8171095
TITLE: Ambassador
NAME: Enrique P. Syquia

Mexico
18th Floor, Ramon Magsaysay Center, 1680 Roxas Boulevard, Pasay, Metro Manila, Philippines
PHONE: +63 (2) 5267461
TITLE: Ambassador
NAME: Enrique Michel

Myanmar
8th Floor, Xanland Centre, 152 Amorsolo Street, Legaspi Village, Makati City, Philippines
PHONE: +63 (2) 8172372
TITLE: Ambassador
NAME: U San Thein

Netherlands
9th Floor, King's Court Building, 2129 Pasong Tamo, Makati, Metro Manila, Philippines
PHONE: +63 (2) 8125981; 8125982; 8125983
TITLE: Ambassador
NAME: George Theodore Eugene Richard Arnold

New Zealand
23rd Floor, Far East Bank Centre, Sen. Gil Puyat Avenue (near Makati Avenue), Makati, Metro Manila, Philippines
PHONE: +63 (2) 8915358
TITLE: Ambassador
NAME: Graeme Charles Waters

Nigeria
2211 Paraiso Street, Dasmarinas Village, Makati, Metro Manila, Philippines
PHONE: +63 (2) 8439866

TITLE: Ambassador
NAME: Ademola Olugbade Aderele

Norway
21st Floor, Petron Mega Plaza Building, 358 Sen. Gil Puyat Avenue, Makati, Metro Manila, Philippines
PHONE: +63 (2) 8863245
TITLE: Ambassador
NAME: Inga Magistad

Pakistan
6th Floor, Alexander House, 132 Amorsolo Street, Legaspi Village, Makati, Metro Manila, Philippines
PHONE: +63 (2) 8172776; 8172772
TITLE: Ambassador
NAME: Azmat Ghayur

Panama
Room 501, Victoria Building, 429 United Nations Avenue, Ermita, Manila, Philippines
PHONE: +63 (2) 5212790; 5211233
TITLE: Ambassador
NAME: Graciela Arauz Arias

Papua New Guinea
2280 Magnolia Street, Dasmarinas Village, Makati, Metro Manila, Philippines
PHONE: +63 (2) 8442060; 8442051
TITLE: Ambassador
NAME: Graham John Ainui

Peru
7th Floor, Unit 7-B, Country Space One Building, Sen. Gil Puyat Avenue, Makati, Metro Manila, Philippines
PHONE: +63 (2) 8138731
TITLE: Ambassador
NAME: Victor Aritomi-Shinto

Portugal
14th Floor, Unit D Trafalgar Plaza, 105 H.V. dela Costa Street, Salcedo Village, Makati City, Philippines
PHONE: +63 (2) 8483789; 8483790
TITLE: Ambassador
NAME: Joao Henrique Araujo Brito Camara

Qatar
1601 Cypress Street, Dasmarinas Village, Makati, Metro Manila, Philippines
PHONE: +63 (2) 8874944; 8874945
TITLE: Ambassador
NAME: Saleh Ibrahim al-Kuwari

Romania
1216 Acacia Road, Dasmarinas Village, Makati, Metro Manila, Philippines
PHONE: +63 (2) 8439014

Russia
1245 Acacia Road, Dasmarinas Village, Makati, Metro Manila, Philippines
PHONE: +63 (2) 8109614; 8930190
TITLE: Ambassador
NAME: Anatoli Khmelnitski

Saudi Arabia
Saudi Embassy Building, 389 Senator Gil J. Puyat Avenue Extension, Makati, Metro Manila, Philippines
PHONE: +63 (2) 8909735
TITLE: Ambassador
NAME: Saleh Mohammad al-Ghamdi

Singapore
6th Floor, ODC International Plaza, 219 Salcedo Street, Legaspi Village, Makati, Metro Manila, Philippines
PHONE: +63 (2) 8161764; 8161765
TITLE: Ambassador
NAME: Simon Tensing De Cruz

Spain
5th Floor, ACT Tower, 135 Sen. Gil Puyat Avenue, Makati, Metro Manila, Philippines
PHONE: +63 (2) 8183561; 8185526
TITLE: Ambassador
NAME: Delfin Colome

Sri Lanka
2260 Avocado Avenue, Dasmarinas Village, Makati City, Philippines
PHONE: +63 (2) 8439813; 8120335
TITLE: Ambassador
NAME: Pitiduwa Gamage Karunasiri

United States
Chancery Building, 1201 Roxas Boulevard, Manila, Philippines
PHONE: +63 (2) 5231001
TITLE: Ambassador
NAME: Thomas C. Hubbard

JUDICIAL SYSTEM
Supreme Court

FURTHER READING
Articles
''Appeals Made for Sobriety, Reason in Rally,'' *The Manila Bulletin*, 18 August 1999.

"Economies: Stealth Technology," *Far Eastern Economic Review,* 15 July 1999.

"Espiritu Bats for Charter Changes," *The Manila Bulletin,* 14 July 1999.

Books

Hamilton-Paterson, James. *America's Boy: A Century of Colonialism in the Philippines.* New York: H. Holt, 1999.

Kirk, Donald. *Looted: the Philippines After the Bases.* New York: St. Martin's Press, 1998.

Roces, Mina. *Women, Power, and Kinship Politics: Female Power in Post-War Philippines.* Westport, CT: Praeger, 1998.

Silliman, G. Sidney and Lela Garner Noble, eds. *Organizing for Democracy: NGOs, civil society, and the Philippine State.* Honolulu: University of Hawai'i Press, 1998.

Internet

The Philippine Senate Home Page. Available Online @ http://senate.hypermart.net/pcgg.html (October 22, 1999.)

Kasaysayan, A Comprehensive Peek at Philippine History, "Social Values and Organization." Available Online @ http://www.pinoys.com/kasaysayan/ph0062.htm (October 22, 1999.)

The Heritage Foundation, "Rebuilding the U.S.-Philippine Alliance," Available Online @ http://www.heritage.org/library/backgrounder/bg1255es.html (October 22, 1999.)

PHILIPPINES: STATISTICAL DATA

For sources and notes see "Sources of Statistics" in the front of each volume.

GEOGRAPHY

Geography (1)

Area:

Total: 300,000 sq km.

Land: 298,170 sq km.

Water: 1,830 sq km.

Area—comparative: slightly larger than Arizona.

Land boundaries: 0 km.

Coastline: 36,289 km.

Climate: tropical marine; northeast monsoon (November to April); southwest monsoon (May to October).

Terrain: mostly mountains with narrow to extensive coastal lowlands.

Natural resources: timber, petroleum, nickel, cobalt, silver, gold, salt, copper.

Land use:

Arable land: 19%

Permanent crops: 12%

Permanent pastures: 4%

Forests and woodland: 46%

Other: 19% (1993 est.).

HUMAN FACTORS

Demographics (2A)

	1990	1995	1998	2000	2010	2020	2030	2040	2050
Population	65,036.6	72,859.9	77,725.9	80,961.4	97,119.3	112,962.9	127,599.0	140,090.5	150,271.8
Net migration rate (per 1,000 population)	NA	NA	NA	NA	NA	NA	NA	NA	NA
Births	NA	NA	NA	NA	NA	NA	NA	NA	NA
Deaths	NA	NA	NA	NA	NA	NA	NA	NA	NA
Life expectancy - males	61.3	62.9	63.6	64.0	66.1	68.0	69.7	71.3	72.6
Life expectancy - females	67.5	68.6	69.3	69.7	71.8	73.8	75.5	77.1	78.4
Birth rate (per 1,000)	32.3	30.0	28.4	27.3	23.5	20.7	18.0	16.3	14.9
Death rate (per 1,000)	7.3	6.7	6.5	6.4	6.1	6.2	6.7	7.5	8.4
Women of reproductive age (15-49 yrs.)	16,240.8	18,566.0	20,054.2	20,987.9	25,669.7	29,994.1	33,269.3	35,583.3	36,558.9
of which are currently married	8,641.2	NA	NA	NA	NA	NA	NA	NA	NA
Fertility rate	4.1	3.8	3.5	3.4	2.8	2.5	2.3	2.2	2.1

Except as noted, values for vital statistics are in thousands; life expectancy is in years.

Health Personnel (3)

Total health expenditure as a percentage of GDP, 1990-1997[a]

Public sector 1.3

Private sector 1.0

Total[b] 2.4

Health expenditure per capita in U.S. dollars, 1990-1997[a]

Purchasing power parity 67

Total 17

Availability of health care facilities per 100,000 people

Hospital beds 1990-1997[a] 110

Doctors 1993[c] 11

Nurses 1993[c] 43

Health Indicators (4)

Life expectancy at birth

1980 61

1997 68

Daily per capita supply of calories (1996) 2,356

Total fertility rate births per woman (1997) 3.6

Maternal mortality ratio per 100,000 live births (1990-97) . . . . .210[d]

Safe water % of population with access (1995) 83

Sanitation % of population with access (1995) 77

Consumption of iodized salt % of households (1992-98)[a] 15

Smoking prevalence

Male % of adults (1985-95)[a] 43

Female % of adults (1985-95)[a] 8

Tuberculosis incidence per 100,000 people (1997) 310

Adult HIV prevalence % of population ages 15-49 (1997) 0.06

Infants and Malnutrition (5)

Under-5 mortality rate (1997) 41

% of infants with low birthweight (1990-97) 9

Births attended by skilled health staff % of total[a] . . .53

% fully immunized (1995-97)

TB 82

DPT 70

Polio 67

Measles 72

Prevalence of child malnutrition under age 5 (1992-97)[b] 30

Ethnic Division (6)

Christian Malay 91.5%

Muslim Malay 4%

Chinese 1.5%

Other 3%

Religions (7)

Roman Catholic 83%

Protestant 9%

Muslim 5%

Buddhist and other 3%

Languages (8)

Pilipino (official, based on Tagalog), English (official).

EDUCATION

Public Education Expenditures (9)

Public expenditure on education (% of GNP)

1980 . . . . .1.7

1996 . . . . .2.2[1]

Expenditure per student

Primary % of GNP per capita

1980 . . . . .5.8

1996 . . . .

Secondary % of GNP per capita

1980 . . . . .4.3

1996 . . . .

Tertiary % of GNP per capita

1980 . . . . .13.8

1996 . . . .

Expenditure on teaching materials

Primary % of total for level (1996) . . . .

Secondary % of total for level (1996) . . . .

Primary pupil-teacher ratio per teacher (1996) 35

Duration of primary education years (1995) 6

Educational Attainment (10)

Age group (1995) . . . . .15+

Total population 42,700,000

Highest level attained (%)

No schooling 3.8

First level

Not completed 20.8

Completed 15.1

Entered second level

S-1 . . . . .17.3

S-2 . . . . .21.2

Postsecondary 22.0

Literacy Rates (11A)

In thousands and percent[1]	1990	1995	2000	2010
Illiterate population (15+ yrs.)	2,350	2,234	2,024	1,639
Literacy rate - total adult pop. (%)	93.6	94.6	95.7	97.3
Literacy rate - males (%)	94.0	95.0	96.0	97.4
Literacy rate - females (%)	93.2	94.3	95.5	97.1

GOVERNMENT & LAW

Political Parties (12)

House of Representatives	No. of seats
People Power-National Union of Christian Democrats (Lakas-NUCD)	126
Democratic Filipino Struggle (LDP)	28
National People's Coalition (NPC)	28
Nacionalista Party (NP)	2
New Society Movement (KBL)	2
Other	18

Military Affairs (14B)

	1990	1991	1992	1993	1994	1995
Military expenditures						
Current dollars (mil.)	1,232	1,231	1,185	1,425	1,368	1,151
1995 constant dollars (mil.)	1,416	1,360	1,275	1,494	1,402	1,151
Armed forces (000)	109	107	107	107	109	110
Gross national product (GNP)						
Current dollars (mil.)	57,200	59,910	62,400	65,690	70,740	76,630
1995 constant dollars (mil.)	65,730	66,200	67,120	68,870	72,510	76,630
Central government expenditures (CGE)						
1995 constant dollars (mil.)	13,240	12,920	12,530	12,960	13,240	13,610
People (mil.)	65.0	66.6	68.1	69.7	71.3	72.9
Military expenditure as % of GNP	2.2	2.1	1.9	2.2	1.9	1.5
Military expenditure as % of CGE	10.7	10.5	10.2	11.5	10.6	8.5
Military expenditure per capita (1995 $)	22	20	19	21	20	16
Armed forces per 1,000 people (soldiers)	1.7	1.6	1.6	1.5	1.5	1.5
GNP per capita (1995 $)	1,011	995	986	989	1,018	1,052
Arms imports[6]						
Current dollars (mil.)	110	140	140	60	90	90
1995 constant dollars (mil.)	126	155	151	63	92	90
Arms exports[6]						
Current dollars (mil.)	0	0	0	0	0	0
1995 constant dollars (mil.)	0	0	0	0	0	0
Total imports[7]						
Current dollars (mil.)	13,040	12,790	15,450	18,750	22,550	28,340
1995 constant dollars (mil.)	14,990	14,130	16,620	19,660	23,110	28,340
Total exports[7]						
Current dollars (mil.)	8,068	8,767	9,752	11,090	13,300	17,500
1995 constant dollars (mil.)	9,272	9,688	10,490	11,630	13,640	17,500
Arms as percent of total imports[8]	.8	1.1	.9	.3	.4	.3
Arms as percent of total exports[8]	0	0	0	0	0	0

Government Budget (13A)

Year: 1997

Total Expenditures: 470,279 Millions of Pesos

Expenditures as a percentage of the total by function:

General public services and public order 17.15

Defense 7.98

Education 20.41

Health 3.21

Social Security and Welfare 2.51

Housing and community amenities 55

Recreational, cultural, and religious affairs 73

Fuel and energy 20

Agriculture, forestry, fishing, and hunting 6.50

Mining, manufacturing, and construction 04

Transportation and communication 13.64

Other economic affairs and services 1.84

Crime (15)

Crime rate (for 1994)

Crimes reported 93,300

Total persons convicted . . . . .NA

Crimes per 100,000 population 139

Persons responsible for offenses

Total number of suspects . . . . .NA

Total number of female suspects . . . . .NA

Total number of juvenile suspects . . . . .NA

LABOR FORCE

Labor Force (16)

Total (million) 29.13

Agriculture 43.4%

Services 22.6%

Government services 17.9%

Industry and commerce .16.1%

Data for 1996 est. Percent distribution for 1995.

Unemployment Rate (17)

8.7% (1997)

PRODUCTION SECTOR

Electric Energy (18)

Capacity . . . . .7.64 million kW (1995)

Production . . . . .25.65 billion kWh (1995)

Consumption per capita . . . . .350 kWh (1995)

Transportation (19)

Highways:

total: 156,997 km (1996 est.)

paved: NA km

unpaved: NA km note: probably less than 30,000 km are designated arterial roads and not all of these are all-weather roads

Waterways: 3,219 km; limited to shallow-draft (less than 1.5 m) vessels

Pipelines: petroleum products 357 km

Merchant marine:

total: 535 ships (1,000 GRT or over) totaling 7,334,164 GRT/11,511,707 DWT

Airports: 262 (1997 est.)

Airports—with paved runways:

total: 75

over 3,047 m: 3

2,438 to 3,047 m: 7

1,524 to 2,437 m: 25

914 to 1,523 m: 30

under 914 m: 10 (1997 est.)

Airports—with unpaved runways:

total: 187

1,524 to 2,437 m: 3

914 to 1,523 m: 63

under 914 m: 121 (1997 est.)

Top Agricultural Products (20)

Rice, coconuts, corn, sugarcane, bananas, pineapples, mangoes; pork, eggs, beef; fish catch of 2 million metric tons annually.

MANUFACTURING SECTOR

GDP & Manufacturing Summary (21)

Detailed value added figures are listed by both International Standard Industry Code (ISIC) and product title.

	1980	1985	1990	1994
GDP ($-1990 mil.)[1]	37,449	35,122	44,050	46,755
Per capita ($-1990)[1]	775	642	725	706
Manufacturing share (%) (current prices)[1]	25.7	25.2	25.0	23.3
Manufacturing				
Value added ($-1990 mil.)[1]	10,067	8,605	11,003	11,311
Industrial production index	100	74	168	175

	1980	1985	1990	1994
Value added ($ mil.)	4,861	3,448	8,852	12,694
Gross output ($ mil.)	17,369	12,081	24,321	34,753
Employment (000)	949	619	1,109	1,029
Profitability (% of gross output)				
Intermediate input(%)	72	71	64	63
Wages and salaries inc. supplements (%)	6	6	8	8
Gross operating surplus	22	22	28	28
Productivity ($)				
Gross output per worker	16,263	19,369	19,805	33,592
Value added per worker	4,552	5,528	7,209	12,334
Average wage (inc. supplements)	1,127	1,257	1,802	2,857
Value added ($ mil.)				
311/2 Food products	969	658	2,206	2,178
313 Beverages	195	423	815	1,124
314 Tobacco products	309	209	420	637
321 Textiles	395	109	393	408
322 Wearing apparel	205	105	509	815
323 Leather and fur products	8	3	25	30
324 Footwear	13	9	18	48
331 Wood and wood products	229	86	164	153
332 Furniture and fixtures	75	22	103	103
341 Paper and paper products	128	97	184	305
342 Printing and publishing	89	46	125	173
351 Industrial chemicals	296	101	277	455
352 Other chemical products	389	205	767	1,502
353 Petroleum refineries	328	715	489	948
354 Miscellaneous petroleum and coal products	2	3	3	16
355 Rubber products	103	34	158	273
356 Plastic products	85	32	111	244
361 Pottery, china and earthenware	33	9	29	59
362 Glass and glass products	42	28	86	115
369 Other non-metal mineral products	63	60	240	402
371 Iron and steel	98	164	236	466
372 Non-ferrous metals	35	28	117	92
381 Metal products	127	49	156	190
382 Non-electrical machinery	98	31	84	150
383 Electrical machinery	260	156	775	1,154
384 Transport equipment	234	35	258	504
385 Professional and scientific equipment	5	5	11	22
390 Other manufacturing industries	49	28	93	127

FINANCE, ECONOMICS, & TRADE

Balance of Payments (23)

	1991	1992	1993	1994	1995
Exports of goods (f.o.b.)	8,840	9,824	11,375	13,483	17,447
Imports of goods (f.o.b.)	−12,051	−14,519	−17,597	−21,333	−26,391
Trade balance	−3,211	−4,695	−6,222	−7,850	−8,944
Services - debits	−4,273	−4,618	−4,990	−6,586	−9,331
Services - credits	5,623	7,497	7,497	10,550	15,415
Private transfers (net)	150	200	139	72	77
Government transfers (net)	677	616	560	864	803
Overall balance	−1,034	−1,000	−3,016	−2,950	−1,980

FINANCE, ECONOMICS, & TRADE

Economic Indicators (22)

National product: GDP—purchasing power parity—$244 billion (1997 est.)

National product real growth rate: 5.1% (1997 est.)

National product per capita: $3,200 (1997 est.)

Inflation rate—consumer price index: 5.1% (1997)

Exchange Rates (24)

Exchange rates:

Philippine pesos (P) per US$1

April 1998	.40.2
May 1997	.26.36
1997	.29.471
1996	.26.216
1995	.25.714
1994	.26.417
1993	.27.120

Top Import Origins (25)

$34 billion (f.o.b., 1997 est.) Data are for 1997 est.

Origins	%
Japan	.21
United States	.20
ASEAN	.12
European Union	.10
Taiwan	.5
Hong Kong	.4
Saudi Arabia	.4

Top Export Destinations (26)

$25 billion (f.o.b., 1997 est.) Data are for 1997 est.

Destinations	%
United States	.34
Japan	.17
European Union	.17
ASEAN	.14
Hong Kong	.4
Taiwan	.4

Economic Aid (27)

Recipient: ODA, $3 billion pledged at December 1997 for 1998.

Import Export Commodities (28)

Import Commodities	Export Commodities
Raw materials and intermediate goods 43%	Electronics and telecommunications 51%
Capital goods 36%	
Consumer goods 9%	Machinery and transport 10%
Fuels 9%	
	Garments 9%
	Other 30% est.

POLAND

Republic of Poland
Rzeczpospolita Polska

INTRODUCTORY SURVEY

RECENT HISTORY

Poland as a whole suffered tremendous losses of life and property during World War II. An estimated 6 million Poles were killed, half of them Jews. The remaining population suffered near starvation throughout the Nazi occupation.

On 17 January 1945, Warsaw was liberated by the Soviet and Polish armies. The Provisional Government of National Unity was formally recognized by the United States and United Kingdom in July 1945. The communists and the socialists merged in December 1948 to form the Polish United Workers' Party (PZPR). The PZPR consistently followed a pro-Soviet policy. It shunned the Marshall Plan (plan to rebuild Europe after World War II) and, in its first two decades, renounced all dealings with the Western powers.

The first decade of communist rule was dominated by tensions with the Roman Catholic Church and the question of Soviet influence. In response to worker riots in Poznán on 28–29 July 1956, a new Polish government, headed by Wladyslaw Gomulka, introduced new freedoms, including improved relations with the Church. By the late 1950s, however, the reform movement had been halted, and the government took a harder line against dissent. In 1968 there were student demonstrations and further government crackdowns.

Following a drought in 1969 and an exceptionally severe winter, demonstrations by shipyard workers in Gdánsk broke out on 16 December 1970

POLAND

0   50   100 Miles

0   50   100 Kilometers

protesting economic conditions. After widespread violence, in which at least 44 people were killed, the government, under a new leader, Edward Gierek, modified its economic policies and reinstated Church control over thousands of religious properties in northwestern Poland.

During the 1970s, Gierek's government vigorously pursued a policy of détente (harmony) with the West. At home, however, the economic situation kept growing worse, and Polish nationalism continued to rise. In an historic public ceremony on 31 August 1980, government officials agreed to allow workers the right to form independent trade unions and the right to strike. The independent labor movement Solidarity, headed by Walesa, the leader of the Gdánsk workers, emerged in early September and soon claimed a membership of about 10 million.

On 13 December 1980, after union leaders in Gdánsk called for a national referendum on forming a non-communist government in Poland, General Wojciech Jaruzelski, prime minister since

February, declared martial law. Almost the whole leadership of Solidarity, including Walesa, was arrested, and the union was suspended.

In the following years, martial law was gradually eased, and the Jaruzelski government restored order on the political level. However, continued declines in the standard of living led to waves of strikes throughout Poland in spring and fall 1988, paralyzing the nation. The demands of strikers, most led by Solidarity, began to become political as well as economic.

By April 1989, the government agreed to establish a Senate with the seats to be filled by open election. In addition, 35% of the seats in the existing parliament, the Sejm, were also made subject to direct election. In elections in June 1989, 99 of the 100 seats in the Senate went to Solidarity members. Tadeusz Mazowiecki took office on 24 August 1989 as the first non-communist prime minister in the eastern bloc (communist nations in eastern Europe).

Across eastern Europe that autumn, other communist countries were quietly breaking loose of the influence of the Soviet Union. This wave of "velvet revolutions" sped up the de-Sovietization of the Polish government. Local elections were held in May 1990, further weakening the communists' grip on power. On 9 December 1990 Lech Walesa, the leader of the Solidarity labor movement, was elected president.

After 1990, the number of political parties grew rapidly, weakening the impact that any one party or group of parties was able to have. This resulted in coalition governments without strong powers, giving Poland five prime ministers and four governments in 1991–93.

In addition, once the communists had been removed from power, splits became more apparent between the 40% of Poland which is rural, and the 60% which is urban. Also important were growing tensions between intellectuals and the powerful Catholic Church, which moved to take close control over social issues like abortion, school curriculum, and women's role in society.

However, local elections held 19 June 1994 suggested that fears of a return to communism under the new government were unfounded. The government of Polish Peasant Party leader Waldemar Pawlak, and his Democratic Left Alliance partner, Aleksander Kwasniewski, remained generally committed to democracy and economic change. In December 1995, Kwasniewski was elected president.

In 1997, the North Atlantic Treaty Organization (NATO) invited Poland, along with the Czech Republic and Hungary, to join the alliance in 1999. On March 12, 1999, all three states formally joined NATO.

GOVERNMENT

Without a new formal constitution, Poland has been functioning on a much-amended form of its communist-era constitution. A package of amendments passed in October 1992 are collectively called the "Little Constitution." A 1990 agreement made the presidency a popularly elected post, rather than one of parliamentary appointment.

The present system combines a presidential and a parliamentary system. The president is directly elected, for a term of six years. The post includes traditional executive duties and powers, such as the duty to sign into law or veto legislation, but also retains many legislative powers, including the right to introduce bills and draft legal amendments.

The parliament consists of two houses: the Sejm, or lower house, with 460 seats; and the Senate, with 100 seats. Seats are filled on the basis of party lists. The government, which appoints the Council of Ministers, is drawn from the party with majority parliamentary representation. In the absence of such a majority, coalitions are necessary.

Under the communists, Poland was divided into 49 administrative districts, called *voivods*. The 1989 Solidarity government replaced these with the *gmina*, or local authority, which chooses its own council and officials. In 1994, there were 2,383 of these local councils.

Judiciary

The Supreme Court, the highest judicial body, functions primarily as a court of appeal. Its judges are elected by the Council of State for five-year terms. It is divided into criminal, civil, military, and labor and social insurance chambers. In addition, there are regional courts, as well as special courts such as military tribunals, children's courts, and courts for cases involving social insurance.

In general the Poles have been reluctant to remove communist-era judges, but fears about the fair-mindedness of people who served the earlier regime damage the public's belief in the judiciary. A 1993 law makes it possible for the Ministry of Justice to recall a judge determined by a disciplinary commission to have failed to exercise "court independence."

Political Parties

After the restrictions of their communist past, the Poles formed a rich variety of political parties. These ranged across the full political spectrum, including even such strange groups as the Polish Beerdrinkers' Party. A full 69 parties participated in the 1991 parliamentary elections, of which 29 gained seats, none of them with more than 14% of the total vote.

By 1993, however, the political scene was showing signs of stabilizing. Only 35 parties took part in that election, and only 5 received seats.

The local elections of 1994 showed Poland dividing into three basic political groupings. On the right in that election were two large coalitions made up of parties including the Christian National Union, the Center Alliance, the Movement for the

Republic, the Peasant Alliance, the Conservative Coalition, the Conservative Party, the Party of Christian Democrats, and the Christian-Peasant Alliance. These parties generally favor a major role for the Catholic Church, and tend to draw their support from Poland's rural areas.

The center is dominated by Freedom Union (UW), which was formed in April 1994 when the Liberal Democratic Congress merged with the Democratic Union. Its position is taken from the intellectual wing of the original Solidarity, favoring radical economic change, while being less concerned with immediate impact upon workers.

The left, which was almost entirely defeated in 1991, has shown remarkable strength. The two major parties are the Democratic Left Alliance (SLD) and the Polish Peasant Party (PSL).

DEFENSE

The conscription (forced military service, or draft) law of January 1959 provides for registration at 18 and service (18 months) at age 20. Polish armed forces numbered 248,500 (147,100 draftees) in 1995, including 178,700 in 13 army divisions and 10 specialized brigades. Navy personnel totaled 17,800. The air force had 52,000 men and 437 combat aircraft of Soviet design. The reserve had about 466,000 active members in 1995. The Ministry of Interior had 16,000 troops and border guards. Defense expenditures for 1995, as officially reported, amounted to $2.6 billion.

Poland provides 1,700 servicemen to three different nations as United Nations observers.

ECONOMIC AFFAIRS

Until recently, Poland had a centrally planned economy that was primarily state-controlled. Since World War II, agriculture's dominant place in the economy has been shrinking. Poland, with its sizable coastline, has become a maritime nation of some importance, having developed three major ports on the Baltic Sea and a greatly expanded shipbuilding industry, which in 1991 produced 53 ships.

Since the government abandoned central planning, Poland has struggled with the transformation of over 8,000 state-owned enterprises into workable private corporations. By 1992, private businesses accounted for almost half of economic activity. The private sector now accounts for 70% of the domestic economy.

During the transition to a market-oriented economy, consumer prices shot up over 600% in 1990–92, and 35% in 1993. The government's careful financial and monetary policies have helped the economy to grow since 1995. Inflation in 1996 (18.5%) and unemployment (13%) remained high.

Public Finance

The annual budget is presented to the *Sejm* in December and becomes effective for the fiscal year beginning on 1 January. The U.S. Central Intelligence Agency (CIA) estimates that, in 1995, government revenues totaled approximately $34.5 billion and expenditures $37.8 billion. External debt totaled $42.1 billion, approximately 64% of which was financed abroad. The government has managed to refrain from increased deficit spending with public debt standing at 60% of GDP in 1996. The 1996 budget deficit was only 2.5% of GDP, well below the 3% Maastricht Treaty requirement for entry into the single European currency (the euro) in 1999.

Income

In 1997, the gross national product (GNP) was $280.7 billion, or about $7,250 per person. For the period 1985–95 the average inflation rate was 91.8%, resulting in a decline in gross national product of 0.4% per person.

Industry

Leading industries in 1993 included food processing (21.5% of total output), fuel (16.2%), metals and metal products (8.9%), and chemicals (5.8%). With the destabilizing effects of the breakup of the bloc of communist countries in Europe and central planning, industrial production fell by 26% in 1990 before returning to positive growth during 1991–95. In 1995, industrial production was still 13% below the 1989 level.

Poland produced 11.9 million tons of steel in 1995. Sulfur is another important industrial commodity. Sulfur production in 1995 totaled 2.4 million tons. The cement industry turned out 13.9 million tons during the same year. In 1993, Poland produced 401,000 automatic washing machines, 584,000 refrigerators and freezers, 841,000 television sets, 307,000 radios, and 21,000 tape recorders and dictaphones.

Banking and Finance

The Banking Law of 1 July 1982 substantially reformed the Polish banking system by giving banks an effective role in setting monetary and credit policy, thereby allowing them to influence economic planning. The Council of Banks, consisting of top bank officers and representatives of the Planning Commission and the Ministry of Finance, is the principal coordinating body.

The National Bank of Poland (Narodowy Bank Polski—NBP), created in 1945 to replace the former Bank of Poland, is a state institution and the bank of issue. It also controls foreign transactions and prepares financial plans for the economy. On 1 January 1970, the National Bank merged with the Investment Bank and has since controlled funds for finance and investment transactions of state enterprises and organizations. The function of the Food Economy Bank and its associated cooperative banks is to supply short- and long-term credits to rural areas. The national commercial bank, Bank Handlowy w Warszawie (BH), finances foreign trade operations. The General Savings Bank (Bank Polska Kasa Opieki—PKO), a central institution for personal savings, also handles financial transfers into Poland of persons living abroad. Total reserves, excluding gold, amounted to $17,451 million in June 1996.

Time, savings, and foreign currency deposits increased from Z 25.1 billion in 1975 to Z 1,351.1 billion in 1985 and Z 25,409 billion in 1992. In March 1985, two types of hard-currency accounts were introduced: ''A'' accounts, bearing interest, for currency earned in an approved way; and ''B'' accounts, for other currency, bearing no interest. ''B'' accounts can be converted into ''A'' accounts after one year. Banking laws in 1989 opened the country's banking system to foreign banks.

Major enterprises in Poland conduct their business by interaccount settlements through the National Bank rather than by check, and wages are paid in cash.

A fundamental reorganization of the banking sector took place between 1990 and 1992. The NBP lost all its central planning functions, including holding the accounts of state enterprises, making transfers among them, crediting their operations, and exercising financial control of their activities. The NBP thus became only a central bank, and state enterprises competed with other businesses for the scarce credits available from commercial banks. Nine independent (so-called commercial), although state-owned, regional banks were created.

In 1993, the first of these, the Poznan-based Wielkopolski Bank Kredytowy (WBK), was privatized. A second highly controversial privatization took place in early 1994 with the sale of the Silesian Bank (Bank Slaski). Also, the Krakow-based Bank Przemyslowo-Handlowy (BPH), was disposed of at the start of 1995 and Bank Gdanski was sold in late 1995. With four major banks privatized, five remained to be sold off in a process that was supposed to have been completed by 1996. With no real hope of meeting this deadline, the Polish government returned in 1996 to proposals for ''bank consolidation'' prior to privatization. Privatization of the Warsaw-based Powszechny Bank Kredytowy was due to begin in the first quarter of 1997.

Genuinely new private banks have emerged alongside privatization. But most banking activity is conducted by the nine commercial banks: Wielkopolski Bank Kredytowy (WBK), Bank Slaski Katowice (BSK), Bank Przemyslowo-Handlowy (BPH), Bank Gdanski, Pomorski Bank Kredytowy, Bank Zachodin, Powszechny Bank Kredytowy, Powszechny Bank Gospodarczy, and Bank Depozytowo-Kredytowy.

In early 1991 important legislation was introduced to regulate securities transactions and establish a stock exchange in Warsaw. At the same time, a securities commission was formed for consumer protection. A year later, the shares of 11 Polish companies were being traded weekly on the new exchange. Restructuring the financial market not only was necessary for increasing the overall efficiency of the economy and accelerating privatization, but also was a precondition for the rapid influx of Western capital critical to economic development.

When the Warsaw Stock Exchange opened in April 1991, it had only five listed companies, but by September 1996 that figure had increased to 63.

Economic Development

After World War II, the economy of Poland was centrally planned and almost completely under state control, especially in nonagricultural sectors. The nationalized industries and businesses operated within the national economic plan and were governed by the directives issued by the pertinent ministries. After 1963, however, centralized planning and management were somewhat relaxed, and state-owned enterprises gained more freedom in the design and implementation of their programs. Private undertakings were confined to personal crafts and trades and agriculture.

Economic planning followed Soviet lines, setting production goals that determined tasks for each sector on a long-term basis. Under the three-year plan for 1947–49, principal emphasis was placed on the reconstruction of war-devastated areas and industries, in order to raise production and living conditions at least to their prewar levels. Under the six-year plan for 1950–55, the emphasis continued to be on heavy industry, and the housing, transport, agriculture, and consumer sectors lagged. The five-year plan for 1956–60, originally cast along the same lines, was modified after the 1956 disturbances. It called for a lessened rate of industrial expansion and for increases in agricultural output, housing, consumer goods, and social services. Under a long-range plan for 1961–75, which governed the three five-year plans falling within that period, emphasis was placed on a direct improvement in living standards. The first and second of these plans (1961–65 and 1966–70) were oriented toward investments intended (1) to develop the raw-material base of the country, especially the newly discovered resources of sulfur, copper, and lignite; (2) to secure employment opportunities for the rapidly growing population of working age; and (3) to improve Poland's international trade balance. The five-year plan for 1961–65 reached its industrial targets but fell short in the areas of agriculture and consumer goods. The period 1966–70 witnessed two poor agricultural years in addition to export lags, and there were shortages of basic food commodities in 1969–70.

In late 1970, violent protests erupted over the government's stepped-up efforts to increase production. After the change in political leadership from Gomulka to Gierek, government emphasis shifted from heavy industry to light, consumer-oriented production. In addition, through a concentration of investment in mechanization, fertilizers, and other farm improvements, the government sought and achieved a 50% increase in food production. Overall, the 1971–75 five-year plan achieved its main targets by a wide margin, with industrial production up about 73%. The 1976–80 plan, which aimed at a 50% increase in industrial production and a 16% increase in agricultural output, ran into difficulty almost from the beginning, and by 1979 the economy had entered a period of decline and dislocation that continued into 1982. An economic reform stressing decentralization of the economy was introduced in January 1982, but it failed to produce any significant improvements. With price rises and consumer goods shortages continuing to fuel popular discontent, the government in March 1983 announced a three-year austerity plan for 1983–85. Its aims included a general consolidation of the economy, self-sufficiency in food production, and increased emphasis on housing and the production of industrial consumer goods. By 1986, the economy had rebounded. The 1986–90 plan expected the national income to grow 3–3.5% annually, industrial output to increase by 3.2% each year, and exports to grow by 5% (in fixed prices) annually. These goals were not reached. A "second stage," proclaimed in 1986, called for more autonomy for individual enterprises and for more efficient management, with top jobs filled without regard to political affiliations.

The Economic Transformation Program adopted in January 1990 aimed to convert Poland from a planned to a market economy. Measures were aimed at drastically reducing the large budget deficit, abolishing all trade monopolies, and selling many state-owned enterprises to private interests.

The slow pace of privatization picked up somewhat in 1995, as 512 smaller state enterprises were transferred to private National Investment Funds under the Mass Privatization Program, but large-scale industry remain largely in state hands. However, as of 1996, the government has made an attempt to privatize such large-scale sectors of the economy as banks and oil, arms, and telecommunications.

SOCIAL WELFARE

A social insurance institute administers social security programs through a network of branch offices. Social security, including social insurance and medical care, covers nearly the entire population.

Old age, disability, and survivors' pensions are provided, as well as family allowances, sickness benefits, maternity benefits, workers' compensation, and unemployment. Special family allowances have been a part of the social security program since 1947 and are paid for each child after the first. Maternity benefits include full wages for a total of 16–18 weeks.

The law prohibits women from working in 90 occupations, and a greater proportion of women than men are unemployed.

Healthcare

In 1993, the population per physician was 456 and the population per hospital bed was 180. About

54% of the physicians and 81% of the dentists were women. Health care suffers from a lack of medicines, many of which must be imported.

Life expectancy in 1995 averaged 72 years. Leading causes of death were: communicable diseases and maternal/perinatal causes; non-communicable diseases; and injuries.

Housing

Almost 40% of all urban dwelling space was destroyed during World War II. Although investment in public housing has increased, the housing shortage remains critical. In the mid-1980s, the average wait for an apartment was about 15 years. As of 1992, there was a shortage of 1.3 million housing units, a figure that was expected to grow to 2.4 million by the year 2000. In 1991, 130,000 new housing units were constructed.

EDUCATION

Practically the entire Polish population is literate. Primary, secondary, and most university and other education is provided by the government. The school system, which is centralized, consists of an 8-year primary school followed by either a 4-year secondary general education school, 5-year technical school, or basic 3-year vocational training school.

In 1994 there were 20,214 primary schools with 5.2 million students and 325,812 teachers, and general secondary schools had 325,812 students. Some 1.7 million students attended vocational schools, studying technology, agriculture, forestry, economy, education, health services, and the arts. Another 747,638 students attended institutions of higher learning in 1993.

Of the 98 third-level institutions, 11 are universities, 18 are polytechnic schools, 17 are art schools, 11 are medical academies, and 3 are theological academies. Jagiellonian University, among the oldest in Europe, was established at Kraków in 1364. Other prominent universities are the Warsaw University, the Higher Theater School (Warsaw), and the Academy of Fine Arts (Kraków).

1999 KEY EVENTS TIMELINE

January

• Prominent clergyman and editor Jerzy Turowicz dies at age 86.

March

• Poland joins the North Atlantic Treaty Organization (NATO) along with Hungary and the Czech Republic.

• Poland supports the NATO air campaign mounted against Yugoslavia in response to Yugoslav "ethnic cleansing" of Albanians from the Yugoslav province of Kosovo.

• Art from several Polish museums is exhibited in the United States at the Walters Art Gallery in Baltimore, Maryland. Works for the exhibition were selected to reflect the history of Poland.

April

• The United States Senate formally ratifies NATO's expansion.

May

• The leaders of the Visegrad Group (Czech Republic, Hungary, Poland, Slovakia) meet in Bratislava.

• Some Polish Catholics refuse to remove crosses from Auschwitz.

June

• Pope John Paul II makes a visit to his native land of Poland.

• *Billboard* magazine reports that singer Kayah's album, "Kayah And Bregovic," on which she collaborates with Goran Bregovic, a musician from Sarajevo, in Bosnia and Herzegovina, is the fastest-selling Polish album of all time. On April 12, the day it was released, 50,000 copies are sold (gold status), with another 100,000 copies (platinum status) sold the following day. By the week ending June 6, Billboard reports that the album had sold 815,000 copies.

July

• Poland is involved in a dispute with the European Union (EU) over a land-purchase law.

August

• Lawyers representing eleven Jews from the United States and England file suit in a New York court to recover family property in Poland, contending that the property was seized in "ethnic cleansing" following World War II.

September

- NATO's multinational Group Northeast opens its headquarters in Poland.

- Warsaw hosts a conference on children's rights.

- The Christian Democratic Party is founded.

- Isuzu Motors Ltd. opens a diesel engine plant in Tychy, Poland. The plant will manufacture engines for General Motors and will pursue business with other diesel vehicle manufacturers. Isuzu currently ships about 130,000 diesel engines from Japan to General Motors Opel division; the new Tychy plant will supply about 200,000 engines each year, primarily for the small car model, Astra. Isuzu hopes to reach sales of 600,000 engines in Europe by 2005.

October

- The prime minister calls for support from his coalition partners.

- EU diplomats say that Poland is falling behind in its bid to join the EU by 2003.

November

- Tobacco advertising, including sponsorships, is banned.

- A tax reform bill, designed to stimulate the economy by cutting taxes, passes in parliament.

- Dariusz Ratajczak, an historian, faces criminal charges for publishing his ideas that the concentration camp gas chambers during the Nazi were built to disinfect people, not to kill them. He has also written that three million Jews died in the Holocaust, not six million as is generally accepted. Making public statements that deny Nazi crimes is illegal in Poland.

December

- Commercial radio stations refuse to play music by Polish recording artists during a three-day protest of high royalties being demanded by Polish musicians' associations.

- Britain's Duchess of York, Sarah Ferguson, receives the Order of Smiles for her work with Children in Crisis, a charity she founded to help seriously ill children in the Tatra mountain region.

ANALYSIS OF EVENTS: 1999

BUSINESS AND THE ECONOMY

Although the Polish economy has continued to grow, Poland received a blow in early October when EU diplomats asserted that Poland most likely would fail to meet the criteria for membership by 2003. The main stumbling block to membership remains the slow process of reform, particularly in agriculture, a field that still employs 2 million of Poland's 40 million citizens. Most farms are unprofitable and experts predict that as many as four-fifths of Poland's farmers will be forced off the land in the next twenty years.

Indeed, the government's attempts at reform are meeting with increasingly stiff popular opposition throughout the country, and not just from farmers. A demonstration in Warsaw in late September was expected to draw over 100,000 demonstrators including farmers, miners, and workers from state industries opposed to health, pension, and civil service reform.

In addition to popular opposition to Buzek's reform, Poland also suffers from an account deficit that its finance ministry blames on the Russian currency crisis of 1998. As a result of this crisis, Polish trade with Russia and Ukraine plummeted. The Polish government plans on floating the zloty (Poland's currency) but will await further divestment before doing so.

Despite these problems, Poland's economy grew for the seventh-straight year in 1998 and has continued growing throughout 1999. It is by far the most robust of the former communist countries in Central Europe and holds great attraction for foreign investment; this fall, the American hotel chain, Best Western, announced plans to build thirty new hotels in the fifteen largest cities in Poland. Developments such as these, coupled with Poland's population of 40 million, bode well for its inclusion in the next round of EU enlargement.

GOVERNMENT AND POLITICS

The past year saw Poland continue making progress in its efforts to shed its postwar communist, Eastern European heritage and become a full-fledged part of Western Europe. Poland, along with Hungary and the Czech Republic, became the first of the former Warsaw Pact states to join the Atlantic Alliance. Yet Poland's course was not all smooth sailing. The goal of joining the EU by 2003 appeared to be in jeopardy and the extreme right and left continued attacking the government of Prime Minister Jerzy Buzek.

Pro-Western President Aleksander Kwasniewski continued leading Poland toward greater integration with Western Europe and scored his first major foreign success in that direction with the entry of Poland into the North Atlantic Treaty Organization (NATO) in March 1999. Within weeks of NATO's enlargement, the Alliance found itself at war for the first time and Poland supported the air campaign against Yugoslavia. With membership in the Western security umbrella secure, Kwasniewski moved to place greater emphasis on his next major goal: membership in the European Union (EU) by 2003. In this regard, however, Poland has fallen on some hard times. The problem is not sluggish economic growth—indeed, Poland's economy continues to grow at a robust rate—rather, Poland's problems are structural and political. According to the EU, much needed reforms, particularly in agriculture, are in order, but Prime Minister Jerzy Buzek's shaky center-right coalition appears too unwieldy to tackle needed reforms. Moreover, Buzek faces increased pressure from those on the right who favor greater Church involvement in politics and those on both the right and the left who hope to crush continuing divestment and restructuring efforts. Indeed, the clerical grouping on the right formed a Christian Democratic Party in late September under the leadership of Antoni Tokarczuk.

Despite the deadlock at home, Poland, under the colorful, cosmopolitan, ex-communist President Kwasniewski has continued making inroads abroad. In May Kwasniewski attended a meeting of the Visegrad Group (Czech Republic, Hungary, Slovakia) in Bratislava, Slovakia, in an effort to renew the cooperation that existed between them in the early 1990s. The process of closer ties among the Visegrad member-states was intended to lead to a quicker integration into the EU. Although wishing to move his country inexorably westward, Kwasniewski has not neglected his eastern neighbors. Indeed, he has polite relations with Russia and Belarus and even claims to support EU expansion farther east, beyond Poland.

Warsaw is already recognized as a key city in central Europe. In the midst of domestic deadlock, Warsaw hosted a major international conference on children's rights throughout the world. Enitled ''Keeping Children Smiling in the New Millennium,'' the conference coincided with the tenth anniversary of the signing of the Convention of the Rights of the Child.

CULTURE AND SOCIETY

Polish society continues to reflect the government's efforts to bring the nation fully into Western Europe. Among those opposed to continuing reform, many farmers disgruntled with rapid Westernization began congregating around the populist nationalist program of Andrzej Lepper who opposes Polish membership in the EU. Another vocal segment of the Polish population favors an enhanced role for the Roman Catholic Church in national affairs, as demonstrated by the strong and enthusiastic reception given Pope John Paul II on his visit to his native land in June. The papal reception—as well as the obituaries of dissident Catholic priest Jerzy Turowicz—reflects the important role still played by organized religion nearly two decades after it became a symbol of resistance to the totalitarian communist regime. The conflict over the Church's place in Polish society also occurred in May following passage of a law that decreed that all crosses be removed from the Auschwitz concentration camp. Many Catholics protested the decision vehemently. The creation of the Christian Democratic Party appears to guarantee that Polish Catholics will continue to play a political rule in their country's future.

Most Poles appear to have adopted a guardedly optimistic attitude toward Westernization. They grudgingly take the reforms in stride while flocking to the latest Western attractions, be they fashions, movies, or music. Indeed, many commentators (including many non-Poles) have criticized this aspect of post-communist culture. Yet not all Polish cultural figures have suffered. One artist who is bucking the trend is the singer/songwriter Czesaw Nieman, a mainstay of Polish pop since the early 1960s. In 1999 Nieman released his first album in ten years to rave reviews. Yet the veneration for Nieman is an exception. Like most in Eastern Europe, the majority of Poles identify their future with the up-to-date West. So long as this need for acceptance persists, Poles will continue to incorporate more aspects of Western European culture into their society.

DIRECTORY

CENTRAL GOVERNMENT

Head of State

President
Aleksander Kwasniewski, Office of the
President, Palac Prezydencki, Krakowskie
Przedmiescie 48/50, 00-071 Warsaw, Poland
PHONE: +48 (22) 6952900
E-MAIL: listy@prezydent.pl

Ministers

Prime Minister
Jerzy Buzek, Office of the Prime Minister, Aleje
Ujazdowskie 1/3, 00-583 Warsaw, Poland
PHONE: +48 (22) 6946000
FAX: +48 (22) 6252637
E-MAIL: cirinfo@kprm.gov.pl

Deputy Prime Minister; Minister of Finance
Leszek Balcerowicz, Ministry of Finance

**Deputy Prime Minister; Minister of Interior
and Administration**
Janusz Tomaszewski, Ministry of Interior and
Administration

Minister of Agriculture and Food Economy
Artur Balazs, Ministry of Agriculture and Food
Economy, ul. Wspólna 30, 00-930 Warsaw,
Poland
PHONE: +48 (22) 6231000
FAX: +48 (22) 6232750; 6232751

Minister of Culture and Arts
Joanna Wnuk-Nazarowa, Ministry of Culture and
Arts, ul. Krakowskie Przedmiescie 15/17, 00-071
Warsaw, Poland
PHONE: +48 (22) 6200231
FAX: +48 (22) 8261922; 8267533
E-MAIL: mkis@warman.com.pl

**Minister of Environmental Protection, Natural
Resources and Forestry**
Jan Szyszko, Ministry of Environmental
Protection, Natural Resources and Forestry, ul.
Wawelska 52/54, 00-922 Warsaw, Poland
PHONE: +48 (22) 250001; 254001
FAX: +48 (22) 253332; 253972
E-MAIL: Info@Mos.Gov.Pl

Minister of Finance
Leszek Balcerowicz, Ministry of Finance, Ul.
Swietokrzyska 12, 00-916 Warsaw, Poland
PHONE: +48 (22) 6945555
FAX: +48 (22) 8265561

Minister of Foreign Affairs
Bronislaw Geremek, Ministry of Foreign Affairs,
Aleja Szucha 23, 00-580 Warsaw, Poland
PHONE: +48 (22) 6239000
FAX: +48 (22) 6290287; 6257652
E-MAIL: mszddpi@atos.warman.com.pl

Minister of Economy
Janusz Steinhoff, Ministry of Economy, Plac
Trzech Krzyza 3/5, 00-950 Warsaw, Poland
PHONE: +48 (22) 6935000
FAX: +48 (22) 6286808

Minister of Health and Social Security
Franciszka Cegielska, Ministry of Health and
Social Security, Ul. Miodowa 15, 00-952
Warsaw, Poland
PHONE: +48 (22) 8313441
FAX: +48 (22) 8312212; 8311553
E-MAIL: mzios001@medianet.com.pl

Minister of Interior and Administration
Janusz Tomaszewski, Ministry of Interior and
Administration, Ul. Batorego 5, 02-514 Warsaw,
Poland
PHONE: +48 (22) 6210251
FAX: +48 (22) 6289983
E-MAIL: bagin@ikp.atm.com.pl

Minister of Justice
Hanna Suchocka, Ministry of Justice, Aleje
Ujazdowskie 11, 00-950 Warsaw, Poland
PHONE: +48 (22) 6284431
FAX: +48 (22) 6281692

Minister of Labor and Social Policy
Longin Komolowski, Ministry of Labor and
Social Policy, Ul. Nowogrodzka 1/3, 00-513
Warsaw, Poland
PHONE: +48 (22) 6616100
FAX: +48 (22) 6284048

Minister of National Defense
Janusz Onyszkiewicz, Ministry of National
Defense, Ul. Klonowa 1, 00-909 Warsaw,
Poland
PHONE: +48 (22) 6210261; 6280031
FAX: +48 (22) 455378
E-MAIL: bpmon@mon.wp.mil.pl

Minister of National Education
Miroslaw Handke, Ministry of National
Education, Aleja Szucha 25, 00-918 Warsaw,
Poland
PHONE: +48 (22) 6297241; 6280461
FAX: +48 (22) 6282746
E-MAIL: root@kaliope.men.waw.pl

Minister of the State Treasury
Emil Wasacz, Ministry of State Treasury, Ul.
Krucza 36, 00-522 Warsaw, Poland
PHONE: +48 (22) 6958000
FAX: +48 (22) 6251114; 6280872
E-MAIL: minister@mst.gov.pl

Minister of Communication
Maciej Srebro, Ministry of Communication, Ul.
Malachowskiego 2, 00-940 Warsaw, Poland
PHONE: +48 (22) 6565000
FAX: +48 (22) 8261071

Minister of Transport and Marine Economy
Eugeniusz Morawski, Ministry of Transport and
Marine Economy, Ul. Chalubinskiego 4/6,
00-928 Warsaw, Poland
PHONE: +48 (22) 6244000
FAX: +48 (22) 6285365

Minister of Scientific Research
Andrzej Wiszniewski, Ministry of Scientific
Research, Ul. Wspolna 1/3, 00-529 Warsaw,
Poland
PHONE: +48 (22) 6284071
FAX: +48 (22) 6280922

Minister of Strategic Studies
Jerzy Kropiwnicki, Ministry of Strategic Studies,
Ul. Wspolna 4, 00-926 Warsaw, Poland
PHONE: +48 (22) 6618600; 6618111
FAX: +48 (22) 6212550

POLITICAL ORGANIZATIONS
Democratic Left Alliance
ul. Grunwaldzka 31, 82-300 Elblag, Poland
PHONE: +48 (55) 2339693
FAX: +48 (55) 2337676
NAME: Leszek Miller

Polish Peasant Party
NAME: Jaroslaw Kalinowski

Freedom Union
NAME: Leszek Balcerowicz

Christian National Union
NAME: Marian Pilka

Center Alliance Party
NAME: Jaroslaw Kaczynski

Peaasant Alliance
NAME: Gabriel Janowski

Solidarity Electoral Action Social Movement
NAME: Jerzy Buzek

Union of Labor
NAME: Aleksander Malachowskij

Conservative Party
NAME: Aleksander Hall

Movement for the Reconstruction of Poland
NAME: Jan Olszewski

Confederation for an Independent Poland
NAME: Adam Slomka

German Minority
NAME: Henryk Kroll

Union of Real Politics
NAME: Stanislaw Michalkiewicz

DIPLOMATIC REPRESENTATION
Embassies in Poland
Afghanistan
ul. Staroscinska 1 lok. 20, 02-516 Warsaw, Poland
PHONE: +48 (22) 8491563

Albania
ul. Sloneczna 15, 00-789 Warsaw, Poland
PHONE: +48 (22) 8498427
FAX: +48 (22) 8484004

Algeria
ul. Dabrowiecka 21, 03-932 Warsaw, Poland
PHONE: +48 (22) 6175855; 6175931
FAX: +48 (22) 6160081

Argentina
ul. Styki 17/19, 03-928 Warsaw, Poland
PHONE: +48 (22) 6176028
FAX: +48 (22) 6177162

Australia
ul. Estonska 3/5, 03-903 Warsaw, Poland
PHONE: +48 (22) 6176081
FAX: +48 (22) 6176756

Austria
ul. Gagarina 34, 00748 Warsaw, Poland
PHONE: +48 (22) 8410081
FAX: +48 (22) 8410085

Bangladesh
ul. Rejtana 15 lok.20/21, 02-516 Warsaw, Poland
PHONE: +48 (22) 8483200; 8480637
FAX: +48 (22) 8484974

Belarus
ul. Atenska 67, 03-798 Warsaw, Poland
PHONE: +48 (22) 6173212
FAX: +48 (22) 6178441

Belgium
ul. Senatorska 34, 00-095 Warsaw, Poland
PHONE: +48 (22) 8270233
FAX: +48 (22) 6355711

Brazil
ul. Poselska 11, 03-931 Warsaw, Poland
PHONE: +48 (22) 6174800; 6178689

Bulgaria
al. Ujazdowskie 33/35, 00-540 Warsaw, Poland
PHONE: +48 (22) 6294071
FAX: +48 (22) 6282271

Canada
ul. Matejki 1/5, 00-481 Warsaw, Poland
PHONE: +48 (22) 6298051
FAX: +48 (22) 6296457

Chile
ul. Staroscinska 1b, appt. 2-3, 02-516 Warsaw, Poland
PHONE: +48 (22) 6469962
FAX: +48 (22) 6462610

China
ul. Bonifraterska 1, 00-203 Warsaw, Poland
PHONE: +48 (22) 8313836
FAX: +48 (22) 6354211

Colombia
ul. Zwyciezcow 29, 03-936 Warsaw, Poland
PHONE: +48 (22) 6170973
FAX: +48 (22) 6176684

Congo
ul. Hoza 38 lok. 35, 00-516 Warsaw, Poland
PHONE: +48 (22) 6213736

Costa Rica
ul. Kubickiego 17, appt. 26, 02-954 Warsaw, Poland
PHONE: +48 (22) 6427832

Croatia
ul. Ignacego Krasickiego 10, 02-628 Warsaw, Poland
PHONE: +48 (22) 8441225
FAX: +48 (22) 8440567

Cuba
ul. Rejtana 15, appt.9, 02-516 Warsaw, Poland
PHONE: +48 (22) 6461178
FAX: +48 (22) 8482231

Cyprus
pl. J.H. Dabrowskiego 1, 00-057 Warsaw, Poland
PHONE: +48 (22) 8267318
FAX: +48 (22) 8264759

Czech Republic
ul. Koszykowa 18, 00-555 Warsaw, Poland
PHONE: +48 (22) 6287221
FAX: +48 (22) 6219880

Denmark
ul. Rakowiecka 19, 02-517 Warsaw, Poland
PHONE: +48 (22) 8482600
FAX: +48 (22) 8487580

Ecuador
ul. Rejtana 15, appt.15, 02-516 Warsaw, Poland
PHONE: +48 (22) 8488196

Egypt
ul. Alzacka 18, 03-972 Warsaw, Poland
PHONE: +48 (22) 6176973
FAX: +48 (22) 6179058

Estonia
ul. Karwinska 1, 02-639 Warsaw, Poland
PHONE: +48 (22) 6464480
FAX: +48 (22) 6464481

Finland
ul. Chopina 4/8, 00-559 Warsaw, Poland
PHONE: +48 (22) 6294091
FAX: +48 (22) 6213442

France
ul. Piekna 1, 00-477 Warsaw, Poland
PHONE: +48 (22) 6288401
FAX: +48 (22) 6296480

Germany
ul. Dabrowiecka 30, 03-932 Warsaw, Poland

Great Britain
al. Roz 1, 00-556 Warsaw, Poland
PHONE: +48 (22) 6281001
FAX: +48 (22) 6217161

Greece
ul. Gornoslaska 35, 00-432 Warsaw, Poland
PHONE: +48 (22) 6229460
FAX: +48 (22) 6229464

Guatemala
ul. Genewska 37, 03-940 Warsaw, Poland
PHONE: +48 (22) 6173303

Hungary
ul. Chopina 2, 00-559 Warsaw, Poland
PHONE: +48 (22) 6284451
FAX: +48 (22) 6218561

Iceland
ul. Slowackiego 30, appt.17, 81-872 Sopot, Poland
PHONE: +48 (58) 5515840

India
ul. Rejtana 15, appt. 2/7, 02-516 Warsaw, Poland
PHONE: +48 (22) 8495800
FAX: +48 (22) 8496705

Indonesia
ul. Wachocka 9, 03-934 Warsaw, Poland
PHONE: +48 (22) 6173917

Iran
ul. Krolowej Aldony 22, 03-928 Warsaw, Poland
PHONE: +48 (22) 6174293
FAX: +48 (22) 6178452

Iraq
ul. Dabrowiecka, 9a Warsaw, Poland
PHONE: +48 (22) 6175773
FAX: +48 (22) 6177065

Ireland
ul. Humanska 10, 00-789 Warsaw, Poland
PHONE: +48 (22) 8496655
FAX: +48 (22) 8498431

Israel
ul. Krzywickiego 24, 02-078 Warsaw, Poland
PHONE: +48 (22) 8250028; 8251607

Italy
pl. J. H. Dabrowskiego 6, 00-055 Warsaw, Poland
PHONE: +48 (22) 8263471
FAX: +48 (22) 8278507

Japan
al. Jana Pawla II 23, 00-854 Warsaw, Poland
PHONE: +48 (22) 6539430
FAX: +48 (22) 6539432

Laos
ul. Rejtana 15, appt. 26, 02-516 Warsaw, Poland
PHONE: +48 (22) 8484786
FAX: +48 (22) 8497122

Latvia
ul. Rejtana 15, appt. 19, 02-516 Warsaw, Poland
PHONE: +48 (22) 8481947
FAX: +48 (22) 8480201

Lebanon
ul. Staroscinska, appt.10, 02-516 Warsaw, Poland
PHONE: +48 (22) 8445065
FAX: +48 (22) 6460030

Libya
ul. Kryniczna 2, 03-934 Warsaw, Poland
PHONE: +48 (22) 6174883
FAX: +48 (22) 6175091

Lithuania
al. Szucha 5, 00-580 Warsaw, Poland
PHONE: +48 (22) 6253368
FAX: +48 (22) 6253440

Luxembourg
ul. Zelazna 28/30, 00-806 Warsaw, Poland
PHONE: +48 (22) 6549559
FAX: +48 (22) 6546498

Macedonia
ul. Dominikanska 15, 02-738 Warsaw, Poland
PHONE: +48 (22) 6444672
FAX: +48 (22) 8431326

Malaysia
ul. Gruzinska 3, 03-902 Warsaw, Poland
PHONE: +48 (22) 6174413

United States
al. Ujazdowskie 29/31, 00-540 Warsaw, Poland
PHONE: +48 (22) 6283041
FAX: +48 (22) 6288298

JUDICIAL SYSTEM
Supreme Court
ul. Ogrodowa 6, 00-951 Warsaw, Poland
PHONE: +48 (22) 6200371
FAX: +48 (22) 6203714

Constitutional Tribunal
Al. Szucha 12 A, 00-918 Warsaw, Poland
PHONE: +48 (22) 6216503

FURTHER READING
Articles

Eckardt, Allison Ledes. "Poland: Where the West Met the East." *The Magazine Antiques* (March 1999): 354.

Harward, Barnaby. "Polish Singer Kayah." *Billboard* (June 19, 1999): 25.

Miller, Joe. "Isuzu's Goal: No. 1 In Diesels: Poland Plant Key to European Effort." *Automotive News,* 27 September 1999, p. 36.

Muravchik, Joshua. ''Poland Ten Years Later: Once Won, Freedom Becomes A Leading Export. (1999 International Human Rights Conference).'' *The American Spectator* (January 1999): 58.

Nagorski, Andrew. ''Reopening Old Wounds: A Suit Renews the Debate over Poles and the Holocaust.'' *Newsweek International* (August 23, 1999): 36.

''Poland's Pig-Headed Farmers.'' *The Economist* (February 20, 1999): 47.

Books

Sanford, George. *Historical Dictionary of Poland.* Metuchen, NJ: Scarecrow Press, 1994.

Internet

Poland Today. Available Online @ http://www.centraleurope.com/polandtoday/. (November 2, 1999).

Polish Embassy. Available Online @ http://www.polishworld.com/ (November 2, 1999).

POLAND: STATISTICAL DATA

For sources and notes see "Sources of Statistics" in the front of each volume.

GEOGRAPHY

Geography (1)

Area:

Total: 312,683 sq km.

Land: 304,510 sq km.

Water: 8,173 sq km.

Area—comparative: slightly smaller than New Mexico.

Land boundaries:

Total: 2,888 km.

Border countries: Belarus 605 km, Czech Republic 658 km, Germany 456 km, Lithuania 91 km, Russia (Kaliningrad Oblast) 206 km, Slovakia 444 km, Ukraine 428 km.

Coastline: 491 km.

Climate: temperate with cold, cloudy, moderately severe winters with frequent precipitation; mild summers with frequent showers and thundershowers.

Terrain: mostly flat plain; mountains along southern border.

Natural resources: coal, sulfur, copper, natural gas, silver, lead, salt.

Land use:

Arable land: 47%

Permanent crops: 1%

Permanent pastures: 13%

Forests and woodland: 29%

Other: 10% (1993 est.).

HUMAN FACTORS

Demographics (2A)

	1990	1995	1998	2000	2010	2020	2030	2040	2050
Population	38,108.9	38,590.2	38,606.9	38,644.2	39,927.7	40,344.1	39,780.5	38,544.7	36,465.2
Net migration rate (per 1,000 population)	NA	NA	NA	NA	NA	NA	NA	NA	NA
Births	NA	NA	NA	NA	NA	NA	NA	NA	NA
Deaths	388.4	NA	NA	NA	NA	NA	NA	NA	NA
Life expectancy - males	66.5	67.6	68.6	69.3	72.1	74.5	76.3	77.8	78.8
Life expectancy - females	75.5	76.4	77.2	77.6	79.8	81.6	83.0	84.1	85.0
Birth rate (per 1,000)	14.3	11.2	9.8	11.5	12.9	9.5	9.2	8.4	7.3
Death rate (per 1,000)	10.2	10.0	9.8	9.7	9.7	10.1	11.2	12.9	13.7
Women of reproductive age (15-49 yrs.)	9,388.1	9,988.2	10,191.7	10,250.0	9,618.7	9,295.6	8,819.8	7,686.4	7,295.0
of which are currently married	31,149.2	NA	NA	NA	NA	NA	NA	NA	NA
Fertility rate	2.0	1.6	1.4	1.5	1.7	1.6	1.5	1.5	1.4

Except as noted, values for vital statistics are in thousands; life expectancy is in years.

Health Personnel (3)

Total health expenditure as a percentage of GDP, 1990-1997[a]

Public sector 4.8

Private sector 0.4

Total[b] 5.2

Health expenditure per capita in U.S. dollars, 1990-1997[a]

Purchasing power parity 297

Total 182

Availability of health care facilities per 100,000 people

Hospital beds 1990-1997[a] 620

Doctors 1993[c] . . . . .NA

Nurses 1993[c] . . . . .NA

Health Indicators (4)

Life expectancy at birth

1980 70

1997 73

Daily per capita supply of calories (1996) 3,344

Total fertility rate births per woman (1997) 1.5

Maternal mortality ratio per 100,000 live births (1990-97) . . . . .5[b]

Safe water % of population with access (1995) . . . .

Sanitation % of population with access (1995) . . . .

Consumption of iodized salt % of households (1992-98)[a] . . . .

Smoking prevalence

Male % of adults (1985-95)[a] 51

Female % of adults (1985-95)[a] 29

Tuberculosis incidence per 100,000 people (1997) 44

Adult HIV prevalence % of population ages 15-49 (1997) 0.06

Infants and Malnutrition (5)

Under-5 mortality rate (1997) 11

% of infants with low birthweight (1990-97) . . . . . .NA

Births attended by skilled health staff % of total[a] . . .98

% fully immunized (1995-97)

TB 94

DPT 95

Polio 95

Measles 91

Prevalence of child malnutrition under age 5 (1992-97)[b] . . . . .NA

Ethnic Division (6)

Polish 97.6%

German 1.3%

Ukrainian 0.6%

Byelorussian . . . . .0.5% (1990 est.)

Religions (7)

Roman Catholic 95%

Eastern Orthodox, Protestant, and other 5%

About 75% of Roman Catholics practice.

Languages (8)

Polish

EDUCATION

Public Education Expenditures (9)

Public expenditure on education (% of GNP)

1980 . . . .

1996 . . . . .5.2[1]

Expenditure per student

Primary % of GNP per capita

1980 . . . . .8.1

1996 . . . . .17.1[1]

Secondary % of GNP per capita

1980 . . . . .14.8

1996 . . . . .16.7[1]

Tertiary % of GNP per capita

1980 . . . . .47.4

1996 . . . . .40.7[1]

Expenditure on teaching materials

Primary % of total for level (1996) . . . .

Secondary % of total for level (1996) . . . . .1.0[1]

Primary pupil-teacher ratio per teacher (1996) . . . . .15[1]

Duration of primary education years (1995) 8

Educational Attainment (10)

Age group (1988) . . . . .25+

Total population 22,986,018

Highest level attained (%)

No schooling 1.5

First level

Not completed 5.6

Completed 37.2

Entered second level

S-1 . . . . .47.8

S-2 . . . . .NA

Postsecondary 7.9

Literacy Rates (11B)

Adult literacy rate

1980

Male 99%

Female 97%

1995

Male . . . .-

Female . . . .-

GOVERNMENT & LAW

Political Parties (12)

Sejm (Lower House)	% of seats
Solidarity Electoral Action (AWS)	.33.8
Democratic Left Alliance (SLD)	.27.1
Freedom Union (UW)	.13.4
Polish Peasant Party (PSL)	.7.3
Movement for the Reconstruction of Poland (ROP)	.5.6

German Minority 0.4

Other 12.4

Government Budget (13A)

Year: 1997

Total Expenditures: 183,289 Millions of Zlotys

Expenditures as a percentage of the total by function:

General public services and public order 8.37

Defense 4.01

Education 6.24

Health 10.23

Social Security and Welfare 50.90

Housing and community amenities 2.20

Recreational, cultural, and religious affairs 1.09

Fuel and energy 55

Agriculture, forestry, fishing, and hunting 1.88

Mining, manufacturing, and construction 45

Transportation and communication 1.90

Other economic affairs and services 62

Military Affairs (14B)

	1990	1991	1992	1993	1994	1995
Military expenditures						
Current dollars (mil.)	8,752[r]	7,362[r]	3,569	3,536	4,644	4,887
1995 constant dollars (mil.)	10,060[r]	8,135[r]	3,839	3,707	4,760	4,887
Armed forces (000)	313	305	270	180	255	278
Gross national product (GNP)						
Current dollars (mil.)	163,300[e]	160,100[e]	165,000	175,800	187,800	208,500
1995 constant dollars (mil.)	187,700[e]	176,900[e]	177,500	184,300	192,800	208,500
Central government expenditures (CGE)						
1995 constant dollars (mil.)	NA	24,750[e]	47,220	58,980	86,050	90,440
People (mil.)	38.1	38.2	38.4	38.5	38.5	38.6
Military expenditure as % of GNP	5.4	4.6	2.2	2.0	2.5	2.3
Military expenditure as % of CGE	NA	32.9	8.1	6.3	5.5	5.4
Military expenditure per capita (1995 $)	264	213	100	96	124	127
Armed forces per 1,000 people (soldiers)	8.2	8.0	7.0	4.7	6.6	7.2
GNP per capita (1995 $)	4,925	4,626	4,627	4,794	4,997	5,404
Arms imports[6]						
Current dollars (mil.)	250	0	0	5	5	90
1995 constant dollars (mil.)	287	0	0	5	5	90
Arms exports[6]						
Current dollars (mil.)	230	110	20	10	50	40
1995 constant dollars (mil.)	264	122	22	10	51	40
Total imports[7]						
Current dollars (mil.)	8,413	15,760	15,700	18,830	21,380	29,050
1995 constant dollars (mil.)	9,669	17,410	16,890	19,750	21,920	29,050
Total exports[7]						
Current dollars (mil.)	13,630	14,900	13,320	14,140	17,040	22,890
1995 constant dollars (mil.)	15,660	16,470	14,330	14,830	17,470	22,890
Arms as percent of total imports[8]	3.0	0	0	0	0	.3
Arms as percent of total exports[8]	1.7	.7	.2	.1	.3	.2

Crime (15)

Crime rate (for 1997)

Crimes reported 992,400

Total persons convicted 568,600

Crimes per 100,000 population 2,550

Persons responsible for offenses

Total number of suspects 410,800

Total number of female suspects 39,400

Total number of juvenile suspects 58,800

LABOR FORCE

Labor Force (16)

Total (million) 17.7

Industry and construction 29.9%

Agriculture 26%

Services 44.1%

Data for 1997 est. Percent distribution for 1996.

Unemployment Rate (17)

12% (1997)

PRODUCTION SECTOR

Electric Energy (18)

Capacity . . . . .33.5 million kW (1997 est.)

Production . . . . .142 billion kWh (1997 est.)

Consumption per capita . . . . .3,360 kWh (1995)

Transportation (19)

Highways:

total: 374,990 km

paved: 245,243 km (including 258 km of expressways)

unpaved: 129,747 km (1996 est.)

Waterways: 3,812 km navigable rivers and canals (1996)

Pipelines: crude oil and petroleum products 2,280 km; natural gas 17,000 km (1996)

Merchant marine:

total: 90 ships (1,000 GRT or over) totaling 1,574,637 GRT/2,446,849 DWT ships by type: bulk 67, cargo 10, chemical tanker 3, container 2, passenger 1, refrigerated cargo 2, roll-on/roll-off cargo 1, short-sea passenger 4 note: Poland owns an additional 35 ships (1,000 GRT or over) totaling 459,793 DWT operating under the registries of the Bahamas, Cyprus, Liberia, Malta, and Vanuatu (1997 est.)

Airports: 83 (1997 est.)

Airports—with paved runways:

total: 68

over 3,047 m: 2

2,438 to 3,047 m: 23

1,524 to 2,437 m: 34

914 to 1,523 m: 6

under 914 m: 3 (1997 est.)

Airports—with unpaved runways:

total: 15

2,438 to 3,047 m: 1

1,524 to 2,437 m: 1

914 to 1,523 m: 8

under 914 m: 5 (1997 est.)

Top Agricultural Products (20)

Potatoes, milk, cheese, fruits, vegetables, wheat; poultry and eggs; pork, beef.

MANUFACTURING SECTOR

GDP & Manufacturing Summary (21)

Detailed value added figures are listed by both International Standard Industry Code (ISIC) and product title.

	1980	1985	1990	1994
GDP ($-1990 mil.)[1]	54,856	54,357	53,290	54,989
Per capita ($-1990)[1]	1,542	1,461	1,398	1,434
Manufacturing share (%) (current prices)[1]	44.0	41.2	47.0	NA
Manufacturing				
Value added ($-1990 mil.)[1]	31,971	29,768	25,072	27,119
Industrial production index	100	98	84	91
Value added ($ mil.)	22,833	24,432	23,017	20,994
Gross output ($ mil.)	55,609	54,448	46,092	55,584
Employment (000)	4,063	3,578	3,014	2,173
Profitability (% of gross output)				
Intermediate input (%)	59	55	50	62
Wages and salaries inc. supplements (%)	12	11	8	11
Gross operating surplus	30	34	42	27
Productivity ($)				
Gross output per worker	12,960	13,487	15,293	25,494
Value added per worker	5,321	6,052	7,637	9,630
Average wage (inc. supplements)	1,575	1,627	1,258	2,775

	1980	1985	1990	1994
Value added ($ mil.)				
311/2 Food products	−889	144	2,595	2,268
313 Beverages	3,062	3,582	1,838	2,864
314 Tobacco products	636	74	379	934
321 Textiles	2,795	2,444	1,222	837
322 Wearing apparel	572	801	432	676
323 Leather and fur products	122	221	120	71
324 Footwear	403	430	263	169
331 Wood and wood products	423	434	325	350
332 Furniture and fixtures	491	500	307	430
341 Paper and paper products	224	269	348	291
342 Printing and publishing	154	208	166	179
351 Industrial chemicals	837	734	1,056	677
352 Other chemical products	961	644	649	827
353 Petroleum refineries	1,058	1,239	1,419	2,306
354 Miscellaneous petroleum and coal products	54	60	249	84
355 Rubber products	317	341	209	229
356 Plastic products	360	296	274	346
361 Pottery, china and earthenware	97	146	107	118
362 Glass and glass products	269	282	227	233
369 Other non-metal mineral products	335	634	602	524
371 Iron and steel	868	1,161	1,887	1,066
372 Non-ferrous metals	602	336	951	201
381 Metal products	1,343	1,347	1,081	942
382 Non-electrical machinery	3,263	3,360	2,604	1,563
383 Electrical machinery	1,558	1,801	1,420	947
384 Transport equipment	2,436	2,255	1,855	1,624
385 Professional and scientific equipment	244	251	173	148
390 Other manufacturing industries	237	438	258	89

FINANCE, ECONOMICS, & TRADE

Economic Indicators (22)

National product: GDP—purchasing power parity—$280.7 billion (1997 est.)

National product real growth rate: 6.9% (1997 est.)

National product per capita: $7,250 (1997 est.)

Inflation rate—consumer price index: 15% (1997 est.)

Exchange Rates (24)

Exchange rates:

Zlotych (Zl) per US$1

January 1998	3.54
1997	3.2793
1996	2.6961
1995	2.4250
1994	22,723
1993	18,115
1992	13,626

A currency reform on 1 January 1995 replaced 10,000 old zlotys with 1 new zloty.

Balance of Payments (23)

	1992	1993	1994	1995	1996
Exports of goods (f.o.b.)	13,929	13,582	18,355	25,041	27,557
Imports of goods (f.o.b.)	−14,060	−17,087	−18,930	−26,687	−34,844
Trade balance	−131	−3,505	−575	−1,646	−7,287
Services - debits	−8,940	−7,823	−6,968	−10,222	−9,031
Services - credits	5,501	4,780	7,245	11,764	11,360
Private transfers (net)	253	139	128	244	82
Government transfers (net)	213	621	1,124	714	1,612
Overall balance	−3,104	−5,788	954	854	−3,264

Top Import Origins (25)

$44.5 billion (f.o.b., 1997 est.) Data are for 1996.

Origins	%
Germany	.26.5
Italy	.10.4
Russia	.7.3
United Kingdom	.6.3
Netherlands	.4.8
France	.4.4

Top Export Destinations (26)

$26.4 billion (f.o.b., 1997 est.) Data are for 1996.

Destinations	%
Germany	.34.5
Russia	.6.8
France	.5.9
Italy	.5.6
United States	.4.8
Netherlands	.4.1

Economic Aid (27)

Recipient: US, $210 million (1995-97).

Import Export Commodities (28)

Import Commodities	Export Commodities
Machinery and transport equipment 32%	Intermediate goods 38%
Intermediate goods 20%	Machinery and transport equipment 23%
Chemicals 15%	Consumer goods 21%
Consumer goods 9%	Foodstuffs 10%
Food 9%	Fuels 7%
Fuels 8%	

PORTUGAL

Portuguese Republic
República Portuguesa

CAPITAL: Lisbon (Lisboa).

FLAG: The national flag, adopted in 1911, consists of a green field at the hoist and a larger red field. At the junction of the two, in yellow, red, blue, and white, is the national coat of arms.

ANTHEM: *A Portuguesa (The Portuguese).*

MONETARY UNIT: The escudo (E) is a paper currency of 100 centavos. There are coins of 1, 2.5, 5, 10, 20, 50, 100, and 200 escudos, and notes of 500, 1,000, 2,000, 5,000 and 10,000 escudos. E1 = $0.00654 (or $1 = E153.005).

WEIGHTS AND MEASURES: The metric system is the legal standard.

HOLIDAYS: New Year's Day, 1 January; Carnival Day, 15 February; Anniversary of the Revolution, 25 April; Labor Day, 1 May; National Day, 10 June; Assumption, 15 August; Republic Day, 5 October; All Saints' Day, 1 November; Independence Day, 1 December; Immaculate Conception, 8 December; Christmas, 25 December. Movable religious holidays include Carnival Day, Good Friday, and Corpus Christi.

TIME: GMT.

LOCATION AND SIZE: The westernmost country of Europe, Portugal occupies most of the western coast of the Iberian Peninsula; it shares the peninsula with Spain. Portugal has an area of 92,080 square kilometers (35,552 square miles), including the Azores Archipelago (island chain) and the islands of Madeira and Porto Santo. The area occupied by Portugal is slightly smaller than the state of Indiana. Portugal has a total boundary length of 3,007 kilometers (1,868 miles).

Portugal's capital city, Lisbon, is located on Portugal's west coast.

CLIMATE: The north has cool summers and rainy winters (average annual rainfall 125–150 centimeters/50–60 inches), with occasional snowfall. Central Portugal has hot summers and cool, rainy winters, with 50–75 centimeters (20–30 inches) average annual rainfall. The southern climate is very dry, with rainfall not exceeding 50 centimeters (20 inches) along the coast. In Lisbon, the average temperature is about 21°C (70°F) in July and 4°C (39°F) in January.

INTRODUCTORY SURVEY

RECENT HISTORY

During World War II (1939–45), Portugal supported the Allies but did not take part in combat. It later became a member of the North Atlantic Treaty Organization (NATO).

Despite its reduced status as a European power, Portugal attempted to maintain its overseas empire, especially its resource-rich African provinces. The United Nations General Assembly passed a resolution in 1965 calling for a worldwide economic and arms boycott of Portugal in order to force it to grant independence to its African dependencies. Meanwhile, guerrilla movements in Angola, Mozambique, and Guinea-Bissau were met by a steadily increasing commitment of Portuguese troops and supplies.

Salazar, who had served as prime minister of Portugal since 1932, was followed in 1968 by Marcello Caetano. The refusal of the Caetano regime to adopt democratic and economic reforms, coupled with growing discontent over the costly colonial war in Africa, led to a military takeover by the left-wing Armed Forces Movement in April 1974. Democratic liberties were immediately granted and opposition political parties legalized. A decolonization program was also begun, resulting in the independence of all of Portugal's African provinces by November 1975.

Continued differences between right and left—and between communist and socialist factions on the left—led to numerous temporary gov-

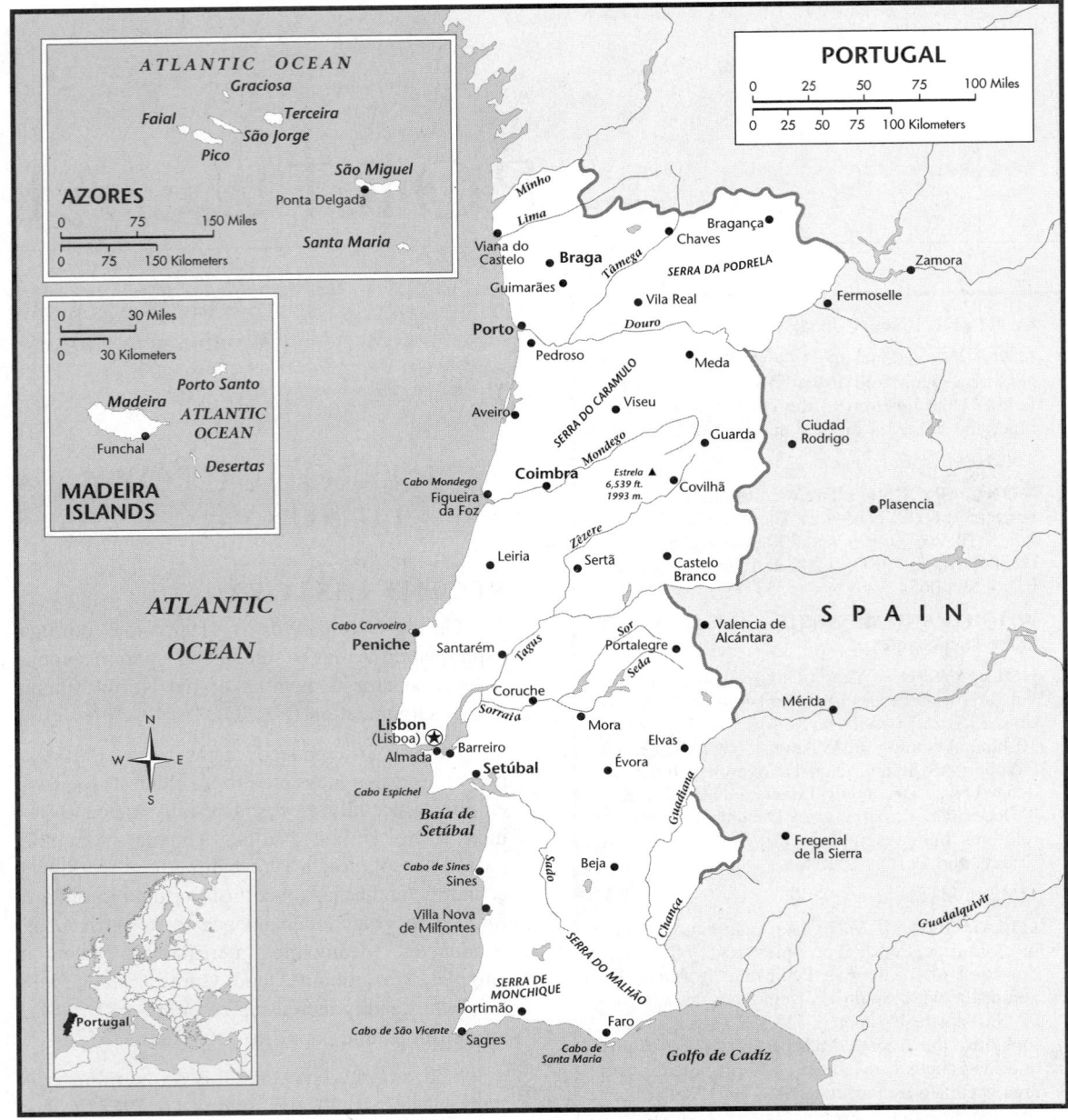

ernments after the 1974 takeover. In April 1975, general elections were held for a Constituent Assembly, whose task was to draw up a new constitution. In April 1976 General António dos Santos Ramalho Eanes was elected president, and the leader of the Portuguese Socialist Party, Mário Alberto Nobre Lopes Soares, became prime minister. This government fell apart in 1978 and was replaced by a temporary cabinet.

After a series of different coalitions, the Socialist Party won a 35% plurality in the parliamentary elections of April 1983, and Soares was again named prime minister, forming a coalition government with the center-right Social Democratic Party (Partido Social Democratico—PSD). Political unrest increased after the election, including, in 1984, urban terrorism. In the following year, Portugal entered the European Community, boosting the economy.

The PSD was returned to power in 1991 and Mario Soares was reelected president for a second five-year term on 13 January 1991. Economic recession, government deficits, and regional development have been major concerns in the 1990s.

Following the Socialist Party's success in the legislative elections in October 1995, Socialist Jorge Sampaio won the presidency in January 1996.

GOVERNMENT

According to the 1976 constitution as amended, the president appoints the prime minister and, at the prime minister's proposal, other members of the government. The main lawmaking body is the single-chamber Assembly of the Republic. Its members (230 in 1997) are directly elected to four-year terms.

Portugal is divided into 22 districts.

Judiciary

Justice is administered by ordinary and special courts, including the Supreme Court of Justice in Lisbon, four courts of appeal, district courts, and special courts.

Political Parties

After the 1974 revolution, various left-wing parties that had functioned underground or in exile were recognized. Among these was the Portuguese Communist Party (Partido Comunista Português—PCP), which is Portugal's oldest political party; the Portuguese Socialist Party (Partido Socialista Português—PSP); and the Popular Democratic Party (Partido Popular Democrático—PPD).

In October 1985, former President Eanes's centrist Democratic Renewal Party (Partido Renovador Democrático—PRD) entered the ballot for the first time, taking 18% of the vote.

In the October 1995 legislative elections, the PSP won 112 seats; PSD, 88; and others, 30.

DEFENSE

The armed forces are maintained by compulsory service, with terms of 8–12 months for all services. As of 1995, the army had 29,700 personnel (15,000 draftees), the navy 12,500 (including 1,800 marines), and the air force, 7,300 personnel and 90 combat aircraft. The defense budget in 1996 was $1.7 billion. The United States maintains an important airbase in the Azores, and the North Atlantic Treaty Organization (NATO) has one headquarters at Lisbon.

ECONOMIC AFFAIRS

Despite the economic progress recorded since World War II, Portugal remains one of the poorest countries in Europe. The largest industries are clothing, textiles, footwear, and food processing. Two traditional Portuguese foreign exchange sources are income from tourism and payments to Portugal by emigrant workers in western Europe.

Portugal's economy was helped by entry into the European Community (EC) in 1985. The domestic economy grew by an average of 3.6% per year during 1985–92, but fell to 0.3% in 1993. Growth has been about 2–3% per year since 1995. The unofficial, or underground, economy is estimated at 20% of the official gross domestic product (GDP).

Public Finance

Portugal's budgets (accounting for the effects of loans and transfers) have been in deficit since 1974. Major factors contributing to the deficit include spending on health and education programs, funding for major public investment projects, and large state-owned enterprise payrolls. To finance the deficit, the government issues bonds in the domestic market, which also serves the monetary policy purpose of absorbing excess liquidity. The governments objective is to join the Economic and Monetary Union (EMU) by 1999. To be eligible, however, the government must first reduce the budget deficit.

The U.S. Central Intelligence Agency (CIA) estimates that in 1995, government revenues totaled approximately $31 billion and expenditures $41 billion. External debt totaled $11.8 billion or about 11% of GDP and 57% of foreign exchange reserves.

Income

In 1997, Portugal's gross national product (GNP) was $149.5 billion, or about $15,200 per person. For the period 1985–95 the average inflation rate was 11.2%, resulting in a real growth rate in GNP of 3.7% per person.

Industry

Portuguese industry is mainly light. The development of heavy industry has been hampered by a shortage of electric power. Textiles are the oldest and most important of Portugal's manufactured products. Other principal industries are automotive assembly, electronics, glass and pottery, footwear, cement, cellulose and paper, rubber and chemicals, cork and cork products, and food industries.

Banking and Finance

All 22 banks in Portugal, except for three foreign-owned ones (Banco do Brasil, Credit Franco-Portugais, and the Bank of London and South America), were nationalized in 1975. A 1983 law, however, permitted private enterprise to return to the banking industry. The Bank of Portugal, the central bank (founded in 1846), functions as a bank of issue and rediscount, controls gold and foreign exchange movements, and sets the discount rate. The money supply in December 1996, as measured by M1, totaled E 4,541 million. Total foreign reserves, excluding gold, amounted to $15.92 billion at the end of 1996.

The state-owned General Savings Bank dominates the savings field, holding over 70% of time deposits. The National Development Bank, established in January 1960, administers long-term loans.

Portugal's two stock exchanges, located in Lisbon and Porto, were closed after the coup of April 1974. The Lisbon exchange reopened in 1976, and the Oporto exchange in 1981. In January 1992 the market was split into three tiers, of which the first is the major liquid market: this at present includes the 11 firms whose shares are traded regularly and which have a minimum market capitalization of E 500 million. Trading outside the stock exchanges is still widespread.

Economic Development

In 1975, radical economic transformations were accomplished through a series of decrees that nationalized the domestically owned parts of major sectors of the national economy. These decrees affected the leading banks, insurance companies (representing 99% of insurance companies' capital), petroleum refineries, the transportation sector, the steel industry, and eventually Portugal's leading privately owned industrial monopoly, Companhia União Fabril. At the same time, large-scale agrarian reform measures led to expropriation of many of the country's privately owned large landholdings; other holdings were seized illegally by peasants. In an attempt to stimulate agricultural production, the government decreed a 30% reduction in the price of fertilizer to farm workers and small and medium farmers. When the nationalization and agrarian reform measures met with only limited success, partly because of liquidity problems, an emergency austerity plan was approved by the Council of Ministers in October 1975. The program included wage and import controls and the reduction of subsidies on consumer goods.

As a result of Portugal's entry into the EC, the highly protected, unresponsive, and inefficient economy is being transformed. State intervention is being reduced, and the physical infrastructure is being modernized. Privatization began in 1989, with the share of GDP for non-financial public enterprises reduced from 17.9% in 1985 to 10.7% in 1991. In 1992, $3.6 billion was raised as banks, insurance companies, and a 25% interest in Petrogal—the state oil company—were sold. The government estimated that privatized companies would represent half of stock market capitalization by the end of 1994.

In 1996 and 1997, a series of important investments and acquisitions were made by companies such as Sonae and Jernimo Martins, Portugal's leading retail distributors; Cimpor, a cement producer; and Portugal Telecom and Electricidade de Portugal, the last of which was recently privatized. The big banks are developing new overseas operations as well.

SOCIAL WELFARE

The government-run social security system provides old-age, disability, sickness, and unemployment benefits, family allowances, and health and medical care. The system is funded by payroll contributions from employers and employees.

According to law, women must receive equal pay for equal work. Human rights conditions improved substantially after the 1974 takeover. Immigrants from Portugal's former African colonies sometimes face social prejudice and discrimination.

Healthcare

The Santa Maria Hospital in Lisbon is the largest hospital in Portugal. There are 2.9 doctors for every 1,000 people.

Average life expectancy in 1995 was 75 years. The leading causes of death are circulatory disorders, cancer, and respiratory disorders.

Housing

In the early 1990s, Portugal built an average of 40,000 housing units annually. The total number of housing units in 1991 was 3.6 million. In May 1993, the government announced a $2 billion program designed to clear urban slums, which included the construction of 20,000 low-income units in Lisbon by 2000.

EDUCATION

In 1990, adult literacy rates were an estimated 85% (88.8% for men and 81.5% for women). As of 1997, a new law requires nine years of compulsory education. Primary level education is compulsory for six years. Secondary level education is in two stages of three years each.

In 1993 primary schools had 910,650 pupils. At the secondary level, during 1993, there were 69,095 teachers and 778,485 pupils. That year, total enrollment in institutions of higher learning was 276,263.

1999 KEY EVENTS TIMELINE

January

• Portugal is one of 11 members of the European Union that adopts the Euro as its currency. The Euro will replace the currency of individual countries by 2002.

February

• John Henry Smithes, maker of Port, dies. He was 88.

March

• With 29 traffic fatalities per 100,000 residents, Portugal's roads are the most dangerous in Europe, The Guardian of London reports.

April

• The foreign ministers of Portugal and Indonesia agree to hold a vote in East Timor that could determine whether the tiny province is integrated into Indonesia or granted independence.

• Paleontologists discover 24,500-year-old skeleton of a young boy in a shallow graveyard in Portugal. They believe his remains show Neanderthals and modern humans coexisted and cohabited for thousands of years.

• Portuguese observe the 25th anniversary of the "Carnation Revolution" that toppled a 40-year dictatorship.

• Portuguese company Amorim signs agreement with Cuba to develop a 250-apartment complex in Havana and develop the country's fishing industry. The deal could bring $50 million in foreign capital to Cuba.

May

• The Portuguese colony of Macao, which is scheduled to revert back to the Chinese in December 1999, gets its first Chinese administrator.

• Portugal, Indonesia sign East Timor autonomy plan.

July

• An official inquiry concludes that Portugal did not knowingly handle gold looted from Holocaust victims by Nazi Germany.

August

• Lieut. Col. Ernesto Melo Antunes, who helped engineer and execute the 1974 Carnation Revolution, dies. He was 65.

September

• East Timorese vote for independence. Portugal celebrates the vote, and urges the United Nations to halt the violence following the vote.

October

• East Timor resistance leader Xanana Gusmao pays an emotional tribute to Portugal for supporting the territory's struggle for independence from Indonesia.

• Luis Sa, a leading member of the Portuguese Communist Party and former member of the European Parliament, dies of a heart attack. He was 47.

• Amalia Rodrigues, the queen of fado, dies in her home in Lisbon. She was 79.

• Prime Minister Antonio Guterres returns to power, but his Socialist Party fails to capture a majority in Portugal's general elections. He is first Socialist to win a second successive term since the 1974 revolution.

• Portugal wins its bid to host the 2004 European soccer championships with a simple slogan: we love soccer. The country will spend $300 million to refurbish five stadiums and build five others.

November

• Portugal's finance minister, Joaquim Pina Moura, unveils a complex deal under which Spain's Banco Santander Central Hispanico will take over two banks within Mundial Confianca, a financial group controlled by Antonio Champalimaud, Portugal's richest man, all to avoid a showdown between Portugal and the European Commission, which had filed a complaint against Portugal at the European Court of Justice for interfering with the Spanish bank's first deal with Champalimaud.

ANALYSIS OF EVENTS: 1999

BUSINESS AND THE ECONOMY

The Socialists find themselves in power during particularly good times for the Portuguese economy. Economic growth, according to government figures, was expected to be 3.2 percent for 1999, above average for European Union countries. But analysts warn the country will have to make tough social reforms if it expects to remain financially healthy. Inflation was running at 2.7 percent by August, the highest in the European Union. Economists, including the International Monetary Fund, said the government needed to control spending to prevent the economy from overheating. The Socialists needed a majority in parliament to push through some harsh social reforms to keep up with greater demands on social security, health and education. Without it, the battle for reform is expected to be tougher. The nation is concerned about social security and health services for the elderly as the population continues to age. The Socialists have promised to cut hospital waiting lists by 2002.

GOVERNMENT AND POLITICS

Prime Minister Antonio Guterres knew he needed a majority in parliament to survive his four-year term, but the Socialist leader didn't get it. The Communists boosted their representation in parliament by two seats, while the Social Democrats lost five seats. Ideologically, the Social Democrats are not too far from Guterres' party, but they were expected to create more problems for his government. Guterres' government has been ruling as a minority since 1995, and it campaigned hard to establish a majority in the October elections. He fell three seats short of the 116 needed to control the 230-seat parliament. Those three seats could be enough to send his government into a crisis. The opposition includes both right-wing parties and extreme-left parties. Together, they could make it nearly impossible for Guterres to carry out social and economic reforms. After the vote, Guterres warned the opposition to be reasonable, but some analysts believe it will be difficult for the prime minister to get much cooperation.

CULTURE AND SOCIETY

On April 25, Portuguese observed the 25th anniversary of the Carnation Revolution, when young army officers collectively known as the Armed Forces Movement staged a coup to end the bloodshed in the colonies. The nearly bloodless coup in 1974 ended 40 years of dictatorship, and marked an abrupt end to its colonial past. But the Portuguese didn't mark the occasion with wild celebrations. The country remained troubled by the legacy of civil wars and deep poverty in its former colonies. Its people wavered between an "uneasy blend of national pride in the country's imperial past and guilt over the catastrophic way it was dismantled," Associated Press reporter Barry Hatton wrote in an article about the anniversary of the revolution.

But the anniversary was not the only remainder of the country's colonial past. During 1999, Portugal took steps to formally cede Macao, its last vestige of a once great empire, to the Chinese by December 1999. The transition was by most estimates going smoothly, but it was events in East Timor that angered the Portuguese.

Indonesia occupied East Timor shortly after the Portuguese left in 1975, but the United Nations continued to recognize Portugal as the administering power in the territory. In May, Portugal and Indonesia signed an accord to settle the future of the former Portuguese territory. On August 30, East Timorese voted for independence, but the vote was followed by bloody attacks by pro-Jakarta militias opposed to the territory's independence. The militias killed several hundred and displaced thousands from their homes. In Portugal many people wore white to protest the bloodshed and tens of thousands formed a human chain linking the embassies of the five permanent members of the United Nations Security Council in Lisbon. In October East Timor resistance leader Xanana Gusmao paid an emotional tribute to Portugal for supporting the territory's struggle for independence. Gusmao, who is expected to become the first leader of an independent East Timor, was given a hero's welcome in Lisbon, where he was addressed as "president" by Portugal President Jorge Sampaio. The Portuguese promised financial and administrative aid to its former colony.

Finally, as if taking her leave at the emergence of a post-colonial, cosmopolitan Portuguese culture, one of the most beloved musicians of a popular Portuguese folk idiom passed away in 1999. Her voice traveled the world, popularizing the obscure lyrics of the Portuguese *fado*. To her fans, she was simply known as Amalia, forever a woman possessed of a dark and tormented beauty, the perfect personification of the sorrowful songs she performed. On October 6, Amalia Rodrigues, who rose from poverty to become a national treasure, died. She was 79.

Prime Minister Antonio Guterres declared three days of national mourning and thousands of Portuguese attended her state funeral. *Fado*, like the blues, expresses longing and sorrow, and is deeply rooted with Moorish and African influences. The music is said to express the unique Portuguese concept known as saudade, which expresses melancholy and nostalgia for what has been lost and for what has never been attained. The *fado* (which roughly translates to fate) is an expression of Portuguese society, and no one expressed it as well as Amalia. She was, Guterres said, the voice of the Portuguese soul.

Amalia was born in a poor Lisbon neighborhood, and raised by her grandparents. She started singing while she sold fruits and other products on the city's waterfront. Soon she was singing in local festivals, even though her family and many Portuguese didn't approve of the vulgar *fado*. To sing *fado* was gutsy. It never seemed to be in favor. Somehow it became a detested symbol of fascist reaction among leftist intellectuals after the 1974 revolution. Amalia always dismissed the criticism, and continued to sing well into her 70s. Thanks to her and to other exponents of *fado*, the music has seen a rebirth in Portugal. No longer vulgar, no longer viewed as a political tool of the fascists, it is just *fado*, the voice of the Portuguese soul.

DIRECTORY

CENTRAL GOVERNMENT

Head of State

President

Jorge Sampaio, Office of the President, Palacio de Belem, P-1300 Lisbon, Portugal
PHONE: +351 (1) 3635768
FAX: +351 (1) 3636603

Prime Minister

Antonio Manuel de Oliveira Guterres, Office of the Prime Minister, Gabinete do Primeiro-Ministro, P-1300 Lisbon, Portugal
E-MAIL: pm@pm.gov.pt

Ministers

Minister of Agriculture and Fisheries

Luis Manuel Capoulas Santos, Ministry of Agriculture and Fisheries, Praça do Comércio, P-1100 Lisbon, Portugal
PHONE: +351 (1) 3463151
FAX: +351 (1) 3473798
E-MAIL: siaza@min-agricultura.pt

Minister of Culture

Manuel Maria Carrilho, Ministry of Culture

Minister of Defense

Jose Veiga Simao, Ministry of Defense, Avenida Ilha da Madeira n° 1, P–1400–204 Lisbon, Portugal
PHONE: +351 (1) 3017485
FAX: +351 (1) 3019280

Minister of Economy

Joaquim Pina Moura, Ministry of Economy, Rua da Horta Seca 15, P-1294 Lisbon, Portugal
PHONE: +351 (1) 3228600
FAX: +351 (1) 3228811
E-MAIL: webmaster@min-economia.pt

Minister of Education

Eduardo Marcal Grilo, Ministry of Education, Av. 5 de Outubro 107, Lisbon, Portugal
PHONE: +351 (1) 7931603
FAX: +351 (1) 7964119
E-MAIL: cirep@min-edu.pt

Minister of the Environment

Elisa Ferreira, Ministry of the Environment

Minister of Finance

Antonio Sousa Franco, Ministry of Finance, Av. Infante D. Henrique n° 1, P-1194 Lisbon, Portugal

Minister of the Treasurer

Ministry of the Treasurer, Rua da Alfândega n°5, 1°, P-1149-008 Lisbon, Portugal
PHONE: +351 (1) 8880631
FAX: +351 (1) 8877580
E-MAIL: tesouro@mail.telepac.pt

Minister of Foreign Affairs

Jaime José Matos da Gama, Ministry of Foreign Affairs, Palácio das Necessidades, Largo do Rilvas, P-1354 Lisbon, Portugal

PHONE: +351 (1) 3969850
FAX: +351 (1) 609708

Minister of Health
Maria de Belem Roseira, Ministry of Health

Minister of Internal Administration
Jorge Coelho, Ministry of the Internal
Administration

Minister of Justice
Jose Vera Jardim, Ministry of Justice

Minister of Parliamentary Affairs
Antonio Costa, Ministry of Parliamentary Affairs

Minister of Planning, Public Works, and Territorial Administration
Joao Cravinho, Ministry of Planning, Public
Works, and Territorial Administration, Palacion
Penafiel, Rua de S. Mamede ao Caldas 21,
P-1149-050 Lisbon, Portugal
PHONE: +351 (1) 8861119
FAX: +351 (1) 8863827

Minister of Science and Technology
Jose Mariano Gago, Ministry of Science and
Technology, Praça do Comercio, Ala Oriental,
P-1194 Lisbon, Portugal
PHONE: +351 (1) 8812000
FAX: +351 (1) 8882434
E-MAIL: geral@mct.pt

Minister of Solidarity, Social Security and Employment
Eduardo Ferro Rodrigues, Ministry of Solidarity,
Social Security and Employment

Minister of Youth, Drug Addiction, and Sports
Jose Socrates, Ministry of Youth, Drug
Addiction, and Sports

High Commissioner for Immigration and Ethnic Minorities
José Maximiano de Albuquerque Almeida
Leitão, Office of the High Commissioner for
Immigration and Ethnic Minorities, Av.
Columbano Bordalo Pinheiro, 86–8°, P-1070-065
Lisbon, Portugal
PHONE: +351 (1) 7210210
FAX: +351 (1) 7271143

Consular for Information
Office of the Consular for Information, Gomes
Teixeira, P–1399–022 Lisbon, Portugal
PHONE: +351 (1) 3977001; 3927600
FAX: +351 (1) 3977814

Consular for Civil Protection
Office of the Consular for Civil Protection,
Gomes Teixeira, P-1399-022 Lisbon, Portugal
PHONE: +351 (1) 4247100
FAX: +351 (1) 4247171

Consular for Internal Security
Office of the Consular for Internal Security,
Terreiro do Paço, P-1149-015 Lisbon, Portugal
PHONE: +351 (1) 3233027
FAX: +351 (1) 3430618

High Commissioner for Immigration and Ethnic Minorities
Joana Morais Sarmento de Barros do
Nascimento Baptista, Office of the High
Commissioner for Immigration and Ethnic
Minorities, Palácio Foz, Praça dos Restauradores,
P-1250-187 Lisbon, Portugal
PHONE: +351 (1) 3219515; 3219516
FAX: +351 (1) 3429114

President of the Commission for Equal Rights and Women's Affairs
Ana Maria Quintans Fernandes Ferreira Braga da
Cruz, Office of the President of the Commission
for Equal Rights and Women's Affairs, Av. da
República 32-1°, P-1050-193 Lisbon, Portugal
PHONE: +351 (1) 7983000
FAX: +351 (1) 7983098

National Consular for Family Affairs
Joana Morais Sarmento de Barros do
Nascimento Baptista, Office of the National
Consular for Family Affairs, Palácio Foz, Praça
dos Restauradores, P-1250-187 Lisbon, Portugal
PHONE: +351 (1) 3219515; 3219516
FAX: +351 (1) 3429114

Secretary General of the Presidency to the Consul of Ministers
Alexandre Alves de Figueiredo, Office of the
Secretary General of the Presidency to the
Consul of Ministers, Rua Prof. Gomes Teixeira,
P-1399-022 Lisbon, Portugal

Director General of Public Administration
Júlio Gabriel Casanova Nabais, Office of the
Director General of Public Administration, Av.
24 de Julho 80 a 80 J, P-1249-084 Lisbon,
Portugal
PHONE: +351 (1) 3972161
FAX: +351 (1) 3900148
E-MAIL: dgap@esoterica.pt

General Director for Commerce and Competition DGCC

Office of the General Director for Commerce and Competition, Av. Visconde de Valmor n° 72, P-1069-041 Lisbon, Portugal
PHONE: +351 (1) 7919100
FAX: +351 (1) 7965158
E-MAIL: dgcomconc@mail. telepac.pt

General Director for Energy

Office of the General Director for Energy, Av. 5 de Outubro 87, P-1069-039 Lisbon, Portugal
PHONE: +351 (1) 7922700; 7922800
FAX: +351 (1) 7939540

Chairman of the Directorate General for Investments, Commerce and Tourism

Guilherme Costa, Office of the Chairman of the Directorate General for Investments, Commerce and Tourism, Avenida 5 de Outubro 101, P-1016 Lisbon, Portugal
PHONE: +351 (1) 7930103
FAX: +351 (1) 7970186

Minister for Labour and Solidarity

Eduardo Luís Barreto Ferro Rodrigues, Ministry for Labour and Solidarity, Rua Rosa Araújo 43-4°, P-1250-194 Lisbon, Portugal
PHONE: +351 (1) 3107800
FAX: +351 (1) 3530085
E-MAIL: ministro@mts.gov.pt

Attorney General

Office of the Attorney General, Rua da Escola Politécnica 140, P-1269-269 Lisbon, Portugal
PHONE: +351 (1) 3921900
FAX: +351 (1) 3975255

POLITICAL ORGANIZATIONS

Partido Socialista-PS (Socialist Party)

Largo do Rato 2, P-1269-143 Lisbon, Portugal
PHONE: +351 (1) 3822000
FAX: +351 (1) 3822016
E-MAIL: info@ps.pt
TITLE: Chairman
NAME: António Guterres

Partido Social Democrata-PSD (Social Democratic Party)

Rua de São Caetano 9, Lisbon, Portugal
PHONE: +351 (1) 3952140
FAX: +351 (1) 3822016
TITLE: President
NAME: Manuel Dias Loureiro

Portuguese Communist Party

Rua Soeiro Pereira Gomes 3, P-1699 Lisbon, Portugal
PHONE: +351 (1) 7813800
FAX: +351 (1) 7969126
E-MAIL: dep.pcp@mail.telepac.pt
NAME: Carlos Carvalhas

Partido Popular-CDS-PP (People's Party)

Largo Adelino Amaro da Costa 5, P-1196 Lisbon, Portugal
PHONE: +351 (1) 8869730
FAX: +351 (1) 8860454
NAME: Paulo Portas

Partido Liberal (Liberal Party)

Centro National Da Liberdade, Apartado 14.061, P-1064 Lisbon, Portugal

DIPLOMATIC REPRESENTATION

Embassies in Portugal

Austria
Av. Infante Santo 43-4, 1350 Lisbon, Portugal
PHONE: +351 (1) 3958220; 3958221; 3958222
FAX: +351 (1) 3958224

Canada
Edifício MCB, Av. da Liberdade 144-4, Lisbon, Portugal
PHONE: +351 (1) 3474892
FAX: +351 (1) 3425628

China
R. S. Caetano 2, 1200 Lisbon, Portugal
PHONE: +351 (1) 3961882
FAX: +351 (1) 3282555

Egypt
Av. D. Vasco da Gama 8, P-1400 Lisbon, Portugal
PHONE: +351 (1) 3018301
FAX: +351 (1) 3017909

France
R. Santos-o-Velho 5, 1200 Lisbon, Portugal
PHONE: +351 (1) 3972652
FAX: +351 (1) 3978327

Germany
Campo Mártires da Pátria 38, 1150 Lisbon, Portugal
PHONE: +351 (1) 8810210
FAX: +351 (1) 8853846

India
R. Pero da Covilha 16, 1400 Lisbon, Portugal
PHONE: +351 (1) 3017291
FAX: +351 (1) 3016576

Italy
Largo Conde Pombeiro 6, 1150 Lisbon, Portugal
PHONE: +351 (1) 3520862
FAX: +351 (1) 3154926

Japan
R. Mouzinho da Silveira 11, 125 Lisbon, Portugal
PHONE: +351 (1) 3310560
FAX: +351 (1) 3534802

South Africa
Av. Luis Bivar 10A, 1050 Lisbon, Portugal
PHONE: +351 (1) 3535041
FAX: +351 (1) 3535713

United Kingdom
Rua de S. Domingos a Lapa 37, Lisbon, Portugal
PHONE: +351 (1) 3961191
FAX: +351 (1) 3976768

United States
Av. das Forcas Armadas, Lisbon, Portugal
PHONE: +351 (1) 7273300
FAX: +351 (1) 7269109

JUDICIAL SYSTEM
Supreme Court

FURTHER READING
Articles
''Amalia Rodrigues, Queen of Fado, Lisbon's Sad Songs,'' *The New York Times* (October 7, 1999).

''Making Memories, Macao Reverts to Chinese Control,'' *The Economist* (August 14, 1999): 66.

''Melo Antunes, a Brainy Soldier and Revolutionary,'' *The Economist* (August 21, 1999): 76.

''Panel Clears Lisbon on Nazi Gold Trade,'' *The New York Times* 5 August 1999.

''Portugal Economy Booms, but Reforms Needed,'' Reuters (October 5, 1999).

''Portugal's Highways of Death,'' *The Guardian of London* 8 March 1999.

''Portugal's Last Days in Macao Marred by Chinese Troop Issue,'' *The New York Times* 23 March 1999.

''Portugal Socialists Fall Short of Majority,'' *The New York Times* 11 October 1999.

''Skeleton Gives Clues that Neanderthals, Modern Man Mated,'' The Associated Press, 17 April 1999.

''Twenty-Five Years After the Carnation Revolution: Portugal Fares Better than Old Colonies,'' The Associated Press 21 April 1999.

PORTUGAL: STATISTICAL DATA

For sources and notes see "Sources of Statistics" in the front of each volume.

GEOGRAPHY

Geography (1)

Area:

Total: 92,391 sq km.

Land: 91,951 sq km.

Water: 440 sq km.

Note: includes Azores and Madeira Islands.

Area—comparative: slightly smaller than Indiana.

Land boundaries:

Total: 1,214 km.

Border countries: Spain 1,214 km.

Coastline: 1,793 km.

Climate: maritime temperate; cool and rainy in north, warmer and drier in south.

Terrain: mountainous north of the Tagus, rolling plains in south.

Natural resources: fish, forests (cork), tungsten, iron ore, uranium ore, marble.

Land use:

Arable land: 26%

Permanent crops: 9%

Permanent pastures: 9%

Forests and woodland: 36%

Other: 20% (1993 est.).

HUMAN FACTORS

Demographics (2A)

	1990	1995	1998	2000	2010	2020	2030	2040	2050
Population	NA	9,920.5	9,927.6	9,902.1	9,642.7	9,238.8	8,757.6	8,099.2	7,255.7
Net migration rate (per 1,000 population)	NA	NA	NA	NA	NA	NA	NA	NA	NA
Births	NA	NA	NA	NA	NA	NA	NA	NA	NA
Deaths	NA	NA	NA	NA	NA	NA	NA	NA	NA
Life expectancy - males	NA	71.2	72.3	72.8	74.9	76.6	77.9	78.9	79.7
Life expectancy - females	NA	78.5	79.2	79.7	81.5	82.9	84.1	85.0	85.7
Birth rate (per 1,000)	NA	11.1	10.6	10.3	8.4	7.2	6.5	5.8	5.4
Death rate (per 1,000)	NA	10.5	10.3	10.2	10.8	11.6	12.8	15.1	17.9
Women of reproductive age (15-49 yrs.)	NA	2,563.7	2,570.9	2,559.3	2,391.3	2,085.8	1,713.0	1,454.4	1,212.8
of which are currently married	NA	NA	NA	NA	NA	NA	NA	NA	NA
Fertility rate	NA	1.4	1.3	1.3	1.3	1.3	1.3	1.3	1.3

Except as noted, values for vital statistics are in thousands; life expectancy is in years.

Health Personnel (3)

Total health expenditure as a percentage of GDP,
1990-1997[a]

Public sector 4.9

Private sector 3.3

Total[b] 8.2

Health expenditure per capita in U.S. dollars,
1990-1997[a]

Purchasing power parity 1,114

Total 805

Availability of health care facilities per 100,000 people

Hospital beds 1990-1997[a] 410

Doctors 1993[c] 291

Nurses 1993[c] 304

Health Indicators (4)

Life expectancy at birth

1980 71

1997 75

Daily per capita supply of calories (1996) 3,658

Total fertility rate births per woman (1997) 1.4

Maternal mortality ratio per 100,000 live births
(1990-97) . . . . .15[c]

Safe water % of population with access (1995) 82

Sanitation % of population with access (1995) . . . .

Consumption of iodized salt % of households
(1992-98)[a] . . . .

Smoking prevalence

Male % of adults (1985-95)[a] 38

Female % of adults (1985-95)[a] 15

Tuberculosis incidence per 100,000 people
(1997) 55

Adult HIV prevalence % of population ages
15-49 (1997) 0.69

Infants and Malnutrition (5)

Under-5 mortality rate (1997) 8

% of infants with low birthweight (1990-97) 5

Births attended by skilled health staff % of total[a] . . .NA

% fully immunized (1995-97)

TB 91

DPT 95

Polio 99

Measles 94

Prevalence of child malnutrition under age 5
(1992-97)[b] . . . . .NA

Ethnic Division (6)

Homogeneous Mediterranean stock in mainland,
Azores, Madeira Islands; citizens of black African
descent who immigrated to mainland during
decolonization number less than 100,000.

Religions (7)

Roman Catholic 97%

Protestant denominations 1%

Other 2%

Languages (8)

Portuguese.

EDUCATION

Public Education Expenditures (9)

Public expenditure on education (% of GNP)

1980 . . . . .3.8

1996 . . . . .5.5[1]

Expenditure per student

Primary % of GNP per capita

1980 . . . . .13.5

1996 . . . . .20.9[1]

Secondary % of GNP per capita

1980 . . . .

1996 . . . . .20.9[1]

Tertiary % of GNP per capita

1980 . . . . .36.2

1996 . . . . .25.2[1]

Expenditure on teaching materials

Primary % of total for level (1996) . . . . .0.2[1]

Secondary % of total for level (1996) . . . .

Primary pupil-teacher ratio per teacher (1996) . . . . .12[1]

Duration of primary education years (1995) 6

Educational Attainment (10)

Age group (1991) . . . . .25+

Total population .6,280,792

Highest level attained (%)

No schooling 16.1

First level

Not completed 61.5

Completed . . . . .NA

Entered second level

S-1 . . . . .14.8

S-2 . . . . .NA

Postsecondary 7.7

Literacy Rates (11B)

Adult literacy rate
1980
  Male 78%
  Female 65%
1995
  Male 92%
  Female 87%

GOVERNMENT & LAW

Political Parties (12)

Assembly of the Republic	% of seats
Social Democratic Party (PSD)	.34.0
Portuguese Socialist Party (PS)	.43.8

United Democratic Coalition (CDU) 8.6
Center Democratic/Popular Party (CDS/PP) 9.1

Government Budget (13B)

Revenues . . . .$48 billion
Expenditures . . . .$52 billion
  Capital expenditures . . . .$7.4 billion

Data for 1996 est.

Crime (15)

Crime rate (for 1997)
  Crimes reported 75,600
  Total persons convicted 26,600
  Crimes per 100,000 population 750
Persons responsible for offenses
  Total number of suspects 39,700
  Total number of female suspects 8,400
  Total number of juvenile suspects . . . . .NA

Military Affairs (14B)

	1990	1991	1992	1993	1994	1995
Military expenditures						
Current dollars (mil.)	2,361	2,457	2,490	2,450	2,442	2,690
1995 constant dollars (mil.)	2,713	2,716	2,678	2,569	2,503	2,690
Armed forces (000)	87	86	80	68	122	78
Gross national product (GNP)						
Current dollars (mil.)	84,390	89,830	94,010	94,590	97,900	102,900[e]
1995 constant dollars (mil.)	96,990	99,270	101,100	99,160	100,400	102,900[e]
Central government expenditures (CGE)						
1995 constant dollars (mil.)	38,760	42,610	41,630	43,300	42,570	NA
People (mil.)	9.9	9.9	9.9	9.9	9.9	9.9
Military expenditure as % of GNP	2.8	2.7	2.6	2.6	2.5	2.6
Military expenditure as % of CGE	7.0	6.4	6.4	5.9	5.0	NA
Military expenditure per capita (1995 $)	275	275	272	261	254	273
Armed forces per 1,000 people (soldiers)	8.8	8.7	8.1	6.9	12.4	7.9
GNP per capita (1995 $)	9,826	10,070	10,260	10,060	10,170	10,430
Arms imports[6]						
Current dollars (mil.)	360	550	130	150	270	90
1995 constant dollars (mil.)	414	608	140	157	277	90
Arms exports[6]						
Current dollars (mil.)	10	5	20	10	100	0
1995 constant dollars (mil.)	11	6	22	10	103	0
Total imports[7]						
Current dollars (mil.)	25,260	26,110	29,580	24,340	26,940	32,340
1995 constant dollars (mil.)	29,030	28,860	31,820	25,510	27,610	32,340
Total exports[7]						
Current dollars (mil.)	16,420	16,280	18,350	15,430	17,900	22,620
1995 constant dollars (mil.)	18,870	17,990	19,740	16,180	18,350	22,620
Arms as percent of total imports[8]	1.4	2.1	.4	.6	1.0	.3
Arms as percent of total exports[8]	.1	0	.1	.1	.6	0

LABOR FORCE

Labor Force (16)

Total (million) 4.53

Services 56%

Manufacturing 23%

Agriculture, forestry, fisheries 11%

Construction 8%

Utilities 1%

Mining 1%

Data for 1996 est. Percent distribution for 1995.

Unemployment Rate (17)

7% (January 1998)

PRODUCTION SECTOR

Electric Energy (18)

Capacity . . . . .8.831 million kW (1995)

Production . . . . .31.446 billion kWh (1995)

Consumption per capita . . . . .3,072 kWh (1995)

Transportation (19)

Highways:

total: 68,732 km

paved: 59,110 km (including 687 km of expressways)

unpaved: 9,622 km (1995 est.)

Waterways: 820 km navigable; relatively unimportant to national economy, used by shallow-draft craft limited to 300 metric-ton cargo capacity

Pipelines: crude oil 22 km; petroleum products 58 km; natural gas 700 km note: the secondary lines for the natural gas pipeline that will be 300 km long have not yet been built

Merchant marine:

total: 107 ships (1,000 GRT or over) totaling 736,478 GRT/1,139,180 DWT ships by type: bulk 8, cargo 60, chemical tanker 10, container 6, liquefied gas tanker 9, oil tanker 8, refrigerated cargo 1, roll-on/roll-off cargo 2, short-sea passenger 3 note: Portugal has created a captive register on Madeira for Portuguese-owned ships; ships on the Madeira Register (MAR) will have taxation and crewing benefits of a flag of convenience (1997 est.)

Airports: 69 (1997 est.)

Airports—with paved runways:

total: 41

over 3,047 m: 5

2,438 to 3,047 m: 8

1,524 to 2,437 m: 4

914 to 1,523 m: 18

under 914 m: 6 (1997 est.)

Airports—with unpaved runways:

total: 28

914 to 1,523 m: 1

under 914 m: 27 (1997 est.)

Top Agricultural Products (20)

Grain, potatoes, olives, grapes; sheep, cattle, goats, poultry, meat, dairy products.

MANUFACTURING SECTOR

GDP & Manufacturing Summary (21)

Detailed value added figures are listed by both International Standard Industry Code (ISIC) and product title.

	1980	1985	1990	1994
GDP ($-1990 mil.)[1]	51,485	53,809	67,271	69,550
Per capita ($-1990)[1]	5,272	5,433	6,817	7,075
Manufacturing share (%) (current prices)[1]	32.5	32.5	32.3	NA
Manufacturing				
Value added ($-1990 mil.)[1]	14,935	14,817	18,765	17,607
Industrial production index	100	103	125	117
Value added ($ mil.)	5,602	4,113	13,182	13,384
Gross output ($ mil.)	17,932	15,534	51,224	54,783
Employment (000)	680	622	489	443
Profitability (% of gross output)				
Intermediate input (%)	69	74	74	76
Wages and salaries inc. supplements (%)	17	14	10	10
Gross operating surplus	14	13	16	15
Productivity ($)				
Gross output per worker	25,887	24,567	50,379	60,926
Value added per worker	8,087	6,505	12,965	14,917
Average wage (inc. supplements)	4,541	3,490	10,129	12,082
Value added ($ mil.)				
311/2 Food products	544	475	1,305	1,164
313 Beverages	135	133	344	362

	1980	1985	1990	1994
314 Tobacco products	64	93	592	*716*
321 Textiles	905	679	1,654	*1,438*
322 Wearing apparel	186	182	985	*1,091*
323 Leather and fur products	41	41	126	*105*
324 Footwear	86	86	452	*454*
331 Wood and wood products	325	150	532	*572*
332 Furniture and fixtures	106	30	233	*305*
341 Paper and paper products	274	276	577	*485*
342 Printing and publishing	180	140	523	*599*
351 Industrial chemicals	147	215	432	*315*
352 Other chemical products	224	190	481	*630*
353 Petroleum refineries	*219*	*-18*	*167*	99
354 Miscellaneous petroleum and coal products	—	—	—	—
355 Rubber products	58	*45*	54	*55*
356 Plastic products	128	*92*	237	*221*
361 Pottery, china and earthenware	80	67	291	*299*
362 Glass and glass products	87	53	173	*177*
369 Other non-metal mineral products	295	200	724	*818*
371 Iron and steel	207	98	273	*239*
372 Non-ferrous metals	33	26	81	*74*

	1980	1985	1990	1994
381 Metal products	323	219	826	*998*
382 Non-electrical machinery	170	143	528	*631*
383 Electrical machinery	319	247	834	*858*
384 Transport equipment	428	222	583	*452*
385 Professional and scientific equipment	15	16	36	*66*
390 Other manufacturing industries	20	11	141	*159*

FINANCE, ECONOMICS, & TRADE

Economic Indicators (22)

National product: GDP—purchasing power parity—$149.5 billion (1997 est.)

National product real growth rate: 3.3% (1997 est.)

National product per capita: $15,200 (1997 est.)

Inflation rate—consumer price index: 2.3% (1997 est.)

Exchange Rates (24)

Exchange rates:

Portuguese escudos (Esc) per US$1

January 1998	185.81
1997	175.31
1996	154.24
1995	151.11
1994	165.99
1993	160.80

Balance of Payments (23)

	1992	1993	1994	1995	1996
Exports of goods (f.o.b.)	18,348	15,931	18,645	24,024	25,527
Imports of goods (f.o.b.)	−27,735	−23,981	−26,966	−32,934	−34,868
Trade balance	−9,387	−8,050	−8,321	−8,910	−9,340
Services - debits	−6,188	−7,717	−8,283	−10,697	−11,445
Services - credits	7,564	9,301	8,987	12,331	12,468
Private transfers (net)	3,032	2,879	1,942	3,750	3,467
Government transfers (net)	4,794	3,819	3,479	3,382	3,359
Overall balance	−184	233	−2,195	−144	−1,491

Top Import Origins (25)

$33.9 billion (c.i.f., 1996) Data are for 1995.

Origins	%
European Union	.72
Other developed	.8
United States	.3
Less developed	.17

Top Export Destinations (26)

$23.8 billion (f.o.b., 1996).

Destinations	%
European Union	.76
Other developed	.9
US	.5

Economic Aid (27)

Donor: ODA, $220 million (1996). Recipient: ODA, $70 million (1993).

Import Export Commodities (28)

Import Commodities	Export Commodities
Machinery and transport equipment	Clothing and footwear
	Machinery
Agricultural products	Cork and paper products
Chemicals	Hides
Petroleum	
Textiles 17%	

PUERTO RICO

Commonwealth of Puerto Rico

INTRODUCTORY SURVEY

RECENT HISTORY

Christopher Columbus, accompanied by a young nobleman named Juan Ponce de León, discovered Puerto Rico on 19 November 1493, landing at the western end of the Island, which he called San Juan Bautista (St. John the Baptist), and claimed it for Spain. But it was not until colonization was well under way that the island would acquire the name Puerto Rico ("rich port"), with the name San Juan Bautista applied to the capital city. The first settlers arrived on 12 August 1508, under the able leadership of Ponce de León, who sought to transplant and adapt Spanish civilization to Puerto Rico's tropical habitat. The small contingent of Spaniards compelled the Taino, numbering perhaps 30,000, to mine for gold; the rigors of forced labor and the losses from rebellion reduced the Taino population to about 4,000 by 1514, by which time the mines were nearly depleted. With the introduction of slaves from Africa, sugarcane growing became the leading economic activity.

Puerto Rico was briefly held by the English in 1598, and San Juan was besieged by the Dutch in 1625; otherwise, Spanish rule continued until the latter part of the 19th century. The island was captured by U.S. forces during the Spanish-American War, and under the Treaty of Paris (December 1898) Puerto Rico was ceded outright to the United States. It remained under direct military rule until 1900, when the U.S Congress established an administration with a governor and an executive council, appointed by the U.S. president, and a

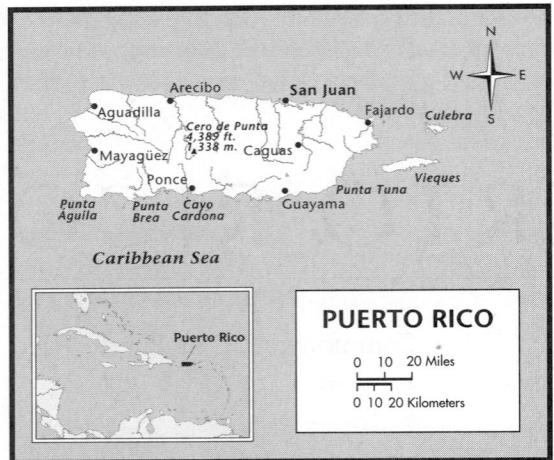

popularly elected House of Delegates. In 1917, Puerto Ricans were granted U.S. citizenship.

In 1947, Congress provided for popular election of the governor; and in 1948, Luis Munoz Marin was elected to that office. A congressional act of 1950, affirmed by popular vote in the island on 4 June 1951, granted Puerto Rico the right to draft its own constitution. The constitution was ratified by popular referendum on 3 March 1952. Puerto Rico's new status as a free commonwealth voluntarily associated with the U.S. became effective on 25 July. The commonwealth status was upheld in a plebiscite in 1967, with 60.5% voting for continuation of the commonwealth and 38.9% for Puerto Rican statehood. In 1993 another plebiscite vote drew nearly 1.7 million voters or 73.6 percent of those eligible. The voters choose to keep the commonwealth status 48.4% to 46.2% for statehood, and 4.4% for independence.

GOVERNMENT

The Commonwealth of Puerto Rico enjoys almost complete internal autonomy. The chief executive is the governor, elected by popular vote to a four-year term. The legislature consists of a 27-member Senate and 51-member House of Representatives elected by popular vote to four-year terms.

Judiciary

The Supreme Court and lower courts are tied in with the U.S. federal judiciary, and appeals from Puerto Rican courts may be carried as far as the U.S. Supreme Court.

Political Parties

The Popular Democratic Party (PDP) was the dominant political party until 1968, when Luis A. Ferro, a New Progressive Party (NPP) candidate, who had supported the statehood position in the 1967 plebiscite, won the governorship. The NPP also won control of the House, while the PDP retained the Senate. The PDP returned to power in 1972 but lost to the NPP in 1976 and again, by a very narrow margin, in 1980; in 1984, it took roughly two-to-one majorities in both houses. The pro-commonwealth PDP remained in control of the government in every election from 1984–92, when Pedro Rossello, a New Progressive and supporter of statehood, was elected governor; Rosello was reelected in 1996. There is a small but vocal independence movement, divided into two wings: the moderates, favoring social democracy, and the radicals, supporting close ties with the Fidel Castro regime in Cuba.

ECONOMIC AFFAIRS

For more than 400 years, the island's economy was based almost exclusively on sugar. Since 1947, agriculture has been diversified, and a thriving manufacturing industry has been established; since 1956 there has been increasing emphasis on hotel building to encourage the expansion of the tourist industry. By 1990/91, the gross commonwealth domestic product reached $30 billion, up from $15.8 billion in 1985/86. In 1991 manufacturing generated $12 billion, or 40% of domestic output.

Income

U.S. taxes do not apply in Puerto Rico, since the commonwealth is not represented in Congress. New or expanding manufacturing and hotel enterprises are granted exemptions of varying lengths and degrees from income taxes and municipal levies. In 1940, when annual income per capita was $118, agricultural workers made as little as 6 cents an hour, and the illiteracy rate was 70%. By 1990/91, however, personal income per capita was $6,330, and by 1996, had increased to $7,882.

Industry

The leading industrial products were pharmaceuticals, clothing, electrical machinery, rum, and processed foods. Sugar processing, once the dominant industry, now plays a lesser role. In 1952, there were only 82 labor-intensive plants on the island but by 1990 there were 2,000 plants in Puerto Rico, most of them capital intensive.

1999 KEY EVENTS TIMELINE

January

- The trial of seven anti-Castro Cuban Americans who were arrested bringing firearms to Puerto Rico has been moved from the island to southern Florida; the U.S. Department of Justice asks Puerto Rico's U.S. district judge to reconsider his decision to move the trial.

April

- One civilian dies and four are injured on April 20 after two U.S. F-18 planes drop bombs in a training exercise in Vieques.

- Governor Roselló appoints a commission to study the presence of the U.S. Navy on the 21-mile long island of Vieques, just off the shore of the main island of Puerto Rico.

May

- Members and sympathizers of the Independence Party trespass on Navy property to protest against the U.S. use of the island of Vieques as a military training camp and site for war games.

- Felix "Tito" Trinidad retains his International Boxing Federation welterweight crown and earns the right to challenge World Boxing Council champion Oscar de la Hoya later in the year.

June

- The Pepsi-Cola Puerto Rico Bottling Company buys two additional bottlers for $309 million, making it the third largest anchor Pepsi bottler in the world.

July

- Protests against a U.S. naval presence in Puerto Rico continue. A majority of Puerto Ricans, including Governor Pedro Roselló, want U.S. armed forces removed from Vieques. A July 4 march in Vieques draws nearly 50,000 protestors.

- Short story author Abelardo Díaz Alfaro dies at age 81.

August

- The U.S. Navy says human error caused the civilian death and injuries during their April war games, and it denies intentions to pull out of Vieques.

- Reverend Jesse Jackson visits Puerto Rico and joins those demanding the Navy leave Vieques.

- The U.S. Army completes a relocation of the U.S. Army South Headquarters from Panama to Puerto Rico.

- José Toledo, the son of Puerto Rico's top police officer and former FBI agent Pedro Toledo, is indicted in Miami, Florida, by the Drug Enforcement Administration (DEA) for smuggling drugs into the United States using American Airlines planes.

September

- U.S. President Bill Clinton makes a clemency offer to sixteen Puerto Rican political prisoners sentenced for terrorist attacks in the 1970s.

- First Lady Hillary Clinton publicly opposes the clemency offer made by her husband to the sixteen Puerto Rican political prisoners. Puerto Rican leaders in the United States and the island publicly criticize Mrs. Clinton and vow not to support her senatorial candidacy.

- Twelve of the sixteen political prisoners accept President Clinton's offer and are released from jail. They are received as heroes in the island, but according to recent polls, most Puerto Ricans reject independence from the United States.

- Republicans in the U.S. Congress criticize President Clinton's clemency offer, but many Democrats, including three Puerto Rican Representatives from New York and Illinois, argue that the twelve convicted political prisoners were serving excessive terms resulting from charges of seditious conspiracy.

- Felix "Tito" Trinidad defeats welterweight world champion and favorite Oscar de la Hoya in a fight on September 17; Puerto Ricans take to the streets to celebrate the victory.

December

- U.S. President Bill Clinton orders the phased withdrawal of U.S. forces from the island of Vieques over the next five years.

ANALYSIS OF EVENTS: 1999

BUSINESS AND THE ECONOMY

The unemployment rate remains high in Puerto Rico. In 1995 the U.S. Congress eliminated tax incentives for labor-intensive companies relocating to Puerto Rico, and since then few new industries have moved to the island, hurting its economy. Elsewhere in the economy, new public work projects and infrastructure development increased with finance from the U.S. federal government, but stagnation in industrial production and agricultural activity have made it difficult for the island to generate new productive employment. Tourism, however, has remained one of the island's key sources of revenue.

The consolidation of the banking industry and the integration of Caribbean nations into the world economy have helped Puerto Rico's economy. The island has been able to position itself as a major banking center in the Caribbean. The modern infrastructure and up-to-date technological advances in electricity, its telecommunications systems, and Puerto Rico's status as a territory of the United States have also made it easier for businesses to establish their Caribbean offices on the island.

GOVERNMENT AND POLITICS

Governor Pedro Roselló announced that he would not seek re-election for a third term in 2000. Upon his announcement a number of prominent political figures began exploring possible gubernatorial campaigns. The highly popular governor feared that recent economic difficulties and the effect of eight years in office would make it difficult for him to secure a third term.

Primary elections were scheduled for November 14, 1999. The governor's party, the pro-statehood New Progressive Party (PNP) has few chances of retaining the governorship in next year's elections, and many prominent leaders within the party have chosen to position themselves for future elections. The opposition party, the pro-commonwealth Popular Democratic Party (PPD) seeks to elect Sila Calderón as the next governor. Calderón would be the first woman to occupy the governor's post on the island and one of the few female Latin American leaders to hold the nation's highest office.

The most relevant event for the year, however, occurred in April when two U.S. F-18 planes killed one Puerto Rican civilian and injured four while conducting war games on the island of Vieques. The U.S. armed forces maintains military bases on Vieques, located off the coast of the main island of Puerto Rico. After the civilian death, nationalist sentiments, together with genuine concern for human safety, unified Puerto Ricans to demand the removal of U.S. military bases. At the least they requested a stop to the war games on the island. Pro-independence groups initiated hunger strikes and attempted to take over some of the bases. The governor asked President Clinton to ban war games and members of Congress of Puerto Rican origin moved to see U.S. military presence reduced on the island.

Vieques and the U.S. military bases were the central political and social issue until late August. At that time President Clinton asked the Pentagon to review the strategic need for conducting war games on the island. The Pentagon report called the games essential to the U.S. armed forces. Politicians and civil society leaders vowed to continue opposing the games, but support for the removal of U.S. military bases from Vieques is not strong. For the most part Puerto Ricans prefer to keep the bases, but want a reduction in the level of active military training.

CULTURE AND SOCIETY

The question of Puerto Rico's long-term political status, however, permeates the entire society. National identity and societal values are influenced by the existing debate between joining the United States as the fifty-first state, maintaining its present commonwealth status, or seeking independence from the United States. After 101 years of U.S. presence in the island, whatever political path Puerto Rico ultimately chooses, it will continue to struggle between Latin American, Caribbean, and U.S. cultural and societal values for many years to come.

As a result of the noted success of artists Jennifer López, Ricky Martin, and Marc Anthony in the mainland United States, Puerto Ricans have once again faced the question of national identity. While pride of Puerto Rico as a nation is strong and healthy, significant cultural and social incorporation into the mainland United States has also reshaped Puerto Rican society.

In late August President Clinton offered clemency to sixteen Puerto Rican political prisoners serving long sentences for conspiracy and sedition. The prisoners were convicted and sentenced in the late 1970s and early 1980s for their involvement in several pro-Puerto Rican independence groups in mainland United States. Analysts criticized Clinton's offer, claiming it was made to boost his wife's popularity among Latino voters in New York, where she is seeking a senate seat. Hillary Clinton, however, publicly denounced the offer, and the issue turned into a political battle between the Clintons and Puerto Rican leaders.

Surprisingly, most Puerto Ricans, regardless of their political ideology, supported the clemency offer and criticized Mrs. Clinton's position. From pro-independence activists to pro-statehood leaders, Puerto Ricans favored healing the wounds of the past and supported the release of the political prisoners. The sense of national unity, however, did not reach far beyond this issue to garner more public support for independence.

DIRECTORY

CENTRAL GOVERNMENT
Head of State

President of the United States
William Jefferson Clinton, Office of the President, 1600 Pensylvania Avenue, Washington, D.C. 20500
PHONE: +(202) 4561414
FAX: +(202) 4562461
E-MAIL: www.whitehouse.gov

Governor of Puerto Rico
Pedro Rossello, Office of the Governor, La Fortzaleza San Juan, Puerto Rico 00901
PHONE: +(787) 7217000
FAX: +(787) 7254569
E-MAIL: www.govpr.org

POLITICAL ORGANIZATIONS
Puerto Rican Independence Party

963 F.D. Roosevelt Avenue, Hato Rey, San Juan, Puerto Rico 00918
PHONE: +(787) 7821455
NAME: Ruben Berrios Martinez

Popular Democratic Party

403 Ponce de Leon Avenue, Puerta de Tierra, San Juan, Puerto Rico 00906
PHONE: +(787) 7251992
NAME: Hector Acevedo

New Progressive Party

La Fortalleza, San Juan, Puerto Rico 00901
PHONE: +(787) 7217000
FAX: +(787) 7254569
E-MAIL: webmaster@govpr.org
TITLE: President
NAME: Pedro Rossello

JUDICIAL SYSTEM
Supreme Court of Puerto Rico

P.O. Box 2392, Puerta de Tierra, San Juan, Puerto Rico 00902
PHONE: +(787) 7243551
FAX: +(787) 7254910

The U.S. District Court for the District of Puerto Rico

150 Carlos Chardon Avenue, Clemente Ruiz Nazario Courthouse, Hato Rey, Puerto Rico, 00918

FURTHER READING
Periodicals

Roman, Ivan. "Puerto Rico Suffers Large Manufacturing Job Losses." Knight-Ridder/Tribune Business News, October 17, 1999.

"Forgive Us Our Revolution: The Political Costs of Freeing the Puerto Rican Nationalists." *Newsweek* (September 20, 1999): 30.

Hirschfeld, Julie R. and Sumana Chatterjee. "House Opposes Clemency For Puerto Rican Nationalists." *Congressional Quarterly Weekly Report* (September 11, 1999): 2124.

Russell, Joel. "Puerto Rico's Economic Puzzle: the Island Commonwealth Searches for Ways to Integrate with the Mainland Economy." *Hispanic Business* (April 1999): 44(1).

Passalacqua, Juan M. Garcia. "Puerto Rico's Redress of Grievances." *Current History* (March 1999): 144(1).

Internet

Puerto Rico Herald. Available Online @ http://www.puertorico-herald.org/ (November 17, 1999).

Puerto Rico USA Citizenship Foundation. Available Online @ http://www.puertoricousa.com (November 17, 1999).

PUERTO RICO: STATISTICAL DATA

For sources and notes see "Sources of Statistics" in the front of each volume.

GEOGRAPHY

Geography (1)

Area:

Total: 9,104 sq km.

Land: 8,959 sq km.

Water: 145 sq km.

Area—comparative: slightly less than three times the size of Rhode Island.

Land boundaries: 0 km.

Coastline: 501 km.

Climate: tropical marine, mild; little seasonal temperature variation.

Terrain: mostly mountains with coastal plain belt in north; mountains precipitous to sea on west coast; sandy beaches along most coastal areas.

Natural resources: some copper and nickel; potential for onshore and offshore oil.

Land use:

Arable land: 4%

Permanent crops: 5%

Permanent pastures: 26%

Forests and woodland: 16%

Other: 49% (1993 est.).

HUMAN FACTORS

Demographics (2A)

	1990	1995	1998	2000	2010	2020	2030	2040	2050
Population	3,536.9	3,731.0	3,860.1	3,909.8	4,051.4	4,104.5	4,118.9	4,053.2	3,913.9
Net migration rate (per 1,000 population)	NA	NA	NA	NA	NA	NA	NA	NA	NA
Births	NA	NA	NA	NA	NA	NA	NA	NA	NA
Deaths	NA	NA	NA	NA	NA	NA	NA	NA	NA
Life expectancy - males	70.0	68.9	70.8	71.1	72.8	74.2	75.3	76.3	77.2
Life expectancy - females	78.9	78.8	79.3	79.5	80.4	81.2	81.9	82.5	83.1
Birth rate (per 1,000)	18.8	17.0	16.2	15.5	12.6	11.4	10.6	9.8	9.4
Death rate (per 1,000)	7.4	8.1	7.8	7.9	8.7	9.8	11.2	12.4	13.7
Women of reproductive age (15-49 yrs.)	935.6	998.2	1,030.1	1,033.0	1,023.4	980.7	898.6	863.1	800.8
of which are currently married	1,151.4	NA	NA	NA	NA	NA	NA	NA	NA
Fertility rate	2.3	2.1	2.0	1.9	1.8	1.7	1.7	1.7	1.7

Except as noted, values for vital statistics are in thousands; life expectancy is in years.

Health Indicators (4)

Life expectancy at birth

  1980 74

  1997 75

Daily per capita supply of calories (1996) . . . .

Total fertility rate births per woman (1997) 1.9

Maternal mortality ratio per 100,000 live births

(1990-97) . . . . .21[b]

Safe water % of population with access (1995) 97

Sanitation % of population with access (1995) . . . .

Consumption of iodized salt % of households

(1992-98)[a] . . . .

Smoking prevalence

  Male % of adults (1985-95)[a] . . . .

  Female % of adults (1985-95)[a] . . . .

Tuberculosis incidence per 100,000 people

(1997) 10

Adult HIV prevalence % of population ages

15-49 (1997) . . . .

Infants and Malnutrition (5)

Under-5 mortality rate (1997) . . . . .NA

% of infants with low birthweight (1990-97) . . . . . .NA

Births attended by skilled health staff % of total[a] . . .99

% fully immunized (1995-97)

  TB . . . . .NA

  DPT . . . . .NA

  Polio . . . . .NA

  Measles . . . . .NA

Prevalence of child malnutrition under age 5

(1992-97)[b] . . . . .NA

Ethnic Division (6)

Hispanic.

Religions (7)

Roman Catholic 85%

Protestant denominations and other 15%

Languages (8)

Spanish, English.

EDUCATION

Public Education Expenditures (9)

Public expenditure on education (% of GNP)

  1980 . . . .

  1996 . . . .

Expenditure per student

  Primary % of GNP per capita

    1980 . . . .

    1996 . . . .

  Secondary % of GNP per capita

    1980 . . . .

    1996 . . . .

  Tertiary % of GNP per capita

    1980 . . . .

    1996 . . . .

Expenditure on teaching materials

  Primary % of total for level (1996) . . . .

  Secondary % of total for level (1996) . . . .

Primary pupil-teacher ratio per teacher (1996) . . . .

Duration of primary education years (1995) 8

Educational Attainment (10)

Age group (1990)[26] . . . . .25+

Total population 1,952,297

Highest level attained (%)

  No schooling 4.6

  First level

    Not completed .31.0

    Completed . . . . .NA

  Entered second level

    S-1 . . . . .35.9

    S-2 . . . . .NA

  Postsecondary 28.7

GOVERNMENT & LAW

Political Parties (12)

House of Representatives	No. of seats
New Progressive Party (PNP)	37
Popular Democratic Party (PPD)	16
Puerto Rican Independence Party (PIP)	1

Government Budget (13B)

Revenues . . . .$5.1 billion

Expenditures . . . .$5.1 billion

  Capital expenditures . . . . .NA

Data for FY94/95. NA stands for not available.

Military Affairs (14A)

Defense is the responsibility of the US.

Crime (15)

Crime rate (for 1997)

Crimes reported 60,000

Total persons convicted . . . . .NA

Crimes per 100,000 population . . . . .NA

Persons responsible for offenses

Total number of suspects . . . . .NA

Total number of female suspects . . . . .NA

Total number of juvenile suspects . . . . .NA

LABOR FORCE

Labor Force (16)

Total (million) 1.3

Government 19%

Manufacturing 13%

Trade 17%

Construction 5%

Other 32%

Unemployed 14%

Data for 1996. Percent distribution for 1996.

Unemployment Rate (17)

13% (FY96/97 est.)

PRODUCTION SECTOR

Electric Energy (18)

Capacity . . . . .4.465 million kW (1995)

Production . . . . .17.34 billion kWh (1995)

Consumption per capita . . . . .4,548 kWh (1995)

Transportation (19)

Highways:

total: 14,400 km

paved: 14,400 km

unpaved: 0 km (1996 est.)

Merchant marine: none

Airports: 30 (1997 est.)

Airports—with paved runways:

total: 21

over 3,047 m: 3

1,524 to 2,437 m: 3

914 to 1,523 m: 9

under 914 m: 6 (1997 est.)

Airports—with unpaved runways:

total: 9

914 to 1,523 m: 2

under 914 m: 7 (1997 est.)

Top Agricultural Products (20)

Livestock products, chickens; sugarcane, coffee, pineapples, plantains, bananas.

MANUFACTURING SECTOR

GDP & Manufacturing Summary (21)

Detailed value added figures are listed by both International Standard Industry Code (ISIC) and product title.

	1980	1985	1990	1994
GDP: $-1990 mil.)[1]	21,294	24,575	30,604	34,511
Per capita ($-1990)[1]	6,642	7,301	8,667	9,466
Manufacturing share (%) (current prices)[1]	37.2	39.2	39.5	*39.0*
Manufacturing				
Value added ($-1990 mil.)[1]	9,068	10,255	12,126	*13,335*
Industrial production index	100	113	134	*147*
Value added ($ mil.)	*5,910*	7,968	12,126	16,309
Gross output ($ mil.)	*24,225*	*27,379*	29,777	23,657
Employment (000)	155	149	162	149
Profitability (% of gross output)				
Intermediate input (%)	*76*	*71*	59	31
Wages and salaries inc. supplements (%)	*6*	*7*	*10*	*14*
Gross operating surplus	*19*	*22*	*31*	*55*
Productivity ($)				
Gross output per worker	*156,636*	*184,027*	*184,210*	*158,631*
Value added per worker	*38,213*	*53,554*	*75,013*	*109,359*
Average wage (inc. supplements)	*8,875*	13,637	*18,666*	*23,088*
Value added ($ mil.)				
311/2 Food products	*401*	*485*	*673*	*694*
313 Beverages	*429*	714	1,117	1,894
314 Tobacco products	*128*	*143*	*171*	*192*
321 Textiles	*31*	*34*	*42*	*47*
322 Wearing apparel	*394*	437	486	524
323 Leather and fur products	*24*	*27*	*26*	*30*
324 Footwear	*48*	*61*	*88*	*143*
331 Wood and wood products	*7*	*7*	*8*	*9*
332 Furniture and fixtures	*34*	*37*	*51*	*58*
341 Paper and paper products	*39*	*56*	*66*	*78*

MANUFACTURING SECTOR

GDP & Manufacturing Summary (21)

	1980	1985	1990	1994
342 Printing and publishing	56	86	164	190
351 Industrial chemicals	56	58	39	35
352 Other chemical products	1,791	2,849	5,334	8,436
353 Petroleum refineries	63	84	117	97
354 Miscellaneous petroleum and coal products	80	81	88	84
355 Rubber products	21	31	43	64
356 Plastic products	42	82	120	180
361 Pottery, china and earthenware	18	21	33	36
362 Glass and glass products	25	28	44	48
369 Other non-metal mineral products	57	65	101	111
371 Iron and steel	3	10	17	13
372 Non-ferrous metals	6	21	38	30
381 Metal products	82	93	116	112
382 Non-electrical machinery	529	502	668	456
383 Electrical machinery	1,013	1,246	1,409	1,598
384 Transport equipment	23	29	68	50
385 Professional and scientific equipment	420	582	889	1,000
390 Other manufacturing industries	89	98	113	99

FINANCE, ECONOMICS, & TRADE

Economic Indicators (22)

National product: GDP—purchasing power parity—$32.9 billion (1997 est.)

National product real growth rate: 3% (1997 est.)

National product per capita: $8,600 (1997 est.)

Inflation rate—consumer price index: 5.5% (1997 est.)

Exchange Rates (24)

Exchange rates: US currency is used

Top Import Origins (25)

$19.1 billion (c.i.f. 1996) Data are for 1995 est.

Origins	%
United States	.62

Top Export Destinations (26)

$22.9 billion (f.o.b. 1996) Data are for 1995 est.

Destinations	%
United States	.88

Economic Aid (27)

None.

Import Export Commodities (28)

Import Commodities	Export Commodities
Chemicals	Pharmaceuticals
Clothing	Electronics
Food	Apparel
Fish	Canned tuna
Petroleum products	Rum
	Beverage concentrates
	Medical equipment

QATAR

State of Qatar
Dawlat Qatar

CAPITAL: Doha (Ad-Dawhah).

FLAG: Maroon with white serrated border at the hoist.

ANTHEM: *Qatar National Anthem.*

MONETARY UNIT: The Qatar riyal (QR) of 100 dirhams was introduced on 13 May 1973. There are coins of 1, 5, 10, 25, and 50 dirhams, and notes of 1, 5, 10, 50, 100, and 500 riyals. QR1 = $0.2747 (or $1 = QR3.64).

WEIGHTS AND MEASURES: The metric system is the legal standard, although some British measures are still in use.

HOLIDAYS: Emir's Succession Day, 22 February; Independence Day, 3 September. Muslim religious holidays include 'Id al-Fitr, 'Id al-'Adha', and Milad an-Nabi.

TIME: 3 PM = noon GMT.

LOCATION AND SIZE: The State of Qatar, a peninsula projecting northward into the Persian Gulf, has an area of 11,000 square kilometers (4,247 square miles), slightly smaller than the state of Connecticut. Qatar also includes a number of islands.

Qatar's capital city, Doha, is located on the Persian Gulf coast.

CLIMATE: Qatar's summer is extremely hot. Mean temperatures in June are 42°C (108°F), dropping to 15°C (59°F) in winter. Rainfall is minimal.

INTRODUCTORY SURVEY

RECENT HISTORY

At the outbreak of World War I (1914–18) Qatar established its independence. In 1916 it signed a treaty with the United Kingdom providing for British protection in exchange for a central role for the United Kingdom in Qatar's foreign affairs.

High-quality oil was discovered at Dukhan in 1940, but full-scale use of the discovery did not begin until 1949.

In January 1968, the United Kingdom announced its intention to withdraw its forces from the Persian Gulf states by the end of 1971. On 3 September 1971, the independent State of Qatar was declared. A new treaty of friendship and cooperation was signed with the United Kingdom, and Qatar was soon admitted to membership in the 20-member Arab League (also known as the League of Arab States) and the United Nations.

On 22 February 1972, Sheikh Khalifa bin Hamad al-Thani seized power in a peaceful coup, deposing his cousin, Sheikh Ahmad. Sheikh Khalifa pursued a vigorous program of economic and social reforms, including the transfer of royal income to the state.

Qatar's boundary disputes with Bahrain disrupted relations between the two countries in the mid-1980s. In December 1992, a minor dispute with Saudi Arabia was resolved with a boundary agreement.

In February 1995, Sheikh Hamad seized power from his father, Sheikh Khalifa. Sheikh Khalifa had put government revenues in his own bank accounts and paid for government services out of those funds. When Sheikh Hamad took over the government, his father froze the bank accounts, which disabled Qatar's treasury.

In 1996, Sheikh Khalifa set up a government in exile in nearby United Arab Emirates. The hostile transfer of power has led to problems among the members of the Gulf Cooperation Council. Budget problems from the lost revenue have caused Sheikh

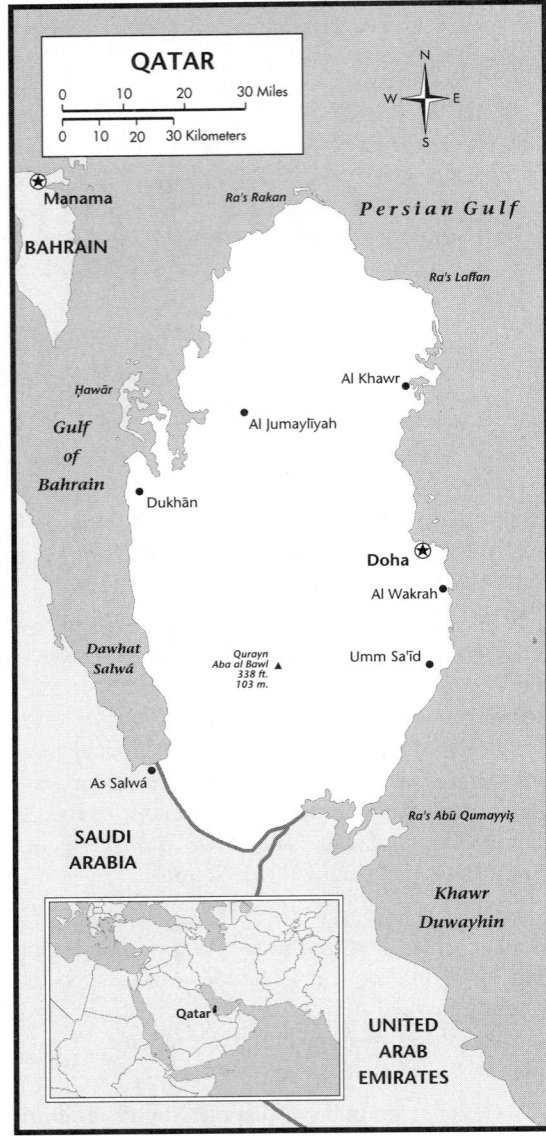

Judiciary

The legal system is based on the Shari'ah (canonical Muslim law). The Basic Law of 1970, however, provided for the creation of an independent judiciary, including the Court of Appeal, which has final jurisdiction in civil and criminal matters; the Higher Criminal Court, which judges major criminal cases; the Lower Criminal Court; the Civil Court; and the Labor Court, which judges claims involving employees and their employers.

Political Parties

There are no organized political parties.

DEFENSE

The Qatar security force consists of 8,500 army, 1,800 naval, and 1,500 air force personnel. Defense spending may have been as high as $326 million in 1995.

ECONOMIC AFFAIRS

Until recent decades, the Qatar peninsula was an impoverished area with a scant living provided by pearl diving, fishing, and nomadic herding. In 1940, oil was discovered at Dūkhan, and since then it has dominated the Qatari economy. The recent discovery of a vast field of natural gas promises to add a new dimension to the economy. The economy performed sluggishly in the early 1990s but recovered somewhat by 1995 because of a surge in oil prices.

Public Finance

Revenues from oil and gas constitute about 90% of total government income. From 1986 to 1990, the government ran a deficit due to the drop in oil revenues from fallen prices. These deficits often have resulted in the procrastination of payments by the government, which creates a financial difficulty for many private companies. The U.S. Central Intelligence Agency estimates that in 1995, government revenues totaled approximately $2.5 billion and expenditures $3.5 billion. External debt totaled $1.5 billion.

Income

In 1997, Qatar's gross national product (GNP) was $11.2 billion at current prices, or about $16,700 per person. During 1985–95, the average annual decline of GNP per person was 2.6%.

Industry

In 1995, Qatar Iron and Steel Co. produced 614,000 tons of crude steel; Qatar Fertilizer Co. produced 653,900 tons of ammonia and 886,000

Hamad to cut government spending. However, the government will need to spend money in order to develop huge offshore natural gas reserves.

GOVERNMENT

Qatar is a monarchy ruled by an emir (ruler of an Islamic country). A Basic Law, including a bill of rights, provides for a 9-member executive Council of Ministers (cabinet) and a 30-member legislative Advisory Council. No electoral system has been instituted, and no provisions for voting have been established.

tons of urea; and Qatar National Cement Co. made 580,000 tons of cement. Qatar Petrochemical Co. produces ethylene, polyethylene, and sulfur.

Banking and Finance

Qatar's monetary and banking system is headed by the Qatar Monetary Agency, established in 1973. The Qatar National Bank handles most government business and some central bank functions. The Qatar Monetary Agency, a quasi-central bank, plays a large role in controlling and supervising the monetary sector.

There is no stock exchange. Shares in Qatari public companies are traded through banks.

Economic Development

Qatar follows a policy of diversifying and extending its industrial and commercial activities to reduce the current dependence on oil. Infrastructure, heavy and light industry, agriculture, and fishing have all been development targets. The Industrial Development Committee encourages investment and supervises industrial growth. The government also uses surplus oil revenues on the international money market to protect the purchasing power of those revenues. Qatar is currently preparing to launch some major/minor projects worth about $7 billion: LNG plant expansion of the present fertilizer and petrochemical plants, aluminum smelter, Al-Wusail power/water desalination plant, new Doha international airport, and upgrading and expanding the offshore oil fields.

Qatar has extended economic assistance to other Arab states, to other developing nations, and to Palestinian organizations.

SOCIAL WELFARE

The Ministry of Labor and Social Affairs provides help to orphans, widows, and other Qatari nationals in need of assistance. Both law and Islamic customs closely restrict the activities of Qatari women, who are largely limited to roles within the home. Non-Muslims may experience discrimination in employment and education.

Healthcare

In 1992, there was about 1 doctor for every 1,000 people. In 1991, 100% of the population had access to health care services. Life expectancy is 72 years.

Housing

A "popular housing" scheme provides dwellings through interest-free loans and repayment on easy terms. In 1993, 100% of the population had access to safe water.

EDUCATION

Adult illiteracy stands at about 21%. As of 1994, there were 169 schools with 5,853 teachers and 52,130 pupils at the primary level. Secondary level schools had 3,858 teachers and 37,635 pupils.

The leading higher educational institution is the University of Qatar. Enrollment in all higher level institutions in 1994 was 7,794 pupils with 637 teaching staff.

1999 KEY EVENTS TIMELINE

January

- Distinct differences in policies towards Iraq are exposed as Arab ministers attempt to organize a full summit.

- Saudi Arabia and Kuwait oppose the summit while Qatar and the United Arab Emierates (UAE) support it.

- Iraqi leader Sadam Hussein's inflammatory call for Arabs to topple their governments provokes the ministers of Saudi Arabia, Kuwait, Bahrain, Oman, Qatar and the United Arab Emirates.

March

- The United States agrees to establish a telephone hot line between Washington, D.C. and Qatar in order to share information on missile launches from Iran or Iraq.

- In a first for Qatar and the Gulf region, the country allows women to vote and run as candidates for election. The poll is monitored by outside observers from nine countries who declare it a fair election; the six women candidates running for a 29-member Municipality Council, however, are all defeated.

- The Arab League meets in Qatar to discuss the creation of a new free trade zone by the year 2007.

- Qatar opposes American and British air strikes against Iraq.

- Qatar's foreign minister, Sheikh Hamad bin Jassim al-Thani, suggests that U.S. attacks on Iraq's no-fly zone are inappropriate and designed to provoke the Iraqis; he requests that the attacks be stopped.

- The Organization of Oil Exporting Countries (OPEC), including Algeria, Indonesia, Iran, Kuwait, Libya, Nigeria, Qatar, Saudi Arabia, the United Arab Emirates, and Venezuela, agrees with non-OPEC members Mexico and Oman to cut oil production, increasing the price of crude oil in 1999. Iraq is the only OPEC country to disagree with the cut.

April

- Several years of negotiation lead to agreement on the final maps defining the border between Qatar and Saudi Arabia.
- Gulf Arabs send donations through local Islamic charities to Muslim Kosovars; Qatar, the UAE, and Kuwait send planes full of aid to the Kosovo refugees.
- Qatar reports that the malicious Chernobyl computer virus, a variant of the CIH virus timed to strike on the anniversary of the nuclear reactor disaster, spread in "epidemic" proportions.

May

- Qatar issues a $1,000 million Eurobond, tapping the international debt market; the bonds have a ten year maturity.

June

- Qatar's satellite news channel's bureau in Kuwait, Al Jazeera, is closed by Kuwait when it broadcasts an Iraqi caller, living in Norway, insulting the Kuwaiti emir.
- The emir of Qatar, Sheikh Hamad al-Thani, acts as a liaison for Saudi Arabia's King Fahd and U.A.E. Foreign Minister Sheikh Hamdan al-Nayahan, helping to settle a disagreement over relations with Iran.
- Emir Sheikh Hamad bin Khalifa al-Thani forms a 32-member committee charged with drawing up a permanent constitution under which Qatar will have an elected parliament.
- The Israeli trade mission in Qatar is evicted.
- Qatar's satellite television station, Al Jezeera, breaks a long-standing taboo by criticizing the traditional state funding that continues to be extended to 3,000 members of the ruling al-Thani family despite the nation's economic recession, government subsidy cutbacks, and unemployment increases.

- Ras Liquefied Natural Gas Company (RasGas) ships its first shipment of 125,000 cubic meters to U.S.-owned CMS Energy in Louisiana.

July

- After three years on the run Sheikh Hamad bin Jassem bin Hamad al-Thani, a former cabinet minister, ex-police chief, and member of the Qatari royal family, is arrested and accused of masterminding a 1996 failed coup attempt.
- The death of King Hassan II of Morocco is marked by three days of official mourning.

August

- The emir of Qatar visits Gaza, becoming the first Gulf leader to visit Palestinian territory.
- Because of Qatar's relations with Israel, the Qatari emir's appearance before the Lebanese parliament is boycotted by nine Lebanese Hezbollah deputies.
- The yacht Constellation, belonging to Qatar's ruling family, defies a court order and leaves Palma, Spain, after allegedly colliding with a ferry and causing over $100,000 in damage.
- The world youth handball championship is held in Qatar despite the withdrawal of the Saudi, Bahraini, and Kuwaiti teams.
- A Qatari Disney franchise owner threatens to close his store over an Arab confrontation with Disney. The controversy stems from Jerusalem being presented as the capital of Israel in an upcoming exhibit; Arab satellite television providers are prepared to discontinue Disney's Arab-dubbed channel over the matter.
- The Ninth Arab Games are held, and the Qatari weight-lifting team is disqualified because four of its members are found to be Bulgarian-born.

September

- Accused of masterminding the foiled coup attempt against the present emir, royal family member Sheikh Hamad bin Jassem bin Hamad al-Thani pleads not guilty.

October

- Qatar's Ras Laffian Liquefied Natural Gas Company (RasGas) takes a 26 percent stake in two LNG projects in India.

- The trial of 120 people accused in the 1996 failed coup attempt involving a cousin of the emir and former military and police officials comes to end; a mass verdict is expected in February.

- Qatar maintains its commitment to OPEC cuts.

- OPEC President Abullah al-Attiyah of Qatar expects that OPEC will not raise production in March 2000 because excess stockpiles are not shrinking fast enough to warrant increasing output.

- Qatar and Jordan hold economic cooperation talks, agreeing to consider a proposal to establish a free trade zone and expand bilateral trade.

- The United Kingdom's *Business Traveler* magazine rates Qatar Airways' economy class service among the top three surveyed.

December

- Qatar and Bahrain establish new relations, agreeing to exchange ambassadors and establishing a special committee charged with resolving the dispute over territories that is currently the subject of a case before the International Court of Justice in the Hague, Netherlands. The case will be withdrawn if the countries can negotiate a settlement on their own.

- Qatar approves the construction of a Catholic Church, the first Christian church to be built in the country.

ANALYSIS OF EVENTS: 1999

BUSINESS AND THE ECONOMY

Qatar, subject to the caprices of international oil markets, sees its oil revenues bounce back from an earlier low. Proven oil reserves in the country ensure continued output at current levels for twenty-three years. Qatar has the third largest natural gas reserves in the world. The Liquefied Natural Gas (LNG) company's earnings are expected to increase as Qatar supplies more natural gas to the Asian market. The production and exportation of natural gas are becoming an increasingly important aspect of the economy.

Qatar's budget is based on an oil price of $10 a barrel. If oil prices remain around $15 a barrel until the end of 1999 Qatar may be able to balance its budget. The country supports the Organization of Oil Exporting Countries (OPEC) and that organization's efforts to increase oil prices by cutting back crude oil production by 4.3 million barrels per day between March 1999 to March 2000. This strategy is intended to more than double the price per barrel from $10 at the end of 1998 to $24 per barrel by September 1999.

Qatar's industrialization program has increased its debt service obligations. In 1998 hydrocarbon revenues dropped by 25%. Business and consumer confidence fell. Revenues for 1999 may succeed in returning economic growth to 1997 levels. To improve and protect its economy Qatar is practicing fiscal discipline and creating low-cost efficiencies. In addition plans are in the works to implement a foreign investment code in agriculture, industry, tourism, and education ventures. Prior to this year Qataris have received water and electricity free of charge, but the government is now developing a tariff structure with a monthly ceiling.

GOVERNMENT AND POLITICS

Qatar's government is a traditional monarchy. The present ruler, Emir Hamad bin Khalifa al-Thani, is encouraging political openness. The emir formed a constitutional committee charged with drawing up a permanent constitution under which Qatar would have an elected parliament. The political openness also extended to the media. Qatar's satellite news channel, Al Jazeera, broke a previous taboo with an open discussion and criticism of the state funding of the ruling family. In addition, women were allowed to vote and to run for office in municipal elections for the first time in the country's history, a significant advancement in the traditional Muslim society.

In 1995 Emir Hamad ousted his father, Emir Khalifa bin Hamad al-Thani, in a bloodless coup. This was followed by another coup attempt in 1996, which failed. The attempt was intended to restore his father to power. In July the emir's cousin, Sheikh Hamad bin Jassem bin Hamid al-Thani, was arrested and accused of masterminding the plot.

Qatar's foreign policy has often been at odds with public opinion in the Persian Gulf, especially on issues relating to Israel, Iran, and Iraq. In 1999 the other member nations of the Gulf Cooperation Council (GCC) have become less critical and more accepting of Qatar's positions.

CULTURE AND SOCIETY

The presence of foreign troops during the 1991 Persian Gulf War and the communications revolution, with its access to Western television, movies, and other media, have become forces for societal change in the region. The Qatari government and society are responding in many ways. Trends in intellectual freedom are epitomized by nude artwork in the classroom, although Islam discourages representations of the human body, and the ability of Qatar's satellite news channel, Al Jazeera, to publicly criticize the country's leadership. Signs of government relaxation can be seen in the opening of municipal elections to female candidates and the hiring of female employees in the research and Internet departments of the Foreign Ministry.

The major ecological issue for Qatar is the country's limited natural fresh water resources and its increasing dependence on large-scale desalination facilities.

DIRECTORY

CENTRAL GOVERNMENT

Head of State

Amir
Hamad bin Khalifa al-Thani

Prime Minister
Abdallah bin Khalifa al-Thani

Ministers

Minister of Defense
Hamad bin Khalifa al Thani, Ministry of Defense, P.O. Box 37, Doha, Qatar
PHONE: +974 404111

Minister of the Interior
Abdallah bin Khalifa al Thani, Ministry of the Interior, P.O. Box 2433, Doha, Qatar
PHONE: +974 330000

Minister of Public Health
Hajar bin Ahmad al-Hajar, Ministry of Public Health, P.O. Box 42, Doha, Qatar
PHONE: +974 441555

Minister of Finance, Economy and Commerce
Yusif Husayh al-Kamal, Ministry of Finance, Economy and Commerce, P.O. Box 83, Doha, Qatar
PHONE: +974 461444

Minister of Justice
Hasan bin Abdallah al-Ghanim, Ministry of Justice, P.O. Box 4796, Doha, Qatar
PHONE: +974 427444

Minister of Foreign Affairs
Ahmad Abdallah al-Mahmud, Ministry of Foreign Affairs, P.O. Box 250, Doha, Qatar
PHONE: +974 415000

Minister of Endowments and Islamic Affairs
Ahmad Abdallah al-Marri, Ministry of Endowments and Islamic Affairs, P.O. Box 232, Doha, Qatar
PHONE: +974 452222

Minister of Education
Muhammad Abd al-Rahim al-Kafud, Ministry of Education, P.O. Box 80, Doha, Qatar
PHONE: +974 413444

Minister of Electricity and Water
Abdallah bin Hamad al-Altiyah, Ministry of Electricity and Water, P.O. Box 41, Doha, Qatar
PHONE: +974 326622

DIPLOMATIC REPRESENTATION

Embassies in Qatar

Italy
Ali bin Abi Talib Street 41, P.O. Box 4188, Doha, Qatar
PHONE: +974 436842
FAX: +974 446466

United Kingdom
P.O. Box 3, Doha, Qatar
PHONE: +974 421991
FAX: +974 438692

JUDICIAL SYSTEM

Court of Appeal

FURTHER READING

Books

Abu Saud, Abeer. *Qatari Women Past and Present.* Essex, England: Longman Group Limited, 1984.

Anscombe, Frederick F. *The Ottoman Gulf: The Creation of Kuwait, Saudi Arabia, and Qatar.* New York: Columbia Press, 1997.

Crystal, Jill. *Oil and Politics in the Gulf: Rulers and Merchants in Kuwait and Qatar.* New York: Cambridge University Press, 1995.

di Cardi, Beatrice, ed. *British Archaeological Expedition in Qatar (1973–1974)*. New York: Oxford University Press, 1978.

El Mallakh, Ragaei. *Qatar, Energy and Development*. London: Croom Helm, 1985.

Graham, Helga. *Arabian Time Machine: Self-Portrait of an Oil State*. New York: Holmes and Meier Publishers, Inc., 1978.

Klaus, Ferdinand. *Bedouins of Qatar*. London: Thames and Hudson, 1993.

Misnad, Sheikha. *The development of modern education in the Gulf*. London: Ithaca Press, 1985.

Nafi, Zuhair Ahmen. *Economic and Social Development in Qatar*. Dover, NH: F. Pinter, 1983.

Rickman, Maureen. *Qatar*. New York: Chelsea House Publishers, 1987.

Vine, Peter and Paula Casey. *The Heritage of Qatar*. London: IMMEL Publishing Limited, 1992.

Zahlan, Rosemarie Said. *The Creation of Qatar*. New York: Harper and Row Publishers, Inc., 1979.

Internet

Gulf Times. Available Online @ http://www.gulf-times.com/ (November 18, 1999).

Qatar On-Line. Available Online @ http://www.qatar-online.com/index-e.htm#Q (November 18, 1999).

QATAR:
STATISTICAL DATA

For sources and notes see "Sources of Statistics" in the front of each volume.

GEOGRAPHY

Geography (1)
Area:

Total: 11,437 sq km.

Land: 11,437 sq km.

Water: 0 sq km.

Area—comparative: slightly smaller than Connecticut.

Land boundaries:

Total: 60 km.

Border countries: Saudi Arabia 60 km.

Coastline: 563 km.

Climate: desert; hot, dry; humid and sultry in summer.

Terrain: mostly flat and barren desert covered with loose sand and gravel.

Natural resources: petroleum, natural gas, fish.

Land use:

Arable land: 1%

Permanent crops: NA%

Permanent pastures: 5%

Forests and woodland: NA%

Other: 94% (1993 est.).

HUMAN FACTORS

Demographics (2A)

	1990	1995	1998	2000	2010	2020	2030	2040	2050
Population	482.2	615.2	697.1	749.5	990.5	1,159.9	1,247.5	1,305.2	1,347.9
Net migration rate (per 1,000 population)	NA	NA	NA	NA	NA	NA	NA	NA	NA
Births	NA	NA	NA	NA	NA	NA	NA	NA	NA
Deaths	NA	NA	NA	NA	NA	NA	NA	NA	NA
Life expectancy - males	68.7	70.4	71.4	72.0	74.6	76.5	77.9	78.8	79.5
Life expectancy - females	73.5	75.5	76.5	77.3	80.1	82.2	83.7	84.8	85.5
Birth rate (per 1,000)	22.9	18.1	17.0	16.6	16.8	15.2	13.9	13.6	12.9
Death rate (per 1,000)	3.6	3.5	3.5	3.6	4.4	6.0	8.3	9.9	10.0
Women of reproductive age (15-49 yrs.)	81.6	105.4	121.6	132.8	185.4	230.5	267.6	281.8	291.9
of which are currently married	NA	NA	NA	NA	NA	NA	NA	NA	NA
Fertility rate	4.4	3.7	3.5	3.3	2.8	2.4	2.2	2.1	2.0

Except as noted, values for vital statistics are in thousands; life expectancy is in years.

Infants and Malnutrition (5)

Under-5 mortality rate (1997) 20

% of infants with low birthweight (1990-97) . . . . . .NA

Births attended by skilled health staff % of total[a] . . .NA

% fully immunized (1995-97)

TB 99

DPT 92

Polio 92

Measles 87

Prevalence of child malnutrition under age 5
(1992-97)[b] . . . . .NA

Ethnic Division (6)

Arab 40%

Pakistani 18%

Indian 18%

Iranian 10%

Other 14%

Religions (7)

Muslim 95%

Languages (8)

Arabic (official), English commonly used as a second
language.

GOVERNMENT & LAW

Military Affairs (14B)

	1990	1991	1992	1993	1994	1995
Military expenditures						
Current dollars (mil.)	NA	934[e]	357[e]	330[e]	302[e]	330[e]
1995 constant dollars (mil.)	NA	1,032[e]	384[e]	346[e]	310[e]	330[e]
Armed forces (000)	11	11	8	8	10	10
Gross national product (GNP)						
Current dollars (mil.)	7,581	7,084	7,644	7,583	7,820	7,445
1995 constant dollars (mil.)	8,713	7,827	8,222	7,949	8,016	7,445
Central government expenditures (CGE)						
1995 constant dollars (mil.)	NA	3,536	3,680	3,766	NA	3,500
People (mil.)	.5	.5	.5	.5	.5	.5
Military expenditure as % of GNP	NA	13.2	4.7	4.3	3.9	4.4
Military expenditure as % of CGE	NA	29.2	10.4	9.2	NA	9.4
Military expenditure per capita (1995 $)	NA	2,196	789	687	597	617
Armed forces per 1,000 people (soldiers)	24.3	23.4	16.4	15.9	19.3	18.7
GNP per capita (1995 $)	19,270	16,660	16,880	15,790	15,450	13,940
Arms imports[6]						
Current dollars (mil.)	100	20	40	0	0	50
1995 constant dollars (mil.)	115	22	43	0	0	50
Arms exports[6]						
Current dollars (mil.)	0	0	0	10	130	0
1995 constant dollars (mil.)	0	0	0	10	133	0
Total imports[7]						
Current dollars (mil.)	1,695	1,720	2,015	1,893	1,927	NA
1995 constant dollars (mil.)	1,948	1,901	2,167	1,985	1,975	NA
Total exports[7]						
Current dollars (mil.)	3,291[e]	3,107	3,736	3,100	2,900[e]	NA
1995 constant dollars (mil.)	3,782[e]	3,433	4,019	3,250	2,973[e]	NA
Arms as percent of total imports[8]	5.9	1.2	2.0	0	0	NA
Arms as percent of total exports[8]	0	0	0	.3	4.5	NA

EDUCATION

Educational Attainment (10)

Age group (1986) . . . . .10+
Total population 211,485
Highest level attained (%)
No schooling[2] 53.5
First level
  Not completed 9.8
  Completed . . . . .NA
Entered second level
  S-1 . . . . .10.1
  S-2 . . . . .13.3
Postsecondary 13.3

Literacy Rates (11A)

In thousands and percent[1]	1990	1995	2000	2010
Illiterate population (15+ yrs.)	80	82	81	74
Literacy rate - total adult pop. (%)	77.2	79.4	81.6	86.0
Literacy rate - males (%)	77.7	79.2	80.8	84.1
Literacy rate - females (%)	75.7	79.9	83.5	89.5

GOVERNMENT & LAW

Political Parties (12)

The legislative branch is a unicameral Advisory Council (35 seats; members appointed by the amir). Note: the constitution calls for elections for part of this consultative body, but no elections have been held since 1970, when there were partial elections to the body. Council members have had their terms extended every four years since. There are no political parties.

Government Budget (13B)

Revenues . . . .$3.7 billion
Expenditures . . . .$4.5 billion
  Capital expenditures . . . .$700 million
Data for FY97/98 est.

Crime (15)

Crime rate (for 1997)
  Crimes reported 5,050
  Total persons convicted 4,400
  Crimes per 100,000 population 850
Persons responsible for offenses
  Total number of suspects 6,050
  Total number of female suspects 275
  Total number of juvenile suspects 100

LABOR FORCE

Labor Force (16)

Total 233,000. 83% of the population in the 15-64 age group is non-national (July 1997 est.). Data for 1993 est.

Unemployment Rate (17)

Rate not available.

PRODUCTION SECTOR

Electric Energy (18)

Capacity . . . . .1.303 million kW (1995)
Production . . . . .5.8 billion kWh (1995)
Consumption per capita . . . . .10,863 kWh (1995)

MANUFACTURING SECTOR

GDP & Manufacturing Summary (21)

	1980	1985	1990	1992	1993	1994
Gross Domestic Product						
Millions of 1990 dollars	7,767	6,285	7,360	7,655	7,755	7,716
Growth rate in percent	7.10	−3.91	7.85	5.60	1.30	−0.50
Per capita (in 1990 dollars)	33,919.1	17,556.4	15,176.2	14,807.4	14,659.7	14,289.2
Manufacturing Value Added						
Millions of 1990 dollars	459	693	948	928	*990*	*1,051*
Growth rate in percent	−12.51	3.64	7.86	6.41	*6.64*	*6.14*
Manufacturing share in percent of current prices	3.3	7.8	12.7	11.6	11.0	*11.2*

Transportation (19)

Highways:

total: 1,230 km

paved: 1,107 km

unpaved: 123 km (1996 est.)

Pipelines: crude oil 235 km; natural gas 400 km

Merchant marine:

total: 21 ships (1,000 GRT or over) totaling 618,447 GRT/1,031,135 DWT ships by type: combination ore/oil 2, container 3, cargo 11, oil tanker 5 (1997 est.)

Airports: 4 (1997 est.)

Airports—with paved runways:

total: 2

over 3,047 m: 2 (1997 est.)

Airports—with unpaved runways:

total: 2

914 to 1,523 m: 1

under 914 m: 1 (1997 est.)

Top Agricultural Products (20)

Fruits, vegetables; poultry, dairy products, beef; fish (all on small scale).

FINANCE, ECONOMICS, & TRADE

Economic Indicators (22)

National product: GDP—purchasing power parity—$11.2 billion (1997 est.)

National product real growth rate: 10% (1997 est.)

National product per capita: $16,700 (1997 est.)

Inflation rate—consumer price index: 2.5% (1996)

Exchange Rates (24)

Exchange rates: Qatari riyals (QR) per US$1—3.6400 riyals (fixed rate)

Top Import Origins (25)

$5 billion (f.o.b., 1997 est.) Data are for 1996.

Origins	%
Italy	14
United Kingdom	12
France	11
Japan	10
Germany	9

Top Export Destinations (26)

$5.8 billion (f.o.b., 1997 est.) Data are for 1996.

Destinations	%
Japan	55
Singapore	11
South Korea	6
Australia	3
UAE	3

Economic Aid (27)

$NA. NA stands for not available.

Import Export Commodities (28)

Import Commodities	Export Commodities
Machinery and equipment	Petroleum products 80%
Consumer goods	Fertilizers
Food	Steel
Chemicals	

RÉUNION

CAPITAL: Saint Denis.

FLAG: The flag of France is used.

ANTHEM: *La Marseillaise*.

MONETARY UNIT: 1 French Franc (F) = 100 centimes.

WEIGHTS AND MEASURES: The metric system is used.

HOLIDAYS: National Day, 14 July.

TIME: 4 PM = noon GMT.

LOCATION AND SIZE: Réunion, about 675 km (420 mi.) E of Madagascar in the Indian Ocean, is the largest island in the Mascarene Archipelago. Réunion lies between 20°52′ and 21°22′S and between 55°13′ and 55°50′E, is 55 km (34 mi.) long and 53 km (33 mi) wide, and has a coastline of 207 km (129 mi.). It has an area of 2,510 sq. km (969 sq. mi.).

CLIMATE: The mean annual temperature is 23°C (73°F) at sea level, but the climate, generally tropical, varies with orientation and altitude. The east coast receives almost daily precipitation, totaling some 350 cm (140 in.) annually, but on the north coast, annual rainfall is only about half that. Cyclones, which threaten from December to April, have devastated Réunion several times. Sea fauna is rich and varied.

INTRODUCTORY SURVEY

RECENT HISTORY

Portugese explorers who first visited Réunion in the early sixteenth century found the island uninhabited. By 1642 Réunion became a French colony when the French East India Company established a lay-over station for trade ships rounding the Cape of Good Hope destined for India. First coffee then sugar plantations worked by African slaves were established on the islands. Upon abolition of slavery in 1848, the plantations imported indentured laborers from India, East Africa, and Indochina. Réunion remained a colony until 1946 when it received full department status with the French government. In 1974 the status was further elevated to an Overseas Department. Even at the close of the twentieth century little local support exists for independence.

GOVERNMENT

The Department of Réunion, more commonly known as Réunion, is an Overseas Department of France operating under the 1958 French constitution. As French citizens, the Réunionese elect five deputies to the French National Assembly. Three representatives are also indirectly elected to the French Senate. Réunion is represented by one councillor on the French Economic and Social Council. The chief of state is the President of France who is represented in Réunionese government affairs by an appointed prefect. The island is administered by a forty-nine member unicameral General Council. Members of the General Council are directly elected to six-year terms by universal popular vote by all residents over eighteen years of age. A forty-five member Regional Council, established in 1974, coordinates economic and social development policies. Members are also elected by universal popular vote to six-year terms. Members of the two councils elect presidents of their respective bodies. The island is further subdivided into four *arrondissements*, twenty-four communes, and forty-seven cantons.

Judiciary

With a judicial system based on French law, the Réunion has three lower courts, two higher

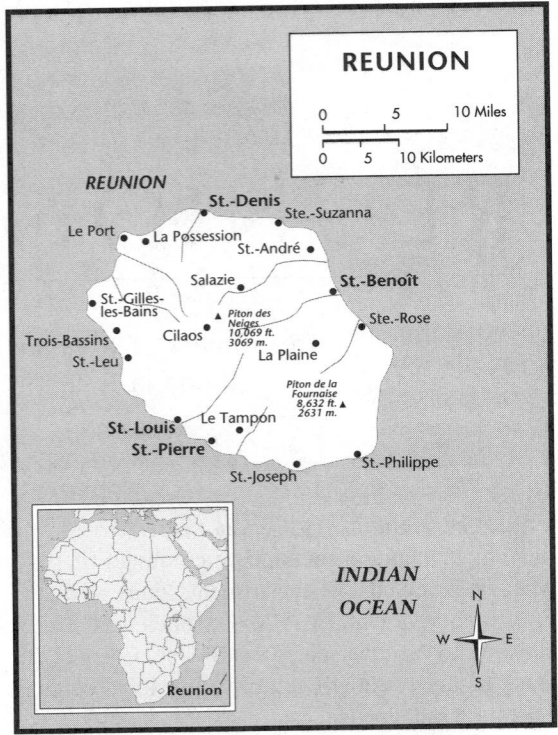

REUNION

0   5   10 Miles

0   5   10 Kilometers

REUNION

St.-Denis
Ste.-Suzanna
Le Port
La Possession
St.-André
Salazie
St.-Gilles-les-Bains
St.-Benoît
Piton des Neiges, 10,069 ft. 3069 m.
Cilaos
Ste.-Rose
Trois-Bassins
La Plaine
St.-Leu
Piton de la Fournaise 8,632 ft. 2631 m.
St.-Louis
Le Tampon
St.-Pierre
St.-Philippe
St.-Joseph

INDIAN OCEAN

N W E S

Reunion

courts, one appeals court, an administrative court, and a conciliation board.

Political Parties

Active political parties on the island include Rally for the Republic (RPR), Union for French Democracy (UDF), Communist Party of Réunion (PCR), France-Réunion Future (FRA), the Socialist Party (PS), Center of Social Democrats (CDS), Union for France (UPF), Free-DOM Movement, and the National Front (FN).

DEFENSE

France is responsible for defense and foreign affairs. Following French withdrawal from nearby Madagascar in 1973, headquarters for French military forces in the Indian Ocean was moved to Réunion. Approximately 4,000 active French troops were stationed on Réunion and the nearby island of Mayotte in 1998. French forces include Army, Navy, Air Force, and Gendarmerie.

ECONOMIC AFFAIRS

Agriculture is a key sector of the economy. For over a century sugar cane has been the principal crop. The sugar cane is milled into sugar at several large milling facilities located on a dozen big estates. In some years sugar constitutes 85% of ex-

ports. Sugar products such as rum and molasses constitutes much of the remaining exports. Exports in 1994 were estimated at US $171.8 million and imports at US $2.4 billion. Most of Réunion's trade is with France. Other crops include vanilla bean, tobacco, geraniums for perfume, and assorted fruits and vegetables.

In 1992 services including transport, trade, finance, and communication contributed 76% of the GDP and employed almost 72% of the workforce. Réunion maintains an exclusive economic zone of two hundred nautical miles.

Réunion is represented by France in the Indian Ocean Commission and, as an integral part of France, is a member of the European Union. In 1992 the Regional Council adopted an economic development program for the island which included establishment of an export free zone and emphasis on growth in tourism. However, a limited land base of less than a thousand square miles, no natural harbors, and frequent occurrence of tropical cyclones hampers economic development. Charges of corruption among Réunion political and business leaders through the 1990s placed a cloud over economic development initiatives. Réunion had the highest unemployment in 1997 of all the departments of France. Additionally, socioeconomic tensions are spurred by a persistent substantial gap between the island's white and Indian communities and indigenous groups.

Public Finance

Réunion is largely dependent on annual French subsidies. Revenues in 1997 were estimated at 7.1 billion francs and expenditures were 14.7 billion francs.

Income

The estimated gross domestic product (GDP) for 1998 was estimated at US $3.4 billion at an annual real growth rate of 3.8%. The per capita GDP was estimated at US $4,800.

Industry

Manufacturing, power generation, and construction constitute 20% of the GDP. In the manufacturing sector key industries include the processing of sugar and production of rum. Other industries include tourism, cigarette production, handicrafts, and extraction of flower oil for perfume. The tourist industry brought over 370,000 visitors in 1997. Réunion had 49 hotels and over 1,800 rooms in that year.

Banking and Finance

The Institut d'émission de Départements d'Outre-Mer is the central bank of Réunion having the right to issue bank notes. The development bank is Banque Populaire Fédérale de Développement. Commercial banks include Banque Française Commerciale Ocean Indien, Banque Nationale de Paris Intercontinentale, Banque de la Réunion, and Caisse Régionale de Crédit Agricole Mutuel de la Réunion.

SOCIAL WELFARE

High unemployment is chronic in Réunion. Another long-term issue is inequality in social benefits between metropolitan France and France's departments including Réunion. Deteriorating economic conditions in the early 1990s led to rioting on Réunion. In 1996 greater equality in social services between France's Overseas Departments and metropolitan France began to emerge.

Healthcare

In 1997 Réunion had two general hospitals, four local hospitals, a psychiatric care facility, and nine private surgical clinics for a total of 2,800 hospital beds. Life expectancy for the total population was estimated in 1999 to be 75.7 years, 72.7 years for males and 78.9 years for females.

EDUCATION

Education in Réunion is modeled after French system. Attendance is compulsory for ten years between ages six and sixteen. In 1998 Réunion had 175 pre-primary schools, 351 primary schools, 111 secondary schools. A university provides higher education in law, politics, economics, and French literature and language. A teacher-training college is also available. In 1982 the literacy rate for those over fifteen years of age was 79%.

1999 KEY EVENTS TIMELINE

July

- On July 19, 1999, the volcano Piton de la Fournaise erupts on the island.

ANALYSIS OF EVENTS: 1999

BUSINESS AND THE ECONOMY

Réunion relies on trade with France, and its chief industry is the production of sugarcane. Tourism is also a big business, as people come to the island's magnificent beaches to surf, scuba dive, and snorkel. Bird watching is also attracting many visitors to the island.

GOVERNMENT AND POLITICS

Réunion remains an overseas territory of France and takes its direction from the current French President Jacques Chirac. The local governing body is headed by Jean-Luc Poudroux, who has served as president of the General Council since 1994. The president of the Regional Council is Margarite Sudre, who is also the head of the political party called the Freedom Movement. The island is represented in the French government by Robert Pommies, in office since 1996.

CULTURE AND SOCIETY

Réunion's population is overwhelmingly of mixed descent. Many in the population have Asian or French ancestry, or are descendants of former slaves. Most citizens are Roman Catholic in religious belief.

DIRECTORY

CENTRAL GOVERNMENT

Head of State

President of France
Jacques Chirac

President of the General Council
Jean-Luc Poudroux, Hotel du Departement, 2, rue Source, 97488 Saint-Denis Cedex, Réunion
PHONE: +262 903030
FAX: +262 903999

Prefect
Robert Pommies, Office of the Prefecture, Avenue Victoire, 97405 Saint-Denis Cedex, Réunion
PHONE: +262 407777
FAX: +262 417374

Ministers

Minister of Tourism
Ministry of Tourism, 4, place du 20 Decembre 1948, Résidence Vétyver BP 1119, 97482 Saint-Denis Cedex, Réunion
PHONE: +262 210041
FAX: +262 418441

Minister of Culture
Ministry of Culture, 31, rue Amiral Lacaze, BP 224, 97400 Saint-Denis, Réunion
PHONE: +262 219171
FAX: +262 416193

Minister of Agriculture
Ministry of Agriculture, BP 134, 24, rue de la Source, 97464 Saint-Denis Cedex, Réunion
PHONE: +262 212588
FAX: +262 210617

Minister of Foreign Affairs
Ministry of Foreign Affairs, 6-10, quai de Seine, 93200 Saint-Denis, Réunion

Minister of Employment
Ministry of Employment, 10, rue Champ Fleury, 97490 Sainte-Clotilde, Réunion
PHONE: +262 902440
FAX: +262 417383

Minister of Youth and Sports
Ministry of Youth and Sports, BP 297, 14, allé des Saphirs, 97487 Saint-Denis Cedex, Réunion
PHONE: +262 901616
FAX: +262 213864

Minister of Social Affairs
Ministry of Social Affairs, BP 199, 28 bis, Avenue Georges Brassens, 97400 Saint-Denis, Réunion
PHONE: +262 486060
FAX: +262 486008

Minister of Work and Employment
Ministry of Work and Employment, 24, rue Maréchal Leclerc, 97488 Saint-Denis Cedex, Réunion
PHONE: +262 486600
FAX: +262 486666

Minister of Trade
Ministry of Trade, 42, rue Jean Cocteau, 97490 Sainte-Clotilde, Réunion
PHONE: +262 210435
FAX: +262 216833

Minister of Commerce and Industry
Ministry of Commerce and Industry, 5 bis, rue de Paris, BP 120, 97463 Saint-Denis Cedex, Réunion
PHONE: +262 942000
FAX: +262 942290

POLITICAL ORGANIZATIONS
Rally for the Republic (RPR)
NAME: Alain Defaud

Unions for French Democracy (UDF)
NAME: Gilbert Gerard

Socialist Party (PS)
NAME: Jean-Claude Fruteau

Freedom Movement
NAME: Marguerite Sudre

Social Democrats (CDS)
France-Réunion Future (FRF)
NAME: Andre Thien ah Koon

JUDICIAL SYSTEM
Court of Appeals

FURTHER READING
Internet
Arapaho Services Internet. Available Online @ http://www.outremer.com (November 12, 1999).

Multimania, Le site de communauté. Available Online @ http://www.multimania.fr/general/pub.perso.html (November 12, 1999).

Welcome to Réunion. Available Online @ http://www.runisland.com/index1.html (November 12, 1999).

RÉUNION: STATISTICAL DATA

For sources and notes see "Sources of Statistics" in the front of each volume.

GEOGRAPHY

Geography (1)

Area:

Total: 2,510 sq km.

Land: 2,500 sq km.

Water: 10 sq km.

Area—comparative: slightly smaller than Rhode Island.

Land boundaries: 0 km.

Coastline: 201 km.

Climate: tropical, but temperature moderates with elevation; cool and dry from May to November, hot and rainy from November to April.

Terrain: mostly rugged and mountainous; fertile lowlands along coast.

Natural resources: fish, arable land.

Land use:

Arable land: 17%

Permanent crops: 2%

Permanent pastures: 5%

Forests and woodland: 35%

Other: 41% (1993 est.).

HUMAN FACTORS

Ethnic Division (6)

French, African, Malagasy, Chinese, Pakistani, Indian.

Religions (7)

Roman Catholic 94%; Hindu, Islam, Buddhist.

Languages (8)

French (official), Creole widely used.

Demographics (2A)

	1990	1995	1998	2000	2010	2020	2030	2040	2050
Population	600.3	666.1	705.1	730.2	847.0	961.8	1,066.9	1,148.7	1,204.5
Net migration rate (per 1,000 population)	NA	NA	NA	NA	NA	NA	NA	NA	NA
Births	NA	NA	NA	NA	NA	NA	NA	NA	NA
Deaths	NA	NA	NA	NA	NA	NA	NA	NA	NA
Life expectancy - males	69.5	71.4	72.4	73.0	75.6	77.4	78.6	79.5	80.0
Life expectancy - females	75.8	77.7	78.6	79.3	81.8	83.5	84.7	85.5	86.0
Birth rate (per 1,000)	26.7	24.6	22.8	21.5	18.2	16.9	14.8	13.3	12.5
Death rate (per 1,000)	5.2	4.8	4.7	4.6	4.7	5.1	5.9	7.3	9.0
Women of reproductive age (15-49 yrs.)	162.9	177.6	185.8	191.7	226.4	238.8	254.6	267.9	266.4
of which are currently married	160.8	NA	NA	NA	NA	NA	NA	NA	NA
Fertility rate	2.9	2.8	2.7	2.6	2.4	2.2	2.1	2.0	2.0

Except as noted, values for vital statistics are in thousands; life expectancy is in years.

GOVERNMENT & LAW

Political Parties (12)

General Council	No. of seats
Communist Party of Reunion (PCR)	12
Socialist Party (PS)	12
Union for French Democracy (UDF)	11
Rally for the Republic (RPR)	5
Others	7

Government Budget (13B)

Revenues ....$856.7 million
Expenditures ....$2.2437 billion
  Capital expenditures ....NA

Data for 1993. NA stands for not available.

Military Affairs (14A)

Military age ....18 years of age
Availability of manpower
  Males age 15-49 (1998 est.) 182,620
Fit for military service
  Males (1998 est.) 93,572
Reaching military age annually
  Males (1998 est.) 5,780

Defense is the responsibility of France.

LABOR FORCE

Labor Force (16)

Total 242,169
Agriculture 8%

Industry 19%
Services 73%

Data for 1993. Percent distribution for 1990.

Unemployment Rate (17)

35% (1994)

PRODUCTION SECTOR

Electric Energy (18)

Capacity ....299,000 kW (1995)
Production ....1.105 billion kWh (1995)
Consumption per capita ....1,659 kWh (1995)

Transportation (19)

Highways:
total: 2,784 km
paved: 2,187 km
unpaved: 597 km (1987 est.)
Merchant marine: none
Airports: 2 (1997 est.)
Airports—with paved runways:
total: 2
2,438 to 3,047 m: 1
914 to 1,523 m: 1 (1997 est.)

Top Agricultural Products (20)

Sugarcane, vanilla, tobacco, tropical fruits, vegetables, corn.

MANUFACTURING SECTOR

GDP & Manufacturing Summary (21)

	1980	1985	1990	1992	1993	1994
Gross Domestic Product						
Millions of 1990 dollars	3,296	4,048	4,959	5,328	5,506	5,775
Growth rate in percent	4.20	3.49	4.00	3.80	3.34	4.89
Per capita (in 1990 dollars)	6,513.0	7,359.4	8,209.7	8,537.9	8,683.9	8,967.3
Manufacturing Value Added						
Millions of 1990 dollars	190	236	300	289	300	313
Growth rate in percent	13.91	11.41	12.79	3.96	3.81	4.32
Manufacturing share in percent of current prices	10.2	8.8	NA	NA	NA	NA

FINANCE, ECONOMICS, & TRADE

Economic Indicators (22)

National product: GDP—purchasing power parity—$3 billion (1996 est.)

National product real growth rate: 4% (1996 est.)

National product per capita: $4,300 (1996 est.)

Inflation rate—consumer price index: NA%

Exchange Rates (24)

Exchange rates:

French francs (F) per US$1

January 1998	.6.0836
1997	.5.8367
1996	.5.1155
1995	.4.9915
1994	.5.5520
1993	.5.6632

Top Import Origins (25)

$2.354 billion (c.i.f., 1994)

Origins	%
France	.NA
Mauritius	.NA
Bahrain	.NA
South Africa	.NA
Italy	.NA
Madagascar	.NA

NA stands for not available.

Top Export Destinations (26)

$171.776 million (f.o.b., 1994) Data are for 1996.

Destinations	%
Japan	.55
Singapore	.11
South Korea	.6
Australia	.3
UAE	.3

Economic Aid (27)

Recipient: substantial annual subsidies from France.

Import Export Commodities (28)

Import Commodities	Export Commodities
Manufactured goods	Sugar 63%
Food	Rum and molasses 4%
Beverages	Perfume essences 2%
Tobacco	Lobster 3%
Machinery and transportation equipment	
Raw materials	
And petroleum products	

ROMANIA

CAPITAL: Bucharest (Bucuresti).

FLAG: The national flag, adopted in 1965, is a tricolor of blue, yellow, and red vertical stripes.

ANTHEM: *Trei culori (Three Colors).*

MONETARY UNIT: The leu (L) is a paper currency of 100 bani. There are coins of 25 bani and 1, 3, 5, 10, 20, 50, and 100 lei, and notes of 10, 25, 50, 100, 200, 500, 1,000, and 5,000 lei. L1 = $0.0003 (or $1 = L3,375.0).

WEIGHTS AND MEASURES: The metric system is the legal standard.

HOLIDAYS: New Year's Day, 1 January; International Labor Day, 1–2 May; Liberation Day, 23 August; National Day, 1 December; Christmas Day, 25 December.

TIME: 2 PM = noon GMT.

LOCATION AND SIZE: Situated in eastern Europe, north of the Balkan Peninsula, Romania has a total area of 237,500 square kilometers (91,699 square miles), slightly smaller than the state of Oregon. Its total boundary length is 2,744 kilometers (1,702 miles). Romania's capital city, Bucharest, is located in the south central part of the country.

CLIMATE: Romania is exposed to northerly cold winds in the winter and moderate westerly winds from the Atlantic Ocean in the summer. Average January temperatures range from −4°C to 0°C (25–32°F). During the summer, the highest temperatures are recorded in the Danube (Dunùrea) River Valley (24°C/75°F). Precipitation averages between 100 and 125 centimeters (about 40 and 50 inches) annually in the mountains and about 38 centimeters (15 inches) in the delta.

INTRODUCTORY SURVEY

RECENT HISTORY

After World War II, a communist-led coalition government under Premier Petru Groza was set up. On 30 December 1947, the Romanian People's Republic was proclaimed.

In international affairs, Romania followed a distinctly pro-Soviet line, becoming a member of the alliance of socialist countries known as the Council for Mutual Economic Assistance (CMEA) and the Warsaw Pact for mutual defense.

During the 1960s, however, and especially after the emergence of Nicolae Ceausescu as Communist Party and national leader, Romania followed a more independent course, increasing its trade with Western nations. In 1968, Romania denounced the intervention by the Soviet Union in Czechoslovakia. In December 1973, President Ceausescu visited Washington, where he signed a joint declaration on economic, industrial, and technical cooperation with the United States.

In contrast to some other East European countries, there was relatively little political dissent in Romania during the first 30 years of communist rule. In 1977, however, about 35,000 miners in the Jiu Valley, west of Bucharest, went on strike because of economic grievances. In the early and mid-1980s, there were a number of work stoppages and strikes caused by food and energy shortages. In early 1987, Ceausescu indicated that Romania would not follow the reform trend initiated by Mikhail Gorbachev in the Soviet Union.

When the Securitate, Romania's dreaded secret police, attempted to deport Laszlo Toekes, a popular clergyman and leading spokesperson for the local Hungarians, thousands of people took to the streets. Troops were summoned, and two days of rioting ensued, during which several thousand citizens were killed.

Upon Ceausescu's return from a visit to Iran, he convened a mass rally at which he attempted to portray his opponents as advocating dictatorship. However, the rally turned into an anti-government demonstration, in which the army sided with the demonstrators. Ceausescu and his wife attempted to flee the country, but were detained, tried, and executed on 25 December 1989.

A hastily assembled Council of National Salvation took power. The council's president was Ion Iliescu, a former secretary of the Communist Party. In February 1990, Iliescu agreed to ban the Communist Party, replacing the 145-member Council of National Salvation with a 241-member Council of National Unity, which included members of opposition parties, national minorities, and former political prisoners.

Parliamentary elections were held in May 1990 against a background of continued civil unrest, especially in the Hungarian west. Iliescu was elected president, with about 85% of the votes, and was reelected in the general elections of September 1992.

Continued political instability and the slow pace of economic change have kept foreign investment quite low. Because of this, Romania has had to rely upon loans from Western sources, especially the International Monetary Fund (IMF), piling up foreign debt at the rate of about $1 billion a year.

Romanians began the 1990s as among the poorest people in Europe, and their economy only grew worse. Inflation for 1992 was 210%, and more than 300% for 1993, while unemployment was almost 10%. Most significantly, production fell for the first few years after the anti-communist revolution. By 1994, however, Romania began to turn its economy around. Presidential and parliamentary elections were held in November 1996. Emil Constantinescu of the Democratic Convention Alliance of Opposition Groups was elected as Romania's first post-communist leader. In March 1998, thousands of citizens protested in Bucharest against high unemployment and recent tax hikes.

GOVERNMENT

The Council for National Unity enacted a new constitution for Romania in November 1991, but the document is similar to Soviet-era constitutions.

The present government has a directly elected president, who is head of state. The legislature is made up of two houses, the Senate, with 143 seats, and the Assembly of Deputies, with 341 seats. Although the legislature has the formal duty to propose and pass laws, in practice the bodies have been weak, so that much of the country's function appears still to be conducted by decrees and orders, as in the past.

Romania is divided into 40 counties, as well as the municipality of Bucharest.

Judiciary

The 1992 law on reorganization of the judiciary establishes a four-level legal system. The four levels consist of courts of first instance, intermediate appellate level courts, a Supreme Court, and a Constitutional Court. The Constitutional Court has responsibility for judicial review of constitutional issues. The intermediate appellate courts had not yet been established as of 1993 due to lack of personnel and funding.

Political Parties

After the overthrow of Nicolae Ceausescu in 1989, some 80 political parties appeared. The dominant party in the 1990 elections proved to be the National Salvation Front (NSF). Due to disagreements over supporting its leader, Ion Iliescu, the NSF has since split into the Party of Social Democracy in Romania (PSDR), the Democratic National Salvation Front, and the Front for National Salvation.

The second-largest party in the 1992 elections was a coalition, called the Democratic Convention of Romania (DCR), which incorporated such parties as the National Peasant Party Christian Democratic, the Movement of Civic Alliance, the Party of Civic Alliance, Liberal Party '93, and the Social Democratic Party.

Smaller parties include the Magyar Democratic Union, the Agrarian Democratic Party, the National Unity Party, Democratic National Salvation Front, and others. There are two ultra-nationalist parties, the Party of Romanian National Unity and the Greater Romania Party, and the Communists have been reborn as the Socialist Labor Party.

In the parliamentary election of November 1996, the DCR became the ruling party, with 53 seats in the Senate and 122 in the Chamber of Deputies. The PSDR, which lost the majority, held 41 and 91 seats, respectively.

DEFENSE

The revolution of 1989–90 destroyed the communist armed forces and security establishment. Reorganization continues. In 1995, the armed forces numbered about 228,400 officers and men: 129,800 in the army, 18,500 in the navy, and 47,600 in the air force, which had 368 combat aircraft and 16 attack helicopters.

Military service is compulsory, and all able-bodied men at the age of 20 may be drafted into the armed forces for 12–18 months. Romania's budgeted defense expenditures in 1995 may have been as high as $872 million, or 1.9% of the gross domestic product (GDP).

ECONOMIC AFFAIRS

Before World War II (1939–45), the economy was mainly agricultural. Under the communists, industry was developed rapidly and surpassed agriculture in importance. Heavy industry, particularly machine-building, was emphasized as opposed to consumer goods. During the late 1970s and 1980s, the continued emphasis on industrial expansion and consequent neglect of agriculture led to food shortages and rationing.

The transition to a market economy in the 1990s has also proved extremely painful. By 1993, industrial output had fallen to 47% of the 1989 level. The domestic economy shrank by 38% between 1989 and 1992 before rising 1% in 1993.

Since then, growth has been 4–7% per year. Unemployment fell from 10.5% of the labor force in 1993 to 6% in 1996.

Public Finance

The annual budget is presented to the Grand National Assembly around December and becomes effective for the fiscal year on 1 January. The state budget, prepared by the Ministry of Finance, is a central part of the financial plan for the whole economy. The reduction of the growth rate of expenditures during the early 1980s was in keeping with an economic stabilization program designed to hold down domestic investment and consumption. As a result of fiscal reforms begun since the fall of the Ceausescu regime in December 1989, adherence to IMF fiscal targets, and an unanticipated inflation-fed revenue windfall during the first half, the central government unofficially recorded a relatively modest deficit for 1991. Deficits increased greatly through the 1990s, reflecting the poor fiscal management and generalized corruption of the Iliescu regime. In 1995, the deficit had ballooned to 2.9 trillion lei.

The U.S. Central Intelligence Agency estimates that, in 1995, government revenues totaled approximately $5.35 billion and expenditures $6.6 billion. External debt totaled $4.7 billion.

Income

In 1997, the gross national product (GNP) was $114.2 billion, or about $5,300 per person. For the period 1985–95 the average inflation rate was 69.1%, resulting in a 4% decline in per person GNP.

Industry

In 1993, industrial production was at only 47% of the 1989 level. Industrial production increased during 1994–96. In 1995, it was 13% higher than in 1992. The leading industries are food and drink, metallurgy, electric power, chemicals and synthetic fibers, and machines and equipment. In 1996, industrial production increased the most in the processing and machine and electronics industries.

Romanian industry manufactures steel, caustic soda, sulfuric acid, chemical fertilizers, automobiles, seagoing vessels, woven goods, artificial fibers, synthetic rubber, and footwear.

Banking and Finance

Romanian banks were nationalized in 1948. Established in 1880, the bank of issue is the National Bank of the Socialist Republic of Romania, which also extends short-term loans to state enterprises and supervises their financial activities. Foreign reserves amounted to about $1.5 billion in mid-1995. Money supply, as measured by M2, amounted to L 30.3 trillion in 1996. The Romanian Bank for Development (1990) finances investments of state enterprises and institutions and grants long-term credit. As investments increased in volume, this bank was required to intensify its control over the use of funds allocated for investment. The Romanian Bank for Foreign Trade conducts operations with foreign countries. Savings are deposited with the Loans and Savings Bank. In 1974, New York's Manufacturers Hanover Trust opened an office in Bucharest, the first such instance for a Western commercial bank in a Communist nation.

Romania has generally been very cautious in its approach to banking reform. Since 1990, the financial sector has undergone a fundamental overhaul, although the pace of change has been slower than elsewhere in the region. The number of banks rose from 5 in December 1990 to 26 by the end of 1994—including 7 branches of foreign banks, one wholly-owned foreign bank, and 10 with foreign capital participation. The system remains highly concentrated, as four of the five state banks still account for over 90% of loans to the business sector. The foreign specialized banks—for development, agriculture, and foreign trade—still handle almost all of the business in these areas. The Romanian Commercial Bank is still the banker to most Romanian firms, while the Savings Bank retains a virtual monopoly on personal savings deposits. Romania has undertaken to privatize at least two of the big state banks, a requirement under loan agreements with the multinationals. A law on financial sector privatization has yet to go to Parliament.

Romania set up its first post-war stock exchange in 1995, after the enabling legislation was delayed for several years.

Economic Development

The economy of Romania before 1990 was centrally planned and, for the most part, under complete state control. The nationalized industries and other economic enterprises operated within the state economic plan and were governed by the directives issued by the pertinent ministries. Economic planning, conducted by the State Planning Commission, emulated the Soviet example.

Nationalization of industry, mining, transportation, banking, and insurance on 11 June 1948 was followed by one-year economic plans in 1949 and 1950. These were succeeded by the first five-year plan (1951–55), which laid the groundwork for rapid industrialization, with emphasis on heavy industry, primarily machine-building. The state's second five-year plan (1956–60) provided for an increase of industrialization by 60–65%. Greater attention was given to consumer goods and to agriculture. A subsequent six-year plan (1960–65) envisaged an overall industrial increase of 110%, especially in producer goods. The five-year plan for 1966–70 realized an overall industrial increase of 73%. The five-year plans for 1971–75, 1976–80, and 1981–85 called for further industrial expansion and, according to official figures, during 1966–85 industrial production grew by 9.5% annually. The eighth five-year plan, for 1986–90, projected a 13.3–14.2% annual increase in Romania's net industrial production.

In the farming sector, the government has assiduously pursued a policy of collectivization. By virtue of the 22 March 1945 land reform, most farms over 50 hectares (123 acres), a total of about 1.5 million hectares (3.7 million acres), were confiscated without compensation. In 1949, the remaining large private farms were seized, and their 500,000 hectares (1,236,000 acres) organized into state farms. Various pressures, including coercion, were used to force peasants into joining. In April 1962, collectivization was announced as virtually completed. Agricultural development in following years was comparatively neglected.

As of 1 January 1979, Romania began implementing the ''new economic-financial mechanism,'' an attempt to introduce into the Romanian economy the principle of workers' self-management as previously developed elsewhere in Eastern Europe, notably in Yugoslavia and Hungary. Accordingly, autonomous production units were expected to plan for their own revenues and expenditures and manpower needs. These separate plans were, however, to be harmonized with the national economic plan, so that Romania's centralized system of goal and price setting was not significantly altered.

One of the major economic targets in the 1980s was the reduction of foreign debt, which was achieved but at the cost of drastic austerity measures and reduced industrial growth. After the fall of Communism, a major objective was the privatization of 6,200 state enterprises. The economy was to be completely restructured, with the emphasis on private ownership and adherence to the market for the allocation of resources. By late 1996, nearly all the country's agricultural land had been returned to private ownership, but only 65% of all eligible recipients had been officially given title.

SOCIAL WELFARE

Social security covers all wage earners. Workers' compensation and unemployment insurance are also provided. Families with children under age 16 receive family allowances and a birth grant for each child.

Legally, women have the same rights and privileges as men, although they face employment discrimination in Romania's harsh economic climate. Ethnic Hungarians are often subjected to discrimination.

Healthcare

In 1992, there were 1.8 doctors per 1,000 people. Through social insurance, all workers and employees, pensioners, and their dependents are covered for medical care and medicine.

The general health of the population has improved, with several previously serious diseases eliminated (recurrent fever, malaria) or greatly reduced (diphtheria, tuberculosis). In 1994, tuberculosis and measles were commonly reported. Major causes of death are communicable diseases, non-communicable diseases, and injuries. Average life expectancy is 69 years.

Housing

Romanian housing suffered from the 1940 earthquake, war damage, neglect, and inadequate repair and maintenance after the war. An increase in the urban population caused by industrialization worsened the problem. Since 1987, construction of new housing units has fallen from 110,400 to 60,400 in 1989 and 28,000 in 1991. The total number of houses was 7.8 million in 1991.

EDUCATION

Average adult illiteracy is about 3% (males, 1% and females, 4%). Since 1968, 10 years of education has been required. Romania's educational system consists of preschool (ages 3–6), primary school (grades 1–4), gymnasium (grades 5–8), lyceum or college in two steps (each consisting of 2 years), vocational schools, higher education, and postgraduate education.

In 1994, there were 6,162 general education schools (primary schools and gymnasiums), with

910,650 students and 61,960 teachers. The total number of secondary level students was 2.3 million with 168,982 teachers. Institutions of higher learning had 250,087 students and 19,130 instructors in 1993. There are universities in Bucharest, Brasov, Craiova, Galati, Iasi, Timisoara, and Cluj-Napoca.

1999 KEY EVENTS TIMELINE

February

- Northern and western Romania experience severe floods due to heavy rains and snowmelt.

- Demonstrating coal miners march on Bucharest and a clash with riot police.

April

- The government concedes $200 million to striking coal miners and promises to keep the mines in operation.

- A NATO communiqué lists Romania among the countries most likely to be admitted to NATO in the coming decade.

May

- Pope John Paul II pays a three-day visit to Romania.

October

- The European Union (EU) announces Romania's candidacy for membership as early as 2003.

- A new facility for Solectron, the world's largest electronics manufacturer, opens in Timisoara.

December

- On December 14, Radu Vasile is dismissed as prime minister by President Emil Constantinescu after seven members of Vasile's own Christian Democratic Party resigned in a move to signal that Vasile no longer had the coalition's support. Mugur Isarescu is appointed prime minister.

ANALYSIS OF EVENTS: 1999

BUSINESS AND THE ECONOMY

The first quarter of 1999 found Romania in danger of defaulting on its foreign debt, suffering from decline in production and growth in the industrial sector, and seemingly losing the war against inflation (at 47%). By the end of the second quarter, liquidation proceedings had begun against 49 industrial companies that had been showing losses, the energy sector had undergone a restructuring that included the closure of several coal mines, and two of Romania's state-owned banks were privatized and sold to foreign investors.

Demonstrations were staged by Romanian coal miners in February which culminated in a march of thousands on Bucharest and a clash with riot police in which one miner was killed and dozens of police and protesters were injured. In April, the government conceded $200 million to the miners and promised to keep the mines in operation. The scale of the anti-government protest has led to speculation that the miners were aided by the increasingly popular ultra-nationalist Greater Romania Party in an effort to overthrow the existing government. Despite its promises, the government had closed 29 coal mines by June.

A new year 2000 compliant trading system introduced in the Romanian stock market in Bucharest in October initially caused investors to be cautious and resulted in a 0.6% drop in average stock prices. Investors were also thought to be waiting for the disbursement of the second half of a $547 million loan from the International Monetary Fund (IMF). The disbursement was expected by the end of the month, though there was some uncertainty given the fact that over the last decade the IMF has suspended four loans before they were fully disbursed due to Romania's inability to meet the free market reform terms of the loans.

The Romanian city of Timisoara became the site of a new facility for Solectron, the Munich, Germany, company that is the world's largest electronics manufacturer. The 200,000-square-foot Timisoara facility occupies 40 acres and employs 1,000 skilled workers, with a planned addition of another 1,000 workers in the next two years.

The executive commission of the European Union (EU) announced in October that Romania was among six countries added to the EU's list of candidates for membership. Entry into the EU for the new candidates could be as early as 2003.

GOVERNMENT AND POLITICS

At the 50th anniversary summit of NATO in Washington in April, a communiqué designated

Romania and Slovenia as the most likely prospective new members for the coming decade.

The Romanian political scene was also being monitored for evidence of graft and corruption. Transparency International, an international group that monitors government corruption around the globe, ranked Romania in 63rd place in a ranking of the world's 99 least corrupt nations. Bulgaria tied with Romania, and Russia took 82nd place.

CULTURE AND SOCIETY

The government apparatus for dealing with natural disasters was put to the test when some 50,000 acres of farmland, over 100 towns and villages, and about 4,000 homes in northern and western Romania were swamped by floods due to heavy rains and snowmelt in February.

The over-taxed state of Romania's catastrophic safety net was apparent to the residents of Tichilesti, Europe's last remaining leper colony. These unfortunates were denied a $150 monthly subsidy by Romania's health ministry which, like the rest of the Romanian government, was seriously short of funds. The lepers of Tichilesti needed the subsidy for medicine that they have to take regularly. A macabre metaphor for the times was present in the Romanian government's well-meaning offer to give the lepers clothing and accessories judged unsatisfactory for inclusion in an upcoming auction of the designer items collected by Romania's late communist dictator, Nicolai Ceausescu, and his wife.

During Pope John Paul II's three-day visit to Romania in May he emphasized ecumenical dialogue and cooperation between the Eastern Orthodox and the Catholic churches. The Pope and the Patriarch of Romania, Teoctist, attended one another's liturgies, and Patriarch Teoctist rode with the pope in the "popemobile." One issue separating Catholics and Orthodox in Romania is the issue of property such as schools confiscated from Catholic parishes by the communists and later given to the Orthodox.

In June, the World-Wide Fund for Nature began assisting Romania in a program to monitor toxic substances in the Danube River. The World-Wide Fund for Nature insists that the Danube must be cleaned of pollutants such as toxic chemicals and oil that it says entered the river as a result of NATO bombing operations in Yugoslavia. In May, the United Nations Environment Program had found no significant levels of pollutants in the Danube.

Heavy rains in July caused the collapse of a dam on a river 170 miles northwest of Bucharest. The collapse triggered flooding and landslides that damaged houses and killed 9 people.

DIRECTORY

CENTRAL GOVERNMENT

Head of State

President
Emil Constantinescu, Office of the President
E-MAIL: guv@kappa.ro

Ministers

Prime Minister
Mugur Isarescu, Office of the Prime Minister,
R-70312 Bucharest, Romania
PHONE: +40 (1) 3143400
FAX: +40 (1) 2225814

Minister of Foreign Affairs
Andrei Gabriel Plesu, Foreign Affairs Office,
Aleea Modrogan 14, Sector 1, R-71274
Bucharest, Romania
PHONE: +40 (1) 6334060; 2122060
FAX: +40 (1) 3127589
E-MAIL: maero@mae.kappa.ro.

Minister of Defense
Victor Babiuc, Ministry of Defense, Izvor Street 13, Sector 5, Bucharest, Romania
PHONE: +40 (1) 4104000
FAX: +40 (1) 3120863

Minister of Justice
Valeriu Stoica, Ministry of Justice, Apolodor Street 17, Sector 5, Bucharest, Romania
PHONE: +40 (1) 3112266
FAX: +40 (1) 3155389

Minister of Finance
Decebal Traian Remes, Ministry of Finance, Al. Modrogan 14, R-70663 Bucharest, Romania
PHONE: +40 (1) 4103400
FAX: +40 (1) 3122077

Minister of Industry and Trade
Radu Mircea Berceanu, Ministry of Industry and Trade, Calea Victoriei 152, Sector 1, R-71274
Bucharest, Romania
PHONE: +40 (1) 2310262
FAX: +40 (1) 3120513

Minister of Labor and Social Protection
Alexandru Athanasiu, Ministry of Labor and
Social Protection, Str. Demetru Dobrescu 2B,
Sector 1, R-70119 Bucharest, Romania
PHONE: +40 (1) 3156563
FAX: +40 (1) 3125268
E-MAIL: ministru@srv.mmps.ro

Minister of the Interior
Constantin Dudu Ionescu, Ministry of the
Interior, Str. Apolodor 17, R-70622 Bucharest,
Romania
PHONE: +40 (1) 3112021
FAX: +40 (1) 6140909

Minister of Agriculture and Food
Ioan Avram Muresan, Ministry of Agriculture
and Food, Bd. Carol I 24, R-70312 Bucharest,
Romania
PHONE: +40 (1) 6144020
FAX: +40 (1) 3124410

Minister of Transport
Traian Basescu, Ministry of Transport, Dinicu
Golescu 38, R-77113 Bucharest, Romania
PHONE: +40 (1) 2230880
FAX: +40 (1) 3120772

Minister of Public Works and Land Planning
Nicolae Stefan Noica, Ministry of Public Works
and Land Planning, Str. Apolodor 17, R-70663
Bucharest, Romania
PHONE: +40 (1) 4101933
FAX: +40 (1) 4111138

**Minister of Waters, Forests and Environment
Protection**
Romica Tomescu, Ministry of Waters, Forestry
and Environmental Protections, Bd. Libertatii 12,
R-76106 Bucharest, Romania
PHONE: +40 (1) 4100482
FAX: +40 (1) 3124227

Minister of Health
Hajdu Gabor, Ministry of Health, Str.
Ministerului 1-3, R-70109 Bucharest, Romania
PHONE: +40 (1) 2223850
FAX: +40 (1) 3124916

Minister of Culture
Ion Caramitru, Ministry of Culture, Piata Presei
Libere 1, R-71341 Bucharest, Romania
PHONE: +40 (1) 2231516
FAX: +40 (1) 2234951

Minister of Youth and Sports
George Crin Antonescu, Ministry of Youth and
Sports, Str. Vasile Conta 16, Sector 2, R-70139
Bucharest, Romania
PHONE: +40 (1) 2111141
FAX: +40 (1) 2111710

Minister of National Education
Andrei Marga, Ministry of National Education,
General Berthlot Street 28-30, Sector 1, R-70749
Bucharest, Romania
PHONE: +40 (1) 3133355
FAX: +40 (1) 3124719

POLITICAL ORGANIZATIONS

Partidul National Taranesc Crestin Democrat-PNTCD (Christian Democratic National Peasants' Party)

Bd. Carol I 34, Sector 2, R-73231 Bucharest,
Romania
PHONE: +40 (1) 6147231
FAX: +40 (1) 6143277
TITLE: Chairman
NAME: Ion Diaconescu

Partidul National Liberal (National Liberal Party)

Bd. Nicolae Balcescu 21, R-70112 Bucharest,
Romania
PHONE: +40 (1) 6143235
FAX: +40 (1) 3239508
TITLE: Presedinte
NAME: Niculae Cerveni

Partidul Democra iei Sociale din Romƒnia (Party of Social Democracy of Romania)

10 Kiseleff Street, Bucharest, Romania
PHONE: +40 (1) 2222955
FAX: +40 (1) 2222879
E-MAIL: pdsr@pdsr.ro
TITLE: President
NAME: Ion Iliescu

Aliantei Civice (Civic Alliance)

Filiala Municipiului Bucuresti, Piata Amzei 13,
Etaj 2, Sector 1, Bucharest, Romania
PHONE: +40 (1) 6595909
FAX: +40 (1) 3125854
E-MAIL: acivica@acivica.sfos.ro
TITLE: Chairman
NAME: Ana Blandiana

Partidul Democrat (PD)

Aleea Modrogan 1, Sector 1, R-7000 Bucharest, Romania
PHONE: +40 (1) 2301332
FAX: +40 (1) 2301332
E-MAIL: office@pd.ro

PUR (Humanist Party)

Calea Victoriei 118, Etaj 5, Sector 1, Bucharest, Romania
PHONE: +40 (1) 6596598; 6507035
FAX: +40 (1) 6504345
E-MAIL: pur@itcnet.ro

Uniunea Fortelor de Dreapta (United Right Wing)

B-dul Regina Elisabeta 3-5, Et. 2, Bucharest, Romania
PHONE: +40 (1) 3124262; 3122511
FAX: +40 (1) 3111528

DIPLOMATIC REPRESENTATION

Embassies in Romania

Argentina

Str. Drobeta 11, Bucharest, Romania
PHONE: +40 (1) 2117290; 2117293
FAX: +40 (1) 2101412
NAME: Diana T. Berruhet

Belgium

B-Dul Dacia 58, Sector 2, Bucharest, Romania
PHONE: +40 (1) 2102969; 2102970
FAX: +40 (1) 2102803
TITLE: Ambassador
NAME: Michel Vantroyen

Bulgaria

Str. Rabat 5, Bucharest, Romania
PHONE: +40 (1) 2302150; 2302159
FAX: +40 (1) 2307654
TITLE: Ambassador
NAME: Kosio Troikov Kitipov

Burundi

Kaloujskaya Plochad, Dom. 1, Ap. 226-227, Bucharest, Romania
PHONE: +40 (1) 2302564
FAX: +40 (1) 2302009
TITLE: Ambassador
NAME: Apollonie Simbizi

Cameroon

Str. Povarskaya 40, Bucharest, Romania
PHONE: +40 (1) 2906549; 2900063
FAX: +40 (1) 2906116

Canada

Str. N. Iorga 36, Sector 1, Bucharest, Romania
PHONE: +40 (1) 2229845
FAX: +40 (1) 3120366; 3129680; 3113128; 3113129
TITLE: Ambassador
NAME: David Collins

China

Sos. Nordului 2, Bucharest, Romania
PHONE: +40 (1) 2321925
FAX: +40 (1) 2307523
TITLE: Charge d'Affaires
NAME: Xu Jian

Democratic Republic of the Congo

Str. Racota 16-18, Bucharest, Romania
PHONE: +40 (1) 2244008
TITLE: Charge d'Affaires
NAME: Phoba-Ki-Kumbu

Republic of the Congo

Str. Sfantul Spiridon 10, Bucharest, Romania
TITLE: Charge d'Affaires
NAME: Georges Ambara

Cyprus

Str. Herodotou 16, Bucharest, Romania
PHONE: +40 (1) 7237883; 7239377; 7232727
FAX: +40 (1) 7231927
TITLE: Ambassador
NAME: Cristodoulos Pasiardis

Czech Republic

Str. Ion Ghica 11, Bucharest, Romania
PHONE: +40 (1) 3159142
FAX: +40 (1) 3122539
TITLE: Ambassador
NAME: Jaromir Plisek

Denmark

Str. Dr. Burghelea 3, Bucharest, Romania
PHONE: +40 (1) 3120352; 3120353; 3120354; 3120355; 3120356
FAX: +40 (1) 3120358
TITLE: Ambassador
NAME: Erik Bom

Germany

Str. Rabat 19, 71272 Bucharest, Romania
PHONE: +40 (1) 2300357; 2302605
FAX: +40 (1) 2302155
TITLE: Ambassador
NAME: Wolf-Dietrich Schilling

India

Str. Uruguay 11, Sector 1, Bucharest, Romania

PHONE: +40 (1) 2225451; 2228715; 2228915
FAX: +40 (1) 2232681
TITLE: Ambassador
NAME: Rajiv Dogra

Indonesia
Str. Orlando 10, Sector 1, Bucharest, Romania
PHONE: +40 (1) 3120742
FAX: +40 (1) 3120214
TITLE: Ambassador
NAME: Tjahjani Sukadi

Mexico
Str. Armeneasca 35, Sector 2, Bucharest, Romania
PHONE: +40 (1) 2104577; 2104728; 2104417
FAX: +40 (1) 2104713
TITLE: Ambassador
NAME: Enrique Fernandez Zapata

United Kingdom
Str. Jules Michelet 24, Bucharest, Romania
PHONE: +40 (1) 3120303
FAX: +40 (1) 3120229
TITLE: Ambassador
NAME: Ralph Richard Peter

United States
Str. Tudor Arghezi 7-9, Bucharest, Romania
PHONE: +40 (1) 2104042; 2100149; 2106384
FAX: +40 (1) 2100395

TITLE: Ambassador
NAME: James C. Rosapepe

JUDICIAL SYSTEM
Constitutional Court
Supreme Court

FURTHER READING
Articles

Fischer, Joannie Schrof. ''From Romania, A Lesson in Resilience.'' *U.S. News and World Report* (September 13, 1999): 50.

''Grey New Year.'' *The Economist* (January 23, 1999): 48.

Jones, Colin. ''On the Road to Reform.'' *The Banker* (June 1999): 47.

Jones, Colin. ''Starting From Scratch.'' *The Banker* (October 1999): 55.

Perlez, Jane. ''A Dictator's Yard Sale.'' *New York Times Magazine* (August 29, 1999): 17.

Rich, Vera. ''Transylvanian Cash Row Sorted.'' *Times Higher Education Supplement* (September 17, 1999): 12.

''Romania.'' *The Economist* (June 19, 1999).

''Romania Told to Close Foreign Trade Bank.'' *The Banker* (October 1999): 53.

ROMANIA: STATISTICAL DATA

For sources and notes see "Sources of Statistics" in the front of each volume.

GEOGRAPHY

Geography (1)

Area:

Total: 237,500 sq km.

Land: 230,340 sq km.

Water: 7,160 sq km.

Area—comparative: slightly smaller than Oregon.

Land boundaries:

Total: 2,508 km.

Border countries: Bulgaria 608 km, Hungary 443 km, Moldova 450 km, Serbia and Montenegro 476 km (all with Serbia), Ukraine (north) 362 km, Ukraine (east) 169 km.

Coastline: 225 km.

Climate: temperate; cold, cloudy winters with frequent snow and fog; sunny summers with frequent showers and thunderstorms.

Terrain: central Transylvanian Basin is separated from the Plain of Moldavia on the east by the Carpathian Mountains and separated from the Walachian Plain on the south by the Transylvanian Alps.

Natural resources: petroleum (reserves declining), timber, natural gas, coal, iron ore, salt.

Land use:

Arable land: 41%

Permanent crops: 3%

Permanent pastures: 21%

Forests and woodland: 29%

Other: 6% (1993 est.).

HUMAN FACTORS

Demographics (2A)

	1990	1995	1998	2000	2010	2020	2030	2040	2050
Population	NA	22,581.7	22,395.8	22,291.2	22,288.1	21,789.3	21,038.3	19,988.9	18,483.4
Net migration rate (per 1,000 population)	NA	NA	NA	NA	NA	NA	NA	NA	NA
Births	NA	NA	NA	NA	NA	NA	NA	NA	NA
Deaths	NA	NA	NA	NA	NA	NA	NA	NA	NA
Life expectancy - males	NA	65.5	66.7	67.4	70.8	73.6	75.8	77.5	78.7
Life expectancy - females	NA	73.4	74.5	75.1	78.1	80.4	82.3	83.8	84.9
Birth rate (per 1,000)	NA	10.4	9.3	10.9	11.1	8.2	8.1	6.8	6.1
Death rate (per 1,000)	NA	12.0	11.6	11.5	11.4	11.4	11.9	13.4	15.1
Women of reproductive age (15-49 yrs.)	NA	5,714.5	5,790.6	5,764.7	5,513.5	5,148.9	4,524.0	3,798.6	3,497.4
of which are currently married	NA	NA	NA	NA	NA	NA	NA	NA	NA
Fertility rate	NA	1.3	1.2	1.4	1.5	1.5	1.4	1.3	1.3

Except as noted, values for vital statistics are in thousands; life expectancy is in years.

Health Personnel (3)

Total health expenditure as a percentage of GDP, 1990-1997[a]

Public sector 2.9

Private sector . . . . .NA

Total[b] . . . . .NA

Health expenditure per capita in U.S. dollars, 1990-1997[a]

Purchasing power parity . . . . .NA

Total . . . . .NA

Availability of health care facilities per 100,000 people

Hospital beds 1990-1997[a] 760

Doctors 1993[c] 176

Nurses 1993[c] 430

Health Indicators (4)

Life expectancy at birth

1980 69

1997 69

Daily per capita supply of calories (1996) 2,943

Total fertility rate births per woman (1997) 1.3

Maternal mortality ratio per 100,000 live births (1990-97) . . . . .41[b]

Safe water % of population with access (1995) 62

Sanitation % of population with access (1995) 44

Consumption of iodized salt % of households (1992-98)[a] . . . .

Smoking prevalence

Male % of adults (1985-95)[a] 68

Female % of adults (1985-95)[a] 32

Tuberculosis incidence per 100,000 people (1997) 121

Adult HIV prevalence % of population ages 15-49 (1997) 0.01

Infants and Malnutrition (5)

Under-5 mortality rate (1997) 26

% of infants with low birthweight (1990-97) 7

Births attended by skilled health staff % of total[a] . . .99

% fully immunized (1995-97)

TB 100

DPT 97

Polio 97

Measles 97

Prevalence of child malnutrition under age 5 (1992-97)[b] 6

Ethnic Division (6)

Romanian 89.1%

Hungarian 8.9%

German 0.4%

Ukrainian, Serb, Croat, Russian, Turk, and Gypsy . .1.6%

Religions (7)

Romanian Orthodox .70%

Roman Catholic 6%

Protestant 6%

Unaffiliated 18%

3% of Roman Cathoics are Uniate.

Languages (8)

Romanian, Hungarian, German.

EDUCATION

Public Education Expenditures (9)

Public expenditure on education (% of GNP)

1980 . . . . .3.3

1996 . . . . .3.6

Expenditure per student

Primary % of GNP per capita

1980 . . . .

1996 . . . . .20.0

Secondary % of GNP per capita

1980 . . . .

1996 . . . . .8.7

Tertiary % of GNP per capita

1980 . . . .

1996 . . . . .31.6

Expenditure on teaching materials

Primary % of total for level (1996) . . . .

Secondary % of total for level (1996) . . . .

Primary pupil-teacher ratio per teacher (1996) 20

Duration of primary education years (1995) 4

Educational Attainment (10)

Age group (1996) . . . . .12+

Total population .19,065,000

Highest level attained (%)

No schooling 4.3

First level

Not completed 20.7

Completed . . . . .NA

Entered second level

S-1 . . . . .69.4

S-2 . . . . .NA

Postsecondary 5.6

Literacy Rates (11B)

Adult literacy rate

1980

  Male 98%

  Female 93%

1995

  Male 99%

  Female 97%

GOVERNMENT & LAW

Political Parties (12)

Chamber of Deputies—	% of seats
The Democratic Convention (CDR) 30.2	
Party of Social Democracy in Romania (PDSR) ...21.5	
Union of Social Democrats (USD) 12.9	
Democratic Union of Hungarians in Romania (UDMR) 6.6	
Romania Mare Party (Greater Romanian Party) (PRM) 4.5	
Romanian National Unity Party (PUNR) 4.4	
Others 19.9	

Military Affairs (14B)

	1990	1991	1992	1993	1994	1995
Military expenditures						
Current dollars (mil.)	3,869[r]	3,747[r]	2,672	1,802	2,178	2,520
1995 constant dollars (mil.)	4,446[r]	4,140[r]	2,874	1,889	2,233	2,520
Armed forces (000)	126	201	172	167	200	209
Gross national product (GNP)						
Current dollars (mil.)	104,900[e]	94,190[e]	82,000	85,610	91,140	98,940
1995 constant dollars (mil.)	120,600[e]	104,100[e]	88,200	89,750	93,430	98,940
Central government expenditures (CGE)						
1995 constant dollars (mil.)	40,750[e]	36,400[e]	36,460	29,190	30,400	22,580
People (mil.)	22.8	22.7	22.7	22.4	22.2	21.9
Military expenditure as % of GNP	3.7	4.0	3.3	2.1	2.4	2.5
Military expenditure as % of CGE	10.9	11.4	7.9	6.5	7.3	11.2
Military expenditure per capita (1995 $)	195	182	127	84	101	115
Armed forces per 1,000 people (soldiers)	5.5	8.8	7.6	7.4	9.0	9.5
GNP per capita (1995 $)	5,294	4,579	3,887	3,999	4,210	4,513
Arms imports[6]						
Current dollars (mil.)	825	170	30	0	0	0
1995 constant dollars (mil.)	948	188	32	0	0	0
Arms exports[6]						
Current dollars (mil.)	0	0	20	10	40	20
1995 constant dollars (mil.)	0	0	22	10	41	20
Total imports[7]						
Current dollars (mil.)	9,843	5,793	6,260	6,522	7,109	9,424
1995 constant dollars (mil.)	11,310	6,401	6,734	6,837	7,287	9,424
Total exports[7]						
Current dollars (mil.)	5,870	4,266	4,363	4,892	6,151	7,548
1995 constant dollars (mil.)	6,746	4,714	4,693	5,129	6,305	7,548
Arms as percent of total imports[8]	8.4	2.9	.5	0	0	0
Arms as percent of total exports[8]	.0	.0	.5	.2	.7	.3

Government Budget (13A)

Year: 1996

Total Expenditures: 34,033 Billions of Lei

Expenditures as a percentage of the total by function:

General public services and public order 7.52
Defense 6.05
Education 10.10
Health 7.38
Social Security and Welfare 28.95
Housing and community amenities 1.24
Recreational, cultural, and religious affairs 1.42
Fuel and energy 3.61
Agriculture, forestry, fishing, and hunting 7.86
Mining, manufacturing, and construction 3.44
Transportation and communication 4.22
Other economic affairs and services 2.71

Crime (15)

Crime rate (for 1997)

Crimes reported 361,100
Total persons convicted .NA
Crimes per 100,000 population 1,600

Persons responsible for offenses

Total number of suspects 249,800
Total number of female suspects 35,500
Total number of juvenile suspects 27,500

LABOR FORCE

Labor Force (16)

Total (million) 10.1
Industry 28.6%
Agriculture 34.4%
Trade 10.4%
Construction 5.1%
Other 21.5%

Data for 1996 est. Percent distribution for 1995.

Unemployment Rate (17)

8.8% (1997 est.)

PRODUCTION SECTOR

Electric Energy (18)

Capacity . . . . .22.06 million kW (1995)
Production . . . . .55.19 billion kWh (1995)
Consumption per capita . . . . .2,412 kWh (1995)

Transportation (19)

Highways:

total: 153,170 km

paved: 78,117 km (including 113 km of expressways)

unpaved: 75,053 km (1995 est.)

Waterways: 1,724 km (1984)

Pipelines: crude oil 2,800 km; petroleum products 1,429 km; natural gas 6,400 km (1992)

Merchant marine:

total: 227 ships (1,000 GRT or over) totaling 2,332,117 GRT/3,464,613 DWT ships by type: bulk 39, cargo 160, container 2, oil tanker 12, passenger 1, passenger-cargo 1, railcar carrier 2, roll-on/roll-off cargo 10 note: Romania owns an additional 11 ships (1,000 GRT or over) totaling 827,625 DWT operating under the registries of the Bahamas, Cyprus, Liberia, and Malta (1997 est.)

Airports: 24 (1997 est.)

Airports—with paved runways:

total: 19
over 3,047 m: 4
2,438 to 3,047 m: 5
1,524 to 2,437 m: 10 (1997 est.)

Airports—with unpaved runways:

total: 5
1,524 to 2,437 m: 1
914 to 1,523 m: 3
under 914 m: 1 (1997 est.)

Top Agricultural Products (20)

Wheat, corn, sugar beets, sunflower seed, potatoes, grapes; milk, eggs, meat.

MANUFACTURING SECTOR

GDP & Manufacturing Summary (21)

Detailed value added figures are listed by both International Standard Industry Code (ISIC) and product title.

	1980	1985	1990	1994
GDP ($-1990 mil.)[1]	36,527	42,674	38,244	29,580
Per capita ($-1990)[1]	1,645	1,878	1,648	1,290
Manufacturing share (%) (current prices)[1]	52.7	53.0	47.4	35.6
Manufacturing				
Value added ($-1990 mil.)[1]	18,912	22,369	18,135	13,662
Industrial production index	100	120	115	71

MANUFACTURING SECTOR

GDP & Manufacturing Summary (21)

	1980	1985	1990	1994
Value added ($ mil.)	8,910	16,862	14,047	7,385
Gross output ($ mil.)	45,225	59,157	47,936	21,380
Employment (000)	2,877	3,051	3,451	2,426
Profitability (% of gross output)				
Intermediate input (%)	80	71	71	65
Wages and salaries inc. supplements (%)	8	9	12	11
Gross operating surplus	11	19	17	24
Productivity ($)				
Gross output per worker	15,719	19,389	13,219	8,434
Value added per worker	3,097	5,527	3,874	2,914
Average wage (inc. supplements)	1,316	1,796	1,725	958
Value added ($ mil.)				
311/2 Food products	1,043	1,729	1,649	1,415
313 Beverages	418	760	642	499
314 Tobacco products	15	27	410	70
321 Textiles	527	1,339	1,449	472
322 Wearing apparel	323	802	691	269
323 Leather and fur products	149	271	67	29
324 Footwear	186	346	366	179
331 Wood and wood products	311	601	312	251
332 Furniture and fixtures	278	455	321	231
341 Paper and paper products	115	222	169	81
342 Printing and publishing	14	41	143	55
351 Industrial chemicals	383	538	111	224
352 Other chemical products	261	480	441	273
353 Petroleum refineries	354	515	−134	286
354 Miscellaneous petroleum and coal products	44	62	36	123
355 Rubber products	188	282	129	121
356 Plastic products	50	144	397	120
361 Pottery, china and earthenware	55	99	571	370
362 Glass and glass products	76	155	120	61
369 Other non-metal mineral products	32	52	40	50
371 Iron and steel	597	978	651	387
372 Non-ferrous metals	278	358	22	33
381 Metal products	294	766	869	366
382 Non-electrical machinery	657	1,793	2,004	443
383 Electrical machinery	641	932	1,208	358
384 Transport equipment	737	1,371	704	427
385 Professional and scientific equipment	164	404	430	153
390 Other manufacturing industries	721	1,340	227	39

FINANCE, ECONOMICS, & TRADE

Economic Indicators (22)

National product: GDP—purchasing power parity—$114.2 billion (1997 est.)

National product real growth rate: -6.6% (1997 est.)

National product per capita: $5,300 (1997 est.)

Inflation rate—consumer price index: 151% (1997 est.)

Exchange Rates (24)

Exchange rates:

Lei (L) per US$1

January 1998	8,293.40
1997	7,167.94
1996	3,084.22
1995	2,033.28
1994	1,655.09
1993	760.05

Top Import Origins (25)

$10.4 billion (f.o.b., 1997 est.) Data are for 1996.

Origins	%
Germany	17.1
Italy	15.6
Russia	12.6
France	5.0
United States	3.8
Egypt	3.8

Top Export Destinations (26)

$8.4 billion (f.o.b., 1997 est.) Data are for 1996.

Destinations	%
Germany	18.1
Italy	16.7
France	5.6
Turkey	5
Netherlands	4.2
China	3.0

Economic Aid (27)

Recipient: $NA. NA stands for not available.

Import Export Commodities (28)

Import Commodities	Export Commodities
Fuels and minerals 24%	Textiles and footwear 27.5%
Machinery and transport equipment 25%	Metals and metal products 16.2%
Food and agricultural goods 7.6%	Mineral products 9.0%
Chemicals 12.5%	Chemicals 11.2%
Other 30.9%	Other 36.1%

Balance of Payments (23)

	1992	1993	1994	1995	1996
Exports of goods (f.o.b.)	4,364	4,892	6,151	7,910	8,085
Imports of goods (f.o.b.)	−5,588	−6,020	−6,562	−9,487	−10,555
Trade balance	−1,194	−1,128	−411	−1,577	−2,470
Services - debits	−1,090	−1,122	−1,460	−2,141	−2,335
Services - credits	713	862	1,160	1,575	1,641
Private transfers (net)	46	111	101	63	47
Government transfers (net)	19	103	182	306	546
Overall balance	−1,506	−1,174	−428	−1,774	−2,571

RUSSIA

Russian Federation
Rossiyskaya Federatsiya

CAPITAL: Moscow.

FLAG: Equal horizontal bands of white (top), blue, and red.

ANTHEM: *Patriotic Song.*

MONETARY UNIT: The ruble (R) is a paper currency of 100 kopecks. There are coins of 1, 2, 3, 5, 10, 15, 20, and 50 kopecks and 1 ruble, and notes of 100, 200, 500, 1,000, 5,000, 10,000 and 50,000 rubles. R1 = $0.00018 (or $1 = R5,455.0).

WEIGHTS AND MEASURES: The metric system is the legal standard.

HOLIDAYS: New Year's Day, 1–2 January; Christmas, 7 January; Women's Day, 8 March; Spring and Labor Day, 1–2 May; Victory Day, 9 May; State Sovereignty Day, 12 June; Socialist Revolution Day, 7 November.

TIME: 3 PM Moscow = noon GMT.

LOCATION AND SIZE: Russia is located in northeastern Europe and northern Asia. It is the largest country in the world—slightly more than 1.8 times the size of the United States, with a total area of 17,075,200 square kilometers (6,592,771 square miles). Russia's capital city, Moscow, is located in the eastern part of the country.

CLIMATE: Most of the country has a continental climate, with long, cold winters and brief summers. Temperatures in January range from 6°C (45°F), on the southeast shore of the Black Sea, to as low as −71°C (−96°F) in northeastern Siberia. The lowest temperatures of any of the world's inhabited regions are found in Siberia. Precipitation varies from 53 centimeters (21 inches) at Moscow to between 20 and 25 centimeters (8–10 inches) in eastern Siberia.

INTRODUCTORY SURVEY

RECENT HISTORY

The USSR was a Communist nation consisting of Russia and much of the surrounding area. After World War II (1939–45), the USSR and the United States regarded one another as enemies. Although they never directly engaged in war, both nations built enormous nuclear arsenals and supported opposing sides in conflicts around the world during the so-called Cold War, which lasted for almost five decades. Increasing frustration with the Soviet political and economic systems prompted Soviet leader Mikhail Gorbachev to initiate reforms in the late 1980s and early 1990s. However, dissatisfaction continued and the USSR began to collapse.

For the first time since 1917, free multiparty elections were held in Russia in March 1990. On 12 June 1991, the first elections to the Russian presidency were won by Boris Yeltsin. On 8 December 1991, Yeltsin, together with the leaders of Ukraine and Belarus, formed the nucleus of the Commonwealth of Independent States (CIS). This spelled the end of the Union of Soviet Socialist Republics (USSR) later that month. Like the other former Soviet republics, Russia had become an independent sovereign state.

In early 1992, Yeltsin sought to reform the economy, but prices rose rapidly and public opposition to his reforms grew. Much of Russian politics in 1993 consisted of bitter squabbling between Yeltsin and the legislature. No progress was made on drafting a new constitution to replace the much

amended Soviet-era constitution that still governed Russia.

On 21 September 1993, Yeltsin dissolved the Supreme Soviet and introduced rule by presidential decree until new parliamentary elections and a referendum on his draft constitution could be held on 12 December. After anti-Yeltsin legislators barricaded themselves inside the parliament building, a state of emergency was declared for a brief period.

The referendum and parliamentary elections were held as planned. The electorate approved the new constitution, which called for a strong presidency. In the parliamentary elections, ten parties won seats. Both communist and nationalist forces won representation.

As Yeltsin tried to stabilize the government, nationalistic feelings grew in the republics inhabited by non-Russians. War broke out in December 1994 in Chechnya when the rebellious region in the Caucasus declared its independence. Russia's military was not able to subdue the region and withdrew. The bloody and unpopular conflict led Yeltsin to sign a peace treaty with Chechen leader

Aslan Maskhadov in May 1997. The treaty agreed to wait five years for a final decision on Chechnya's status.

In a show of power, on 23 March 1998 President Yeltsin dismissed the entire cabinet, including Prime Minister Chernomyrdin. Several ministers retained their positions, and Yeltsin's new picks consisted largely of young reformists not associated with Moscow's politics, such as Sergei Kiriyenko, who became the new prime minister. The Russian economy continued to sink, however, as did Yeltsin's authority. In August Yeltsin sought to reappoint Chernomyrdin as prime minister, but the legislature rejected the nomination.

In mid-1998 the International Monetary Fund agreed to loan Russia $11.2 billion. Despite the promised bailout, the stock market plunged as interest rates soared, and Russia moved to devalue its currency.

GOVERNMENT

A new constitution for Russia was approved in a referendum held 12 December 1993. The constitution established a two-chamber legislature known as the Federal Assembly. The lower house (State Duma) consists of 450 elected deputies while the 178-member upper house (Council of the Federation) is composed of representatives of the provinces and autonomous republics that make up Russia. The president is elected separately for a five-year term.

The president appoints the cabinet members and other top government posts subject to confirmation by the legislature. The president may declare war or a state of emergency on his own authority. Impeachment of the president is provided for in the constitution, but is very difficult.

The State Duma has jurisdiction over the budget and economic policy. The Council has jurisdiction over issues affecting the provinces and autonomous republics, including border changes and the use of force within the Russian Federation.

Judiciary

A Constitutional Court has been established to rule on disputes between the executive and legislative branches. The Supreme Court reviews charges brought against the executive and legislative branches. The High Court of Arbitration is the highest court for matters between businesses.

Political Parties

After elections to the State Duma held in December 1995, the Communist Party held 157 of 450 seats. They are supported by two socialist factions, Power to the People (9 seats) and the Agrarians (45). The center-right Our Home is Russia held 55 seats, Vladimir Zhirinovsky's nationalist Liberal Democratic Party had 51 seats, the moderate-reformist Yabloko Bloc had 45 seats, independents won 78 seats, and other parties held 35 seats.

DEFENSE

Although equipment numbers and force structure are impressive, Russian armed forces have declined significantly since the breakup of the Soviet Union. The active Russian armed forces may number about 1.3 million. The Russian army has 460,000 soldiers, of whom perhaps 144,000 are draftees. The air force claims 145,000 airmen (about 44,000 draftees). The Russian navy of 190,000 retains the vast majority of the combat capability of the former Soviet navy. It remains organized in four major fleets with regional and global missions. The fleets are stationed in Arctic

Russia, four Baltic bases, three Black Sea bases, and Vladivostok.

Russia remains the world's second most formidable nation when it comes to nuclear weapons, after the United States. The Strategic Rocket Forces (144,000) control 1,400 silo-based and mobile intercontinental ballistic missiles (ICBMs) with 6,620 warheads, and provide ground defense forces to defend ICBM launch sites and warhead storage facilities.

In addition to troops remaining in two Commonwealth of Independent States (CIS) member nations, Russia maintains major military missions or units in Cuba, Cambodia, Syria, Mongolia, Bosnia, and Vietnam. Russian units participate in four separate peacekeeping missions, two sponsored by the United Nations. Russia has assumed the treaty responsibilities of the former Soviet Union to reduce its strategic arsenal and conventional forces in Europe.

ECONOMIC AFFAIRS

Russia's economic situation has deteriorated steadily since the break-up of the Soviet Union in 1991. It is undergoing a transformation from a centrally planned economy to a market-oriented one, with limited public ownership. Industry accounted for 41% of the gross domestic product (GDP) in 1996, while agriculture contributed just 6%. There is a serious demand for goods that is not being met, especially for consumer goods. A stabilization plan started in 1995 tightened the budget, opened up trade, and lowered inflation. The inflation rate fell from 214% in 1994 to just 3% in 1997. Unemployment is around 8%.

Public Finance

Since the breakup of the Soviet Union, trade disruptions and friction between Russia and the governments of the former Soviet republics have led to an enormous expansion of the fiscal deficit. Consequently, the government has sharply restrained spending in an attempt to keep the federal budget deficit to under 6% of GDP. The deficit is financed largely through sales of domestic government securities and borrowing from international financial institutions.

Income

In 1997, the gross national product (GNP) was $692 billion, or about $4,700 per person. For the period 1985–95 the average inflation rate was

148.9% and the average annual decline of GNP per person was 5.1%.

Industry

Major manufacturing industries include crude steel, cars and trucks, aircraft, chemicals (including fertilizers), plastics, cement and other building materials, paper, television sets, and appliances. Military production, which dominated industrial output in the former Soviet Union, is being replaced by other types of manufacturing, often consumer goods and food processing.

Banking and Finance

The Central Bank of the Russian Federation was created in January 1992 from the old Soviet banking system headed by Gosbank (The Soviet State Bank). Foreign reserves totaled $12.4 billion in July 1996. Money supply, as measured by M2, was Rb804,080 billion at the end of June 1995. The bank heads a two-tier banking system, and implements a monetary policy and regulates the commercial banking sector by setting the reserve requirements and the discount rate. The currency unit of Russia is the ruble, a currency that is in the process of becoming fully convertible with world currency. Russia, along with a few other countries of the former Soviet Union, decided to keep the ruble as its currency. The other important state bank is the Rosevneshtorgbank (Bank for Foreign Trade of the Russian Federation).

Currently, around 2,000 commercial banks operate in Russia, a third of which are former specialized state banks. The rest are new institutions. Commercial banks include the Commercial Bank Industriaservis, the Commercial Credit Bank, the Commercial Conservation Bank, the Commercial Innovation Bank, the International Moscow Bank, St. Petersburg's Investment Bank, and the Construction Bank. The International Bank is a bank whose shares are owned by western banks, such as Citibank (US) and the Barclays Groups (UK), interested in doing business in the country.

Sberbank held around 86% of the population's savings in 1994. Having around 42,000 branches, it is by far the largest banking institution in the country. Sberbank became a joint-stock company in 1991, with the Central Bank taking a 20% shareholding. In addition to Sberbank (the Savings Bank), there were four other specialized banks: the Foreign Trade Bank (Vneshtorgbank), the Bank for Construction and Industry (Promstroibank), the Agriculture Bank (Agroprombank), and the Social Sector Bank (Zhilotsbank). Formerly these were joint-stock banks but they relied on cheap credit from Gosbank.

Russia had a small stock market in 1992. The market is considered an emerging market by western investors with the potential for significant growth in coming years. Although the first stock market opened in Moscow in 1991, over 100 were in operation by 1996. The range, as well as the volume, of securities traded has been rapidly expanding. Inadequate regulation and custody registration systems have been the main bottlenecks in development. A Commission for Securities and Stock Market was established in late 1994. The second half of 1996 witnessed a huge rally in the value of Russian equity as it became clear that economic reforms would continue following the re-election of Boris Yeltsin as president.

Economic Development

In 1991, Russia's parliament enacted legislation aimed at fully privatizing the commercial and service sector by 1994 and placing about half the medium and large companies in private hands by 1995. By the end of 1992, about 6,000 firms had applied to become joint-stock companies, and 1,560 had completed the process; almost one-third of Russia's approximately 250,000 small businesses had been privatized. Housing privatization began late in 1992, and over 2.6 million apartments, about 8% of the total, had been privatized by the end of 1993. In 1996, the government claimed that the non-state sector produced approximately 70% of GDP, up from 62% in 1995. Russia's Communist-dominated parliament, however, is quick to criticize the government's privatization efforts which they think are responsible for the economic decline. In March of 1997, over two million people took part in a national strike protesting the economic hardships of privatization and over 100,000 attended rallies in Moscow and St. Petersburg. The government, however, is committed to privatization and has largely ignored the parliament and the protests.

SOCIAL WELFARE

The Russian Republic had enacted its own pension legislation in November 1990, before the collapse of the Soviet Union. While it followed the Soviet Union model in many respects, it linked pensions to a ''minimum subsistence'' figure instead of to the minimum wage. However, rapid price increases in 1992 pressured the Yeltsin government into once again tying pensions to the minimum wage.

Social security legislation was updated in 1992 and 1993 to provide medical care for all residents. Pensions are also provided for all employed and self-employed persons, and for independent farmers.

The constitution prohibits discrimination based on race, sex, religion, language, and social status. Despite the provisions, there is employment discrimination against minorities and women.

Healthcare

There are 3.8 physicians per 1,000 people. In 1991, there were 13.8 hospital beds per 1,000 population. Average life expectancy is 66 years.

Housing

In 1989, 46.7% of all privately owned urban housing had running water, 36.3% had central heating, and 17.2% had hot water. In 1990, Russia had 16.4 square meters of housing space per capita.

EDUCATION

The adult illiteracy rate is estimated at about 2%. Education, mostly state-funded, is also compulsory for 10 years. In 1993, there were 66,235 primary schools and 7.8 million students, while secondary schools had 13.7 million students. The state provides a stipend for higher education. There were 4.5 million university students in 1994.

1999 KEY EVENTS TIMELINE

January

- Three academic institutions are sanctioned by the United States under allegations of aiding Iran's nuclear weapons research program.

- President Yeltsin is hospitalized with a large gastric ulcer.

- The Russian government estimates over 1.5 million Chinese are illegally residing in Russia.

February

- International Monetary Fund (IMF) officials meet with Prime Minister Primakov to discuss payment of Russia's debt.

- Russia's central bank confirms that about $50 billion in foreign exchange reserves have se-

cretly been managed by a small offshore company for the last five years.

- Chechnya's president, Aslan Maskhadov, mandates Islamic law and calls for an Islamic-based constitution.

- The Duma ratifies treaty with Ukraine abandoning Russia's claim to Crimea.

- World premiere of The Barber of Siberia, the most expensive Russian film ever made, directed by Nikita Mikhalkov.

- Russian Space Agency and NASA arrange schedule for the International Space Station.

March

- Bombing in the city of Vladikavkaz kills 62 and wounds 100 more.

- The Duma adopts censorship law to set moral standards for media, establishing a Supreme Council that will determine morality and set fines for violations.

April

- New oil pipeline opens through Georgia, threatening Russia's monopoly over the shipment of Azerbaijani oil to the Black Sea.

- The government defaults on bonds issued from hard currency that had once been deposited in Soviet banks.

- Russo-Chinese Demarcation Commission completes seven-year mapping project of the countries' common border.

May

- President Yeltsin fires Prime Minister Yevgeny Primakov amid Russia's economic crisis.

- Russia participates with Group of Eight countries in drafting plan to end fighting in Yugoslavia.

- Parliament rejects the five counts of impeachment brought against President Yeltsin.

- Parliament confirms Sergei Stepashin as new prime minister.

June

- Chechen rebels fire on Russian outposts near the border, killing several Russian troops and policemen. The government closes most of the checkpoints between Russia and Chechnya.

- Russian troops seize the airport at Pristina, Yugoslavia, amid NATO's military occupation of Kosovo.

July

- Russia begins artillery fire on rebel military forces in Chechnya after another border attack kills more Russian troops.

August

- Bank of New York is connected with $4.2 billion in money laundering by Russian gangster.

- Russia boycotts NATO-sponsored military exercise to protest the April bombings in Kosovo.

September

- Three apartment buildings are bombed in Moscow and two more are bombed in southern cities, resulting in 300 fatalities.

- Russian aircraft strike Grozny, the capital of Chechnya, in a two-week air campaign of bombings and missile attacks.

- Russian ground troops and tanks launch an offensive into northern Chechnya.

October

- Russian prime minister Vladimir Putin insists that negotiations with Chechnya will not occur until the Chechen government hands over all suspected ''terrorists.''

November

- Russia opens border crossings with the breakaway Caucasus republic of Chechnya after mounting criticism of the treatment of refugees trying to flee the conflict.

- Political consensus over Chechnya is shattered when the liberal Yabloko party calls for a halt to the mass bombardment of the separatist Caucasian region and the opening of political talks with Chechen president, Aslan Maskhadov.

- Media mogul Vladimir Gusinsky's company, Media-Most, is pursued through Russian courts for a $42.2m loan; a Gusinsky spokesman claims the purpose is to drive Gusinsky's popular television station off the air before next month's general election.

- President Boris Yeltsin travels to Turkey to meet with 50 other world leaders at a summit in Istanbul; a diplomatic disaster over the war in Chechnya is carefully averted.

- The Kremlin's forces escalate their assault on the town of Urus-Martan, just south of the Chechen capital of Grozny, with the stated goal of surrounding the Chechen capital by mid-December.

December

- Belarus and Russia agree in principle to form an economic alliance.

- Russian forces tell residents of Grozny, the capital of the breakaway republic of Chechnya, to leave the city or face bombardment. The Russian military and rebel forces in Grozny engage in vicious fighting through the end of the year.

- In the general election held December 19, the political parties of Vladimir Putin and the Kremlin win broad support.

- On December 31, President Boris Yeltsin surprises the world by resigning in a televised speech to the Russian people, and names Vladimir Putin acting president. Elections will be held March 26.

ANALYSIS OF EVENTS: 1999

BUSINESS AND THE ECONOMY

Russia's economy in early 1999 was still ailing from the financial collapse in August 1998 that caused the ruble's value to plummet as the government defaulted on $40 billion in ruble bonds. The decline of the country's banking system had also been initiated by a poor autumn harvest and a reduction of foreign exchange due to the fall in world oil prices by the beginning of 1999. Furthermore, a new oil pipeline from Azerbaijan through Georgia was opened in the spring, bypassing the need for overland transport through Russia and causing the country to lose its monopoly over the shipment of Azerbaijani oil to the Black Sea.

By early 1999, Russia's capital losses were totaling some $2 billion per month. In February, with the government badly in debt, Prime Minister Primakov met with International Monetary Fund (IMF) officials to discuss how the country would schedule debt payments to the IMF and World Bank that were anticipated to total $4.8 billion for 1999. Russia owed an estimated $17.5 billion in interest and principal to foreign banks, but it would be unable to keep up payments without more aid.

As the economic situation worsened, Russia's central bank confirmed that about $50 billion in foreign exchange reserves had been secretly managed by a small offshore company since 1994. The government defaulted on bonds issued from hard currency that had once been deposited in former Soviet banks. More accounts of large-scale money laundering resurfaced in the summer with reports that between October 1998 and March 1999, approximately $4.2 billion had allegedly been funneled through the Bank of New York by Semyon Yukovich Mogilevich, a Russian mobster.

GOVERNMENT AND POLITICS

In 1999, scandals involving corruption and money laundering dominated Russian politics. Meanwhile, Russia's foreign affairs were dominated by two military operations: in the Kosovo region of Yugoslavia in the spring, and in Chechnya (in the Caucasus area of the Russian Federation) during the summer and fall.

Late in March 1999 Prime Minister Primakov went to Belgrade, Yugoslavia as a moderator to meet with Slobodan Milosevic in order to help facilitate an end to the NATO bombing campaign of Yugoslavia that had begun on March 24. In April, Russia's envoy to Yugoslavia, Viktor Chernomyrdin, was informed by Milosevic that Yugoslavia would agree to a UN-led operation within Kosovo.

By May, Russia and other Group of Eight (leading industrial countries) began drafting a cease-fire plan that would remove Serbian troops from Kosovo and replace them with an international peacekeeping force. Russia then suspended its ties with NATO after its request for a temporary halt to the bombings was denied. In June, 200 Russian troops suddenly seized the airport at Pristina, Yugoslavia amid NATO's military occupation of Kosovo, a move which allowed Russia to assert its influence. About 3,600 Russian peacekeepers eventually were sent to Kosovo under a hastily made joint military agreement with the United States. Russia later boycotted NATO-sponsored military exercises in August to protest NATO's handling of the situation in Kosovo.

Late in 1998, Chechnya's parliament was suspended by the republic's supreme Islamic court, which decreed it that it was not in accord with Islamic law. As the Chechen disagreement resurfaced, Russia's government was initially hesitant to return troops to Grozny, Chechnya's capital. The city was the center of intense fighting during a devastating 1994–96 war with Russia in which Chechen rebels effectively won autonomy but not total independence from Russia. In February 1999,

Chechnya's president, Aslan Maskhadov, mandated Islamic law and called for an Islamic-based constitution, thus furthering the rift between Chechnya and the Russian Federation.

During 1999, Russia endured sustained political uncertainty, as President Yeltsin's health was still faltering—early in the year he was hospitalized with a large gastric ulcer—and his dismissal of key officials within his administration contributed to the sense of political instability. The political muckraking and news about scandals was also seen as a precursor to the general elections held on December 19th. In May, President Yeltsin fired Prime Minister Primakov amid Russia's continued economic crisis. Parliament confirmed Sergei Stepashin as new prime minister. That month also, the Duma (parliament) rejected the five counts of impeachment that had been brought against President Yeltsin by its Communist Party members. In August, Stepashin was fired without explanation. Yeltsin nominated Vladimir Putin, former KGB official, head of the FSB, and secretary of the Russian Security Council. Putin became the fourth prime minister in 18 months. On December 31, with his popularity among Russia's citizens very low, Yeltsin resigned, naming Prime Minister Putin, who was the leading candidate for the March 2000 presidential elections, as acting president.

Russia also worked on resolving several territorial disputes that originated during the Soviet and imperial eras. In February, the Duma ratified a treaty with Ukraine that gave up Russia's claim to the Crimean peninsula along the Black Sea. However, Ukraine would still permit Russia's Black Sea fleet to operate in the Crimea from the port of Sevastopol. In April, the Russo-Chinese Demarcation Commission completed a seven-year mapping of the two countries' border, ending three centuries of ongoing border disputes. The only remaining uncertainty concerned the status of three large islands which were to remain under Russia's control until their final territorial status was determined. Russia also conducted talks with Japan over the status of the Kuril Islands, which both countries claimed after the end of World War II. During the mid-1990s, the two countries had set a goal of resolving the issue by 2000, but the negotiations remained deadlocked during 1999.

CULTURE AND SOCIETY

Urban terrorism became an important social issue, as a wave of apartment building bombings occurred throughout 1999. In March, a bombing in the city of Vladikavkaz (in the North Ossetia region of the Caucasus within the Russian Federation) killed 62 and wounded 100 more. The government suspected Chechen rebels but had no convincing evidence to determine responsibility. In June, Chechen rebels started firing on Russian outposts near the border, killing several Russian troops and policemen. As tension rose, the Russian government closed most of the checkpoints between Russia and Chechnya. In September, three apartment buildings were bombed in Moscow and two more were bombed in southern cities, resulting in 300 fatalities. The government blamed Chechen rebels again for the bombings, but there was still no conclusive proof, and Chechen authorities denied any responsibility.

Frustrated, the administration began to publicly ridicule its own 1996 peace accord with Chechnya as a political misstep. Later that month, Russia began to shell rebel military forces in Chechnya after another border attack killed more Russian troops. As the internal border skirmish intensified, Russian aircraft then struck Grozny, the capital of Chechnya, in a two-week air campaign of bombings and missile attacks. Chechen leaders claimed that over 300 civilians were killed during the first five days of the bombings. Russian ground troops and tanks launched an offensive into northern Chechnya and proceeded to the outskirts of Grozny. Some 100,000 people in Chechnya fled to neighboring Ingushetia (also within the Russian Federation).

During Russia's efforts to settle the final status of its border with China, Russian authorities determined that over 1.5 million Chinese were living illegally within Russia.

In February, the Russian Space Agency and NASA arranged a schedule for the construction of the International Space Station. In July the agency also determined that it could not afford to spend the estimated $250 million needed to keep the 13-year-old beleaguered Mir space station in orbit. The agency and NASA began coordinating for the planned descent and destruction of Mir in 2000. Three Russian academic institutions are sanctioned by the United States under allegations of aiding Iran's nuclear weapons research program.

In March, the Duma adopted a censorship law to set moral standards for media. The law called for the establishment of a 12-member appointed Supreme Council that would define and determine morality and set up a schedule of fines for violations.

DIRECTORY

CENTRAL GOVERNMENT
Head of State

Prime Minister and Acting President
Vladimir Vladimirovich Putin, Office of the President, Kremlin, Moscow, Russia
PHONE: +7 (095) 9100766
FAX: +7 (095) 2068510
E-MAIL: president@gov.ru

First Deputy Premier
Nikolay Yemelyanovich Aksenenko, Office of the First Deputy Premier

First Deputy Premier
Viktor Borisovich Khristenko, Office of the First Deputy Premier

Deputy Premier
Ilya Iosifovich Klebanov, Office of the Deputy Premier

Deputy Premier
Valentina Ivanovna Matviyenko, Office of the Deputy Premier

Deputy Premier
Vladimir Nikolayevich Shcherbak, Office the Deputy Premier

Ministers

Minister of Agriculture and Food
Aleksey Vasilyevich Gordeyev, Ministry of Agriculture and Food, Orlikov, l-11, 107139 Moscow, Russia
PHONE: +7 2076742
FAX: +7 2078362

Minister of Anti-Monopoly Policy and Enterprise Support
Ilya Arturovich Yuzhanov, Ministry of Anti-Monopoly Policy and Enterprise Support

Minister of Nuclear Atomic Energy
Yevgeniy Olegovich Adamov, Ministry of Nuclear Atomic Energy, Ordynka B, 24-26, 109017 Moscow, Russia
PHONE: +7 2394753

Minister of CIS Affairs
Leonid Vladimirovich Drachevskiy, Ministry of CIS Affairs, Varvarka, 7, 103012 Moscow, Russia

PHONE: +7 2061365

Minister of Civil Defense, Emergencies, and Natural Disasters

Sergey Kuzhugetovich Shoygu, Ministry of Civil Defense, Emergencies, and Natural Disasters, Teatralnyj, 3, 103012 Moscow, Russia
PHONE: +7 9263901
FAX: +7 9241946

Minister of Culture

Vladimir Konstantinovich Yegorov, Ministry of Culture, Kitaigorodsky, 7103693 Moscow, Russia
PHONE: +7 9251195
FAX: +7 9281791

Minister of Defense

Marshall Igor Dmitriyevich Sergeyev, Ministry of Defense
PHONE: +7 2968900

Minister of Economy

Andrey Georgiyevich Shapovalyants, Ministry of Economy, Arbat Novyj, 19, 103025 Moscow, Russia
PHONE: +7 2037534

Minister of Education

Vladimir Mikhaylovich Filippov, Ministry of Education, Chistoprudnyj, 6, 101856 Moscow, Russia
PHONE: +7 9270568
FAX: +7 9246989

Minister of Federation and National Policy

Vyacheslav Aleksandrovich Mikhaylov, Ministry of Federation and National Policy, Trubnikovskij, 19, 121803 Moscow, Russia
PHONE: +7 2488408
FAX: +7 2024490

Minister of Finance

Mikhail Mikhaylovich Kasyanov, Ministry of Finances, Iljinka, 9, 103097 Moscow, Russia
PHONE: +7 2989101
FAX: +7 9250889

Minister of Foreign Affairs

Igor Sergeyevich Ivanov, Ministry of Foreign Affairs, Smolenskaya Sennaya, 32-34, 121200 Moscow, Russia
PHONE: +7 2441606
FAX: +7 2302130

Minister of Fuel and Energy

Viktor Ivanovich Kalyuzhnyy, Ministry of Fuel and Energy, Kitajgorodskij, 7, 103074 Moscow, Russia

PHONE: +7 2205500
FAX: +7 2068107

Minister of Health

Yuriy Leonidovich Shevchenko, Ministry of Health, Rakhmanovsky 3, 101431 Moscow, Russia
PHONE: +7 9272848
FAX: +7 9210195

Minister of Internal Affairs

Vladimir Borisovich Rushaylo, Ministry of Internal Affairs, Zhitnaya, 16, 117049 Moscow, Russia
PHONE: +7 2377585
FAX: +7 2226669

Minister of Justice

Yuriy Yakovlevich Chayka, Ministry of Justice, Voroncovo Pole, 109830 Moscow, Russia
PHONE: +7 2060554

Minister of Labor and Social Development

Sergey Vyacheslavovich Kalashnikov, Ministry of Labor and Social Development, Birzevaja, 1, 103706 Moscow, Russia
PHONE: +7 2612030
FAX: +7 2302407

Minister of Natural Resources

Boris Aleksandrovich Yatskevich, Ministry of Natural Resources, Gruyinskaja B, 4-6, 123812 Moscow, Russia
PHONE: +7 2542766
FAX: +7 2548283

Minister of Press, Television and Radio Broadcasting, and Mass Communication

Mikhail Yuryevich Lesin, Ministry of Press, Television and Radio Broadcasting, and Mass Communication, Tverskaja, 7, 103375 Moscow, Russia
PHONE: +7 2927144

Minister of Railroads

Nikolay Yemel'yanovich Aksenenko, Ministry of Railroads, Basmannaja Novaja, 2, 107174 Moscow, Russia
PHONE: +7 2629901
FAX: +7 2629095

Minister of Science and Technology

Mikhail Petrovich Kirpichnikov, Ministry of Science and Technology, Tverskaja, 11, 103905 Moscow, Russia
PHONE: +7 2291192
FAX: +7 302660

Minister of Sports and Tourism
Boris Viktorovich Ivanyuzhenkov, Ministry of
Sports and Tourism

Minister of State Property
Farit Rafikovich Gazizullin, Ministry of State
Property

Minister of Taxes and Levies
Aleksandr Petrovich Pochinok, Ministry of Taxes
and Levies

Minister of Trade
Mikhail Yefimovich Fradkov, Ministry of Trade,
Smolyenskaya Sennaya, 32-34, 121200 Moscow,
Russia
PHONE: +7 2442450
FAX: +7 2443068

Minister of Transportation
Sergey Ottovich Frank, Ministry of
Transportation, Sadovaja-Samotechnaja, 10,
101433 Moscow, Russia
PHONE: +7 2000809
FAX: +7 2993996

POLITICAL ORGANIZATIONS
Yabloko Bloc
NAME: Grigoriy Alekseyevich Yavlinskiy

Just Cause
NAME: Yegor Timurovich Gaydar; Anatoliy
Borisovich Chubays; Boris Yefimovich Nemtsov;
Sergey Vladlenovich Kiriyenko

Fatherland
NAME: Yuriy Mikhailovich Luzhkov

Russian People's Republican Party
NAME: Aleksandr Ivanovich Lebed

Our Home Is Russia
NAME: Viktor Stepanovich Chernomyrdin

Communist Party of the Russian Federation
NAME: Gennadiy Andreyevich Zyuganov

Liberal Democratic Party of Russia
NAME: Vladimir Vol'fovich Zhirinovskiy

Agrarian Party
NAME: Mikhail Ivanovich Lapshin

Working Russia
NAME: Viktor Ivanovich Anpilov; Stanislav
Terekhov

Russian National Unity
NAME: Aleksandr Barkashov

Russia's Democratic Choice
Power To the People
Congress of Russian Communities
Forward, Russia!
Women of Russia

DIPLOMATIC REPRESENTATION
Embassies in the Russian Federation
Afghanistan
Svertchkov str., 3/2, Moscow, Russia
PHONE: +7 9287278
FAX: +7 9219563

Albania
Mitnaya str., 3 Ap.23, Moscow, Russia
PHONE: +7 2307732
FAX: +7 2307635

Algeria
Krapivinsky str., 1-a, Moscow, Russia
PHONE: +7 2006642; 9248620; 9230298
FAX: +7 2000222

Angola
Uloph Palme str., 6, Moscow, Russia
PHONE: +7 1436324

Argentina
Sadovaya-Triumphalnaya str., 4/10, Moscow,
Russia
PHONE: +7 2990367; 2992329; 2991670;
2998261
FAX: +7 2004218

Armenia
Armiansky str., 2, Moscow, Russia
PHONE: +7 9241269; 9234784

Australia
Kropotkinsky str., 13, Moscow, Russia
PHONE: +7 9566070
FAX: +7 9566170

Austria
Starokonushenny str., 1, Moscow, Russia
PHONE: +7 2017379; 2012166; 2012169;
2017307

Azerbaijan
Leontievsky str., 16, Moscow, Russia
PHONE: +7 2291649
FAX: +7 2025072

Bahrain
Ordinka str.,18, Moscow, Russia
PHONE: +7 2300013

Bangladesh
Zemledelchesky str.,6, Moscow, Russia
PHONE: +7 2467804
FAX: +7 2483185

Belarus
Maroseyka str., 17/6, Moscow, Russia
PHONE: +7 9247031

Belgium
Moltchanovka str., 7, Moscow, Russia
PHONE: +7 2916027; 2916018; 2910531; 2911604
FAX: +7 2916005

Benin
Uspensky str., 4a, Moscow, Russia
PHONE: +7 2992360
FAX: +7 2000226

Bolivia
Lopuhinsky str., 5, Moscow, Russia
PHONE: +7 2012508; 2012513
FAX: +7 2012508

Brazil
Nikitinskaya str., 54, Moscow, Russia
PHONE: +7 2904022; 2904023; 2904024; 2904025; 2904026

Bulgaria
Mosfilmovskaya str., 66, Moscow, Russia
PHONE: +7 1439022; 1439023; 1439027
FAX: +7 2323302

Burundi
Kalujskaya sq. 1, Ap. 226-227, Moscow, Russia
PHONE: +7 2302564
FAX: +7 2302009

Cape Verde
Rublevskoe str., 26, Ap. 180, Moscow, Russia
PHONE: +7 4154503
FAX: +7 4154504

Cambodia
Starokonushenny str., 16, Moscow, Russia
PHONE: +7 2014736; 2013925; 2012115
FAX: +7 9566573

Cameroon
Povarskaya str., 40, Moscow, Russia

PHONE: +7 2906549; 2900063
FAX: +7 2906116

Canada
Starokonushenny str., 23, Moscow, Russia
PHONE: +7 9566666; 9566158

Central African Republic
26 Bakinskikh Kommisarov str., 9, Ap. 124-125, Moscow, Russia
PHONE: +7 4344520

Chad
Rublevskoe str., 26/1, Moscow, Russia
PHONE: +7 4154139; 4154122
FAX: +7 4152941

Chile
Junnosti str., 11, Building 1, Moscow, Russia
PHONE: +7 3739571; 3739176
FAX: +7 3737725

China
Drujbi str., 6, Moscow, Russia
PHONE: +7 9561169

Colombia
Burdenko str., 18, Moscow, Russia
PHONE: +7 2483042; 2483073
FAX: +7 2483025

Congo
Donskaya str., 7, Moscow, Russia
PHONE: +7 2363368

Democratic Republic of Congo
Pretchistensky str., 12, Moscow, Russia
PHONE: +7 2017948

Costa Rica
Rublevskoe str., 26, Ap. 23-24, Moscow, Russia
PHONE: +7 4154014
FAX: +7 4154042

Côte d'Ivoire
Korobeinikov str., 14/9, Moscow, Russia
PHONE: +7 2012375; 2012400
FAX: +7 2001292

Croatia
Korobeinikov str., 16/10, Moscow, Russia
PHONE: +7 2013222; 2013868; 2013977
FAX: +7 2014624

Cuba
Leontievsky str., 9, Moscow, Russia
PHONE: +7 2902882; 2028261

Cyprus
Nikitskaya str., 51, Moscow, Russia
PHONE: +7 2902154; 2906523
FAX: +7 2001254

Czech Republic
Uliusa Futchika str., 12/14, Moscow, Russia
PHONE: +7 2510540; 2510545
FAX: +7 2501523

Denmark
Pretchistensky str., 9, Moscow, Russia
PHONE: +7 2017860; 2017868; 2012227;
2012232
FAX: +7 2015357; 2012295

Ecuador
Gorohovsky str., 12, Moscow, Russia
PHONE: +7 2615544; 2612739
FAX: +7 2677079
E-MAIL: mosecual2@glas.apc.org
PHONE: +7 24397645

Eritrea
Meshanskaya str., 17, Moscow, Russia
PHONE: +7 9710620
FAX: +7 9713767

Estonia
Maly Kislovsky str., 5, Moscow, Russia
PHONE: +7 2905013; 2904661; 2915807
FAX: +7 2023830

Ethiopia
Orlovo-Davidovsky str., 6, Moscow, Russia
PHONE: +7 2801616; 2801676
FAX: +7 2806608

Finland
Kropotkinsky str., 15/17, Moscow, Russia
PHONE: +7 2464027
FAX: +7 2473301

France
Bolshaya Yakimanka str., 45, Moscow, Russia
PHONE: +7 2360003
FAX: +7 2371956

Gabon
Denejny str., 16, Moscow, Russia
PHONE: +7 2411585; 2410080
FAX: +7 2440694

Georgia
Maly Rjevsky str., 6, Moscow, Russia
PHONE: +7 2906902
FAX: +7 2915990

Germany
Mosfilmovskaya str., 56, Moscow, Russia
PHONE: +7 9561080
FAX: +7 9362401

Ghana
Skatertny str., 14, Moscow, Russia

PHONE: +7 2021870; 2021871; 2021890
FAX: +7 2022941

Greece
Leontievsky str., 4, Moscow, Russia
PHONE: +7 2905742; 2911446; 2904558
FAX: +7 2001252

Guatemala
Korovy Val str., 7, Ap. 92, Moscow, Russia
PHONE: +7 2382214
FAX: +7 9566270

Guinea
Pomerancev str., 6, Moscow, Russia
PHONE: +7 2013601
FAX: +7 2202138

Hungary
Mosfilmovskaya str., 62, Moscow, Russia
PHONE: +7 1438611; 1438612; 1438613;
1438614; 1438615
FAX: +7 1434625; 1478156
E-MAIL: huembmow@glasnet.ru

Indonesia
Novokuznetskaya str., 12, Moscow, Russia
PHONE: +7 9519549; 9519550; 9519551

Iraq
Pogodinskaya str., 12, Moscow, Russia
PHONE: +7 2465506
FAX: +7 2302922

Iran
Pokrovsky str., 7, Moscow, Russia
PHONE: +7 9178440; 9177282
FAX: +7 2302897

Ireland
Groholsky str., 5, Moscow, Russia
PHONE: +7 7420907
FAX: +7 9752066

Israel
Bolshaya Ordinka str., 56, Moscow, Russia
PHONE: +7 2306700
FAX: +7 2381346

Italy
Denejny str., 5, Moscow, Russia
PHONE: +7 2411533; 2411534; 2411535

Jamaica
Korovy Val str., 7, Ap. 70-71, Moscow, Russia
PHONE: +7 2372320
FAX: +7 2302102

Japan
Kalashny str., 12, Moscow, Russia
PHONE: +7 2918500; 2918501

Jordan
Mamonovsky str., 3, Moscow, Russia
PHONE: +7 2991242; 2992845; 2994344
FAX: +7 2994354

Kazakstan
Tchistoprudny str., 3a, Moscow, Russia
PHONE: +7 9271820
FAX: +7 2082650

Kenya
Bolshaya Ordinka str., 70, Moscow, Russia
PHONE: +7 2373462; 2374541; 2374702
FAX: +7 2302340

North Korea
Mosfilmovskaya str., 72, Moscow, Russia
PHONE: +7 1436249
FAX: +7 9382195

South Korea
Spiridonovka str., 14, Moscow, Russia
PHONE: +7 9561474
FAX: +7 9562434; 2035087

Kuwait
Mosfilmovskaya str., 44, Moscow, Russia
PHONE: +7 1474441; 1470040; 1473488
FAX: +7 9566032

Kyrgyzstan
Bolshaya Ordinka str., 64, Moscow, Russia
PHONE: +7 2374601; 2374882

Laos
Malaya Nikitskaya str., 18, Moscow, Russia
PHONE: +7 2902560
FAX: +7 2904246

Latvia
Chapligina str., 3, Moscow, Russia
PHONE: +7 9252707; 9248886
FAX: +7 9239295

Lebanon
Sadovaya-Samotechnaya str., 14, Moscow, Russia
PHONE: +7 2000022; 2002083

Libya
Mosfilmovskaya str., 38, Moscow, Russia
PHONE: +7 1430354; 1437722; 1437700
FAX: +7 1430354; 1437722; 1437700

Lithuania
Borisoglebsky str., 10, Moscow, Russia
PHONE: +7 2912643; 2911698
FAX: +7 2023516; 2039155

Luxembourg
Hruschevsky str., 3, Moscow, Russia

PHONE: +7 2022171; 2025381
FAX: +7 2005243

Macedonia
Dmitria Ulianova str., 16, Building 2, Ground floor, Moscow, Russia
PHONE: +7 1243357
FAX: +7 1243359

Madagascar
Kursovoi str., 5, Moscow, Russia
PHONE: +7 2900214
FAX: +7 2023453

Malaysia
Mosfilmovskaya str., 50, Moscow, Russia
PHONE: +7 1471514; 1471523; 9566817
FAX: +7 1471526; 9379602

Mali
Novokuznetskaya str., 11, Moscow, Russia
PHONE: +7 2310655; 2312784
FAX: +7 2302889

Malta
Dmitria Ulianova str., 7, Ap. 219, Moscow, Russia
PHONE: +7 2371939; 2302524
FAX: +7 2372158

Mauritania
Bolshaya Ordinka str., 66, Moscow, Russia
PHONE: +7 2373792; 2371132
FAX: +7 2372861

Mexico
Bolshoi Levshinsky str., 4, Moscow, Russia
PHONE: +7 2015631; 2012593
FAX: +7 2302042

Moldova
Kuznetsky Most str., 18, Moscow, Russia
PHONE: +7 9246342
FAX: +7 9249590

Mongolia
Borisoglebsky str., 11, Moscow, Russia
PHONE: +7 2906792

Morocco
Pretchistensky str., 8, Moscow, Russia
PHONE: +7 2017351; 2017395; 2017284

Mozambique
Giliarovskogo str., 20, Moscow, Russia
PHONE: +7 2844007; 2844319
FAX: +7 2004235

Myanmar
Nikitskaya str., 41, Moscow, Russia
PHONE: +7 2910534

Namibia
2 Kazatchy str., 7, Moscow, Russia
PHONE: +7 2303275
FAX: +7 2302274

Nepal
2 Neopalimovsky str., 14/7, Moscow, Russia
PHONE: +7 2440215; 2416943
FAX: +7 2440000

Nigeria
Malaya Nikitskaya str., 13, Moscow, Russia
PHONE: +7 2903783; 2903785
FAX: +7 9562825
E-MAIL: nigeriamosco@glasnet.ru

Norway
Povarskaya str., 7, Moscow, Russia
PHONE: +7 9562005
FAX: +7 9562647; 9562483

Oman
Staromonetny str., 14, Buildings 6 and 7,
Moscow, Russia
PHONE: +7 2302587; 2301255; 2302052
FAX: +7 2301544

Pakistan
Sadovaya-Kudrinskaya str., 17, Moscow, Russsia
PHONE: +7 2503991; 2549791

Palestine
Kropotkinsky str., 26, Moscow, Russia
PHONE: +7 2014340; 2013682
FAX: +7 2302083

Panama
Mosfilmovskaya str., 50, Building 1, Moscow,
Russia
PHONE: +7 9560729; 1430631
FAX: +7 9560730

Paraguay
Gruzinsky str., 3, Ap. 41-42, Moscow, Russia
PHONE: +7 2547223
FAX: +7 2549055

Peru
Smolensky str., 22/14, Ap. 15, Moscow, Russia
PHONE: +7 2487738; 2486794; 2482302
FAX: +7 2302000

Philippines
Karmanicsky str., 6, Moscow, Russia
PHONE: +7 2410563

Poland
Klimashkina str., 4, Moscow, Russia
PHONE: +7 2550017

Portugal
Botanichesky str., 1, Moscow, Russia
PHONE: +7 2803319; 2801228
FAX: +7 2809203

Qatar
Korovy Val str., 7, Ap. 196-198, Moscow,
Russia
PHONE: +7 2301577
FAX: +7 2302240

Romania
Mosfilmovskaya str., 64, Moscow, Russia
PHONE: +7 1430424

Saudi Arabia
2 Neopalimovsky str., 4, Moscow, Russia
PHONE: +7 2452310; 2453491; 2453970
FAX: +7 2469471

Serbia
Mosfilmovskaya str., 46, Moscow, Russia
FAX: +7 1474106; 1479008

Sierra Leone
Rublevskoe str., 26, Building 1, Ap. 58-59,
Moscow, Russia
PHONE: +7 4154166
FAX: +7 4152985

Singapore
Kamennaya Sloboda str., 5, Moscow, Russia
PHONE: +7 2413913; 2413914

Slovakia
Uliusa Fuchika str., 17/19, Moscow, Russia
PHONE: +7 9564923
FAX: +7 9732081; 2501591

Slovenia
Malaya Dmitrovka str., 14, Building 1, Moscow,
Russia
PHONE: +7 2090203; 2090815; 2090825
FAX: +7 2001568

Somalia
Kutuzovsky str., 13, Ap. 131-132, Moscow,
Russia
PHONE: +7 2439563
FAX: +7 2439563

South Africa
Bolshoi Strochenovsky str., 22/25, Moscow,
Russia
PHONE: +7 2306869
FAX: +7 2001230
E-MAIL: saembmsk@glasnet.ru

Sri Lanka
Shepkina str., 24, Moscow, Russia

PHONE: +7 2881620; 2881463; 2881651
FAX: +7 2881757

Sudan
Povarskaya str., 9, Moscow, Russia
PHONE: +7 2903732
FAX: +7 2903985

Sweden
Mosfilmovskaya str., 60, Moscow, Russia
PHONE: +7 9561200
FAX: +7 9561203

Switzerland
Ogorodnaya Sloboda str., 2/5, Moscow, Russia
PHONE: +7 2583830
FAX: +7 9211627

Syria
Mansurovsky str., 4, Moscow, Russia
PHONE: +7 2031521; 2031528

Tajikistan
Granatny str., 13, Moscow, Russia
PHONE: +7 2906102

Tanzania
Piatnitskaya str., 33, Moscow, Russia
PHONE: +7 2349045
FAX: +7 9530785

Thailand
Bolshaya Spasskaya str., 9, Moscow, Russia
PHONE: +7 2080817; 2080856
FAX: +7 9612090

Togo
Gruzinsky str., 3, Ap. 227-228, Moscow, Russia
PHONE: +7 2542012
FAX: +7 2541965

Tunisia
Malaya Nikitskaya str., 28/1, Moscow, Russia
PHONE: +7 2912858; 2912869; 2916223
FAX: +7 2917588

Turkey
7-th Rostovsky str., 12, Moscow, Russia
PHONE: +7 2460009; 2460010; 2461989
FAX: +7 2456348

Turkmenistan
Philippovsky str., 22, Moscow, Russia
PHONE: +7 2916636
FAX: +7 2910935

Uganda
Mamonovsky str., 5, Moscow, Russia
PHONE: +7 2510060; 2510061; 2510062;
2998397; 2993093
FAX: +7 2004200

Ukraine
Stanislavskogo str., 18, Moscow, Russia
PHONE: +7 2293542
FAX: +7 9246862

Unitied Arab Emirates
Ulofa Palme str., 4, Moscow, Russia
PHONE: +7 1476286; 1470066; 1436413;
1436414

United Kingdom
Sofyskaya str., 14, Moscow, Russia
PHONE: +7 9567200
FAX: +7 9567420

United States
Novinsky str., 19/23, Moscow, Russia
PHONE: +7 2522451; 2522452; 2522453;
2522454; 2522455; 2522456; 2522457; 2522458;
2522459

Uruguay
Lomonosovky str., 38, Moscow, Russia
PHONE: +7 1430401; 1430404
FAX: +7 9382045; 1430404; 2388918
E-MAIL: ururus@glasnet.ru

Vietnam
Pirogovskaya str., 13, Moscow, Russia
PHONE: +7 2450925

Yemen
2 Neopalimovsky str., 6, Moscow, Russia
PHONE: +7 2461531

Zambia
Mira str., 52a, Moscow, Russia
PHONE: +7 2885001; 2885083

Zimbabwe
Serpov str., 6, Moscow, Russia
PHONE: +7 2483150; 2484367; 2484364
FAX: +7 2302497

JUDICIAL SYSTEM
The Constitutional Court
Supreme Court
The High Court of Arbitration

FURTHER READING
Articles
Cullison, Alan S. "Russian Tanks and Troops Drive Deeper into Chechnya." *Wall Street Journal* 6 October 1999, p. A18.

DeGregorio, Paul. "Bombings Increase Tension, But Russian Democracy Holds On." *St. Louis Post-Dispatch* 20 September 1999, p. D17.

Hoffman, David. "Russia, One Year After the Fall: Ruble's Crash Has Pumped New Life Into Some Industries." *Washington Post* 17 August 1999, p. A1.

"Money Can't Buy Me Love." *The Economist* (February 6, 1999): 23–25.

Reeves, Phil. "The Last Film Tsar of All the Russias." *Independent* (February 20, 1999): 14.

"Russia's Economic Quagmire." *The Economist* (April 24, 1999): 69–70.

"Russia, Financial Outcast." *The Economist* (February 6, 1999): 17–18.

"Russia's Political Battle Looms." *The Economist* (September 4, 1999): 49–50.

"Russia's Violent Southern Rim." *The Economist* (March 27, 1999): 53.

Internet

Institute for the Study of Conflict, Ideology and Policy. Available Online @ http://www.bu.edu/iscip (November 16, 1999).

Russia Today. Available Online @ http://www.russiatoday.com (November 16, 1999).

RUSSIA: STATISTICAL DATA

For sources and notes see "Sources of Statistics" in the front of each volume.

GEOGRAPHY

Geography (1)

Area:

Total: 17,075,200 sq km.

Land: 16,995,800 sq km.

Water: 79,400 sq km.

Area—comparative: slightly less than 1.8 times the size of the US.

Land boundaries:

Total: 19,917 km.

Border countries: Azerbaijan 284 km, Belarus 959 km, China (southeast) 3,605 km, China (south) 40 km, Estonia 294 km, Finland 1,313 km, Georgia 723 km, Kazakhstan 6,846 km, North Korea 19 km, Latvia 217 km, Lithuania (Kaliningrad Oblast) 227 km, Mongolia 3,441 km, Norway 167 km, Poland (Kaliningrad Oblast) 206 km, Ukraine 1,576 km.

Coastline: 37,653 km.

Climate: ranges from steppes in the south through humid continental in much of European Russia; subarctic in Siberia to tundra climate in the polar north; winters vary from cool along Black Sea coast to frigid in Siberia; summers vary from warm in the steppes to cool along Arctic coast.

Terrain: broad plain with low hills west of Urals; vast coniferous forest and tundra in Siberia; uplands and mountains along southern border regions.

Natural resources: wide natural resource base including major deposits of oil, natural gas, coal, and many strategic minerals, timber.

Note: formidable obstacles of climate, terrain, and distance hinder exploitation of natural resources.

HUMAN FACTORS

Demographics (2A)

	1990	1995	1998	2000	2010	2020	2030	2040	2050
Population	148,088.1	148,123.9	146,861.0	145,904.5	143,917.8	141,311.0	136,396.5	130,426.2	121,776.6
Net migration rate (per 1,000 population)	NA	NA	NA	NA	NA	NA	NA	NA	NA
Births	NA	NA	NA	NA	NA	NA	NA	NA	NA
Deaths	NA	NA	NA	NA	NA	NA	NA	NA	NA
Life expectancy - males	63.4	57.7	58.6	59.1	62.9	67.7	71.6	74.6	76.8
Life expectancy - females	73.9	71.1	71.6	71.8	74.4	77.5	80.1	82.1	83.6
Birth rate (per 1,000)	13.9	9.6	9.6	9.7	12.9	9.1	9.0	7.9	6.9
Death rate (per 1,000)	11.2	15.1	14.9	15.0	14.1	12.6	12.4	13.7	14.4
Women of reproductive age (15-49 yrs.)	35,998.0	38,187.2	39,004.8	39,191.1	36,660.6	33,546.5	31,515.8	26,109.5	24,469.2
of which are currently married	NA	NA	NA	NA	NA	NA	NA	NA	NA
Fertility rate	1.9	1.4	1.3	1.3	1.7	1.6	1.5	1.4	1.4

Except as noted, values for vital statistics are in thousands; life expectancy is in years.

GEOGRAPHY

Land use:

Arable land: 8%

Permanent crops: 0%

Permanent pastures: 4%

Forests and woodland: 46%

Other: 42% (1993 est.).

HUMAN FACTORS

Health Personnel (3)

Total health expenditure as a percentage of GDP, 1990-1997[a]

Public sector 4.1

Private sector 0.6

Total[b] 5.8

Health expenditure per capita in U.S. dollars, 1990-1997[a]

Purchasing power parity 262

Total 117

Availability of health care facilities per 100,000 people

Hospital beds 1990-1997[a] 1170

Doctors 1993[c] 380

Nurses 1993[c] 659

Ethnic Division (6)

Russian 81.5%

Tatar 3.8%

Ukrainian 3%

Chuvash 1.2%

Bashkir 0.9%

Byelorussian 0.8%

Moldavian 0.7%

Other 8.1%

Religions (7)

Russian Orthodox, Muslim, other.

Languages (8)

Russian, other.

EDUCATION

Educational Attainment (10)

Age group (1989) . . . . .25+

Total population .86,016,990

Highest level attained (%)

No schooling . . . . .NA

First level

Not completed 36.9

Completed . . . . .NA

Entered second level

S-1 . . . . .49.0

S-2 . . . . .NA

Postsecondary 14.1

Literacy Rates (11B)

Adult literacy rate

1980

Male . . . .-

Female . . . .-

1995

Male 100

Female 99

GOVERNMENT & LAW

Political Parties (12)

State Duma	No. of seats
Liberal Democratic Party of Russia	11.2
Our Home Is Russia	10.1
Yabloko Bloc	6.9

Only parties with 5% or more of the vote can participate in the Duma.

Government Budget (13A)

Year: 1995

Total Expenditures: 391,103 Millions of Rubles

Expenditures as a percentage of the total by function:

General public services and public order . . . . .14.14[p]

Defense . . . . .12.22[p]

Education . . . . .2.21[p]

Health . . . . .1.74[p]

Social Security and Welfare . . . . .27.67[p]

Housing and community amenities . . . .

Recreational, cultural, and religious affairs . . . .74[p]

Fuel and energy . . . .

Agriculture, forestry, fishing, and hunting . . . .

Mining, manufacturing, and construction . . . .

Transportation and communication . . . .

Other economic affairs and services . . . .

Military Affairs (14B)

	1992	1993	1994	1995
Military expenditures				
Current dollars (mil.)	159,200	125,000	93,000	76,000
1995 constant dollars (mil.)	171,200	131,000	95,330	76,000
Armed forces (000)	1,900	1,500	1,400	1,400
Gross national product (GNP)				
Current dollars (bil.)	806,900	757,700	676,300	664,000
1995 constant dollars (bil.)	867,900	794,300	693,200	664,000
Central government expenditures (CGE)				
1995 constant dollars (mil.)	544,400	NA	250,500	NA
People (mil.)	148.6	148.5	148.4	148.3
Military expenditure as % of GNP[2]	19.7	16.5	13.8	11.4
Military expenditure as % of CGE[2]	31.5	NA	37.1	NA
Military expenditure per capita (1995 $)	1,152	882	643	513
Armed forces per 1,000 people (soldiers)	12.8	10.1	9.4	9.4
GNP per capita (1995 $)	5,841	5,349	4,673	4,478
Arms imports[6]				
Current dollars (mil.)	0	0	0	0
1995 constant dollars (mil.)	0	0	0	0
Arms exports[6]				
Current dollars (mil.)	2,500	3,100	1,500	3,300
1995 constant dollars (mil.)	2,689	3,250	1,538	3,300
Total imports[7]				
Current dollars (mil.)	36,900	43,700	51,600	55,000
1995 constant dollars (mil.)	39,690	45,810	52,890	50,000
Total exports[7]				
Current dollars (mil.)	42,400	58,200	66,600	77,000
1995 constant dollars (mil.)	45,610	61,020	68,270	77,000
Arms as percent of total imports[8]	0.0	0	0	0
Arms as percent of total exports[8]	5.9	5.3	2.3	4.3

Crime (15)

Crime rate (for 1997)

Crimes reported 2,397,300

Total persons convicted 1,730,900

Crimes per 100,000 population 1,650

Persons responsible for offenses

Total number of suspects 1,372,200

Total number of female suspects 186,600

Total number of juvenile suspects 161,900

LABOR FORCE

Labor Force (16)

Total 66 million (1997).

Unemployment Rate (17)

9% (1997 est.) with considerable additional underemployment.

PRODUCTION SECTOR

Electric Energy (18)

Capacity . . . . .214.687 million kW (1995)

Production . . . . .834 billion kWh (1997)

Consumption per capita . . . . .5,508 kWh (1995)

Transportation (19)

Highways:

total: 948,000 km (including 416,000 km which serve specific industries or farms and are not maintained by governmental highway maintenance departments)

Waterways: total navigable routes in general use 101,000 km; routes with navigation guides serving the Russian River Fleet 95,900 km; routes with night navigational aids 60,400 km; man-made navigable routes 16,900 km (1 January 1994)

Pipelines: crude oil 48,000 km; petroleum products 15,000 km; natural gas 140,000 km (30 June 1993)

Merchant marine:

total: 540 ships (1,000 GRT or over) totaling 4,531,937 GRT/6,253,940 DWT ships by type: barge carrier 1, bulk 18, cargo 291, combination bulk 21, combination ore/oil 12, container 24, multifunction large-load carrier

2, oil tanker 107, passenger 2, passenger-cargo 4, refrigerated cargo 20, roll-on/roll-off cargo 28, short-sea passenger 9, specialized tanker 1 note: Russia owns an additional 176 ships (1,000 GRT or over) totaling 3,240,776 DWT operating under the registries of The Bahamas, Cambodia, Cyprus, Honduras, Liberia, Malta, Panama, Saint Vincent and the Grenadines, and Singapore (1997 est.)

Airports: 2,517 (1994 est.)

Airports—with paved runways:

total: 630

over 3,047 m: 54

2,438 to 3,047 m: 202

1,524 to 2,437 m: 108

914 to 1,523 m: 115

under 914 m: 151 (1994 est.)

Airports—with unpaved runways:

total: 1,887

over 3,047 m: 25

2,438 to 3,047 m: 45

1,524 to 2,437 m: 134

914 to 1,523 m: 291

under 914 m: 1,392 (1994 est.)

Top Agricultural Products (20)

Grain, sugar beets, sunflower seed, vegetables, fruits (because of its northern location does not grow citrus, cotton, tea, and other warm climate products); meat, milk.

MANUFACTURING SECTOR

GDP & Manufacturing Summary (21)

Detailed value added figures are listed by both International Standard Industry Code (ISIC) and product title.

	1980	1985	1990	1994
GDP ($-1990 bil.)[1]	540,061	638,631	608,121	371,895
Per capita ($-1990)[1]	3,900	4,465	4,111	2,524
Manufacturing share (%) (current prices)[1]	36.6	33.2	27.8	27.1
Manufacturing				
Value added ($-1990 mil.)[1]	NA	NA	169,135	86,698
Industrial production index	NA	NA	NA	NA
Value added ($ mil.)	NA	NA	NA	54,150
Gross output ($ mil.)	NA	NA	537,070	116,955
Employment (000)	NA	NA	NA	12,533
Profitability (% of gross output)				
Intermediate input (%)	NA	NA	NA	54
Wages and salaries inc. supplements (%)	NA	NA	NA	13
Gross operating surplus	NA	NA	NA	34
Productivity ($)				
Gross output per worker	NA	NA	NA	9,332
Value added per worker	NA	NA	NA	4,321
Average wage (inc. supplements)	NA	NA	NA	1,185
Value added ($ mil.)				
311/2 Food products	NA	NA	NA	8,697
313 Beverages	NA	NA	NA	715
314 Tobacco products	NA	NA	NA	150
321 Textiles	NA	NA	NA	1,342
322 Wearing apparel	NA	NA	NA	853
323 Leather and fur products	NA	NA	NA	235
324 Footwear	NA	NA	NA	307
331 Wood and wood products	NA	NA	NA	949
332 Furniture and fixtures	NA	NA	NA	583
341 Paper and paper products	NA	NA	NA	889
342 Printing and publishing	NA	NA	NA	428
351 Industrial chemicals	NA	NA	NA	3,902
352 Other chemical products	NA	NA	NA	1,189
353 Petroleum refineries	NA	NA	NA	2,186
354 Miscellaneous petroleum and coal products	NA	NA	NA	713
355 Rubber products	NA	NA	NA	669
356 Plastic products	NA	NA	NA	279
361 Pottery, china and earthenware	NA	NA	NA	255
362 Glass and glass products	NA	NA	NA	243
369 Other non-metal mineral products	NA	NA	NA	3,489
371 Iron and steel	NA	NA	NA	4,861
372 Non-ferrous metals	NA	NA	NA	4,486
381 Metal products	NA	NA	NA	951
382 Non-electrical machinery	NA	NA	NA	7,218
383 Electrical machinery	NA	NA	NA	1,470

	1980	1985	1990	1994
384 Transport equipment	NA	NA	NA	5,355
385 Professional and scientific equipment	NA	NA	NA	881
390 Other manufacturing industries	NA	NA	NA	856

FINANCE, ECONOMICS, & TRADE

Economic Indicators (22)

National product: GDP—purchasing power parity—$692 billion (1997 est.)

National product real growth rate: 0.4% (1997 est.)

National product per capita: $4,700 (1997 est.)

Inflation rate—consumer price index: 11% (1997 est.)

Exchange Rates (24)

Exchange rates:

Rubles per US$1

December 1997	5,941
1997	5,785
1996	5,121
1995	4,559
1994	2,191
1993	992

Top Import Origins (25)

$66.9 billion (1997)

Origins	%
Europe	NA
North America	NA
Japan	NA
Third World countries	NA

NA stands for not available.

Top Export Destinations (26)

$86.7 billion (1997) Data are for 1995 est.

Destinations	%
United States	88

Economic Aid (27)

Recipient: ODA, $15 billion drawn (1990-97). Note: US commitments, including Ex-Im, $15 billion (1990-96); other countries, ODA and OOF bilateral commitments (1990-96), $125 billion.

Import Export Commodities (28)

Import Commodities	Export Commodities
Machinery and equipment	Petroleum and petroleum products
Consumer goods	Natural gas
Medicines	Wood and wood products
Meat	
Grain	Metals
Sugar	Chemicals
Semifinished metal products	And a wide variety of civilian and military manufactures

Balance of Payments (23)

	1994	1995	1996
Exports of goods (f.o.b.)	67,826	82,663	90,232
Imports of goods (f.o.b.)	−48,446	−60,716	−67,406
Trade balance	19,380	21,947	22,826
Services - debits	−20,147	−26,428	−28,040
Services - credits	11,601	14,351	16,449
Private transfers (net)	−99	128	176
Government transfers (net)	−12	−20	−12
Overall balance	10,723	9,978	11,399

RWANDA

Republic of Rwanda
Republika y'u Rwanda

CAPITAL: Kigali.

FLAG: The national flag is a tricolor of red, yellow, and green vertical stripes. The letter ''R'' in black appears in the center of the yellow stripe.

ANTHEM: *Rwanda Rwacu (Our Rwanda).*

MONETARY UNIT: The Rwanda franc (RFr) is a paper currency. There are coins of 1, 5, 10, 20, and 50 francs and notes of 100, 500, 1,000, and 5,000 francs. RFr1 = $0.00322 (or $1 = RFr310.42).

WEIGHTS AND MEASURES: The metric system is the legal standard.

HOLIDAYS: New Year's Day, 1 January; Democracy Day, 28 January; Labor Day, 1 May; Independence Day, 1 July; Peace and National Unity Day, 5 July; Assumption, 15 August; Anniversary of 1961 Referendum, 25 September; Armed Forces' Day, 26 October; All Saints' Day, 1 November; Christmas, 25 December. Movable religious holidays include Easter Monday, Ascension, and Pentecost Monday.

TIME: 2 PM = noon GMT.

LOCATION AND SIZE: Rwanda, a landlocked country in east-central Africa, has an area of 26,340 square kilometers (10,170 square miles), slightly smaller than the state of Maryland. It has a total boundary length of 893 kilometers (555 miles). Rwanda's capital city, Kigali, is located near the center of the country.

CLIMATE: The high altitude of Rwanda provides the country with a pleasant tropical highland climate. At Kigali, on the central plateau, the average temperature is 19°C (66°F). A long rainy season lasts from February to May and a short one from November through December. Annual rainfall averages as much as 160 centimeters (63 inches) in the west.

INTRODUCTORY SURVEY

RECENT HISTORY

Liberation movements in other African countries after World War II (1939–45) led the Hutu to demand social and political equality with the Tutsis. In November 1959, a Hutu revolution began, continuing sporadically for the next few years. Many Tutsi either were killed or fled to neighboring territories. On 27 June 1962, the United Nations General Assembly passed a resolution providing for the independent states of Rwanda and Burundi, and on 1 July, Rwanda became an independent country. In December 1963, following an unsuccessful invasion by Tutsi refugees from Burundi, a massacre of the remaining resident Tutsi population caused the death of an estimated 12,000 Tutsi and more fled into neighboring countries.

In January 1964, the economic union that had existed between Burundi and Rwanda was terminated. This resulted in severe economic difficulties and internal unrest. The unstable political and economic situation led the Rwandan army to overthrow the government in July 1973. Major General Juvénal Habyarimana assumed the presidency. In 1975, his military regime created a one-party state under the National Revolutionary Movement for Development (MRND). A system of ethnic quotas was introduced that formally limited the Tutsi minority to 14% of the positions in the workplace and in the schools.

Popular discontent grew through the 1980s. In October 1990, over 1,000 Tutsi refugees invaded Rwanda from Uganda; government forces

RWANDA

0   25   50 Miles

0   25   50 Kilometers

retaliated by massacring Tutsi. In spite of cease-fires negotiated between the government and Tutsi rebels in 1991 and 1992, tensions remained high.

On the political front, Habyarimana liberalized his government in the early 1990s. A power sharing agreement between Hutus and Tutsis was signed in Tanzania in January 1993 but failed to end the fighting. The United Nations Security Council authorized a peacekeeping force, but unrest continued.

In 1994, a total breakdown occurred. In February, the minister of public works was assassinated. In April, a rocket downed an airplane carrying the presidents of Rwanda and Burundi. The president was a Hutu. They were returning to Kigali from regional peace talks in Tanzania. All aboard were killed. From that point on, Rwanda was lawless, as members of the Rwandan army and other bands of armed Hutu set out to murder all the Tutsi they could find. Hundreds of thousands, mostly Tutsi, were killed.

In July 1994, Tutsi rebels gained control of the government, prompting Hutus to flee to refugee camps in Tanzania, Zaire (now the Democratic Re-

public of the Congo), and Burundi. After 1994, the government of Zaire began to force Rwandans to return home from the refugee camps. From April 1994 to 1997, an estimated 100,000 refugees died or disappeared.

Between the end of the genocide and 1997, almost 90,000 suspected killers had been arrested in Rwanda. In February 1995, the United Nations Security Council created the International Criminal Tribunal for Rwanda in order to bring the killers to justice. By 1997, 1,946 of the accused had been indicted.

In October 1996, Rwandan military forces began fighting in neighboring Zaire in order to get rid of that country's long-time dictator, Mobutu Sese-Seko. Rwanda stepped in when it became clear that the United Nations did not have the political motivation to close down the refugee camps in Zaire. The Tutsi-based Rwandan Patriotic Front (RPF) saw the camps as little more than training bases for Hutu rebels. Rwandan officials also believed that Mobutu might even support another Hutu militia movement in Rwanda, and so they began supporting a long-time Zairian revolutionary, Laurent Désiré Kabila. Kabila's forces managed to overthrow Mobuto's government in less than eight months. In the process, refugee camps with Hutus were destroyed and thousands of Hutus were killed. In 1997, a million refugees returned to Rwanda; many were former Hutu soldiers from the defeated army.

On 24 April 1998, the Rwandan government conducted its first public executions of people convicted in local courts of crimes from the 1994 genocide. There were concerns, however, that the trials of these first 22 people had been conducted unfairly.

GOVERNMENT

A peace accord with the Rwandan Patriotic Front (RPF) was signed on 4 August 1993. By 1994, the RPF had established control over the country, instituting a government of national unity, headed by a Hutu president. In May 1995, the Transitional National Assembly created a new constitution.

Judiciary

There are district courts, provincial courts, and courts of appeal. Also functioning are a constitutional court, a court of accounts, which examines public accounts, and a court of state security for treason and national security cases. As of 1996, the judicial system was functioning on a limited basis. Rwanda has sought help from the international community to rebuild the judiciary and appoint lower court officials.

Political Parties

The Tutsi-based Rwandan Patriotic Front (RPF), an army once in exile, is now firmly entrenched within Rwanda.

The Transitional National Assembly is structured as follows: RPF, 19 seats; Democratic Republican Movement (MDR), 13; Democratic and Socialist Party (PSD), 13; Liberal Party (PL), 13; Christian Democrats (PDC), 6; Rwandan Socialist Party (PDI), 2; and others, 2.

DEFENSE

Rwanda's armed forces totaled 33,000 in 1995, of which all but 200 air corps personnel were in the army. The national police numbers 1,200.

ECONOMIC AFFAIRS

Rwanda has an agricultural economy with relatively few mineral resources. The manufacturing base is limited to a few basic products. Soil erosion has limited growth in the agricultural sector. Poor markets, lack of natural resources, and difficult transportation problems all painted a discouraging picture for the economy. However, these problems are insignificant in comparison to those brought about in 1994 by the civil war.

Public Finance

Rwanda has both an ordinary budget for recurrent operations and a development budget for controlling development projects. In the 1960s and 1970s, prudent public finance management and generous foreign aid helped keep deficits and inflation low. With the fall of coffee prices during the 1980s, however, the government increased its control over the economy, and raised annual budget deficits to the equivalent of 11% of GDP by 1990. In 1995, the budget deficit amounted to RFr11 billion.

In 1992, Rwanda had total outstanding debt of RFr131,613 million, of which RFr95,817 million was financed abroad. The cost of servicing the debt in 1994 was equivalent to 12.5% of total exports.

Income

In 1997 Rwanda's gross national product (GNP) was $3 billion, or about $440 per person. For the period 1985–95 the average inflation rate was 10.4%, resulting in a decline in per person GNP of 5%.

Industry

Rwanda has light industry that produces sugar, coffee, tea, flour, cigars, beer, wine, soft drinks, metal products, and assembled radios. There are also textile mills, soap factories, auto repair shops, a match factory, a pyrethrum (insecticide) refinery, and plants for producing paint, pharmaceuticals, and furniture. Industrial production includes soap, cement, radios, cigarettes, beer, soft drinks, and plastic shoes. The average annual growth rate of manufacturing in 1990–95 was − 16.4%.

Banking and Finance

From 1922 until the independence of Zaire (Belgian Congo, now DROC) in 1960, the monetary and banking systems of Rwanda and Burundi were integrated with those of the Congo. In July 1962, upon becoming independent, Rwanda and Burundi formed a joint monetary union administered by a common central bank. This bank was dissolved, and its functions as a central banking institution were transferred, in April 1964, to the National Bank of the Republic of Rwanda. The Banque nationale du Rwanda (BNR) was looted in July 1994 but reopened later in the year and has since reopened its branches in Butare and Ruhengeri. The bank imposes foreign exchange controls and administers the import licensing system. It is eager for independence and is wary of excessive government borrowing from it. As of September 1996, the money supply, as measured by M2, totaled RFr68,472 million.

There are four main commercial banks, of which two pre-date the war and two were established in 1995. The former are the Banque de Kigali, which is jointly owned by the state and two Belgian institutions—Belgolaise Bank and Générale de Banque—and the Banque commerciale du Rwanda, which is majority state-owned. The new institutions are the Banque de commerce, développement, et l'industrie (BCDI), whose main shareholders are Rwandans, and the Gold Trust Bank of Rwanda, whose main shareholders are Ugandan Asians. Rwanda also has a savings bank and a postal savings bank. The Rwandese Bank of Development and the People's Bank of Rwanda are the nation's development banks. The Banque Rwandaise de Développement (BRD) was also looted but reopened in mid-1995 with RFr3 billion of bad debt. The extensive rural credit network was shattered and is slowly reestablishing itself. There is no stock exchange in Rwanda.

Economic Development

Rwanda's attempt to establish food self-sufficiency has delayed many of its development plans in other sectors. Rwanda typically receives foreign aid from various European donors and the EU. After the 1994 genocide, Rwandan officials requested $1.4 billion from the UN for reconstruction. Net concessional aid from international financial institutions and UN organizations in 1994 amounted to $226 million.

SOCIAL WELFARE

Old age pensions for workers, family allowances, and payments for those injured on the job are provided for all wage earners. In 1994, there was a total breakdown of all governmental services throughout the country.

There are government- and missionary-sponsored mutual aid societies, which increasingly supply the many social services once provided by the clan and family under Rwanda's traditional social structure.

Healthcare

In 1995, some 500,000–800,000 Rwandan refugees fled to neighboring Zaire (now the Democratic Republic of the Congo). Almost 50,000 died during the first month of the influx. In peaceful times, malnutrition is the greatest health problem in Rwanda. Kwashiorkor, a protein-calorie deficiency, is common, increasing the severity of other prevalent diseases, among them pneumonia, tuberculosis, measles, whooping cough, and dysentery. In 1994, an estimated 7.2% of the adult population was infected with HIV (the virus that causes AIDS). There were 10,706 new AIDS cases reported in 1996. Average life expectancy is 41 years.

In 1990, there were 1.7 hospital beds per 1,000 inhabitants. There is about 1 doctor per 73,796 people. In 1993, 80% of the population had access to health care services.

Housing

The basic type of housing in the rural areas is made of mud bricks and poles, and covered with thatch. These residences are dispersed in the collines, or family farms.

EDUCATION

In 1995, adult illiteracy was estimated at 40% (males, 30.2%; females, 48.4%). Education is free and compulsory for all children aged 7 to 15. In 1991, there were 1,710 primary schools, with 18,937 teachers and 1.1 million pupils attending. In that same year, there were 94,586 pupils in secondary schools. The National University of Rwanda is located at Butare. Other known institutions are the African and Mauritian Institute of Statistics and Applied Economics in Kigali. In 1989, all higher level institutions had 3,389 pupils and 646 teaching staff.

1999 KEY EVENTS TIMELINE

January

- The Tutsi-led government proposes a controversial program supposedly designed to transform Rwanda's troubled northwest province and protect the civilian population from war: government troops force Hutu peasant refugees into temporary camps where living conditions are poor, and disease runs rampant.

- The Tutsi-led government appeals to western aid donors to help fulfill its promise that the deplorable camps will one day have proper housing and facilities.

March

- Ugandan and Rwandan soldiers join forces in a manhunt for Rwandan Hutu rebels who hacked to death eight foreign tourists visiting a jungle famous for its rare gorillas.

- A UN tribunal prosecuting crimes related to the 1994 Rwandan genocide decides to free Bernard Ntuyahaga, former Rwandan army officer involved in the killing of ten Belgian peacekeepers.

April

- Rwanda holds its first election since the 1994 genocide wherein Hutu militiamen killed hundreds of Tutsi civilians in the small town of Taba; the elections are local, and democracy is limited.

- Rwandan pastor Elizaphan Ntakirutimana, accused of leading Hutu soldiers to his church to slaughter hundreds of Tutsis hiding inside in April of 1994, faces a U.S. federal appeals court that rules he should be handed over to UN officials in Tanzania; he appeals and waits to hear whether he will be extradited for trial.

- Vice president of the Rwandan Interhamwe militia group, Georges Rutaganda, charged with genocide in the 1994 massacre, testifies on his own behalf before the International Criminal Tribunal for Rwanda.

May

- In a three-page statement issued by the Vatican press entitled ''Rwandan Genocide: the Last Act,'' the Vatican accuses Rwandan leaders of waging a defamatory campaign against the Roman Catholic church that blocks reconciliation efforts in Rwanda and threatens peaceful ethnic coexistence throughout Africa.

June

- Seven plant extracts used by traditional Rwandan healers to treat infections are tested by researchers in Belgium for antimicrobial and antiviral properties; two of the plants show true antiviral activity, and all exhibit virucidal properties.

July

- African foreign and defense ministers from six countries, including Rwanda, sign a draft ceasefire plan to formally end the eleven-month-old civil war in Congo; however, two squabbling rebel leaders refuse to sign, and it remains unclear whether fighting will actually stop.

August

- Former Foreign Minister Jerome Bicamumpaka, former Commerce Minister Justin Mugenzi, and former Civil Service Minister Prosper Mugiraneza, all charged with genocide and crimes against humanity in the 1994 genocide, are transferred from Cameroon to Tanzania to await trial before a UN tribunal.

- South African President Thabo Mbeki begins talks with the presidents of Rwanda, Uganda, and Tanzania in an effort to end the war in the Democratic Republic of the Congo.

- Congolese President Laurent Kabila's information minister blames Rwanda and Uganda for clashes between rival rebel factions, accusing them of trying to undermine the July peace deal.

- Prosecutors at the UN tribunal on Rwanda's 1994 genocide press for joint trials of top suspects in an attempt to finish their work before the court's mandate expires in 2003.

- Former Rwandan minister Pauline Nyiramasuhuko is indicted for rape in the 1994 genocide by the International Criminal Tribunal for Rwanda sitting in Tanzania.

- Uganda and Rwanda agree on an immediate cease-fire to end three days of heavy fighting between their troops in the Democratic Republic of the Congo; leaders agree to meet for talks to revive their alliance and persuade rebel factions to sign a peace deal.

- Congolese rebel leaders and their Rwandan and Ugandan backers gather in the Zambian capital for a landmark ceasefire ceremony; the ceasefire is signed by members of the Congolese Rally for Democracy, whose rival factions are backed by Rwanda and Uganda.

- Ugandan President Yoweri Museveni warns Rwanda's Vice President Major-General Paul Kagame to tread carefully despite the recent ceasefire agreement; if provoked, Uganda will respond with heavy counter attacks.

September

- A United Nations commission set up to look into the international community's response to the 1994 Rwanda genocide arrives in Rwanda on a three-day fact-finding visit.

- South African President Thabo Mbeki holds talks with Rwandan military strongman Paul Kagame as part of an attempt to strengthen the shaky ceasefire deal in the Democratic Republic of Congo.

- Roman Catholic Bishop Augustin Misago, accused of attending high level meetings that organized the 1994 genocide, denies the charges against him at the start of his trial in a Kigali court.

- Former Rwandan Mayor Ignace Bagilishema pleads not guilty to seven counts of genocide and crimes against humanity at a U.N. tribunal.

- Burundi President Pierre Buyoya denies after weekend talks with Rwandan counterpart Pasteur Bizimungu that Rwanda sent troops to his country to help counter an upsurge in rebel guerilla attacks.

- The extradition trial in Tanzania of former Rwandan army officier Bernard Ntuyahaga, accused of murdering 10 Belgian peacekeepers during the 1994 genocide, is postponed.

October

- Rwanda adopts a new national flag and motto in an attempt to bury the old symbols, seen as representatives of the ideology that lay behind the 1994 genocide.

- Despite the five-week-old ceasefire deal, Congolese rebels kill more than 200 Rwandan Hutu militia operating in the northeast of the Democratic Republic of Congo in a joint effort with the Rwandan army; Congolese Rally for Democracy leader Jean Pierre Ondekane insists neither his forces nor the allied Rwandan army units violated the ceasefire as they were defending themselves from imminent attack.

- Two Rwandan cabinet ministers, Social Affairs Minister Charles Ntakirutinka and Minister in the President's Office Anastase Gasana, are forced to resign after losing a parliamentary no–confidence vote over their alleged involvement in a business scandal that cost the government $1 million.

- A Ugandan delegation arrives in Kigali to open talks with Rwandan officials on improving relations that were damaged by the battle between their armies in the neighboring Democratic Republic of the Congo in August.

November

- Rwanda declares itself at odds with the UN's International Criminal Tribunal for Rwanda because of the release of Jean-Bosco Barayagwiza, one of the 50 genocide suspects to have been indicted by the tribunal, and denies a visa to Carla Del Ponte, the UN's chief prosecutor of war crimes in Rwanda and ex-Yugoslavia.

December

- A United Nations tribunal meeting in Tanzania convicts Hutu businessman and rebel leader Georges Rutaganda of genocide, crimes against humanity, and murder stemming from the 1994 massacres when an estimated 500,000 Tutsis were killed.

- A report by a panel of international experts charges that the both the United States and United Nations are partially responsible, by not taking stronger action, for the genocide of hundreds of thousands of people in Rwanda in 1994.

ANALYSIS OF EVENTS: 1999

BUSINESS AND THE ECONOMY

In 1999 Rwanda was the most densely populated country in Africa. Most of its people were engaged in subsistence agriculture. Its per capita Gross National Product for 1998 was estimated at an abysmal $690. The average life expectancy at birth in 1998 was only 43 years. Its infant mortality rate stood at 113 per thousand live births. (The infant mortality rate for Nigeria, by comparison, was 70 per thousand live births. In Switzerland it was five per thousand.) Land–locked and with few marketable natural resources, Rwanda had seen its economy disintegrate during the 1994 genocide of the ethnic Tutsis by the majority Hutus.

Rwanda's economy had been plagued by indemic poverty and ethnic conflict for decades. Ethnic tensions between the Hutus and Tutsis led to the 1959 Hutu uprising against the Tutsi king and attacks on the Tutsi population. Tens of thousands of Tutsis went into exile. The children of the exiles formed a rebel group, the Rwandan Patriotic Front (RPF), and precipitated a civil war in October 1990. In early 1994 the majority Hutus rose up and killed about 800,000 Tutsis and moderate Hutus. Once again, the Tutsis fought a guerrilla war against the Hutu regime and overthrew it in July 1994.

In the aftermath, two million Hutus, fearing retribution, fled to neighboring nations, including Burundi, Tanzania, Uganda, and the Democratic Republic of the Congo (DROC). In 1996 and 1997 nearly 1.3 million Hutus returned to Rwanda. The UN Office of the High Commissioner for Refugees established camps for those returning. With so much of the population without permanent settlement, economic development was nearly impossible. Rwandan troops continued a low-level war against the Tutsis in the northwestern corner of the country. Rwandan troops are also involved in a crisis engulfing neighboring DROC.

GOVERNMENT AND POLITICS

In 1998 and 1999, Rwandan society began to recover, at least on paper. The gross domestic product had grown by 10.5 percent in 1998. Inflation was also brought under control, a considerable improvement in comparisons to the intense inflation that followed the 1994 genocide (10 percent in 1998). Rwanda continued to struggle to control its debt and to attract foreign investment. In mid-1998 the country joined the Enhanced Structural Adjustment Facility (ESAF) with the International Monetary Fund, and received pledges of financial support from IMF supporting governments. Rwanda continued to develop the processing and packaging of coffee and tea and developed new fields such as cement, beverages, soap, furniture, shoes, plastic goods, textiles, and cigarettes.

CULTURE AND SOCIETY

Almost ninety percent of Rwandans are engaged in subsistence agriculture. The 1994 genocide triggered severe poverty and left many women with no means for even the most basic existence. However, by the end of 1999, the population was beginning to recover its stability, and people were beginning to return to the way of life they had engaged in prior to the 1994 genocide.

DIRECTORY

CENTRAL GOVERNMENT

Head of State

President
Pasteur Bizimungu, Office of the President, PO Box 15, Kigali, Rwanda
FAX: +250 84769; 84390

Prime Minister
Pierre-Célestin Rwigema, Office of the Prime Minister, PO Box 1334, Kigali, Rwanda
PHONE: +250 85444
FAX: +250 83714

Ministers

Minister of Defense
Major General Paul Kagame, Ministry of Defense, PO Box 23, Kigali, Rwanda
PHONE: +250 77942
FAX: +250 72431

Minister of International Affairs
Sheikh Abdul Karim Harelimana, Ministry of International Affairs, PO Box 446, Kigali, Rwanda
PHONE: +280 85477
FAX: +250 84373

Minister of Foreign Affairs Regional Cooperation
Amri Sued, Ministry of Foreign Affairs Regional Cooperation, PO Box 179, Kigali, Rwanda
PHONE: +250 74522
FAX: +250 72409

Minister of Justice
Jean de Dieu Mucyo, Ministry of Justice, PO Box 160, Kigali, Rwanda
PHONE: +250 86561
FAX: +250 86509

Minister of Education
Emmanuel Mudidi, Ministry of Education
PHONE: +250 83051
FAX: +250 82162

Minister of Finance and Economic Planning
Donald Kaberuka, Ministry of Finance and Economic Planning
PHONE: +250 75777
FAX: +250 75719

Minister of Commerce, Industry and Tourism
Marc Rugenera, Ministry of Commerce, Industry and Tourism
PHONE: +250 74725
FAX: +250 75465

Minister of Health
Ezechias Rwabuhihi, Ministry of Health
PHONE: +250 73482
FAX: +250 76853

Minister of Local Government
Désiré Nyandwi, Ministry of Local Government

Minister of Public Service and Labor
Jean Népomuscène Nayinzira, Public Service and Labor
PHONE: +250 85714
FAX: +250 83374

Minister of Public Works, Transport and Communications
Vincent Biruta, Ministry of Public Works, Transport and Communications
PHONE: +250 75750
FAX: +250 76641

Minister of Women in Development
Angeline Muganza, Ministry of Women in Development
PHONE: +250 77626
FAX: +250 77543

Minister of Agriculture, Animal Resources and Forestry
Ephraim Kabayua, Ministry of Agriculture, Animal Resources and Forestry
PHONE: +250 85155
FAX: +250 85057

Minister of Youth, Sport and Trades
François Ngarambe, Ministry of Youth, Sport and Trades
PHONE: +250 82572
FAX: +250 87010

Minister of Information
Augustin Iyamuremye, Ministry of Information
PHONE: +250 84654
FAX: +250 84607

Minister of State
Emmanuel Habyarimana, Ministry of State

Minister of State
Emmanuel Ndahimana, Ministry of State

Minister of State
Laurien Ngirabanzi, Ministry of State

Minister of Energy, Water and Natural Resources
Bonaventure Niybizi, Ministry of Energy, Water and Natural Resources

Minister of Lands, Human Resettlement and Environment Protection
Jospeh Nsengimana, Ministry of Lands, Human Resettlement and Environment Protection

Minister of State
Sylvie Zayinabo Kayitesi, Ministry of State

Minister of Social Affairs
Charles Ntakirutinka, Ministry of Social Affairs

POLITICAL ORGANIZATIONS

Parti Démocratique Chrêtien (Christian Democratic Party)

Mouvement Démocratique Républicain-MDR (Democratic Republican Movement)

Parti Social-Democratique-PSD (Democratic and Socialist Party)

Partie Démocratique Islamique-PDI (Islamic Democratic Party)

Parti Libéral-PL (Liberal Party)

Mouvement Républicain National pour la Démocratie et le Développement-MRNDD (National Republican Movement for Democracy and Development)

Front Patriottique Rwandais-FPR (Rwandan Patriotic Front)

TITLE: Chairman
NAME: Alexis Kanyarengwe

Parti Socialiste Rwandais-PSR (Rwandan Socialist Party)

DIPLOMATIC REPRESENTATION
Embassies in Rwanda

United Kingdom
Parcelle No. 1071 Kimihurura, Kigali, Rwanda
PHONE: +250 84098
FAX: +250 82044

United States
BP 29, Kigali, Rwanda
PHONE: +250 75601; 75602; 75603; 72126; 77147
TITLE: Ambassador
NAME: Robert Gribbin III

JUDICIAL SYSTEM
Constitutional Court

FURTHER READING
Articles

Boyles, Salynn and Sandra W. Key. "Plants Tested for Antiviral/Antimicrobial Activity." *Antiviral Weekly* (June 28, 1999): 5.

Cahn, Dianna. "Soldiers in Manhunt for Rwandan Insurgents." *The Associated Press*, 3 March 1999.

"Group Trials." *The Economist* (August 14, 1999): 36.

Kantz, Matt. "Rwandans Accused of Defaming Church." *National Catholic Reporter* (June 4, 1999): 9.

"Neither Hutu nor Tutsi, Just Rwandan." *The Economist* (April 3, 1999): 37.

"Now for Some Imudugudusisation." *The Economist* (January 23, 1999): 43.

Pitman, Todd. "Gorillas Threatened In Africa's War-Torn Heart." Reuters, August 19, 1999.

"Rwanda: State v. Church." *The Economist* (September 18, 1999): 52.

''Uganda and Rwanda: Old Friends, New War.'' *The Economist* (August 21, 1999): 37.

Books

Carr, Rosamond Halsey. *Land of a Thousand Hills: My Life in Rwanda.* New York: Viking, 1999.

Pierce, Julian R. *Speak Rwanda.* New York: Picador, 1999.

Uvin, Peter. *Aiding Violence: the Development Enterprise in Rwanda.* West Hartford, CT: Kumarian Press, 1998.

Internet

Africa New Online. Available Online @ http://www.africanews.org/ (November 30, 1999).

Stories from Rwanda. Available Online @ http://www.historyplace.com/pointsofview/rwanda.html (December 1, 1999).

World Full Coverage. Available Online @ http://fullcoverage.yahoo.com/Full_Coverage/World/Rwanda (December 1, 1999).

RWANDA:
STATISTICAL DATA

For sources and notes see "Sources of Statistics" in the front of each volume.

GEOGRAPHY

Geography (1)

Area:

Total: 26,340 sq km.

Land: 24,950 sq km.

Water: 1,390 sq km.

Area—comparative: slightly smaller than Maryland.

Land boundaries:

Total: 893 km.

Border countries: Burundi 290 km, Democratic Republic of the Congo 217 km, Tanzania 217 km, Uganda 169 km.

Coastline: 0 km (landlocked).

Climate: temperate; two rainy seasons (February to April, November to January); mild in mountains with frost and snow possible.

Terrain: mostly grassy uplands and hills; relief is mountainous with altitude declining from west to east.

Natural resources: gold, cassiterite (tin ore), wolframite (tungsten ore), natural gas, hydropower.

Land use:

Arable land: 35%

Permanent crops: 13%

Permanent pastures: 18%

Forests and woodland: 22%

Other: 12% (1993 est.).

HUMAN FACTORS

Demographics (2A)

	1990	1995	1998	2000	2010	2020	2030	2040	2050
Population	7,160.8	5,980.2	7,956.2	8,337.0	9,881.2	11,303.5	13,272.1	16,262.2	19,607.3
Net migration rate (per 1,000 population)	NA	NA	NA	NA	NA	NA	NA	NA	NA
Births	NA	NA	NA	NA	NA	NA	NA	NA	NA
Deaths	NA	NA	NA	NA	NA	NA	NA	NA	NA
Life expectancy - males	47.1	39.0	41.5	40.2	37.6	41.8	54.6	67.4	71.6
Life expectancy - females	49.2	39.7	42.4	41.2	37.5	42.1	57.3	72.4	77.1
Birth rate (per 1,000)	43.0	39.4	39.0	38.9	37.3	32.5	29.8	25.5	21.3
Death rate (per 1,000)	16.0	20.6	19.0	20.0	23.1	19.1	10.7	5.2	4.3
Women of reproductive age (15-49 yrs.)	1,544.6	1,364.5	1,870.9	1,996.2	2,367.5	2,761.2	3,484.9	4,339.5	5,285.3
of which are currently married	NA	NA	NA	NA	NA	NA	NA	NA	NA
Fertility rate	6.7	6.1	5.9	5.7	5.0	4.2	3.5	3.0	2.6

Except as noted, values for vital statistics are in thousands; life expectancy is in years.

Health Personnel (3)

Total health expenditure as a percentage of GDP, 1990-1997[a]

Public sector 1.9

Private sector . . . . .NA

Total[b] . . . . .NA

Health expenditure per capita in U.S. dollars, 1990-1997[a]

Purchasing power parity . . . . .NA

Total . . . . .NA

Availability of health care facilities per 100,000 people

Hospital beds 1990-1997[a] 170

Doctors 1993[c] . . . . .NA

Nurses 1993[c] . . . . .NA

Health Indicators (4)

Life expectancy at birth

1980 46

1997 40

Daily per capita supply of calories (1996) 2,142

Total fertility rate births per woman (1997) 6.2

Maternal mortality ratio per 100,000 live births (1990-97) . . . . .1,300[c]

Safe water % of population with access (1995) . . . .

Sanitation % of population with access (1995) 94

Consumption of iodized salt % of households (1992-98)[a] 95

Smoking prevalence

Male % of adults (1985-95)[a] . . . .

Female % of adults (1985-95)[a] . . . .

Tuberculosis incidence per 100,000 people (1997) 276

Adult HIV prevalence % of population ages 15-49 (1997) 12.75

Infants and Malnutrition (5)

Under-5 mortality rate (1997) 170

% of infants with low birthweight (1990-97) 17

Births attended by skilled health staff % of total[a] . . .26

% fully immunized (1995-97)

TB 79

DPT 77

Polio 77

Measles 66

Prevalence of child malnutrition under age 5 (1992-97)[b] 29

Ethnic Division (6)

Hutu 80%

Tutsi 19%

Twa (Pygmoid) 1%

Religions (7)

Roman Catholic 65%

Protestant 9%

Muslim 1%

Indigenous beliefs and other 25%

Languages (8)

Kinyarwanda (official) universal Bantu vernacular, French (official), English (official), Kiswahili (Swahili) used in commercial centers.

EDUCATION

Public Education Expenditures (9)

Public expenditure on education (% of GNP)

1980 . . . . .2.7

1996 . . . .

Expenditure per student

Primary % of GNP per capita

1980 . . . . .11.1

1996 . . . .

Secondary % of GNP per capita

1980 . . . .

1996 . . . .

Tertiary % of GNP per capita

1980 . . . . .902.6

1996 . . . .

Expenditure on teaching materials

Primary % of total for level (1996) 3.5

Secondary % of total for level (1996) . . . .

Primary pupil-teacher ratio per teacher (1996) . . . .

Duration of primary education years (1995) 7

Literacy Rates (11A)

In thousands and percent[1]	1990	1995	2000	2010
Illiterate population (15+ yrs.)	1,677	1,695	1,683	1,588
Literacy rate - total adult pop. (%)	54.3	60.5	66.4	76.0
Literacy rate - males (%)	65.1	69.8	74.2	81.0
Literacy rate - females (%)	44.0	51.6	59.0	71.3

GOVERNMENT & LAW

Political Parties (12)

Transitional National Assembly	No. of seats
RPF	19
Democratic Republican Movement (MDR)	13
Democratic and Socialist Party (PSD)	13
Liberal Party (PL)	13
Christian Democratic Party (PDC)	6
Rwandan Socialist Party (PSR)	2
Islamic Democratic Party (PDI)	2
Other	2

The distribution of seats was predetermined. The Transitional National Assembly is a power-sharing body established on 12 December 1994 following a multi-party protocol of understanding.

Government Budget (13B)

Revenues	$231 million
Expenditures	$319 million
Capital expenditures	$13 million

Data for 1996 est.

LABOR FORCE

Labor Force (16)

Total (million)	3.6
Agriculture	93%
Government and services	5%
Industry and commerce	2%

Military Affairs (14B)

	1990	1991	1992	1993	1994	1995
Military expenditures						
Current dollars (mil.)	149	275[e]	262[e]	286[e]	448[e]	118[e]
1995 constant dollars (mil.)	171	303[e]	282[e]	300[e]	459[e]	118[e]
Armed forces (000)	6	30	30	30	40	33[e]
Gross national product (GNP)						
Current dollars (mil.)	3,553	3,917	4,155	3,834	1,782	2,274
1995 constant dollars (mil.)	4,084	4,328	4,469	4,020	1,826	2,274
Central government expenditures (CGE)						
1995 constant dollars (mil.)	864	976	1,124	1,288	NA	NA
People (mil.)	7.1	7.3	7.5	7.7	6.6	6.0
Military expenditure as % of GNP	4.2	7.0	6.3	7.5	25.1	5.2
Military expenditure as % of CGE	19.8	31.1	25.1	23.3	NA	NA
Military expenditure per capita (1995 $)	24	41	38	39	69	20
Armed forces per 1,000 people (soldiers)	.8	4.1	4.0	3.9	6.0	5.5
GNP per capita (1995 $)	571	590	595	524	276	378
Arms imports[6]						
Current dollars (mil.)	0	0	0	10	80	0
1995 constant dollars (mil.)	0	0	0	10	82	0
Arms exports[6]						
Current dollars (mil.)	0	0	0	0	0	0
1995 constant dollars (mil.)	0	0	0	0	0	0
Total imports[7]						
Current dollars (mil.)	194	307	287	332	125	207
1995 constant dollars (mil.)	223	340	309	348	128	207
Total exports[7]						
Current dollars (mil.)	112	93	67	65	29[e]	49[e]
1995 constant dollars (mil.)	128	102	72	68	30[e]	49[e]
Arms as percent of total imports[8]	0	0	0	3.0	64.1	0
Arms as percent of total exports[8]	0	0	0	0	0	0

Unemployment Rate (17)

Rate not available.

PRODUCTION SECTOR

Electric Energy (18)

Capacity . . . . .34,000 kW (1995)

Production . . . . .169 million kWh (1995)

Consumption per capita . . . . .21 kWh (1995)

Transportation (19)

Highways:

total: 12,000 km

paved: 1,000 km

unpaved: 11,000 km (1997 est.)

Waterways: Lac Kivu navigable by shallow-draft barges and native craft

Airports: 7 (1997 est.)

Airports—with paved runways:

total: 4

over 3,047 m: 1

914 to 1,523 m: 2

under 914 m: 1 (1997 est.)

Airports—with unpaved runways:

total: 3

914 to 1,523 m: 1

under 914 m: 2 (1997 est.)

Top Agricultural Products (20)

Coffee, tea, pyrethrum (insecticide made from chrysanthemums), bananas, beans, sorghum, potatoes; livestock.

MANUFACTURING SECTOR

GDP & Manufacturing Summary (21)

	1980	1985	1990	1992	1993	1994
Gross Domestic Product						
Millions of 1990 dollars	1,905	2,206	2,337	2,420	2,499	1,249
Growth rate in percent	6.01	4.41	−2.00	2.49	3.25	−50.00
Per capita (in 1990 dollars)	368.9	364.2	334.5	328.7	330.8	161.2
Manufacturing Value Added						
Millions of 1990 dollars	276	289	316	330	343	*132*
Growth rate in percent	26.49	6.96	2.86	2.91	3.79	*−61.53*
Manufacturing share in percent of current prices	15.8	14.2	13.9	11.0	14.8	NA

FINANCE, ECONOMICS, & TRADE

Balance of Payments (23)

	1992	1993	1994	1995	1996
Exports of goods (f.o.b.)	69	68	36	57	64
Imports of goods (f.o.b.)	−240	−268	−481	−214	−213
Trade balance	−172	−200	−445	−157	−148
Services - debits	−131	−155	−143	−172	−169
Services - credits	36	37	—	42	27
Private transfers (net)	161	165	463	328	261
Government transfers (net)	22	23	58	17	30
Overall balance	−83	−129	−67	57	1

FINANCE, ECONOMICS, & TRADE

Economic Indicators (22)

National product: GDP—purchasing power parity—$3 billion (1996 est.)

National product real growth rate: 13.3% (1996)

National product per capita: $440 (1996 est.)

Inflation rate—consumer price index: 7.4% (1996)

Exchange Rates (24)

Exchange rates:

Rwandan francs (RF) per US$1

January 1998	302.28
1997	301.53
1996	306.82
1995	262.20
1993	144.31

Top Import Origins (25)

$202.4 million (f.o.b., 1996 est.)

Origins	%
United States	NA
European Union	NA
Kenya	NA
Tanzania	NA

NA stands for not available.

Top Export Destinations (26)

$62.3 million (f.o.b., 1996 est.)

Destinations	%
Brazil	NA
European Union	NA

NA stands for not available.

Economic Aid (27)

Recipient: ODA, $NA. Note: in October 1990 Rwanda launched a Structural Adjustment Program with the IMF; since September 1991, the EU has given $46 million and the US $25 million in support of this program (1993). NA stands for not available.

Import Export Commodities (28)

Import Commodities	Export Commodities
Foodstuffs 35%	Coffee 74%
Machines and equipment	Tea
Capital goods	Cassiterite
Steel	Wolframite
Petroleum products	Pyrethrum
Cement and construction material